# CUMULATIVE PROBABILITIES FOR THE STANDARD NORMAL DISTRIBUTION

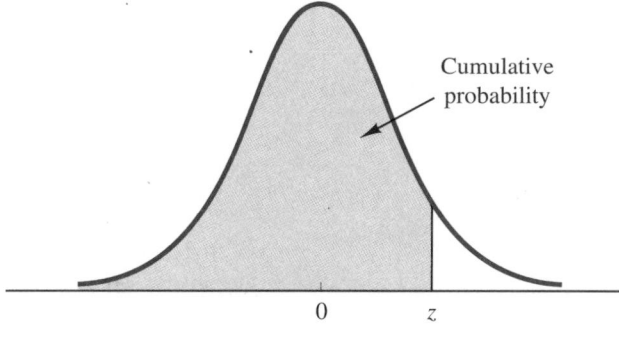

Cumulative probability

Entries in the table give the area under the curve to the left of the $z$ value. For example, for $z = 1.25$ the cumulative probability is .8944.

| z | .00 | .01 | .02 | .03 | .04 | .05 | .06 | .07 | .08 | .09 |
|---|---|---|---|---|---|---|---|---|---|---|
| .0 | .5000 | .5040 | .5080 | .5120 | .5160 | .5199 | .5239 | .5279 | .5319 | .5359 |
| .1 | .5398 | .5438 | .5478 | .5517 | .5557 | .5596 | .5636 | .5675 | .5714 | .5753 |
| .2 | .5793 | .5832 | .5871 | .5910 | .5948 | .5987 | .6026 | .6064 | .6103 | .6141 |
| .3 | .6179 | .6217 | .6255 | .6293 | .6331 | .6368 | .6406 | .6443 | .6480 | .6517 |
| .4 | .6554 | .6591 | .6628 | .6664 | .6700 | .6736 | .6772 | .6808 | .6844 | .6879 |
| .5 | .6915 | .6950 | .6985 | .7019 | .7054 | .7088 | .7123 | .7157 | .7190 | .7224 |
| .6 | .7257 | .7291 | .7324 | .7357 | .7389 | .7422 | .7454 | .7486 | .7517 | .7549 |
| .7 | .7580 | .7611 | .7642 | .7673 | .7704 | .7734 | .7764 | .7794 | .7823 | .7852 |
| .8 | .7881 | .7910 | .7939 | .7967 | .7995 | .8023 | .8051 | .8078 | .8106 | .8133 |
| .9 | .8159 | .8186 | .8212 | .8238 | .8264 | .8289 | .8315 | .8340 | .8365 | .8389 |
| 1.0 | .8413 | .8438 | .8461 | .8485 | .8508 | .8531 | .8554 | .8577 | .8599 | .8621 |
| 1.1 | .8643 | .8665 | .8686 | .8708 | .8729 | .8749 | .8770 | .8790 | .8810 | .8830 |
| 1.2 | .8849 | .8869 | .8888 | .8907 | .8925 | .8944 | .8962 | .8980 | .8997 | .9015 |
| 1.3 | .9032 | .9049 | .9066 | .9082 | .9099 | .9115 | .9131 | .9147 | .9162 | .9177 |
| 1.4 | .9192 | .9207 | .9222 | .9236 | 9.251 | .9265 | .9279 | .9292 | .9306 | .9319 |
| 1.5 | .9332 | .9345 | .9357 | .9370 | .9382 | .9394 | .9406 | .9418 | .9429 | .9441 |
| 1.6 | .9452 | .9463 | .9474 | .9484 | .9495 | .9505 | .9515 | .9525 | .9535 | .9545 |
| 1.7 | .9554 | .9564 | .9573 | .9582 | .9591 | .9599 | .9608 | .9616 | .9625 | .9633 |
| 1.8 | .9641 | .9649 | .9656 | .9664 | .9671 | .9678 | .9686 | .9693 | .9699 | .9706 |
| 1.9 | .9713 | .9719 | .9726 | .9732 | .9738 | .9744 | .9750 | .9756 | .9761 | .9767 |
| 2.0 | .9772 | .9778 | .9783 | .9788 | .9793 | .9798 | .9803 | .9808 | .9812 | .9817 |
| 2.1 | .9821 | .9826 | .9830 | .9834 | .9838 | .9842 | .9846 | .9850 | .9854 | .9857 |
| 2.2 | .9861 | .9864 | .9868 | .9871 | .9875 | .9878 | .9881 | .9884 | .9887 | .9890 |
| 2.3 | .9893 | .9896 | .9898 | .9901 | .9904 | .9906 | .9909 | .9911 | .9913 | .9913 |
| 2.4 | .9918 | .9920 | .9922 | .9925 | .9927 | .9929 | .9931 | .9932 | .9934 | .9936 |
| 2.5 | .9938 | .9940 | .9941 | .9943 | .9945 | .9946 | .9948 | .9949 | .9951 | .9952 |
| 2.6 | .9953 | .9955 | .9956 | .9957 | .9959 | .9960 | .9961 | .9962 | .9963 | .9964 |
| 2.7 | .9965 | .9966 | .9967 | .9968 | .9969 | .9970 | .9971 | .9972 | .9973 | .9974 |
| 2.8 | .9974 | .9975 | .9976 | .9977 | .9977 | .9978 | .9979 | .9979 | .9980 | .9981 |
| 2.9 | .9981 | .9982 | .9982 | .9983 | .9984 | .9984 | .9985 | .9985 | .9986 | .9986 |
| 3.0 | .9986 | .9987 | .9987 | .9988 | .9988 | .9989 | .9989 | .9989 | .9990 | .9990 |

# MODERN BUSINESS STATISTICS

## WITH MICROSOFT® EXCEL

**David R. Anderson**
University of Cincinnati

**Dennis J. Sweeney**
University of Cincinnati

**Thomas A. Williams**
Rochester Institute of Technology

SOUTH-WESTERN
™
THOMSON LEARNING

Australia · Canada · Mexico · Singapore · Spain · United Kingdom · United States

*Dedicated to*
*Krista, Justin, Mark, and Colleen*
*Mark, Linda, Brad, Tim, Scott, and Lisa*
*Cathy, David, and Kristin*

*Modern Business Statistics with Microsoft® Excel, 1st edition* by Anderson, Sweeney, and Williams
Publisher: Melissa Acuna
Sr. Acquisitions Editor: Charles E. McCormick, Jr.
Sr. Developmental Editor: Alice C. Denny
Sr. Marketing Manager: Joseph A. Sabatino
Sr. Production Editor: Deanna R. Quinn
Media Technology Editor: Diane Van Bakel
Media Developmental Editor: Chris Wittmer
Media Production Editor: Robin Browning
Manufacturing Coordinator: Diane Lohman
Internal Design: Craig Ramsdell Design
Cover Design: Paul Ness Design and Casey Gilbertson
Cover Image: DigitalVision/Gordon Bennett, Photographer
Production House and Compositor: BookMasters, Inc.
Printer: R.R. Donnelley & Sons Company

Printed in the United States of America
1   2   3   4   5   04   03   02   01

For more information contact South-Western, 5101 Madison Road, Cincinnati, Ohio, 45227 or find us on the Internet at http://www.swcollege.com

**For permission to use material from this text or product, contact us by**
• **telephone: 1-800-730-2214**
• **fax: 1-800-730-2215**
• **web: http://www.thomsonrights.com**

**Library of Congress Cataloging-in-Publication Data**

Anderson, David Ray
    Modern business statistics with Microsoft® Excel / David R. Anderson, Dennis J. Sweeney, Thomas A. Williams.
        p.   cm.
    Includes bibliographical references and index.
    ISBN 0–324–12174–1 (package)
    ISBN 0–324–12175–X (book)
    ISBN 0–324–12176-8 (CD-ROM)
    1. Commercial statistics.   2. Microsoft Excel for Windows.   I. Sweeney, Dennis J.
II. Williams, Thomas Arthur.   III. Title.
HF1017.A533   2003
005.369—dc21                                                          2001049276

# Brief Contents

# Contents

## Chapter 3
### Descriptive Statistics: Numerical Methods  79

## Chapter 4
**Introduction to Probability  140**

## Chapter 5
**Discrete Probability Distributions 184**

## Chapter 6
**Continuous Probability Distributions 223**

## Chapter 9
## Hypothesis Testing  335

## Chapter 10
**Statistical Inferences About Means and Proportions for Two Populations 397**

## Chapter 11
### Inferences About Population Variances  446

## Chapter 12
### Tests of Goodness of Fit and Independence  473

## Chapter 17
**Nonparametric Methods  748**

# Preface

The purpose of *Modern Business Statistics with Microsoft® Excel* is to give students, primarily in the fields of business administration and economics, an introduction to the field of statistics and its many applications. The text is applications oriented and written with the needs of the nonmathematician in mind; the mathematical prerequisite is knowledge of algebra.

Applications of data analysis and statistical methodology are an integral part of the organization and presentation of the text material. The discussion and development of each technique is presented in an application setting, with the statistical results providing insights to decisions and solutions to problems.

Although the book is applications oriented, we have taken care to provide a sound methodological development and to use notation that is generally accepted for the topic being covered. Hence, students will find that this text provides good preparation for the study of more advanced material. A bibliography to guide further study is included in an appendix.

## USE OF MICROSOFT® EXCEL FOR STATISTICAL ANALYSIS

*Modern Business Statistics with Microsoft® Excel* is first and foremost a statistics textbook that emphasizes statistical concepts and applications. But, since most practical problems are too large to be solved using hand calculations, some type of statistical software package is required to solve these problems. There are several excellent statistical packages available today. However, because most students and potential employers value spreadsheet experience, many colleges and universities now use a spreadsheet package in their statistics courses. Microsoft Excel is the most widely used spreadsheet package in business as well as in colleges and universities. We have written *Modern Business Statistics with Microsoft® Excel* especially for statistics courses in which Excel is used as the software package.

Excel has been integrated within each of the chapters, and plays an integral part in providing an application orientation. We assume that readers using this text are familiar with Excel basics such as selecting cells, entering formulas, copying, and so on. We build on that familiarity by showing how to use the appropriate Excel statistical functions and data analysis tools.

The discussion of using Excel to perform a statistical procedure appears in a subsection immediately following the discussion of the statistical procedure. We believe that this style enables us to fully integrate the use of Excel throughout the text, but still maintain the primary emphasis on the statistical methodology being discussed. In each of these subsections, we use a standard format for setting up a worksheet for statistical analysis. There are three primary tasks: Enter Data, Enter Functions and Formulas, and Apply Tools. We believe a consistent framework for applying Excel helps users to focus on the statistical methodology without getting bogged down in the details of using Excel.

In presenting worksheet figures we often use a nested approach in which the worksheet shown in the background of the figure displays the formulas and the worksheet shown in the foreground shows the values computed using the formulas.

Following is Figure 2.1 from the text, which is displayed to illustrate the use of color in Excel figures. We use brown to highlight the data from the sample (soft drink purchases in this figure) and yellow to highlight the cells containing Excel functions and formulas.

The yellow cells show the functions and formulas in the background worksheet and they show the values obtained using the formulas in the foreground worksheet. A third color (blue) is used in certain figures to highlight material that is printed by Excel as result of using one of the data analysis tools.

Note: Rows 11–44 are hidden.

| | A | B | C | D | E |
|---|---|---|---|---|---|
| 1 | Brand Purchased | | Soft Drink | Frequency | |
| 2 | Coke Classic | | Coke Classic | =COUNTIF($A$2:$A$51,C2) | |
| 3 | Diet Coke | | Diet Coke | =COUNTIF($A$2:$A$51,C3) | |
| 4 | Pepsi-Cola | | Dr. Pepper | =COUNTIF($A$2:$A$51,C4) | |
| 5 | Diet Coke | | Pepsi-Cola | =COUNTIF($A$2:$A$51,C5) | |
| 6 | Coke Classic | | Sprite | =COUNTIF($A$2:$A$51,C6) | |
| 7 | Coke Classic | | | | |
| 8 | Dr. Pepper | | | | |
| 9 | Diet Coke | | | | |
| 10 | Pepsi-Cola | | | | |
| 45 | Pepsi-Cola | | | | |
| 46 | Pepsi-Cola | | | | |
| 47 | Pepsi-Cola | | | | |
| 48 | Coke Classic | | | | |
| 49 | Dr. Pepper | | | | |
| 50 | Pepsi-Cola | | | | |
| 51 | Sprite | | | | |
| 52 | | | | | |

| | A | B | C | D | E |
|---|---|---|---|---|---|
| 1 | Brand Purchased | | Soft Drink | Frequency | |
| 2 | Coke Classic | | Coke Classic | 19 | |
| 3 | Diet Coke | | Diet Coke | 8 | |
| 4 | Pepsi-Cola | | Dr. Pepper | 5 | |
| 5 | Diet Coke | | Pepsi-Cola | 13 | |
| 6 | Coke Classic | | Sprite | 5 | |
| 7 | Coke Classic | | | | |
| 8 | Dr. Pepper | | | | |
| 9 | Diet Coke | | | | |
| 10 | Pepsi-Cola | | | | |
| 45 | Pepsi-Cola | | | | |
| 46 | Pepsi-Cola | | | | |
| 47 | Pepsi-Cola | | | | |
| 48 | Coke Classic | | | | |
| 49 | Dr. Pepper | | | | |
| 50 | Pepsi-Cola | | | | |
| 51 | Sprite | | | | |
| 52 | | | | | |

We have provided over 200 data sets on the CD-ROM accompanying the text. Many of the data sets are used as examples to illustrate statistical concepts in the text; others contain the data for exercises and case problems. For the data sets used as examples in the text we have also included any worksheets used in the analysis. Students can use these worksheets as templates for solving problems in the text. A listing of the data sets is contained inside the back cover of the text.

## FEATURES AND PEDAGOGY

The significant features in this text are summarized below.

## Examples and Exercises Based on Real Data

Over 300 exercises and examples are based on real data and recent sources referencing statistical information. Using the Census Bureau, *The Wall Street Journal, USA Today, Fortune, Barron's,* and a variety of other sources, we have drawn on actual studies to develop scenarios and to create exercises that demonstrate uses of statistics in business and economics. We believe that the use of realistic data helps generate more student interest in the material and enables the student to be more creative in identifying possible applications of statistical methodology.

## Case Problems

We have 24 case problems that appear at the end of the supplementary exercises in many chapters. The case problems provide users with the opportunity to analyze somewhat larger data sets and prepare managerial reports that are based on the results of the analysis.

## Data Files Accompany the Text

Over 200 data files are available and are packaged with the text. The data files can be accessed using Excel 97 as well as Excel 2000. Data files for all case problems, as well as for larger data sets in text illustrations and exercises, are included.

## Statistics in Practice

To emphasize how companies use statistics, each chapter begins with an application supplied by a practitioner. These chapter openings briefly describe an organization and a problem in which the statistical methodology introduced in the chapter has been applied.

## Margin Annotations and Notes & Comments

Margin annotations that highlight key points and provide additional insights for the student are a key feature of this text. These annotations, which appear in the margins, are designed to provide emphasis and enhance understanding of the terms and concepts being presented in the text.

At the end of many sections, we provide "Notes & Comments" designed to give the reader additional insights about the statistical methodology and its application. These notes include warnings about limitations of the methodology, recommendations for application, brief descriptions of technical considerations, and other matters.

## Methods Exercises and Applications Exercises

The end-of-section exercises are split into two parts: Methods and Applications. The Methods exercises require users to use the formulas and make computations. The Applications exercises require students to apply the chapter material in real-world situations. Thus, students focus on the computational "nuts and bolts" and then move on to the subtleties of statistical applications and the interpretation of the statistical output.

## Self-Test Exercises

Some exercises are identified as self-test exercises. Completely worked-out solutions for these exercises are provided in an appendix at the end of the book. Students can attempt the self-text exercises and immediately check the solutions to evaluate their understanding of the concepts presented in the chapter.

## Ancillary Teaching and Learning Materials

WebTutor™, a brand new electronic ancillary, is available with this first edition of *Modern Business Statistics with Microsoft® Excel.* There are two main formats for this product:

- WebTutor is used by an entire class under the direction of the instructor. It provides web-based learning resources to students as well as powerful communication and other course management tools including course calendar, chat, and e-mail for instructors. WebTutor is available on WebCT and Blackboard. See *http://webtutor. thomsonlearning.com* for more information.

- Personal WebTutor provides the learning resources for individual students to purchase, and use for study and review. See *http://pwt.swcollege.com* for more information about this product.

A valuable resource is available to students either through their bookstore or for direct purchase through the on-line catalog at *www.swcollege.com*.

- The **Study Guide** (ISBN: 0-324-12177-6) prepared by John Loucks of St. Edward's University, will provide the student with significant supplementary study materials. For each chapter, it contains key concepts, review materials, example problems worked out in full detail, exercises with answers, and self-test questions with answers.

Instructor support materials are available to adopters from the Thomson Learning™ Academic Resource Center at 800-423-0563 or through *www.swcollege.com*. All instructor ancillaries are provided on a single **Instructor's Resource CD-ROM** (ISBN: 0-324-12179-2). Included in this convenient format are:

- **Solutions Manual**—The *Solutions Manual* prepared by the authors, includes solutions for all problems in the text.
- **Instructor's Manual**—The *Instructor's Manual,* also prepared by the authors, contains solutions to all case problems presented in the text.
- **PowerPoint™ Presentation Slides**—Prepared also by John Loucks, the presentation slides contain a teaching outline that incorporates graphics to help instructors create even more stimulating lectures. The PowerPoint 97 slides may be adapted using PowerPoint software to facilitate classroom use.
- **Test Bank** and **ExamView™**—Prepared by Sarai Hedges of the University of Cincinnati, the Test Bank includes multiple choice questions and problems for each chapter. ExamView computerized testing software allows instructors to create, edit, store and print exams.

Also, at the request of the instructor, a print version of the *Solutions Manual* can be packaged with the text for student purchase.

## ACKNOWLEDGMENTS

We would like to acknowledge the work of our reviewers who provided comments and suggestions of ways to continue to improve our text. Thanks to:

Darl Bien, University of Denver

Thomas W. Bolland, Ohio University

Terry Dielman, Texas Christian University

Mohammed A. El-Saidi, Ferris State University (Michigan)

Abe Feinberg, California State University, Northridge

V. Daniel Guide, Duquesne University

Alan Humphrey, University of Rhode Island

Kenneth Klassen, California State University Northridge

June Lapidus, Roosevelt University

Lynne Pastor, Carnegie Mellon University

William Struning, Seton Hall University

We would like to recognize the following individuals who have helped us in the past and continue to influence our writing.

Glen Archibald, University of Mississippi

Mike Bourke, Houston Baptist University

Peter Bryant, University of Colorado,

Terri L. Byczkowski, University of Cincinnati

Robert Carver, Stonehill College

Ying Chien, University of Scranton

Robert Cochran, University of Wyoming

Murray Côté, University of Florida

David W. Cravens, Texas Christian University

Robert Carver, Stonehill College

Tom Dahlstrom, Eastern College

Ronald Ehresman, Baldwin-Wallace College

Nicholas Farnum, California State University-Fullerton

Michael Ford, Rochester Institute of Technology

Phil Fry, Boise State University

Paul Guy, California State University-Chico

Alan Humphrey, University of Rhode Island

Ann Hussein, Philadelphia College of Textiles and Science

C. Thomas Innis, University of Cincinnati

Ben Isselhardt, Rochester Institute of Technology

Jeffery Jarrett, University of Rhode Island

Barry Kadets, Bryant College

David Krueger, St. Cloud State University

Martin S. Levy, University of Cincinnati

Don Marx, University of Alaska, Anchorage

Ka-sing Man, Georgetown University

John McClain, Cornell University

Tom McCullough, University of California - Berkeley

Mario Miranda, The Ohio State University

Mitchell Muesham, Sam Houston State University

Richard O'Connell, Miami University of Ohio

Alan Olinsky, Bryant College

Tom Pray, Rochester Institute of Technology

Harold Rahmlow, St. Joseph's University

Derrick Reagle, Fordham University

Tom Ryan, Case Western Reserve University

Bill Seaver, University of Tennessee

Alan Smith, Robert Morris College

David Tufte, University of New Orleans

Jack Vaughn, University of Texas-El Paso

Ari Wijetunga, Morehead State University

J. E. Willis, Louisiana State University

Mustafa Yilmaz, Northeastern University

Sarai Hedges, at the University of Cincinnati, made a major contribution to this textbook by reading every chapter and offering numerous suggestions and criticisms. A special thanks is owed to our associates from business and industry who supplied the "Statistics in Practice" features. We recognize them individually by a credit line in each of the articles. Finally, we are also indebted to our senior acquisitions editor Charles McCormick, Jr., our senior developmental editor Alice Denny, our senior production editor Deanna Quinn, our senior marketing manager Joe Sabatino, and others at South-Western/Thomson Learning for their editorial counsel and support during the preparation of this text.

*David R. Anderson*
*Dennis J. Sweeney*
*Thomas A. Williams*

# About the Authors

**David R. Anderson.**    David R. Anderson is Professor of Quantitative Analysis in the College of Business Administration at the University of Cincinnati. Born in Grand Forks, North Dakota, he earned his B.S., M.S., and Ph.D. degrees from Purdue University. Professor Anderson has served as Head of the Department of Quantitative Analysis and Operations Management and as Associate Dean of the College of Business Administration. In addition, he was the coordinator of the college's first Executive Program.

At the University of Cincinnati, Professor Anderson has taught introductory statistics for business students as well as graduate-level courses in regression analysis, multivariate analysis, and management science. He has also taught statistical courses at the Department of Labor in Washington, D.C. He has been honored with nominations and awards for excellence in teaching and excellence in service to student organizations.

Professor Anderson has coauthored ten textbooks in the areas of statistics, management science, linear programming, and production and operations management. He is an active consultant in the field of sampling and statistical methods.

**Dennis J. Sweeney.**    Dennis J. Sweeney is Professor of Quantitative Analysis and founder of the Center for Productivity Improvement at the University of Cincinnati. Born in Des Moines, Iowa, he earned a B.S.B.A. degree from Drake University and his M.B.A. and D.B.A. degrees from Indiana University where he was an NDEA Fellow. During 1978–79, Professor Sweeney worked in the management science group at Procter & Gamble; during 1981–82, he was a visiting professor at Duke University. Professor Sweeney served as Head of the Department of Quantitative Analysis and as Associate Dean of the College of Business Administration at the University of Cincinnati.

Professor Sweeney has published more than 30 articles and monographs in the area of management science and statistics. The National Science Foundation, IBM, Procter & Gamble, Federated Department Stores, Kroger, and Cincinnati Gas & Electric have funded his research, which has been published in *Management Science*, *Operations Research*, *Mathematical Programming*, *Decision Sciences*, and other journals.

Professor Sweeney has coauthored ten textbooks in the areas of statistics, management science, linear programming, and production and operations management.

**Thomas A. Williams.**    Thomas A. Williams is Professor of Management Science in the College of Business at Rochester Institute of Technology. Born in Elmira, New York, he earned his B.S. degree at Clarkson University. He did his graduate work at Rensselaer Polytechnic Institute, where he received his M.S. and Ph.D. degrees.

Before joining the College of Business at RIT, Professor Williams served for seven years as a faculty member in the College of Business Administration at the University of Cincinnati, where he developed the undergraduate program in Information Systems and then served as its coordinator. At RIT he was the first chairman of the Decision Sciences Department. He teaches courses in management science and statistics, as well as graduate courses in regression and decision analysis.

Professor Williams is the coauthor of eleven textbooks in the areas of management science, statistics, production and operations management, and mathematics. He has been a consultant for numerous *Fortune* 500 companies and has worked on projects ranging from the use of data analysis to the development of large-scale regression models.

# DATA AND STATISTICS

**CONTENTS**

## STATISTICS IN PRACTICE

### BUSINESS WEEK*
*New York, New York*

With a global circulation of more than 1 million, *Business Week* is the most widely read business magazine in the world. More than 200 dedicated reporters and editors in 26 bureaus worldwide deliver a variety of articles of interest to the business and economic community. Along with feature articles on current topics, the magazine contains regular sections on International Business, Economic Analysis, Information Processing, and Science & Technology. Information in the feature articles and the regular sections help readers stay abreast of current developments and assess the impact of those developments on business and economic conditions.

Most issues of *Business Week* provide an in-depth report on a topic of current interest. Often, the in-depth reports contain statistical facts and summaries that help the reader understand the business and/or economic information. For instance, the January 8, 2001, issue contained a report on the top 25 managers of the year, and the March 19, 2001, issue contained a report on the banking crisis in Japan. The June 18, 2001, issue provided a variety of statistics on the top 100 information technology companies. In addition, the weekly *Business Week Investor* contains statistics about the state of the economy including production indexes, stock prices, mutual funds, and interest rates.

*Business Week* also uses statistics and statistical information to help manage its own business. For example, an annual survey of subscribers helps the company learn about subscriber demographics, reading habits, likely purchases, lifestyles, and so on. *Business Week* managers use the statistical summaries from the

*Business Week* uses statistical facts and summaries in many of its articles. © Deanna Ettinger/South-Western.

survey to provide better services to subscribers and advertisers. For instance, a recent North American subscriber survey indicated that 90% of *Business Week* subscribers have a personal computer at home and that 64% of *Business Week* subscribers are involved with computer purchases at work. Such statistics alert *Business Week* managers to subscriber interest in articles about new developments in computers. The results of the survey are also made available to potential advertisers. The high percentage of subscribers using personal computers at home and the high percentage of subscribers involved with computer purchases at work would be an incentive for a computer manufacturer to consider advertising in *Business Week*.

In this chapter, we discuss the types of data that are available for statistical analysis and describe how the data are obtained. We introduce descriptive statistics and statistical inference as ways of converting data into meaningful and easily interpreted statistical information.

*The authors are indebted to Charlene Trentham, Research Manager at *Business Week,* for providing this Statistics in Practice.

Frequently, we see the following kinds of statements in newspaper and magazine articles:

- The average price of a movie ticket is $5.60, and the average amount spent by a family of four at the concession stand is $8 (*Money,* April 2001).
- Last year less than 40% of stock mutual funds actually had positive returns. But, net inflows to stock funds have increased by $2 billion (*Forbes Best of the Web,* February 26, 2001).
- Starbucks plans to offer wire-free Internet access in 2,100 of its 3,000 North American coffee shops (*Inc. Tech* 2001).
- Last year Corning sold about $2.85 billion of fiber and cabling, or about 40% of its total revenue of $7.1 billion (*Fortune,* March 19, 2001).

* In Hong Kong, Disney has paid only $310 million for a 43% stake in a venture that is valued at around $4 billion (*Time,* February 19, 2001).

The numerical facts in the preceding statements ($5.60, $8, 40%, $2 billion, 2100, 3000, $2.85 billion, 40%, $7.1 billion, $310 million, 43%, and $4 billion) are called statistics. Thus, in everyday usage, the term *statistics* refers to numerical facts. However, the field, or subject, of statistics involves much more than numerical facts. In a broad sense, statistics is the art and science of collecting, analyzing, presenting, and interpreting data. Particularly in business and economics, a major reason for collecting, analyzing, presenting, and interpreting data is to give managers and decision makers a better understanding of the business and economic environment and thus enable them to make more informed and better decisions. In this text, we emphasize the use of statistics for business and economic decision making.

Chapter 1 begins with some illustrations of the applications of statistics in business and economics. In Section 1.2 we define the term *data* and introduce the concept of a data set. This section also introduces key terms such as *variables* and *observations,* discusses the difference between quantitative and qualitative data, and illustrates the difference between cross-sectional and time series data. Section 1.3 discusses how data can be obtained from existing sources or through survey and experimental studies designed to obtain new data. The important role that the Internet now plays in obtaining data is also highlighted. The use of data in developing descriptive statistics and in making statistical inferences is described in Sections 1.4 and 1.5, and Section 1.6 concludes with an introduction to the use of Microsoft Excel for statistical analysis.

## 1.1   APPLICATIONS IN BUSINESS AND ECONOMICS

In today's global business and economic environment, vast amounts of statistical information are available. The most successful managers and decision makers are the ones who can understand the information and use it effectively. In this section, we provide examples that illustrate some of the uses of statistics in business and economics.

### Accounting

Public accounting firms use statistical sampling procedures when conducting audits for their clients. For instance, suppose an accounting firm wants to determine whether the amount of accounts receivable shown on a client's balance sheet fairly represents the actual amount of accounts receivable. Usually the number of individual accounts receivable is so large that reviewing and validating every account would be too time-consuming and expensive. The common practice in such situations is for the audit staff to select a subset of the accounts called a sample. After reviewing the accuracy of the sampled accounts, the auditors draw a conclusion as to whether the accounts receivable amount shown on the client's balance sheet is acceptable.

### Finance

Financial analysts use a variety of statistical information to guide their investment recommendations. In the case of stocks, the analysts review a variety of financial data including price/earnings ratios and dividend yields. By comparing the information for an individual stock with information about the stock market averages, a financial analyst can begin to draw a conclusion as to whether an individual stock is over- or undervalued. For example, *Barron's* (January 10, 2000) reported that the average price/earnings ratio for the 30 stocks in the Dow Jones Industrial Average was 24.7. Philip Morris had a price/earnings ratio of

9. In this case, the statistical information on price/earnings ratios showed that Philip Morris had a lower price in comparison to its earnings than the average for the Dow Jones stocks. Therefore, a financial analyst might have concluded that Philip Morris was currently underpriced. This and other information about Philip Morris would help the analyst make buy, sell, or hold recommendations for the stock.

## Marketing

Electronic scanners at retail checkout counters are being used to collect data for a variety of marketing research applications. For example, data suppliers such as ACNielsen and Information Resources, Inc., purchase point-of-sale scanner data from grocery stores, process the data, and then sell statistical summaries of the data to manufacturers. Manufacturers spent an average of $387,325 per product category to obtain this type of scanner data (Scanner Data User Survey, Mercer Management Consulting, Inc., April 1997). Manufacturers also purchase data and statistical summaries on promotional activities such as special pricing and the use of in-store displays. Brand managers can review the scanner statistics and the promotional activity statistics to gain a better understanding of the relationship between promotional activities and sales. Such analyses are helpful in establishing future marketing strategies for the various products.

## Production

With today's emphasis on quality, quality control is an important application of statistics in production. A variety of statistical quality control charts are used to monitor the output of a production process. In particular, an $x$-bar chart is used to monitor the average output. Suppose, for example, that a machine is being used to fill containers with 12 ounces of a soft drink. Periodically, a sample of containers is selected and the average number of ounces in the sample containers is computed. This average, or $x$-bar value, is plotted on an $x$-bar chart. A plotted value above the chart's upper control limit indicates overfilling, and a plotted value below the chart's lower control limit indicates underfilling. The process is termed "in control" and allowed to continue as long as the plotted $x$-bar values are between the chart's upper and lower control limits. Properly interpreted, an $x$-bar chart can help determine when adjustments are necessary to correct a production process.

## Economics

Economists are frequently asked to provide forecasts about the future of the economy or some aspect of it. They use a variety of statistical information in making such forecasts. For instance, in forecasting inflation rates, economists use statistical information on such indicators as the Producer Price Index, the unemployment rate, and manufacturing capacity utilization. Often these statistical indicators are entered into computerized forecasting models that predict inflation rates.

Applications of statistics such as those described in this section are an integral part of this text. Such examples provide an overview of the breadth of statistical applications. To supplement these examples, we have asked practitioners in the fields of business and economics to provide chapter-opening Statistics in Practice articles that introduce the material covered in each chapter. The Statistics in Practice applications show the importance of statistics in a wide variety of decision-making situations.

## 1.2 DATA

Data are the facts and figures that are collected, analyzed, and summarized for presentation and interpretation. Together, the data collected in a particular study are referred to as the data set for the study. Table 1.1 shows a data set containing information for 25 of

**TABLE 1.1**    A DATA SET FOR 25 SHADOW STOCKS

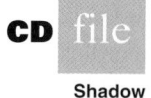

**CD** file

Shadow

| Company | Exchange | Ticker Symbol | Annual Sales ($ millions) | Earnings per Share ($) | Price/ Earnings Ratio |
|---|---|---|---|---|---|
| Advanced Comm. Systems | OTC | ACSC | 75.10 | 0.32 | 39.10 |
| Ag-Chem Equipment Co. | OTC | AGCH | 321.10 | 0.48 | 23.40 |
| Aztec Manufacturing Co. | NYSE | AZZ | 79.70 | 1.18 | 7.80 |
| Cal-Maine Foods, Inc. | OTC | CALM | 314.10 | 0.38 | 11.70 |
| Chesapeake Utilities | NYSE | CPK | 174.50 | 1.13 | 16.20 |
| Dataram Corporation | AMEX | DTM | 73.10 | 0.86 | 11.00 |
| EnergySouth, Inc. | OTC | ENSI | 74.00 | 1.67 | 13.20 |
| Gencor Industries, Inc. | AMEX | GX | 263.30 | 1.96 | 4.70 |
| Industrial Scientific | OTC | ISCX | 43.50 | 2.03 | 11.50 |
| Keystone Consolidated | NYSE | KES | 365.70 | 0.86 | 9.40 |
| LandCare USA, Inc. | NYSE | GRW | 111.40 | 0.33 | 29.40 |
| Market Facts, Inc. | OTC | MFAC | 126.70 | 0.98 | 26.50 |
| Meridian Diagnostics, Inc. | OTC | KITS | 36.30 | 0.46 | 14.70 |
| Merit Medical Systems | OTC | MMSI | 67.20 | 0.27 | 24.50 |
| Met-Pro Corporation | NYSE | MPR | 61.90 | 1.01 | 12.40 |
| Nobility Homes, Inc. | OTC | NOBH | 45.80 | 0.87 | 14.70 |
| Omega Research, Inc. | OTC | OMGA | 27.60 | 0.11 | 27.30 |
| Point of Sale Limited | OTC | POSIF | 12.30 | 0.28 | 25.40 |
| Psychemedics Corp. | AMEX | PMD | 17.60 | 0.13 | 39.40 |
| Roadhouse Grill, Inc. | OTC | GRLL | 118.40 | 0.26 | 20.80 |
| Selas Corp. of America | AMEX | SLS | 97.10 | 0.77 | 10.70 |
| Toymax International, Inc. | OTC | TMAX | 104.50 | 1.08 | 4.70 |
| VSI Holdings, Inc. | AMEX | VIS | 166.8 | 0.25 | 21 |
| Warrantech Corporation | OTC | WTEC | 207.30 | 0.13 | 29.80 |
| Webco Industries, Inc. | AMEX | WEB | 153.50 | 0.88 | 7.50 |

*Source:* American Association of Individual Investors web site, March 1999.

the shadow stocks tracked by the American Association of Individual Investors. Shadow stocks are common stocks of smaller companies that are not closely followed by Wall Street analysts.

## Elements, Variables, and Observations

Elements are the entities on which data are collected. For the data set in Table 1.1, each individual company's stock is an element. With 25 stocks, the data set contains 25 elements.

A **variable** is a characteristic of interest for the elements. The data set in Table 1.1 has the following five variables:

* *Exchange:* Where the stock is traded—NYSE (New York Stock Exchange), AMEX (American Stock Exchange), and OTC (Over-the-Counter).
* *Ticker Symbol:* The abbreviation used to identify the stock on the exchange listing.
* *Annual Sales:* Total sales for the company for the most recent 12 months in millions of dollars.
* *Earnings per Share:* Total earnings per share for the latest 12 months in dollars.
* *Price/Earnings Ratio:* Market price per share divided by the most recent 12 months' earnings per share.

Data are obtained by collecting measurements on each variable for every element in a study. The set of measurements obtained for a particular element is called an observation. Referring to Table 1.1, we see that the set of measurements for the first observation (Advanced Comm. Systems) is OTC, ACSC, 75.10, 0.32, and 39.10. The set of measurements for the second observation (Ag-Chem Equipment Co.) is OTC, AGCH, 321.10, 0.48, and 23.40; and so on. Because the data set contains 25 elements, it has 25 observations.

## Scales of Measurement

Data are obtained using one of the following scales of measurement: nominal, ordinal, interval, and ratio. The scale of measurement determines the amount of information contained in the data and indicates the data summarization and statistical analyses that are most appropriate.

The scale of measurement for a variable is a nominal scale when the data are labels or names used to identify an attribute of the element. For example, referring to the data in Table 1.1, we see that the scale of measurement for the exchange variable is nominal because NYSE, AMEX, and OTC are labels used to identify where the company's stock is traded. In cases where the scale of measurement is nominal, a numeric code as well as nonnumeric labels may be used. For example, to facilitate data collection and to prepare the data for entry into a computer database, we might use a numeric code by letting 1 denote the New York Stock Exchange, 2 denote the American Stock Exchange, and 3 denote over-the-counter. In this case the numeric values 1, 2, and 3 are the labels used to identify where the stock is traded. The scale of measurement is nominal even though the data are shown as numeric values.

The scale of measurement for a variable is an ordinal scale if the data have the properties of nominal data and the order or rank of the data is meaningful. For example, Eastside Automotive sends customers a questionnaire designed to obtain data on the quality of its automotive repair service. Each customer provides a repair service rating of excellent, good, or poor. Because the data obtained are the labels—excellent, good, or poor—the data have the properties of nominal data. In addition, the data can be ranked, or ordered, with respect to the service quality. Data recorded as excellent indicate the best service, followed by good and then poor. Thus, the scale of measurement is ordinal. Note that the ordinal data can also be recorded using a numeric code. For example, we could use 1 for excellent, 2 for good, and 3 for poor to maintain the properties of ordinal data. Thus, data for an ordinal scale may be either nonnumeric or numeric.

The scale of measurement for a variable is an interval scale if the data have the properties of ordinal data and the interval between observations is expressed in terms of a fixed unit of measure. Interval data are always numeric. Scholastic Aptitude Test (SAT) scores are an example of interval-scaled data. For example, three students with SAT scores of 1120, 1050, and 970 can be ranked or ordered in terms of best performance to poorest performance. In addition, the differences between the scores are meaningful. For instance, student 1 scored $1120 - 1050 = 70$ points more than student 2, while student 2 scored $1050 - 970 = 80$ points more than student 3.

The scale of measurement for a variable is a ratio scale if the data have all the properties of interval data and the ratio of two values is meaningful. Variables such as distance, height, weight, and time use the ratio scale of measurement. A requirement of this scale is that it must contain a zero value that indicates that nothing exists for the variable at the zero point. For example, consider the cost of an automobile. A zero value for the cost would indicate that the automobile has no cost and is free. In addition, if we compare the cost of $30,000 for one automobile to the cost of $15,000 for a second automobile, the ratio property shows that the first automobile is $30,000/$15,000 = 2 times, or twice, the cost of the second automobile.

## Qualitative and Quantitative Data

Data can be further classified as being either qualitative or quantitative. Qualitative data are labels or names used to identify an attribute of each element. Qualitative data use either the nominal or ordinal scale of measurement and may be nonnumeric or numeric. Quantitative data are numeric values that indicate how much or how many. Quantitative data are obtained using either the interval or ratio scale of measurement.

The statistical method appropriate for summarizing data depends upon whether the data are qualitative or quantitative

A qualitative variable is a variable with qualitative data, and a quantitative variable is a variable with quantitative data. The statistical analysis that is appropriate for a particular variable depends upon whether the variable is qualitative or quantitative. If the variable is qualitative, the statistical analysis is rather limited. We can summarize qualitative data by counting the number of observations in each qualitative category or by computing the proportion of the observations in each qualitative category. However, even when the qualitative data have a numeric code, arithmetic operations such as addition, subtraction, multiplication, and division do not provide meaningful results. Section 2.1 provides ways for summarizing qualitative data.

On the other hand, arithmetic operations often provide meaningful results for a quantitative variable. For example, for a quantitative variable, the data may be added and then divided by the number of observations to compute the average value. This average is usually meaningful and easily interpreted. In general, more alternatives for statistical analysis are possible when the data are quantitative. Section 2.2 and Chapter 3 provide ways of summarizing quantitative data.

## Cross-Sectional and Time Series Data

For purposes of statistical analysis, distinguishing between cross-sectional data and time series data is important. Cross-sectional data are data collected at the same or approximately the same point in time. The data in Table 1.1 are cross-sectional because they describe the five variables for the 25 shadow stocks at the same point in time. Time series data are data collected over several time periods. For example, Figure 1.1 is a graph of the

**FIGURE 1.1**    U.S. CITY AVERAGE PRICE PER GALLON FOR UNLEADED REGULAR GASOLINE

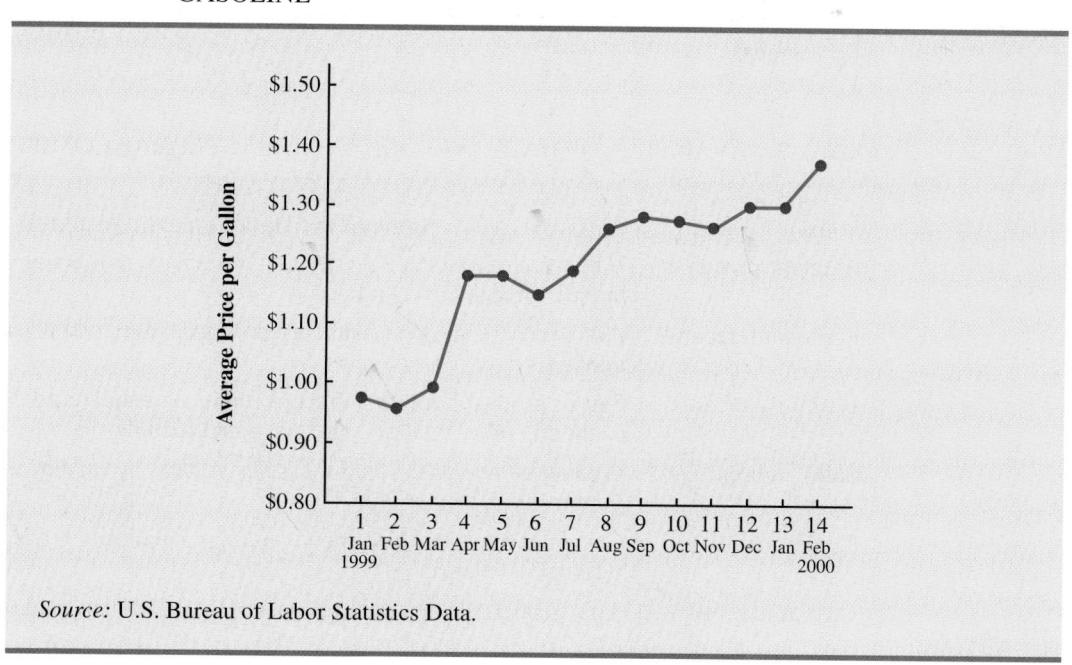

*Source:* U.S. Bureau of Labor Statistics Data.

U.S. city average price per gallon for unleaded regular gasoline. It shows that the average price per gallon has grown from approximately $0.97 per gallon in January 1999 to $1.37 per gallon in February 2000. Most of the statistical methods presented in this text apply to cross-sectional data.

---

### NOTES AND COMMENTS

1. An observation is the set of measurements obtained for each element in a data set. Hence, the number of observations is always the same as the number of elements. The number of measurements obtained for each element is equal to the number of variables. Hence, the total number of data items is the number of observations multiplied by the number of variables.

2. Quantitative data may be discrete or continuous. Quantitative data that measure how many are discrete. Quantitative data that measure how much are continuous because they have no separation between the possible data values.

---

## 1.3   DATA SOURCES

Data can be collected from existing sources or from surveys and experimental studies designed to obtain new data.

### Existing Sources

In some cases, data needed for a particular application may already exist within a firm or organization. All companies maintain a variety of databases about their employees, customers, and business operations. Data on employee salaries, ages, and years of experience can usually be obtained from internal personnel records. Data on sales, advertising expenditures, distribution costs, inventory levels, and production quantities are generally available from other internal records. Most companies also maintain detailed data about their customers. Table 1.2 shows some of the data commonly available from internal company records.

**TABLE 1.2   EXAMPLES OF DATA AVAILABLE FROM INTERNAL COMPANY RECORDS**

| Source | Some of the Data Typically Available |
|---|---|
| Employee records | Name, address, social security number, salary, number of vacation days, number of sick days, and bonus |
| Production records | Part or product number, quantity produced, direct labor cost, and materials cost |
| Inventory records | Part or product number, number of units on hand, reorder level, economic order quantity, and discount schedule |
| Sales records | Product number, sales volume, sales volume by region, and sales volume by customer type |
| Credit records | Customer name, address, phone number, credit limit, and accounts receivable balance |
| Customer profile | Age, gender, income level, household size, address, and preferences |

Substantial amounts of business and economic data are now available from organizations that specialize in collecting and maintaining data. Companies obtain access to these external data sources through leasing arrangements or by purchase. Dun & Bradstreet, Bloomberg, and Dow Jones & Company are three firms that provide extensive business database services to clients. ACNielsen and Information Resources, Inc., have built successful businesses collecting and processing data that they sell to advertisers and product manufacturers.

Data are also available from a variety of industry associations and special interest organizations. The Travel Industry Association of America maintains travel-related information such as the number of tourists and travel expenditures by states. Such data would be of interest to firms and individuals in the travel industry. The Graduate Management Admission Council maintains data on test scores, student characteristics, and graduate management education programs. Most of the data from these types of sources are available to qualified users at a modest cost.

In recent years, the Internet has become an important source of data. Almost all companies have Internet web sites and provide public access to them. Figure 1.2 shows the

**FIGURE 1.2**   INTERNET ADDRESSES FOR SELECTED COMPANIES

| | | |
|---|---|---|
| **ACNielsen Corporation**<br>www.acnielsen.com | **Disney**<br>www.disney.com | **Morton International, Inc.**<br>www.morton.com |
| **Alcoa Inc.**<br>www.alcoa.com | **Dollar General Corporation**<br>www.dollargeneral.com | **Motorola, Inc.**<br>www.motorola.com |
| **Amazon.com, Inc.**<br>www.amazon.com | **Dow Chemical Company**<br>www.dowchemical.com | **Nielsen Media Research, Inc.**<br>www.nielsenmedia.com |
| **American Airlines Inc.**<br>www.aa.com | **E.I. DuPont de Nemours and Company**<br>www.dupont.com | **Novell, Inc.**<br>www.novell.com |
| **American Association of Individual Investors**<br>www.aaii.com | **E*TRADE Securities, Inc.**<br>www.etrade.com | **Oracle Corporation**<br>www.oracle.com |
| **American Express Company**<br>www.americanexpress.com | **Ford Motor Company**<br>www.ford.com | **Polaroid Corporation**<br>www.polaroid.com |
| **Andersen Consulting**<br>www.ac.com | **General Electric Company**<br>www.ge.com | **Procter & Gamble Co.**<br>www.pg.com |
| **America Online, Inc.**<br>www.aol.com | **General Motors Corporation**<br>www.gm.com | **The Prudential Insurance Company of America**<br>www.prudential.com |
| **AT&T**<br>www.att.com | **The Goodyear Tire & Rubber Company**<br>www.goodyear.com | **Quicken.com**<br>www.quicken.com |
| **BMW of North America**<br>www.bmw.com | **Harris Corporation**<br>www.harris.com | **SAP America, Inc.**<br>www.sap.com |
| **The Boeing Company**<br>www.boeing.com | **Hewlett-Packard Company**<br>www.hp.com | **Sears Roebuck and Company**<br>www.sears.com |
| **Business Week**<br>www.businessweek.com | **The Home Depot, Inc.**<br>www.homedepot.com | **Siebel Systems, Inc.**<br>www.siebel.com |
| **BUY.COM, Inc.**<br>www.buy.com | **Honeywell**<br>www.honeywell.com | **Sprint Corporation**<br>www.sprint.com |
| **Caterpillar, Inc.**<br>www.caterpillar.com | **IBM Corporation**<br>www.ibm.com | **Toyota Motor Corporation**<br>www.toyota.com |
| **Charles Schwab & Co.**<br>www.charlesschwab.com | **International Paper**<br>www.ipaper.com | **The Travelers Insurance Company**<br>www.travelers.com |
| **Chemdex Corporation**<br>www.chemdex.com | **Johnson & Johnson**<br>www.johnsonjohnson.com | **Union Carbide**<br>www.unioncarbide.com |
| **Chevron Corporation**<br>www.chevron.com | **L.L. Bean, Inc.**<br>www.llbean.com | **United Way of America**<br>www.unitedway.org |
| **Cisco Systems, Inc.**<br>www.cisco.com | **Lucent Technologies**<br>www.lucent.com | **US Airways, Inc.**<br>www.usair.com |
| **Citibank**<br>www.citibank.com | **McDonald's Corporation**<br>www.mcdonalds.com | **Visa International**<br>www.visa.com |
| **The CocaCola Company**<br>www.cocacola.com | **Mead Corporation**<br>www.mead.com | **Wal-Mart Stores, Inc.**<br>www.walmart.com |
| **Colgate-Palmolive Company**<br>www.colgate.com | **Microsoft Corporation**<br>www.microsoft.com | **Xerox Corporation**<br>www.xerox.com |
| **Dell Computer Corporation**<br>www.dell.com | **Minnesota Mining and Manufacturing (3M)**<br>www.mmm.com | **The Yankee Group**<br>www.yankeegroup.com |
| **Delta Air Lines**<br>www.delta-air.com | | |

Internet addresses for a variety of companies, including the companies that contributed the Statistics in Practice applications that appear at the beginning of each chapter. By accessing these web sites, one can easily obtain a variety of product and other types of information concerning these companies. In addition, a number of companies now specialize in making information available over the Internet. As a result, one can obtain access to stock quotes, meal prices at restaurants, salary data, and an almost infinite variety of information.

Government agencies are another important source of existing data. For instance, the U.S. Department of Labor maintains considerable data on employment rates, wage rates, size of the labor force, and union membership. Table 1.3 lists selected governmental agencies and some of the data they provide. Most government agencies that collect and process data also make the results available through a web site. For instance, the U.S. Census Bureau has a wealth of data at its web site, *www.census.gov*. Figure 1.3 shows the home page for the U.S. Census Bureau.

## Statistical Studies

Sometimes the data needed for a particular application are not available through existing sources. In such cases, the data can often be obtained by conducting a statistical study. Statistical studies can be classified as either *experimental* or *observational*.

*The largest experimental statistical study ever conducted is believed to be the 1954 Public Health Service experiment for the Salk polio vaccine. Nearly two million children in grades 1, 2, and 3 were selected from throughout the United States*

In an experimental study, a variable of interest is first identified. Then one or more other variables are identified and controlled so that data can be obtained about how they influence the variable of interest. For example, a pharmaceutical firm might be interested in conducting an experiment to learn about how a new drug affects blood pressure. Blood pressure is the variable of interest in the study. The dosage level of the new drug is another variable that is hoped to have a causal effect on blood pressure. To obtain data about the effect of the new drug, a sample of individuals is selected. The dosage level of the new drug is controlled, with different groups of individuals being given different dosage levels. Data on blood pressure are collected for each group. Statistical analysis of the experimental data can help determine how the new drug affects blood pressure.

*Studies of smokers and nonsmokers are observational studies because researchers do not determine or control who will smoke and who will not smoke.*

In nonexperimental, or observational, statistical studies, no attempt is made to control the variables of interest. A survey is perhaps the most common type of observational study. For instance, in a personal interview survey, research questions are first identified. Then a questionnaire is designed and administered to a sample of individuals. Some restaurants use observational studies to obtain data about their customers' opinions of the quality of food, service, atmosphere, and so on. A questionnaire used by the Lobster Pot Restaurant in Red-

**TABLE 1.3**   EXAMPLES OF DATA AVAILABLE FROM SELECTED GOVERNMENT
AGENCIES

| Government Agency | Some of the Data Available |
| --- | --- |
| Bureau of the Census<br>www.census.gov | Population data and their distribution, data on number of households and their distribution, data on household income and their distribution |
| Federal Reserve Board<br>www.bog.frb.fed.us | Data on the money supply, installment credit, exchange rates, and discount rates |
| Office of Management and Budget<br>www.whitehouse.gov/omb | Data on revenue, expenditures, and debt of the federal government |
| Department of Commerce<br>www.doc.gov | Data on business activity, value of shipments by industry, level of profits by industry, and growing and declining industries |

**FIGURE 1.3**    U.S. CENSUS BUREAU HOMEPAGE

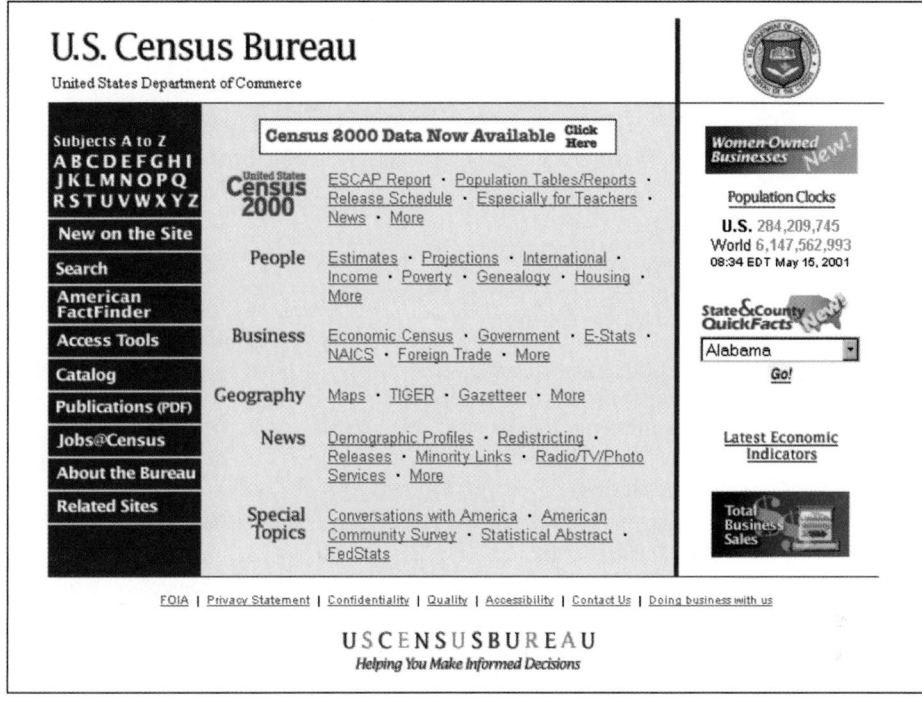

ington Shores, Florida, is shown in Figure 1.4. Note that the customers completing the questionnaire are asked to provide ratings for five variables: food quality, friendliness of service, promptness of service, cleanliness, and management. The response categories of excellent, good, satisfactory, and unsatisfactory provide data that enable Lobster Pot's managers to assess the quality of the restaurant's operation.

Managers wanting to use data and statistical analyses as an aid to decision making must be aware of the time and cost required to obtain the data. The use of existing data sources is desirable when data must be obtained in a relatively short period of time. If important data are not readily available from an existing source, the additional time and cost involved in obtaining the data must be taken into account. In all cases, the decision maker should consider the contribution of the statistical analysis to the decision-making process. The cost of data acquisition and the subsequent statistical analysis should not exceed the savings generated by using the information to make a better decision.

## Data Acquisition Errors

Managers should always be aware of the possibility of data errors in statistical studies. Using erroneous data can be worse than not using any data at all. An error in data acquisition occurs whenever the data value obtained is not equal to the true or actual value that would have been obtained with a correct procedure. Such errors can occur in a number of ways. For example, an interviewer might make a recording error, such as a transposition in writing the age of a 24-year-old person as 42, or the person answering an interview question might misinterpret the question and provide an incorrect response.

Experienced data analysts take great care in collecting and recording data to ensure that errors are not made. Special procedures can be used to check for internal consistency of the data. For instance, such procedures would indicate that the analyst should review the

**FIGURE 1.4**   CUSTOMER OPINION QUESTIONNAIRE USED BY THE LOBSTER POT RESTAURANT, REDINGTON SHORES, FLORIDA

accuracy of data for a respondent who is shown to be 22 years of age but who reports 20 years of work experience. Data analysts also review data with unusually large and small values, called outliers, which are candidates for possible data errors. In Chapter 3 we present some of the methods statisticians use to identify outliers.

Errors often occur during data acquisition. Blindly using any data that happen to be available or using data that were acquired with little care can provide poor and misleading information and lead to bad decisions. Thus, taking steps to acquire accurate data can help ensure reliable and valuable decision-making information.

## 1.4   DESCRIPTIVE STATISTICS

Most of the statistical information in newspapers, magazines, company reports, and other publications consists of data that are summarized and presented in a form that is easy for the reader to understand. Such summaries of data, which may be tabular, graphical, or numerical, are referred to as **descriptive statistics.**

Refer again to the data set in Table 1.1 where data on 25 shadow stocks are presented. Methods of descriptive statistics can be used to provide summaries of the information in this data set. For example, a tabular summary of the data for the qualitative variable Exchange is shown in Table 1.4. A graphical summary of the same data, called a bar graph, is

**TABLE 1.4**   FREQUENCIES AND PERCENT FREQUENCIES FOR THE EXCHANGE
VARIABLE

| Exchange | Frequency | Percent Frequency |
|---|---|---|
| New York Stock Exchange (NYSE) | 5 | 20 |
| American Stock Exchange (AMEX) | 6 | 24 |
| Over-the-counter (OTC) | 14 | 56 |
| Totals | 25 | 100 |

shown in Figure 1.5. The purpose of these types of tabular and graphical summaries is to make the data easier to interpret. Referring to Table 1.4 and Figure 1.5, we can see easily that the majority of the stocks in the data set are traded over the counter. On a percentage basis, 56% are traded over the counter, 24% are traded on the American Stock Exchange, and 20% are traded on the New York Stock Exchange.

A graphical summary of the data for the quantitative variable Price/Earnings Ratio for the shadow stocks, called a histogram, is provided in Figure 1.6. From the histogram, it is easy to see that the price/earnings ratios range from 0.0 to 39.9, with the highest concentrations between 8.0 and 15.9.

In addition to tabular and graphical displays, numerical descriptive statistics are used to summarize data. The most common numerical descriptive statistic is the average, or mean. Using the data on annual sales for the shadow stocks in Table 1.1, we can compute the average annual sales by adding the annual sales for all 25 stocks and dividing the sum by 25. Doing so provides average annual sales of $125.54 million. This average is taken as a measure of the central tendency, or central location, of the data.

In recent years interest has grown in statistical methods that can be used for developing and presenting descriptive statistics. Chapters 2 and 3 are devoted to the tabular, graphical, and numerical methods of descriptive statistics.

**FIGURE 1.5**   BAR GRAPH FOR THE EXCHANGE VARIABLE

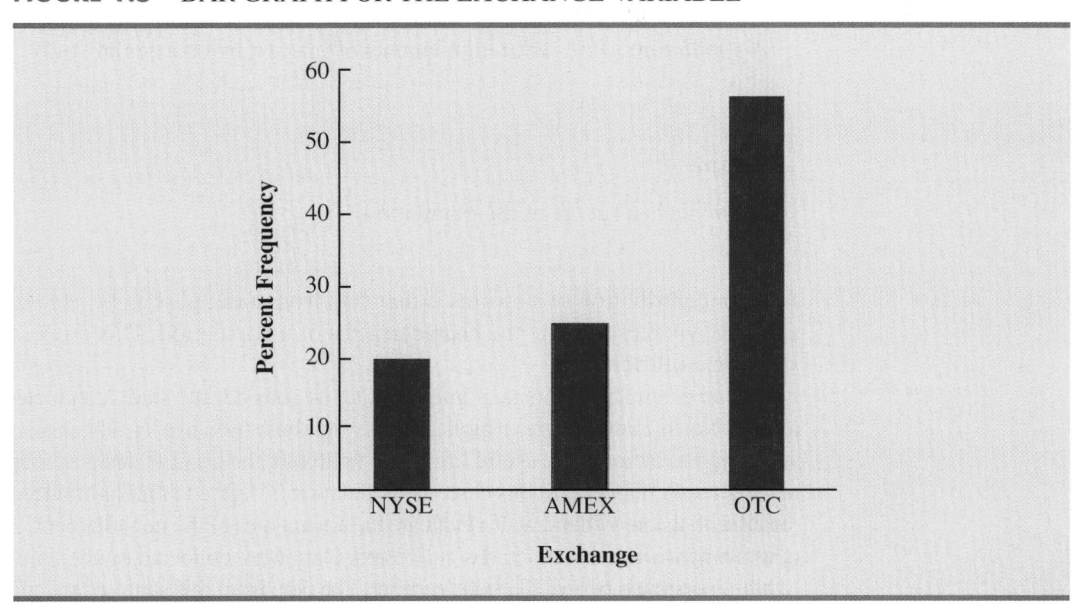

**FIGURE 1.6**    HISTOGRAM FOR 25 SHADOW STOCKS

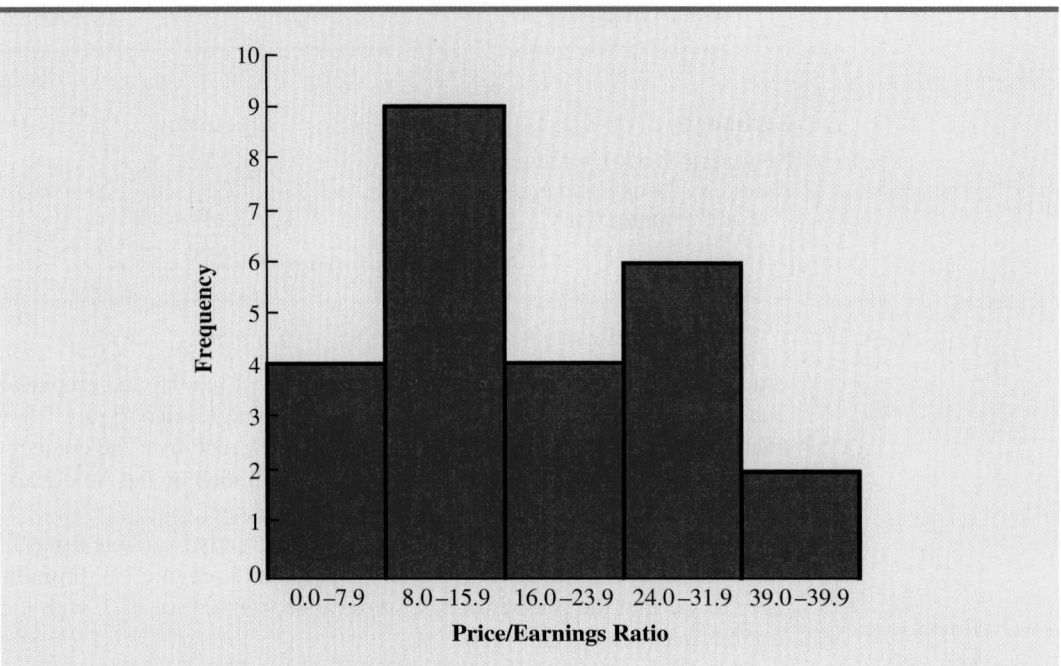

## 1.5    STATISTICAL INFERENCE

In many situations, data are sought for a large group of elements (individuals, companies, voters, households, products, customers, and so on). Because of time, cost, and other considerations, data are collected from only a small portion of the group. The larger group of elements in a particular study is called the **population**, and the smaller group is called the **sample**. Formally, we use the following definitions.

> **Population**
>
> A *population* is the set of all elements of interest in a particular study.

> **Sample**
>
> A *sample* is a subset of the population.

A major contribution of statistics is that data from a sample can be used to make estimates and test hypotheses about the characteristics of a population. This process is referred to as **statistical inference.**

     As an example of statistical inference, let us consider the study conducted by Norris Electronics. Norris manufactures a high-intensity lightbulb used in a variety of electrical products. In an attempt to increase the useful life of the lightbulb, the product design group has developed a new lightbulb filament. In this case, the population is defined as all lightbulbs that could be produced with the new filament. To evaluate the advantages of the new filament, 200 bulbs with the new filament were manufactured and tested. Data were collected on the number of hours each lightbulb operated before filament burnout. The data from this sample are reported in Table 1.5.

**TABLE 1.5** HOURS UNTIL BURNOUT FOR A SAMPLE OF 200 LIGHTBULBS FOR NORRIS ELECTRONICS

| | | | | | | | | | |
|---|---|---|---|---|---|---|---|---|---|
| 107 | 73 | 68 | 97 | 76 | 79 | 94 | 59 | 98 | 57 |
| 54 | 65 | 71 | 70 | 84 | 88 | 62 | 61 | 79 | 98 |
| 66 | 62 | 79 | 86 | 68 | 74 | 61 | 82 | 65 | 98 |
| 62 | 116 | 65 | 88 | 64 | 79 | 78 | 79 | 77 | 86 |
| 74 | 85 | 73 | 80 | 68 | 78 | 89 | 72 | 58 | 69 |
| 92 | 78 | 88 | 77 | 103 | 88 | 63 | 68 | 88 | 81 |
| 75 | 90 | 62 | 89 | 71 | 71 | 74 | 70 | 74 | 70 |
| 65 | 81 | 75 | 62 | 94 | 71 | 85 | 84 | 83 | 63 |
| 81 | 62 | 79 | 83 | 93 | 61 | 65 | 62 | 92 | 65 |
| 83 | 70 | 70 | 81 | 77 | 72 | 84 | 67 | 59 | 58 |
| 78 | 66 | 66 | 94 | 77 | 63 | 66 | 75 | 68 | 76 |
| 90 | 78 | 71 | 101 | 78 | 43 | 59 | 67 | 61 | 71 |
| 96 | 75 | 64 | 76 | 72 | 77 | 74 | 65 | 82 | 86 |
| 66 | 86 | 96 | 89 | 81 | 71 | 85 | 99 | 59 | 92 |
| 68 | 72 | 77 | 60 | 87 | 84 | 75 | 77 | 51 | 45 |
| 85 | 67 | 87 | 80 | 84 | 93 | 69 | 76 | 89 | 75 |
| 83 | 68 | 72 | 67 | 92 | 89 | 82 | 96 | 77 | 102 |
| 74 | 91 | 76 | 83 | 66 | 68 | 61 | 73 | 72 | 76 |
| 73 | 77 | 79 | 94 | 63 | 59 | 62 | 71 | 81 | 65 |
| 73 | 63 | 63 | 89 | 82 | 64 | 85 | 92 | 64 | 73 |

**CD** file

**Norris**

Suppose Norris is interested in using the sample data to make an inference about the average hours of useful life for the population of all lightbulbs that could be produced with the new filament. Adding the 200 values in Table 1.5 and dividing the total by 200 provides the sample average lifetime for the lightbulbs: 76 hours. We can use this sample result to estimate that the average lifetime for the lightbulbs in the population is 76 hours. Figure 1.7 is a graphical summary of the statistical inference process for Norris Electronics.

**FIGURE 1.7** THE PROCESS OF STATISTICAL INFERENCE FOR THE NORRIS ELECTRONICS EXAMPLE

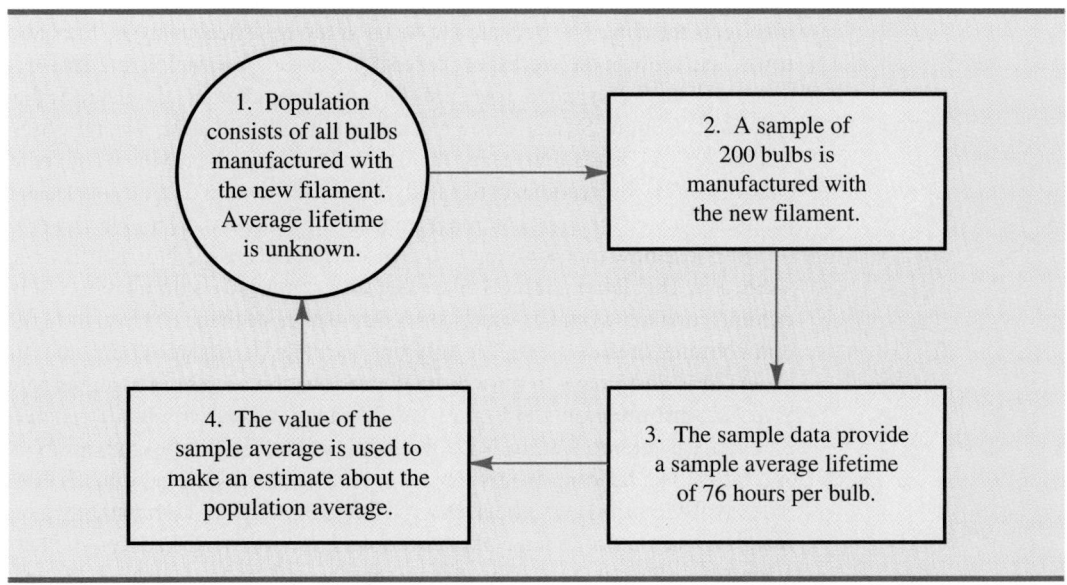

Whenever statisticians use a sample to estimate population characteristics of interest, they usually provide a statement of the quality, or precision, associated with the estimate. For the Norris example, the statistician might state that the estimate of the average lifetime for the population of new lightbulbs is 76 hours with a margin of error of ±4 hours. Thus, an interval estimate of the average lifetime for all lightbulbs produced with the new filament is 72 hours to 80 hours. The statistician can also state how confident he or she is that the interval from 72 hours to 80 hours contains the population average.

## 1.6   STATISTICAL ANALYSIS USING MICROSOFT EXCEL

Because statistical analysis typically involves working with large amounts of data, computer software is frequently used to conduct the analysis. Often the data that is to be analyzed resides in a spreadsheet. Given the data management, data analysis, and presentation capabilities of modern spreadsheet packages, it is now possible to conduct statistical analyses using them. In this book we show how statistical analysis can be performed using Microsoft Excel.

We want to emphasize that this book is about statistics; it is not a book about spreadsheets. Thus our focus is on showing the appropriate statistical procedures for collecting, analyzing, presenting, and interpreting data. Because Excel is widely available in business organizations, you can expect to put the knowledge gained here to use in the setting where you currently, or soon will, work. If in the process of studying this material you become more proficient in Excel, so much the better.

Our focus is on statistical applications. Most sections begin with an application scenario in which a statistical procedure is useful. After showing what the statistical procedure is and how it is used, we turn to showing how to implement the procedure using Excel. Thus, you should gain an understanding of what the procedure is, the situations in which it is useful, and how to implement it using the capabilities of Excel.

### Data Sets and Excel Worksheets

Data sets are organized in Excel worksheets in much the same way as the data set for the 25 shadow stocks appears in Table 1.1. Figure 1.8 shows an Excel worksheet for that data set. Note that row 1 contains headings. Cells B1:F1 contain the variable names. Cells A2:A26 contain the observation names, and cells B2:F26 contain the data that were collected. A brown screen highlights the data. The data are the focus of the statistical analysis. Excluding the headings in row 1, each row in the worksheet corresponds to an observation and each column corresponds to a variable. For instance, row 2 of the worksheet contains the data for the first observation, Advanced Comm. Systems, row 3 contains the data for the second observation, Ag-Chem Equipment Co., and so on. Thus, the names in column A provide a convenient way to refer to each of the 25 observations in the study. Note that column 2 of the worksheet contains the data for the variable Exchange, column 3 contains the data for the variable Ticker Symbol, and so on.

Suppose now that we want to use Excel to analyze the Norris Electronics data shown in Table 1.5. The data in Table 1.5 are organized into 10 columns with 20 data values in each column so that it would fit nicely on a single page of the text. Even though the table has several columns, it shows data for only one variable (hours until burnout). In statistical worksheets, it is customary to put all the data for each variable in a single column. Refer to the Excel worksheet shown in Figure 1.9. To make it easier to identify each observation in the data set, we entered the heading Observation into cell A1 and the numbers 1–200 into cells A2:A201. The heading Hours until Burnout has been entered into cell B1, and the data for the 200 observations have been entered into cells B2:B201. Displaying a worksheet with this many rows on a single page of a textbook is not practical. In cases such as this we will hide

**FIGURE 1.8**    EXCEL WORKSHEET FOR THE SHADOW STOCK DATA SET

| | A | B | C | D | E | F | G |
|---|---|---|---|---|---|---|---|
| 1 | Company | Exchange | Ticker Symbol | Annual Sales ($ Million) | Earnings Per Share ($) | Price-Earnings Ratio | |
| 2 | Advanced Comm. Systems | OTC | ACSC | 75.10 | 0.32 | 39.10 | |
| 3 | Ag-Chem Equipment Co. | OTC | AGCH | 321.10 | 0.48 | 23.40 | |
| 4 | Aztec Manufacturing Co. | NYSE | AZZ | 79.70 | 1.18 | 7.80 | |
| 5 | Cal-Maine Foods, Inc. | OTC | CALM | 314.10 | 0.38 | 11.70 | |
| 6 | Chesapeake Utilities | NYSE | CPK | 174.50 | 1.13 | 16.20 | |
| 7 | Dataram Corporation | AMEX | DTM | 73.10 | 0.86 | 11.00 | |
| 8 | EnergySouth, Inc. | OTC | ENSI | 74.00 | 1.67 | 13.20 | |
| 9 | Gencor Industries, Inc. | AMEX | GX | 263.30 | 1.96 | 4.70 | |
| 10 | Industrial Scientific | OTC | ISCX | 43.50 | 2.03 | 11.50 | |
| 11 | Keystone Consolidated | NYSE | KES | 365.70 | 0.86 | 9.40 | |
| 12 | LandCare USA, Inc. | NYSE | GRW | 111.40 | 0.33 | 29.40 | |
| 13 | Market Facts, Inc. | OTC | MFAC | 126.70 | 0.98 | 26.50 | |
| 14 | Meridian Diagnostics, Inc. | OTC | KITS | 36.30 | 0.46 | 14.70 | |
| 15 | Merit Medical Systems | OTC | MMSI | 67.20 | 0.27 | 24.50 | |
| 16 | Met-Pro Corporation | NYSE | MPR | 61.90 | 1.01 | 12.40 | |
| 17 | Nobility Homes, Inc. | OTC | NOBH | 45.80 | 0.87 | 14.70 | |
| 18 | Omega Research, Inc. | OTC | OMGA | 27.60 | 0.11 | 27.30 | |
| 19 | Point of Sale Limited | OTC | POSIF | 12.30 | 0.28 | 25.40 | |
| 20 | Psychemedics Corp. | AMEX | PMD | 17.60 | 0.13 | 39.40 | |
| 21 | Roadhouse Grill, Inc. | OTC | GRLL | 118.40 | 0.26 | 20.80 | |
| 22 | Selas Corp. of America | AMEX | SLS | 97.10 | 0.77 | 10.70 | |
| 23 | Toymax International, Inc | OTC | TMAX | 104.50 | 1.08 | 4.70 | |
| 24 | VSI Holdings, Inc. | AMEX | VIS | 166.8 | 0.25 | 21 | |
| 25 | Warrantech Corporation | OTC | WTEC | 207.30 | 0.13 | 29.80 | |
| 26 | Webco Industries, Inc. | AMEX | WEB | 153.50 | 0.88 | 7.50 | |
| 27 | | | | | | | |

**FIGURE 1.9**    EXCEL WORKSHEET FOR THE NORRIS ELECTRONICS DATA SET

Note: Rows 7–195 are hidden.

| | A | B | C |
|---|---|---|---|
| 1 | Observation | Hours until Burnout | |
| 2 | 1 | 107 | |
| 3 | 2 | 54 | |
| 4 | 3 | 66 | |
| 5 | 4 | 62 | |
| 6 | 5 | 74 | |
| 196 | 195 | 45 | |
| 197 | 196 | 75 | |
| 198 | 197 | 102 | |
| 199 | 198 | 76 | |
| 200 | 199 | 65 | |
| 201 | 200 | 73 | |
| 202 | | | |

selected rows to conserve space. In the Excel worksheet for the Norris Electronics problem we have hidden rows 7 through 195 (observations 6 through 194) to conserve space.*

## Using Excel for Statistical Analysis

In this text, we are careful to separate the discussion of a statistical procedure from the discussion of using Excel to implement the procedure. The material that discusses the use of Excel will be set apart in sections with headings such as Using Excel's COUNTIF Function to Construct a Frequency Distribution, Using Excel's Chart Wizard to Construct Bar Graphs and Pie Charts, and so on. In using Excel for statistical analysis, three tasks may be needed: Enter Data; Enter Functions and Formulas; and Apply Tools.

**Enter Data:**   Select cell locations for the data and enter the data along with appropriate descriptive labels.

**Enter Functions and Formulas:**   Select cell locations, enter Excel functions and formulas, and provide descriptive material to identify the results.

**Apply Tools:**   Use Excel's tools for data management, data analysis, and presentation.

Our approach will be to describe how these tasks are performed each time we use Excel to implement a statistical procedure. It will always be necessary to enter data. But, depending upon the complexity of the statistical analysis, only one of the last two tasks may be needed.

To illustrate how the discussion of using Excel will appear throughout the book, we will show how to use Excel's AVERAGE function to compute the average lifetime for the 200 burnout times in Table 1.5. Refer to Figure 1.10 as we describe the tasks involved. The worksheet shown in the foreground of Figure 1.10 displays the data for the problem and

**FIGURE 1.10**   COMPUTING THE AVERAGE LIFETIME OF LIGHTBULBS FOR NORRIS ELECTRONICS USING EXCEL'S AVERAGE FUNCTION

Note: Rows 7–195 are hidden.

---

shows the results of the analysis. It is called a **value worksheet.** The worksheet shown in the background displays the Excel formula used to compute the average lifetime and is called the **formula worksheet.** A brown screen is used to highlight the data in both worksheets. In addition, a yellow screen is used to highlight functions and formulas in the formula worksheet and the corresponding results in the value worksheet.

**Enter Data:**    The labels Observation and Hours Until Burnout are entered into cells A1:B1. The numbers 1–200 are entered into cells A2:A201 to identify each of the observations, and the data showing the hours until burnout for each observation are entered into cells B2:B201 of the worksheet.

**Enter Functions and Formulas:**    Excel's AVERAGE function can be used to compute the average lifetime for the 200 lightbulbs. We can compute the average lifetime by entering the following formula into cell E2:

$$=AVERAGE(B2:B201)$$

To identify the result, the label Average Lifetime is entered into cell D2. Note that for this problem, the Apply Tools task was not required. The value worksheet shows that the value computed using the AVERAGE function is 76 hours.

## SUMMARY

Statistics is the art and science of collecting, analyzing, presenting, and interpreting data. Nearly every college student majoring in business or economics is required to take a course in statistics. We began the chapter by describing typical statistical applications for business and economics.

Data are the facts and figures that are collected and analyzed. Four scales of measurement are used to obtain data on a particular variable: nominal, ordinal, interval, and ratio. The scale of measurement for a variable is nominal when the data are labels or names used to identify an attribute of an element. The scale is ordinal if the data have the properties of nominal data and the order or rank of the data is meaningful. The scale is interval if the data have the properties of ordinal data and the interval between observations is expressed in terms of a fixed unit of measure. Finally, the scale of measurement is ratio if the data have all the properties of interval data and the ratio of two values is meaningful.

For purposes of statistical analysis, data can be classified as qualitative or quantitative. Qualitative data are labels or names used to identify an attribute of each element. Qualitative data use either the nominal or ordinal scale of measurement and may be nonnumeric or numeric. Quantitative data are numeric values that indicate how much or how many. Quantitative data use either the interval or ratio scale of measurement. Ordinary arithmetic operations are meaningful only if the data are quantitative. Therefore, statistical computations used for quantitative data are not always appropriate for qualitative data.

In Sections 1.4 and 1.5 we introduced the topics of descriptive statistics and statistical inference. Descriptive statistics are the tabular, graphical, and numerical methods used to summarize data. Statistical inference is the process of using data obtained from a sample to make estimates or test hypotheses about the characteristics of a population.

In the last section of the chapter we provided an introduction to the use of Excel for statistical analysis. We showed that data sets are organized in Excel worksheets in much the same way as the data set for the shadow stocks presented in Table 1.1. That is, the columns in the worksheet correspond to variables in the data set and the rows correspond to observations. We also introduced the approach that will be used throughout the text to describe the use of Excel for statistical analysis. Three tasks may be needed: Enter Data; Enter Functions and Formulas; and Apply Tools. As an illustration, we showed how Excel's AVERAGE function could be used to compute the average lifetime for the 200 observations in the Norris Electronics data set.

## GLOSSARY

**Statistics**   The art and science of collecting, analyzing, presenting, and interpreting data.

**Data**   The facts and figures that are collected, analyzed, and interpreted.

**Data set**   All the data collected in a particular study.

**Elements**   The entities on which data are collected.

**Variable**   A characteristic of interest for the elements.

**Observation**   The set of measurements obtained for a single element.

**Nominal scale**   A scale of measurement for a variable that uses a label or name to identify an attribute of an element. Nominal data may be nonnumeric or numeric.

**Ordinal scale**   A scale of measurement for a variable that has the properties of nominal data and can be used to rank or order the data. Ordinal data may be nonnumeric or numeric.

**Interval scale**   A scale of measurement for a variable that has the properties of ordinal data and the interval between observations is expressed in terms of a fixed unit of measure. Interval data are always numeric.

**Ratio scale**   A scale of measurement for a variable that has all the properties of interval data and the ratio of two values is meaningful. Ratio data are always numeric.

**Qualitative data**   Data that are labels or names used to identify an attribute of each element. Qualitative data use the nominal or ordinal scale of measurement and may be nonnumeric or numeric.

**Quantitative data**   Data that indicate how much or how many of something. Quantitative data use the interval or ratio scale of measurement and are always numeric.

**Qualitative variable**   A variable with qualitative data.

**Quantitative variable**   A variable with quantitative data.

**Cross-sectional data**   Data collected at the same or approximately the same point in time.

**Time series data**   Data collected at several successive periods of time.

**Descriptive statistics**   Tabular, graphical, and numerical summaries of data.

**Population**   The set of all elements of interest in a particular study.

**Sample**   A subset of the population.

**Statistical inference**   The process of using data obtained from a sample to make estimates or test hypotheses about the characteristics of a population.

**Value worksheet**   A worksheet that displays the data for the problem and shows the results of the analysis.

**Formula worksheet**   A worksheet that displays the Excel formulas used to create the results shown in the value worksheet.

## EXERCISES

1. Discuss the differences between statistics as numerical facts and statistics as a discipline or field of study.

2. *Condé Nast Traveler* conducts an annual poll of subscribers in order to determine the best places to stay throughout the world. Table 1.6 is a sample of nine European hotels from their most recent poll. The price of a standard double room during the hotel's high season ranges from $ (lowest price) to $$$$ (highest price). The overall score includes sub-

**TABLE 1.6**    RATINGS FOR NINE PLACES TO STAY IN EUROPE

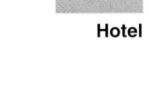

**Hotel**

| Name of Property | Country | Room Rate | Number of Rooms | Overall Score |
|---|---|---|---|---|
| Graveteye Manor | England | $$ | 18 | 83.6 |
| Villa d'Este | Italy | $$$$ | 166 | 86.3 |
| Hotel Prem | Germany | $ | 54 | 77.8 |
| Hotel d'Europe | France | $$ | 47 | 76.8 |
| Palace Luzern | Switzerland | $$ | 326 | 80.9 |
| Royal Crescent Hotel | England | $$$ | 45 | 73.7 |
| Hotel Sacher | Austria | $$$ | 120 | 85.5 |
| Duc de Bourgogne | Belgium | $ | 10 | 76.9 |
| Villa Gallici | France | $$ | 22 | 90.6 |

*Source:* Condé Nast Traveler, January 2000.

scriber's evaluations of each hotel's rooms, service, restaurants, location/atmosphere, and public areas; higher overall scores correspond to a higher level of satisfaction.

   **a.** How many elements are in this data set?
   **b.** How many variables are in this data set?
   **c.** Which variables are qualitative and which variables are quantitative?
   **d.** What type of measurement scale is used for each of the variables?

**3.** Refer to Table 1.6.
   **a.** What is the average number of rooms for the nine hotels?
   **b.** Compute the average overall score.
   **c.** What is the percentage of hotels located in England?
   **d.** What is the percentage of hotels with a room rate of $$?

**4.** *Fortune* magazine provides data on how the 500 largest U.S. industrial corporations rank in terms of revenues and profits. Data for a sample of *Fortune* 500 companies are given in Table 1.7.
   **a.** How many elements are in this data set?
   **b.** What is the population?
   **c.** Compute the average revenue for the sample.
   **d.** Using the results in part (c), what is the estimate of the average revenue for the population?

**TABLE 1.7**    A SAMPLE OF 10 *FORTUNE* 500 COMPANIES

**Fortune**

| Company | Revenue ($ millions) | Profit ($ millions) | Industry Code |
|---|---|---|---|
| US Airways Group | 8688.0 | 538.0 | 3 |
| International Paper | 19500.0 | 213.0 | 23 |
| Tyson Foods | 7414.1 | 25.1 | 20 |
| Hewlett-Packard | 47061.0 | 2945.0 | 13 |
| Intel | 26273.0 | 6068.0 | 49 |
| Northrup Grumman | 8902.0 | 214.0 | 2 |
| Seagate Technology | 6819.0 | −530.0 | 11 |
| Unisys | 7208.4 | 387.0 | 10 |
| Westvaco | 2904.7 | 132.0 | 23 |
| Campbell Soup | 7505.0 | 660.0 | 20 |

*Source: Fortune,* April 26, 1999.

5.    Consider the data set for the sample of *Fortune* 500 companies in Table 1.7.
   a.    How many variables are in the data set?
   b.    Which of the variables are qualitative and which are quantitative?
   c.    Compute the average profit for the sample.
   d.    What percentage of the companies earned a profit over $100 million?
   e.    What percentage of the companies have an industry code of 3?

6.    Columbia House provides CDs and tapes to its mail-order club members. A Columbia House Music Survey asked new club members to complete an 11-question survey. Some of the questions asked were:
   a.    How many CDs and tapes have you bought in the last 12 months?
   b.    Are you currently a member of a national mail-order book club? (Yes or No)
   c.    What is your age?
   d.    Including yourself, how many people (adults and children) are in your household?
   e.    What kind of music are you interested in buying? (15 categories were listed, including hard rock, soft rock, adult contemporary, heavy metal, rap, and country.)
   Comment on whether each question provides qualitative or quantitative data.

7.    A California state agency classifies worker occupations as professional, white collar, or blue collar. The data are recorded with 1 denoting professional, 2 denoting white collar, and 3 denoting blue collar.
   a.    The variable is worker occupation. Is it a qualitative or quantitative variable?
   b.    What type of measurement scale is used for this variable?

8.    A *Wall Street Journal*/NBC News poll asked 2013 adults, "How satisfied are you with the state of the U.S. economy today?" (*The Wall Street Journal,* December 12, 1997). Response categories were Dissatisfied, Satisfied, and Not Sure.
   a.    What was the sample size for this survey?
   b.    Are the data qualitative or quantitative?
   c.    Would it make more sense to use averages or percentages as a summary of the data for this question?
   d.    Of the respondents, 28% said that they were dissatisfied with the state of the U.S. economy. How many individuals provided this response?

9.    The Commerce Department reported receiving the following applications for the Malcolm Baldrige National Quality Award: 23 from large manufacturing firms, 18 from large service firms, and 30 from small businesses.
   a.    Is type of business a qualitative or quantitative variable?
   b.    What percentage of the applications came from small businesses?

10.    State whether each of the following variables is qualitative or quantitative and indicate its measurement scale.
   a.    Age
   b.    Gender
   c.    Class rank
   d.    Make of automobile
   e.    Number of people favoring the death penalty

11.    State whether each of the following variables is qualitative or quantitative and indicate its measurement scale.
   a.    Annual sales
   b.    Soft-drink size (small, medium, large)
   c.    Employee classification (GS1 through GS18)
   d.    Earnings per share
   e.    Method of payment (cash, check, credit card)

12.    The Hawaii Visitors Bureau collects data on visitors to Hawaii. The following questions were among 16 asked in a questionnaire handed out to passengers during incoming airline flights in June.

- This trip to Hawaii is my: 1st, 2nd, 3rd, 4th, etc.
- The primary reason for this trip is: (10 categories including vacation, convention, honeymoon)
- Where I plan to stay: (11 categories including hotel, apartment, relatives, camping)
- Total days in Hawaii

a. What is the population being studied?

b. Is the use of a questionnaire a good way to reach the population of passengers on incoming airline flights?

c. Comment on each of the four questions in terms of whether it will provide qualitative or quantitative data.

13. Figure 1.11 is a bar graph providing data on the number of riverboat casinos over the years 1991–1997.

a. Are the data qualitative or quantitative?

b. Are the data time series or cross-sectional?

c. What is the variable of interest?

d. Comment on the trend over time. Would you expect to see an increase or a decrease in 1998?

14. The following data set provides a snapshot of the financial performance of Ameritech Corporation (*Barrons,* December 29, 1997).

|  | **1993** | **1994** | **1995** | **1996** |
|---|---|---|---|---|
| Earnings per Share ($) | 2.78 | 2.13 | 3.41 | 3.83 |
| Revenues ($ billions) | 11.87 | 12.57 | 13.43 | 14.92 |
| Net Income ($ billions) | 1.51 | 1.17 | 1.89 | 2.12 |
| Book Value per Share ($) | 14.35 | 10.98 | 12.67 | 13.98 |

a. How many variables are there?

b. Are the data qualitative or quantitative?

c. Are they cross-sectional or time series data? Why?

**FIGURE 1.11    RIVERBOAT CASINOS IN THE UNITED STATES**

15. Refer again to the data in Table 1.7 for *Fortune* 500 companies. Are they cross-sectional or time series data? Why?

16. The marketing group at your company has come up with a new diet soft drink that it claims will capture a large share of the young adult market.
    a. What data would you want to see before deciding to invest substantial funds in introducing the new product into the marketplace?
    b. How would you expect the data mentioned in part (a) to be obtained?

17. A manager of a large corporation has recommended that a $10,000 raise be given to keep a valued subordinate from moving to another company. What internal and external sources of data might be used to decide whether such a salary increase is appropriate?

18. In a recent study of causes of death in men 60 years of age and older, a sample of 120 men indicated that 48 died as a result of some form of heart disease.
    a. Develop a descriptive statistic that can be used as an estimate of the percentage of men 60 years of age or older who die from some form of heart disease.
    b. Are the data on cause of death qualitative or quantitative?
    c. Discuss the role of statistical inference in this type of medical research.

19. The *Business Week* 1996 North American subscriber study collected data from a sample of 2861 subscribers. Fifty-nine percent of the respondents indicated that their annual income was $75,000 or more, and 50% reported having an American Express credit card.
    a. What is the population of interest in this study?
    b. Is annual income a qualitative or quantitative variable?
    c. Is ownership of an American Express card a qualitative or quantitative variable?
    d. Does this study involve cross-sectional or time series data?
    e. Describe any statistical inferences Business Week might make on the basis of the survey.

20. A Scanner Data User Survey of 50 companies provided the following findings (Mercer Management Consulting, Inc., April 24, 1997):
    • ACNielsen earned 56% of the dollar-share of the market.
    • The average amount spent on scanner data per category of consumer goods was $387,325.
    • On a scale of 1 (very dissatisfied) to 5 (very satisfied), the average level of overall satisfaction with scanner data was 3.73.
    a. Cite two descriptive statistics.
    b. Make an inference of the overall satisfaction in the population of all users of scanner data.
    c. Make an inference about the average amount spent per category for scanner data for consumer goods.

21. A seven-year medical research study reported that women whose mothers took the drug DES during pregnancy were *twice* as likely to develop tissue abnormalities that might lead to cancer as women whose mothers did not take the drug.
    a. This study involved the comparison of two populations. What were the populations?
    b. Do you suppose the data were obtained in a survey or an experiment?
    c. For the population of women whose mothers took the drug DES during pregnancy, a sample of 3980 women showed 63 developed tissue abnormalities that might lead to cancer. Provide a descriptive statistic that could be used to estimate the number of women out of 1000 in this population who have tissue abnormalities.
    d. For the population of women whose mothers did not take the drug DES during pregnancy, what is the estimate of the number of women out of 1000 who would be expected to have tissue abnormalities?
    e. Medical studies often use a relatively large sample (in this case, 3980). Why?

22. A firm is interested in testing the advertising effectiveness of a new television commercial. As part of the test, the commercial is shown on a 6:30 P.M. local news program in Denver, Colorado. Two days later, a market research firm conducts a telephone survey to obtain in-

formation on recall rates (percentage of viewers who recall seeing the commercial) and impressions of the commercial.

    **a.**  What is the population for this study?

    **b.**  What is the sample for this study?

    **c.**  Why would a sample be used in this situation? Explain.

**23.**  ACNielsen conducts weekly surveys of television viewing throughout the United States. The ACNielsen statistical ratings indicate the size of the viewing audience for each major network television program. Rankings of the television programs and of the viewing audience market shares for each network are published each week.

    **a.**  What is the ACNielsen organization attempting to measure?

    **b.**  What is the population?

    **c.**  Why would a sample be used for this situation?

    **d.**  What kinds of decisions or actions are based on the ACNielsen studies?

**24.**  A sample of midterm grades for five students showed the following results: 72, 65, 82, 90, 76. Which of the following statements are correct, and which should be challenged as being too generalized?

    **a.**  The average midterm grade for the sample of five students is 77.

    **b.**  The average midterm grade for all students who took the exam is 77.

    **c.**  An estimate of the average midterm grade for all students who took the exam is 77.

    **d.**  More than half of the students who take this exam will score between 70 and 85.

    **e.**  If five other students are included in the sample, their grades will be between 65 and 90.

# Chapter 2

# DESCRIPTIVE STATISTICS: TABULAR AND GRAPHICAL METHODS

**CONTENTS**

## STATISTICS IN PRACTICE

### COLGATE-PALMOLIVE COMPANY*
*New York, New York*

The Colgate-Palmolive Company started as a small soap and candle shop in New York City in 1806. Today, Colgate-Palmolive is a $9 billion company whose products can be found in more than 200 countries and territories around the world. Although best known for its brand names of Colgate, Palmolive, Ajax, and Fab, the company also markets Mennen, Hill's Science Diet, and Hill's Prescription Diet products.

The Colgate-Palmolive Company uses statistics in its quality assurance program for home laundry detergent products. One concern is customer satisfaction with the quantity of detergent in a carton. Every carton in each size category is filled with the same amount of detergent by weight, but the volume of detergent is affected by the density of the detergent powder. For instance, if the powder density is on the heavy side, a smaller volume of detergent is needed to reach the carton's specified weight. As a result, the carton may appear to be underfilled when opened by the consumer.

To control the problem of heavy detergent powder, limits are placed on the acceptable range of powder density. Statistical samples are taken periodically, and the density of each powder sample is measured. Data summaries are then provided for operating personnel so that corrective action can be taken if necessary to keep the density within the desired quality specifications.

A frequency distribution for the densities of 150 samples taken over a one-week period and a histogram are shown in the accompanying table and figure. Density levels above .40 are unacceptably high. The frequency distribution and histogram show that the operation is meeting its quality guidelines with all of the densities less than or equal to .40. Managers viewing these statistical summaries would be pleased with the quality of the detergent production process.

In this chapter, you will learn about tabular and graphical methods of descriptive statistics such as frequency distributions, bar graphs, histograms, stem-and-leaf displays, crosstabulations, and others. The

Statistical summaries help maintain the quality of these Colgate-Palmolive products. © Joe Higgins/South-Western.

goal of these methods is to summarize data so that they can be easily understood and interpreted.

### Frequency Distribution of Density Data

| Density | Frequency |
|---------|-----------|
| .29–.30 | 30 |
| .31–.32 | 75 |
| .33–.34 | 32 |
| .35–.36 | 9 |
| .37–.38 | 3 |
| .39–.40 | 1 |
| Total | 150 |

### HISTOGRAM OF DENSITY DATA

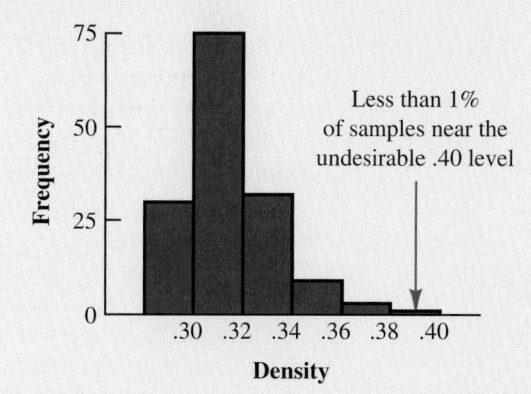

*The authors are indebted to William R. Fowle, Manager of Quality Assurance, Colgate-Palmolive Company, for providing this Statistics in Practice.

As indicated in Chapter 1, data can be classified as either **qualitative** or **quantitative.** Qualitative data are labels or names used to identify categories of like items. Quantitative data are numerical values that indicate how much or how many.

The purpose of this chapter is to introduce tabular and graphical methods commonly used to summarize both qualitative and quantitative data. Tabular and graphical summaries of data can be found in annual reports, newspaper articles, and research studies. Everyone is exposed to these types of presentations. Hence, it is important to understand how they are prepared and how they should be interpreted. We begin with tabular and graphical methods for summarizing data concerning a single variable. The last section introduces methods for summarizing data when the relationship between two variables is of interest.

Excel's wide variety of functions and tools for descriptive statistics are used extensively in this chapter. The Chart Wizard and Pivot Table tool are two Excel tools that are extremely valuable in summarizing and presenting data. The Chart Wizard has extensive capabilities for developing graphical presentations and the PivotTable tool is useful in preparing crosstabulations for data sets involving more than one variable.

## 2.1  SUMMARIZING QUALITATIVE DATA

### Frequency Distribution

We begin the discussion of how tabular and graphical methods can be used to summarize qualitative data with the definition of a **frequency distribution.**

> **Frequency Distribution**
>
> A frequency distribution is a tabular summary of data showing the number (frequency) of items in each of several nonoverlapping classes.

Let us use the following example to demonstrate the construction and interpretation of a frequency distribution for qualitative data. According to *Beverage Digest,* Coke Classic, Diet Coke, Dr. Pepper, Pepsi-Cola, and Sprite are the five top-selling soft drinks (*The Wall Street Journal Almanac,* 1998). Assume that the data in Table 2.1 show the soft drink selected for a sample of 50 soft drink purchases.

To develop a frequency distribution for these data, we count the number of times each soft drink appears in Table 2.1. Coke Classic appears 19 times, Diet Coke appears 8 times, Dr. Pepper appears 5 times, Pepsi-Cola appears 13 times, and Sprite appears 5 times. These counts are summarized in the frequency distribution in Table 2.2.

This frequency distribution provides a summary of how the 50 soft drink purchases are distributed across the five soft drinks. This summary provides more insight than the original data shown in Table 2.1. Viewing the frequency distribution, we see that Coke Classic is the leader, Pepsi-Cola is second, Diet Coke is third, and Sprite and Dr. Pepper are tied for fourth. The frequency distribution has provided information about the relative popularity of the five best-selling soft drinks.

Counting the number of times each soft drink appears in the data was not too difficult for the sample of 50 soft drink purchases. However, the effort needed to develop an accurate count for each soft drink would have been greater had the sample size been larger. Let us now see how Excel can be used to count the frequencies and construct a frequency distribution for the soft drink data in Table 2.1.

**TABLE 2.1**    DATA FROM A SAMPLE OF 50 SOFT DRINK PURCHASES

**SoftDrink**

| | | |
|---|---|---|
| Coke Classic | Sprite | Pepsi-Cola |
| Diet Coke | Coke Classic | Coke Classic |
| Pepsi-Cola | Diet Coke | Coke Classic |
| Diet Coke | Coke Classic | Coke Classic |
| Coke Classic | Diet Coke | Pepsi-Cola |
| Coke Classic | Coke Classic | Dr. Pepper |
| Dr. Pepper | Sprite | Coke Classic |
| Diet Coke | Pepsi-Cola | Diet Coke |
| Pepsi-Cola | Coke Classic | Pepsi-Cola |
| Pepsi-Cola | Coke Classic | Pepsi-Cola |
| Coke Classic | Coke Classic | Pepsi-Cola |
| Dr. Pepper | Pepsi-Cola | Pepsi-Cola |
| Sprite | Coke Classic | Coke Classic |
| Coke Classic | Sprite | Dr. Pepper |
| Diet Coke | Dr. Pepper | Pepsi-Cola |
| Coke Classic | Pepsi-Cola | Sprite |
| Coke Classic | Diet Coke | |

## Using Excel's COUNTIF Function to Construct a Frequency Distribution

Two tasks are involved in using Excel's COUNTIF function to construct a frequency distribution: Enter Data and Enter Functions and Formulas. Refer to Figure 2.1 as we describe the tasks involved. The formula worksheet is in the background; the value worksheet is in the foreground.

**Enter Data:**    The label "Brand Purchased" and the data for the 50 soft drink purchases are entered into cells A1:A51.

Excel's Function Wizard can help with the proper use of this function (see Appendix F).

**Enter Functions and Formulas:**    Excel's COUNTIF function can be used to count the number of times each soft drink appears in cells A2:A51. We first entered a label and the soft drink names into cells C1:C6 and D1. Then, to count the number of times that Coke Classic appears, we entered the following formula into cell D2:

$$=COUNTIF(\$A\$2:\$A\$51,C2)$$

**TABLE 2.2**

FREQUENCY DISTRIBUTION OF SOFT DRINK PURCHASES

| Soft Drink | Frequency |
|---|---|
| Coke Classic | 19 |
| Diet Coke | 8 |
| Dr. Pepper | 5 |
| Pepsi-Cola | 13 |
| Sprite | 5 |
| Total | 50 |

To count the number of times the other soft drinks appear, we copied the same formula into cells D3:D6.

The value worksheet, in the foreground of Figure 2.1, shows the values computed using these cell formulas; we see that the Excel worksheet shows the same frequency distribution that we developed in Table 2.2.

## Relative Frequency and Percent Frequency Distributions

A frequency distribution shows the number (frequency) of items in each of several non-overlapping classes. However, we are often interested in the proportion, or percentage, of items in each class. The *relative frequency* of a class is the fraction or proportion of items

**FIGURE 2.1** FREQUENCY DISTRIBUTION FOR SOFT DRINK PURCHASES CONSTRUCTED USING EXCEL'S COUNTIF FUNCTION

Note: Rows 11–44 are hidden.

| | A | B | C | D | E |
|---|---|---|---|---|---|
| 1 | Brand Purchased | | Soft Drink | Frequency | |
| 2 | Coke Classic | | Coke Classic | =COUNTIF($A$2:$A$51,C2) | |
| 3 | Diet Coke | | Diet Coke | =COUNTIF($A$2:$A$51,C3) | |
| 4 | Pepsi-Cola | | Dr. Pepper | =COUNTIF($A$2:$A$51,C4) | |
| 5 | Diet Coke | | Pepsi-Cola | =COUNTIF($A$2:$A$51,C5) | |
| 6 | Coke Classic | | Sprite | =COUNTIF($A$2:$A$51,C6) | |
| 7 | Coke Classic | | | | |
| 8 | Dr. Pepper | | | | |
| 9 | Diet Coke | | | | |
| 10 | Pepsi-Cola | | | | |
| 45 | Pepsi-Cola | | | | |
| 46 | Pepsi-Cola | | | | |
| 47 | Pepsi-Cola | | | | |
| 48 | Coke Classic | | | | |
| 49 | Dr. Pepper | | | | |
| 50 | Pepsi-Cola | | | | |
| 51 | Sprite | | | | |
| 52 | | | | | |

| | A | B | C | D | E |
|---|---|---|---|---|---|
| 1 | Brand Purchased | | Soft Drink | Frequency | |
| 2 | Coke Classic | | Coke Classic | 19 | |
| 3 | Diet Coke | | Diet Coke | 8 | |
| 4 | Pepsi-Cola | | Dr. Pepper | 5 | |
| 5 | Diet Coke | | Pepsi-Cola | 13 | |
| 6 | Coke Classic | | Sprite | 5 | |
| 7 | Coke Classic | | | | |
| 8 | Dr. Pepper | | | | |
| 9 | Diet Coke | | | | |
| 10 | Pepsi-Cola | | | | |
| 45 | Pepsi-Cola | | | | |
| 46 | Pepsi-Cola | | | | |
| 47 | Pepsi-Cola | | | | |
| 48 | Coke Classic | | | | |
| 49 | Dr. Pepper | | | | |
| 50 | Pepsi-Cola | | | | |
| 51 | Sprite | | | | |
| 52 | | | | | |

belonging to a class. For a data set with $n$ observations, the relative frequency of each class is as follows:

**Relative Frequency**

$$\text{Relative Frequency of a Class} = \frac{\text{Frequency of the Class}}{n} \qquad (2.1)$$

The *percent frequency* of a class is the relative frequency multiplied by 100.

A **relative frequency distribution** is a tabular summary of data showing the relative frequency for each class. A **percent frequency distribution** is a tabular summary of data showing the percent frequency for each class. Table 2.3 shows a relative frequency distribution and a percent frequency distribution for the soft drink data. In Table 2.3 we see that the relative frequency for Coke Classic is 19/50 = .38, the relative frequency for Diet Coke is 8/50 = .16, and so on. From the percent frequency distribution, we see that 38% of the purchases were Coke Classic, 16% of the purchases were Diet Coke, and so on. We can also note that 38% + 26% + 16% = 80% of the purchases were of the top three soft drinks.

**TABLE 2.3**   RELATIVE AND PERCENT FREQUENCY DISTRIBUTIONS OF SOFT DRINK
PURCHASES

| Soft Drink | Relative Frequency | Percent Frequency |
|---|---|---|
| Coke Classic | .38 | 38 |
| Diet Coke | .16 | 16 |
| Dr. Pepper | .10 | 10 |
| Pepsi-Cola | .26 | 26 |
| Sprite | .10 | 10 |
| Total | 1.00 | 100 |

## Using Excel to Construct Relative Frequency and Percent Frequency Distributions

Extending the worksheet shown in Figure 2.1, we can develop the relative frequency and percent frequency distributions shown in Table 2.3. Refer to Figure 2.2 as we describe the tasks involved. The formula worksheet is in the background; the value worksheet is in the foreground.

**FIGURE 2.2**   RELATIVE FREQUENCY AND PERCENT FREQUENCY DISTRIBUTIONS OF SOFT DRINK
PURCHASES CONSTRUCTED USING EXCEL

| | A | B | C | D | E | F | G |
|---|---|---|---|---|---|---|---|
| 1 | Brand Purchased | | Soft Drink | Frequency | Relative Frequency | Percent Frequency | |
| 2 | Coke Classic | | Coke Classic | =COUNTIF(A2:A51,"Coke Classic") | =D2/$D$7 | =E2*100 | |
| 3 | Diet Coke | | Diet Coke | =COUNTIF(A2:A51,"Diet Coke") | =D3/$D$7 | =E3*100 | |
| 4 | Pepsi-Cola | | Dr. Pepper | =COUNTIF(A2:A51,"Dr. Pepper") | =D4/$D$7 | =E4*100 | |
| 5 | Diet Coke | | Pepsi-Cola | =COUNTIF(A2:A51,"Pepsi-Cola") | =D5/$D$7 | =E5*100 | |
| 6 | Coke Classic | | Sprite | =COUNTIF(A2:A51,"Sprite") | =D6/$D$7 | =E6*100 | |
| 7 | Coke Classic | | Total | =SUM(D2:D6) | =SUM(E2:E6) | =SUM(F2:F6) | |
| 8 | Dr. Pepper | | | | | | |
| 9 | Diet Coke | | | | | | |
| 10 | Pepsi-Cola | | | | | | |
| 45 | Pepsi-Cola | | | | | | |
| 46 | Pepsi-Cola | | | | | | |
| 47 | Pepsi-Cola | | | | | | |
| 48 | Coke Classic | | | | | | |
| 49 | Dr. Pepper | | | | | | |
| 50 | Pepsi-Cola | | | | | | |
| 51 | Sprite | | | | | | |
| 52 | | | | | | | |

| | A | B | C | D | E | F | G |
|---|---|---|---|---|---|---|---|
| 1 | Brand Purchased | | Soft Drink | Frequency | Relative Frequency | Percent Frequency | |
| 2 | Coke Classic | | Coke Classic | 19 | 0.38 | 38 | |
| 3 | Diet Coke | | Diet Coke | 8 | 0.16 | 16 | |
| 4 | Pepsi-Cola | | Dr. Pepper | 5 | 0.1 | 10 | |
| 5 | Diet Coke | | Pepsi-Cola | 13 | 0.26 | 26 | |
| 6 | Coke Classic | | Sprite | 5 | 0.1 | 10 | |
| 7 | Coke Classic | | Total | 50 | 1.00 | 100 | |
| 8 | Dr. Pepper | | | | | | |
| 9 | Diet Coke | | | | | | |
| 10 | Pepsi-Cola | | | | | | |
| 45 | Pepsi-Cola | | | | | | |
| 46 | Pepsi-Cola | | | | | | |
| 47 | Pepsi-Cola | | | | | | |
| 48 | Coke Classic | | | | | | |
| 49 | Dr. Pepper | | | | | | |
| 50 | Pepsi-Cola | | | | | | |
| 51 | Sprite | | | | | | |
| 52 | | | | | | | |

Note: Rows 11–44 are hidden.

**Enter Data:**    The label "Brand Purchased" and the data for the 50 soft drink purchases are entered into cells A1:A51.

**Enter Functions and Formulas:**    The information in cells C1:D6 is the same as in Figure 2.1. Excel's SUM function is used in cell D7 to compute the sum of the frequencies in cells D2:D6. The resulting value of 50 is the number of observations in the data set. To compute the relative frequency for Coke Classic using Equation (2.1), we entered the formula = D2/$D$7 into cell E2; the result, 0.38, is the relative frequency for Coke Classic. Copying cell E2 to cells E3:E6 computes the relative frequencies for each of the other soft drinks.

To compute the percent frequency for Coke Classic we entered the formula = E2*100 into cell F2. The result, 38, indicates that 38% of the soft drink purchases were Coke Classic. Copying cell F2 to cells F3:F6 computes the percent frequencies for each of the other soft drinks. Finally, copying cell D7 to cells E7:F7 computes the total of the relative frequencies (1.00) and the total of the percent frequencies (100).

## Bar Graphs and Pie Charts

In quality control applications, bar graphs are used to identify the most important causes of problems. When the bars are arranged in descending order of height from left to right with the most frequently occurring cause appearing first, the bar graph is called a *pareto diagram.* This diagram is named for its founder, Vilfredo Pareto, an Italian economist.

A **bar graph** is a graphical device for depicting qualitative data that have been summarized in a frequency, relative frequency, or percent frequency distribution. On one axis of the graph (usually the horizontal axis), we specify the labels that are used for the classes (categories) of data. A frequency, relative frequency, or percent frequency scale can be used for the other axis of the graph (usually the vertical axis). Then, using a bar of fixed width drawn above each class label, we extend the length of the bar until we reach the frequency, relative frequency, or percent frequency of the class. For qualitative data, the bars should be separated to emphasize the fact that each class (category) is separate. Figure 2.3 is a bar graph of the frequency distribution for the 50 soft drink purchases. Note how the graphical presentation shows Coke Classic, Pepsi-Cola, and Diet Coke to be the most preferred brands.

The **pie chart** is another graphical device for presenting relative frequency and percent frequency distributions for qualitative data. To construct a pie chart, we first draw a circle to

**FIGURE 2.3**    BAR GRAPH OF SOFT DRINK PURCHASES

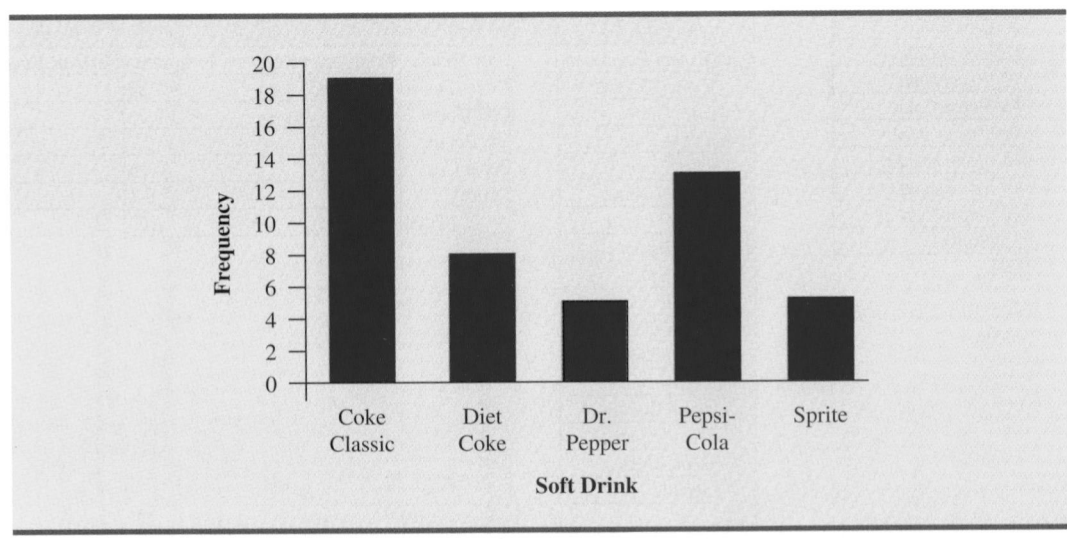

represent all of the data. Then we use the relative frequencies to subdivide the circle into sectors, or parts, that correspond to the relative frequency for each class. For example, because a circle has 360 degrees and Coke Classic has a relative frequency of .38, the sector of the pie chart labeled Coke Classic consists of .38(360) = 136.8 degrees. The sector of the pie chart labeled Diet Coke consists of .16(360) = 57.6 degrees. Similar calculations for the other classes yield the pie chart in Figure 2.4. The numerical values shown for each sector can be frequencies, relative frequencies, or percent frequencies.

## Using Excel's Chart Wizard to Construct Bar Graphs and Pie Charts

Excel's Chart Wizard provides a general tool for constructing a variety of graphical displays, including bar graphs and pie charts. We will illustrate the use of Excel's Chart Wizard by showing how to construct the bar graph for soft drink purchases. The Chart Wizard is an Excel tool that allows us to go beyond what can be done with functions and formulas alone. When such tools are used, a third task is needed for worksheet construction: Apply Tools.

The same data and functions and formulas that were used in Figure 2.1 are used here. Thus, the chart we are going to develop is an extension of that worksheet. Refer to Figure 2.5 as we describe the Apply Tools task. The value worksheet is in the background; the chart developed using the Excel Chart Wizard is in the foreground.

**Enter Data:**    Same as in Figure 2.1.

**Enter Functions and Formulas:**    Same as in Figure 2.1.

**Apply Tools:**    The following steps describe how to use Excel's Chart Wizard to construct a bar graph for the soft drink data using the frequency distribution appearing in cells C1:D6.

   **Step 1.**  Select cells C1:D6
   **Step 2.**  Select the **Chart Wizard** button on the Standard toolbar (or select the **Insert** pull-down menu and choose the **Chart** option)

**FIGURE 2.4**    PIE CHART OF SOFT DRINK PURCHASES

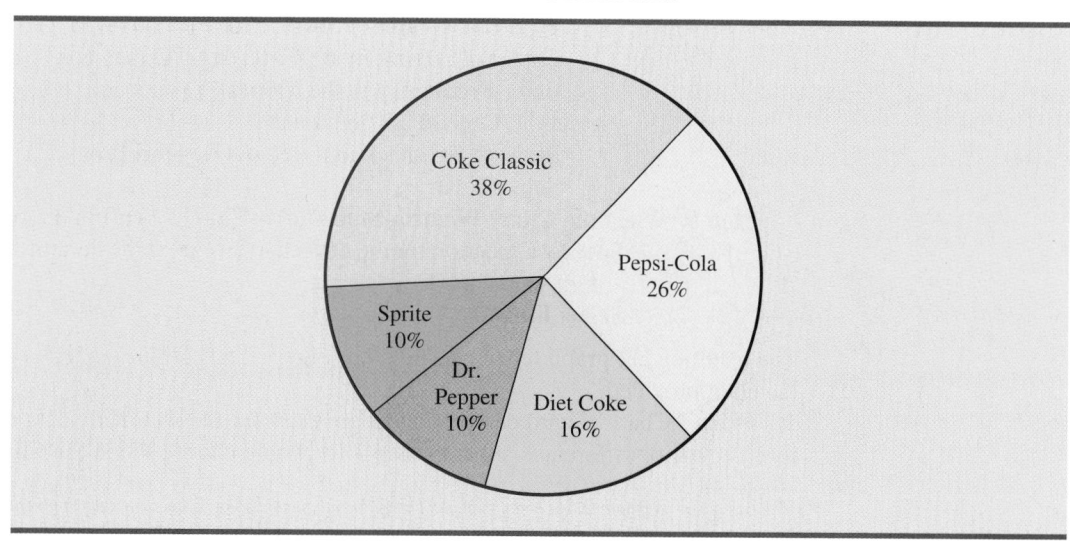

**FIGURE 2.5**    BAR GRAPH OF SOFT DRINK PURCHASES CONSTRUCTED USING EXCEL'S CHART WIZARD

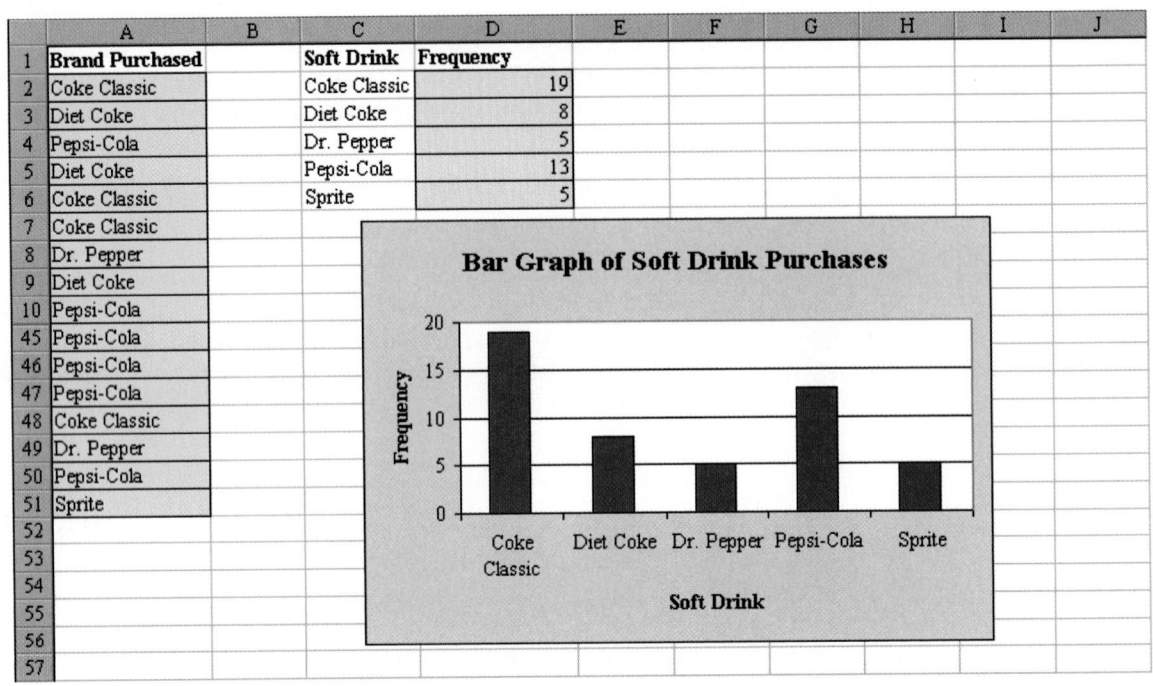

**Step 3.**  When the **Chart Wizard–Step 1 of 4–Chart Type** dialog box appears:
Choose **Column** in the **Chart type** list
Choose **Clustered Column** from the **Chart sub-type** display
Select **Next >**

**Step 4.**  When the **Chart Wizard–Step 2 of 4–Chart Source Data** dialog box appears:
Select **Next >**

**Step 5.**  When the **Chart Wizard–Step 3 of 4–Chart Options** dialog box appears:
Select the **Titles** tab and then
Type **Bar Graph of Soft Drink Purchases** in the **Chart title** box
Enter **Soft Drink** in the **Category (X)** axis box
Enter **Frequency** in the **Values (Y)** axis box
Select the **Legend** tab and then
Remove the check in the **Show Legend** Box
Select **Next >**

**Step 6.**  When the **Chart Wizard–Step 4 of 4–Chart Location** dialog box appears:
Specify a location for the new chart (we used the default setting of the current worksheet)
Select **Finish**

The resulting bar graph (chart) is shown in Figure 2.5.* A blue screen is used to highlight the chart provided.

Excel's Chart Wizard can produce a pie chart for the soft drink data in a similar fashion. The major difference is that in Step 3 we would choose Pie in the Chart type list.

---

*The bar graph in Figure 2.5 is slightly larger than what was provided by Excel after selecting **Finish.** Resizing an Excel chart is not difficult. First, select the chart. Small black squares, called sizing handles, will appear on the chart border. Click on the sizing handles and drag them to resize the figure to your preference.

## NOTES AND COMMENTS

**1.** Often the number of classes in a frequency distribution is the same as the number of categories found in the data, as is the case for the soft drink purchase data in this section. The data involve only five soft drinks, and a separate frequency distribution class was defined for each one. Data that included all soft drinks would require many categories, most of which would have a small number of purchases. Most statisticians recommend that classes with smaller frequencies be grouped into an aggregate class called "other." Classes with frequencies of 5 percent or less would most often be treated in this fashion.

**2.** The sum of the frequencies in any frequency distribution always equals the number of observations. The sum of the relative frequencies in any relative frequency distribution always equals 1.00, and the sum of the percentages in a percent frequency distribution always equals 100.

## EXERCISES

### Methods

**1.** The response to a question has three alternatives: A, B, and C. A sample of 120 responses provides 60 A, 24 B, and 36 C. Show the frequency and relative frequency distributions.

**2.** A partial relative frequency distribution is given.

| Class | Relative Frequency |
|-------|--------------------|
| A | .22 |
| B | .18 |
| C | .40 |
| D | |

**a.** What is the relative frequency of class D?
**b.** The total sample size is 200. What is the frequency of class D?
**c.** Show the frequency distribution.
**d.** Show the percent frequency distribution.

**3.** A questionnaire provides 58 yes, 42 no, and 20 no-opinion answers.
**a.** In the construction of a pie chart, how many degrees would be in the section of the pie showing the yes answers?
**b.** How many degrees would be in the section of the pie showing the no answers?
**c.** Construct a pie chart.
**d.** Construct a bar graph.

### Applications

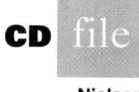

**Nielsen**

**4.** According to Nielsen Media Research, the top four TV shows at 8:00 P.M., April 6, 2000, were Millionaire, Frasier, Chicago Hope, and Charmed (*USA Today,* April 13, 2000). Data for a sample of 50 viewers follow.

| | | | | |
|---|---|---|---|---|
| Millionaire | Millionaire | Millionaire | Frasier | Charmed |
| Frasier | Frasier | Millionaire | Millionaire | Frasier |
| Frasier | Millionaire | Millionaire | Chicago Hope | Millionaire |
| Charmed | Millionaire | Frasier | Chicago Hope | Millionaire |
| Chicago Hope | Charmed | Frasier | Frasier | Millionaire |
| Millionaire | Frasier | Millionaire | Millionaire | Chicago Hope |
| Frasier | Millionaire | Millionaire | Charmed | Chicago Hope |
| Chicago Hope | Millionaire | Millionaire | Millionaire | Millionaire |
| Frasier | Frasier | Millionaire | Frasier | Frasier |
| Millionaire | Millionaire | Chicago Hope | Millionaire | Frasier |

**TABLE 2.4**

THE EIGHT
BEST-SELLING
PAPERBACK
BUSINESS BOOKS

- *The 7 Habits of Highly Effective People*
- *Investing for Dummies*
- *The Ernst & Young Tax Guide 2000*
- *The Millionaire Next Door*
- *The Motley Fool Investment Guide*
- *Rich Dad, Poor Dad*
- *The Wall Street Journal Guide to Understanding Money and Investing*
- *What Color is Your Parachute? 2000*

a. Are these qualitative or quantitative data?
b. Provide frequency and percent frequency distributions.
c. Construct a bar graph and a pie chart.
d. On the basis of the sample, which show has the largest market share? Which one is second?

5. Freshmen entering the College of Business at Eastern University were asked to indicate their preferred major. The following data were obtained.

| Major | Number |
|---|---|
| Management | 55 |
| Accounting | 51 |
| Finance | 28 |
| Marketing | 82 |

Summarize the data by constructing:
a. Relative and percent frequency distributions.
b. A bar graph.
c. A pie chart.

6. The eight best-selling paperback business books in February 2000 are listed in Table 2.4 (*Business Week*, April 3, 2000). Suppose a sample of book purchases in the Denver, Colorado, area provided the following data for these eight books.

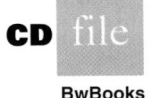

**BwBooks**

| | | | | | |
|---|---|---|---|---|---|
| 7 Habits | Dad | 7 Habits | Millionaire | Millionaire | WSJ Guide |
| Motley | Millionaire | Tax Guide | 7 Habits | Dad | Dummies |
| Millionaire | Motley | Dad | Dad | Parachute | Dad |
| Dad | 7 Habits | WSJ Guide | WSJ Guide | WSJ Guide | 7 Habits |
| Motley | WSJ Guide | Millionaire | 7 Habits | Millionaire | Millionaire |
| Millionaire | 7 Habits | Millionaire | 7 Habits | Motley | Motley |
| Motley | 7 Habits | Dad | Dad | Dad | Dad |
| 7 Habits | WSJ Guide | Tax Guide | Millionaire | Motley | Tax Guide |
| Motley | Motley | Millionaire | Millionaire | Dad | Dummies |
| Millionaire | Millionaire | Millionaire | Dad | Millionaire | Dad |

a. Construct frequency and percent frequency distributions for the data. Group any books with a frequency of 5% or less in an "other" category.
b. Rank the best-selling books.
c. What percentage of the sales are represented by *The Millionaire Next Door* and *Rich Dad, Poor Dad*?

7. Leverock's Waterfront Steakhouse in Maderia Beach, Florida, uses a questionnaire to ask customers how they rate the server, food quality, cocktails, prices, and atmosphere at the restaurant. Each characteristic is rated on a scale of outstanding (O), very good (V), good (G), average (A), and poor (P). Use descriptive statistics to summarize the following data collected on food quality. What is your feeling about the food quality ratings at the restaurant?

| | | | | | | | | | | | | |
|---|---|---|---|---|---|---|---|---|---|---|---|---|
| G | O | V | G | A | O | V | O | V | G | O | V | A |
| V | O | P | V | O | G | A | O | O | O | G | O | V |
| V | A | G | O | V | P | V | O | O | G | O | O | V |
| O | G | A | O | V | O | O | G | V | A | G | | |

8. Data for a sample of 55 members of the Baseball Hall of Fame in Cooperstown, New York, are shown here. Each observation indicates the primary position played by the Hall of Famers: pitcher (P), catcher (H), 1st base (1), 2nd base (2), 3rd base (3), shortstop (S), left field (L), center field (C), and right field (R).

| L | P | C | H | 2 | P | R | 1 | S | S | 1 | L | P | R | P |
|---|---|---|---|---|---|---|---|---|---|---|---|---|---|---|
| P | P | P | R | C | S | L | R | P | C | C | P | P | R | P |
| 2 | 3 | P | H | L | P | 1 | C | P | P | P | S | 1 | L | R |
| R | 1 | 2 | H | S | 3 | H | 2 | L | P |   |   |   |   |   |

a. Use frequency and relative frequency distributions to summarize the data.
b. What position provides the most Hall of Famers?
c. What position provides the fewest Hall of Famers?
d. What outfield position (L, C, or R) provides the most Hall of Famers?
e. Compare infielders (1, 2, 3, and S) to outfielders (L, C, and R).

9. The flextime system at Electronics Associates allows employees to begin their working day at 7:00, 7:30, 8:00, 8:30, or 9:00 A.M. The following data represent a sample of the starting times selected by the employees.

7:00(3)  8:30(7)  9:00(2)  8:00(4)  7:30(4)  7:30    8:30    8:30    7:30    7:00
8:30     8:30     8:00     8:00     7:30     8:30    7:00    9:00    8:30    8:00

Summarize the data by constructing the following:
a. A frequency distribution
b. A percent frequency distribution
c. A bar graph
d. A pie chart
e. What do the summaries tell you about employee preferences in the flextime system?

10. Students in the College of Business Administration at the University of Cincinnati are asked to fill out a course evaluation questionnaire upon completion of their courses. The questionnaire consists of a variety of questions that have a five-category response scale. One of the questions follows.

Compared to other courses you have taken, what is the overall quality of the course you are now completing?

| ___ | ___ | ___ | ___ | ___ |
|-----|-----|-----|-----|-----|
| Poor | Fair | Good | Very Good | Excellent |

A sample of 60 students completing a course in business statistics during the spring quarter of 2001 provided the following responses. To aid in computer processing of the questionnaire results, the responses were coded as follows: 1 = poor, 2 = fair, 3 = good, 4 = very good, and 5 = excellent.

| 3 | 4 | 4 | 5 | 1 | 5 | 3 | 4 | 5 | 2 | 4 | 5 | 3 | 4 | 4 |
|---|---|---|---|---|---|---|---|---|---|---|---|---|---|---|
| 4 | 5 | 5 | 4 | 1 | 4 | 5 | 4 | 2 | 5 | 4 | 2 | 4 | 4 | 4 |
| 5 | 5 | 3 | 4 | 5 | 5 | 2 | 4 | 3 | 4 | 5 | 4 | 3 | 5 | 4 |
| 4 | 3 | 5 | 4 | 5 | 4 | 3 | 5 | 3 | 4 | 4 | 3 | 5 | 3 | 3 |

a. Comment on why these are qualitative data.
b. Provide a frequency distribution and a relative frequency distribution summary of the data.
c. Provide a bar graph and a pie chart.
d. On the basis of your summaries, comment on the students' overall evaluation of the course.

## 2.2   SUMMARIZING QUANTITATIVE DATA

## Frequency Distribution

As defined in Section 2.1, a frequency distribution is a tabular summary showing the number (frequency) of items in each of several nonoverlapping classes. This definition holds for quantitative as well as qualitative data. However, with quantitative data we have to be more careful in defining the nonoverlapping classes to be used in the frequency distribution.

**TABLE 2.5**

YEAR-END AUDIT
TIMES (IN DAYS)

| | | | |
|---|---|---|---|
| 12 | 14 | 19 | 18 |
| 15 | 15 | 18 | 17 |
| 20 | 27 | 22 | 23 |
| 22 | 21 | 33 | 28 |
| 14 | 18 | 16 | 13 |

**CD** file

**Audit**

Making the classes the
same width reduces the
chance of inappropriate
interpretations by the user.

No single frequency
distribution is best for a
data set. Different people
may construct different,
but equally acceptable,
frequency distributions.
The goal is to reveal the
natural grouping and
variation in the data.

For example, consider the quantitative data in Table 2.5. These data provide the time in days required to complete year-end audits for a sample of 20 clients of Sanderson and Clifford, a small public accounting firm. The three steps necessary to define the classes for a frequency distribution with quantitative data are:

1. Determine the number of nonoverlapping classes.
2. Determine the width of each class.
3. Determine the class limits.

Let us demonstrate these steps by developing a frequency distribution for the audit time data in Table 2.5.

**Number of Classes.**    Classes are formed by specifying ranges that will be used to group the data. As a general guideline, we recommend using between five and 20 classes. For a small number of data items, as few as five or six classes may be used to summarize the data. For a larger number of data items, a larger number of classes is usually required. The goal is to use enough classes to show the variation in the data, but not so many classes that they contain only a few data items. Because the number of data items in Table 2.5 is relatively small ($n = 20$), we chose to develop a frequency distribution with five classes.

**Width of the Classes.**    The second step in constructing a frequency distribution for quantitative data is to choose a width for the classes. As a general guideline, we recommend that the width be the same for each class. Thus the choices of the number of classes and the width of classes are not independent decisions. A larger number of classes means a smaller class width, and vice versa. To determine an approximate class width, we begin by identifying the largest and smallest data values. Then, once the desired number of classes has been specified, we can use the following expression to determine the approximate class width.

$$\text{Approximate Class Width} = \frac{\text{Largest Data Value} - \text{Smallest Data Value}}{\text{Number of Classes}} \quad \textbf{(2.2)}$$

The approximate class width given by Equation (2.2) can be rounded to a more convenient value based on the preference of the person developing the frequency distribution. For example, an approximate class width of 9.28 might be rounded to 10 simply because 10 is a more convenient class width to use in presenting a frequency distribution.

For the data involving the year-end audit times, the largest value is 33 and the smallest value is 12. Because we decided to summarize the data with five classes, using Equation (2.2) provides an approximate class width of $(33 - 12)/5 = 4.2$. We therefore decided to use a class width of five days in the frequency distribution.

In practice, the number of classes and the appropriate class width are determined by trial and error. Once a possible number of classes is chosen, Equation (2.2) is used to find the approximate class width. The process can be repeated for a different number of classes. Ultimately, the analyst uses judgment to determine the combination of the number of classes and class width that provides the best frequency distribution for summarizing the data.

For the audit time data in Table 2.5, after deciding to use five classes, each with a width of five days, the next task is to specify the class limits for each of the classes.

**Class Limits.**    Class limits must be chosen so that each data item belongs to one and only one class. The *lower class limit* identifies the smallest possible data value assigned to the class. The *upper class limit* identifies the largest possible data value assigned to the class. In developing frequency distributions for qualitative data, we did not need to specify class limits because each data item naturally fell into a separate class (category). But with quantitative data, such as the audit times in Table 2.5, class limits are necessary to determine where each data value belongs.

For the audit time data in Table 2.5 we defined the class limits as 10–14, 15–19, 20–24, 25–29, and 30–34. The smallest data value, 12, is included in the 10–14 class. The largest data value, 33, is included in the 30–34 class. For the 10–14 class, 10 is the lower class limit and 14 is the upper class limit. The difference between the lower class limits of adjacent classes is the class width. Using the first two lower class limits of 10 and 15, we see that the class width is $15 - 10 = 5$.

Once the number of classes, class width, and class limits have been determined, a frequency distribution can be obtained by counting the number of data values belonging to each class. For example, the data in Table 2.5 show that four values—12, 14, 14, and 13—belong to the 10–14 class. Thus, the frequency for the 10–14 class is 4. Continuing this counting process for the 15–19, 20–24, 25–29, and 30–34 classes provides the frequency distribution in Table 2.6. Using this frequency distribution, we can observe that:

**TABLE 2.6**

FREQUENCY DISTRIBUTION FOR THE AUDIT TIME DATA

| Audit Time (days) | Frequency |
| --- | --- |
| 10–14 | 4 |
| 15–19 | 8 |
| 20–24 | 5 |
| 25–29 | 2 |
| 30–34 | 1 |
| Total | 20 |

1. The most frequently occurring audit times are in the class of 15–19 days. Eight of the 20 audit times belong to this class.
2. Only one audit required 30 or more days.

Other conclusions are possible, depending on the interests of the person viewing the frequency distribution. The value of a frequency distribution is that it provides insights about the data that are not easily obtained by viewing the data in their original unorganized form.

**Class Midpoint.**   In some applications, we want to know the midpoints of the classes in a frequency distribution for quantitative data. The **class midpoint** is the value halfway between the lower and upper class limits. For the audit time data, the five class midpoints are 12, 17, 22, 27, and 32.

## Using Excel's FREQUENCY Function to Construct a Frequency Distribution

Constructing a frequency distribution for quantitative data using Excel's COUNTIF function is cumbersome. Here we show how to use Excel's FREQUENCY function to construct a frequency distribution for quantitative data. The FREQUENCY function involves the use of array formulas that provide multiple values (in this case the class frequencies) as output. Refer to Figure 2.6 as we describe the tasks involved. The formula worksheet is in the background; the value worksheet is in the foreground

**Enter Data:**   The label Audit Time and the data for the 20 audit times have been entered into cells A1:A21.

*Excel's Function Wizard can help with the proper use of this function. See Appendix F.*

**Enter Functions and Formulas:**   Descriptive labels have been entered into cells C1 and D1 and the class limits 10–14, 15–19, and so on, have been entered using text format into cells C2:C6. Unlike simple Excel functions, the FREQUENCY function is capable of providing multiple values. In this case, the multiple values are the class frequencies. A formula that can return multiple values is called an array formula and must be entered in a special way. The following steps describe how to create and enter an array formula that uses the FREQUENCY function to calculate the frequencies for the audit time data.

**Step 1.** Select cells D2:D6, the cells in which we want the frequencies to appear
**Step 2.** Type the following formula:
  =FREQUENCY(A2:A21,{14,19,24,29,34})

*You must hold down Ctrl and Shift while pressing Enter to enter an array formula.*

**Step 3.** Press CTRL + SHIFT + ENTER and the array formula will be entered into each of the cells D2:D6

**FIGURE 2.6** FREQUENCY DISTRIBUTION FOR AUDIT TIME DATA CONSTRUCTED USING EXCEL'S FREQUENCY FUNCTION

| | A | B | C | D | E |
|---|---|---|---|---|---|
| 1 | Audit Time | | Audit Time | Frequency | |
| 2 | 12 | | 10-14 | =FREQUENCY(A2:A21,{14,19,24,29,34}) | |
| 3 | 15 | | 15-19 | =FREQUENCY(A2:A21,{14,19,24,29,34}) | |
| 4 | 20 | | 20-24 | =FREQUENCY(A2:A21,{14,19,24,29,34}) | |
| 5 | 22 | | 25-29 | =FREQUENCY(A2:A21,{14,19,24,29,34}) | |
| 6 | 14 | | 30-34 | =FREQUENCY(A2:A21,{14,19,24,29,34}) | |
| 7 | 14 | | | | |
| 8 | 15 | | | | |
| 9 | 27 | | | | |
| 10 | 21 | | | | |
| 11 | 18 | | | | |
| 12 | 19 | | | | |
| 13 | 18 | | | | |
| 14 | 22 | | | | |
| 15 | 33 | | | | |
| 16 | 16 | | | | |
| 17 | 18 | | | | |
| 18 | 17 | | | | |
| 19 | 23 | | | | |
| 20 | 28 | | | | |
| 21 | 13 | | | | |
| 22 | | | | | |

| | A | B | C | D | E |
|---|---|---|---|---|---|
| 1 | Audit Time | | Audit Time | Frequency | |
| 2 | 12 | | 10-14 | 4 | |
| 3 | 15 | | 15-19 | 8 | |
| 4 | 20 | | 20-24 | 5 | |
| 5 | 22 | | 25-29 | 2 | |
| 6 | 14 | | 30-34 | 1 | |
| 7 | 14 | | | | |
| 8 | 15 | | | | |
| 9 | 27 | | | | |
| 10 | 21 | | | | |
| 11 | 18 | | | | |
| 12 | 19 | | | | |
| 13 | 18 | | | | |
| 14 | 22 | | | | |
| 15 | 33 | | | | |
| 16 | 16 | | | | |
| 17 | 18 | | | | |
| 18 | 17 | | | | |
| 19 | 23 | | | | |
| 20 | 28 | | | | |
| 21 | 13 | | | | |
| 22 | | | | | |

The results are shown in Figure 2.6. Because we entered an array formula into cells D2:D6, the formula that Excel displays in each of these cells is the same. But, the values calculated are not. They are the frequencies for each class (see Table 2.6). The class upper limits in the second argument of the FREQUENCY function (between the braces in Step 2) tell Excel which frequency to put in each cell within the range of the array formula. The frequency for the class with an upper limit of 14 is placed in the first cell (D2), the frequency for the class with an upper limit of 19 is placed in the second cell (D3), and so on.

## Relative Frequency and Percent Frequency Distributions

We define the relative frequency and percent frequency distributions for quantitative data in the same manner as for qualitative data. First, recall that the relative frequency is simply the proportion of the observations belonging to a class. With $n$ observations,

$$\text{Relative Frequency of Class} = \frac{\text{Frequency of the Class}}{n}$$

The percent frequency of a class is the relative frequency multiplied by 100.

**TABLE 2.7**    RELATIVE AND PERCENT FREQUENCY DISTRIBUTIONS FOR THE AUDIT TIME DATA

| Audit Time (days) | Relative Frequency | Percent Frequency |
|---|---|---|
| 10–14 | .20 | 20 |
| 15–19 | .40 | 40 |
| 20–24 | .25 | 25 |
| 25–29 | .10 | 10 |
| 30–34 | .05 | 5 |
| Total | 1.00 | 100 |

Based on the class frequencies in Table 2.6 and with $n = 20$, Table 2.7 shows the relative frequency distribution and percent frequency distribution for the audit time data. Note that .40 of the audits, or 40%, required from 15 to 19 days. Only .05 of the audits, or 5%, required 30 or more days. Again, additional interpretations and insights can be obtained by using Table 2.7.

## Histogram

A common graphical presentation of quantitative data is a **histogram.** This graphical summary can be prepared for data that have been previously summarized in either a frequency, relative frequency, or percent frequency distribution. A histogram is constructed by placing the variable of interest on the horizontal axis and the frequency, relative frequency, or percent frequency on the vertical axis. The frequency, relative frequency, or percent frequency of each class is shown by drawing a rectangle whose base is the class interval on the horizontal axis and whose height is the corresponding frequency, relative frequency, or percent frequency.

Figure 2.7 is a histogram for the audit time data. Note that the class with the greatest frequency is shown by the rectangle appearing above the class of 15–19 days. The height of the rectangle shows that the frequency of this class is 8. A histogram for the relative or percent frequency distribution of this data would look the same as the histogram

**FIGURE 2.7**    HISTOGRAM FOR THE AUDIT TIME DATA

in Figure 2.7 with the exception that the vertical axis would be labeled with relative or percent frequency values.

As Figure 2.7 shows, the adjacent rectangles of a histogram touch one another. Unlike a bar graph, a histogram has no natural separation between the rectangles of adjacent classes. This format is the usual convention for histograms. Because the class limits for the audit time data are stated as 10–14, 15–19, 20–24, 25–29, and 30–34, one-unit intervals of 14 to 15, 19 to 20, 24 to 25, and 29 to 30 appear between the classes. These spaces are eliminated by drawing the vertical lines of the histogram halfway between the class limits. The vertical lines separating the classes for the histogram in Figure 2.7 are at 9.5, 14.5, 19.5, 24.5, 29.5, and 34.5. This minor adjustment to eliminate the spaces between classes in a histogram helps show that, even though the data are rounded, all values between the lower limit of the first class and the upper limit of the last class are possible.

## Using Excel's Chart Wizard to Construct a Histogram

We can use Excel's Chart Wizard to construct a histogram for the audit time data. Refer to Figure 2.8 as we describe the tasks involved.

**Enter Data:**   Same as in in Figure 2.6.

**Enter Functions and Formulas:**   Same as in Figure 2.6.

**Apply Tools:**   The following steps describe how to use Excel's Chart Wizard to produce a histogram for the audit time data using the frequency distribution appearing in cells C2:D6 of the worksheet shown in Figure 2.8.

> **Step 1.**  Select cells C1:D6
> **Step 2.**  Select the **Chart Wizard** button on the Standard toolbar (or select the **Insert** pull-down menu and choose the **Chart** option)

**FIGURE 2.8**   INITIAL HISTOGRAM CONSTRUCTED USING EXCEL FOR THE AUDIT-TIME DATA

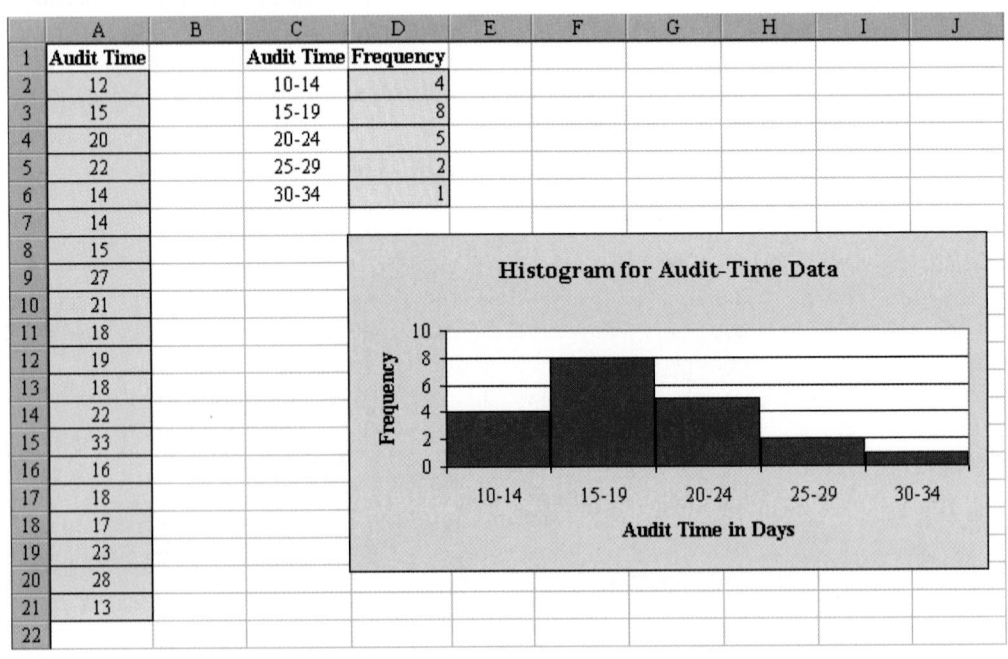

> **Step 3.** When the **Chart Wizard–Step 1 of 4–Chart Type** dialog box appears:
> Choose **Column** in the **Chart type** list
> Choose **Clustered Column** from the **Chart sub-type** display
> Select **Next >**
>
> **Step 4.** When the **Chart Wizard–Step 2 of 4–Chart Source Data** dialog box appears:
> Select **Next >**
>
> **Step 5.** When the **Chart Wizard–Step 3 of 4–Chart Options** dialog box appears:
> Select the **Titles** tab and then
> Type **Histogram for Audit-Time Data** in the **Chart title** box
> Enter **Audit Time in Days** in the **Category (X)** axis box
> Enter **Frequency** in the **Values (Y)** axis box
> Select the **Legend** tab and then
> Remove the check in the **Show Legend** Box
> Select **Next >**
>
> **Step 6.** When the **Chart Wizard–Step 4 of 4–Chart Location** dialog box appears:
> Specify a location for the chart (we used the default setting of the current worksheet)
> Select **Finish**

The worksheet displayed in Figure 2.8 shows the column chart produced by Excel. Note the gaps between the rectangles. Because the adjacent rectangles in a histogram must touch, we need to edit the chart in order to eliminate the gap between each of the rectangles. The following steps describe this process. Refer to Figure 2.9 as we describe the steps.

> **Step 1.** Right click on any rectangle in the column chart to produce a list of options
> **Step 2.** Select the **Format Data Series** option
> **Step 3.** When the **Format Data Series** dialog box appears:
> Select the **Options** tab and then
> Enter **0** in the **Gap width** box
> Click **OK**

Figure 2.10 displays the histogram produced by Excel. With the exception of the labels on the horizontal axis, it is the same histogram that we developed earlier in Figure 2.7. The size of the chart can now be adjusted to suit user preference.

## Cumulative Distributions

A variation of the frequency distribution that provides another tabular summary of quantitative data is the cumulative frequency distribution. The cumulative frequency distribution uses the number of classes, class widths, and class limits that were developed for the frequency distribution. However, rather than showing the frequency of each class, the cumulative frequency distribution shows the number of data items with values *less than or equal to the upper class limit* of each class. The first two columns of Table 2.8 provide the cumulative frequency distribution for the audit time data.

To understand how the cumulative frequencies are determined, consider the class with the description "less than or equal to 24." The cumulative frequency for this class is simply the sum of the frequencies for all classes with data values less than or equal to 24. For the frequency distribution in Table 2.6, the sum of the frequencies for classes 10–14, 15–19, and 20–24 indicates that $4 + 8 + 5 = 17$ data values are less than or equal to 24. Hence, the cumulative frequency for this class is 17. In addition, the cumulative frequency distribution in Table 2.8 shows that four audits were completed in 14 days or less and 19 audits were completed in 29 days or less.

As a final point, we note that a cumulative relative frequency distribution shows the proportion of data items, and a cumulative percent frequency distribution shows the

**FIGURE 2.9**     REMOVING THE GAPS BETWEEN CLASSES TO DISPLAY A HISTOGRAM FOR THE
AUDIT-TIME DATA

percentage of data items with values less than or equal to the upper limit of each class. The
cumulative relative frequency distribution can be computed either by summing the relative
frequencies in the relative frequency distribution or by dividing the cumulative frequencies
by the total number of items. Using the latter approach, we found the cumulative relative
frequencies in column 3 of Table 2.8 by dividing the cumulative frequencies in column 2
by the total number of items ($n = 20$). The cumulative percent frequencies were again computed by multiplying the relative frequencies by 100. The cumulative relative and percent

**FIGURE 2.10**    FINAL HISTOGRAM CONSTRUCTED USING EXCEL FOR THE
AUDIT-TIME DATA

| | A | B | C | D | E | F | G | H | I | J |
|---|---|---|---|---|---|---|---|---|---|---|
| 1 | **Audit Time** | | **Audit Time** | **Frequency** | | | | | | |
| 2 | 12 | | 10-14 | 4 | | | | | | |
| 3 | 15 | | 15-19 | 8 | | | | | | |
| 4 | 20 | | 20-24 | 5 | | | | | | |
| 5 | 22 | | 25-29 | 2 | | | | | | |
| 6 | 14 | | 30-34 | 1 | | | | | | |
| 7 | 14 | | | | | | | | | |
| 8 | 15 | | | | | Histogram for Audit-Time Data | | | | |
| 9 | 27 | | | | | | | | | |
| 10 | 21 | | | | | | | | | |
| 11 | 18 | | | | | | | | | |
| 12 | 19 | | | | | | | | | |
| 13 | 18 | | | | | | | | | |
| 14 | 22 | | | | | | | | | |
| 15 | 33 | | | | | | | | | |
| 16 | 16 | | | | | | | | | |
| 17 | 18 | | | | | | | | | |
| 18 | 17 | | | | | | | | | |
| 19 | 23 | | | | | | | | | |
| 20 | 28 | | | | | | | | | |
| 21 | 13 | | | | | | | | | |
| 22 | | | | | | | | | | |

frequency distributions show that .85 of the audits, or 85%, were completed in 24 days or less, .95 of the audits, or 95%, were completed in 29 days or less, and so on.

## Ogive

A graph of a cumulative distribution is called an **ogive.** The data values are shown on the horizontal axis and either the cumulative frequencies, the cumulative relative frequencies, or the cumulative percent frequencies are shown on the vertical axis. Figure 2.11 is the ogive for the cumulative frequencies of the audit time data in Table 2.8.

**TABLE 2.8**    CUMULATIVE FREQUENCY, CUMULATIVE RELATIVE FREQUENCY,
AND CUMULATIVE PERCENT FREQUENCY DISTRIBUTIONS FOR THE
AUDIT-TIME DATA

| Audit Time (days) | Cumulative Frequency | Cumulative Relative Frequency | Cumulative Percent Frequency |
|---|---|---|---|
| Less than or equal to 14 | 4 | .20 | 20 |
| Less than or equal to 19 | 12 | .60 | 60 |
| Less than or equal to 24 | 17 | .85 | 85 |
| Less than or equal to 29 | 19 | .95 | 95 |
| Less than or equal to 34 | 20 | 1.00 | 100 |

**FIGURE 2.11**     OGIVE FOR THE AUDIT-TIME DATA

The ogive is constructed by plotting a point corresponding to the cumulative frequency of each class. Because the class limits for the audit time data are 10–14, 15–19, 20–24, and so on, one-unit gaps appear from 14 to 15, 19 to 20, and so on. As with the histogram, these gaps are eliminated by plotting points halfway between the class limits. Thus, 14.5 is used for the 10–14 class, 19.5 is used for the 15–19 class, and so on. The "less than or equal to 14" class with a cumulative frequency of 4 is shown on the ogive in Figure 2.11 by the point located at 14.5 on the horizontal axis and 4 on the vertical axis. The "less than or equal to 19" class with a cumulative frequency of 12 is shown by the point located at 19.5 on the horizontal axis and 12 on the vertical axis. Note that one additional point is plotted at the left end of the ogive. This point starts the ogive by showing that no data values fall below the 10–14 class. It is plotted at 9.5 on the horizontal axis and 0 on the vertical axis. The plotted points are connected by straight lines to complete the ogive.

## NOTES AND COMMENTS

1. A bar graph and a histogram are essentially the same thing; both are graphical presentations of the data in a frequency distribution. A histogram is just a bar graph with no separation between bars. The separation between bars is appropriate for qualitative data because the data are discrete; no intermediate values are possible. For some quantitative data, a separation between bars is appropriate. Consider, for example, the number of classes in which a college student is enrolled. The data may only assume integer values. Intermediate values such as 1.5, 2.73, and so on are not possible. With continuous quantitative data, such as the audit times in Table 2.5, a separation between bars is not appropriate.

2. The appropriate values for the class limits with quantitative data depend on the level of accuracy

of the data. For instance, with the audit time data of Table 2.5 the limits used were integer values because the data had been rounded to the nearest day. If the data were rounded to the nearest tenth of a day (e.g., 12.3, 14.4, and so on), then the limits would have been stated in tenths of days. For instance, the first class limits would have been 10.0–14.9. If the data were rounded to the nearest hundredth of a day (e.g., 12.34, 14.45, and so on), the limits would have been stated in hundredths of days. For instance, the first class limits would have been 10.00–14.99.

3. An *open-end* class is one that has only a lower class limit or an upper class limit. For example, in the audit time data of Table 2.5, suppose two of the audits had taken 58 and 65 days. Rather than continue with the classes of width 5 with

class intervals 35–39, 40–44, 45–49, and so on, we could simplify the frequency distribution to show an open-end class of "35 or more." This class would have a frequency of 2. Most often the open-end class appears at the upper end of the distribution. Sometimes an open-end class appears at the lower end of the distribution, and occasionally such classes appear at both ends.

**4.** The last entry in a cumulative frequency distribution is always the total number of observations. The last entry in a cumulative relative frequency distribution is always 1.00 and the last entry in a cumulative percent frequency distribution is always 100.

**5.** In addition to the FREQUENCY function to construct a frequency distribution for quantitative data, and the Chart Wizard for constructing a histogram, Excel has a Histogram tool in its Data Analysis add-in. It can be used to construct both a frequency distribution and a histogram in one series of steps. We show how it can be used to construct a frequency distribution and histogram for the audit time data in Appendix 2.1. We note there the advantages and disadvantages to the use of this tool. Other tools in the Data Analysis add-in will be introduced in Chapter 3.

## EXERCISES

## Methods

**11.** Consider the following data.

| | | | | |
|---|---|---|---|---|
| 14 | 21 | 23 | 21 | 16 |
| 19 | 22 | 25 | 16 | 16 |
| 24 | 24 | 25 | 19 | 16 |
| 19 | 18 | 19 | 21 | 12 |
| 16 | 17 | 18 | 23 | 25 |
| 20 | 23 | 16 | 20 | 19 |
| 24 | 26 | 15 | 22 | 24 |
| 20 | 22 | 24 | 22 | 20 |

  **a.** Develop a frequency distribution using class limits of 12–14, 15–17, 18–20, 21–23, and 24–26.

  **b.** Develop a relative frequency distribution and a percent frequency distribution using the class limits in part (a).

**12.** Consider the following frequency distribution.

| Class | Frequency |
|---|---|
| 10–19 | 10 |
| 20–29 | 14 |
| 30–39 | 17 |
| 40–49 | 7 |
| 50–59 | 2 |

Construct a cumulative frequency distribution and a cumulative relative frequency distribution.

**13.** Construct a histogram and an ogive for the data in Exercise 12.

**14.** Consider the following data.

| | | | | | | | | | |
|---|---|---|---|---|---|---|---|---|---|
| 8.9 | 10.2 | 11.5 | 7.8 | 10.0 | 12.2 | 13.5 | 14.1 | 10.0 | 12.2 |
| 6.8 | 9.5 | 11.5 | 11.2 | 14.9 | 7.5 | 10.0 | 6.0 | 15.8 | 11.5 |

  **a.** Construct a frequency distribution.

  **b.** Construct a percent frequency distribution.

## Applications

15. A doctor's office staff has studied the waiting times for patients who arrive at the office with a request for emergency service. The following data were collected over a one-month period (the waiting times are in minutes).

    2   5   10   12   4   4   5   17   11   8   9   8   12   21   6   8   7   13   18   3

    Use classes of 0–4, 5–9, and so on in the following:
    a. Show the frequency distribution.
    b. Show the relative frequency distribution.
    c. Show the cumulative frequency distribution.
    d. Show the cumulative relative frequency distribution.
    e. What proportion of patients needing emergency service has a waiting time of nine minutes or less?

16. A sample of 25 computer hardware companies taken from the *Stock Invester Pro* database is shown in Table 2.9.
    a. Develop tabular summaries and a histogram for the stock price data. Comment on typical stock prices and the distribution of stock prices.
    b. Develop tabular summaries and a histogram for the earnings per share data. Comment on your results.

**TABLE 2.9**   DATA SET FOR 25 COMPUTER HARDWARE COMPANIES

**Stocks**

| Company | Stock Price | Institutional Ownership (%) | Price/Book Value | Earnings per Share (Annual $) |
|---|---|---|---|---|
| Amdahl | 12.31 | 45.4 | 2.49 | −2.49 |
| Auspex Systems | 11.00 | 66.1 | 2.22 | 0.85 |
| Compaq Computer | 65.50 | 83.0 | 6.84 | 2.01 |
| Data General | 35.94 | 91.5 | 4.25 | 1.15 |
| Digi International | 15.00 | 33.4 | 2.04 | −0.89 |
| Digital Equipment Corp. | 43.00 | 58.8 | 1.92 | −2.93 |
| En Pointe Technologies | 14.25 | 11.8 | 3.47 | 0.80 |
| Equitrac | 16.25 | 20.9 | 2.38 | 0.76 |
| Franklin Electronic Pbls. | 12.88 | 30.8 | 1.41 | 0.82 |
| Gateway 2000 | 39.13 | 36.0 | 6.45 | 1.74 |
| Hewlett-Packard | 61.50 | 50.2 | 4.35 | 2.64 |
| Ingram Micro | 28.75 | 14.4 | 4.53 | 1.01 |
| Maxwell Technologies | 30.50 | 26.5 | 8.07 | 0.46 |
| MicroAge | 27.19 | 76.6 | 2.16 | 1.25 |
| Micron Electronics | 16.31 | 18.8 | 4.48 | 1.06 |
| Network Computing Devices | 11.88 | 39.8 | 3.34 | 0.15 |
| Pomeroy Computer Resource | 33.00 | 56.9 | 3.29 | 1.81 |
| Sequent Computer Systems | 28.19 | 57.0 | 2.65 | 0.36 |
| Silicon Graphics | 27.44 | 63.0 | 3.01 | 0.44 |
| Southern Electronics | 15.13 | 41.9 | 2.46 | 0.99 |
| Stratus Computer | 55.50 | 77.2 | 2.48 | 2.52 |
| Sun Microsystems | 48.00 | 59.3 | 7.50 | 1.67 |
| Tandem Computers | 34.25 | 61.3 | 3.61 | 1.02 |
| Tech Data | 38.94 | 82.3 | 3.80 | 1.50 |
| Unisys | 11.31 | 34.8 | 16.64 | 0.08 |

*Source: Stock Investor Pro,* American Association of Individual Investors, August 31, 1997.

**17.** National Airlines accepts flight reservations by telephone. The following data show the call durations (in minutes) for a sample of 20 telephone reservations. Construct frequency and relative frequency distributions for the data. Also provide a histogram.

| 2.1 | 4.8 | 5.5 | 10.4 |
|-----|-----|-----|------|
| 3.3 | 3.5 | 4.8 | 5.8 |
| 5.3 | 5.5 | 2.8 | 3.6 |
| 5.9 | 6.6 | 7.8 | 10.5 |
| 7.5 | 6.0 | 4.5 | 4.8 |

**18.** Wageweb conducts surveys of salary data and presents summaries on its web site. Using salary data as of January 1, 2000, Wageweb reported that salaries of marketing vice presidents ranged from $85,090 to $190,054 (*Wageweb.com*, April 12, 2000). Assume the following data are a sample of the annual salaries for 50 marketing vice presidents. Data are in thousands of dollars.

**CD** file

**Wageweb**

| 145 | 95 | 148 | 112 | 132 |
|-----|-----|-----|-----|-----|
| 140 | 162 | 118 | 170 | 144 |
| 145 | 127 | 148 | 165 | 138 |
| 173 | 113 | 104 | 141 | 142 |
| 116 | 178 | 123 | 141 | 138 |
| 127 | 143 | 134 | 136 | 137 |
| 155 | 93 | 102 | 154 | 142 |
| 134 | 165 | 123 | 124 | 124 |
| 138 | 160 | 157 | 138 | 131 |
| 114 | 135 | 151 | 138 | 157 |

**a.** What are the lowest and highest salaries?
**b.** Use a class width of $15,000 and prepare tabular summaries of the annual salary data.
**c.** What proportion of the annual salaries are $135,000 or less?
**d.** What percentage of the annual salaries are more than $150,000?
**e.** Prepare a histogram.

**19.** The data for the numbers of units produced by a production employee during the most recent 20 days are shown here.

| 160 | 170 | 181 | 156 | 176 |
|-----|-----|-----|-----|-----|
| 148 | 198 | 179 | 162 | 150 |
| 162 | 156 | 179 | 178 | 151 |
| 157 | 154 | 179 | 148 | 156 |

Summarize the data by constructing the following:
**a.** A frequency distribution
**b.** A relative frequency distribution
**c.** A cumulative frequency distribution
**d.** A cumulative relative frequency distribution
**e.** An ogive

**20.** The U.S. Bureau of the Census publishes a variety of information on the U.S. population. Shown here is the percent frequency distribution of the U.S. population by age as of July 1, 2000 (*The World Almanac and Book of Facts 2000*).

| Age | Percent Frequency |
|-----|-------------------|
| 0–13 | 20.0 |
| 14–17 | 5.7 |
| 18–24 | 9.6 |
| 25–34 | 13.6 |
| 35–44 | 16.3 |
| 45–54 | 13.5 |
| 55–64 | 8.7 |
| 65 or over | 12.6 |
| | 100.0 |

a. What percentage of the population is 34 years old or younger?
b. What percentage of the population is between 25 and 54 years old inclusively?
c. What percentage of the population is older than 34 years old?
d. The total population is 275 million. How many people are younger than 25 years old?
e. Suppose you believe that half the people in the 55–64 class are retired and that approximately all of the people 65 or older are retired. Estimate the number of retired people in the population.

21. The *Nielsen Home Technology Report* (February 20, 1996) reported on home technology and its usage by persons aged 12 and older. The following data are the hours of personal computer usage during one week for a sample of 50 persons.

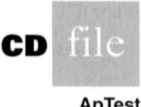

**CD** file

Computer

| | | | | | | | | | |
|---|---|---|---|---|---|---|---|---|---|
| 4.1 | 1.5 | 10.4 | 5.9 | 3.4 | 5.7 | 1.6 | 6.1 | 3.0 | 3.7 |
| 3.1 | 4.8 | 2.0 | 14.8 | 5.4 | 4.2 | 3.9 | 4.1 | 11.1 | 3.5 |
| 4.1 | 4.1 | 8.8 | 5.6 | 4.3 | 3.3 | 7.1 | 10.3 | 6.2 | 7.6 |
| 10.8 | 2.8 | 9.5 | 12.9 | 12.1 | 0.7 | 4.0 | 9.2 | 4.4 | 5.7 |
| 7.2 | 6.1 | 5.7 | 5.9 | 4.7 | 3.9 | 3.7 | 3.1 | 6.1 | 3.1 |

Summarize the data by constructing the following:
a. A frequency distribution (use a class width of three hours)
b. A relative frequency distribution
c. A histogram
d. An ogive
e. Comment on what the data indicate about personal computer usage at home.

## 2.3 EXPLORATORY DATA ANALYSIS: THE STEM-AND-LEAF DISPLAY

The techniques of exploratory data analysis consist of simple arithmetic and easy-to-draw graphs that can be used to summarize data quickly. One technique — referred to as a stem-and-leaf display — can be used to show both the rank order and shape of a data set simultaneously.

To illustrate the use of a stem-and-leaf display, consider the data in Table 2.10. These data are the result of a 150-question aptitude test given to 50 individuals who were recently interviewed for a position at Haskens Manufacturing. The data values indicate the number of questions answered correctly.

To develop a stem-and-leaf display, we first arrange the leading digits of each data value to the left of a vertical line. To the right of the vertical line, we record the last digit for each

**TABLE 2.10**    NUMBER OF QUESTIONS ANSWERED CORRECTLY ON AN APTITUDE TEST

**CD** file

ApTest

| | | | | |
|---|---|---|---|---|
| 112 | 72 | 69 | 97 | 107 |
| 73 | 92 | 76 | 86 | 73 |
| 126 | 128 | 118 | 127 | 124 |
| 82 | 104 | 132 | 134 | 83 |
| 92 | 108 | 96 | 100 | 92 |
| 115 | 76 | 91 | 102 | 81 |
| 95 | 141 | 81 | 80 | 106 |
| 84 | 119 | 113 | 98 | 75 |
| 68 | 98 | 115 | 106 | 95 |
| 100 | 85 | 94 | 106 | 119 |

data value as we pass through the observations in the order they were recorded. The last digit for each data value is placed on the line corresponding to its first digit as follows:

```
 6 | 9  8
 7 | 2  3  6  3  6  5
 8 | 6  2  3  1  1  0  4  5
 9 | 7  2  2  6  2  1  5  8  8  5  4
10 | 7  4  8  0  2  6  6  0  6
11 | 2  8  5  9  3  5  9
12 | 6  8  7  4
13 | 2  4
14 | 1
```

With this organization of the data, sorting the digits on each line into rank order is simple. Doing so leads to the stem-and-leaf display shown here.

```
 6 | 8  9
 7 | 2  3  3  5  6  6
 8 | 0  1  1  2  3  4  5  6
 9 | 1  2  2  2  4  5  5  6  7  8  8
10 | 0  0  2  4  6  6  6  7  8
11 | 2  3  5  5  8  9  9
12 | 4  6  7  8
13 | 2  4
14 | 1
```

The numbers to the left of the line (6, 7, 8, 9, 10, 11, 12, 13, and 14) form the *stem,* and each digit to the right of the line is a *leaf.* For example, consider the first line with a stem value of 6 and leaves of 8 and 9.

$$6 \mid 8 \quad 9$$

This indicates that there are two data values that have a first digit of six. The leaves show that the data values are 68 and 69. Similarly, the second line

$$7 \mid 2 \quad 3 \quad 3 \quad 5 \quad 6 \quad 6$$

indicates that six data values have a first digit of seven. The leaves show that the data values are 72, 73, 73, 75, 76, and 76.

To focus on the shape indicated by the stem-and-leaf display, let us use a rectangle to contain the leaves of each stem. Doing so, we obtain the following.

```
 6 | 8 9
 7 | 2 3 3 5 6 6
 8 | 0 1 1 2 3 4 5 6
 9 | 1 2 2 2 4 5 5 6 7 8 8
10 | 0 0 2 4 6 6 6 7 8
11 | 2 3 5 5 8 9 9
12 | 4 6 7 8
13 | 2 4
14 | 1
```

Rotating this page counterclockwise onto its side provides a picture of the data that is similar to a histogram with classes of 60–69, 70–79, 80–89, and so on.

Although the stem-and-leaf display may appear to offer the same information as a histogram, it has two primary advantages.

1. The stem-and-leaf display is easier to construct by hand.
2. Within a class interval, the stem-and-leaf display provides more information than the histogram because the stem-and-leaf shows the actual data values.

*In a stretched stem-and-leaf display, whenever a stem value is stated twice, the first value corresponds to leaf values of 0–4, and the second value corresponds to leaf values of 5–9.*

Just as a frequency distribution or histogram has no absolute number of classes, neither does a stem-and-leaf display have an absolute number of rows or stems. If we believe that our original stem-and-leaf display has condensed the data too much, we can easily stretch the display by using two or more stems for each leading digit(s). For example, to use two stems for each leading digit(s), we would place all data values ending in 0, 1, 2, 3, and 4 on one line and all values ending in 5, 6, 7, 8, and 9 on a second line. The following stretched stem-and-leaf display illustrates this approach.

```
 6 | 8 9
 7 | 2 3 3
 7 | 5 6 6
 8 | 0 1 1 2 3 4
 8 | 5 6
 9 | 1 2 2 2 4
 9 | 5 5 6 7 8 8
10 | 0 0 2 4
10 | 6 6 6 7 8
11 | 2 3
11 | 5 5 8 9 9
12 | 4
12 | 6 7 8
13 | 2 4
13 |
14 | 1
```

Note that values 72, 73, and 73 have leaves in the 0–4 range and are shown with the first stem value of 7. The values 75, 76, and 76 have leaves in the 5–9 range and are shown with the second stem value of 7. This stretched stem-and-leaf display is similar to a frequency distribution with intervals of 65–69, 70–74, 75–79, and so on.

The preceding example showed a stem-and-leaf display for data having up to three digits. Stem-and-leaf displays for data with more than three digits are possible. For example, consider the following data on the number of hamburgers sold by a fast-food restaurant for each of 15 weeks.

| 1565 | 1852 | 1644 | 1766 | 1888 | 1912 | 2044 | 1812 |
|------|------|------|------|------|------|------|------|
| 1790 | 1679 | 2008 | 1852 | 1967 | 1954 | 1733 |      |

A stem-and-leaf display of these data follows.

Leaf Unit = 10

```
15 | 6
16 | 4  7
17 | 3  6  9
18 | 1  5  5  8
19 | 1  5  6
20 | 0  4
```

A single digit is used to define each leaf in a stem-and-leaf display. The leaf unit indicates how to multiply the stem-and-leaf numbers in order to approximate the original data. Leaf units may be 100, 10, 1, 0.1, and so on.

Note that a single digit is used to define each leaf and that only the first three digits of each observation have been used to construct the display. At the top of the display we have specified Leaf Unit = 10. To illustrate how to interpret the values in the display, consider the first stem, 15, and its associated leaf, 6. Combining these numbers, we obtain 156. To reconstruct an approximation of the original observation, we must multiply this number by 10, the value of the *leaf unit*. Thus, $156 \times 10 = 1560$ is an approximation of the original observation used to construct the stem-and-leaf display. Although it is not possible to reconstruct the exact data from this stem-and-leaf display, the convention of using a single digit for each leaf enables stem-and-leaf displays to be constructed for data having a large number of digits. For stem-and-leaf displays where the leaf unit is not shown, it is assumed to equal 1.

## EXERCISES

## Methods

**22.** Construct a stem-and-leaf display for the following data.

| 70 | 72 | 75 | 64 | 58 | 83 | 80 | 82 |
|----|----|----|----|----|----|----|----|
| 76 | 75 | 68 | 65 | 57 | 78 | 85 | 72 |

**23.** Construct a stem-and-leaf display for the following data.

| 11.3 | 9.6 | 10.4 | 7.5 | 8.3 | 10.5 | 10.0 |
|------|-----|------|-----|-----|------|------|
| 9.3  | 8.1 | 7.7  | 7.5 | 8.4 | 6.3  | 8.8  |

**24.** Construct a stem-and-leaf display for the following data. Use a leaf unit of 10.

| 1161 | 1206 | 1478 | 1300 | 1604 | 1725 | 1361 | 1422 |
|------|------|------|------|------|------|------|------|
| 1221 | 1378 | 1623 | 1426 | 1557 | 1730 | 1706 | 1689 |

## Applications

25. A psychologist developed a new test of adult intelligence. The test was administered to 20 individuals, and the following data were obtained.

| 114 | 99 | 131 | 124 | 117 | 102 | 106 | 127 | 119 | 115 |
|-----|-----|-----|-----|-----|-----|-----|-----|-----|-----|
| 98 | 104 | 144 | 151 | 132 | 106 | 125 | 122 | 118 | 118 |

Construct a stem-and-leaf display for the data.

26. The earnings per share data for a sample of 20 companies from the *Business Week* Corporate Scoreboard follow (*Business Week*, November 17, 1997):

| Company | Earnings per Share ($) | Company | Earnings per Share ($) |
|---------|------------------------|---------|------------------------|
| Barnes & Noble | 0.78 | Hershey Foods | 1.97 |
| Citicorp | 7.10 | Hewlett-Packard | 2.82 |
| Compaq Computer | 2.16 | Humana | 0.89 |
| Dana | 3.42 | Microsoft | 2.66 |
| Dell Computer | 2.03 | Procter & Gamble | 2.53 |
| Digital Equipment | 1.28 | Quaker State | 0.41 |
| General Dynamics | 4.82 | Sara Lee | 2.08 |
| Goodyear | 0.94 | Snap-On Tools | 2.38 |
| Harley-Davidson | 1.11 | Sunstrand | 2.53 |
| Heinz | 0.98 | Xerox | 3.95 |

Develop a stem-and-leaf display for the data. Use a leaf unit of 0.1. Comment on what you learned about the earnings per share for these companies.

27. In a study of job satisfaction, a series of tests was administered to 50 subjects. The following data were obtained; higher scores represent greater dissatisfaction.

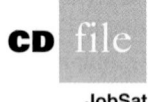

**JobSat**

| 87 | 76 | 67 | 58 | 92 | 59 | 41 | 50 | 90 | 75 | 80 | 81 | 70 |
|----|----|----|----|----|----|----|----|----|----|----|----|----|
| 73 | 69 | 61 | 88 | 46 | 85 | 97 | 50 | 47 | 81 | 87 | 75 | 60 |
| 65 | 92 | 77 | 71 | 70 | 74 | 53 | 43 | 61 | 89 | 84 | 83 | 70 |
| 46 | 84 | 76 | 78 | 64 | 69 | 76 | 78 | 67 | 74 | 64 | | |

Construct a stem-and-leaf display for the data.

28. Periodically *Barron's* publishes earnings forecasts for the companies listed in the Dow Jones Industrial Average. The following are the 2000 forecasts of price/earnings (P/E) ratios for these companies implied by *Barron's* earnings forecasts (*Barron's*, February 14, 2000).

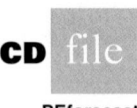

**PEforecast**

| Company | 2000 P/E Forecast | Company | 2000 P/E Forecast |
|---------|-------------------|---------|-------------------|
| AT&T | 23 | Honeywell | 13 |
| Alcoa | 15 | IBM | 28 |
| American Express | 25 | Intel | 37 |
| Boeing | 16 | International Paper | 14 |
| Caterpillar | 13 | Johnson & Johnson | 23 |
| Citigroup | 17 | McDonald's | 23 |
| Coca-Cola | 39 | Merck | 25 |
| Disney | 47 | Microsoft | 60 |
| Dupont | 18 | Minnesota Mining | 19 |
| Eastman Kodak | 11 | J. P. Morgan | 11 |
| Exxon/Mobil | 22 | Philip Morris | 5 |
| General Electric | 37 | Procter & Gamble | 26 |
| General Motors | 8 | SBC Comm. | 19 |
| Hewlett-Packard | 36 | United Technologies | 14 |
| Home Depot | 48 | Wal-Mart | 40 |

a. Develop a stem-and-leaf display for the data.
b. Use the results of the stem-and-leaf display to develop a frequency distribution and percent frequency distribution.

2.4    **CROSSTABULATIONS AND SCATTER DIAGRAMS**

Crosstabulations and scatter diagrams are used to summarize data in a way that reveals the relationship between two variables.

Thus far in this chapter, we have focused on tabular and graphical methods that are used to summarize the data for *one variable at a time*. Often a manager or decision maker is interested in tabular and graphical methods that will assist in the understanding of the *relationship between two variables*. Crosstabulation and scatter diagrams are two such methods.

## Crosstabulation

Crosstabulation is a method that can be used to summarize the data for two variables simultaneously. Let us illustrate the use of a crosstabulation by considering the following application. Zagat's Restaurant Review is a service that provides data on restaurants located throughout the world. Data on a variety of variables such as the restaurant's quality rating and typical meal price are reported. Quality rating is a qualitative variable with rating categories of good, very good, and excellent. Meal price is a quantitative variable that generally ranges from $10 to $49. The quality rating and the meal price data were collected for a sample of 300 restaurants located in the Los Angeles area. Table 2.11 shows the data for the first 10 restaurants.

A crosstabulation of the data for this application is shown in Table 2.12. The left and top margin labels define the classes for the two variables. In the left margin, the row labels (good, very good, and excellent) correspond to the three classes of the quality rating variable. In the top margin, the column labels ($10–19, $20–29, $30–39, and $40–49) correspond to the four classes of the meal price variable. Each restaurant in the sample provides a quality rating and a meal price. Thus, each restaurant in the sample is associated with a cell appearing in one of the rows and one of the columns of the crosstabulation. For example, restaurant 5 is identified as having a very good quality rating and a meal price of $33. This restaurant belongs to the cell in row 2 and column 3 of Table 2.12. In constructing a crosstabulation, we simply count the number of restaurants that belong to each of the cells in the crosstabulation table.

In reviewing Table 2.12, we see that the greatest number of restaurants in the sample (64) have a very good rating and a meal price in the $20–29 range. Only two restaurants have an excellent rating and a meal price in the $10–19 range. Similar interpretations of the other frequencies can be made. In addition, note that the right and bottom margins of the crosstabulation provide the frequency distributions for quality rating and meal price separately. From the frequency distribution in the right margin, we see that data on quality ratings show 84 good restaurants, 150 very good restaurants, and 66 excellent restaurants. Similarly, the bottom margin shows the frequency distribution for the meal price variable.

**TABLE 2.11**    QUALITY RATING AND MEAL PRICE FOR LOS ANGELES RESTAURANTS

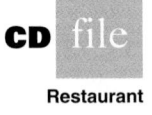

**CD** file

**Restaurant**

| Restaurant | Quality Rating | Meal Price ($) |
|---|---|---|
| 1 | Good | 18 |
| 2 | Very Good | 22 |
| 3 | Good | 28 |
| 4 | Excellent | 38 |
| 5 | Very Good | 33 |
| 6 | Good | 28 |
| 7 | Very Good | 19 |
| 8 | Very Good | 11 |
| 9 | Very Good | 23 |
| 10 | Good | 13 |
| . | . | . |
| . | . | . |
| . | . | . |

**TABLE 2.12**   CROSSTABULATION OF QUALITY RATING AND MEAL PRICE FOR 300 LOS ANGELES RESTAURANTS

| Quality Rating | Meal Price | | | | Total |
|---|---|---|---|---|---|
| | $10–19 | $20–29 | $30–39 | $40–49 | |
| Good | 42 | 40 | 2 | 0 | 84 |
| Very Good | 34 | 64 | 46 | 6 | 150 |
| Excellent | 2 | 14 | 28 | 22 | 66 |
| **Total** | 78 | 118 | 76 | 28 | 300 |

The value of a crosstabulation is that it provides insight about the relationship between the variables. From the results in Table 2.12, higher meal prices appear to be associated with the higher quality restaurants and the lower meal prices appear to be associated with the lower quality restaurants.

Converting the entries in the table into row percentages or column percentages can afford additional insight about the relationship between the variables. For row percentages, the results of dividing each frequency in Table 2.12 by its corresponding row total are shown in Table 2.13. For example, the percentage in the first row and first column, 50.0, is calculated by dividing 42 by 84 and multiplying by 100 ($42/84 \times 100 = 50.0\%$). Of the restaurants with the lowest (good) quality rating, we see that the greatest percentages are for the less expensive restaurants (50.0% have $10–19 meal prices and 47.6% have $20–29 meal prices). Of the restaurants with the highest (excellent) quality rating, we see that the greatest percentages are for the more expensive restaurants (42.4% have $30–39 meal prices and 33.4% have $40–49 meal prices). Thus, we continue to see that the more expensive meals are associated with the higher quality restaurants.

Crosstabulation is widely used for examining the relationship between two variables. In practice, final reports for many statistical surveys include a large number of crosstabulation tables. In the Los Angeles restaurant sample, the crosstabulation is based on one qualitative variable (quality rating) and one quantitative variable (meal price). Crosstabulations can also be developed when both variables are qualitative and when both variables are quantitative.

## Using Excel's PivotTable Report to Construct a Crosstabulation

Excel's PivotTable Report provides a general tool for summarizing the data for two or more variables simultaneously. We will illustrate the use of Excel's PivotTable Report by showing how to develop a crosstabulation of quality ratings and meal prices for the sample of 300 restaurants located in the Los Angeles area.

**TABLE 2.13**   ROW PERCENTAGES FOR EACH QUALITY RATING CATEGORY

| Quality Rating | Meal Price | | | | Total |
|---|---|---|---|---|---|
| | $10–19 | $20–29 | $30–39 | $40–49 | |
| Good | 50.0 | 47.6 | 2.4 | 0.0 | 100 |
| Very Good | 22.7 | 42.7 | 30.6 | 4.0 | 100 |
| Excellent | 3.0 | 21.2 | 42.4 | 33.4 | 100 |

**Enter Data:**   The labels "Restaurant," "Quality Rating," and "Meal Price ($)" have been entered into cells A1:C1 of the worksheet shown in Figure 2.12. The data for each of the 300 restaurants in the sample has been entered into cells B2:C301.

**Enter Functions and Formulas:**   No functions and formulas are needed.

**Apply Tools:**   The crosstabulation shown in Table 2.12 has three rows under the heading Quality Rating, corresponding to the three quality categories, Good, Very Good, and Excellent. Unless we specify differently, the PivotTable Report will order the labels alphabetically causing the quality ratings to be listed in the order Excellent, Good, and Very Good. Because we want the quality ratings in the order Good, Very Good, Excellent, we must change the default order for the PivotTable Report. The following steps will do so:

**Step 1.** Select the **Tools** pull-down menu
**Step 2.** Choose **Options**
**Step 3.** When the Options dialog box appears (see Figure 2.13):
   Select the **Custom Lists** tab
   In the **List entries:** box, type **Good** and press Enter; type **Very Good** and press Enter; and type **Excellent**
   Select **Add**
   Click **OK**

We are now ready to use the PivotTable Report to construct a crosstabulation of the data for quality rating and meal price. Starting with the worksheet in Figure 2.12, the following steps are necessary:

**Step 1.** Select the **Data** pull down menu
**Step 2.** Choose the **PivotTable and PivotChart** Report
**Step 3.** When the **PivotTable and PivotChart Wizard–Step 1 of 3** dialog box appears:
   Choose **Microsoft Excel list or database**

**FIGURE 2.12**   EXCEL WORKSHEET CONTAINING RESTAURANT DATA

**CD** file

**Restaurant**

Note: Rows 12–291 are hidden.

|  | A | B | C | D |
|---|---|---|---|---|
| 1 | Restaurant | Quality Rating | Meal Price ($) | |
| 2 | 1 | Good | 18 | |
| 3 | 2 | Very Good | 22 | |
| 4 | 3 | Good | 28 | |
| 5 | 4 | Excellent | 38 | |
| 6 | 5 | Very Good | 33 | |
| 7 | 6 | Good | 28 | |
| 8 | 7 | Very Good | 19 | |
| 9 | 8 | Very Good | 11 | |
| 10 | 9 | Very Good | 23 | |
| 11 | 10 | Good | 13 | |
| 292 | 291 | Very Good | 23 | |
| 293 | 292 | Very Good | 24 | |
| 294 | 293 | Excellent | 45 | |
| 295 | 294 | Good | 14 | |
| 296 | 295 | Good | 18 | |
| 297 | 296 | Good | 17 | |
| 298 | 297 | Good | 16 | |
| 299 | 298 | Good | 15 | |
| 300 | 299 | Very Good | 38 | |
| 301 | 300 | Very Good | 31 | |
| 302 | | | | |

**FIGURE 2.13**    DIALOG BOX FOR CHANGING SORT ORDER IN EXCEL PivotTable

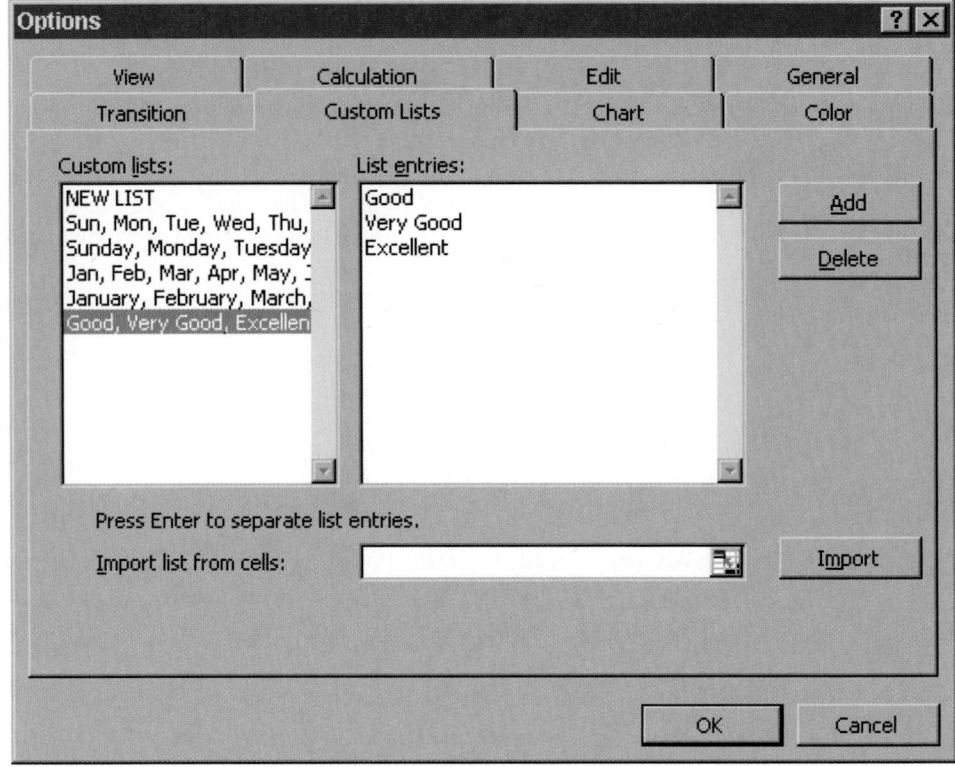

> Choose **PivotTable**
> Select **Next >**

**Step 4.**   When the **PivotTable and PivotChart Wizard–Step 2 of 3** dialog box appears:
> Enter A1:C301 in the **Range:** box
> Select **Next >**

**Step 5.**   When the **PivotTable and PivotChart Wizard–Step 3 of 3** dialog box appears:
> Select **New Worksheet**
> Click on the **Layout** button
> When the **PivotTable and PivotChart Wizard–Layout** diagram appears (See Figure 2.14):
>> Drag the **Quality Rating** field button to the **ROW** section of the diagram
>> Drag the **Meal Price ($)** field button to the **COLUMN** section of the diagram
>> Drag the **Restaurant** field button to the **DATA** section of the diagram
>> Double click the **Sum of Restaurant** field button in the data section
>> When the **PivotTable Field** dialog box appears:
>>> Choose **Count** under **Summarize by:**
>>> Click **OK** (Figure 2.15 shows the completed layout diagram)
>> Click **OK**
> When the **PivotTable and PivotChart Wizard–Step 3 of 3** dialog box reappears:
>> Select **Finish>**

**FIGURE 2.14**   PivotTable AND PivotChart WIZARD-LAYOUT DIAGRAM

**FIGURE 2.15**   COMPLETED LAYOUT DIAGRAM

A portion of the output generated by Excel is shown in Figure 2.16. Note that the output that appears in columns D through AK has been hidden so the results can be shown in a reasonably sized figure. The row labels (Good, Very Good, and Excellent) and row totals (84, 150, 66, and 300) that appear in Figure 2.16 are the same as the row labels and row totals shown in Table 2.12. But, in Figure 2.16, one column is designated for each possible value of meal price. For example, column B contains a count of restaurants with a $10 meal price, column C contains a count of restaurants with an $11 mean price, and so on. To view the PivotTable Report in a form similar to that shown in Table 2.12, we must group the columns into four price categories: $10–19, $20–29, $30–39, and $40–49. The steps necessary to group the columns for the worksheet shown in Figure 2.16 follow.

**Step 1.** Right click on Meal Price ($) in cell B3 of the PivotTable
**Step 2.** Select **Group and Outline** and then **Group**
**Step 3.** When the **Grouping** dialog box appears
  Enter 10 in the **Starting at** box
  Enter 49 in the **Ending at** box
  Enter 10 in the **By** box
  Click **OK**

The revised PivotTable output is shown in Figure 2.17. It is the final PivotTable. Note that it provides the same information as the crosstabulation shown in Table 2.12.

## Scatter Diagram

A **scatter diagram** is a graphical presentation of the relationship between two quantitative variables. As an illustration of a scatter diagram, consider the situation of a stereo and sound equipment store in San Francisco. On 10 occasions during the past three months, the store has used weekend television commercials to promote sales at its stores. The managers want to investigate whether a relationship can be demonstrated between the number of commercials shown and the sales at the store during the following week. Sample data for the 10 weeks with sales in hundreds of dollars are shown in Table 2.14.

**FIGURE 2.16**   INITIAL PivotTable REPORT OUTPUT (COLUMNS D:AK ARE HIDDEN.)

| | A | B | C | AL | AM | AN | AO |
|---|---|---|---|---|---|---|---|
| 1 | | | | | | | |
| 2 | | | | | | | |
| 3 | Count of Restaurant | Meal Price ($) ▾ | | | | | |
| 4 | Quality Rating ▾ | 10 | 11 | 47 | | 48 | Grand Total |
| 5 | Good | 6 | 4 | | | | 84 |
| 6 | Very Good | 1 | 4 | | 1 | | 150 |
| 7 | Excellent | | | 2 | 2 | | 66 |
| 8 | Grand Total | 7 | 8 | 2 | 3 | | 300 |
| 9 | | | | | | | |
| 10 | | | | | | | |
| 11 | | | | | | | |
| 12 | | | | | | | |
| 13 | | | | | | | |
| 14 | | | | | | | |
| 15 | | | | | | | |
| 16 | | PivotTable ☒ | | | | | |
| 17 | | PivotTable ▾ | | | | | |
| 18 | | | | | | | |

**FIGURE 2.17**    FINAL PivotTable REPORT FOR RESTAURANT DATA

| | A | B | C | D | E | F | G |
|---|---|---|---|---|---|---|---|
| 1 | | | | | | | |
| 2 | | | | | | | |
| 3 | Count of Restaurant | Meal Price ($) ▼ | | | | | |
| 4 | Quality Rating ▼ | 10-19 | 20-29 | 30-39 | 40-49 | Grand Total | |
| 5 | Good | 42 | 40 | 2 | | 84 | |
| 6 | Very Good | 34 | 64 | 46 | 6 | 150 | |
| 7 | Excellent | 2 | 14 | 28 | 22 | 66 | |
| 8 | Grand Total | 78 | 118 | 76 | 28 | 300 | |
| 9 | | | | | | | |
| 10 | | | | | | | |
| 11 | | | | | | | |
| 12 | | | | | | | |
| 13 | | | | | | | |
| 14 | | | | | | | |
| 15 | | | | | | | |
| 16 | | PivotTable ⊠ | | | | | |
| 17 | | PivotTable ▼  🖽 🖾 🔃  ⬚ᷔ ᷔᷔ ᷔ ❗ ᷤ 🖽 | | | | | |
| 18 | | | | | | | |

Figure 2.18 is the scatter diagram for the data in Table 2.14. The number of commercials ($x$) is shown on the horizontal axis and the sales ($y$) are shown on the vertical axis. For week 1, $x = 2$ and $y = 50$. A point with those coordinates is plotted on the scatter diagram. Similar points are plotted for the other nine weeks. Note that during two of the weeks one commercial was shown, on two of the weeks two commercials were shown, and so on.

The completed scatter diagram in Figure 2.18 indicates a positive relationship between the number of commercials and sales. Higher sales are associated with a higher number of commercials. The relationship is not perfect in that all points are not on a straight line. However, the general pattern of the points suggests that the overall relationship is positive.

Some general scatter diagram patterns and the types of relationships they suggest are shown in Figure 2.19. The top left panel depicts a positive relationship similar to the one we saw for the number of commercials and sales example. In the top right panel, the

**TABLE 2.14**    SAMPLE DATA FOR THE STEREO AND SOUND EQUIPMENT STORE

CD file

Stereo

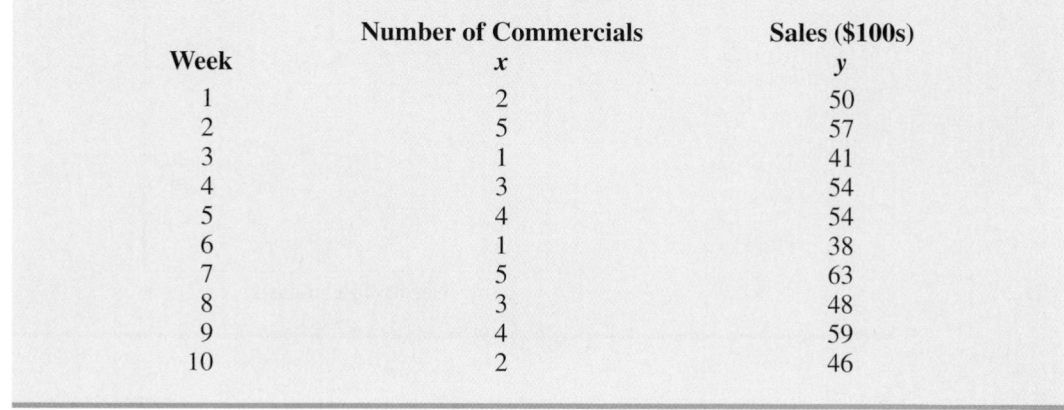

| Week | Number of Commercials $x$ | Sales ($100s) $y$ |
|---|---|---|
| 1 | 2 | 50 |
| 2 | 5 | 57 |
| 3 | 1 | 41 |
| 4 | 3 | 54 |
| 5 | 4 | 54 |
| 6 | 1 | 38 |
| 7 | 5 | 63 |
| 8 | 3 | 48 |
| 9 | 4 | 59 |
| 10 | 2 | 46 |

**FIGURE 2.18    SCATTER DIAGRAM FOR THE STEREO AND SOUND EQUIPMENT STORE**

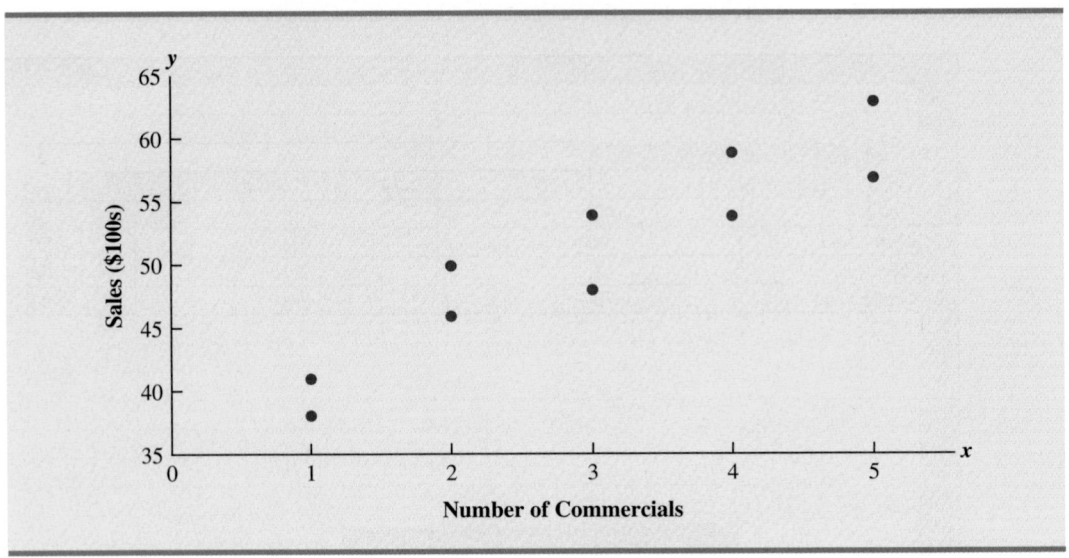

**FIGURE 2.19    TYPES OF RELATIONSHIPS DEPICTED BY SCATTER DIAGRAMS**

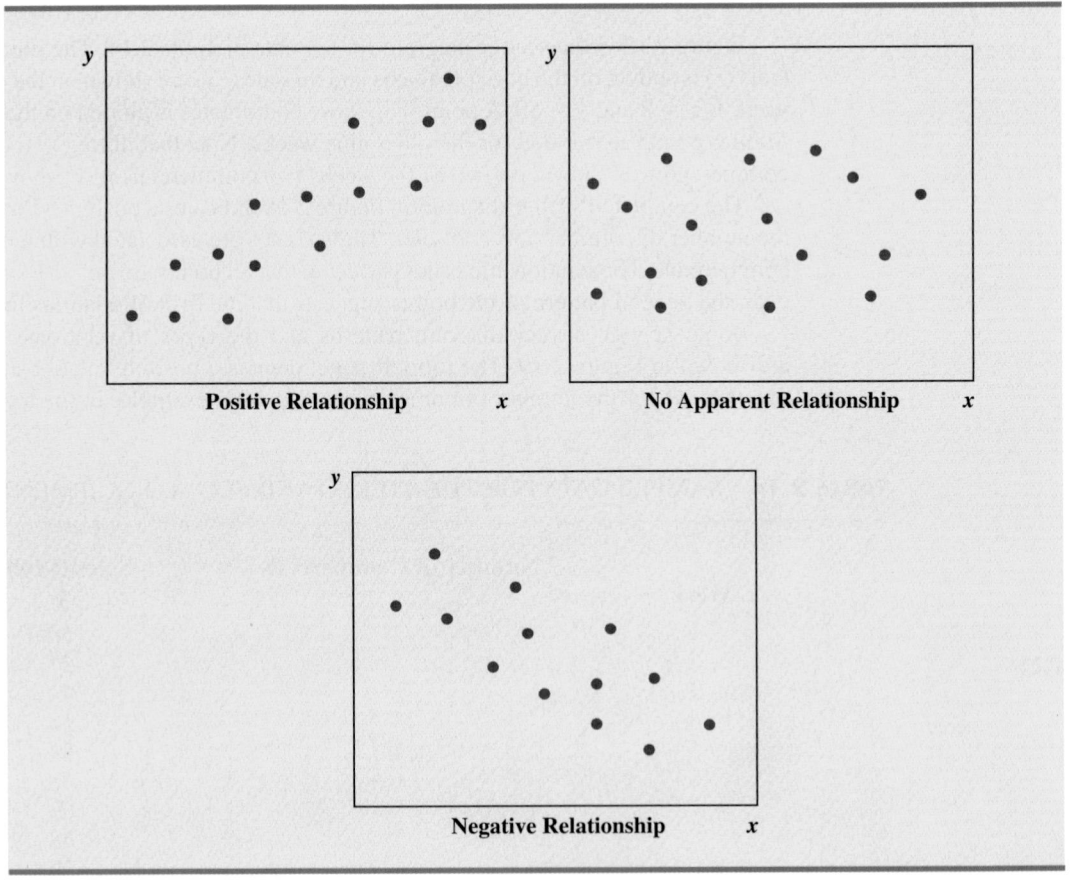

scatter diagram shows no apparent relationship between the variables. The bottom panel depicts a negative relationship where *y* tends to decrease as *x* increases.

## Using Excel's Chart Wizard to Construct a Scatter Diagram

We can use Excel's Chart Wizard to construct a scatter diagram for the stereo and sound equipment store data. Refer to Figures 2.20 and 2.21 as we describe the tasks involved.

**FIGURE 2.20   WORKSHEET WITH STEREO AND SOUND EQUIPMENT STORE DATA**

| | A | B | C | D |
|---|---|---|---|---|
| 1 | Week | No. of Commercials | Sales Volume | |
| 2 | 1 | 2 | 50 | |
| 3 | 2 | 5 | 57 | |
| 4 | 3 | 1 | 41 | |
| 5 | 4 | 3 | 54 | |
| 6 | 5 | 4 | 54 | |
| 7 | 6 | 1 | 38 | |
| 8 | 7 | 5 | 63 | |
| 9 | 8 | 3 | 48 | |
| 10 | 9 | 4 | 59 | |
| 11 | 10 | 2 | 46 | |
| 12 | | | | |

**FIGURE 2.21   SCATTER DIAGRAM FOR STEREO AND SOUND EQUIPMENT STORE USING EXCEL'S CHART WIZARD**

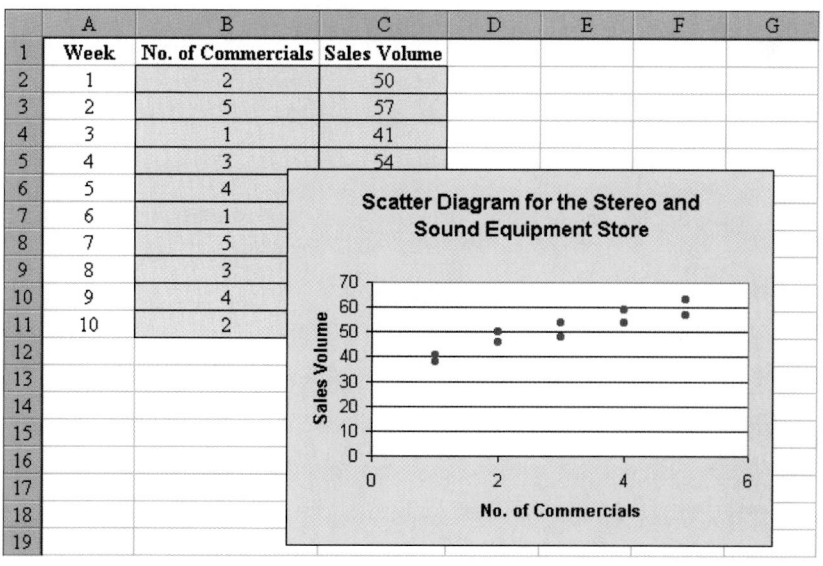

**Enter Data:** Appropriate labels and the sample data have been entered into cells A1:C11 of the worksheet shown in Figure 2.20.

**Enter Functions and Formulas:** No functions and formulas are needed.

**Apply Tools:** The following steps describe how to use Excel's Chart Wizard to produce a scatter diagram from the data in the worksheet.

> **Step 1.** Select cells B1:C11
> **Step 2.** Select the **Chart Wizard** (or select the **Insert** pull-down menu and choose the **Chart** option)
> **Step 3.** When the **Chart Wizard–Step 1 of 4–Chart Type** dialog box appears:
> > Choose **XY (Scatter)** in the **Chart type** list
> > Choose **Scatter** from the **Chart sub-type** display
> > Select **Next >**
> **Step 4.** When the **Chart Wizard–Step 2 of 4–Chart Source Data** dialog box appears:
> > Select **Next >**
> **Step 5.** When the **Chart Wizard–Step 3 of 4–Chart Options** dialog box appears:
> > Select the **Titles** tab and then
> > > Type **Scatter Diagram for the Stereo and Sound Equipment Store** in the **Chart title:** box
> > > Enter **No. of Commercials** in the **Value (X) axis:** box
> > > Enter **Sales Volume** in the **Value (Y) axis:** box
> > Select the **Legend** tab and then
> > > Remove the check in the **Show Legend** box
> > > Select **Next >**
> **Step 6.** When the **Chart Wizard–Step 4 of 4–Chart Location** dialog box appears:
> > Specify a location for the new chart (we used the default setting of the current worksheet)
> > Select **Finish**

The worksheet displayed in Figure 2.21 shows the scatter diagram produced by Excel. We have enlarged the scatter diagram slightly.

## EXERCISES

## Methods

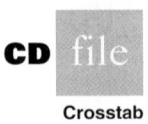

Crosstab

**29.** The following data are for 30 observations on two qualitative variables, $x$ and $y$. The categories for $x$ are A, B, and C; the categories for $y$ are 1 and 2.

| Observation | $x$ | $y$ | Observation | $x$ | $y$ |
|---|---|---|---|---|---|
| 1 | A | 1 | 13 | C | 2 |
| 2 | B | 1 | 14 | C | 2 |
| 3 | B | 1 | 15 | C | 2 |
| 4 | C | 2 | 16 | B | 2 |
| 5 | B | 1 | 17 | C | 1 |
| 6 | C | 2 | 18 | B | 1 |
| 7 | B | 1 | 19 | C | 1 |
| 8 | C | 2 | 20 | B | 1 |
| 9 | A | 1 | 21 | C | 2 |
| 10 | B | 1 | 22 | B | 1 |
| 11 | A | 1 | 23 | C | 2 |
| 12 | B | 1 | 24 | A | 1 |

| Observation | x | y | Observation | x | y |
|---|---|---|---|---|---|
| 25 | B | 1 | 28 | A | 1 |
| 26 | C | 2 | 29 | B | 1 |
| 27 | C | 2 | 30 | B | 2 |

**a.** Develop a crosstabulation for the data, with $x$ in the rows and $y$ in the columns.
**b.** Compute the row percentages.
**c.** Compute column percentages.
**d.** What is the relationship, if any, between $x$ and $y$?

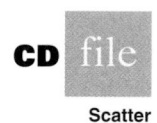
**SELF** test

30. The following 20 observations are for two quantitative variables, $x$ and $y$.

**CD** file

**Scatter**

| Observation | x | y | Observation | x | y |
|---|---|---|---|---|---|
| 1 | −22 | 22 | 11 | −37 | 48 |
| 2 | −33 | 49 | 12 | 34 | −29 |
| 3 | 2 | 8 | 13 | 9 | −18 |
| 4 | 29 | −16 | 14 | −33 | 31 |
| 5 | −13 | 10 | 15 | 20 | −16 |
| 6 | 21 | −28 | 16 | −3 | 14 |
| 7 | −13 | 27 | 17 | −15 | 18 |
| 8 | −23 | 35 | 18 | 12 | 17 |
| 9 | 14 | −5 | 19 | −20 | −11 |
| 10 | 3 | −3 | 20 | −7 | −22 |

**a.** Develop a scatter diagram for the relationship between $x$ and $y$.
**b.** What is the relationship, if any, between $x$ and $y$?

## Applications

31. Compute column percentages for the restaurant data in Table 2.12. What is the relationship between quality rating and meal price?

32. Shown in Table 2.15 are financial data for a sample of 36 companies whose stock is traded on the New York Stock Exchange (*Investor's Business Daily,* April 7, 2000). The data on Sales/Margins/ROE is a composite rating based on a company's sales growth rate, its profit margins, and its return on equity (ROE). EPS Rating is a measure of growth in earnings per share for the company.
    **a.** Prepare a crosstabulation of the data on Sales/Margins/ROE (rows) and EPS Rating (columns). Use classes of 0–19, 20–39, 40–59, 60–79, and 80–99 for EPS Rating.
    **b.** Compute row percentages and comment on any relationship between the variables.

33. Refer to the data in Table 2.15.
    **a.** Prepare a crosstabulation of the data on Sales/Margins/ROE and Industry Group Relative Strength.
    **b.** Prepare a frequency distribution for the data on Sales/Margins/ROE.
    **c.** Prepare a frequency distribution for the data on Industry Group Relative Strength.
    **d.** How has the crosstabulation helped in preparing the frequency distributions in parts (b) and (c)?

34. Refer to the data in Table 2.15.
    **a.** Prepare a scatter diagram of the data on EPS Rating and Relative Price Strength.
    **b.** Comment on the relationship, if any, between the variables. (The meaning of the EPS Rating is described in Exercise 32. Relative Price Strength is a measure of the change in the stock's price over the past 12 months. Higher values indicate greater strength.)

**TABLE 2.15** FINANCIAL DATA FOR A SAMPLE OF 36 COMPANIES

| Company | EPS Rating | Relative Price Strength | Industry Group Relative Strength | Sales/Margins/ROE |
|---|---|---|---|---|
| Advo | 81 | 74 | B | A |
| Alaska AirGp | 58 | 17 | C | B |
| Alliant Tech | 84 | 22 | B | B |
| Atmos Engy | 21 | 9 | C | E |
| Bank of Am. | 87 | 38 | C | A |
| Bowater PLC | 14 | 46 | C | D |
| Callaway Golf | 46 | 62 | B | E |
| Central Parking | 76 | 18 | B | C |
| Dean Foods | 84 | 7 | B | C |
| Dole Food | 70 | 54 | E | C |
| Elec. Data Sys | 72 | 69 | A | B |
| Fed. Dept. Stor. | 79 | 21 | D | B |
| Gateway | 82 | 68 | A | A |
| Goodyear | 21 | 9 | E | D |
| Hanson PLC | 57 | 32 | B | B |
| ICN Pharm. | 76 | 56 | A | D |
| Jefferson plt | 80 | 38 | D | C |
| Kroger | 84 | 24 | D | A |
| Mattel | 18 | 20 | E | D |
| McDermott | 6 | 6 | A | C |
| Monaco | 97 | 21 | D | A |
| Murphy Oil | 80 | 62 | B | B |
| Nordstrom | 58 | 57 | B | C |
| NYMAGIC | 17 | 45 | D | D |
| Office Depot | 58 | 40 | B | B |
| Payless Shoes | 76 | 59 | B | B |
| Praxair | 62 | 32 | C | B |
| Reebok | 31 | 72 | C | E |
| Safeway | 91 | 61 | D | A |
| Teco Energy | 49 | 48 | D | B |
| Texaco | 80 | 31 | D | C |
| US West | 60 | 65 | B | A |
| United Rental | 98 | 12 | C | A |
| Wachovia | 69 | 36 | E | B |
| Winnebago | 83 | 49 | D | A |
| York Intl. | 28 | 14 | D | B |

*Source: Investor's Business Daily, April 7, 2000.*

35. The following data show the hotel revenue and the gaming revenue, in millions of dollars, for 10 Las Vegas casino hotels (*Cornell Hotel And Restaurant Administration Quarterly,* October 1997).

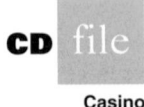

| Company | Hotel Revenue ($millions) | Gaming Revenue ($millions) |
|---|---|---|
| Boyd Gaming | 303.5 | 548.2 |
| Circus Circus Enterprises | 664.8 | 664.8 |
| Grand Casinos | 121.0 | 270.7 |
| Hilton Corp. Gaming Div. | 429.6 | 511.0 |
| MGM Grand, Inc. | 373.1 | 404.7 |
| Mirage Resorts | 670.9 | 782.8 |
| Primadonna Resorts | 66.4 | 130.7 |
| Rio Hotel & Casino | 105.8 | 105.5 |

| Company | Hotel Revenue ($millions) | Gaming Revenue ($millions) |
|---|---|---|
| Sahara Gaming | 102.4 | 148.7 |
| Station Casinos | 135.8 | 358.5 |

**a.** Develop a scatter diagram of the data on Hotel Revenue and Gaming Revenue.

**b.** Comment on the relationship, if any, between the variables.

## SUMMARY

A set of data, even if modest in size, is often difficult to interpret directly in the form in which it is gathered. Tabular and graphical methods provide procedures for organizing and summarizing data so that patterns are revealed and the data are more easily interpreted. Frequency distributions, relative frequency distributions, percent frequency distributions, bar graphs, and pie charts were presented as tabular and graphical procedures for summarizing qualitative data. Frequency distributions, relative frequency distributions, percent frequency distributions, histograms, cumulative frequency distributions, cumulative relative frequency distributions, cumulative percent frequency distributions, and ogives were presented as ways of summarizing quantitative data. A stem-and-leaf display was presented as an exploratory data analysis technique that can be used to summarize quantitative data. Crosstabulation was presented as a tabular method for summarizing data for two variables. The scatter diagram was introduced as a graphical method for showing the relationship between two quantitative variables. Figure 2.22 is a summary of the tabular and graphical methods presented in this chapter.

**FIGURE 2.22**   TABULAR AND GRAPHICAL METHODS FOR SUMMARIZING DATA

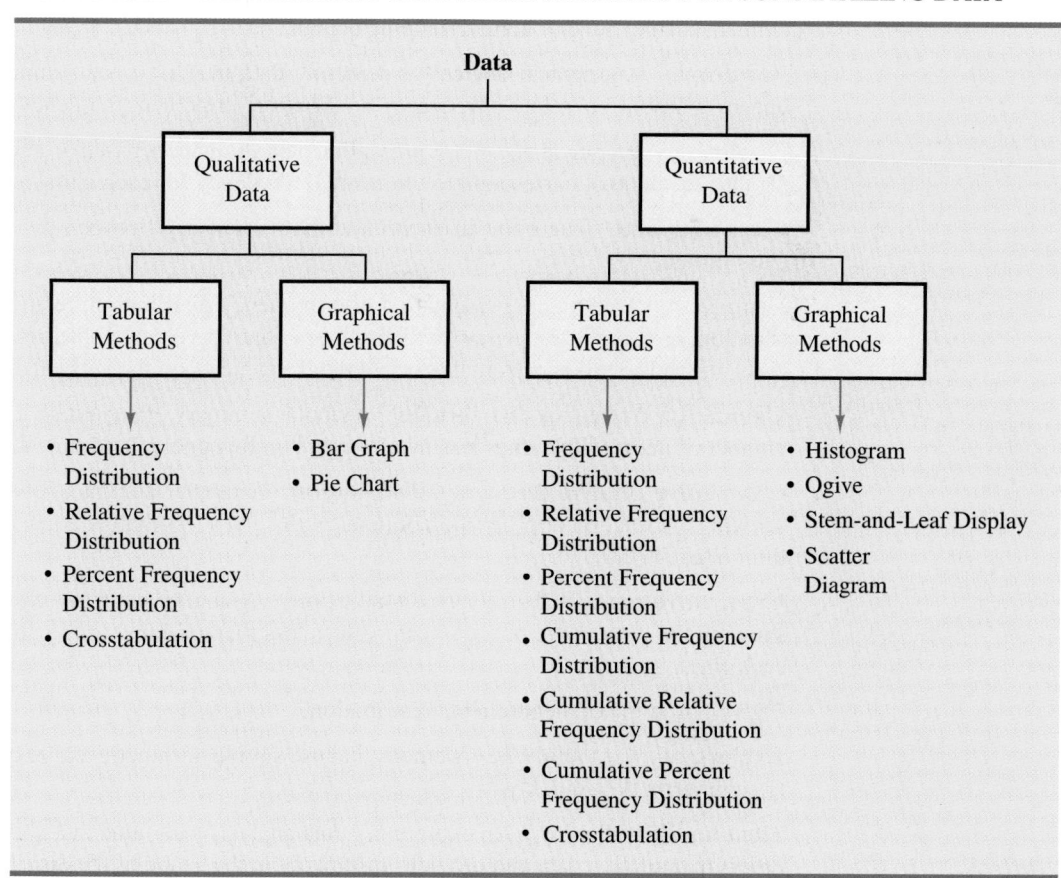

For most of the statistical methods introduced, we have shown how they can be implemented with Excel. The COUNTIF and FREQUENCY functions help to construct frequency distributions for a single variable, and the PivotTable Report can be used to prepare a cross-tabulation for a two-variable data set. The Chart Wizard provides extensive graphical presentations. We have shown how it can be used to construct bar graphs, pie charts, histograms, and scatter diagrams. In the chapter appendix, we show how to use the Histogram tool as an alternative for constructing a frequency distribution and histogram for quantitative data.

If you have trouble recalling which Excel function to use in a particular situation, or have difficulty using a function, Excel's Function Wizard has been designed to provide help. We describe how to use the Function Wizard in Appendix F: Excel Functions and the Function Wizard.

## GLOSSARY

**Qualitative data**   Data that are labels or names used to identify categories of like items.

**Quantitative data**   Data that indicate how much or how many.

**Frequency distribution**   A tabular summary of data showing the number (frequency) of items in each of several nonoverlapping classes.

**Relative frequency distribution**   A tabular summary of data showing the fraction or proportion (relative frequency) of data items in each of several nonoverlapping classes.

**Percent frequency distribution**   A tabular summary of data showing the percentage of items in each of several nonoverlapping classes.

**Bar graph**   A graphical device for depicting data that have been summarized in a frequency distribution, relative frequency distribution, or percent frequency distribution.

**Pie chart**   A graphical device for presenting data summaries based on subdivision of a circle into sectors that correspond to the relative frequency for each class.

**Class midpoint**   The point in each class that is halfway between the lower and upper class limits.

**Histogram**   A graphical presentation of a frequency distribution, relative frequency distribution, or percent frequency distribution of quantitative data constructed by placing the class intervals on the horizontal axis and the frequencies on the vertical axis.

**Cumulative frequency distribution**   A tabular summary of quantitative data showing the number of items with values less than or equal to the upper class limit of each class.

**Cumulative relative frequency distribution**   A tabular summary of quantitative data showing the fraction or proportion of items with values less than or equal to the upper class limit of each class.

**Cumulative percent frequency distribution**   A tabular summary of quantitative data showing the percentage of items with values less than or equal to the upper class limit of each class.

**Ogive**   A graph of a cumulative distribution.

**Exploratory data analysis**   Methods that use simple arithmetic and easy-to-draw graphs to summarize data quickly.

**Stem-and-leaf display**   An exploratory data analysis technique that simultaneously rank orders quantitative data and provides insight about the shape of the distribution.

**Crosstabulation**   A tabular summary of data for two variables. The classes for one variable are represented by the rows; the classes for the other variable are represented by the columns.

**Scatter diagram**   A graphical presentation of the relationship between two quantitative variables. One variable is shown on the horizontal axis and the other variable is shown on the vertical axis.

## KEY FORMULAS

**Relative Frequency**

$$\frac{\text{Frequency of the Class}}{n} \qquad \textbf{(2.1)}$$

**Approximate Class Width**

$$\frac{\text{Largest Data Value} - \text{Smallest Data Value}}{\text{Number of Classes}} \qquad \textbf{(2.2)}$$

## SUPPLEMENTARY EXERCISES

**36.** *Autodata* and *USA Today* research provided data on the best-selling vehicle models for March 2000 (*USA Today,* April 4, 2000). Among those listed were Chevrolet Silverado/ C/K pickup, Ford F-Series pickup, Ford Taurus, Honda Accord, and Toyota Camry. Data from a sample of 50 vehicle purchases are presented in Table 2.16.

**TABLE 2.16**   DATA FOR 50 VEHICLE PURCHASES

**Vehicles**

| | | | | |
|---|---|---|---|---|
| Silverado | Taurus | Accord | F-Series | Silverado |
| F-Series | Accord | Silverado | Camry | Taurus |
| Silverado | F-Series | Camry | Silverado | F-Series |
| Taurus | F-Series | Taurus | F-Series | Camry |
| Taurus | F-Series | F-Series | Accord | Camry |
| Silverado | Silverado | Silverado | Silverado | Taurus |
| Camry | Silverado | Accord | F-Series | F-Series |
| Taurus | F-Series | Accord | Camry | Accord |
| F-Series | Silverado | F-Series | F-Series | Taurus |
| Camry | Silverado | F-Series | F-Series | F-Series |

**a.** Develop a frequency and percent frequency distribution.
**b.** What are the two top-selling vehicles?
**c.** Show a pie chart.

**37.** Each of the *Fortune* 1000 companies is classified as belonging to one of several industries (*Fortune,* April 17, 2000). A sample of 20 companies with their corresponding industry classification follows.

| Company | Industry Classification | Company | Industry Classification |
|---|---|---|---|
| IBP | Food | Borden | Food |
| Intel | Electronics | McDonnell Douglas | Aerospace |
| Coca-Cola | Beverage | Morton International | Chemicals |

(*continued*)

| Company | Industry Classification | Company | Industry Classification |
|---|---|---|---|
| Union Carbide | Chemicals | Quaker Oats | Food |
| General Electric | Electronics | Pepsico | Beverage |
| Motorola | Electronics | Maytag | Electronics |
| Kellogg | Food | Textron | Aerospace |
| Dow Chemical | Chemicals | Sara Lee | Food |
| Campbell Soup | Food | Harris | Electronics |
| Ralston Purina | Food | Eaton | Electronics |

    **a.** Provide a frequency distribution showing the number of companies in each industry.

    **b.** Provide a percent frequency distribution.

    **c.** Provide a bar graph for the data.

**38.** During 1998 and 1999, *Time* magazine carried cover stories on the following movies: *Blair Witch Project, Phantom Menace, Beloved, Primary Colors,* and *Truman Show. Time* keeps track of mail received on its cover stories; the number of pieces of mail received on these movies was 159, 89, 85, 57, and 51 respectively (*Time,* September 27, 1999).

    **a.** Develop a percent frequency distribution for the mail data.

    **b.** Develop a pie chart.

    **c.** The cover stories on the *Blair Witch Project* and *Phantom Menace* were run in 1999; the others were run in 1998. What percent of the mail pertained to 1999 cover stories?

**39.** The data in Table 2.17 represent sales in millions of dollars for 20 companies in the health care services industry during the third quarter of 1997 (*Business Week,* November 17, 1997).

    **a.** Construct a frequency distribution to summarize the data. Use a class width of 500.

    **b.** Develop a relative frequency distribution.

    **c.** Construct a cumulative frequency distribution.

    **d.** Construct a cumulative relative frequency distribution.

    **e.** Construct a histogram as a graphical representation of the data.

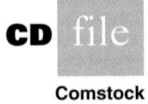

**Comstock**

**40.** The closing prices of 40 common stocks follow (*The Wall Street Journal,* March 17, 2000).

| | | | | | | | | | |
|---|---|---|---|---|---|---|---|---|---|
| $29\frac{5}{8}$ | 34 | $43\frac{1}{4}$ | $8\frac{3}{4}$ | $37\frac{7}{8}$ | $8\frac{5}{8}$ | $7\frac{5}{8}$ | $30\frac{3}{8}$ | $35\frac{1}{4}$ | $19\frac{3}{8}$ |
| $9\frac{1}{4}$ | $16\frac{1}{2}$ | 38 | $53\frac{3}{8}$ | $16\frac{5}{8}$ | $1\frac{1}{4}$ | $48\frac{3}{8}$ | 18 | $9\frac{3}{8}$ | $9\frac{1}{4}$ |
| 10 | 37 | 18 | 8 | $28\frac{1}{2}$ | $24\frac{1}{4}$ | $21\frac{5}{8}$ | $18\frac{1}{2}$ | $33\frac{5}{8}$ | $31\frac{1}{8}$ |
| $32\frac{1}{4}$ | $29\frac{5}{8}$ | $79\frac{3}{8}$ | $11\frac{3}{8}$ | $38\frac{7}{8}$ | $11\frac{1}{2}$ | 52 | 14 | 9 | $33\frac{1}{2}$ |

    **a.** Construct frequency and relative frequency distributions.

    **b.** Construct cumulative frequency and cumulative relative frequency distributions.

    **c.** Construct a histogram.

    **d.** Using your summaries, make comments and observations about the price of common stock.

**TABLE 2.17**    SALES IN HEALTH CARE SERVICES FOR THIRD QUARTER, 1997

| | | | |
|---|---|---|---|
| Beverly Ent. | 805 | Novacare | 357 |
| Coventry | 307 | Phycor | 284 |
| Express Scripts | 320 | Quest Diag. | 374 |
| Healthsouth | 748 | Quorum Health | 393 |
| Horizon | 445 | Sun Healthcare | 486 |
| Humana | 1968 | Tenet Healthcare | 2331 |
| Int. Health | 472 | U. Wisconsin | 389 |
| Lab. Corp. Am. | 377 | Univ. Health | 362 |
| Manor Care | 274 | Vencor | 845 |
| Medpartners | 1614 | Wellpoint | 1512 |

*Source: Business Week,* November 17, 1997.

**41.** Ninety-four new shadow stocks were reported by the American Association of Individual Investors (*AAII Journal,* February 1997). The term *shadow* indicates stocks for small to medium-sized firms not followed closely by the major brokerage houses. Information on where the stock was traded—New York Stock Exchange (NYSE), American Stock Exchange (AMEX), and over-the-counter (OTC)—the earnings per share, and the price/earnings ratio was provided for the following sample of 20 shadow stocks.

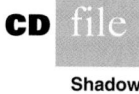

**CD** file

**Shadow**

| Stock | Exchange | Earnings per Share ($) | Price/ Earnings Ratio |
|---|---|---|---|
| Chemi-Trol | OTC | .39 | 27.30 |
| Candie's | OTC | .07 | 36.20 |
| TST/Impreso | OTC | .65 | 12.70 |
| Unimed Pharm. | OTC | .12 | 59.30 |
| Skyline Chili | AMEX | .34 | 19.30 |
| Cyanotech | OTC | .22 | 29.30 |
| Catalina Light. | NYSE | .15 | 33.20 |
| DDL Elect. | NYSE | .10 | 10.20 |
| Euphonix | OTC | .09 | 49.70 |
| Mesa Labs | OTC | .37 | 14.40 |
| RCM Tech. | OTC | .47 | 18.60 |
| Anuhco | AMEX | .70 | 11.40 |
| Hello Direct | OTC | .23 | 21.10 |
| Hilite Industries | OTC | .61 | 7.80 |
| Alpha Tech. | OTC | .11 | 34.60 |
| Wegener Group | OTC | .16 | 24.50 |
| U.S. Home & Garden | OTC | .24 | 8.70 |
| Chalone Wine | OTC | .27 | 44.40 |
| Eng. Support Sys. | OTC | .89 | 16.70 |
| Int. Remote Imaging | AMEX | .86 | 4.70 |

a. Provide frequency and relative frequency distributions for the exchange data. Where are most shadow stocks listed?

b. Provide frequency and relative frequency distributions for the earnings per share and price/earnings ratio data. Use class limits of 0.00–0.19, 0.20–0.39, and so on, for the earnings per share data and class limits of 0.0–9.9, 10.0–19.9, and so on for the price/ earnings ratio data. What observations and comments can you make about the shadow stocks?

**42.** A state-by-state listing of per capita personal income for 1998 follows (Bureau of Economic Analysis, *Current Population Survey,* March 2000).

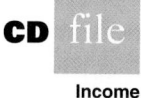

**CD** file

**Income**

| | | | | | |
|---|---|---|---|---|---|
| Ala. | 21,500 | Ky. | 21,551 | N.D. | 21,708 |
| Alaska | 25,771 | La. | 21,385 | Ohio | 25,239 |
| Ariz. | 23,152 | Maine | 23,002 | Okla. | 21,056 |
| Ark. | 20,393 | Md. | 30,023 | Ore. | 24,775 |
| Calif. | 27,579 | Mass. | 32,902 | Penn. | 26,889 |
| Colo. | 28,821 | Mich. | 25,979 | R.I. | 26,924 |
| Conn. | 37,700 | Minn. | 27,667 | S.C. | 21,387 |
| Del. | 29,932 | Miss. | 18,998 | S.D. | 22,201 |
| D.C. | 37,325 | Mo. | 24,447 | Tenn. | 23,615 |
| Fla. | 25,922 | Mont. | 20,247 | Texas | 25,028 |
| Ga. | 25,106 | Neb. | 24,786 | Utah | 21,096 |
| Hawaii | 26,210 | Nev. | 27,360 | Vt. | 24,217 |
| Idaho | 21,080 | N.H. | 29,219 | Va. | 27,489 |
| Ill. | 28,976 | N.J. | 33,953 | Wash. | 28,066 |
| Ind. | 24,302 | N.M. | 20,008 | W. Va. | 19,373 |
| Iowa | 24,007 | N.Y. | 31,679 | Wis. | 25,184 |
| Kan. | 25,049 | N.C. | 24,122 | Wyo. | 23,225 |

Develop a frequency distribution, a relative frequency distribution, and a histogram.

**43.** The conclusion from a 40-state poll conducted by the Joint Council on Economic Education is that students do not learn enough economics. The findings were based on test results from 11th- and 12th-grade students who took a 46-question, multiple-choice test on basic economic concepts such as profit and the law of supply and demand. The following table gives sample data on the number of questions answered correctly.

| 12 | 10 | 16 | 24 | 12 | 14 | 18 | 23 |
| 31 | 14 | 15 | 19 | 17 | 9  | 19 | 28 |
| 24 | 16 | 21 | 13 | 20 | 12 | 22 | 18 |
| 22 | 18 | 30 | 16 | 26 | 18 | 16 | 14 |
| 8  | 25 | 22 | 15 | 33 | 24 | 17 | 19 |

Summarize these data using the following:
a. Stem-and-leaf display
b. Frequency distribution
c. Relative frequency distribution
d. Cumulative frequency distribution
e. On the basis of these data, do you agree with the claim that students are not learning enough economics? Explain.

**44.** The daily high and low temperatures for 20 cities follow (*USA Today,* May 9, 2000).

**HighLow**

| City | High | Low | City | High | Low |
|------|------|-----|------|------|-----|
| Athens | 75 | 54 | Melbourne | 66 | 50 |
| Bangkok | 92 | 74 | Montreal | 64 | 52 |
| Cairo | 84 | 57 | Paris | 77 | 55 |
| Copenhagen | 64 | 39 | Rio de Janeiro | 80 | 61 |
| Dublin | 64 | 46 | Rome | 81 | 54 |
| Havana | 86 | 68 | Seoul | 64 | 50 |
| Hong Kong | 81 | 72 | Singapore | 90 | 75 |
| Johannesburg | 61 | 50 | Sydney | 68 | 55 |
| London | 73 | 48 | Tokyo | 79 | 59 |
| Manila | 93 | 75 | Vancouver | 57 | 43 |

a. Prepare a stem-and-leaf display for the high temperatures.
b. Prepare a stem-and-leaf display for the low temperatures.
c. Compare the stem-and-leaf displays from parts (a) and (b), and make some comments about the differences between daily high and low temperatures.
d. Use the stem-and-leaf display from part (a) to determine the number of cities having a high temperature of 80 degrees or above.
e. Provide frequency distributions for both high and low temperature data.

**45.** Refer to the data set for high and low temperatures for 20 cities in Exercise 44.
a. Develop a scatter diagram to show the relationship between the two variables, high temperature and low temperature.
b. Comment on the relationship between high and low temperature.

**46.** A study of job satisfaction was conducted for four occupations. Job satisfaction was measured using an 18-item questionnaire with each question receiving a response score of 1 to 5 with higher scores indicating greater satisfaction. The sum of the 18 scores provides the job satisfaction score for each individual in the sample. The data obtained are shown below.

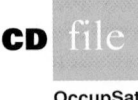

**OccupSat**

| Occupation | Satisfaction Score | Occupation | Satisfaction Score | Occupation | Satisfaction Score |
|------------|-----|------------|-----|------------|-----|
| Lawyer | 42 | Physical Therapist | 78 | Systems Analyst | 60 |
| Physical Therapist | 86 | Systems Analyst | 44 | Physical Therapist | 59 |
| Lawyer | 42 | Systems Analyst | 71 | Cabinetmaker | 78 |
| Systems Analyst | 55 | Lawyer | 50 | Physical Therapist | 60 |

| Occupation | Satisfaction Score | Occupation | Satisfaction Score | Occupation | Satisfaction Score |
|---|---|---|---|---|---|
| Lawyer | 38 | Lawyer | 48 | Physical Therapist | 50 |
| Cabinetmaker | 79 | Cabinetmaker | 69 | Cabinetmaker | 79 |
| Lawyer | 44 | Physical Therapist | 80 | Systems Analyst | 62 |
| Systems Analyst | 41 | Systems Analyst | 64 | Lawyer | 45 |
| Physical Therapist | 55 | Physical Therapist | 55 | Cabinetmaker | 84 |
| Systems Analyst | 66 | Cabinetmaker | 64 | Physical Therapist | 62 |
| Lawyer | 53 | Cabinetmaker | 59 | Systems Analyst | 73 |
| Cabinetmaker | 65 | Cabinetmaker | 54 | Cabinetmaker | 60 |
| Lawyer | 74 | Systems Analyst | 76 | Lawyer | 64 |
| Physical Therapist | 52 | | | | |

    **a.** Provide a crosstabulation of occupation and job satisfaction score.
    **b.** Compute the row percentages for your crosstabulation in part (a).
    **c.** What observations can you make concerning the level of job satisfaction for these occupations?

**47.** Do larger companies generate more revenue? The following data show the number of employees and annual revenue for a sample of 20 *Fortune* 1000 companies (*Fortune,* April 17, 2000).

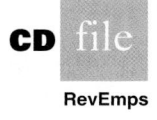

**RevEmps**

| Company | Employees | Revenue ($millions) | Company | Employees | Revenue ($millions) |
|---|---|---|---|---|---|
| Sprint | 77,600 | 19,930 | American Financial | 9,400 | 3,334 |
| Chase Manhattan | 74,801 | 33,710 | Fluor | 53,561 | 12,417 |
| Computer Sciences | 50,000 | 7,660 | Phillips Petroleum | 15,900 | 13,852 |
| Wells Fargo | 89,355 | 21,795 | Cardinal Health | 36,000 | 25,034 |
| Sunbeam | 12,200 | 2,398 | Borders Group | 23,500 | 2,999 |
| CBS | 29,000 | 7,510 | MCI Worldcom | 77,000 | 37,120 |
| Time Warner | 69,722 | 27,333 | Consolidated Edison | 14,269 | 7,491 |
| Steelcase | 16,200 | 2,743 | IBP | 45,000 | 14,075 |
| Georgia-Pacific | 57,000 | 17,796 | Super Value | 50,000 | 17,421 |
| Toro | 1,275 | 4,673 | H&R Block | 4,200 | 1,669 |

    **a.** Prepare a scatter diagram to show the relationship between the variables Revenue and Employees.
    **b.** Comment on any relationship that is apparent between the variables.

**48.** A survey of commercial buildings served by the Cincinnati Gas & Electric Company was concluded in 1992 (CG&E Commercial Building Characteristics Survey, November 25, 1992). One question asked what main heating fuel was used and another asked the year the commercial building was constructed. A partial crosstabulation of the findings follows.

| Year Constructed | Fuel Type | | | | |
|---|---|---|---|---|---|
| | Electricity | Natural Gas | Oil | Propane | Other |
| 1973 or before | 40 | 183 | 12 | 5 | 7 |
| 1974–1979 | 24 | 26 | 2 | 2 | 0 |
| 1980–1986 | 37 | 38 | 1 | 0 | 6 |
| 1987–1991 | 48 | 70 | 2 | 0 | 1 |

    **a.** Complete the crosstabulation by showing the row totals and column totals.
    **b.** Show the frequency distributions for year constructed and for fuel type.
    **c.** Prepare a crosstabulation showing column percentages.
    **d.** Prepare a crosstabulation showing row percentages.
    **e.** Comment on the relationship between year constructed and fuel type.

**TABLE 2.18**    DATA FOR A SAMPLE OF 50 *FORTUNE* 500 COMPANIES

| Company | Stockholders' Equity ($thousands) | Market Value ($thousands) | Profit ($thousands) |
|---|---|---|---|
| AGCO | 982.1 | 372.1 | 60.6 |
| AMP | 2698.0 | 12017.6 | 2.0 |
| Apple Computer | 1642.0 | 4605.0 | 309.0 |
| Baxter International | 2839.0 | 21743.0 | 315.0 |
| Bergen Brunswick | 629.1 | 2787.5 | 3.1 |
| Best Buy | 557.7 | 10376.5 | 94.5 |
| Charles Schwab | 1429.0 | 35340.6 | 348.5 |
| . | . | . | . |
| . | . | . | . |
| . | . | . | . |
| Walgreen | 2849.0 | 30324.7 | 511.0 |
| Westvaco | 2246.4 | 2225.6 | 132.0 |
| Whirlpool | 2001.0 | 3729.4 | 325.0 |
| Xerox | 5544.0 | 35603.7 | 395.0 |

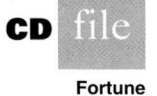

**CD file**

**Fortune**

49. Table 2.18 contains a portion of the data on the file named Fortune on the CD ROM at the back of the book. It provides data on stockholders' equity, market value, and profits for a sample of 50 *Fortune* 500 companies (*Fortune,* April 26, 1999).
    a. Prepare a crosstabulation for the variables Stockholders' Equity and Profit. Use classes of 0–200, 200–400, . . . , 1000–1200 for Profit, and classes of 0–1200, 1200–2400, . . . , 4800–6000 for Stockholders' Equity.
    b. Compute the row percentages for your crosstabulation in part (a)
    c. What relationship, if any, do you notice between Profit and Stockholders' Equity?

50. Refer to the data set in Table 2.18.
    a. Prepare a crosstabulation for the variables Market Value and Profit.
    b. Compute the row percentages for your crosstabulation in part (a).
    c. Comment on any relationship that is apparent between the variables.

51. Refer to the data set in Table 2.18.
    a. Prepare a scatter diagram to show the relationship between the variables Profit and Stockholders' Equity.
    b. Comment on any relationship that is apparent between the variables.

52. Refer to the data set in Table 2.18.
    a. Prepare a scatter diagram to show the relationship between the variables Market Value and Stockholders' Equity.
    b. Comment on any relationship that is apparent between the variables.

## Case Problem    **CONSOLIDATED FOODS**

Consolidated Foods operates a chain of supermarkets in New Mexico, Arizona, and California. A promotional campaign has advertised the chain's offering of a credit card policy whereby Consolidated Foods' customers have the option of paying for their purchases with credit cards, such as Visa and MasterCard, in addition to the usual options of cash or personal check. The policy is being implemented on a trial basis with the hope that the credit card option will encourage customers to make larger purchases.

After the first month of operation, a random sample of 100 customers was selected over a one-week period. Data were collected on the method of payment and how much was spent

**TABLE 2.19**    PURCHASE AMOUNT AND METHOD OF PAYMENT FOR A SAMPLE OF
100 CONSOLIDATED FOODS CUSTOMERS

**Consolid**

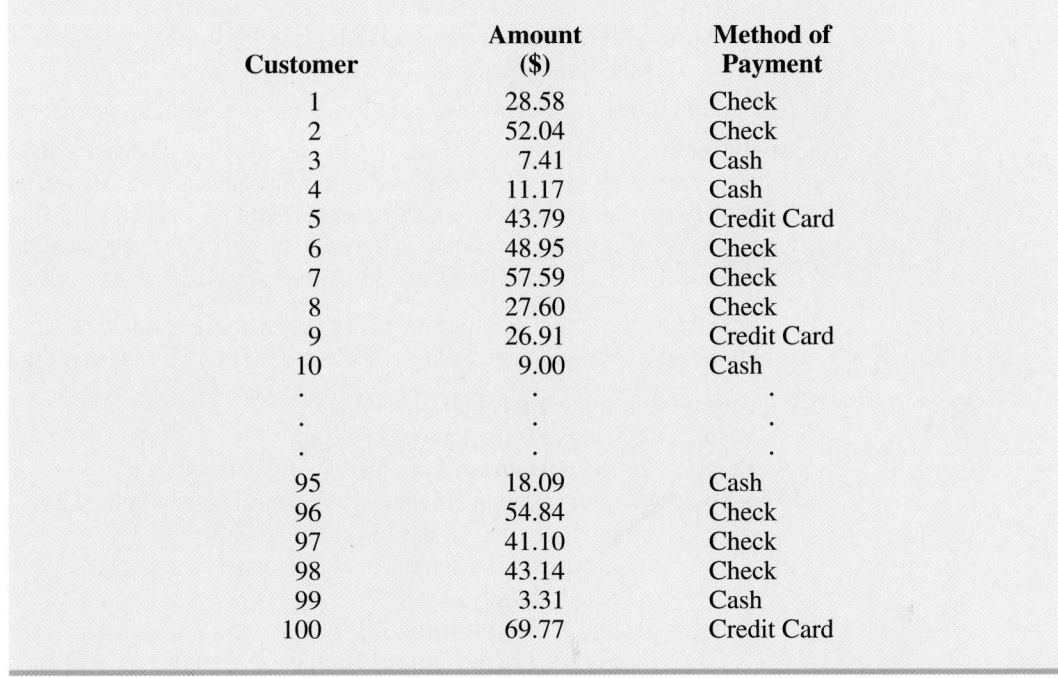

| Customer | Amount ($) | Method of Payment |
|----------|------------|-------------------|
| 1 | 28.58 | Check |
| 2 | 52.04 | Check |
| 3 | 7.41 | Cash |
| 4 | 11.17 | Cash |
| 5 | 43.79 | Credit Card |
| 6 | 48.95 | Check |
| 7 | 57.59 | Check |
| 8 | 27.60 | Check |
| 9 | 26.91 | Credit Card |
| 10 | 9.00 | Cash |
| . | . | . |
| . | . | . |
| . | . | . |
| 95 | 18.09 | Cash |
| 96 | 54.84 | Check |
| 97 | 41.10 | Check |
| 98 | 43.14 | Check |
| 99 | 3.31 | Cash |
| 100 | 69.77 | Credit Card |

by each of the 100 customers. A portion of the sample data are shown in Table 2.19. Prior
to the new credit card policy, approximately 50% of Consolidated Foods' customers paid
in cash and approximately 50% paid by personal check.

## Managerial Report

Use the tabular and graphical methods of descriptive statistics to summarize the sample data
in the data set named Consolid. Your report should contain summaries such as the following.

1. A frequency and relative frequency distribution for the method of payment.
2. A bar graph or pie chart for the method of payment.
3. Frequency and relative frequency distributions for the amount spent in each method of payment.
4. Histograms and/or stem-and-leaf plots for the amount spent in each method of payment.
5. A crosstabulation for the variables method of payment and amount spent.

What preliminary insights do you have about the amounts spent and method of payment at
Consolidated Foods?

## Appendix 2.1    USING EXCEL'S HISTOGRAM TOOL TO CONSTRUCT A FREQUENCY DISTRIBUTION AND HISTOGRAM

In illustrating how to use Excel to summarize quantitative data, we used the FREQUENCY
function to construct a frequency distribution and the Chart Wizard to construct a histogram. Microsoft Excel also provides a set of data analysis tools that can be accessed
through the Tools pull-down menu. The data analysis tool for constructing frequency
distributions and histograms is the Histogram tool. It can save steps when both a frequency

distribution and a histogram are desired. Here we show how it is used by constructing a frequency distribution and a histogram for the audit time data in Table 2.5. As we did in section 2.2, we will use 5 classes, each with a width of 5 days.

**Enter Data:**  The label Audit Time and the data for the 20 audit times have been entered into cells A1:A21 of the worksheet shown in Figure 2.23.

**Enter Functions and Formulas:**  No functions and formulas are needed.

**Apply Tools:**  Excel's Histogram tool requires the user to first identify what are called *bins* for each class in the frequency distribution using the class upper limits. Hence, five bins with upper limits of 14, 19, 24, 29, and 34 are needed for the audit time data. The bin upper limits must be entered in ascending order in a column or row of the worksheet. We have entered the bin upper limits into cells C10:C14 and the label Audit Time into cell C9 of the worksheet in Figure 2.23.

The following steps describe how to use the Histogram tool to produce a frequency distribution and a histogram consisting of 5 classes, or bins, for the audit time data.

**Step 1.** Select the **Tools** pull-down menu
**Step 2.** Choose the **Data Analysis** option
**Step 3.** Choose **Histogram** from the list of Analysis Tools
**Step 4.** When the **Histogram** dialog box appears (see Figure 2.24):
  Enter A1:A21 in the **Input Range** box
  Enter C9:C14 in the **Bin Range** box
  Select **Labels**
  Select **Output Range**
  Enter C1 in the **Output Range** box (it tells Excel where to display the frequency distribution)
  Select **Chart Output** (to request a histogram)
  Click **OK**

**FIGURE 2.23**  WORKSHEET FOR AUDIT TIME DATA AFTER CREATING BINS USING CLASS UPPER LIMITS

| | A | B | C | D |
|---|---|---|---|---|
| 1 | Audit Time | | | |
| 2 | 12 | | | |
| 3 | 15 | | | |
| 4 | 20 | | | |
| 5 | 22 | | | |
| 6 | 14 | | | |
| 7 | 14 | | | |
| 8 | 15 | | | |
| 9 | 27 | | Audit Time | |
| 10 | 21 | | 14 | |
| 11 | 18 | | 19 | |
| 12 | 19 | | 24 | |
| 13 | 18 | | 29 | |
| 14 | 22 | | 34 | |
| 15 | 33 | | | |
| 16 | 16 | | | |
| 17 | 18 | | | |
| 18 | 17 | | | |
| 19 | 23 | | | |
| 20 | 28 | | | |
| 21 | 13 | | | |
| 22 | | | | |

**FIGURE 2.24**    DIALOG BOX FOR HISTOGRAM TOOL

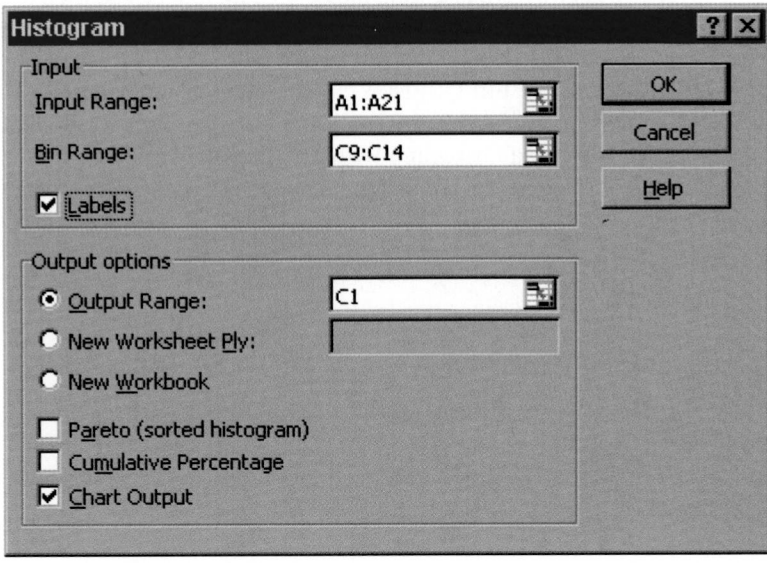

The worksheet shown in Figure 2.25 displays the frequency distribution and the histogram created using these steps. The frequency distribution is displayed in cells C1:D6. Note that Excel has also added a row to the frequency distribution with a label of "More" in order to provide for the possibility that we might have entered too few bin values. You can simply delete this row. Also, the histogram produced using the Histogram tool has gaps

**FIGURE 2.25**    FREQUENCY DISTRIBUTION AND HISTOGRAM CONSTRUCTED USING HISTOGRAM TOOL

| | A | B | C | D | E | F | G | H | I | J | K | L |
|---|---|---|---|---|---|---|---|---|---|---|---|---|
| 1 | **Audit Time** | | *Audit Time* | *Frequency* | | | | | | | | |
| 2 | 12 | | 14 | 4 | | | | | | | | |
| 3 | 15 | | 19 | 8 | | | | | | | | |
| 4 | 20 | | 24 | 5 | | | | | | | | |
| 5 | 22 | | 29 | 2 | | | | | | | | |
| 6 | 14 | | 34 | 1 | | | | | | | | |
| 7 | 14 | | More | 0 | | | | | | | | |
| 8 | 15 | | | | | | | | | | | |
| 9 | 27 | | **Audit Time** | | | | | | | | | |
| 10 | 21 | | 14 | | | | | | | | | |
| 11 | 18 | | 19 | | | | | | | | | |
| 12 | 19 | | 24 | | | | | | | | | |
| 13 | 18 | | 29 | | | | | | | | | |
| 14 | 22 | | 34 | | | | | | | | | |
| 15 | 33 | | | | | | | | | | | |
| 16 | 16 | | | | | | | | | | | |
| 17 | 18 | | | | | | | | | | | |
| 18 | 17 | | | | | | | | | | | |
| 19 | 23 | | | | | | | | | | | |
| 20 | 28 | | | | | | | | | | | |
| 21 | 13 | | | | | | | | | | | |
| 22 | | | | | | | | | | | | |

between the rectangles. We encountered this same situation when using the Chart Wizard to construct a histogram. We can remove the gaps the same way we did then (see Figure 2.9).

As we have just seen, the Histogram tool can be used to construct both a frequency distribution and histogram in one series of steps. In the chapter, we showed how to use the FREQUENCY function and the Chart Wizard to accomplish the same thing. The advantage of using the FREQUENCY function and Chart Wizard is that the results remain linked to the data. Thus, a change in the data will prompt an automatic update of the frequency distribution and histogram. With the Histogram tool, the results are not linked to the data so a change in the data requires that we reconstruct the frequency distribution and histogram.

# DESCRIPTIVE STATISTICS: NUMERICAL METHODS

**Chapter 3**

**CONTENTS**

## STATISTICS IN PRACTICE

### SMALL FRY DESIGN*
*Santa Ana, California*

Founded in 1997, Small Fry Design is a toy and accessory company that designs and imports products for infants. The company's product line includes teddy bears, mobiles, musical toys, rattles, and security blankets, and features high-quality soft toy designs with an emphasis on color, texture, and sound. The products are designed in the United States and manufactured in China.

Small Fry Design uses independent representatives to sell the products to infant furnishing retailers, children's accessory and apparel stores, gift shops, upscale department stores, and major catalog companies. Currently, Small Fry Design products are distributed in more than 1000 retail outlets throughout the United States.

Cash flow management is one of the most critical activities in the day-to-day operation of this company. Ensuring sufficient incoming cash to meet both current and ongoing debt obligations can mean the difference between business success and failure. A critical factor in cash flow management is the analysis and control of accounts receivable. By measuring the average age and dollar value of outstanding invoices, management can predict cash availability and monitor changes in the status of accounts receivable. The company has set the following goals: the average age for outstanding invoices should not exceed 45 days and the dollar value of invoices more than 60 days old should not exceed 5% of the dollar value of all accounts receivable.

In a recent summary of accounts receivable status, the following descriptive statistics were provided for the age of outstanding invoices:

Some of the Small Fry Design products. © Photo courtesy of Small Fry Design.

| Mean | 40 days |
|------|---------|
| Median | 35 days |
| Mode | 31 days |

Interpretation of these statistics shows that the mean or average age of an invoice is 40 days. The median shows that half of the invoices have been outstanding 35 days or more. The mode of 31 days is the most frequent invoice age indicating that the most common length of time an invoice has been outstanding is 31 days. The statistical summary also showed that only 3% of the dollar value of all accounts receivable was over 60 days old. Based on the statistical information, management was satisfied that accounts receivable and incoming cash flow were under control.

In this chapter, you will learn how to compute and interpret some of the statistical measures used by Small Fry Design. In addition to the mean, median, and mode, you will learn about other descriptive statistics such as the range, variance, standard deviation, percentiles, and correlation. These numerical measures will assist in the understanding and interpretation of data.

---

* The authors are indebted to John A. McCarthy, president of Small Fry Design, for providing this Statistics in Practice.

---

In Chapter 2 we discussed tabular and graphical methods used to summarize data. In this chapter, we present several numerical methods of descriptive statistics that provide additional alternatives for summarizing data.

We start by developing numerical summaries for data sets consisting of a single variable. When a data set contains more than one variable, the same numerical summaries can be computed separately for each variable. However, in the two-variable case, we will also develop measures of the relationship between the variables.

Several numerical measures of location, dispersion, and association are introduced. If the measures are computed for data from a sample, they are called **sample statistics.**

If the measures are computed for data from a population, they are called **population parameters.**

Several more of Excel's statistical functions are introduced in this chapter. In most cases we introduce them with little digression from the flow of the statistical material. But, at the end of section 2, we pause to show how Excel's Descriptive Statistics tool can be used to perform the work of several functions by providing a summary of the most commonly used descriptive statistics. If you have trouble using any of the statistical functions, recall that Excel's Function Wizard has been designed to provide help (see Appendix F: Excel Functions and the Function Wizard).

## 3.1   MEASURES OF LOCATION

### Mean

Perhaps the most important measure of location is the **mean,** or average value, for a variable. The mean provides a measure of central location. If the data are from a sample, the mean is denoted by $\bar{x}$; if the data are from a population, the mean is denoted by the Greek letter $\mu$.

In statistical formulas, it is customary to denote the value of variable $x$ for the first observation by $x_1$, the value of $x$ for the second observation by $x_2$, and so on. In general, the value of $x$ for the $i$th observation is denoted by $x_i$. For a sample with $n$ observations, the formula for the sample mean is as follows.

**Sample Mean**

$$\bar{x} = \frac{\Sigma x_i}{n} \tag{3.1}$$

In the preceding formula, the numerator is the sum of the values of the $n$ observations. That is,

$$\Sigma x_i = x_1 + x_2 + \cdots + x_n$$

The Greek letter $\Sigma$ is the summation sign.

To illustrate the computation of a sample mean, let us consider the following class size data for a sample of five college classes.

$$46 \quad 54 \quad 42 \quad 46 \quad 32$$

We use the notation $x_1, x_2, x_3, x_4, x_5$ to represent the number of students in each of the five classes.

$$x_1 = 46 \qquad x_2 = 54 \qquad x_3 = 42 \qquad x_4 = 46 \qquad x_5 = 32$$

Hence, to compute the sample mean, we can write

$$\bar{x} = \frac{\Sigma x_i}{n} = \frac{x_1 + x_2 + x_3 + x_4 + x_5}{5} = \frac{46 + 54 + 42 + 46 + 32}{5} = 44$$

The sample mean class size is 44 students.

Another illustration of the computation of a sample mean is given in the following situation. Suppose that a college placement office sent a questionnaire to a sample of business school graduates requesting information on starting salaries. Table 3.1 shows the data that

**TABLE 3.1**    MONTHLY STARTING SALARIES FOR A SAMPLE OF 12 BUSINESS SCHOOL GRADUATES

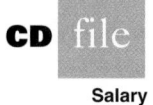

**Salary**

| Graduate | Monthly Starting Salary ($) | Graduate | Monthly Starting Salary ($) |
|----------|-----------------------------|----------|-----------------------------|
| 1 | 2850 | 7 | 2890 |
| 2 | 2950 | 8 | 3130 |
| 3 | 3050 | 9 | 2940 |
| 4 | 2880 | 10 | 3325 |
| 5 | 2755 | 11 | 2920 |
| 6 | 2710 | 12 | 2880 |

have been collected. The mean monthly starting salary for the sample of 12 business college graduates is computed as

$$\bar{x} = \frac{\Sigma x_i}{n} = \frac{x_1 + x_2 + \ldots + x_{12}}{12}$$

$$= \frac{2850 + 2950 + \cdots + 2880}{12}$$

$$= \frac{35{,}280}{12} = 2940$$

Equation (3.1) shows how the mean is computed for a sample with $n$ observations. The formula for computing the mean of a population is the same, but we use different notation to indicate that we are working with the entire population. The number of observations in a population is denoted by $N$ and the symbol for a population mean is $\mu$.

**Population Mean**

$$\mu = \frac{\Sigma x_i}{N} \tag{3.2}$$

## Median

The **median** is another measure of central location for a variable. The median is the value in the middle when the data are arranged in ascending order (smallest value to largest value). With an odd number of observations, the median is the middle value. An even number of observations has no single middle value. In this case, we follow the convention of defining the median to be the average of the values for the middle two observations. For convenience the definition of the median is restated as follows.

**Median**

Arrange the data in ascending order (smallest value to largest value).

    **(a)** For an odd number of observations the median is the middle value.
    **(b)** For an even number of observations, the median is the average of the middle two values.

Let us apply this definition to compute the median class size for the sample of five college classes. Arranging the data in ascending order provides the following list.

$$32 \quad 42 \quad 46 \quad 46 \quad 54$$

Because $n = 5$ is odd, the median is the middle value. Thus the median class size is 46 students. Even though this data set has two observations with values of 46, each observation is treated separately when we arrange the data in ascending order.

Suppose we also compute the median starting salary for 12 business college graduates. We first arrange the data in Table 3.1 in ascending order.

$$2710 \quad 2755 \quad 2850 \quad 2880 \quad 2880 \quad \underbrace{2890 \quad 2920}_{\text{Middle Two Values}} \quad 2940 \quad 2950 \quad 3050 \quad 3130 \quad 3325$$

Because $n = 12$ is even, we identify the middle two values: 2890 and 2920. The median is the average of these values.

$$\text{Median} = \frac{2890 + 2920}{2} = 2905$$

The median is the measure of location most often reported for annual income and property value data because a few extremely large incomes or property values can inflate the mean. In such cases, the median is a better measure of central location.

Although the mean is the more commonly used measure of central location, in some situations the median is preferred. The mean is influenced by extremely small and large data values. For instance, suppose that one of the graduates (see Table 3.1) had a starting salary of $10,000 per month (maybe the individual's family owns the company). If we change the highest monthly starting salary in Table 3.1 from $3325 to $10,000 and recompute the mean, the sample mean changes from $2940 to $3496. The median of $2905, however, is unchanged, because $2890 and $2920 are still the middle two values. With the extremely high starting salary included, the median provides a better measure of central location than the mean. We can generalize to say that whenever a data set has extreme values, the median is the preferred measure of central location.

## Mode

A third measure of location is the **mode.** The mode is defined as follows.

> **Mode**
>
> The mode is the value that occurs with greatest frequency.

To illustrate the identification of the mode, consider the sample of five class sizes. The only value that occurs more than once is 46. Because this value, occurring with a frequency of 2, has the greatest frequency, it is the mode. As another illustration, consider the sample of starting salaries for the business school graduates. The only monthly starting salary that occurs more than once is $2880. Because this value has the greatest frequency, it is the mode.

Situations can arise for which the greatest frequency occurs at two or more different values. In these instances more than one mode exists. If the data have exactly two modes, we say that the data are *bimodal.* If data have more than two modes, we say that the data are *multimodal.* In multimodal cases the mode is almost never reported because listing three or more modes would not be particularly helpful in describing a location for the data.

The mode is an important measure of location for qualitative data. For example, the qualitative data set in Table 2.2 resulted in the following frequency distribution for soft drink purchases.

| Soft Drink | Frequency |
|---|---|
| Coke Classic | 19 |
| Diet Coke | 8 |
| Dr. Pepper | 5 |
| Pepsi-Cola | 13 |
| Sprite | 5 |
| Total | 50 |

The mode, or most frequently purchased soft drink, is Coke Classic. For this type of data it obviously makes no sense to speak of the mean or median. The mode provides the information of interest, the most frequently purchased soft drink.

## Using Excel to Compute the Mean, Median, and Mode

Excel provides functions for computing the mean, median, and mode. We illustrate the use of these Excel functions by computing the mean, median, and mode for the starting salary data in Table 3.1. Refer to Figure 3.1 as we describe the tasks involved. The formula worksheet is in the background; the value worksheet is in the foreground.

**Enter Data:**  Labels and the starting salary data are entered into cells A1:B13 of the worksheet.

**Enter Functions and Formulas:**  Excel's AVERAGE function can be used to compute the mean by entering the following formula into cell E1:

$$=AVERAGE(B2:B13)$$

**FIGURE 3.1**    EXCEL WORKSHEET USED TO COMPUTE THE MEAN, MEDIAN, AND MODE FOR STARTING SALARIES

If the data are bimodal or multimodal, Excel's MODE function will incorrectly identify a single mode.

Similarly, the formulas =MEDIAN(B2:B13) and =MODE(B2:B13) are entered into cells E2 and E3, respectively, to compute the median and the mode. The labels Mean, Median, and Mode are entered into cells D1:D3 to identify the output.

The formulas in cells E1:E3 are displayed in the formula worksheet in the background of Figure 3.1. The worksheet in the foreground shows the values computed using the Excel functions. Note that the mean (2940), median (2905), and mode (2880) are the same as we computed earlier.

## Percentiles

A **percentile** provides information about how the data are spread over the interval from the smallest value to the largest value. For data that do not have numerous repeated values, the $p$th percentile divides the data into two parts. Approximately $p$ percent of the observations have values less than the $p$th percentile; approximately $(100 - p)$ percent of the observations have values greater than the $p$th percentile. The $p$th percentile is formally defined as follows.

> **Percentile**
>
> The $p$th percentile is a value such that *at least* $p$ percent of the observations are less than or equal to this value and *at least* $(100 - p)$ percent of the observations are greater than or equal to this value.

Admission test scores for colleges and universities are frequently reported in terms of percentiles. For instance, suppose an applicant obtains a raw score of 54 on the verbal portion of an admission test. How this student performed in relation to other students taking the same test may not be readily apparent. However, if the raw score of 54 corresponds to the 70th percentile, we know that approximately 70% of the students had scores lower than this individual's and approximately 30% of the students had scores higher than this individual's.

The following procedure can be used to compute the $p$th percentile.

> **Calculating the $p$th Percentile**
>
> **Step 1.** Arrange the data in ascending order (smallest value to largest value).
>
> **Step 2.** Compute an index $i$
>
> $$i = \left(\frac{p}{100}\right)n$$
>
> where $p$ is the percentile of interest and $n$ is the number of observations.
>
> **Step 3.** (a) If $i$ *is not an integer, round up*. The next integer *greater* than $i$ denotes the position of the $p$th percentile.
>
> (b) If $i$ *is an integer*, the $p$th percentile is the average of the values in positions $i$ and $i + 1$.

Following these steps makes it easy to calculate percentiles.

As an illustration of this procedure, let us determine the 85th percentile for the starting salary data in Table 3.1.

**Step 1.** Arrange the data in ascending order.

2710   2755   2850   2880   2880   2890   2920   2940   2950   3050   3130   3325

**Step 2.**

$$i = \left(\frac{p}{100}\right)n = \left(\frac{85}{100}\right)12 = 10.2$$

**Step 3.** Because $i$ is not an integer, *round up*. The position of the 85th percentile is the next integer greater than 10.2, the 11th position.

Returning to the data, we see that the 85th percentile is the data value in the 11th position, or 3130.

As another illustration of this procedure, let us consider the calculation of the 50th percentile for the starting salary data. Applying step 2, we obtain

$$i = \left(\frac{50}{100}\right)12 = 6$$

Because $i$ is an integer, step 3(b) states that the 50th percentile is the average of the sixth and seventh data values; thus the 50th percentile is $(2890 + 2920)/2 = 2905$. Note that the *50th percentile is also the median.*

## Quartiles

Quartiles are just specific percentiles; thus, the steps for computing percentiles can be applied directly in the computation of quartiles.

It is often desirable to divide data into four parts, with each part containing approximately one-fourth, or 25% of the observations. Figure 3.2 shows a data set divided into four parts. The division points are referred to as the **quartiles** and are defined as

$Q_1$ = first quartile, or 25th percentile

$Q_2$ = second quartile, or 50th percentile (also the median)

$Q_3$ = third quartile, or 75th percentile.

The starting salary data are again arranged in ascending order. $Q_2$, the second quartile (median), has already been identified as 2905.

2710  2755  2850  2880  2880  2890  2920  2940  2950  3050  3130  3325

The computations of quartiles $Q_1$ and $Q_3$ require the use of the rule for finding the 25th and 75th percentiles. These calculations follow.

**FIGURE 3.2**  LOCATION OF THE QUARTILES

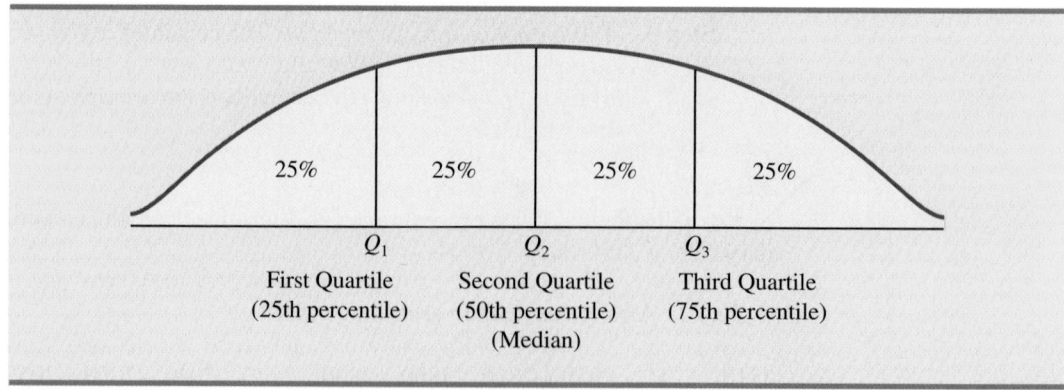

For $Q_1$,

$$i = \left(\frac{p}{100}\right)n = \left(\frac{25}{100}\right)12 = 3$$

Because $i$ is an integer, step 3(b) indicates that the first quartile, or 25th percentile, is the average of the third and fourth data values; thus, $Q_1 = (2850 + 2880)/2 = 2865$.
For $Q_3$,

$$i = \left(\frac{p}{100}\right)n = \left(\frac{75}{100}\right)12 = 9$$

Again, because $i$ is an integer, step 3(b) indicates that the third quartile, or 75th percentile, is the average of the ninth and tenth data values; thus, $Q_3 = (2950 + 3050)/2 = 3000$.
    The quartiles have divided the starting salary data into four parts, with each part containing 25% of the observations.

| 2710 | 2755 | 2850 | 2880 | 2880 | 2890 | 2920 | 2940 | 2950 | 3050 | 3130 | 3325 |

$$Q_1 = 2865 \qquad\qquad Q_2 = 2905 \qquad\qquad Q_3 = 3000$$
$$\text{(Median)}$$

We have defined the quartiles as the 25th, 50th, and 75th percentiles. Thus, we have computed the quartiles in the same way as percentiles. However, other conventions are sometimes used to compute quartiles, and the actual values reported for quartiles may vary slightly depending on the convention used. Nevertheless, the objective of all procedures for computing quartiles is to divide the data into four equal parts.

## Using Excel to Sort Data and to Compute Percentiles and Quartiles

Excel provides functions for computing percentiles and quartiles. However, for small data sets (such as the starting salary data), these functions do not always provide results that satisfy the definition of a percentile. We show here how to use Excel to compute percentiles another way. We first sort the data and then select the appropriate percentile from its position in the data set. This procedure also provides quartiles and the median because they are also percentiles. We will illustrate this approach to computing the 25th, 50th, 75th, and 85th percentiles for the starting salary data in Table 3.1. Refer to Figure 3.3 as we present the steps involved. The worksheet containing the original starting salary data is in the background; the worksheet obtained after sorting the data is in the foreground.

**Enter Data:**   Labels and the starting salary data are entered into cells A1:B13.

**Enter Functions and Formulas:**   No functions and formulas are needed.

**Apply Tools:**   The following steps will sort the data into ascending order.

   **Step 1.** Select any cell containing data in column B
   **Step 2.** Select the **Data** pull-down menu
   **Step 3.** Choose the **Sort** option
   **Step 4.** When the **Sort** dialog box appears:
             In the **Sort by** box, make sure that **Starting Salary** appears and that **Ascending** is selected
             Click **OK** (the sorted data appear in the worksheet shown in the foreground of Figure 3.3)

**FIGURE 3.3**     EXCEL WORKSHEET USED TO COMPUTE PERCENTILES AND QUARTILES FOR STARTING SALARIES

| | A | B | C | D | E |
|---|---|---|---|---|---|
| 1 | Graduate | Starting Salary | | | |
| 2 | 1 | 2850 | | | |
| 3 | 2 | 2950 | | | |
| 4 | 3 | 3050 | | | |
| 5 | 4 | 2880 | | | |
| 6 | 5 | 2755 | | | |
| 7 | 6 | 2710 | | | |
| 8 | 7 | 2890 | | | |
| 9 | 8 | 3130 | | | |
| 10 | 9 | 2940 | | | |
| 11 | 10 | 3325 | | | |
| 12 | 11 | 2920 | | | |
| 13 | 12 | 2880 | | | |
| 14 | | | | | |

| | A | B | C | D | E |
|---|---|---|---|---|---|
| 1 | Graduate | Starting Salary | | | |
| 2 | 6 | 2710 | | | |
| 3 | 5 | 2755 | | | |
| 4 | 1 | 2850 | | | |
| 5 | 4 | 2880 | | $Q_1 = 2865$ | |
| 6 | 12 | 2880 | | | |
| 7 | 7 | 2890 | | | |
| 8 | 11 | 2920 | | $Q_2 = 2905$ | |
| 9 | 9 | 2940 | | | |
| 10 | 2 | 2950 | | | |
| 11 | 3 | 3050 | | $Q_3 = 3000$ | |
| 12 | 8 | 3130 | | 85th percentile = 3130 | |
| 13 | 10 | 3325 | | | |
| 14 | | | | | |

In the previous subsection, we showed how to calculate the $p$th percentile by first arranging the data in ascending order and then computing an index that can be used to identify the position of the $p$th percentile. Recall that for the starting salary data the 25th percentile ($Q_1$) was the average of the 3rd and 4th values, the 50th percentile ($Q_2$ and the median) was the average of the 6th and 7th values, the 75th percentile ($Q_3$) was the average of the 9th and 10th values, and the 85th percentile was the 11th data value. Using the sorted data shown in Figure 3.3, it is easy to identify the position of these values in the data (the row number minus one) and hence compute the percentile values by hand.

## NOTES AND COMMENTS

It is better to use the median than the mean as a measure of central location when a data set contains extreme values. Another measure, sometimes used when extreme values are present, is the *trimmed mean*. It is obtained by deleting a percentage of the smallest and largest values from a data set and then computing the mean of the remaining values. For example, the 5% trimmed mean would be obtained by removing the smallest 5% and the largest 5% of the data values and then computing the mean of the remaining values. Using the sample with $n = 12$ starting salaries, $0.05(12) = 0.6$. Rounding this value to 1 indicates that the 5% trimmed mean would remove the 1 smallest data value and the 1 largest data value. The 5% trimmed mean using the 10 remaining observations is 2924.50.

## EXERCISES

### Methods

1. Consider a sample with data values of 10, 20, 12, 17, and 16. Compute the mean and median.
2. Consider a sample with data values of 10, 20, 21, 17, 16, and 12. Compute the mean and median.

3. Consider a sample with data values of 27, 25, 20, 15, 30, 34, 28, and 25. Compute the 20th, 25th, 65th, and 75th percentiles.

4. Consider a sample with data values of 53, 55, 70, 58, 64, 57, 53, 69, 57, 68, and 53. Compute the mean, median, and mode.

## Applications

5. According to a salary survey conducted by the National Association of Colleges and Employers, bachelor's degree candidates in accounting received starting offers averaging $34,500 per year in 1999 (Bureau of Labor Statistics, *Occupational Outlook Handbook,* 2000–01 Edition). A sample of 30 students who graduated in 2000 with a bachelor's degree in accounting resulted in the following starting salaries. Data are in thousands of dollars.

**AcctSal**

| | | | | |
|---|---|---|---|---|
| 36.8 | 34.9 | 35.2 | 37.2 | 36.2 |
| 35.8 | 36.8 | 36.1 | 36.7 | 36.6 |
| 37.3 | 38.2 | 36.3 | 36.4 | 39.0 |
| 38.3 | 36.0 | 35.0 | 36.7 | 37.9 |
| 38.3 | 36.4 | 36.5 | 38.4 | 39.4 |
| 38.8 | 35.4 | 36.4 | 37.0 | 36.4 |

a. What is the mean starting salary?
b. What is the median starting salary?
c. What is the mode?
d. What is the first quartile?
e. What is the third quartile?

6. More and more investors are turning to discount brokers to save money when buying and selling shares of stock. The American Association of Individual Investors conducts an annual survey of discount brokers. The commissions charged by a sample of 20 discount brokers for two types of trades, 500 shares at $50 per share and 1000 shares at $5 per share, are shown in Table 3.2.

**TABLE 3.2**    COMMISSIONS CHARGED BY DISCOUNT BROKERS

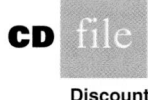

**Discount**

| Broker | 500@$50 | 1000@$5 |
|---|---|---|
| AcuTrade | 38.00 | 48.00 |
| Bank of San Francisco | 140.00 | 79.50 |
| Burke Christensen & Lewis | 34.00 | 34.00 |
| Bush Burns Securities | 35.00 | 35.00 |
| Charles Schwab | 155.00 | 90.00 |
| Downstate Discount | 55.00 | 60.00 |
| Dreyfus Lion Account | 154.50 | 88.50 |
| First Union Brokerage | 140.00 | 90.00 |
| Levitt & Levitt | 35.00 | 70.00 |
| Max Ule | 195.00 | 70.00 |
| Mongerson & Co | 95.00 | 66.00 |
| Quick & Reilly | 119.50 | 60.50 |
| Scottsdale Securities, Inc. | 50.00 | 63.00 |
| Seaport Securities Corp. | 50.00 | 70.00 |
| St. Louis Discount | 66.00 | 64.00 |
| Summit Financial Services | 95.00 | 60.50 |
| T. Rowe Price Brokerage | 134.00 | 80.00 |
| Unified Financial Services | 154.00 | 90.00 |
| Wall Street Access | 45.00 | 45.00 |
| Your Discount Broker | 55.00 | 70.00 |

*Source: AAII Journal,* January 2000.

a. Compute the mean, median, and mode for the commission charged on a trade of 500 shares at $50 per share.
b. Compute the mean, median, and mode for the commission charged on a trade of 1000 shares at $5 per share.
c. Which costs the most: trading 500 shares at $50 per share or trading 1000 shares at $5 per share?
d. Does the cost of a transaction seem to be related to the amount of the transaction?

7. The average person spends 45 minutes a day listening to recorded music (*Des Moines Register,* December 5, 1997). The following data were obtained for the number of minutes spent listening to recorded music for a sample of 30 individuals.

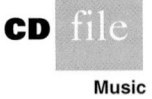

**CD** file

**Music**

| | | | | |
|------|-------|------|------|------|
| 88.3 | 4.3 | 4.6 | 7.0 | 9.2 |
| 0.0 | 99.2 | 34.9 | 81.7 | 0.0 |
| 85.4 | 0.0 | 17.5 | 45.0 | 53.3 |
| 29.1 | 28.8 | 0.0 | 98.9 | 64.5 |
| 4.4 | 67.9 | 94.2 | 7.6 | 56.6 |
| 52.9 | 145.6 | 70.4 | 65.1 | 63.6 |

a. Compute the mean.
b. Do these data appear to be consistent with the average reported by the newspaper?
c. Compute the median.
d. Compute the first and third quartiles.
e. Compute and interpret the 40th percentile.

8. Millions of Americans get up each morning and go to work in their offices at home. The growing use of personal computers is suggested as one of the reasons more people can operate at-home businesses. Following is a sample of age data for individuals working at home.

**SELF** test

| | | | | | | | | | |
|----|----|----|----|----|----|----|----|----|----|
| 22 | 58 | 24 | 50 | 29 | 52 | 57 | 31 | 30 | 41 |
| 44 | 40 | 46 | 29 | 31 | 37 | 32 | 44 | 49 | 29 |

a. Compute the mean and mode.
b. The median age of the population of all adults is 35.1 years (U.S. Census Bureau, November 1, 1997). Use the median age of the preceding data to comment on whether the at-home workers tend to be younger or older than the population of all adults.
c. Compute the first and third quartiles.
d. Compute and interpret the 32nd percentile.

9. Media Matrix collected data showing the most popular websites when browsing at home and at work (*Business 2.0,* January 2000). The following data show the number of unique visitors (thousands) for the top 25 websites when browsing at home.

**CD** file

**Websites**

| Website | Unique Visitors (thousands) |
|---------|------------------------------|
| about.com | 5538 |
| altavista.com | 7391 |
| amazon.com | 7986 |
| angelfire.com | 8917 |
| aol.com | 23863 |
| bluemountainarts.com | 6786 |
| ebay.com | 8296 |
| excite.com | 10479 |
| geocities.com | 15321 |
| go.com | 14330 |
| hotbot.com | 5760 |
| hotmail.com | 11791 |
| icq.com | 5052 |
| looksmart.com | 5984 |

| Website | Unique Visitors (thousands) |
|---|---|
| lycos.com | 9950 |
| microsoft.com | 15593 |
| msn.com | 23505 |
| netscape.com | 14470 |
| passport.com | 11299 |
| real.com | 6785 |
| snap.com | 5730 |
| tripod.com | 7970 |
| xoom.com | 5652 |
| yahoo.com | 26796 |
| zdnet.com | 5133 |

a. Compute the mean and median.
b. Do you think it would be better to use the mean or the median as the measure of central tendency for these data? Explain.
c. Compute the first and third quartiles.
d. Compute and interpret the 85th percentile.

10. The *Los Angeles Times* regularly reports the air quality index for various areas of Southern California. Index ratings of 0–50 are considered good, 51–100 moderate, 101–200 unhealthy, 201–275 very unhealthy, and over 275 hazardous. Recent air quality indexes for Pomona were 28, 42, 58, 48, 45, 55, 60, 49, and 50.
   a. Compute the mean, median, and mode for the data. Should the Pomona air quality index be considered good?
   b. Compute the 25th percentile and 75th percentile for the Pomona air quality data.

11. In automobile mileage and gasoline-consumption testing, 13 automobiles were road tested for 300 miles in both city and highway driving conditions. The following data were recorded for miles-per-gallon performance.

   *City:*    16.2  16.7  15.9  14.4  13.2  15.3  16.8  16.0  16.1  15.3  15.2  15.3  16.2
   *Highway:*  19.4  20.6  18.3  18.6  19.2  17.4  17.2  18.6  19.0  21.1  19.4  18.5  18.7

   Use the mean, median, and mode to make a statement about the difference in performance for city and highway driving.

12. Because of recent technological advances, today's digital cameras produce better-looking pictures than their predecessors did a year ago. The following data show the street price, maximum picture capacity, and battery life (minutes) for 20 of the latest models (*PC World*, January 2000).

**Cameras**

| Camera | Price ($) | Maximum Picture Capacity | Battery Life (minutes) |
|---|---|---|---|
| Agfa Ephoto CL30 | 349 | 36 | 25 |
| Canon PowerShot A50 | 499 | 106 | 75 |
| Canon PowerShot Pro70 | 999 | 96 | 118 |
| Epson PhotoPC 800 | 699 | 120 | 99 |
| Fujifilm DX-10 | 299 | 30 | 229 |
| Fujifilm MX-2700 | 699 | 141 | 124 |
| Fujifilm MX-2900 Zoom | 899 | 141 | 88 |
| HP PhotoSmart C200 | 299 | 80 | 68 |
| Kodak DC215 Zoom | 399 | 54 | 159 |
| Kodak DC265 Zoom | 899 | 180 | 186 |

(*continued*)

| Camera | Price ($) | Maximum Picture Capacity | Battery Life (minutes) |
|---|---|---|---|
| Kodak DC280 Zoom | 799 | 245 | 143 |
| Minolta Dimage EX Zoom 1500 | 549 | 105 | 38 |
| Nikon Coolpix 950 | 999 | 32 | 88 |
| Olympus D-340R | 299 | 122 | 161 |
| Olympus D-450 Zoom | 499 | 122 | 62 |
| Richo RDC-500 | 699 | 99 | 56 |
| Sony Cybershot DSC-F55 | 699 | 63 | 69 |
| Sony Mavica MVC-FD73 | 599 | 40 | 186 |
| Sony Mavica MVC-FD88 | 999 | 40 | 88 |
| Toshiba PDR-M4 | 599 | 124 | 142 |

**a.** Compute the mean price.
**b.** Compute the mean maximum picture capacity.
**c.** Compute the mean battery life.
**d.** If you had to select one camera from this list, what camera would you choose? Explain.

## 3.2   MEASURES OF VARIABILITY

In addition to measures of location, it is often desirable to consider measures of variability, or dispersion. For example, suppose that you are a purchasing agent for a large manufacturing firm and that you regularly place orders with two different suppliers. After several months of operation, you find that the mean number of days required to fill orders is 10 days for both of the suppliers. The histograms summarizing the number of working days required to fill orders from the suppliers are shown in Figure 3.4. Although the mean number of days is 10 for both suppliers, do the two suppliers have the same degree of reliability in terms of making deliveries on schedule? Note the dispersion, or variability, in delivery times indicated by the histograms. Which supplier would you prefer?

For most firms, receiving materials and supplies on schedule is important. The seven- or eight-day deliveries shown for J. C. Clark Distributors might be viewed favorably; how-

**FIGURE 3.4**   HISTORICAL DATA SHOWING THE NUMBER OF DAYS REQUIRED TO FILL ORDERS

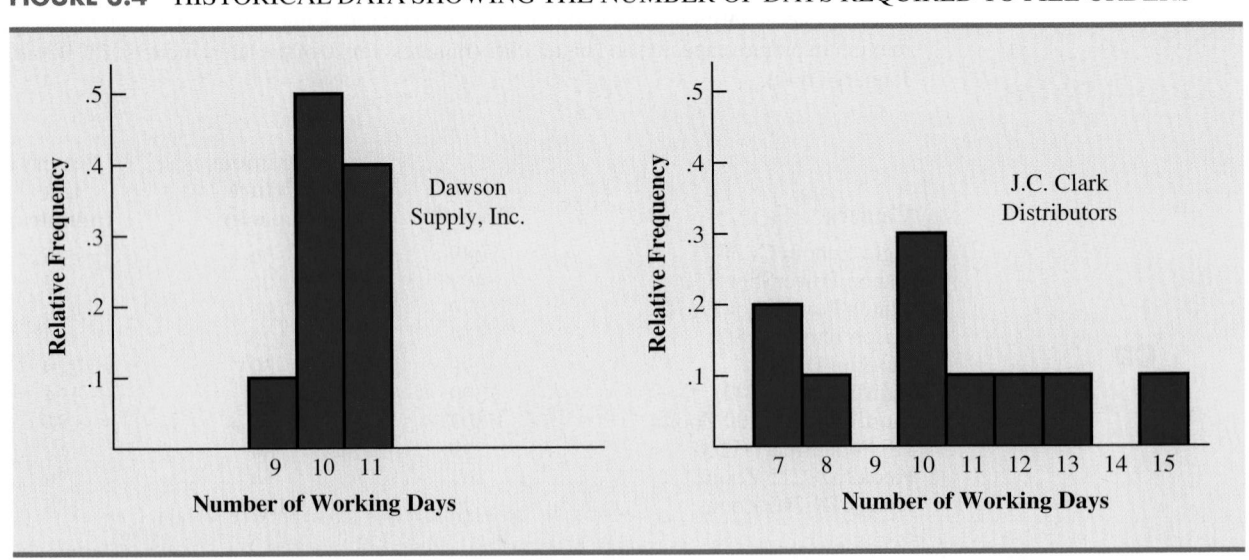

ever, a few of the slow 13- to 15-day deliveries could be disastrous in terms of keeping a workforce busy and production on schedule. This example illustrates a situation in which the variability in the delivery times may be an overriding consideration in selecting a supplier. For most purchasing agents, the lower variability shown for Dawson Supply, Inc., would make Dawson the preferred supplier.

We turn now to a discussion of some commonly used measures of variability

## Range

The simplest measure of variability is the **range.**

> **Range**
>
> $$\text{Range} = \text{Largest Value} - \text{Smallest Value}$$

*The range is easy to compute, but it is sensitive to just two data values: the largest and smallest.*

Let us refer to the data on starting salaries for business school graduates in Table 3.1. The largest starting salary is 3325 and the smallest is 2710. The range is $3325 - 2710 = 615$.

Although the range is the easiest of the measures of variability to compute, it is seldom used as the only measure. The reason is that the range is based on only two of the observations and thus is highly influenced by extreme values. Suppose one of the graduates had a starting salary of $10,000 per month. In this case, the range would be $10,000 - 2710 = 7290$ rather than 615. This large value for the range would not be especially descriptive of the variability in the data because 11 of the 12 starting salaries are closely grouped between 2710 and 3130.

## Interquartile Range

A measure of variability that overcomes the dependency on extreme values is the **interquartile range** (IQR). This measure of variability is simply the difference between the third quartile, $Q_3$, and the first quartile, $Q_1$. In other words, the interquartile range is the range for the middle 50% of the data.

> **Interquartile Range**
>
> $$\text{IQR} = Q_3 - Q_1 \tag{3.3}$$

For the data on monthly starting salaries, the quartiles are $Q_3 = 3000$ and $Q_1 = 2865$. Thus, the interquartile range is $3000 - 2865 = 135$.

## Variance

The **variance** is a measure of variability that utilizes all the data. The variance is based on the difference between the value of each observation ($x_i$) and the mean. The difference between each $x_i$ and the mean ($\bar{x}$ for a sample, $\mu$ for a population) is called a *deviation about the mean.* For a sample, a deviation about the mean is written ($x_i - \bar{x}$); for a population, it is written ($x_i - \mu$). In the computation of the variance, the deviations about the mean are *squared.*

If the data are for a population, the average of the squared deviations is called the *population variance.* The population variance is denoted by the Greek symbol $\sigma^2$. For a population of $N$ observations and with $\mu$ denoting the population mean, the definition of the population variance is as follows.

**Population Variance**

$$\sigma^2 = \frac{\Sigma(x_i - \mu)^2}{N}$$

(3.4)

In most statistical applications, the data being analyzed are for a sample. When we compute a sample variance, we are often interested in using it to estimate the population variance $\sigma^2$. Although a detailed explanation is beyond the scope of this text, it can be shown that if the sum of the squared deviations about the sample mean is divided by $n - 1$, and not $n$, the resulting sample variance provides an unbiased estimate of the population variance. For this reason, the *sample variance,* denoted by $s^2$, is defined as follows.

**Sample Variance**

$$s^2 = \frac{\Sigma(x_i - \bar{x})^2}{n - 1}$$

(3.5)

To illustrate the computation of the variance for a sample, we will use the data on class size for the sample of five college classes as presented in Section 3.1. A summary of the data, including the computation of the deviations about the mean and the squared deviations about the mean, is shown in Table 3.3. The sum of squared deviations about the mean is $\Sigma(x_i - \bar{x})^2 = 256$. Hence, with $n - 1 = 4$, the sample variance is

$$s^2 = \frac{\Sigma(x_i - \bar{x})^2}{n - 1} = \frac{256}{4} = 64$$

Before moving on, let us note that the units associated with the sample variance often cause confusion. Because the values being summed in the variance calculation, $(x_i - \bar{x})^2$, are squared, the units associated with the sample variance are also *squared*. For instance, the sample variance for the class size data is $s^2 = 64$ (students)$^2$. The squared units associ-

**TABLE 3.3** COMPUTATION OF DEVIATIONS AND SQUARED DEVIATIONS ABOUT THE MEAN FOR THE CLASS SIZE DATA

| Number of Students in Class $(x_i)$ | Mean Class Size $(\bar{x})$ | Deviation About the Mean $(x_i - \bar{x})$ | Squared Deviation About the Mean $(x_i - \bar{x})^2$ |
|---|---|---|---|
| 46 | 44 | 2 | 4 |
| 54 | 44 | 10 | 100 |
| 42 | 44 | −2 | 4 |
| 46 | 44 | 2 | 4 |
| 32 | 44 | −12 | 144 |
| | | 0 | 256 |
| | | $\Sigma(x_i - \bar{x})$ | $\Sigma(x_i - \bar{x})^2$ |

The variance is useful in comparing the variability of two or more variables.

ated with variance make it difficult to obtain an intuitive understanding and interpretation of the numerical value of the variance. We recommend that you think of the variance as a measure useful in comparing the amount of variability for two or more variables. In a comparison of the variables, the one with the larger variance has the most variability. Further interpretation of the value of the variance may not be necessary.

As another illustration of computing a sample variance, consider the starting salaries listed in Table 3.1 for the 12 business school graduates. In Section 3.1, we showed that the sample mean starting salary was 2940. A summary of the data, including the computation of the deviations about the mean and the squared deviations about the mean, is shown in Figure 3.5. The worksheet in the background shows the Excel formulas used to compute the results shown in the value worksheet in the foreground. The sum of the squared deviations about the mean is $\Sigma(x_i - \bar{x})^2 = 301,850$ (see cell E14). Hence, with $n - 1 = 11$, the sample variance is

$$s^2 = \frac{\Sigma(x_i - \bar{x})^2}{n - 1} = \frac{301,850}{11} = 27,440.91$$

**FIGURE 3.5**  EXCEL WORKSHEET USED TO COMPUTE THE DEVIATIONS AND SQUARED DEVIATIONS ABOUT THE MEAN FOR THE STARTING SALARIES

| | A | B | C | D | E | F |
|---|---|---|---|---|---|---|
| 1 | Graduate | Starting Salary | Sample Mean | Deviation about the Mean | Squared Deviation about the Mean | |
| 2 | 1 | 2850 | =AVERAGE($B$2:$B$13) | =B2-C2 | =D2^2 | |
| 3 | 2 | 2950 | =AVERAGE($B$2:$B$13) | =B3-C3 | =D3^2 | |
| 4 | 3 | 3050 | =AVERAGE($B$2:$B$13) | =B4-C4 | =D4^2 | |
| 5 | 4 | 2880 | =AVERAGE($B$2:$B$13) | =B5-C5 | =D5^2 | |
| 6 | 5 | 2755 | =AVERAGE($B$2:$B$13) | =B6-C6 | =D6^2 | |
| 7 | 6 | 2710 | =AVERAGE($B$2:$B$13) | =B7-C7 | =D7^2 | |
| 8 | 7 | 2890 | =AVERAGE($B$2:$B$13) | =B8-C8 | =D8^2 | |
| 9 | 8 | 3130 | =AVERAGE($B$2:$B$13) | =B9-C9 | =D9^2 | |
| 10 | 9 | 2940 | =AVERAGE($B$2:$B$13) | =B10-C10 | =D10^2 | |
| 11 | 10 | 3325 | =AVERAGE($B$2:$B$13) | =B11-C11 | =D11^2 | |
| 12 | 11 | 2920 | =AVERAGE($B$2:$B$13) | =B12-C12 | =D12^2 | |
| 13 | 12 | 2880 | =AVERAGE($B$2:$B$13) | =B13-C13 | =D13^2 | |
| 14 | | | | =SUM(D2:D13) | =SUM(E2:E13) | |
| 15 | | | | | | |

| | A | B | C | D | E | F |
|---|---|---|---|---|---|---|
| 1 | Graduate | Starting Salary | Sample Mean | Deviation about the Mean | Squared Deviation about the Mean | |
| 2 | 1 | 2850 | 2940 | -90 | 8100 | |
| 3 | 2 | 2950 | 2940 | 10 | 100 | |
| 4 | 3 | 3050 | 2940 | 110 | 12100 | |
| 5 | 4 | 2880 | 2940 | -60 | 3600 | |
| 6 | 5 | 2755 | 2940 | -185 | 34225 | |
| 7 | 6 | 2710 | 2940 | -230 | 52900 | |
| 8 | 7 | 2890 | 2940 | -50 | 2500 | |
| 9 | 8 | 3130 | 2940 | 190 | 36100 | |
| 10 | 9 | 2940 | 2940 | 0 | 0 | |
| 11 | 10 | 3325 | 2940 | 385 | 148225 | |
| 12 | 11 | 2920 | 2940 | -20 | 400 | |
| 13 | 12 | 2880 | 2940 | -60 | 3600 | |
| 14 | | | | 0 | 301850 | |
| 15 | | | | | | |

Using the definition to compute the sample variance helps us to realize that the variance measures variability as a function of the squared deviations about the mean.

    The method we used for computing the sample variance for starting salaries is the same method that we used to compute the sample variance for the class size data (see Table 3.3). We used the definition as given by equation (3.5). The only difference is that this time we use an Excel worksheet to ease the computational burden. Later we will see that Excel provides a function for obtaining the sample variance directly without entering all the formulas needed to compute the sum of the squared deviations about the mean.

    Note that in Table 3.3 and Figure 3.5 we show both the sum of the deviations about the mean and the sum of the squared deviations about the mean. For any data set, the sum of the deviations about the mean will *always equal zero*. Note that in Table 3.3 and Figure 3.5, $\Sigma(x_i - \bar{x}) = 0$. The positive deviations and negative deviations cancel each other, causing the sum of the deviations about the mean to equal zero.

## Standard Deviation

The **standard deviation** is defined to be the positive square root of the variance. Following the notation we adopted for a sample variance and a population variance, we use $s$ to denote the sample standard deviation and $\sigma$ to denote the population standard deviation. The standard deviation is derived from the variance in the following way.

---

**Standard Deviation**

$$\text{Sample Standard Deviation} = s = \sqrt{s^2} \tag{3.6}$$

$$\text{Population Standard Deviation} = \sigma = \sqrt{\sigma^2} \tag{3.7}$$

---

Recall that the sample variance for the sample of class sizes in five college classes is $s^2 = 64$. Thus the sample standard deviation is $s = \sqrt{64} = 8$. For the data on starting salaries, the sample standard deviation is $s = \sqrt{27,440.91} = 165.65$.

The standard deviation is easier to interpret than the variance because the standard deviation is measured in the same units as the data.

    What is gained by converting the variance to its corresponding standard deviation? Recall that the units associated with the variance are squared. For example, the sample variance for the starting salary data of business school graduates is $s^2 = 27,440.91$ (dollars)$^2$. Because the standard deviation is the square root of the variance, the units of the variance, dollars squared, are converted to dollars in the standard deviation. Thus, the standard deviation of the starting salary data is $165.65. In other words, the standard deviation is measured in the same units as the original data. For this reason the standard deviation is more easily compared to the mean and other statistics that are measured in the same units as the original data.

## Using Excel to Compute the Sample Variance and Sample Standard Deviation

Excel provides functions for computing the sample variance and sample standard deviation, which we will illustrate using the starting salary data. Refer to Figure 3.6 as we describe the steps involved. Figure 3.6 is an extension of Figure 3.1 where we showed how to use Excel functions to compute the mean, median, and mode. The formula worksheet is in the background; the value worksheet is in the foreground.

**Enter Data:**    Labels and the starting salary data are entered into cells A1:B13 of the worksheet.

**Enter Functions and Formulas:**    The Excel AVERAGE, MEDIAN, and MODE functions are entered into cells E1:E3 as described earlier. Excel's VAR function can be used to compute the sample variance by entering the following formula into cell E4:

$$=\text{VAR(B2:B13)}$$

**FIGURE 3.6**   EXCEL WORKSHEET USED TO COMPUTE THE SAMPLE VARIANCE AND THE SAMPLE STANDARD DEVIATION FOR STARTING SALARIES

Similarly, the formula =STDEV(B2:B13) is entered into cell E5 to compute the sample standard deviation. Appropriate labels are entered into cells D1:D5 to identify the output.

The value worksheet, in the foreground, shows the values computed using the Excel functions. Note that the sample variance and sample standard deviation are the same as we computed earlier using the definitions.

## Coefficient of Variation

The coefficient of variation is a relative measure of variability; it measures the standard deviation relative to the mean.

In some situations we may be interested in a descriptive statistic that indicates how large the standard deviation is relative to the mean. This measure is called the **coefficient of variation** and is computed as follows.

**Coefficient of Variation**

$$\frac{\text{Standard Deviation}}{\text{Mean}} \times 100 \qquad \text{(3.8)}$$

For the class size data, we found a sample mean of 44 and a sample standard deviation of 8. The coefficient of variation is (8/44) × 100 = 18.2. In words, the coefficient of variation tells us that the sample standard deviation is 18.2% of the value of the sample mean. For the starting salary data with a sample mean of 2940 and a sample standard deviation of 165.65, the coefficient of variation, (165.65/2940) × 100 = 5.6, tells us the sample standard deviation is only 5.6% of the value of the sample mean. In general, the coefficient of variation is a useful statistic for comparing the variability of variables that have different standard deviations and different means.

## Using Excel's Descriptive Statistics Tool

As we have seen, Excel provides statistical functions to compute descriptive statistics for a data set. These functions can be used to compute one statistic at a time (e.g., mean, variance, etc.). Excel also provides a variety of Data Analysis Tools. One of these, called Descriptive Statistics, allows the user to compute a variety of descriptive statistics at once. We show here how it can be used to compute descriptive statistics for the starting salary data in Table 3.1. Refer to Figures 3.7 and 3.8 as we describe the steps involved.

**Enter Data:**   Labels and the starting salary data are entered into cells A1:B13 of the worksheet.

**Enter Functions and Formulas:**   No functions and formulas are needed.

**Apply Analysis Tools:**   The following steps describe how to use Excel's descriptive statistics tool for these data:

> **Step 1.** Select the **Tools** pull-down menu
> **Step 2.** Choose the **Data Analysis** option
> **Step 3.** Choose **Descriptive Statistics** from the list of Analysis Tools
> **Step 4.** When the **Descriptive Statistics** dialog box appears (see Figure 3.8):
>> Enter B1:B13 in the **Input Range** box
>> Select **Grouped By Columns**
>> Select **Labels in First Row**
>> Select **Output Range**
>> Enter D1 in the **Output Range** box (to identify the upper left corner of the section of the worksheet where the descriptive statistics will appear)
>> Select **Summary Statistics**
>> Click **OK**

Cells D1:E15 of Figure 3.7 show the descriptive statistics provided by Excel. A blue screen is used to highlight the results. The boldfaced entries are the descriptive statistics we have covered in this chapter. The descriptive statistics that are not boldfaced are either covered subsequently in the text or discussed in more advanced texts.

**FIGURE 3.7**   USING EXCEL TO COMPUTE DESCRIPTIVE STATISTICS FOR STARTING SALARIES

| | A | B | C | D | E | F |
|---|---|---|---|---|---|---|
| 1 | Graduate | Starting Salary | | Starting Salary | | |
| 2 | 1 | 2850 | | | | |
| 3 | 2 | 2950 | | Mean | 2940 | |
| 4 | 3 | 3050 | | Standard Error | 47.8199 | |
| 5 | 4 | 2880 | | Median | 2905 | |
| 6 | 5 | 2755 | | Mode | 2880 | |
| 7 | 6 | 2710 | | Standard Deviation | 165.653 | |
| 8 | 7 | 2890 | | Sample Variance | 27440.91 | |
| 9 | 8 | 3130 | | Kurtosis | 1.718884 | |
| 10 | 9 | 2940 | | Skewness | 1.091109 | |
| 11 | 10 | 3325 | | Range | 615 | |
| 12 | 11 | 2920 | | Minimum | 2710 | |
| 13 | 12 | 2880 | | Maximum | 3325 | |
| 14 | | | | Sum | 35280 | |
| 15 | | | | Count | 12 | |
| 16 | | | | | | |

**FIGURE 3.8**   DESCRIPTIVE STATISTICS DIALOG BOX FOR THE STARTING
SALARY DATA

---

### NOTES AND COMMENTS

The standard deviation is a commonly used measure of the risk associated with investing in stock and stock funds (*Business Week,* January 17, 2000). It provides a measure of how monthly returns fluctuate around the long-run average return.

---

## EXERCISES

## Methods

**13.**  Consider a sample with data values of 10, 20, 12, 17, and 16. Compute the range and interquartile range.

**14.**  Consider a sample with data values of 10, 20, 12, 17, and 16. Compute the variance and standard deviation.

**15.**  Consider a sample with data values of 27, 25, 20, 15, 30, 34, 28, and 25. Compute the range, interquartile range, variance, and standard deviation.

## Applications

**16.**  A bowler's scores for six games were 182, 168, 184, 190, 170, and 174. Using these data as a sample, compute the following descriptive statistics.
  **a.**  Range
  **b.**  Variance
  **c.**  Standard deviation
  **d.**  Coefficient of variation

17. *PC World* provided ratings for 15 notebook PCs (*PC World*, February 2000). A 100-point scale was used to provide an overall rating for each notebook. A score in the 90s is exceptional, while one in the 70s is above average. The overall ratings for the 15 notebooks are shown here.

**CD** file

Notebook

| Notebook | Overall Rating |
|---|---|
| AMS Tech Roadster 15CTA380 | 67 |
| Compaq Armada M700 | 78 |
| Compaq Prosignia Notebook 150 | 79 |
| Dell Inspiron 3700 C466GT | 80 |
| Dell Inspiron 7500 R500VT | 84 |
| Dell Latitude Cpi A366XT | 76 |
| Enpower ENP-313 Pro | 77 |
| Gateway Solo 9300LS | 92 |
| HP Pavillion Notebook PC | 83 |
| IBM ThinkPad I Series 1480 | 78 |
| Micro Express NP7400 | 77 |
| Micron TransPort NX PII-400 | 78 |
| NEC Versa SX | 78 |
| Sceptre Soundx 5200 | 73 |
| Sony VAIO PCG-F340 | 77 |

Compute the range, interquartile range, variance, and standard deviation for this sample of notebook PCs.

18. The Hawaii Visitors Bureau collects data on the number of visitors to the islands. The following data are a representative sample of visitors (in thousands) for several days in November.

*From the mainland, Canada, and Europe:*

| 108.70 | 112.25 | 94.01 | 144.03 | 162.44 | 161.61 | 76.20 |
|---|---|---|---|---|---|---|
| 102.11 | 110.87 | 79.36 | 129.04 | 95.16 | 114.16 | 121.88 |

*From Asia and the Pacific:*

| 29.89 | 41.13 | 40.67 | 40.41 | 43.07 | 24.86 |
|---|---|---|---|---|---|
| 31.61 | 21.60 | 27.34 | 64.57 | 32.98 | 41.31 |

a. Compute the mean and median number of daily visitors from the two sources.
b. Compute the range, the standard deviation, and the coefficient of variation for the two sources of visitors.
c. What comparisons can you make between the numbers of visitors from the two sources?

19. The *Los Angeles Times* regularly reports the air quality index for various areas of Southern California. A sample of air quality index values for Pomona provided the following data: 28, 42, 58, 48, 45, 55, 60, 49, and 50.
a. Compute the range and interquartile range.
b. Compute the sample variance and sample standard deviation.
c. A sample of air quality index readings for Anaheim provided a sample mean of 48.5, a sample variance of 136, and a sample standard deviation of 11.66. What comparisons can you make between the air quality in Pomona and that in Anaheim on the basis of these descriptive statistics?

20. Assume that the following data were used to construct the histograms of the number of days required to fill orders for Dawson Supply, Inc., and J. C. Clark Distributors (see Figure 3.4).

| *Dawson Supply Days for Delivery:* | 11 | 10 | 9 | 10 | 11 | 11 | 10 | 11 | 10 | 10 |
|---|---|---|---|---|---|---|---|---|---|---|
| *Clark Distributors Days for Delivery:* | 8 | 10 | 13 | 7 | 10 | 11 | 10 | 7 | 15 | 12 |

Use the range and standard deviation to support the previous observation that Dawson Supply provides the more consistent and reliable delivery times.

**21.** Police records show the following numbers of daily crime reports for a sample of days during the winter months and a sample of days during the summer months.

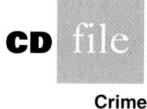

**Crime**

| Winter | Summer |
|--------|--------|
| 18 | 28 |
| 20 | 18 |
| 15 | 24 |
| 16 | 32 |
| 21 | 18 |
| 20 | 29 |
| 12 | 23 |
| 16 | 38 |
| 19 | 28 |
| 20 | 18 |

   **a.**  Compute the range and interquartile range for each period.
   **b.**  Compute the variance and standard deviation for each period.
   **c.**  Compute the coefficient of variation for each period.
   **d.**  Compare the variability of the two periods.

**Discount**

**22.** The American Association of Individual Investors conducts an annual survey of discount brokers (*AAII Journal,* January 2000). The commissions charged by a sample of 20 discount brokers for two types of trades, 500 shares at $50 per share and 1000 shares at $5 per share, are shown in Table 3.2.
   **a.**  Compute the range and interquartile range for each type of trade.
   **b.**  Compute the variance and standard deviation for each type of trade.
   **c.**  Compute the coefficient of variation for each type of trade.
   **d.**  Compare the variability of cost for the two types of trades.

**23.** A production department uses a sampling procedure to test the quality of newly produced items. The department employs the following decision rule at an inspection station: If a sample of 14 items has a variance of more than .005, the production line must be shut down for repairs. Suppose the following data have just been collected:

| | | | | | | |
|------|------|------|------|------|------|------|
| 3.43 | 3.45 | 3.43 | 3.48 | 3.52 | 3.50 | 3.39 |
| 3.48 | 3.41 | 3.38 | 3.49 | 3.45 | 3.51 | 3.50 |

Should the production line be shut down? Why or why not?

**24.** The following times were recorded by the quarter-mile and mile runners of a university track team (times are in minutes).

| *Quarter-mile Times:* | .92 | .98 | 1.04 | .90 | .99 |
|-----------------------|------|------|------|------|------|
| *Mile Times:* | 4.52 | 4.35 | 4.60 | 4.70 | 4.50 |

After viewing this sample of running times, one of the coaches commented that the quarter-milers turned in the more consistent times. Use the standard deviation and the coefficient of variation to summarize the variability in the data. Does the use of the coefficient of variation indicate that the coach's statement should be qualified?

## 3.3    MEASURES OF RELATIVE LOCATION AND DETECTING OUTLIERS

We have described several measures of location and variability for data. The mean is the most widely used measure of location, whereas the standard deviation and variance are the most widely used measures of variability. Using the mean and the standard deviation together, we also can learn about the relative location of observations in a data set.

### z-Scores

By using both the mean and standard deviation, we can determine the relative location of any observation. Suppose we have a sample of $n$ observations, with the values denoted by $x_1$, $x_2, \ldots, x_n$. In addition, assume that the sample mean, $\bar{x}$, and the sample standard deviation, $s$, have been computed. Associated with each value, $x_i$, is another value called its z-score. Equation (3.9) shows how the z-score is computed for each $x_i$.

Excel's STANDARDIZE function can be used to compute the z-score. But it is just as easy to enter a cell formula to compute $z_i$.

**z-Score**

$$z_i = \frac{x_i - \bar{x}}{s} \qquad (3.9)$$

where

$$z_i = \text{the z-score for } x_i$$
$$\bar{x} = \text{the sample mean}$$
$$s = \text{the sample standard deviation}$$

The z-score is often called the *standardized value*. The z-score, $z_i$, can be interpreted as the *number of standard deviations $x_i$ is from the mean $\bar{x}$*. For example, $z_1 = 1.2$ would indicate that $x_1$ is 1.2 standard deviations greater than the sample mean. Similarly, $z_2 = -.5$ would indicate that $x_2$ is .5, or 1/2, standard deviation less than the sample mean. A z-score greater than zero occurs for observations with a value greater than the mean, and a z-score less than zero occurs for observations with a value less than the mean. A z-score of zero indicates that the value of the observation is equal to the mean.

The z-score for any observation can be interpreted as a measure of the relative location of the observation in a data set. Thus, observations in two different data sets with the same z-score can be said to have the same relative location in terms of being the same number of standard deviations from the mean.

The z-scores for the class size data are computed in Table 3.4. Recall that the sample mean, $\bar{x} = 44$, and sample standard deviation, $s = 8$, have been computed previously. The z-score of $-1.50$ for the fifth observation shows it is farthest from the mean; it is 1.50 standard deviations below the mean.

**TABLE 3.4** z-SCORES FOR THE CLASS SIZE DATA

The calculations in this table can be easily made in an Excel worksheet.

| Number of Students in Class ($x_i$) | Deviation About the Mean ($x_i - \bar{x}$) | z-score $\left(\dfrac{x_i - \bar{x}}{s}\right)$ | |
|---|---|---|---|
| 46 | 2 | 2/8 = | .25 |
| 54 | 10 | 10/8 = | 1.25 |
| 42 | -2 | -2/8 = | -.25 |
| 46 | 2 | 2/8 = | .25 |
| 32 | -12 | -12/8 = | -1.50 |

## Chebyshev's Theorem

Chebyshev's theorem enables us to make statements about the proportion of data values that must be within a specified number of standard deviations of the mean.

### Chebyshev's Theorem

At least $(1 - 1/z^2)$ of the data values must be within $z$ standard deviations of the mean, where $z$ is any value greater than 1.

Some of the implications of this theorem, with $z = 2, 3,$ and 4 standard deviations, follow.

- At least .75, or 75%, of the data values must be within $z = 2$ standard deviations of the mean.
- At least .89, or 89%, of the data values must be within $z = 3$ standard deviations of the mean.
- At least .94, or 94%, of the data values must be within $z = 4$ standard deviations of the mean.

For an example using Chebyshev's theorem, suppose that the midterm test scores for 100 students in a college business statistics course had a mean of 70 and a standard deviation of 5. How many students had test scores between 60 and 80? How many students had test scores between 58 and 82?

For the test scores between 60 and 80, we note that 60 is two standard deviations below the mean and 80 is two standard deviations above the mean. Using Chebyshev's theorem, we see that at least .75, or at least 75%, of the observations must have values within two standard deviations of the mean. Thus, at least 75% of the students must have scored between 60 and 80.

Chebyshev's theorem requires $z > 1$; but $z$ need not be an integer.

For the test scores between 58 and 82, we see that $(58 - 70)/5 = -2.4$ indicates 58 is 2.4 standard deviations below the mean and that $(82 - 70)/5 = +2.4$ indicates 82 is 2.4 standard deviations above the mean. Applying Chebyshev's theorem with $z = 2.4$, we have

$$\left(1 - \frac{1}{z^2}\right) = \left[1 - \frac{1}{(2.4)^2}\right] = .826$$

At least 82.6% of the students must have test scores between 58 and 82.

## Empirical Rule

The empirical rule is based on the normal probability distribution, which will be introduced in Chapter 6. The normal distribution is used extensively throughout the text.

One of the advantages of Chebyshev's theorem is that it applies to any data set regardless of the shape of the distribution of the data. In practical applications, however, it has been found that many data sets have a mound-shaped or bell-shaped distribution like the one shown in Figure 3.9. When the data are believed to approximate this distribution, the **empirical rule** can be used to determine the percentage of data values that must be within a specified number of standard deviations of the mean.

### Empirical Rule

For data having a bell-shaped distribution:

- Approximately 68% of the data values will be within one standard deviation of the mean.
- Approximately 95% of the data values will be within two standard deviations of the mean.
- Almost all of the data values will be within three standard deviations of the mean.

**FIGURE 3.9**     A MOUND-SHAPED OR BELL-SHAPED DISTRIBUTION

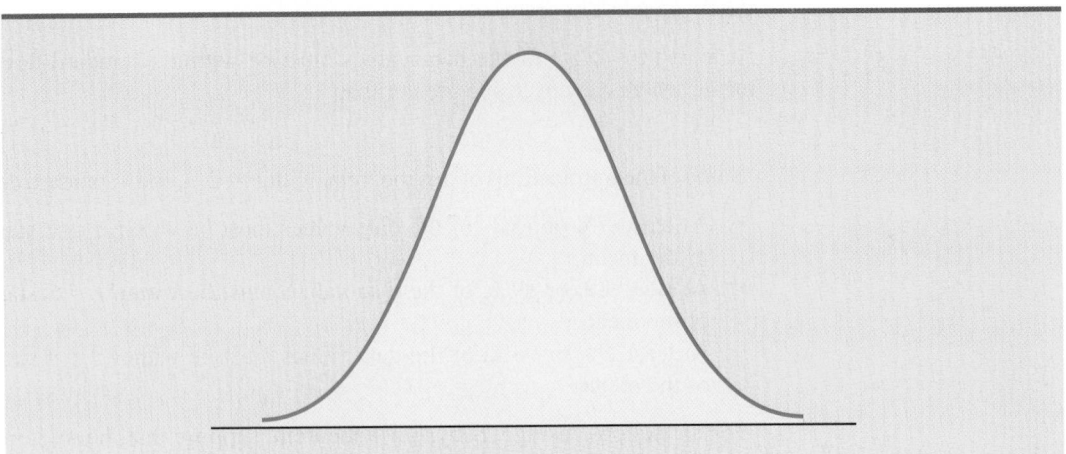

For example, liquid detergent cartons are filled automatically on a production line. Filling weights frequently have a bell-shaped distribution. If the mean filling weight is 16 ounces and the standard deviation is .25 ounces, we can use the empirical rule to draw the following conclusions.

- Approximately 68% of the filled cartons will have weights between 15.75 and 16.25 ounces (that is, within one standard deviation of the mean).
- Approximately 95% of the filled cartons will have weights between 15.50 and 16.50 ounces (that is, within two standard deviations of the mean).
- Almost all filled cartons will have weights between 15.25 and 16.75 ounces (that is, within three standard deviations of the mean).

## Detecting Outliers

Sometimes a data set will have one or more observations with unusually large or unusually small values. Extreme values such as these are called **outliers.** Experienced statisticians take steps to identify outliers and then review each one carefully. An outlier may be a data value that has been incorrectly recorded. If so, it can be corrected before further analysis. An outlier may also be from an observation that was incorrectly included in the data set; if so, it can be removed. Finally, an outlier may be an unusual data value that has been recorded correctly and belongs in the data set. In such cases it should remain.

Standardized values ($z$-scores) can be used to identify outliers. Recall that the empirical rule allows us to conclude that for data with a bell-shaped distribution, almost all the data values will be within three standard deviations of the mean. Hence, in using $z$-scores to identify outliers, we recommend treating any data value with a $z$-score less than $-3$ or greater than $+3$ as an outlier. Such data values can then be reviewed for accuracy and to determine whether they belong in the data set.

Refer to the $z$-scores for the class size data in Table 3.4. The $z$-score of $-1.50$ shows the fifth class size is farthest from the mean. However, this standardized value is well within the $-3$ to $+3$ guideline for outliers. Thus, the $z$-scores do not indicate that outliers are present in the class size data.

*It is a good idea to check for outliers before making decisions based on data analysis. Errors are often made in recording data and entering it into the computer. Outliers should not necessarily be deleted, but their accuracy and appropriateness should be verified before further analysis.*

## NOTES AND COMMENTS

1. Chebyshev's theorem is applicable for any data set and can be used to state the minimum number of data values that will be within a certain number of standard deviations of the mean. If the data are known to be approximately bell-shaped, more can be said. For instance, the empirical rule allows us to say that *approximately* 95% of the data values will be within two standard deviations of the mean; Chebyshev's theorem allows us to conclude only that at least 75% of the data values will be in that interval.

2. Before analyzing a data set, statisticians usually make a variety of checks to ensure the validity of data. In a large study it is not uncommon for errors to be made in recording data values or in entering the values into a computer. Identifying outliers is one tool used to check the validity of data.

## EXERCISES

## Methods

**25.** Consider a sample with data values of 10, 20, 12, 17, and 16. Compute the $z$-score for each of the five observations.

**26.** Consider a sample with a mean of 500 and a standard deviation of 100. What are the $z$-scores for the following data values: 520, 650, 500, 450, and 280?

**27.** Consider a sample with a mean of 30 and a standard deviation of 5. Use Chebyshev's theorem to determine the percentage of the data within each of the following ranges.
   **a.**   20 to 40
   **b.**   15 to 45
   **c.**   22 to 38
   **d.**   18 to 42
   **e.**   12 to 48

**28.** Suppose the data have a bell-shaped distribution with a mean of 30 and a standard deviation of 5. Use the empirical rule to determine the percentage of data within each of the following ranges.
   **a.**   20 to 40
   **b.**   15 to 45
   **c.**   25 to 35

## Applications

**29.** The results of a national survey of 1154 adults showed that on average, adults sleep 6.9 hours per day during the workweek (2000 Omnibus Sleep in America Poll). Suppose that the standard deviation is 1.2 hours.
   **a.**   Use Chebyshev's theorem to calculate the percentage of individuals that sleeps between 4.5 and 9.3 hours per day.
   **b.**   Use Chebyshev's theorem to calculate the percentage of individuals that sleeps between 3.9 and 9.9 hours per day.
   **c.**   Assume that the number of hours of sleep is bell-shaped. Use the empirical rule to calculate the percentage of individuals that sleeps between 4.5 and 9.3 hours per day. How does this result compare to the value that you obtained using Chebyshev's theorem in part (a)?

30. According to Nielsen Media Research, kids aged 12 to 17 watched an average of 3 hours of television per day for the broadcast year that ended in August (*Barron's,* November 8, 1999). Suppose that the standard deviation is 1 hour and that the distribution of the time spent watching television has a bell-shaped distribution.
    a. What percentage of kids aged 12 to 17 watches television between 2 and 3 hours per day?
    b. What percentage of kids aged 12 to 17 watches television between 1 and 4 hours per day?
    c. What percentage of kids aged 12 to 17 watches television more than 4 hours per day?

31. Suppose that IQ scores have a bell-shaped distribution with a mean of 100 and a standard deviation of 15.
    a. What percentage of people should have an IQ score between 85 and 115?
    b. What percentage of people should have an IQ score between 70 and 130?
    c. What percentage of people should have an IQ score of more than 130?
    d. A person with an IQ score greater than 145 is considered a genius. Does the empirical rule support this statement? Explain.

32. The average labor cost for color TV repair in Chicago is $90.06 (*The Wall Street Journal,* January 2, 1998). Suppose the standard deviation is $20.00.
    a. What is the $z$-score for a repair job with a labor cost of $71.00?
    b. What is the $z$-score for a repair job with a labor cost of $168.00?
    c. Interpret the $z$-scores in parts (a) and (b). Comment on whether either should be considered an outlier.

33. Wageweb conducts surveys of salary data and presents summaries on its web site. Using salary data as of January 1, 2000, Wageweb reported that salaries of benefits managers ranged from $50,935 to $79,577 (Wageweb.com, April 12, 2000). Assume the following data are a sample of the annual salaries for 30 benefits managers (data are in thousands of dollars).

**WageWeb**

| 57.7 | 64.4 | 62.1 | 59.1 | 71.1 |
|------|------|------|------|------|
| 63.0 | 64.7 | 61.2 | 66.8 | 61.8 |
| 64.2 | 63.3 | 62.2 | 61.2 | 59.4 |
| 63.0 | 66.7 | 60.3 | 74.0 | 62.8 |
| 68.7 | 63.8 | 59.2 | 60.3 | 56.6 |
| 59.3 | 69.5 | 61.7 | 58.9 | 63.1 |

a. Compute the mean and standard deviation for the sample data.
b. Using the mean and standard deviation computed in part (a) as estimates of the mean and standard deviation of salary for the population of benefits managers, use Chebyshev's theorem to determine the percentage of benefits managers with an annual salary between $55,000 and $71,000.
c. Develop a histogram for the sample data. Does it appear reasonable to assume that the distribution of annual salary can be approximated by a bell-shaped distribution?
d. Assume that the distribution of annual salary is bell-shaped. Using the mean and standard deviation computed in part (a) as estimates of the mean and standard deviation of salary for the population of benefits managers, use the empirical rule to determine the percentage of benefits managers with an annual salary between $55,000 and $71,000. Compare your answer with the value computed in part (b).
e. Do the sample data contain any outliers?

34. A sample of 10 National Basketball Association (NBA) scores provided the following data (*USA Today,* April 14, 2000).

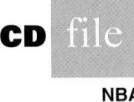

**NBA**

| Winning Team | Points Scored Winning Team | Losing Team | Points Scored Losing Team | Winning Margin |
|---|---|---|---|---|
| Philadelphia | 93 | Washington | 84 | 9 |
| Charlotte | 119 | Atlanta | 87 | 32 |
| Milwaukee | 101 | Cleveland | 100 | 1 |
| Indiana | 77 | Toronto | 73 | 4 |

| Winning Team | Points Scored Winning Team | Losing Team | Points Scored Losing Team | Winning Margin |
|---|---|---|---|---|
| Seattle | 110 | Minnesota | 83 | 27 |
| Boston | 95 | Orlando | 91 | 4 |
| Detroit | 90 | Miami | 73 | 17 |
| New York | 91 | New Jersey | 89 | 2 |
| Utah | 102 | L.A. Clippers | 93 | 9 |
| Phoenix | 122 | Vancouver | 116 | 6 |

**a.** Compute the mean and standard deviation for the points scored by the winning teams.
**b.** Assume that the points scored by the winning teams for all NBA games are bell-shaped. Using the mean and standard deviation computed in part (a) as estimates of the mean and standard deviation of the points scored for the population of all NBA games, estimate the percentage of all NBA games in which the winning team will score 100 or more points. Estimate the percentage of games in which the winning team will score more than 114 points.
**c.** Compute the mean and standard deviation for the winning margin. Do the winning margin data contain outliers? Explain.

**35.** *Consumer Review* posts reviews and ratings of a variety of products on the Internet. The following is a sample of 20 speaker systems and the ratings posted on January 2, 1998 (see *www.audioreview.com*). The ratings are on a scale of 1 to 5, with 5 being best.

**CD file**

**Speakers**

| Speaker | Rating | Speaker | Rating |
|---|---|---|---|
| Infinity Kappa 6.1 | 4.00 | ACI Sapphire III | 4.67 |
| Allison One | 4.12 | Bose 501 Series | 2.14 |
| Cambridge Ensemble II | 3.82 | DCM KX-212 | 4.09 |
| Dynaudio Contour 1.3 | 4.00 | Eosone RSF1000 | 4.17 |
| Hsu Rsch. HRSW12V | 4.56 | Joseph Audio RM7si | 4.88 |
| Legacy Audio Focus | 4.32 | Martin Logan Aerius | 4.26 |
| Mission 73li | 4.33 | Omni Audio SA 12.3 | 2.32 |
| PSB 400i | 4.50 | Polk Audio RT12 | 4.50 |
| Snell Acoustics D IV | 4.64 | Sunfire True Subwoofer | 4.17 |
| Thiel CS1.5 | 4.20 | Yamaha NS-A636 | 2.17 |

**a.** Compute the mean and the median.
**b.** Compute the first and third quartiles.
**c.** Compute the standard deviation.
**d.** What are the *z*-scores associated with Allison One and Omni Audio?
**e.** Do the data contain any outliers? Explain.

## 3.4    EXPLORATORY DATA ANALYSIS

In Chapter 2 we introduced the stem-and-leaf display as a technique of exploratory data analysis. Recall that exploratory data analysis enables us to use simple arithmetic and easy-to-draw pictures to summarize data. In this section we continue exploratory data analysis by considering five-number summaries and box plots.

### Five-Number Summary

In a **five-number summary,** the following five numbers are used to summarize the data.

**1.** Smallest value
**2.** First quartile ($Q_1$)
**3.** Median ($Q_2$)
**4.** Third quartile ($Q_3$)
**5.** Largest value

In Section 3.1, we showed how Excel can be used to put the starting salary data in ascending order.

The easiest way to develop a five-number summary is to first place the data in ascending order. Then it is easy to identify the smallest value, the three quartiles, and the largest value. The monthly starting salaries shown in Table 3.1 for a sample of 12 business school graduates are repeated here in ascending order.

2710   2755   2850 | 2880   2880   2890 | 2920   2940   2950 | 3050   3130   3325

$Q_1 = 2865$ ......... $Q_2 = 2905$ ......... $Q_3 = 3000$
.................... (Median)

The median of 2905 and the quartiles $Q_1 = 2865$ and $Q_3 = 3000$ were computed in Section 3.1. Reviewing the data shows a smallest value of 2710 and a largest value of 3325. Thus the five-number summary for the salary data is 2710, 2865, 2905, 3000, 3325. Approximately one-fourth, or 25%, of the observations are between adjacent numbers in a five-number summary.

## Box Plot

A box plot is a graphical summary of data that is based on a five-number summary. A key to the development of a box plot is the computation of the median and the quartiles, $Q_1$ and $Q_3$. The interquartile range, IQR $= Q_3 - Q_1$, is also used. Figure 3.10 is the box plot for the monthly starting salary data. The steps used to construct the box plot follow.

Box plots provide another way to identify outliers. But they do not necessarily identify the same values as those with a z-score less than $-3$ or greater than $+3$. Either, or both, procedures may be used.

1. A box is drawn with the ends of the box located at the first and third quartiles. For the salary data, $Q_1 = 2865$ and $Q_3 = 3000$. This box contains the middle 50% of the data.
2. A vertical line is drawn in the box at the location of the median (2905 for the salary data).
3. By using the interquartile range, IQR $= Q_3 - Q_1$, *limits* are located. The limits for the box plot are 1.5(IQR) below $Q_1$ and 1.5(IQR) above $Q_3$. For the salary data, IQR $= Q_3 - Q_1 = 3000 - 2865 = 135$. Thus, the limits are $2865 - 1.5(135) = 2662.5$ and $3000 + 1.5(135) = 3202.5$. Data outside these limits are considered *outliers*.

**FIGURE 3.10**   BOX PLOT OF THE STARTING SALARY DATA WITH LINES SHOWING THE LOWER AND UPPER LIMITS

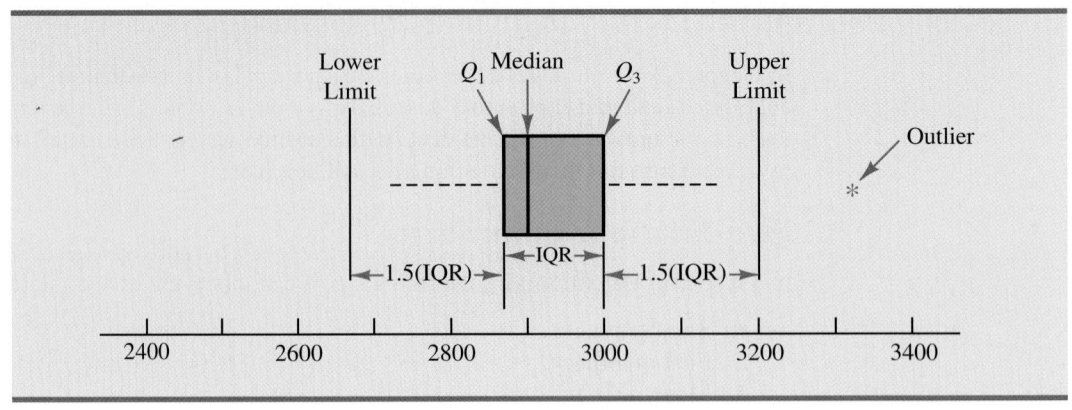

4. The dashed lines in Figure 3.10 are called *whiskers.* The whiskers are drawn from the ends of the box to the smallest and largest values *inside the limits* computed in step 3. Thus the whiskers end at salary values of 2710 and 3130.

5. Finally, the location of each outlier is shown with the symbol *. In Figure 3.10 we see one outlier, 3325.

In Figure 3.10 we have included lines showing the location of the upper and lower limits. These lines were drawn to show how the limits are computed and where they are located for the salary data. Although the limits are always computed, generally they are not drawn on the box plots. Figure 3.11 shows the usual appearance of a box plot for the salary data.

**FIGURE 3.11**   BOX PLOT OF THE STARTING SALARY DATA

### NOTES AND COMMENTS

1. When using a box plot, we may or may not identify the same outliers as the ones we select when using $z$-scores less than $-3$ and greater than $+3$. However, the objective of both approaches is simply to identify extreme data values that should be reviewed to ensure the validity of the data. Outliers identified by either procedure should be reviewed.

2. An advantage of the exploratory data analysis procedures is that they are easy to use; few numerical calculations are necessary. We simply sort the data values into ascending order and identify the five-number summary. The box plot can then be constructed. It is not necessary to compute the mean and the standard deviation for the data.

3. The basic Excel package does not contain a tool for constructing box plots. The Chart Wizard can be used for this purpose, but it is rather awkward and probably not worth the effort.

### EXERCISES

## Methods

36. Consider a sample with data values of 27, 25, 20, 15, 30, 34, 28, and 25. Provide the five-number summary for the data.

37. Show the box plot for the data in Exercise 36.

38. Show the five-number summary and the box plot for the following data: 5, 15, 18, 10, 8, 12, 16, 10, 6.

39. A data set has a first quartile of 42 and a third quartile of 50. Compute the lower and upper limits for the corresponding box plot. Should a data value of 65 be considered an outlier?

## Applications

**40.** A goal of management is to help their company earn as much as possible relative to the capital invested. One measure of success is return on equity—the ratio of net income to stockholders' equity. Shown here are return on equity percentages for 25 companies (*Standard & Poor's Stock Reports,* November 1997).

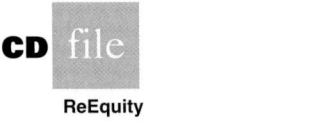

**CD** file

**ReEquity**

| | | | | |
|---|---|---|---|---|
| 9.0 | 19.6 | 22.9 | 41.6 | 11.4 |
| 15.8 | 52.7 | 17.3 | 12.3 | 5.1 |
| 17.3 | 31.1 | 9.6 | 8.6 | 11.2 |
| 12.8 | 12.2 | 14.5 | 9.2 | 16.6 |
| 5.0 | 30.3 | 14.7 | 19.2 | 6.2 |

    **a.** Provide a five-number summary.
    **b.** Compute the lower and upper limits.
    **c.** Do the data contain any outliers? How would this information be helpful to a financial analyst?
    **d.** Show a box plot.

**41.** Annual sales, in millions of dollars, for 21 pharmaceutical companies follow.

**SELF** test

| | | | | | |
|---|---|---|---|---|---|
| 8408 | 1374 | 1872 | 8879 | 2459 | 11413 |
| 608 | 14138 | 6452 | 1850 | 2818 | 1356 |
| 10498 | 7478 | 4019 | 4341 | 739 | 2127 |
| 3653 | 5794 | 8305 | | | |

    **a.** Provide a five-number summary.
    **b.** Compute the lower and upper limits.
    **c.** Do the data contain any outliers?
    **d.** Johnson & Johnson's sales are the largest in the list at $14,138 million. Suppose a data entry error (a transposition) had been made and the sales had been entered as $41,138 million. Would the method of detecting outliers in part (c) have identified the problem and allowed correction of the data entry error?
    **e.** Show a box plot.

**42.** Corporate share repurchase programs are often touted as a benefit for shareholders. But, Robert Gabele, director of insider research for First Call/Thomson Financial, has noted that many of these programs have been undertaken solely to acquire stock to use for incentive options for top managers. Across all companies, existing stock options in 1998 represented 6.2 percent of all common shares outstanding. The following data show the number of shares covered by option grants and the number of shares outstanding for 15 companies. *Blooomberg* identified these companies as the ones that would need to repurchase the highest percentage of outstanding shares to cover their option grants (*Bloomberg Personal Finance,* January/February 2000).

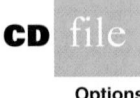

**CD** file

**Options**

| Company | Shares Covered by Option Grants (millions) | Common Shares Outstanding (millions) |
|---|---|---|
| Adobe Systems | 20.3 | 61.8 |
| Apple Computer | 52.7 | 160.9 |
| Applied Materials | 109.1 | 375.4 |
| Autodesk | 15.7 | 58.9 |
| Best Buy | 44.2 | 203.8 |
| Cendant | 183.3 | 718.1 |
| Dell Computer | 720.8 | 2540.9 |
| Fruit of the Loom | 14.2 | 66.9 |
| ITT Industries | 18.0 | 87.9 |
| Merrill Lynch | 89.9 | 365.5 |
| Novell | 120.2 | 335.0 |

| Company | Shares Covered by Option Grants (millions) | Common Shares Outstanding (millions) |
|---|---|---|
| Parametric Technology | 78.3 | 269.3 |
| Reebok International | 12.8 | 56.1 |
| Silicon Graphics | 52.6 | 188.8 |
| Toys R Us | 54.8 | 247.6 |

**a.** What are the mean and median number of shares covered by option grants?

**b.** What are the first and third quartiles for the number of shares covered by option grants?

**c.** Do the number of shares covered by option grants show any outliers? Show a box plot.

**d.** For each company, compute the percentage of shares outstanding that are covered by option grants. How does the mean of this percentage compare to the 1998 percentage of 6.2 reported for all companies?

**43.** The Highway Loss Data Institute's Injury and Collision Loss Experience report rates car models on the basis of the number of insurance claims filed after accidents. Index ratings near 100 are considered average. Lower ratings are better, indicating a safer car model. Shown are ratings for 20 midsize cars and 20 small cars.

| *Midsize cars:* | 81 | 91 | 93 | 127 | 68 | 81 | 60 | 51 | 58 | 75 |
|---|---|---|---|---|---|---|---|---|---|---|
| | 100 | 103 | 119 | 82 | 128 | 76 | 68 | 81 | 91 | 82 |
| *Small cars:* | 73 | 100 | 127 | 100 | 124 | 103 | 119 | 108 | 109 | 113 |
| | 108 | 118 | 103 | 120 | 102 | 122 | 96 | 133 | 80 | 140 |

Summarize the data for the midsize and small cars separately.

**a.** Provide a five-number summary for midsize cars and for small cars.

**b.** Show the box plots.

**c.** Make a statement about what your summaries indicate about the safety of midsize cars in comparison to small cars.

**44.** Birinyi Associates, Inc., conducted a survey of stock markets around the world to assess their performance during 1997. Table 3.5 summarizes the findings for a sample of 30 countries.

**a.** What are the mean and median percentage changes for these countries?

**b.** What are the first and third quartiles?

**c.** Do the data contain any outliers? Show a box plot.

**d.** What percentile would you report for the United States?

**TABLE 3.5**   1997 PERCENT CHANGE IN VALUE FOR WORLD STOCK MARKETS

| Country | Percent Change | Country | Percent Change |
|---|---|---|---|
| Argentina | 24.70 | India | 18.60 |
| Australia | 7.91 | Israel | 27.91 |
| Bahrain | 49.67 | Japan | −21.19 |
| Barbados | 48.29 | Lithuania | 16.82 |
| Bermuda | 51.92 | Mexico | 54.92 |
| Brazil | 44.84 | Namibia | 6.52 |
| Chile | 12.80 | Nigeria | −7.97 |
| Colombia | 69.60 | Panama | 59.40 |
| Croatia | −1.07 | Poland | 2.27 |
| Czech Republic | −3.25 | Russia | 125.89 |
| Ecuador | 5.37 | Slovenia | 18.71 |
| Estonia | 62.34 | Sri Lanka | 15.49 |
| Finland | 32.31 | Taiwan | 18.08 |
| Germany | 47.11 | Turkey | 254.45 |
| Greece | 59.19 | United States | 22.64 |

*Source: The Wall Street Journal, January 2, 1998.*

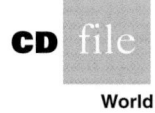

## 3.5     MEASURES OF ASSOCIATION BETWEEN TWO VARIABLES

Thus far we have examined numerical methods used to summarize the data for *one variable at a time*. Often a manager or decision maker is interested in the *relationship between two variables*. In this section we present covariance and correlation as descriptive measures of the relationship between two variables.

We begin by reconsidering the application concerning a stereo and sound equipment store in San Francisco as presented in Section 2.4. The store's manager is interested in investigating the relationship between the number of weekend television commercials shown and the sales at the store during the following week. Sample data with sales expressed in hundreds of dollars are provided in Table 3.6. It shows 10 observations ($n = 10$), one for each week. The scatter diagram in Figure 3.12 shows a positive relationship, with higher sales ($y$) associated with a greater number of commercials ($x$). In fact, the scatter diagram suggests that a straight line could be used as an approximation of the relationship. In the following discussion, we introduce **covariance** as a descriptive measure of the linear association between two variables.

**TABLE 3.6**     SAMPLE DATA FOR THE STEREO AND SOUND EQUIPMENT STORE

| Week | Number of Commercials $x$ | Sales Volume ($100s) $y$ |
|------|-----------------------------|----------------------------|
| 1 | 2 | 50 |
| 2 | 5 | 57 |
| 3 | 1 | 41 |
| 4 | 3 | 54 |
| 5 | 4 | 54 |
| 6 | 1 | 38 |
| 7 | 5 | 63 |
| 8 | 3 | 48 |
| 9 | 4 | 59 |
| 10 | 2 | 46 |

**FIGURE 3.12**     SCATTER DIAGRAM FOR THE STEREO AND SOUND EQUIPMENT STORE

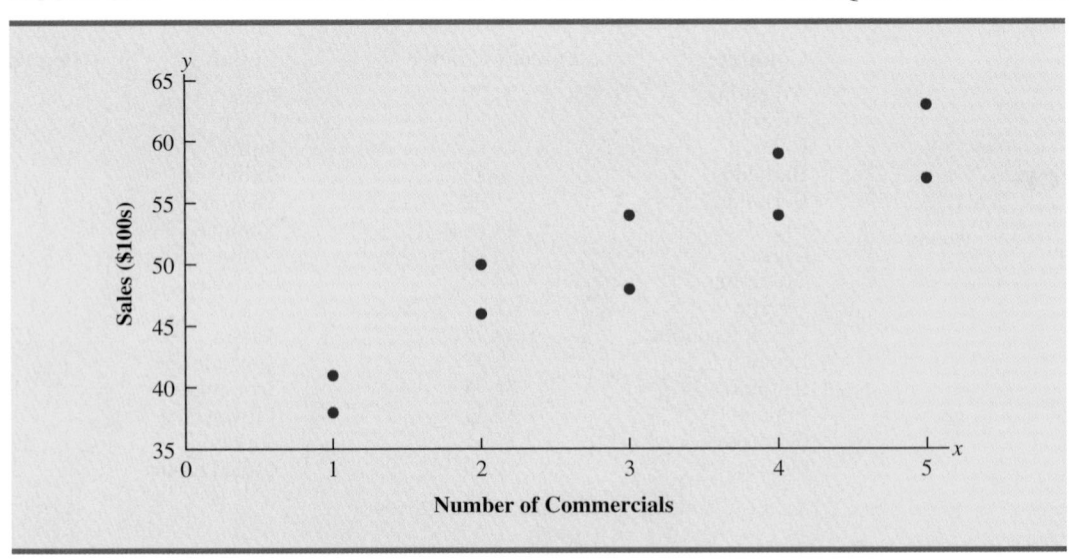

## Covariance

For a sample of size $n$ with the observations $(x_1, y_1)$, $(x_2, y_2)$, and so on, the sample covariance is defined as follows:

**Sample Covariance**

$$s_{xy} = \frac{\Sigma(x_i - \bar{x})(y_i - \bar{y})}{n - 1} \tag{3.10}$$

In this formula each $x_i$ is paired with a $y_i$. We then sum the products obtained by multiplying the deviation of each $x_i$ from its sample mean $\bar{x}$ by the deviation of the corresponding $y_i$ from its sample mean $\bar{y}$; this sum is then divided by $n - 1$.

To measure the strength of the linear relationship between the number of commercials $x$ and the sales volume $y$ in the stereo and sound equipment store problem, we use equation (3.10) to compute the sample covariance. The calculations in Table 3.7 show the computation of $\Sigma(x_i - \bar{x})(y_i - \bar{y})$. Note that $\bar{x} = 30/10 = 3$ and $\bar{y} = 510/10 = 51$. Using equation (3.10), we obtain a sample covariance of

$$s_{xy} = \frac{\Sigma(x_i - \bar{x})(y_i - \bar{y})}{n - 1} = \frac{99}{9} = 11$$

The formula for computing the covariance of a population of size $N$ is similar to equation (3.10), but we use different notation to indicate that we are working with the entire population.

**Population Covariance**

$$\sigma_{xy} = \frac{\Sigma(x_i - \mu_x)(y_i - \mu_y)}{N} \tag{3.11}$$

**TABLE 3.7** CALCULATIONS FOR THE SAMPLE COVARIANCE

The calculations in this table can be easily made in an Excel worksheet.

| | $x_i$ | $y_i$ | $x_i - \bar{x}$ | $y_i - \bar{y}$ | $(x_i - \bar{x})(y_i - \bar{y})$ |
|---|---|---|---|---|---|
| | 2 | 50 | −1 | −1 | 1 |
| | 5 | 57 | 2 | 6 | 12 |
| | 1 | 41 | −2 | −10 | 20 |
| | 3 | 54 | 0 | 3 | 0 |
| | 4 | 54 | 1 | 3 | 3 |
| | 1 | 38 | −2 | −13 | 26 |
| | 5 | 63 | 2 | 12 | 24 |
| | 3 | 48 | 0 | −3 | 0 |
| | 4 | 59 | 1 | 8 | 8 |
| | 2 | 46 | −1 | −5 | 5 |
| Totals | 30 | 510 | 0 | 0 | 99 |

$$s_{xy} = \frac{\Sigma(x_i - \bar{x})(y_i - \bar{y})}{n - 1} = \frac{99}{10 - 1} = 11$$

In equation (3.11) we use the notation $\mu_x$ for the population mean of the variable $x$ and $\mu_y$ for the population mean of the variable $y$. The population covariance $\sigma_{xy}$ is defined for a population of size $N$.

## Interpretation of the Covariance

To aid in the interpretation of the sample covariance, consider Figure 3.13. It is the same as the scatter diagram of Figure 3.12 with a vertical dashed line at $\bar{x} = 3$ and a horizontal dashed line at $\bar{y} = 51$. Four quadrants have been identified on the graph. Points in quadrant I correspond to $x_i$ greater than $\bar{x}$ and $y_i$ greater than $\bar{y}$, points in quadrant II correspond to $x_i$ less than $\bar{x}$ and $y_i$ greater than $\bar{y}$, and so on. Thus, the value of $(x_i - \bar{x})(y_i - \bar{y})$ must be positive for points in quadrant I, negative for points in quadrant II, positive for points in quadrant III, and negative for points in quadrant IV.

> The covariance is a measure of the linear association between two variables.

If the value of $s_{xy}$ is positive, the points that have had the greatest influence on $s_{xy}$ must be in quadrants I and III. Hence, a positive value for $s_{xy}$ is indicative of a positive linear association between $x$ and $y$; that is, as the value of $x$ increases, the value of $y$ increases. If the value of $s_{xy}$ is negative, however, the points that have had the greatest influence on $s_{xy}$ are in quadrants II and IV. Hence, a negative value for $s_{xy}$ is indicative of a negative linear association between $x$ and $y$; that is, as the value of $x$ increases, the value of $y$ decreases. Finally, if the points are evenly distributed across all four quadrants, the value of $s_{xy}$ will be close to zero, indicating no linear association between $x$ and $y$. Figure 3.14 shows the values of $s_{xy}$ that can be expected with three different types of scatter diagrams.

Referring again to Figure 3.13, we see that the scatter diagram for the stereo and sound equipment store follows the pattern in the top panel of Figure 3.14. As we should expect, the value of the sample covariance indicates a positive linear relationship with $s_{xy} = 11$.

From the preceding discussion, it might appear that a large positive value for the covariance is indicative of a strong positive linear relationship and that a large negative value is indicative of a strong negative linear relationship. However, one problem with using covariance as a measure of the strength of the linear relationship is that the value of the covariance depends on the units of measurement for $x$ and $y$. For example, suppose we are interested in the relationship between height $x$ and weight $y$ for individuals. Clearly the strength of the relationship should be the same whether we measure height in feet or inches. When height is mea-

**FIGURE 3.13** PARTITIONED SCATTER DIAGRAM FOR THE STEREO AND SOUND EQUIPMENT STORE

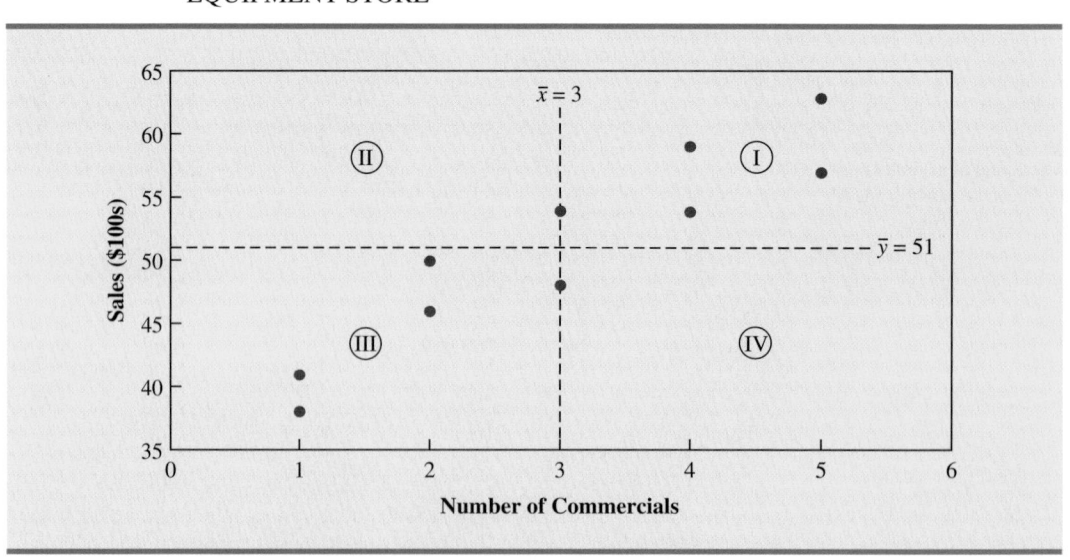

**FIGURE 3.14**   INTERPRETATION OF SAMPLE COVARIANCE

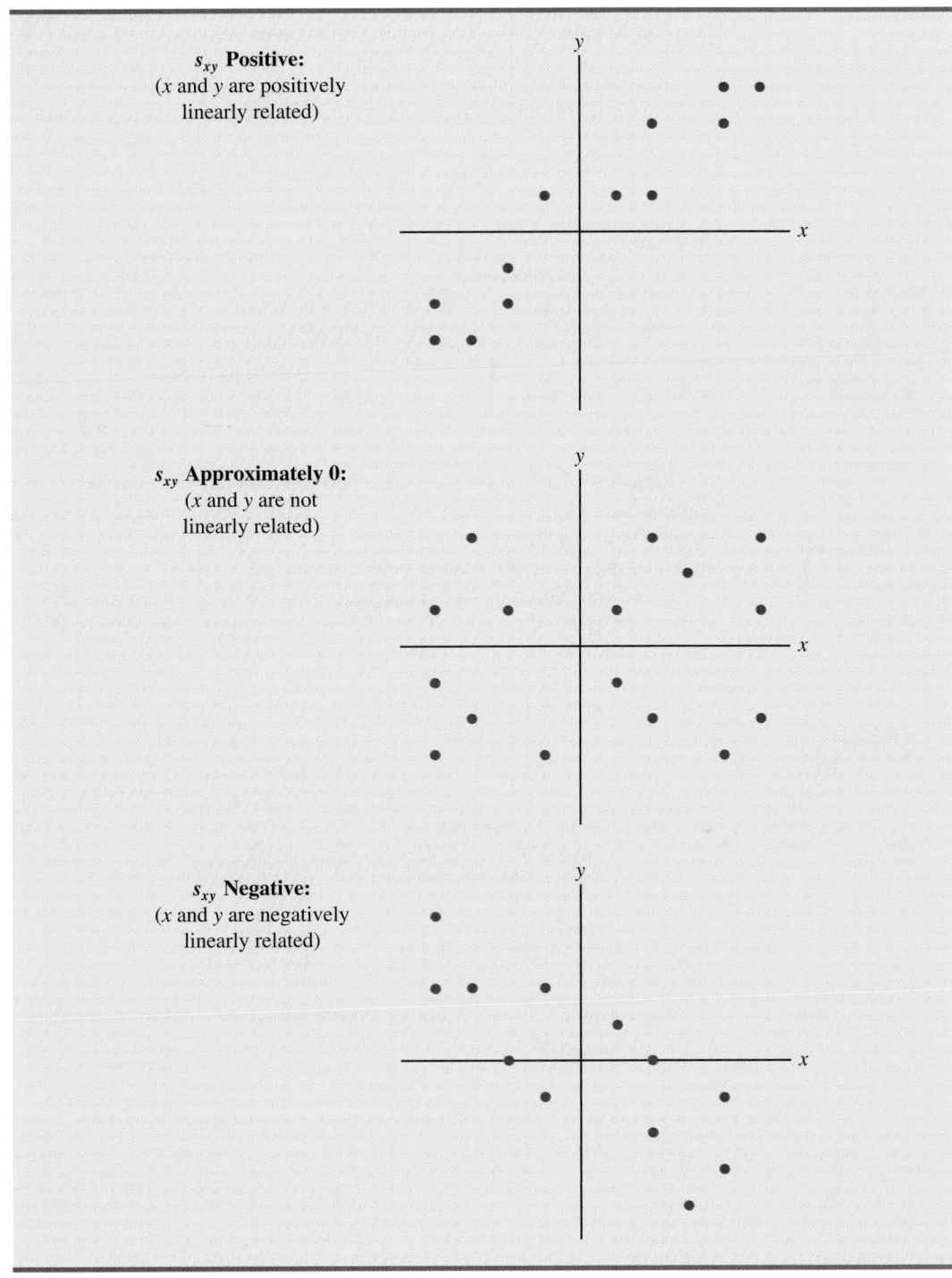

sured in inches, however, we have much larger numerical values for $(x_i - \bar{x})$ than we have when height is measured in feet. Thus, with height measured in inches, we would obtain a larger value for the numerator $\Sigma(x_i - \bar{x})(y_i - \bar{y})$ in equation (3.10)—and hence a larger covariance—when in fact the relationship does not change. A measure of the relationship between two variables that avoids this difficulty is the **correlation coefficient.**

## Correlation Coefficient

For sample data, the Pearson product moment correlation coefficient is defined as follows.

**Pearson Product Moment Correlation Coefficient: Sample Data**

$$r_{xy} = \frac{s_{xy}}{s_x s_y} \tag{3.12}$$

where

$$r_{xy} = \text{sample correlation coefficient}$$
$$s_{xy} = \text{sample covariance}$$
$$s_x = \text{sample standard deviation of } x$$
$$s_y = \text{sample standard deviation of } y$$

Equation (3.12) shows that the Pearson product moment correlation coefficient for sample data (commonly referred to more simply as the *sample correlation coefficient*) is computed by dividing the sample covariance by the product of the sample standard deviation of $x$ and the sample standard deviation of $y$.

Let us now compute the sample correlation coefficient for the stereo and sound equipment store. Using the data in Table 3.7, we can compute the sample standard deviations for the two variables.

$$s_x = \sqrt{\frac{\Sigma(x_i - \bar{x})^2}{n - 1}} = \sqrt{\frac{20}{9}} = 1.49$$

$$s_y = \sqrt{\frac{\Sigma(y_i - \bar{y})^2}{n - 1}} = \sqrt{\frac{566}{9}} = 7.93$$

Now, because $s_{xy} = 11$, we have a sample correlation coefficient of

$$r_{xy} = \frac{s_{xy}}{s_x s_y} = \frac{11}{(1.49)(7.93)} = +.93$$

The formula for computing the correlation coefficient for a population, denoted by the Greek letter $\rho_{xy}$ (rho, pronounced "row"), follows.

**Pearson Product Moment Correlation Coefficient: Population Data**

$$\rho_{xy} = \frac{\sigma_{xy}}{\sigma_x \sigma_y} \tag{3.13}$$

where

$$\rho_{xy} = \text{population correlation coefficient}$$
$$\sigma_{xy} = \text{population covariance}$$
$$\sigma_x = \text{population standard deviation for } x$$
$$\sigma_y = \text{population standard deviation for } y$$

The sample correlation coefficient $r_{xy}$ is an estimate of the population correlation coefficient $\rho_{xy}$.

## Interpretation of the Correlation Coefficient

First let us consider a simple example that illustrates the concept of a perfect positive linear relationship. The scatter diagram in Figure 3.15 depicts the relationship between $x$ and $y$ based on the following sample data.

| $x_i$ | $y_i$ |
|-------|-------|
| 5 | 10 |
| 10 | 30 |
| 15 | 50 |

The straight line drawn through each of the three points shows a perfect linear relationship between $x$ and $y$. In order to apply equation (3.12) to compute the sample correlation we must first compute $s_{xy}$, $s_x$, and $s_y$. Some of the necessary computations are contained in Table 3.8. Using the results in Table 3.8, we find

$$s_{xy} = \frac{\Sigma(x_i - \bar{x})(y_i - \bar{y})}{n - 1} = \frac{200}{2} = 100$$

$$s_x = \sqrt{\frac{\Sigma(x_i - \bar{x})^2}{n - 1}} = \sqrt{\frac{50}{2}} = 5$$

$$s_y = \sqrt{\frac{\Sigma(y_i - \bar{y})^2}{n - 1}} = \sqrt{\frac{800}{2}} = 20$$

$$r_{xy} = \frac{s_{xy}}{s_x s_y} = \frac{100}{5(20)} = 1$$

Thus, we see that the value of the sample correlation coefficient is 1.

**FIGURE 3.15**   SCATTER DIAGRAM DEPICTING A PERFECT POSITIVE LINEAR RELATIONSHIP

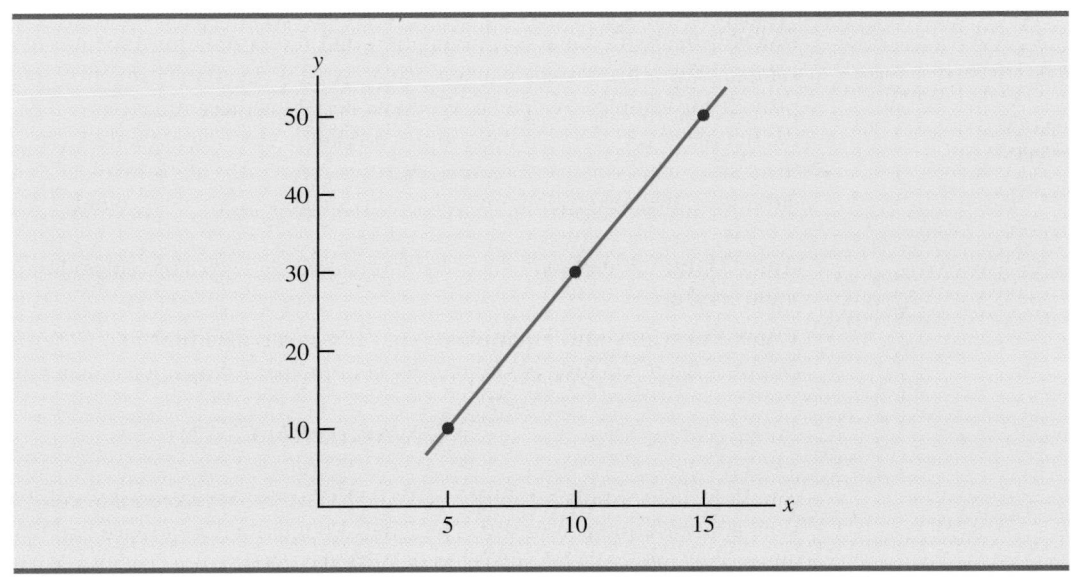

**TABLE 3.8**    COMPUTATIONS USED IN CALCULATING THE SAMPLE CORRELATION
COEFFICIENT

| | $x_i$ | $y_i$ | $x_i - \bar{x}$ | $(x_i - \bar{x})^2$ | $y_i - \bar{y}$ | $(y_i - \bar{y})^2$ | $(x_i - \bar{x})(y_i - \bar{y})$ |
|---|---|---|---|---|---|---|---|
| | 5 | 10 | −5 | 25 | −20 | 400 | 100 |
| | 10 | 30 | 0 | 0 | 0 | 0 | 0 |
| | 15 | 50 | 5 | 25 | 20 | 400 | 100 |
| Totals | 30 | 90 | 0 | 50 | 0 | 800 | 200 |

$$\bar{x} = 10 \quad \bar{y} = 30$$

In general, it can be shown that if all the points in a data set are on a straight line having positive slope, the value of the sample correlation coefficient is +1; that is, a sample correlation coefficient of +1 corresponds to a perfect positive linear relationship between $x$ and $y$. Moreover, if the points in the data set are on a straight line having negative slope, the value of the sample correlation coefficient is −1; that is, a sample correlation coefficient of −1 corresponds to a perfect negative linear relationship between $x$ and $y$.

> The correlation coefficient ranges from −1 to +1. Values close to −1 or +1 indicate a strong linear relationship. The closer the correlation is to zero the weaker the relationship.

Let us now suppose that a certain data set indicates a positive linear relationship between $x$ and $y$ but that the relationship is not perfect. The value of $r_{xy}$ will be less than 1, indicating that the points in the scatter diagram are not all on a straight line. As the points deviate more and more from a perfect positive linear relationship, the value of $r_{xy}$ becomes smaller and smaller. A value of $r_{xy}$ equal to zero indicates no linear relationship between $x$ and $y$, and values of $r_{xy}$ near zero indicate a weak linear relationship.

For the data involving the stereo and sound equipment store, recall that $r_{xy} = +.93$. Therefore, we conclude that a strong positive linear relationship occurs between the number of commercials and sales. More specifically, an increase in the number of commercials is associated with an increase in sales.

## Using Excel to Compute the Covariance and Correlation Coefficient

Excel provides functions that can be used to compute the covariance and correlation coefficient. But, you must be careful when using these functions because the covariance function treats the data as a population and the correlation function treats the data as a sample. Thus, the result obtained using Excel's covariance function must be adjusted to provide the sample covariance. We show here how these functions can be used to compute the sample covariance and the sample correlation coefficient for the stereo and sound equipment store data. Refer to Figure 3.16 as we present the steps involved. The formula worksheet is in the background; the value worksheet is in the foreground.

> Excel's COVAR function is designed for a population and Excel's CORREL function is designed for a sample.

**Enter Data:**   Labels and data on commercials and sales are entered into cells A1:C11 of the worksheet.

**Enter Functions and Formulas:**   Excel's covariance function, COVAR, can be used to compute the population covariance by entering the following formula into cell F1:

$$=\text{COVAR(B2:B11,C2:C11)}$$

Similarly, the formula =CORREL(B2:B11,C2:C11) is entered into cell F2 to compute the sample correlation coefficient. The labels Population Covariance and Sample Correlation are entered into cells E1 and E2 to identify the output.

**FIGURE 3.16**    EXCEL WORKSHEET USED TO COMPUTE THE COVARIANCE
AND CORRELATION COEFFICIENT

| | A | B | C | D | E | F | G |
|---|---|---|---|---|---|---|---|
| 1 | Week | Commercials | Sales | | Population Covariance | =COVAR(B2:B11,C2:C11) | |
| 2 | 1 | 2 | 50 | | Sample Correlation | =CORREL(B2:B11,C2:C11) | |
| 3 | 2 | 5 | 57 | | | | |
| 4 | 3 | 1 | 41 | | | | |
| 5 | 4 | 3 | 54 | | | | |
| 6 | 5 | 4 | 54 | | | | |
| 7 | 6 | 1 | 38 | | | | |
| 8 | 7 | 5 | 63 | | | | |
| 9 | 8 | 3 | 48 | | | | |
| 10 | 9 | 4 | 59 | | | | |
| 11 | 10 | 2 | 46 | | | | |
| 12 | | | | | | | |

| | A | B | C | D | E | F | G |
|---|---|---|---|---|---|---|---|
| 1 | Week | Commercials | Sales | | Population Covariance | 9.9 | |
| 2 | 1 | 2 | 50 | | Sample Correlation | 0.9305 | |
| 3 | 2 | 5 | 57 | | | | |
| 4 | 3 | 1 | 41 | | | | |
| 5 | 4 | 3 | 54 | | | | |
| 6 | 5 | 4 | 54 | | | | |
| 7 | 6 | 1 | 38 | | | | |
| 8 | 7 | 5 | 63 | | | | |
| 9 | 8 | 3 | 48 | | | | |
| 10 | 9 | 4 | 59 | | | | |
| 11 | 10 | 2 | 46 | | | | |
| 12 | | | | | | | |

The formulas in cells F1:F2 are displayed in the worksheet in the background of
Figure 3.16. The worksheet in the foreground shows the values computed using the Excel
functions. Note that, except for rounding, the value of the sample correlation coefficient
(.9305) is the same as we computed earlier using equation (3.12). However, the result provided by Excel COVAR function, 9.9, was obtained by treating the data as a population.
Thus, we must adjust the Excel result of 9.9 to obtain the sample covariance. The adjustment
is rather simple. First, note that the formula for the population covariance, equation (3.11),
requires dividing by the total number of observations in the data set. But, the formula for the
sample covariance, equation (3.10), requires dividing by the total number of observations
minus 1. So to use the Excel result of 9.9 to compute the sample covariance, we simply multiply 9.9 by $n/(n-1)$. With $n = 10$, we obtain

$$s_{xy} = \left(\frac{10}{9}\right)9.9 = 11$$

Thus, the sample covariance for the stereo and sound equipment data is 11.

## EXERCISES

## Methods

**45.**    Five observations taken for two variables follow.

| $x_i$ | 4 | 6 | 11 | 3 | 16 |
|---|---|---|---|---|---|
| $y_i$ | 50 | 50 | 40 | 60 | 30 |

**a.**    Develop a scatter diagram with $x$ on the horizontal axis.
**b.**    What does the scatter diagram developed in part (a) indicate about the relationship between the two variables?
**c.**    Compute and interpret the sample covariance.
**d.**    Compute and interpret the sample correlation coefficient.

**46.** Five observations taken for two variables follow.

| $x_i$ | 6 | 11 | 15 | 21 | 27 |
|-------|---|----|----|----|----|
| $y_i$ | 6 | 9 | 6 | 17 | 12 |

   **a.** Develop a scatter diagram for these data.
   **b.** What does the scatter diagram indicate about a relationship between $x$ and $y$?
   **c.** Compute and interpret the sample covariance.
   **d.** Compute and interpret the sample correlation coefficient.

## Applications

**47.** A high school guidance counselor collected the following data about the grade point averages (GPA) and the SAT mathematics test scores for six seniors.

| **GPA** | 2.7 | 3.5 | 3.7 | 3.3 | 3.6 | 3.0 |
|---------|-----|-----|-----|-----|-----|-----|
| **SAT** | 450 | 560 | 700 | 620 | 640 | 570 |

   **a.** Develop a scatter diagram for the data with GPA on the horizontal axis.
   **b.** Is any relationship evident between the GPA and the SAT mathematics test score? Explain.
   **c.** Compute and interpret the sample covariance.
   **d.** Compute the sample correlation coefficient. What does this value tell us about the relationship between the two variables?

**48.** A department of transportation's study on driving speed and mileage for midsize automobiles resulted in the following data.

| **Driving Speed** | 30 | 50 | 40 | 55 | 30 | 25 | 60 | 25 | 50 | 55 |
|-------------------|----|----|----|----|----|----|----|----|----|----|
| **Mileage** | 28 | 25 | 25 | 23 | 30 | 32 | 21 | 35 | 26 | 25 |

Compute and interpret the sample correlation coefficient.

**49.** *PC World* provided ratings for 15 notebook PCs (*PC World*, February 2000). The performance score is a measure of how fast a PC can run a mix of common business applications as compared to a baseline machine. For example, a PC with a performance score of 200 is twice as fast as the baseline machine. A 100-point scale was used to provide an overall rating for each notebook tested in the study. A score in the 90s is exceptional, while one in the 70s is above average. Table 3.9 shows the performance scores and the overall ratings for the 15 notebooks.

**TABLE 3.9**  PERFORMANCE SCORES AND OVERALL RATINGS FOR 15 NOTEBOOK PCs

PCs

| Notebook | Performance Score | Overall Rating |
|----------|-------------------|----------------|
| AMS Tech Roadster 15CTA380 | 115 | 67 |
| Compaq Armada M700 | 191 | 78 |
| Compaq Prosignia Notebook 150 | 153 | 79 |
| Dell Inspiron 3700 C466GT | 194 | 80 |
| Dell Inspiron 7500 R500VT | 236 | 84 |
| Dell Latitude Cpi A366XT | 184 | 76 |
| Enpower ENP-313 Pro | 184 | 77 |
| Gateway Solo 9300LS | 216 | 92 |
| HP Pavilion Notebook PC | 185 | 83 |
| IBM ThinkPad I Series 1480 | 183 | 78 |
| Micro Express NP7400 | 189 | 77 |
| Micron TransPort NX PII-400 | 202 | 78 |
| NEC Versa SX | 192 | 78 |
| Sceptre Soundx 5200 | 141 | 73 |
| Sony VAIO PCG-F340 | 187 | 77 |

   **a.** Compute the sample correlation coefficient.
   **b.** What does the sample correlation coefficient tell about the relationship between the performance score and the overall rating?

50. The Dow Jones Industrial Average (DJIA) and the Standard & Poor's (S&P) 500 Index are both used as measures of overall movement in the stock market. The DJIA is based on the price movements of 30 large companies; the S&P 500 is an index composed of 500 stocks. Some say the S&P 500 is a better measure of stock market performance because it is broader based. The closing price for the DJIA and the S&P 500 for 10 weeks, beginning with February 11, 2000, are shown (*Barron's*, April 17, 2000).

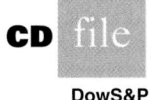

DowS&P

| Date | Dow Jones | S&P 500 |
|------|-----------|---------|
| February 11 | 10425 | 1387 |
| February 18 | 10220 | 1346 |
| February 25 | 9862 | 1333 |
| March 3 | 10367 | 1409 |
| March 10 | 9929 | 1395 |
| March 17 | 10595 | 1464 |
| March 24 | 11113 | 1527 |
| March 31 | 10922 | 1499 |
| April 7 | 11111 | 1516 |
| April 14 | 10306 | 1357 |

   **a.** Compute the sample correlation coefficient for these data.
   **b.** Are they poorly correlated, or do they have a close association?

51. The daily high and low temperatures for 20 cities follow (*USA Today*, May 9, 2000).

HighLow

| City | High | Low |
|------|------|-----|
| Athens | 75 | 54 |
| Bangkok | 92 | 74 |
| Cairo | 84 | 57 |
| Copenhagen | 64 | 39 |
| Dublin | 64 | 46 |
| Havana | 86 | 68 |
| Hong Kong | 81 | 72 |
| Johannesburg | 61 | 50 |
| London | 73 | 48 |
| Manila | 93 | 75 |
| Melbourne | 66 | 50 |
| Montreal | 64 | 52 |
| Paris | 77 | 55 |
| Rio de Janeiro | 80 | 61 |
| Rome | 81 | 54 |
| Seoul | 64 | 50 |
| Singapore | 90 | 75 |
| Sydney | 68 | 55 |
| Tokyo | 79 | 59 |
| Vancouver | 57 | 43 |

What is the correlation between the high and low temperatures?

## 3.6 THE WEIGHTED MEAN AND WORKING WITH GROUPED DATA

In Section 3.1, we presented the mean as one of the most important measures of central location. The formula for the mean of a sample with $n$ observations is restated as follows.

$$\bar{x} = \frac{\Sigma x_i}{n} = \frac{x_1 + x_2 + \cdots + x_n}{n} \tag{3.14}$$

In this formula, each $x_i$ is given equal importance or weight. Although this practice is most common, in some instances, the mean is computed by giving each observation a weight that reflects its importance. A mean computed in this manner is referred to as a **weighted mean.**

## Weighted Mean

The weighted mean is computed as follows:

**Weighted Mean**

$$\bar{x} = \frac{\Sigma w_i x_i}{\Sigma w_i}$$  (3.15)

where

$$x_i = \text{value of observation } i$$
$$w_i = \text{weight for observation } i$$

When the data are from a sample, equation (3.15) provides the weighted sample mean. When the data are from a population, $\mu$ replaces $\bar{x}$ and equation (3.15) provides the weighted population mean.

As an example of the need for a weighted mean, consider the following sample of five purchases of a raw material over the past three months.

| Purchase | Cost per Pound ($) | Number of Pounds |
|----------|--------------------|------------------|
| 1 | 3.00 | 1200 |
| 2 | 3.40 | 500 |
| 3 | 2.80 | 2750 |
| 4 | 2.90 | 1000 |
| 5 | 3.25 | 800 |

Note that the cost per pound has varied from $2.80 to $3.40 and the quantity purchased has varied from 500 to 2750 pounds. Suppose that a manager has asked for information about the mean cost per pound of the raw material. Because the quantities ordered vary, we must use the formula for a weighted mean. The five cost-per-pound data values are $x_1 = 3.00$, $x_2 = 3.40, x_3 = 2.80, x_4 = 2.90$, and $x_5 = 3.25$. The weighted mean cost per pound is found by weighting each cost by its corresponding quantity. For this example, the weights are $w_1 = 1200, w_2 = 500, w_3 = 2750, w_4 = 1000$, and $w_5 = 800$. Using equation (3.15), the weighted mean is calculated as follows:

$$\bar{x} = \frac{1200(3.00) + 500(3.40) + 2750(2.80) + 1000(2.90) + 800(3.25)}{1200 + 500 + 2750 + 1000 + 800}$$

$$= \frac{18,500}{6250} = 2.96$$

Thus, the weighted mean computation shows that the mean cost per pound for the raw material is $2.96. Note that using equation (3.14) rather than the weighted mean formula would have provided misleading results. In this case, the mean of the five cost-per-pound values is $(3.00 + 3.40 + 2.80 + 2.90 + 3.25)/5 = 15.35/5 = \$3.07$, which overstates the actual mean cost per pound purchased.

The choice of weights for a particular weighted mean computation depends upon the application. An example that is well known to college students is the computation of a grade point average (GPA). In this computation, the data values generally used are 4 for an A grade, 3 for a B grade, 2 for a C grade, 1 for a D grade, and 0 for an F grade. The weights are the number of credits hours earned for each grade. Exercise 54 at the end of this section provides an example of this weighted mean computation. In other weighted mean computations, quantities such as pounds, dollars, and/or volume are frequently used as weights. In any case, when observations vary in importance, the analyst must choose the weight that best reflects the importance of each observation in the determination of the mean.

*Computing a grade point average is a good example of the use of a weighted mean.*

## Grouped Data

In most cases, measures of location and variability are computed by using the individual data values. Sometimes, however, we have data in only a grouped or frequency distribution form. In the following discussion, we show how the weighted mean formula can be used to obtain approximations of the mean, variance, and standard deviation for **grouped data.**

In Section 2.2 we provided a frequency distribution of the time in days required to complete year-end audits for the public accounting firm of Sanderson and Clifford. The frequency distribution of audit times based on a sample of 20 clients is shown again in Table 3.10. Based on this frequency distribution, what is the sample mean audit time?

To compute the mean using only the grouped data, we treat the midpoint of each class as being representative of the items in the class. Let $M_i$ denote the midpoint for class $i$ and let $f_i$ denote the frequency of class $i$. The weighted mean formula (3.15) is then used with the data values denoted as $M_i$ and the weights given by the frequencies $f_i$. In this case, the denominator of equation (3.15) is the sum of the frequencies, which is the sample size $n$. That is, $\Sigma f_i = n$. Thus, the equation for the sample mean for grouped data is as follows.

**Sample Mean for Grouped Data**

$$\bar{x} = \frac{\Sigma f_i M_i}{n} \qquad (3.16)$$

where

$$M_i = \text{the midpoint for class } i$$
$$f_i = \text{the frequency for class } i$$
$$n = \text{the sample size}$$

**TABLE 3.10**  FREQUENCY DISTRIBUTION OF AUDIT TIMES

| Audit Time (days) | Frequency |
|---|---|
| 10–14 | 4 |
| 15–19 | 8 |
| 20–24 | 5 |
| 25–29 | 2 |
| 30–34 | 1 |
| Total | 20 |

With the class midpoints, $M_i$, halfway between the class limits, the first class of 10–14 in Table 3.10 has a midpoint at $(10 + 14)/2 = 12$. The five class midpoints and the weighted mean computation for the audit time data are summarized in Table 3.11. As can be seen, the sample mean audit time is 19 days.

To compute the variance for grouped data, we use a slightly altered version of the formula for the variance provided in equation (3.5). In equation (3.5), the squared deviations of the data about the sample mean $\bar{x}$ were written $(x_i - \bar{x})^2$. However, with grouped data, the values are not known. In this case, we treat the class midpoint, $M_i$, as being representative of the $x_i$ values in the corresponding class. Thus the squared deviations about the sample mean, $(x_i - \bar{x})^2$, are replaced by $(M_i - \bar{x})^2$. Then, just as we did with the sample mean calculations for grouped data, we weight each value by the frequency of the class, $f_i$. The sum of the squared deviations about the mean for all the data is approximated by $\Sigma f_i(M_i - \bar{x})^2$. The term $n - 1$ rather than $n$ appears in the denominator in order to make the sample variance the estimate of the population variance. Thus, the following formula is used to obtain the sample variance for grouped data.

**Sample Variance for Grouped Data**

$$s^2 = \frac{\Sigma f_i(M_i - \bar{x})^2}{n - 1} \tag{3.17}$$

The calculation of the sample variance for audit times based on the grouped data from Table 3.10 is shown in Table 3.12. As can be seen, the sample variance is 30.

The standard deviation for grouped data is simply the square root of the variance for grouped data. For the audit time data, the sample standard deviation is $s = \sqrt{30} = 5.48$.

Before closing this section on computing measures of location and dispersion for grouped data, we note that formulas (3.16) and (3.17) are for a sample. Population summary measures are computed similarly. The grouped data formulas for a population mean and variance follow.

**Population Mean for Grouped Data**

$$\mu = \frac{\Sigma f_i M_i}{N} \tag{3.18}$$

**TABLE 3.11** COMPUTATION OF THE SAMPLE MEAN AUDIT TIME FOR GROUPED DATA

The calculations in this table can be easily made in an Excel worksheet.

| Audit Time (days) | Class Midpoint $(M_i)$ | Frequency $(f_i)$ | $f_i M_i$ |
|---|---|---|---|
| 10–14 | 12 | 4 | 48 |
| 15–19 | 17 | 8 | 136 |
| 20–24 | 22 | 5 | 110 |
| 25–29 | 27 | 2 | 54 |
| 30–34 | 32 | 1 | 32 |
| | | 20 | 380 |

$$\text{Sample mean } \bar{x} = \frac{\Sigma f_i M_i}{n} = \frac{380}{20} = 19 \text{ days}$$

**Population Variance for Grouped Data**

$$\sigma^2 = \frac{\Sigma f_i(M_i - \mu)^2}{N}$$

(3.19)

**TABLE 3.12**   COMPUTATION OF THE SAMPLE VARIANCE OF AUDIT TIMES
FOR GROUPED DATA (SAMPLE MEAN $\bar{x} = 19$)

The calculations in this table can be easily made in an Excel worksheet.

| Audit Time (days) | Class Midpoint $(M_i)$ | Frequency $(f_i)$ | Deviation $(M_i - \bar{x})$ | Squared Deviation $(M_i - \bar{x})^2$ | $f_i(M_i - \bar{x})^2$ |
|---|---|---|---|---|---|
| 10–14 | 12 | 4 | −7 | 49 | 196 |
| 15–19 | 17 | 8 | −2 | 4 | 32 |
| 20–24 | 22 | 5 | 3 | 9 | 45 |
| 25–29 | 27 | 2 | 8 | 64 | 128 |
| 30–34 | 32 | 1 | 13 | 169 | 169 |
| | | 20 | | | 570 |

$$\Sigma f_i(M_i - \bar{x})^2$$

$$\text{Sample variance } s^2 = \frac{\Sigma f_i(M_i - \bar{x})^2}{n - 1} = \frac{570}{19} = 30$$

## NOTES AND COMMENTS

In computing descriptive statistics for grouped data, the class midpoints are used to approximate the data values in each class. As a result, the descriptive statistics for grouped data are approximations of the descriptive statistics that would result from using the original data directly. We therefore recommend computing descriptive statistics from the original data rather than from grouped data whenever possible.

## EXERCISES

## Methods

**52.** Consider the following data and corresponding weights.

| $x_i$ | Weight $(w_i)$ |
|---|---|
| 3.2 | 6 |
| 2.0 | 3 |
| 2.5 | 2 |
| 5.0 | 8 |

    **a.** Compute the weighted mean.
    **b.** Compute the sample mean of the four data values without weighting. Note the difference in the results provided by the two computations.

**53.** Consider the sample data in the following frequency distribution.

| Class | Midpoint | Frequency |
|-------|----------|-----------|
| 3–7 | 5 | 4 |
| 8–12 | 10 | 7 |
| 13–17 | 15 | 9 |
| 18–22 | 20 | 5 |

a. Compute the sample mean.
b. Compute the sample variance and sample standard deviation.

## Applications

**54.** The grade point average for college students is based on a weighted mean computation. For most colleges, the grades are given the following data values: A (4), B (3), C (2), D (1), and F (0). After 60 credit hours of course work, a student at State University has earned 9 credit hours of A, 15 credit hours of B, 33 credit hours of C, and 3 credit hours of D.
a. Compute the student's grade point average.
b. Students at State University must have a 2.5 grade point average for their first 60 credit hours of course work in order to be admitted to the business college. Will this student be admitted?

**55.** The dividend yield is the percentage of the value of a share of stock that will be paid as an annual dividend to the stockholder. A sample of eight stocks held by Innis Investments had the following dividend yields (*Barron's,* January 5, 1998). The amount Innis has invested in each stock is also shown. What is the mean dividend yield for the portfolio?

| Company | Dividend Yield | Amount Invested ($) |
|---------|----------------|---------------------|
| Apple Computer | 0.00 | 37,830 |
| Chevron | 2.98 | 27,667 |
| Eastman Kodak | 2.77 | 31,037 |
| ExxonMobil | 2.65 | 27,336 |
| Merck | 1.58 | 37,553 |
| Franklin Resources | 0.57 | 17,812 |
| Sears | 2.00 | 32,660 |
| Woolworth | 0.00 | 17,775 |

**56.** A service station has recorded the following frequency distribution for the number of gallons of gasoline sold per car in a sample of 680 cars.

| Gasoline (gallons) | Frequency |
|--------------------|-----------|
| 0–4 | 74 |
| 5–9 | 192 |
| 10–14 | 280 |
| 15–19 | 105 |
| 20–24 | 23 |
| 25–29 | 6 |
| Total | 680 |

Compute the mean, variance, and standard deviation for these grouped data. If the service station expects to service about 120 cars on a given day, what is an estimate of the total number of gallons of gasoline that will be sold?

**57.** In a survey of subscribers to *Fortune* magazine, the following question was asked: "How many of the last four issues have you read or looked through?" Suppose that the following frequency distribution summarizes 500 responses.

| Number Read | Frequency |
|:---:|:---:|
| 0 | 15 |
| 1 | 10 |
| 2 | 40 |
| 3 | 85 |
| 4 | 350 |
| Total | 500 |

**a.** What is the mean number of issues read by a *Fortune* subscriber?
**b.** What is the standard deviation of the number of issues read?

## SUMMARY

In this chapter we introduced several descriptive statistics that can be used to summarize the location and variability of data. Unlike the tabular and graphical procedures introduced in Chapter 2, the measures introduced in this chapter summarize the data in terms of numerical values. When the numerical values obtained are for a sample, they are called sample statistics. When the numerical values obtained are for a population, they are called population parameters. Some of the notation used for sample statistics and population parameters follow.

| | Sample Statistic | Population Parameter |
|---|:---:|:---:|
| Mean | $\bar{x}$ | $\mu$ |
| Variance | $s^2$ | $\sigma^2$ |
| Standard deviation | $s$ | $\sigma$ |
| Covariance | $s_{xy}$ | $\sigma_{xy}$ |
| Correlation | $r_{xy}$ | $\rho_{xy}$ |

As measures of central location, we defined the mean, median, and mode. Then the concept of percentiles was used to describe other locations in the data set. Next, we presented the range, interquartile range, variance, standard deviation, and coefficient of variation as measures of variability or dispersion. We then described how the mean and standard deviation could be used, applying Chebyshev's theorem and the empirical rule, to provide more information about the distribution of data and to identify outliers.

In Section 3.4 we showed how to develop a five-number summary and a box plot to provide simultaneous information about the location, variability, and shape of the distribution. In Section 3.5 we introduced covariance and the correlation coefficient as measures of association between two variables. In the final section, we showed how to compute a weighted mean and how to calculate a mean, variance, and standard deviation for grouped data.

Most of the descriptive statistics we have discussed can be developed using the functions and tools available in Excel. We have shown how to use many of these functions as well as the Descriptive Statistics tool.

# GLOSSARY

**Sample statistic** A numerical value used as a summary measure for a sample (e.g., the sample mean, $\bar{x}$, the sample variance, $s^2$, and the sample standard deviation, $s$).

**Population parameter** A numerical value used as a summary measure for a population (e.g., the population mean, $\mu$, the population variance, $\sigma^2$, and the population standard deviation, $\sigma$).

**Mean** A measure of central location. It is computed by summing the data values and dividing by the number of observations.

**Median** A measure of central location. It is the value in the middle when the data are arranged in ascending order.

**Mode** A measure of location, defined as the value that occurs with greatest frequency.

**Percentile** A value such that at least $p$ percent of the observations are less than or equal to this value and at least $(100 - p)$ percent of the observations are greater than or equal to this value. The 50th percentile is the median.

**Quartiles** The 25th, 50th, and 75th percentiles are the first quartile, the second quartile (median), and third quartile, respectively. The quartiles can be used to divide a data set into four parts, with each part containing approximately 25% of the data.

**Range** A measure of variability, defined to be the largest value minus the smallest value.

**Interquartile range (IQR)** A measure of variability, defined to be the difference between the third and first quartiles.

**Variance** A measure of variability based on the squared deviations of the data values about the mean.

**Standard deviation** A measure of variability computed by taking the positive square root of the variance.

**Coefficient of variation** A measure of relative variability computed by dividing the standard deviation by the mean and multiplying by 100.

**z-score** A value computed by dividing the deviation about the mean $(x_i - \bar{x})$ by the standard deviation $s$. A $z$-score is referred to as a standardized value and denotes the number of standard deviations $x_i$ is from the mean.

**Chebyshev's theorem** A theorem that can be used to make statements about the proportion of data values that must be within a specified number of standard deviations of the mean.

**Empirical rule** A rule that can be used to compute the percentage of data values that must be within one, two, and three standard deviations of the mean for data having a bell-shaped distribution.

**Outlier** An unusually small or unusually large data value.

**Five-number summary** An exploratory data analysis technique that uses five numbers to summarize the data: smallest value, first quartile, median, third quartile, and largest value.

**Box plot** A graphical summary of data that is based on a five-number summary.

**Covariance** A measure of linear association between two variables. Positive values indicate a positive relationship; negative values indicate a negative relationship.

**Correlation coefficient** A measure of linear association between two variables that takes on values between $-1$ and $+1$. Values near $+1$ indicate a strong positive linear relationship, values near $-1$ indicate a strong negative linear relationship, and values near zero indicate the lack of a linear relationship.

**Weighted mean**    The mean obtained by assigning each observation a weight that reflects its importance.

**Grouped data**    Data available in class intervals as summarized by a frequency distribution. Individual values of the original data are not available.

## KEY FORMULAS

**Sample Mean**

$$\bar{x} = \frac{\Sigma x_i}{n} \tag{3.1}$$

**Population Mean**

$$\mu = \frac{\Sigma x_i}{N} \tag{3.2}$$

**Interquartile Range**

$$IQR = Q_3 - Q_1 \tag{3.3}$$

**Population Variance**

$$\sigma^2 = \frac{\Sigma(x_i - \mu)^2}{N} \tag{3.4}$$

**Sample Variance**

$$s^2 = \frac{\Sigma(x_i - \bar{x})^2}{n - 1} \tag{3.5}$$

**Standard Deviation**

$$\text{Sample Standard Deviation} = s = \sqrt{s^2} \tag{3.6}$$
$$\text{Population Standard Deviation} = \sigma = \sqrt{\sigma^2} \tag{3.7}$$

**Coefficient of Variation**

$$\frac{\text{Standard Deviation}}{\text{Mean}} \times 100 \tag{3.8}$$

**z-score**

$$z_i = \frac{x_i - \bar{x}}{s} \tag{3.9}$$

**Sample Covariance**

$$s_{xy} = \frac{\Sigma(x_i - \bar{x})(y_i - \bar{y})}{n - 1} \tag{3.10}$$

**Population Covariance**

$$\sigma_{xy} = \frac{\Sigma(x_i - \mu_x)(y_i - \mu_y)}{N} \qquad (3.11)$$

**Pearson Product Moment Correlation Coefficient: Sample Data**

$$r_{xy} = \frac{s_{xy}}{s_x s_y} \qquad (3.12)$$

**Pearson Product Moment Correlation Coefficient: Population Data**

$$\rho_{xy} = \frac{\sigma_{xy}}{\sigma_x \sigma_y} \qquad (3.13)$$

**Weighted Mean**

$$\bar{x} = \frac{\Sigma w_i x_i}{\Sigma w_i} \qquad (3.15)$$

**Sample Mean for Grouped Data**

$$\bar{x} = \frac{\Sigma f_i M_i}{n} \qquad (3.16)$$

**Sample Variance for Grouped Data**

$$s^2 = \frac{\Sigma f_i (M_i - \bar{x})^2}{n - 1} \qquad (3.17)$$

**Population Mean for Grouped Data**

$$\mu = \frac{\Sigma f_i M_i}{N} \qquad (3.18)$$

**Population Variance for Grouped Data**

$$\sigma^2 = \frac{\Sigma f_i (M_i - \mu)^2}{N} \qquad (3.19)$$

## SUPPLEMENTARY EXERCISES

**58.** The average American spends $65.88 per month dining out (*The Des Moines Register,* December 5, 1997). A sample of young adults provided the following dining out expenditures (in dollars) over the past month.

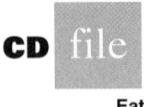

Eat

| 253 | 101 | 245 | 467 | 131 | 0 | 225 |
| 80 | 113 | 69 | 198 | 95 | 129 | 124 |
| 11 | 178 | 104 | 161 | 0 | 118 | 151 |
| 55 | 152 | 134 | 169 | | | |

   **a.** Compute the mean, median, and mode.
   **b.** Considering your results in part (a), do these young adults seem to spend about the same as an average American eating out?
   **c.** Compute the first and third quartiles.
   **d.** Compute the range and interquartile range.
   **e.** Compute the variance and standard deviation.
   **f.** Do the data contain any outliers?

**59.** The total annual compensation for a board member at one of the nation's 100 biggest public companies is based in part on the cash retainer, an annual payment for serving on the board. In addition to the cash retainer, a board member may receive a stock retainer, a stock grant, a stock option, and a fee for attending board meetings. The total compensation can easily exceed $100,000 even with an annual retainer as low as $15,000. The following data show the cash retainer for a sample of 20 of the nation's biggest public companies (*USA Today,* April 17, 2000).

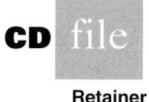

**Retainer**

| Company | Cash Retainer |
|---|---|
| American Express | 64 |
| Bank of America | 36 |
| Boeing | 26 |
| Chevron | 35 |
| Dell Computer | 40 |
| DuPont | 35 |
| ExxonMobil | 40 |
| Ford Motor | 30 |
| General Motors | 60 |
| International Paper | 36 |
| Kroger | 28 |
| Lucent Technologies | 50 |
| Motorola | 20 |
| Procter & Gamble | 55 |
| Raytheon | 40 |
| Sears Roebuck | 30 |
| Texaco | 15 |
| United Parcel Service | 55 |
| Wal-Mart Stores | 25 |
| Xerox | 40 |

Compute the following descriptive statistics.
**a.** Mean, median, and mode
**b.** The first and third quartiles
**c.** The range and interquartile range
**d.** The variance and the standard deviation
**e.** Coefficient of variation

**60.** A survey was conducted concerning the ability of computer manufacturers to handle problems quickly (*PC Computing,* November 1997). The following results were obtained.

| Company | Days to Resolve Problems | Company | Days to Resolve Problems |
|---|---|---|---|
| Compaq | 13 | Gateway | 21 |
| Packard Bell | 27 | Digital | 27 |
| Quantex | 11 | IBM | 12 |
| Dell | 14 | Hewlett-Packard | 14 |
| NEC | 14 | AT&T | 20 |
| AST | 17 | Toshiba | 37 |
| Acer | 16 | Micron | 17 |

**a.** What are the mean and median number of days needed to resolve problems?
**b.** What is the variance and standard deviation?
**c.** Which manufacturer has the best record?
**d.** What is the $z$-score for Packard Bell?
**e.** What is the $z$-score for IBM?
**f.** Do the data contain any outliers?

**61.** According to Forrester Research, Inc., approximately 19% of Internet users play games online. The following data show the number of unique users (in thousands) for the month of March for 10 game sites (*The Wall Street Journal*, April 17, 2000).

| Site | Unique Users |
|------|-------------|
| AOLGames.aol | 9416 |
| extremelotto.com | 3955 |
| freelotto.com | 12901 |
| gamesville.com | 4844 |
| iwin.com | 7410 |
| prizecentral.com | 4899 |
| shockwave.com | 5582 |
| speedyclick.com | 6628 |
| uproar.com | 8821 |
| webstakes.com | 7499 |

Using these data, compute the mean, median, variance, and standard deviation.

**62.** The typical household income for a sample of 20 cities follow (*Places Rated Almanac,* 2000). Data are in thousands of dollars.

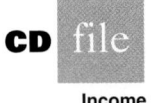

**Income**

| City | Income |
|------|--------|
| Akron, OH | 74.1 |
| Atlanta, GA | 82.4 |
| Birmingham, AL | 71.2 |
| Bismark, ND | 62.8 |
| Cleveland, OH | 79.2 |
| Columbia, SC | 66.8 |
| Danbury, CT | 132.3 |
| Denver, CO | 82.6 |
| Detroit, MI | 85.3 |
| Fort Lauderdale, FL | 75.8 |
| Hartford, CT | 89.1 |
| Lancaster, PA | 75.2 |
| Madison, WI | 78.8 |
| Naples, FL | 100.0 |
| Nashville, TN | 77.3 |
| Philadelphia, PA | 87.0 |
| Savannah, GA | 67.8 |
| Toledo, OH | 71.2 |
| Trenton, NJ | 106.4 |
| Washington, DC | 97.4 |

**a.** Compute the mean and standard deviation for the sample data.

**b.** Using the mean and standard deviation computed in part (a) as estimates of the mean and standard deviation of household income for the population of all cities, use Chebyshev's theorem to determine the range within which 75% of the household incomes for the population of all cities must fall.

**c.** Assume that the distribution of household income is bell-shaped. Using the mean and standard deviation computed in part (a) as estimates of the mean and standard deviation of household income for the population of all cities, use the empirical rule to determine the range within which 95% of the household incomes for the population of all cities must fall. Compare your answer with the value in part (b).

**d.** Do the sample data contain any outliers?

**63.** Public transportation and the automobile are two methods an employee can use to get to work each day. Samples of times recorded for each method are shown. Times are in minutes.

| *Public Transportation:* | 28 | 29 | 32 | 37 | 33 | 25 | 29 | 32 | 41 | 34 |
|---|---|---|---|---|---|---|---|---|---|---|
| *Automobile:* | | 29 | 31 | 33 | 32 | 34 | 30 | 31 | 32 | 35 | 33 |

a. Compute the sample mean time to get to work for each method.
b. Compute the sample standard deviation for each method.
c. On the basis of your results from parts (a) and (b), which method of transportation should be preferred? Explain.
d. Develop a box plot for each method. Does a comparison of the box plots support your conclusion in part (c)?

**64.** The typical household income and typical home price for a sample of 20 cities follow (*Places Rated Almanac,* 2000). Data are in thousands of dollars.

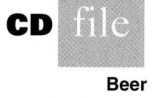

**Cities**

| City | Income | Home Price |
|---|---|---|
| Bismark, ND | 62.8 | 92.8 |
| Columbia, SC | 66.8 | 116.7 |
| Savannah, GA | 67.8 | 108.1 |
| Birmingham, AL | 71.2 | 130.9 |
| Toledo, OH | 71.2 | 101.1 |
| Akron, OH | 74.1 | 114.9 |
| Lancaster, PA | 75.2 | 125.9 |
| Fort Lauderdale, FL | 75.8 | 145.3 |
| Nashville, TN | 77.3 | 125.9 |
| Madison, WI | 78.8 | 145.2 |
| Cleveland, OH | 79.2 | 135.8 |
| Atlanta, GA | 82.4 | 126.9 |
| Denver, CO | 82.6 | 161.9 |
| Detroit, MI | 85.3 | 145.0 |
| Philadelphia, PA | 87.0 | 151.5 |
| Hartford, CT | 89.1 | 162.1 |
| Washington, DC | 97.4 | 191.9 |
| Naples, FL | 100.0 | 173.6 |
| Trenton, NJ | 106.4 | 168.1 |
| Danbury, CT | 132.3 | 234.1 |

a. What is the value of the sample covariance? Does it indicate a positive or a negative linear relationship?
b. What is the sample correlation coefficient?

**65.** The following data show the media expenditures ($ millions) and shipments in millions of barrels (bbls.) for 10 major brands of beer (*Superbrands'* 98, October 20, 1997).

| Brand | Media Expenditures ($millions) | Shipments in bbls. (millions) |
|---|---|---|
| Budweiser | 120.0 | 36.3 |
| Bud Light | 68.7 | 20.7 |
| Miller Lite | 100.1 | 15.9 |
| Coors Light | 76.6 | 13.2 |
| Busch | 8.7 | 8.1 |
| Natural Light | 0.1 | 7.1 |
| Miller Genuine Draft | 21.5 | 5.6 |
| Miller High Lite | 1.4 | 4.4 |
| Busch Lite | 5.3 | 4.3 |
| Milwaukee's Best | 1.7 | 4.3 |

**Beer**

a. What is the sample covariance? Does it indicate a positive or negative relationship?
b. What is the sample correlation coefficient?

**66.** *Road & Track* provided the following sample of the tire ratings and load-carrying capacity of automobiles tires.

| Tire Rating | Load-Carrying Capacity |
|---|---|
| 75 | 853 |
| 82 | 1047 |
| 85 | 1135 |
| 87 | 1201 |
| 88 | 1235 |
| 91 | 1356 |
| 92 | 1389 |
| 93 | 1433 |
| 105 | 2039 |

**a.** Develop a scatter diagram for the data with tire rating on the $x$-axis.
**b.** What is the sample correlation coefficient, and what does it tell you about the relationship between tire rating and load-carrying capacity?

**67.** The following data show the trailing 52-weeks primary share earnings and book values as reported by 10 companies (*The Wall Street Journal,* March 13, 2000).

| Company | Book Value | Earnings |
|---|---|---|
| Am Elec | 25.21 | 2.69 |
| Columbia En | 23.20 | 3.01 |
| Con Ed | 25.19 | 3.13 |
| Duke Energy | 20.17 | 2.25 |
| Edison Int'l | 13.55 | 1.79 |
| Enron Cp. | 7.44 | 1.27 |
| Peco | 13.61 | 3.15 |
| Pub Sv Ent | 21.86 | 3.29 |
| Southn Co. | 8.77 | 1.86 |
| Unicom | 23.22 | 2.74 |

**a.** Develop a scatter diagram for the data with book value on the $x$-axis.
**b.** What is the sample correlation coefficient, and what does it tell you about the relationship between the earnings per share and the book value?

**68.** A forecasting technique referred to as moving averages uses the average or mean of the most recent $n$ periods to forecast the next value for time series data. With a three-period moving average, the most recent three periods of data are used in the forecast computation. Consider a product with the following demand for the first three months of the current year: January (800 units), February (750 units), and March (900 units).
**a.** What is the three-month moving average forecast for April?
**b.** A variation of this forecasting technique is called weighted moving averages. The weighting allows the more recent time series data to receive more weight or more importance in the computation of the forecast. For example, a weighted three-month moving average might give a weight of 3 to data one month old, a weight of 2 to data two months old, and a weight of 1 to data three months old. Use the data given to provide a three-month weighted moving average forecast for April.

**69.** The days to maturity for a sample of five money market funds are shown here. The dollar amounts invested in the funds are provided. Use the weighted mean to determine the mean number of days to maturity for dollars invested in these five money market funds.

| Days to Maturity | Dollar Value ($million) |
|---|---|
| 20 | 20 |
| 12 | 30 |
| 7 | 10 |
| 5 | 15 |
| 6 | 10 |

70. Automobiles traveling on a road that has a posted speed limit of 55 miles per hour are checked for speed by a state police radar system. Following is a frequency distribution of speeds.

| Speed (miles per hour) | Frequency |
|---|---|
| 45–49 | 10 |
| 50–54 | 40 |
| 55–59 | 150 |
| 60–64 | 175 |
| 65–69 | 75 |
| 70–74 | 15 |
| 75–79 | 10 |
| Total | 475 |

    **a.** What is the mean speed of the automobiles traveling on this road?
    **b.** Compute the variance and the standard deviation.

71. Dinner check amounts at La Maison French Restaurant have the frequency distribution shown as follows. Compute the mean, variance, and standard deviation.

| Dinner Check ($) | Frequency |
|---|---|
| 25–34 | 2 |
| 35–44 | 6 |
| 45–54 | 4 |
| 55–64 | 4 |
| 65–74 | 2 |
| 75–84 | 2 |
| Total | 20 |

## Case Problem 1    CONSOLIDATED FOODS, INC.

Consolidated Foods, Inc., operates a chain of supermarkets in New Mexico, Arizona, and California. Data showing the dollar amounts and method of payment were collected for a sample of 100 customers. A portion of the data is shown in Table 3.13. The complete data set is available on the data disk in the file named Consolid. Consolidated's managers requested the sample be taken to learn about payment practices of the store's customers. In particular, managers are interested in learning about how a new credit card payment option is related to the customers' purchase amounts.

### Managerial Report

Use the methods of descriptive statistics presented in Chapter 3 to summarize the sample data. Provide summaries of the dollar purchase amounts for cash customers, personal check customers, and credit card customers separately. Your report should contain the following summaries and discussions.

    **1.** A comparison and interpretation of means and medians.
    **2.** A comparison and interpretation of measures of variability such as the range and standard deviation.
    **3.** The identification and interpretation of the five-number summaries for each method of payment.

**TABLE 3.13** PURCHASE AMOUNT AND METHOD OF PAYMENT FOR A SAMPLE OF 100 CONSOLIDATED FOODS CUSTOMERS

**Consolid**

| Customer | Amount ($) | Method of Payment |
|---|---|---|
| 1 | 28.58 | Check |
| 2 | 52.04 | Check |
| 3 | 7.41 | Cash |
| 4 | 11.17 | Cash |
| 5 | 43.79 | Credit Card |
| 6 | 48.95 | Check |
| 7 | 57.59 | Check |
| 8 | 27.60 | Check |
| 9 | 26.91 | Credit Card |
| 10 | 9.00 | Cash |
| . | . | . |
| . | . | . |
| . | . | . |
| 95 | 18.09 | Cash |
| 96 | 54.84 | Check |
| 97 | 41.10 | Check |
| 98 | 43.14 | Check |
| 99 | 3.31 | Cash |
| 100 | 69.77 | Credit Card |

Use the summary section of your report to provide a discussion of what you have learned about the method of payment and the amounts of payments for Consolidated Foods' customers.

## Case Problem 2 NATIONAL HEALTH CARE ASSOCIATION

The National Health Care Association is concerned about the shortage of nurses the health care profession is projecting for the future. To learn the current degree of job satisfaction among nurses, the association has sponsored a study of hospital nurses throughout the country. As part of this study, 50 nurses in a sample were asked to indicate their degree of satisfaction in their work, their pay, and their opportunities for promotion. Each of the three aspects of satisfaction was measured on a scale from 0 to 100, with larger values indicating higher degrees of satisfaction. The data collected also showed the type of hospital employing the nurses. The types of hospitals were Private, Veterans Administration (VA), and University. A portion of the data is shown in Table 3.14. The complete data set is on the data disk in the file named Health.

## Managerial Report

Use methods of descriptive statistics to summarize the data. Present the summaries that will be beneficial in communicating the results to others. Discuss your findings. Specifically, comment on the following questions.

1. On the basis of the entire data set and the three job satisfaction variables, what aspect of the job is most satisfying for the nurses? What appears to be the least

**TABLE 3.14**    SATISFACTION SCORE DATA FOR A SAMPLE OF 50 NURSES

**Health**

| Nurse | Hospital | Work | Pay | Promotion |
|-------|----------|------|-----|-----------|
| 1 | Private | 74 | 47 | 63 |
| 2 | VA | 72 | 76 | 37 |
| 3 | University | 75 | 53 | 92 |
| 4 | Private | 89 | 66 | 62 |
| 5 | University | 69 | 47 | 16 |
| 6 | Private | 85 | 56 | 64 |
| 7 | University | 89 | 80 | 64 |
| 8 | Private | 88 | 36 | 47 |
| 9 | University | 88 | 55 | 52 |
| 10 | Private | 84 | 42 | 66 |
| . | . | . | . | . |
| . | . | . | . | . |
| . | . | . | . | . |
| 45 | University | 79 | 59 | 41 |
| 46 | University | 84 | 53 | 63 |
| 47 | University | 87 | 66 | 49 |
| 48 | VA | 84 | 74 | 37 |
| 49 | VA | 95 | 66 | 52 |
| 50 | Private | 72 | 57 | 40 |

satisfying? In what area(s), if any, do you feel improvements should be made? Discuss.

2. On the basis of descriptive measures of variability, what measure of job satisfaction appears to generate the greatest difference of opinion among the nurses? Explain.

3. What can be learned about the types of hospitals? Does any particular type of hospital seem to have better levels of job satisfaction than the other types? Do your results suggest any recommendations for learning about and/or improving job satisfaction? Discuss.

4. What additional descriptive statistics and insights can you use to learn about and possibly improve job satisfaction?

## Case Problem 3    BUSINESS SCHOOLS OF ASIA-PACIFIC

The pursuit of a higher education degree in business is now international. A survey shows that more and more Asians are choosing the Master of Business Administration degree route to corporate success (*Asia, Inc.,* September 1997). The number of applicants for MBA courses at Asia-Pacific schools is rising by about 30 percent a year. In 1997, the 74 business schools in the Asia-Pacific region reported a record 170,000 applications for the 11,000 full-time MBA degrees to be awarded in 1999. A main reason for the surge in demand is that an MBA can greatly enhance earning power.

**Asian**

Across the region, thousands of Asians are showing an increasing willingness to temporarily shelve their careers and spend two years in pursuit of a theoretical business qualification. Courses in these schools are notoriously tough and include economics, banking, marketing, behavioral sciences, labor relations, decision making, strategic thinking, business law, and more. *Asia, Inc.* provided the data set in Table 3.15, which shows some of the characteristics of the leading Asia-Pacific business schools.

**TABLE 3.15** DATA FOR 25 ASIA-PACIFIC BUSINESS SCHOOLS

| Business School | Full-Time Enrollment | Students per Faculty | Local Tuition ($) | Foreign Tuition ($) | Age | %Foreign | GMAT | English Test | Work Experience | Starting Salary ($) |
|---|---|---|---|---|---|---|---|---|---|---|
| Melbourne Business School | 200 | 5 | 24,420 | 29,600 | 28 | 47 | Yes | No | Yes | 71,400 |
| University of New South Wales (Sydney) | 228 | 4 | 19,993 | 32,582 | 29 | 28 | Yes | No | Yes | 65,200 |
| Indian Institute of Management (Ahmedabad) | 392 | 5 | 4,300 | 4,300 | 22 | 0 | No | No | No | 7,100 |
| Chinese University of Hong Kong | 90 | 5 | 11,140 | 11,140 | 29 | 10 | Yes | No | No | 31,000 |
| International University of Japan (Niigata) | 126 | 4 | 33,060 | 33,060 | 28 | 60 | Yes | Yes | No | 87,000 |
| Asian Institute of Management (Manila) | 389 | 5 | 7,562 | 9,000 | 25 | 50 | Yes | No | No | 22,800 |
| Indian Institute of Management (Bangalore) | 380 | 5 | 3,935 | 16,000 | 23 | 1 | Yes | No | No | 7,500 |
| National University of Singapore | 147 | 6 | 6,146 | 7,170 | 29 | 51 | Yes | Yes | Yes | 43,300 |
| Indian Institute of Management (Calcutta) | 463 | 8 | 2,880 | 16,000 | 23 | 0 | No | No | No | 7,400 |
| Australian National University (Canberra) | 42 | 2 | 20,300 | 20,300 | 30 | 80 | Yes | Yes | Yes | 46,600 |
| Nanyang Technological University (Singapore) | 50 | 5 | 8,500 | 8,500 | 32 | 20 | Yes | No | Yes | 49,300 |
| University of Queensland (Brisbane) | 138 | 17 | 16,000 | 22,800 | 32 | 26 | No | No | Yes | 49,600 |
| Hong Kong University of Science and Technology | 60 | 2 | 11,513 | 11,513 | 26 | 37 | Yes | No | Yes | 34,000 |
| Macquarie Graduate School of Management (Sydney) | 12 | 8 | 17,172 | 19,778 | 34 | 27 | No | No | Yes | 60,100 |
| Chulalongkorn University (Bangkok) | 200 | 7 | 17,355 | 17,355 | 25 | 6 | Yes | No | Yes | 17,600 |
| Monash Mt. Eliza Business School (Melbourne) | 350 | 13 | 16,200 | 22,500 | 30 | 30 | Yes | Yes | Yes | 52,500 |
| Asian Institute of Management (Bangkok) | 300 | 10 | 18,200 | 18,200 | 29 | 90 | No | Yes | Yes | 25,000 |
| University of Adelaide | 20 | 19 | 16,426 | 23,100 | 30 | 10 | No | No | Yes | 66,000 |
| Massey University (Palmerston North, New Zealand) | 30 | 15 | 13,106 | 21,625 | 37 | 35 | No | Yes | Yes | 41,400 |
| Royal Melbourne Institute of Technology Business Graduate School | 30 | 7 | 13,880 | 17,765 | 32 | 30 | No | Yes | Yes | 48,900 |
| Jamnalal Bajaj Institute of Management Studies (Bombay) | 240 | 9 | 1,000 | 1,000 | 24 | 0 | No | No | Yes | 7,000 |
| Curtin Institute of Technology (Perth) | 98 | 15 | 9,475 | 19,097 | 29 | 43 | Yes | No | Yes | 55,000 |
| Lahore University of Management Sciences | 70 | 14 | 11,250 | 26,300 | 23 | 2.5 | No | No | No | 7,500 |
| Universiti Sains Malaysia (Penang) | 30 | 5 | 2,260 | 2,260 | 32 | 15 | No | Yes | Yes | 16,000 |
| De La Salle University (Manila) | 44 | 17 | 3,300 | 3,600 | 28 | 3.5 | Yes | No | Yes | 13,100 |

# Managerial Report

Use the methods of descriptive statistics to summarize the data in Table 3.15. Discuss your findings.

1. Include a summary for each variable in the data set. Make comments and interpretations based on maximums and minimums, as well as the appropriate means and proportions. What new insights do these descriptive statistics provide concerning Asia-Pacific business schools?
2. Summarize the data to compare the following:
   a. Any difference between local and foreign tuition costs.
   b. Any difference between mean starting salaries for schools requiring and not requiring work experience.
   c. Any difference between starting salaries for schools requiring and not requiring English tests.
3. Do starting salaries appear to be related to tuition?
4. Present any additional graphical and numerical summaries that will be beneficial in communicating the data in Table 3.15 to others.

# Chapter 4

# INTRODUCTION TO PROBABILITY

**CONTENTS**

## STATISTICS IN PRACTICE

### MORTON INTERNATIONAL*
*Chicago, Illinois*

Morton International is a company with businesses in salt, household products, rocket motors, and specialty chemicals. Carstab Corporation, a subsidiary of Morton International, produces specialty chemicals and offers a variety of chemicals designed to meet the unique specifications of its customers. For one particular customer, Carstab produced an expensive catalyst used in chemical processing. Some, but not all, of the lots produced by Carstab met the customer's specifications for the product.

Carstab's customer agreed to test each lot after receiving it and determine whether the catalyst would perform the desired function. Lots that did not pass the customer's test would be returned to Carstab. Over time, Carstab found that the customer was accepting 60% of the lots and returning 40%. In probability terms, each Carstab shipment to the customer had a .60 probability of being accepted and a .40 probability of being returned.

Neither Carstab nor its customer was pleased with these results. In an effort to improve service, Carstab explored the possibility of duplicating the customer's test prior to shipment. However, the high cost of the special testing equipment made that alternative infeasible. Carstab's chemists then proposed a new, relatively low-cost test designed to indicate whether a lot would pass the customer's test. The probability question of interest was: What is the probability that a lot will pass the customer's test if it has passed the new Carstab test?

Morton Salt: "When It Rains It Pours." © Joe Higgins/ South-Western.

A sample of lots was produced and subjected to the new Carstab test. Only lots that passed the new test were sent to the customer. Probability analysis of the data indicated that if a lot passed the Carstab test, it had a .909 probability of passing the customer's test and being accepted. Alternatively, if a lot passed the Carstab test, it had only a .091 probability of being returned. The probability analysis provided key supporting evidence for the adoption and implementation of the new testing procedure at Carstab. The new test resulted in an immediate improvement in customer service and a substantial reduction in shipping and handling costs for returned lots.

The probability of a lot being accepted by the customer after passing the new Carstab test is called a conditional probability. In this chapter, you will learn how to compute this and other probabilities that are helpful in decision making.

*The authors are indebted to Michael Haskell of Morton International for providing this Statistics in Practice.

---

Business decisions are often based on an analysis of uncertainties such as the following:

1. What are the chances that sales will decrease if we increase prices?
2. What is the likelihood a new assembly method will increase productivity?
3. How likely is it that the project will be finished on time?
4. What is the chance that a new investment will be profitable?

*Some of the earliest work on probability originated in a series of letters between Pierre de Fermat and Blaise Pascal in the 1650s.*

**Probability** is a numerical measure of the likelihood that an event will occur. Thus, probabilities could be used as measures of the degree of uncertainty associated with the four events previously listed. If probabilities were available, we could determine the likelihood of each event occurring.

Probability values are always assigned on a scale from 0 to 1. A probability near zero indicates an event is unlikely to occur; a probability near 1 indicates an event is almost certain to occur. Other probabilities between 0 and 1 represent degrees of likelihood that an event will occur. For example, if we consider the event "rain tomorrow," we understand that when the weather report indicates "a near-zero probability of rain," it means almost no chance of rain. However, if a .90 probability of rain is reported, we know that rain is likely to occur. A .50 probability indicates that rain is just as likely to occur as not. Figure 4.1 depicts the view of probability as a numerical measure of the likelihood of an event occurring.

**FIGURE 4.1**  PROBABILITY AS A NUMERICAL MEASURE OF THE LIKELIHOOD OF AN EVENT OCCURRING

## 4.1 EXPERIMENTS, COUNTING RULES, AND ASSIGNING PROBABILITIES

In discussing probability, we define an **experiment** as a process that generates well-defined outcomes. On any single repetition of an experiment, one and only one of the possible experimental outcomes will occur. Several examples of experiments and their associated outcomes follow.

| Experiment | Experimental Outcomes |
|---|---|
| Toss a coin | Head, tail |
| Select a part for inspection | Defective, nondefective |
| Conduct a sales call | Purchase, no purchase |
| Roll a die | 1, 2, 3, 4, 5, 6 |
| Play a football game | Win, lose, tie |

When we have specified all possible experimental outcomes, we have identified the **sample space** for an experiment.

**Sample Space**

The sample space for an experiment is the set of all experimental outcomes.

Experimental outcomes are also called sample points.

An experimental outcome is also called a **sample point** to identify it as an element of the sample space.

Consider the first experiment in the preceding table—tossing a coin. The experimental outcomes (sample points) are determined by the upward face of the coin—a head or a tail. If we let *S* denote the sample space, we can use the following notation to describe the sample space.

$$S = \{\text{Head, Tail}\}$$

The sample space for the second experiment in the table—selecting a part for inspection—has the following sample space and sample points.

$$S = \{\text{Defective, Nondefective}\}$$

Both of the experiments just described have two experimental outcomes (sample points). However, suppose we consider the fourth experiment listed in the table—rolling a die. The possible experimental outcomes, defined as the number of dots appearing on the upward face of the die, are the six points in the sample space for this experiment.

$$S = \{1, 2, 3, 4, 5, 6\}$$

## Counting Rules, Combinations, and Permutations

Being able to identify and count the experimental outcomes is a necessary step in assigning probabilities. We now discuss three counting rules that are useful.

**Multiple-Step Experiments.**   The first counting rule is for multiple-step experiments. Consider the experiment of tossing two coins. Let the experimental outcomes be defined in terms of the pattern of heads and tails appearing on the upward faces of the two coins. How many experimental outcomes are possible for this experiment? The experiment of tossing two coins can be thought of as a two-step experiment in which step 1 is the tossing of the first coin and step 2 is the tossing of the second coin. If we use $H$ to denote a head and $T$ to denote a tail, $(H, H)$ indicates the experimental outcome with a head on the first coin and a head on the second coin. Continuing this notation, we can describe the sample space ($S$) for this coin-tossing experiment as follows:

$$S = \{(H, H), (H, T), (T, H), (T, T)\}$$

Thus, we see that four experimental outcomes are possible. In this case, it is not difficult to list all of the experimental outcomes.

The counting rule for multiple-step experiments makes it possible to determine the number of experimental outcomes without listing them.

---

**A Counting Rule for Multiple-Step Experiments**

If an experiment can be described as a sequence of $k$ steps with $n_1$ possible outcomes on the first step, $n_2$ possible outcomes on the second step, and so on, then the total number of experimental outcomes is given by $(n_1) (n_2) \ldots (n_k)$.

---

Viewing the experiment of tossing two coins as a sequence of first tossing one coin ($n_1 = 2$) and then tossing the other coin ($n_2 = 2$), we can see from the counting rule that there are $(2)(2) = 4$ distinct experimental outcomes. As shown, they are $S = \{(H, H), (H, T), (T, H), (T, T)\}$. The number of experimental outcomes in an experiment involving tossing six coins is $(2)(2)(2)(2)(2)(2) = 64$.

A graphical representation that is helpful in visualizing a multiple-step experiment is a **tree diagram.** Figure 4.2 shows a tree diagram for the experiment of tossing two coins. The sequence of steps is depicted by moving from left to right through the tree. Step 1 corresponds to tossing the first coin. Step 2 corresponds to tossing the second coin. For each step, there are two possible outcomes: head or tail. Note that for each possible outcome at step 1 there are two branches corresponding to the two possible outcomes at step 2. Each of the

*Without the tree diagram, one might think only three experimental outcomes are possible for two tosses of a coin: 0 heads, 1 head, and 2 heads.*

**FIGURE 4.2**    TREE DIAGRAM FOR THE EXPERIMENT OF TOSSING TWO COINS

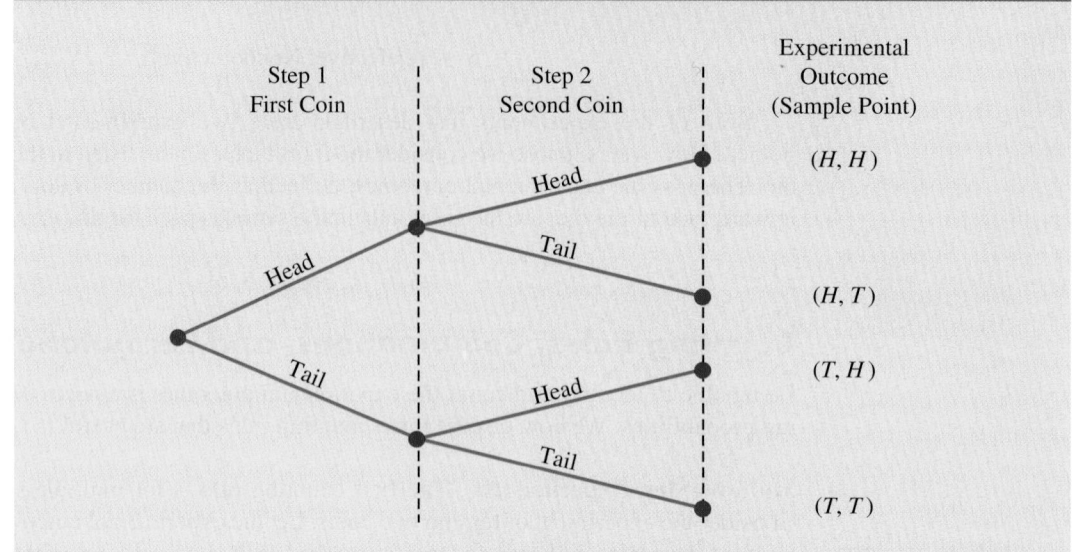

points on the right end of the tree corresponds to an experimental outcome. Each path through the tree from the leftmost node to one of the nodes at the right side of the tree corresponds to a unique sequence of outcomes.

Let us now see how the counting rule for multiple-step experiments can be used in the analysis of a capacity expansion project faced by the Kentucky Power & Light Company (KP&L). KP&L is starting a project designed to increase the generating capacity of one of its plants in northern Kentucky. The project is divided into two sequential stages or steps: stage 1 (design) and stage 2 (construction). Even though each stage will be scheduled and controlled as closely as possible, management cannot predict beforehand the exact time required to complete each stage of the project. An analysis of similar construction projects has shown completion times for the design stage of 2, 3, or 4 months and completion times for the construction stage of 6, 7, or 8 months. In addition, because of the critical need for additional electrical power, management has set a goal of 10 months for the completion of the entire project.

Because this project has three possible completion times for the design stage (step 1) and three possible completion times for the construction stage (step 2), the counting rule for multiple-step experiments can be applied here to determine a total of (3)(3) = 9 experimental outcomes. To describe the experimental outcomes, we will use a two-number notation; for instance, (2, 6) will indicate that the design stage is completed in 2 months and the construction stage is completed in 6 months. This experimental outcome results in a total of 2 + 6 = 8 months to complete the entire project. Table 4.1 summarizes the nine experimental outcomes for the KP&L problem. The tree diagram in Figure 4.3 shows how the nine outcomes (sample points) occur.

The counting rule and tree diagram have been used to help the project manager identify the experimental outcomes and determine the possible project completion times. From the information in Figure 4.3, we see that the project will be completed in 8 to 12 months, with six of the nine experimental outcomes providing the desired completion time of 10 months or less. Although it has been helpful to identify the experimental outcomes, we

**TABLE 4.1**   EXPERIMENTAL OUTCOMES (SAMPLE POINTS) FOR THE KP&L PROBLEM

| Completion Time (months) | | | |
|---|---|---|---|
| **Stage 1 (Design)** | **Stage 2 (Construction)** | **Notation for Experimental Outcome** | **Total Project Completion Time (months)** |
| 2 | 6 | (2, 6) | 8 |
| 2 | 7 | (2, 7) | 9 |
| 2 | 8 | (2, 8) | 10 |
| 3 | 6 | (3, 6) | 9 |
| 3 | 7 | (3, 7) | 10 |
| 3 | 8 | (3, 8) | 11 |
| 4 | 6 | (4, 6) | 10 |
| 4 | 7 | (4, 7) | 11 |
| 4 | 8 | (4, 8) | 12 |

**FIGURE 4.3**   TREE DIAGRAM FOR THE KP&L PROJECT

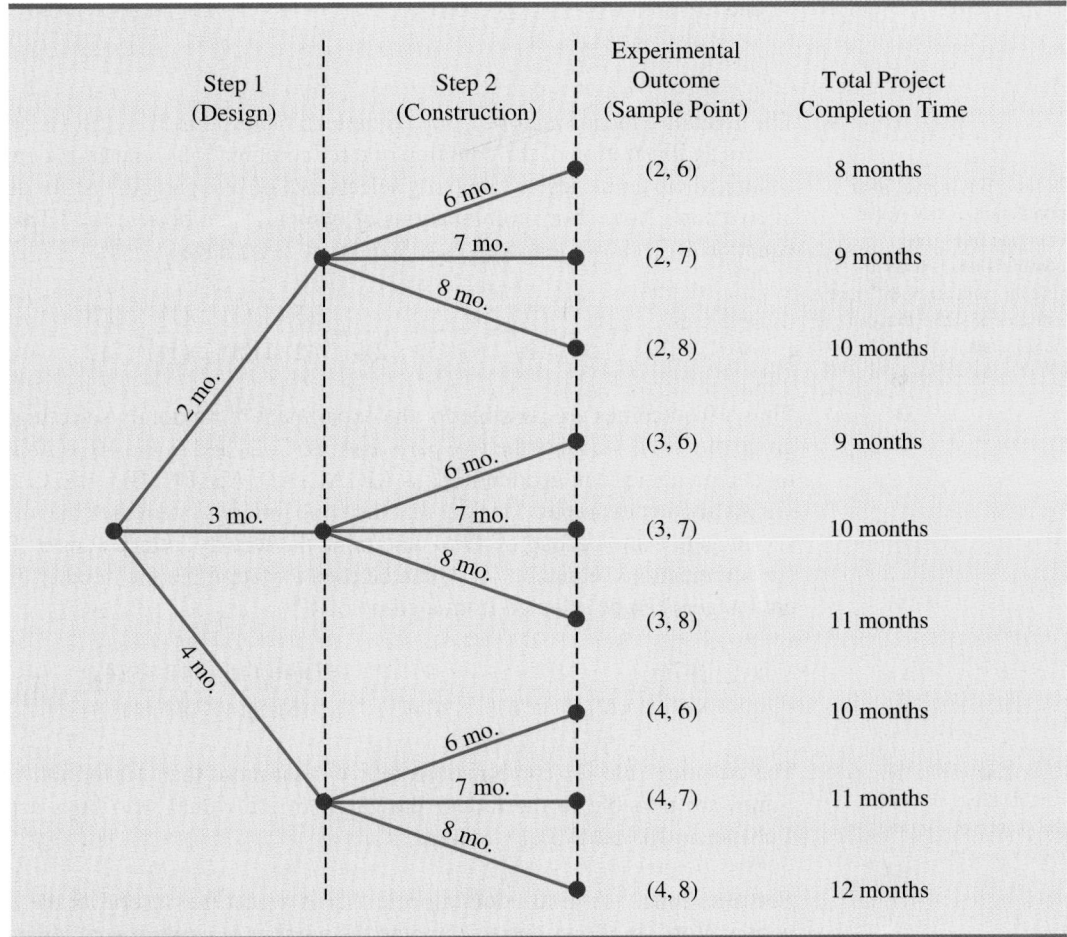

will need to consider how probability values can be assigned to the experimental outcomes before making an assessment of the probability that the project will be completed within the desired 10 months.

**Combinations.** A second counting rule that is often useful allows one to count the number of experimental outcomes when the experiment involves selecting $n$ objects from a (usually larger) set of $N$ objects. It is called the counting rule for combinations.

> **Counting Rule for Combinations**
>
> The number of combinations of $N$ objects taken $n$ at a time is
>
> $$C_n^N = \binom{N}{n} = \frac{N!}{n!(N-n)!} \tag{4.1}$$
>
> where
> $$N! = N(N-1)(N-2)\cdots(2)(1)$$
> $$n! = n(n-1)(n-2)\cdots(2)(1)$$
>
> and
> $$0! = 1$$

The notation ! means *factorial;* for example, 5 factorial is $5! = (5)(4)(3)(2)(1) = 120$.

As an illustration of the counting rule for combinations, consider a quality control procedure where an inspector randomly selects two of five parts to test for defects. In a group of five parts, how many combinations of two parts can be selected? The counting rule in equation (4.1) shows that with $N = 5$ and $n = 2$, we have

In sampling from a finite population of size $N$, the counting rules for combinations is used to find the number of different samples of size $n$ that can be selected.

$$C_2^5 = \binom{5}{2} = \frac{5!}{2!(5-2)!} = \frac{(5)(4)(3)(2)(1)}{(2)(1)(3)(2)(1)} = \frac{120}{12} = 10$$

Thus, 10 outcomes are possible for the experiment of randomly selecting two parts from a group of five. If we label the five parts as A, B, C, D, and E, the 10 combinations or experimental outcomes can be identified as AB, AC, AD, AE, BC, BD, BE, CD, CE, and DE.

As another example, consider that the Ohio lottery system uses the random selection of six integers from a group of 47 to determine the weekly lottery winner. The counting rule for combinations, equation (4.1), can be used to determine the number of ways six different integers can be selected from a group of 47.

$$\binom{47}{6} = \frac{47!}{6!(47-6)!} = \frac{47!}{6!41!} = \frac{(47)(46)(45)(44)(43)(42)}{(6)(5)(4)(3)(2)(1)} = 10,737,573$$

The counting rule for combinations shows that the chance of winning the lottery is slim.

The counting rule for combinations tells us that more than 10 million experimental outcomes are possible in the lottery drawing. An individual who buys a lottery ticket has 1 chance in 10,737,573 of winning.

**Permutations.** A third counting rule that is sometimes useful is the counting rule for permutations. It allows one to compute the number of experimental outcomes when $n$ objects are to be selected from a set of $N$ objects where the order of selection is important. The same $n$ objects selected in a different order is considered a different experimental outcome.

**Counting Rule for Permutations**

The number of permutations of $N$ objects taken $n$ at a time is given by

$$P_n^N = n!\binom{N}{n} = \frac{N!}{(N-n)!} \tag{4.2}$$

The counting rule for permutations is closely related to the one for combinations; however, an experiment will have more permutations than combinations for the same number of objects because every selection of $n$ objects has $n!$ different ways to order them.

As an example, consider again the quality control process in which an inspector selects two of five parts to inspect for defects. How many permutations may be selected? The counting rule in equation (4.2) shows that with $N = 5$ and $n = 2$, we have

$$P_2^5 = \frac{5!}{(5-2)!} = \frac{5!}{3!} = \frac{(5)(4)(3)(2)(1)}{(3)(2)(1)} = (5)(4) = 20$$

Thus, 20 outcomes are possible for the experiment of randomly selecting two parts from a group of five when the order of selection must be taken into account. If we label the parts A, B, C, D, and E, the 20 permutations are AB, BA, AC, CA, AD, DA, AE, EA, BC, CB, BD, DB, BE, EB, CD, DC, CE, EC, DE, and ED.

## Assigning Probabilities

Now let us see how probabilities can be assigned to experimental outcomes. The three approaches most frequently used are the classical, relative frequency, and subjective methods. Regardless of the method used, there are two **basic requirements for assigning probabilities.**

**Basic Requirements for Assigning Probabilities**

1. The probability assigned to each experimental outcome must be between 0 and 1, inclusively. If we let $E_i$ denote the $i$th experimental outcome and $P(E_i)$ its probability, then this requirement can be written as

$$0 \le P(E_i) \le 1 \text{ for all } i \tag{4.3}$$

2. The sum of the probabilities for all the experimental outcomes must equal 1. For $n$ experimental outcomes, this requirement can be written as

$$P(E_1) + P(E_2) + \cdots + P(E_n) = 1 \tag{4.4}$$

The **classical method** of assigning probabilities is appropriate when all the experimental outcomes are equally likely. If $n$ experimental outcomes are possible, a probability of $1/n$ is assigned to each experimental outcome. When using this approach, the two basic requirements for assigning probabilities are automatically satisfied.

For an example, consider the experiment of tossing a fair coin, the two experimental outcomes—head and tail—are equally likely. Because one of the two equally likely outcomes is a head, the probability of observing a head is 1/2, or .50. Similarly, the probability of observing a tail is also 1/2, or .50.

As another example, consider the experiment of rolling a die. It would seem reasonable to conclude that the six possible outcomes are equally likely, and hence each outcome is assigned a probability of 1/6. If $P(1)$ denotes the probability that one dot appears on the upward face of the die, then $P(1) = 1/6$. Similarly, $P(2) = 1/6$. $P(3) = 1/6$, $P(4) = 1/6$, $P(5) = 1/6$, and $P(6) = 1/6$. Note that the requirements of equations (4.3) and (4.4) are both satisfied because each of the probabilities is greater than or equal to zero and they sum to one.

The **relative frequency method** of assigning probabilities is appropriate when data are available to estimate the proportion of the time the experimental outcome will occur if the experiment is repeated a large number of times. As an example consider a study of waiting times in the X-ray department for a local hospital. The number of patients waiting for service at 9:00 A.M. was recorded for 20 successive days. The following results were obtained.

| Number Waiting | Number of Days Outcome Occurred |
|:---:|:---:|
| 0 | 2 |
| 1 | 5 |
| 2 | 6 |
| 3 | 4 |
| 4 | 3 |
| Total | 20 |

These data show that on 2 of the 20 days, zero patients were waiting for service; on 5 of the days, one patient was waiting for service; and so on. Using the relative frequency method, we would assign a probability of 2/20 = .10 to the experimental outcome of zero patients waiting for service, 5/20 = .25 to the experimental outcome of one patient waiting, 6/20 = .30 to two patients waiting, 4/20 = .20 to three patients waiting, and 3/20 = .15 to four patients waiting.

As with the classical method, the two basic requirements of equations (4.3) and (4.4) are automatically satisfied when the relative frequency method is used.

The **subjective method** of assigning probabilities is most appropriate when it is unrealistic to assume that the experimental outcomes are equally likely and when little relevant data are available. When the subjective method is used to assign probabilities to the experimental outcomes, we may use any information available, such as our experience or intuition. After considering all available information, a probability value that expresses our *degree of belief* (on a scale from 0 to 1) that the experimental outcome will occur is specified. Because subjective probability expresses a person's degree of belief, it is personal. Using the subjective method, different people can be expected to assign different probabilities to the same experimental outcome.

When using the subjective probability assignment method, extra care must be taken to ensure that the requirements of equations (4.3) and (4.4) are satisfied. Regardless of a person's degree of belief, the probability value assigned to each experimental outcome must be between 0 and 1, inclusive, and the sum of all the probabilities for the experimental outcome must equal one.

Consider the case in which Tom and Judy Elsbernd have just made an offer to purchase a house. Two outcomes are possible:

$$E_1 = \text{their offer is accepted}$$
$$E_2 = \text{their offer is rejected}$$

Judy believes that the probability their offer will be accepted is .8; thus, Judy would set $P(E_1) = .8$ and $P(E_2) = .2$. Tom, however, believes that the probability that their offer will be accepted is .6; hence, Tom would set $P(E_1) = .6$ and $P(E_2) = .4$. Note that Tom's probability estimate for $E_1$ reflects the fact that he is a bit more pessimistic than Judy about their offer being accepted.

Both Judy and Tom have assigned probabilities that satisfy the two basic requirements. The fact that their probability estimates are different emphasizes the personal nature of the subjective method.

Even in business situations where either the classical or the relative frequency approach can be applied, managers may want to provide subjective probability estimates. In such cases, the best probability estimates often are obtained by combining the estimates from the classical or relative frequency approach with subjective probability estimates.

> Bayes' theorem (see Section 4.5) provides a means for combining subjectively determined prior probabilities with probabilities obtained by other means to obtain revised, or posterior, probabilities.

## Probabilities for the KP&L Project

To perform further analysis on the KP&L project, we must develop probabilities for each of the nine experimental outcomes listed in Table 4.1. On the basis of experience and judgment, management concluded that the experimental outcomes were not equally likely. Hence, the classical method of assigning probabilities could not be used. Management then decided to conduct a study of the completion times for similar projects undertaken by KP&L over the past three years. The results of a study of 40 similar projects are summarized in Table 4.2.

After reviewing the results of the study, management decided to employ the relative frequency method of assigning probabilities. Management could have provided subjective probability estimates, but felt that the current project was quite similar to the 40 previous projects. Thus, the relative frequency method was judged best.

In using the data in Table 4.2 to compute probabilities, we note that outcome (2, 6)—stage 1 completed in 2 months and stage 2 completed in 6 months—occurred six times in the 40 projects. We can use the relative frequency method to assign a probability of $6/40 = .15$ to this outcome. Similarly, outcome (2, 7) also occurred in six of the 40 projects, providing a $6/40 = .15$ probability. Continuing in this manner, we obtain the probability assignments for the sample points of the KP&L project shown in Table 4.3. Note that $P(2, 6)$ represents the probability of the sample point (2, 6), $P(2, 7)$ represents the probability of the sample point (2, 7), and so on.

**TABLE 4.2**    COMPLETION RESULTS FOR 40 KP&L PROJECTS

| Completion Time (months) | | Sample Point | Number of Past Projects Having These Completion Times |
|---|---|---|---|
| **Stage 1** | **Stage 2** | | |
| 2 | 6 | (2, 6) | 6 |
| 2 | 7 | (2, 7) | 6 |
| 2 | 8 | (2, 8) | 2 |
| 3 | 6 | (3, 6) | 4 |
| 3 | 7 | (3, 7) | 8 |
| 3 | 8 | (3, 8) | 2 |
| 4 | 6 | (4, 6) | 2 |
| 4 | 7 | (4, 7) | 4 |
| 4 | 8 | (4, 8) | 6 |
| | | Total | 40 |

**TABLE 4.3** PROBABILITY ASSIGNMENTS FOR THE KP&L PROBLEM BASED ON THE RELATIVE FREQUENCY METHOD

| Sample Point | Project Completion Time | Probability of Sample Point |
|:---:|:---:|:---:|
| (2, 6) | 8 months | $P(2, 6) = 6/40 = .15$ |
| (2, 7) | 9 months | $P(2, 7) = 6/40 = .15$ |
| (2, 8) | 10 months | $P(2, 8) = 2/40 = .05$ |
| (3, 6) | 9 months | $P(3, 6) = 4/40 = .10$ |
| (3, 7) | 10 months | $P(3, 7) = 8/40 = .20$ |
| (3, 8) | 11 months | $P(3, 8) = 2/40 = .05$ |
| (4, 6) | 10 months | $P(4, 6) = 2/40 = .05$ |
| (4, 7) | 11 months | $P(4, 7) = 4/40 = .10$ |
| (4, 8) | 12 months | $P(4, 8) = 6/40 = \underline{.15}$ |
| | | Total      1.00 |

## NOTES AND COMMENTS

1. In statistics, the notion of an experiment is somewhat different from the notion of an experiment in the physical sciences. In the physical sciences, an experiment is usually conducted in a laboratory or a controlled environment in order to learn about cause and effect. In statistical experiments, the outcomes are determined by probability. Even though the experiment is repeated in exactly the same way, an entirely different outcome may occur. Because of this influence of probability on the outcome, the experiments of statistics are sometimes called *random experiments*.

2. When drawing a random sample without replacement from a population of size $N$, the counting rule for combinations is used to find the number of different samples of size $n$ that can be selected.

## EXERCISES

### Methods

1. An experiment has three steps with three outcomes possible for the first step, two outcomes possible for the second step, and four outcomes possible for the third step. How many experimental outcomes exist for the entire experiment?

2. How many ways can three items be selected from a group of six items? Use the letters A, B, C, D, E, and F to identify the items, and list each of the different combinations of three items.

3. How many permutations of three items can be selected from a group of six? Use the letters A, B, C, D, E, and F to identify the items, and list each of the permutations of the three items (B, D, F).

4. Consider the experiment of tossing a coin three times.
   a. Develop a tree diagram for the experiment.
   b. List the experimental outcomes.
   c. What is the probability for each experimental outcome?

5. Suppose an experiment has five equally likely outcomes: $E_1, E_2, E_3, E_4, E_5$. Assign probabilities to each outcome and show that the conditions in equations (4.3) and (4.4) are satisfied. What method did you use?

6. An experiment with three outcomes has been repeated 50 times, and it was learned that $E_1$ occurred 20 times, $E_2$ occurred 13 times, and $E_3$ occurred 17 times. Assign probabilities to the outcomes. What method did you use?

7. A decision maker has subjectively assigned the following probabilities to the four outcomes of an experiment: $P(E_1) = .10$, $P(E_2) = .15$, $P(E_3) = .40$, and $P(E_4) = .20$. Are these valid probability assignments? Check to see whether equations (4.3) and (4.4) are satisfied.

## Applications

8. In the city of Milford, applications for zoning changes go through a two-step process: a review by the planning commission and a final decision by the city council. At step 1 the planning commission will review the zoning change request and make a positive or negative recommendation concerning the change. At step 2 the city council will review the planning commission's recommendation and then vote to approve or to disapprove the zoning change. An application for a zoning change has just been submitted by the developer of an apartment complex. Consider the application process as an experiment.
   a. How many sample points are there for this experiment? List the sample points.
   b. Construct a tree diagram for the experiment.

9. Simple random sampling uses a sample of size $n$ from a population of size $N$ to obtain data that can be used to make inferences about the characteristics of a population. Suppose we have a population of 50 bank accounts and want to take a random sample of four accounts in order to learn about the population. How many different random samples of four accounts are possible?

10. The availability of venture capital has provided a big boost in funds available to companies in recent years. According to Venture Economics (*Investor's Business Daily,* April 28, 2000), 2,374 venture capital disbursements were made in 1999. Of these, 1,434 were to companies in California, 390 were to companies in Massachusetts, 217 were to companies in New York, and 112 were to companies in Colorado. Twenty-two percent of the companies receiving funds were in the early stages of development and 55% of the companies were in an expansion stage.

   Suppose you want to randomly choose one of these companies to learn about how they used the funds.
   a. What is the probability the company chosen will be from California?
   b. What is the probability the company chosen will not be from one of the four states mentioned?
   c. What is the probability the company will not be in the early stages of development?
   d. Assuming the companies in the early stages of development were evenly distributed across the country, how many Massachusetts companies receiving venture capital funds were in their early stages of development?
   e. The total amount of funds invested was $32.4 billion. Estimate the amount that went to Colorado.

11. Strom Construction has made bids on two contracts. The owner has identified the possible outcomes and subjectively assigned the following probabilities.

| Experimental Outcome | Obtain Contract 1 | Obtain Contract 2 | Probability |
|---|---|---|---|
| 1 | Yes | Yes | .15 |
| 2 | Yes | No | .15 |
| 3 | No | Yes | .30 |
| 4 | No | No | .25 |

   a. Are these valid probability assignments? Why or why not?
   b. What would have to be done to make the probability assignments valid?

12. State lotteries have become popular means of fund raising. The Powerball lottery is open to participants across several states. When entering the Powerball lottery, a participant selects five numbers from the digits 1 through 49 and then selects a Powerball number from the digits 1 through 42. One week in 1998 the Powerball lottery jackpot reached $150,000,000, in addition to a payoff of $100,000 for anybody selecting the first five numbers correctly.
    a. Compute the number of ways the first five numbers can be selected.
    b. What is the probability of winning the $100,000 prize by selecting the first five numbers correctly?
    c. What is the probability of winning the Powerball jackpot?

13. A company that manufactures toothpaste is studying five different package designs. Assuming that one design is just as likely to be selected by a consumer as any other design, what selection probability would you assign to each of the package designs? In an actual experiment, 100 consumers were asked to pick the design they preferred. The following data were obtained. Do the data appear to confirm the belief that one design is just as likely to be selected as another? Explain.

| Design | Number of Times Preferred | |
|--------|---------------------------|------|
| 1 | 5 | .05 |
| 2 | 15 | .15 |
| 3 | 30 | .30 |
| 4 | 40 | .40 |
| 5 | 10 | .10 |

## 4.2   EVENTS AND THEIR PROBABILITIES

In the introduction to this chapter we used the term event much as it would be used in every-day language. Then, in Section 4.1 we introduced the concept of an experiment and its associated experimental outcomes or sample points. Sample points and events provide the foundation for the study of probability. As a result, we must now introduce the formal definition of an **event** as it relates to sample points. Doing so will provide the basis for determining the probability of an event.

> **Event**
>
> An event is a collection of sample points.

For an example, let us return to the KP&L problem and assume that the project manager is interested in the event that the entire project can be completed in 10 months or less. Referring to Table 4.3, we see that six sample points—(2, 6), (2, 7), (2, 8), (3, 6), (3, 7), and (4, 6)—provide a project completion time of 10 months or less. Let $C$ denote the event that the project is completed in 10 months or less; we write

$$C = \{(2, 6), (2, 7), (2, 8), (3, 6), (3, 7), (4, 6)\}$$

Event $C$ is said to occur if *any one* of these six sample points appears as the experimental outcome.

Other events that might be of interest to KP&L management include the following.

$L$ = The event that the project is completed in *less* than 10 months
$M$ = The event that the project is completed in *more* than 10 months

Using the information in Table 4.3, we see that these events consist of the following sample points.

$$L = \{(2, 6), (2, 7), (3, 6)\}$$
$$M = \{(3, 8), (4, 7), (4, 8)\}$$

A variety of additional events can be defined for the KP&L problem, but in each case the event must be identified as a collection of sample points for the experiment.

Given the probabilities of the sample points shown in Table 4.3, we can use the following definition to compute the probability of any event that KP&L management might want to consider.

### Probability of an Event

The probability of any event is equal to the sum of the probabilities of the sample points in the event.

Using this definition, we calculate the probability of a particular event by adding the probabilities of the sample points (experimental outcomes) that make up the event. We can now compute the probability that the project will take 10 months or less to complete. Because this event is given by $C = \{(2, 6), (2, 7), (2, 8), (3, 6), (3, 7), (4, 6)\}$, the probability of event $C$, denoted $P(C)$, is given by

$$P(C) = P(2, 6) + P(2, 7) + P(2, 8) + P(3, 6) + P(3, 7) + P(4, 6)$$

Refer to the sample point probabilities in Table 4.3; we have

$$P(C) = .15 + .15 + .05 + .10 + .20 + .05 = .70$$

Similarly, because the event that the project is completed in less than 10 months is given by $L = \{(2, 6), (2, 7), (3, 6)\}$, the probability of this event is given by

$$P(L) = P(2, 6) + P(2, 7) + P(3, 6)$$
$$= .15 + .15 + .10 = .40$$

Finally, for the event that the project is completed in more than 10 months, we have $M = \{(3, 8), (4, 7), (4, 8)\}$ and thus

$$P(M) = P(3, 8) + P(4, 7) + P(4, 8)$$
$$= .05 + .10 + .15 = .30$$

Using these probability results, we can now tell KP&L management that there is a .70 probability that the project will be completed in 10 months or less, a .40 probability that the project will be completed in less than 10 months, and a .30 probability that the project will be completed in more than 10 months. This procedure of computing event probabilities can be repeated for any event of interest to the KP&L management.

Any time that we can identify all the sample points of an experiment and assign probabilities to each, we can compute the probability of an event using the definition. However, in many experiments the number of sample points is large and the identification of the sample points, as well as the determination of their associated probabilities, is extremely cumbersome, if not impossible. In the remaining sections of this chapter, we present some basic probability relationships that can be used to compute the probability of an event without knowledge of all the sample point probabilities.

## NOTES AND COMMENTS

1. The sample space, $S$, is an event. Because it contains all the experimental outcomes, it has a probability of 1; that is, $P(S) = 1$.
2. When the classical method is used to assign probabilities, the assumption is that the experimental outcomes are equally likely. In such cases, the probability of an event can be computed by counting the number of experimental outcomes in the event and dividing the result by the total number of experimental outcomes.

## EXERCISES

### Methods

**14.** An experiment has four equally likely outcomes: $E_1$, $E_2$, $E_3$, and $E_4$.
   **a.** What is the probability that $E_2$ occurs?
   **b.** What is the probability that any two of the outcomes occur (e.g., $E_1$ or $E_3$)?
   **c.** What is the probability that any three of the outcomes occur (e.g., $E_1$ or $E_2$ or $E_4$)?

**15.** Consider the experiment of selecting a card from a deck of 52 cards. Each card corresponds to a sample point with a 1/52 probability.
   **a.** List the sample points in the event an ace is selected.
   **b.** List the sample points in the event a club is selected.
   **c.** List the sample points in the event a face card (jack, queen, or king) is selected.
   **d.** Find the probabilities associated with each of the events in (a), (b), and (c).

**16.** Consider the experiment of rolling a pair of dice. Suppose that we are interested in the sum of the face values showing on the dice.
   **a.** How many sample points are possible? (Hint: Use the counting rule for multiple-step experiments.)
   **b.** List the sample points.
   **c.** What is the probability of obtaining a value of 7?
   **d.** What is the probability of obtaining a value of 9 or greater?
   **e.** Because each roll has six possible even values (2, 4, 6, 8, 10, and 12) and only five possible odd values (3, 5, 7, 9, and 11), the dice should show even values more often than odd values. Do you agree with this statement? Explain.
   **f.** What method did you use to assign the probabilities requested?

### Applications

**17.** Refer to the KP&L sample points and sample point probabilities in Tables 4.2 and 4.3.
   **a.** The design stage (stage 1) will run over budget if it takes 4 months to complete. List the sample points in the event the design stage is over budget.
   **b.** What is the probability that the design stage is over budget?
   **c.** The construction stage (stage 2) will run over budget if it takes 8 months to complete. List the sample points in the event the construction stage is over budget.
   **d.** What is the probability that the construction stage is over budget?
   **e.** What is the probability that both stages are over budget?

**18.** Suppose that a manager of a large apartment complex provides the following subjective probability estimates about the number of vacancies that will exist next month.

| Vacancies | Probability |
|-----------|-------------|
| 0 | .05 |
| 1 | .15 |
| 2 | .35 |
| 3 | .25 |
| 4 | .10 |
| 5 | .10 |

List the sample points in each of the following events and provide the probability of the event.
  **a.** No vacancies
  **b.** At least four vacancies
  **c.** Two or fewer vacancies

**19.** The manager of a furniture store sells from 0 to 4 china hutches each week. On the basis of past experience, the following probabilities are assigned to sales of 0, 1, 2, 3, or 4 hutches: $P(0) = .08$; $P(1) = .18$; $P(2) = .32$; $P(3) = .30$; and $P(4) = .12$.
  **a.** Are these valid probability assignments? Why or why not?
  **b.** Let $A$ be the event that 2 or fewer are sold in one week. Find $P(A)$.
  **c.** Let $B$ be the event that 4 or more are sold in one week. Find $P(B)$.

**20.** *Fortune* magazine publishes an annual issue containing information on *Fortune* 500 companies. The following data show the six states with the largest number of *Fortune* 500 companies as well as the number of companies headquartered in those states (*Fortune*, April 17, 2000).

| State | Number of Companies |
|-------|---------------------|
| New York | 56 |
| California | 53 |
| Texas | 43 |
| Illinois | 37 |
| Ohio | 28 |
| Pennsylvania | 28 |

Suppose a *Fortune* 500 company is chosen for a follow-up questionnaire. What are the probabilities of the following events?
  **a.** Let $N$ be the event the company is headquartered in New York. Find $P(N)$.
  **b.** Let $T$ be the event the company is headquartered in Texas. Find $P(T)$.
  **a.** Let $B$ be the event the company is headquartered in one of these six states. Find $P(B)$.

**21.** A survey of 50 students at Tarpon Springs College about the number of extracurricular activities resulted in the data shown.

| Number of Activities | Frequency |
|----------------------|-----------|
| 0 | 8 |
| 1 | 20 |
| 2 | 12 |
| 3 | 6 |
| 4 | 3 |
| 5 | 1 |

  **a.** Let $A$ be the event that a student participates in at least 1 activity. Find $P(A)$.
  **b.** Let $B$ be the event that a student participates in 3 or more activities. Find $P(B)$.
  **c.** What is the probability that a student participates in exactly 2 activities?

## 4.3 SOME BASIC RELATIONSHIPS OF PROBABILITY

### Complement of an Event

Given an event $A$, the complement of $A$ is defined to be the event consisting of all sample points that are *not in A*. The complement of $A$ is denoted by $A^c$. Figure 4.4 is a diagram, known as a **Venn diagram,** which illustrates the concept of a complement. The rectangular area represents the sample space for the experiment and as such contains all possible sample points. The circle represents event $A$ and contains only the sample points that belong to $A$. The shaded region of the rectangle contains all sample points not in event $A$, and is by definition the complement of $A$.

In any probability application, either event $A$ or its complement $A^c$ must occur. Therefore, we have

$$P(A) + P(A^c) = 1$$

Solving for $P(A)$, we obtain the following result.

> **Computing Probability Using the Complement**
>
> $$P(A) = 1 - P(A^c) \tag{4.5}$$

Equation (4.5) shows that the probability of an event $A$ can be computed easily if the probability of its complement, $P(A^c)$, is known.

As an example, consider the case of a sales manager who, after reviewing sales reports, states that 80% of new customer contacts result in no sale. By allowing $A$ to denote the event of a sale and $A^c$ to denote the event of no sale, the manager is stating that $P(A^c) = .80$. Using equation (4.5), we see that

$$P(A) = 1 - P(A^c) = 1 - .80 = .20$$

We can conclude that a new customer contact has a .20 probability of resulting in a sale.

In another example, a purchasing agent states a .90 probability that a supplier will send a shipment that is free of defective parts. Using the complement, we can conclude that there is a $1 - .90 = .10$ probability that the shipment will contain defective parts.

**FIGURE 4.4**   COMPLEMENT OF EVENT $A$

## Addition Law

The addition law is helpful when we have two events and are interested in knowing the probability that at least one of the events occurs. That is, with events $A$ and $B$ we are interested in knowing the probability that event $A$ or event $B$ or both occur.

Before we present the addition law, we need to discuss two concepts related to the combination of events: the *union* of events and the *intersection* of events. Given two events $A$ and $B$, the **union of events** $A$ **and** $B$ is defined as follows.

> ### Union of Two Events
>
> The *union* of $A$ and $B$ is the event containing *all* sample points belonging to $A$ *or* $B$ *or both*. The union is denoted by $A \cup B$.

The Venn diagram in Figure 4.5 depicts the union of events $A$ and $B$. Note that the two circles contain all the sample points in event $A$ as well as all the sample points in event $B$. The fact that the circles overlap indicates that some sample points are contained in both $A$ and $B$.

The definition of the **intersection of events** $A$ **and** $B$ follows.

> ### Intersection of Two Events
>
> Given two events $A$ and $B$, the *intersection* of $A$ and $B$ is the event containing the sample points belonging to *both A and B*. The intersection is denoted by $A \cap B$.

The Venn diagram depicting the intersection of the two events is shown in Figure 4.6. The area where the two circles overlap is the intersection; it contains the sample points that are in both $A$ and $B$.

Let us now continue with a discussion of the addition law. The **addition law** provides a way to compute the probability of event $A$ or $B$ or both $A$ and $B$ occurring. In other words, the addition law is used to compute the probability of the union of two events, $A \cup B$. The addition law is written as follows.

> ### Addition Law
>
> $$P(A \cup B) = P(A) + P(B) - P(A \cap B)$$
>
> **(4.6)**

**FIGURE 4.5**   UNION OF EVENTS $A$ AND $B$

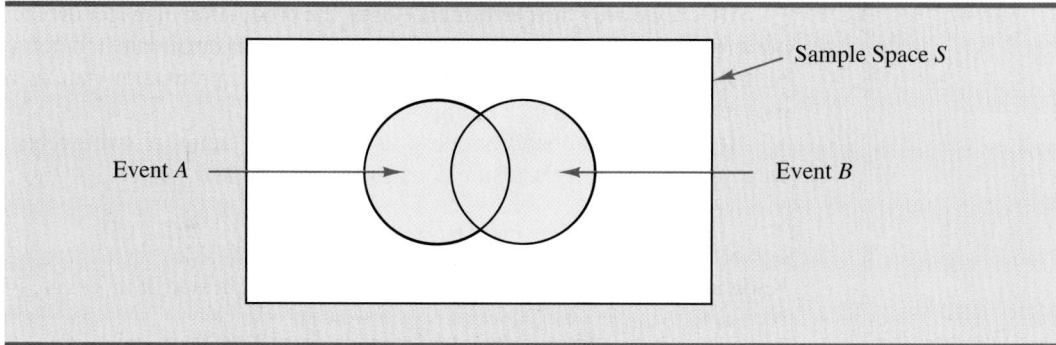

**FIGURE 4.6**   INTERSECTION OF EVENTS $A$ AND $B$

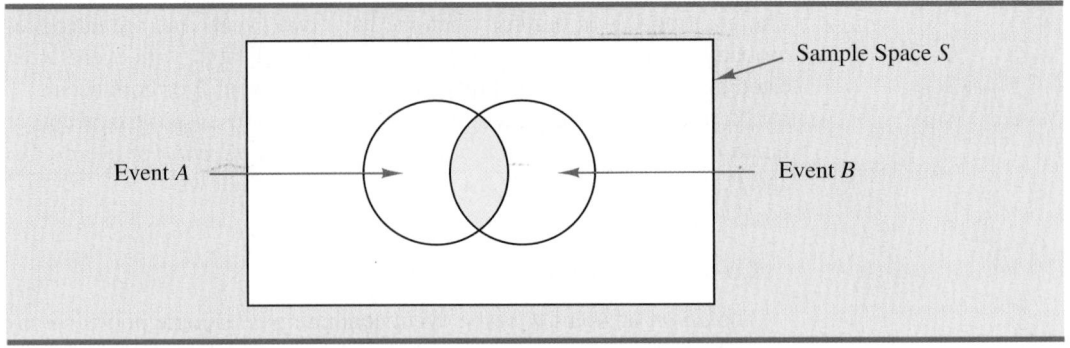

To understand the addition law intuitively, note that the first two terms in the addition law, $P(A) + P(B)$, account for all the sample points in $A \cup B$. However, because the sample points in the intersection $A \cap B$ are in both $A$ and $B$, when we compute $P(A) + P(B)$, we are in effect counting each of the sample points in $A \cap B$ twice. We correct for this over-counting by subtracting $P(A \cap B)$.

As an example of an application of the addition law, let us consider the case of a small assembly plant with 50 employees. Each worker is expected to complete work assignments on time and in such a way that the assembled product will pass a final inspection. On occasion, some of the workers fail to meet the performance standards by completing work late and/or assembling a defective product. At the end of a performance evaluation period, the production manager found that 5 of the 50 workers had completed work late, 6 of the 50 workers had assembled a defective product, and 2 of the 50 workers had both completed work late *and* assembled a defective product.

Let

$$L = \text{the event that the work is completed late}$$
$$D = \text{the event that the assembled product is defective}$$

The relative frequency information leads to the following probabilities.

$$P(L) = \frac{5}{50} = .10$$

$$P(D) = \frac{6}{50} = .12$$

$$P(L \cap D) = \frac{2}{50} = .04$$

After reviewing the performance data, the production manager decided to assign a poor performance rating to any employee whose work was either late or defective; thus the event of interest is $L \cup D$. What is the probability that the production manager assigned an employee a poor performance rating?

Note that the probability question is about the union of two events. Specifically, we want to know $P(L \cup D)$. Using equation (4.6), we have

$$P(L \cup D) = P(L) + P(D) - P(L \cap D)$$

Knowing values for the three probabilities on the right side of this expression, we can write

$$P(L \cup D) = .10 + .12 - .04 = .18$$

This calculation tells us that there is a .18 probability that a randomly selected employee received a poor performance rating.

As another example of the addition law, consider a recent study conducted by the personnel manager of a major computer software company. It was found that 30% of the employees who left the firm within two years did so primarily because they were dissatisfied with their salary, 20% left because they were dissatisfied with their work assignments, and 12% of the former employees indicated dissatisfaction with *both* their salary and their work assignments. What is the probability that an employee who leaves within two years does so because of dissatisfaction with salary, dissatisfaction with the work assignment, or both?

Let

$$S = \text{the event that the employee leaves because of salary}$$
$$W = \text{the event that the employee leaves because of work assignment}$$

We have $P(S) = .30$, $P(W) = .20$, and $P(S \cap W) = .12$. Using equation (4.6), the addition law, we have

$$P(S \cup W) = P(S) + P(W) - P(S \cap W) = .30 + .20 - .12 = .38.$$

We find a .38 probability that an employee leaves for salary or work assignment reasons.

Before we conclude our discussion of the addition law, let us consider a special case that arises for **mutually exclusive events.**

**Mutually Exclusive Events**

Two events are said to be mutually exclusive if the events have no sample points in common.

Events $A$ and $B$ are mutually exclusive if, when one event occurs, the other cannot occur. Thus, a requirement for $A$ and $B$ to be mutually exclusive is that their intersection must contain no sample points. The Venn diagram depicting two mutually exclusive events $A$ and $B$ is shown in Figure 4.7. In this case $P(A \cap B) = 0$ and the addition law can be written as follows.

**Addition Law for Mutually Exclusive Events**

$$P(A \cup B) = P(A) + P(B)$$

**FIGURE 4.7**    MUTUALLY EXCLUSIVE EVENTS

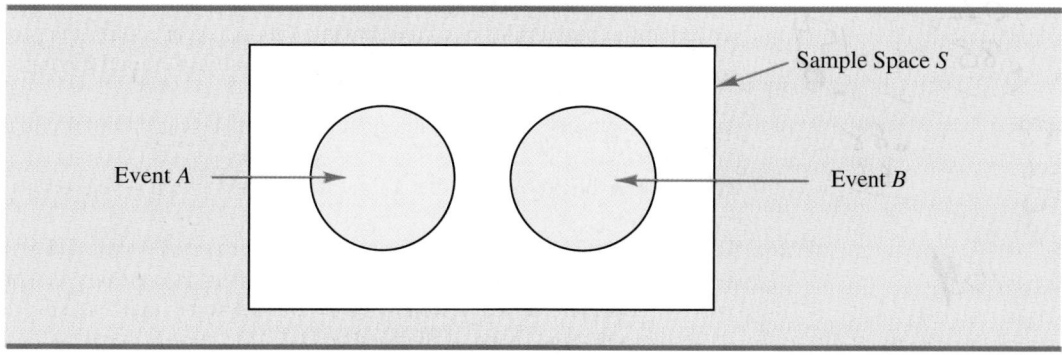

## EXERCISES

### Methods

22. Suppose that we have a sample space with five equally likely experimental outcomes: $E_1$, $E_2$, $E_3$, $E_4$, $E_5$. Let

$$A = \{E_1, E_2\}$$
$$B = \{E_3, E_4\}$$
$$C = \{E_2, E_3, E_5\}$$

a. Find $P(A)$, $P(B)$, and $P(C)$.
b. Find $P(A \cup B)$. Are $A$ and $B$ mutually exclusive?
c. Find $A^c$, $C^c$, $P(A^c)$, and $P(C^c)$.
d. Find $A \cup B^c$ and $P(A \cup B^c)$.
e. Find $P(B \cup C)$.

23. Suppose that we have a sample space $S = \{E_1, E_2, E_3, E_4, E_5, E_6, E_7\}$, where $E_1, E_2, \ldots$, $E_7$ denote the sample points. The following probability assignments apply: $P(E_1) = .05$, $P(E_2) = .20$, $P(E_3) = .20$, $P(E_4) = .25$, $P(E_5) = .15$, $P(E_6) = .10$, and $P(E_7) = .05$. Let

$$A = \{E_1, E_4, E_6\}$$
$$B = \{E_2, E_4, E_7\}$$
$$C = \{E_2, E_3, E_5, E_7\}$$

a. Find $P(A)$, $P(B)$, and $P(C)$.
b. Find $A \cup B$ and $P(A \cup B)$.
c. Find $A \cap B$ and $P(A \cap B)$.
d. Are events $A$ and $C$ mutually exclusive?
e. Find $B^c$ and $P(B^c)$.

### Applications

24. According to a *Business Week*/Harris poll, 14% of adults felt the chance of a big crash in the stock market during 1998 was very likely, and 43% felt the chance of a big crash during 1998 was somewhat likely (*Business Week,* December 29, 1997). If we were to choose an adult at random, what is the probability that she or he would indicate a crash was not likely?

25. Data on the 30 largest bond funds provides 1-year and 5-year percentage returns for the period ending March 31, 2000 (*The Wall Street Journal,* April 10, 2000). Suppose we consider a 1-year return in excess of 2% to be high and a 5-year return in excess of 44% to be high. One-half of the funds had a 1-year return in excess of 2%, 12 of the funds had a 5-year return in excess of 44%, and six of the funds had a 1-year return in excess of 2% and a 5-year return in excess of 44%.

a. Find the probability of a fund having a high 1-year return, the probability of a fund having a high 5-year return, and the probability of a fund having both a high 1-year return and a high 5-year return.
b. What is the probability that a fund has a high 1-year return or a high 5-year return or both?
c. What is the probability that a fund has neither a high 1-year return nor a high 5-year return?

26. Data on the 30 largest stock and balanced funds provided 1-year and 5-year percentage returns for the period ending March 31, 2000 (*The Wall Street Journal,* April 10, 2000). Suppose we consider a 1-year return in excess of 50% to be high and a 5-year return in excess of 300% to be high. Nine of the funds had 1-year returns in excess of 50%, seven of the

funds had 5-year returns in excess of 300%, and five of the funds had both 1-year returns in excess of 50% and 5-year returns in excess of 300%.

    **a.**   What is the probability of a high 1-year return and what is the probability of a high 5-year return?

    **b.**   What is the probability of both a high 1-year return and a high 5-year return?

    **c.**   What is the probability of neither a high 1-year return nor a high 5-year return?

**27.**   *Business Week* surveyed its subscribers concerning whether they consumed or served wine during an average week. The findings were that 57% consumed or served domestic wine, 33% consumed or served imported wine, and 63% consumed or served wine (*Business Week* 1996 Worldwide Subscriber Study). What is the probability that a *Business Week* subscriber consumes or serves both domestic and imported wine in an average week?

**28.**   A survey of magazine subscribers showed that 45.8% rented a car during the past 12 months for business reasons, 54% rented a car during the past 12 months for personal reasons, and 30% rented a car during the past 12 months for both business and personal reasons.

    **a.**   What is the probability that a subscriber rented a car during the past 12 months for business or personal reasons?

    **b.**   What is the probability that a subscriber did not rent a car during the past 12 months for either business or personal reasons?

**29.**   According to the Census Bureau, deaths in the United States occur at a rate of 2,425,000 per year. The National Center for Health Statistics reported that the three leading causes of death during 1997 were heart disease (725,790), cancer (537,390), and stroke (159,877). Let $H$, $C$, and $S$ represent the events that a person dies of heart disease, cancer, and stroke, respectively.

    **a.**   Use the data to estimate $P(H)$, $P(C)$, and $P(S)$.

    **b.**   Are events $H$ and $C$ mutually exclusive? Find $P(H \cap C)$.

    **c.**   What is the probability that a person dies from heart disease or cancer?

    **d.**   What is the probability that a person dies from cancer or a stroke?

    **e.**   Find the probability that someone dies from a cause other than one of these three.

## 4.4   CONDITIONAL PROBABILITY

Often, the probability of an event is influenced by whether a related event has occurred. Suppose we have an event $A$ with probability $P(A)$. If we obtain new information and learn that a related event, denoted by $B$, has occurred, we will want to take advantage of this information by calculating a new probability for event $A$. This new probability of event $A$ is called a **conditional probability** and is written $P(A \mid B)$. The notation | is used to denote the fact that we are considering the probability of event $A$ *given* the condition that event $B$ has occurred. Hence, the notation $P(A \mid B)$ is read "the probability of A given B."

As an illustration of the application of conditional probability, consider the situation of the promotion status of male and female officers of a major metropolitan police force in the eastern United States. The police force consists of 1200 officers, 960 men and 240 women. Over the past two years, 324 officers on the police force have been awarded promotions. The specific breakdown of promotions for male and female officers is shown in Table 4.4.

After reviewing the promotion record, a committee of female officers raised a discrimination case on the basis that 288 male officers had received promotions but only 36 female officers had received promotions. The police administration argued that the relatively low number of promotions for female officers was due not to discrimination, but to the fact that relatively few females are members of the police force. Let us show how conditional probability could be used to analyze the discrimination charge.

**TABLE 4.4**    PROMOTION STATUS OF POLICE OFFICERS OVER THE PAST TWO YEARS

|  | Men | Women | Totals |
|---|---|---|---|
| **Promoted** | 288 | 36 | 324 |
| **Not Promoted** | 672 | 204 | 876 |
| **Totals** | 960 | 240 | 1200 |

Let

$$M = \text{event an officer is a man}$$
$$W = \text{event an officer is a woman}$$
$$A = \text{event an officer is promoted}$$
$$A^c = \text{event an officer is not promoted}$$

Dividing the data values in Table 4.4 by the total of 1200 officers enables us to summarize the available information with the following probability values.

$P(M \cap A) = 288/1200 = .24 =$ probability that a randomly selected officer is a man *and* is promoted

$P(M \cap A^c) = 672/1200 = .56 =$ probability that a randomly selected officer is a man *and* is not promoted

$P(W \cap A) = 36/1200\ \ = .03 =$ probability that a randomly selected officer is a woman *and* is promoted

$P(W \cap A^c) = 204/1200 = .17 =$ probability that a randomly selected officer is a woman *and* is not promoted

Because each of these values gives the probability of the intersection of two events, the probabilities are called **joint probabilities.** Table 4.5, which provides a summary of the probability information for the police officer promotion situation, is referred to as a *joint probability table.*

The values in the margins of the joint probability table provide the probabilities of each event separately. That is, $P(M) = .80$, $P(W) = .20$, $P(A) = .27$, and $P(A^c) = .73$. These probabilities are referred to as **marginal probabilities** because of their location in the margins of the joint probability table. We note that the marginal probabilities are found by summing the joint probabilities in the corresponding row or column of the joint probability

**TABLE 4.5**    JOINT PROBABILITY TABLE FOR PROMOTIONS

Joint probabilities appear in the body of the table.

| | **Men ($M$)** | **Women ($W$)** | **Totals** |
|---|---|---|---|
| **Promoted ($A$)** | .24 | .03 | .27 |
| **Not Promoted ($A^c$)** | .56 | .17 | .73 |
| **Totals** | .80 | .20 | 1.00 |

Marginal probabilities appear in the margins of the table.

table. For instance, the marginal probability of being promoted is $P(A) = P(M \cap A) + P(W \cap A) = .24 + .03 = .27$. From the marginal probabilities, we see that 80% of the force is male, 20% of the force is female, 27% of all officers received promotions, and 73% were not promoted.

Let us begin the conditional probability analysis by computing the probability that an officer is promoted given that the officer is a man. In conditional probability notation, we are attempting to determine $P(A \mid M)$. To calculate $P(A \mid M)$, we first realize that this notation simply means that we are considering the probability of the event $A$ (promotion) given that the condition designated as event $M$ (the officer is a man) is known to exist. Thus $P(A \mid M)$ tells us that we are now concerned only with the promotion status of the 960 male officers. Because 288 of the 960 male officers received promotions, the probability of being promoted given that the officer is a man is $288/960 = .30$. In other words, given that an officer is a man, that officer has a 30% chance of receiving a promotion over the past two years.

This procedure was easy to apply because the values in Table 4.4 show the number of officers in each category. We now want to demonstrate how conditional probabilities such as $P(A \mid M)$ can be computed directly from related event probabilities rather than the frequency data of Table 4.4.

We have shown that $P(A \mid M) = 288/960 = .30$. Let us now divide both the numerator and denominator of this fraction by 1200, the total number of officers in the study.

$$P(A \mid M) = \frac{288}{960} = \frac{288/1200}{960/1200} = \frac{.24}{.80} = .30$$

We now see that the conditional probability $P(A \mid M)$ can be computed as .24/.80. Refer to the joint probability table (Table 4.5). Note in particular that .24 is the joint probability of $A$ and $M$; that is, $P(A \cap M) = .24$. Also note that .80 is the marginal probability that a randomly selected officer is a man; that is, $P(M) = .80$. Thus, the conditional probability $P(A \mid M)$ can be computed as the ratio of the joint probability $P(A \cap M)$ to the marginal probability $P(M)$.

$$P(A \mid M) = \frac{P(A \cap M)}{P(M)} = \frac{.24}{.80} = .30$$

The fact that conditional probabilities can be computed as the ratio of a joint probability to a marginal probability provides the following general formula for conditional probability calculations for two events $A$ and $B$.

**Conditional Probability**

$$P(A \mid B) = \frac{P(A \cap B)}{P(B)} \qquad\qquad \textbf{(4.7)}$$

or

$$P(B \mid A) = \frac{P(A \cap B)}{P(A)} \qquad\qquad \textbf{(4.8)}$$

The Venn diagram in Figure 4.8 is helpful in obtaining an intuitive understanding of conditional probability. The circle on the right shows that event $B$ has occurred; the portion of the circle that overlaps with event $A$ denotes the event $(A \cap B)$. We know that once event

**FIGURE 4.8    CONDITIONAL PROBABILITY** $P(A \mid B) = P(A \cap B)/P(B)$

$B$ has occurred, the only way that we can also observe event $A$ is for the event $(A \cap B)$ to occur. Thus, the ratio $P(A \cap B)/P(B)$ provides the conditional probability that we will observe event $A$ given event $B$ has already occurred.

Let us return to the issue of discrimination against the female officers. The marginal probability in row 1 of Table 4.5 shows that the probability of promotion of an officer is $P(A) = .27$ (regardless of whether that officer is male or female). However, the critical issue in the discrimination case involves the two conditional probabilities $P(A \mid M)$ and $P(A \mid W)$. That is, what is the probability of a promotion *given* that the officer is a man, and what is the probability of a promotion *given* that the officer is a woman? If these two probabilities are equal, a discrimination argument has no basis because the chances of a promotion are the same for male and female officers. However, a difference in the two conditional probabilities will support the position that male and female officers are treated differently in promotion decisions.

We have already determined that $P(A \mid M) = .30$. Let us now use the probability values in Table 4.5 and the basic relationship of conditional probability in equation (4.7) to compute the probability that an officer is promoted given that the officer is a woman; that is, $P(A \mid W)$. Using equation (4.7) with $W$ replacing $B$, we obtain

$$P(A \mid W) = \frac{P(A \cap W)}{P(W)} = \frac{.03}{.20} = .15$$

What conclusion do you draw? The probability of a promotion given that the officer is a man is .30, twice the .15 probability of a promotion given that the officer is a woman. Even though the use of conditional probability does not in itself prove that discrimination exists in this case, the conditional probability values support the argument presented by the female officers.

## Independent Events

In the preceding illustration, $P(A) = .27$, $P(A \mid M) = .30$, and $P(A \mid W) = .15$. We see that the probability of a promotion (event $A$) is affected or influenced by whether the officer is a man or a woman. Particularly, because $P(A \mid M) \neq P(A)$, we would say that events $A$ and $M$ are dependent events. That is, the probability of event $A$ (promotion) is altered or affected by knowing event $M$ (the officer is a man) exists. Similarly, with $P(A \mid W) \neq P(A)$, we would say that events $A$ and $W$ are *dependent events*. However, if the probability of event $A$ is not changed by the existence of event $M$—that is, $P(A \mid M) = P(A)$—we would say that events $A$

and *M* are **independent events.** This situation leads to the following definition of the independence of two events.

**Independent Events**

Two events *A* and *B* are independent if

$$P(A \mid B) = P(A) \tag{4.9}$$

or

$$P(B \mid A) = P(B) \tag{4.10}$$

Otherwise, the events are dependent.

## Multiplication Law

Whereas the addition law of probability is used to compute the probability of a union of two events, the multiplication law is used to compute the probability of an intersection of two events. The multiplication law is based on the definition of conditional probability. Using equations (4.7) and (4.8) and solving for $P(A \cap B)$, we obtain the **multiplication law.**

**Multiplication Law**

$$P(A \cap B) = P(B)P(A \mid B) \tag{4.11}$$

or

$$P(A \cap B) = P(A)P(B \mid A) \tag{4.12}$$

To illustrate the use of the multiplication law, consider a newspaper circulation department where it is known that 84% of the households in a particular neighborhood subscribe to the daily edition of the paper. If we let *D* denote the event that a household subscribes to the daily edition, $P(D) = .84$. In addition, it is known that the probability that a household who already holds a daily subscription also subscribes to the Sunday edition (event *S*) is .75; that is, $P(S \mid D) = .75$. What is the probability that a household subscribes to both the Sunday and daily editions of the newspaper? Using the multiplication law, we compute the desired $P(S \cap D)$ as

$$P(S \cap D) = P(D)P(S \mid D) = .84(.75) = .63$$

We now know that 63% of the households subscribe to both the Sunday and daily editions.

Before concluding this section, let us consider the special case of the multiplication law when the events involved are independent. Recall that events *A* and *B* are independent whenever $P(A \mid B) = P(A)$ or $P(B \mid A) = P(B)$. Hence, using equations (4.11) and (4.12) for the special case of independent events, we obtain the following multiplication law.

**Multiplication Law for Independent Events**

$$P(A \cap B) = P(A)P(B) \tag{4.13}$$

To compute the probability of the intersection of two independent events, we simply multiply the corresponding probabilities. Note that the multiplication law for independent events provides another way to determine whether $A$ and $B$ are independent. That is, if $P(A \cap B) = P(A)P(B)$, then $A$ and $B$ are independent; if $P(A \cap B) \neq P(A)P(B)$, then $A$ and $B$ are dependent.

As an application of the multiplication law for independent events, consider the situation of a service station manager who knows from past experience that 80% of the customers use a credit card when they purchase gasoline. What is the probability that the next two customers purchasing gasoline will each use a credit card? If we let

$A$ = the event that the first customer uses a credit card

$B$ = the event that the second customer uses a credit card

then the event of interest is $A \cap B$. Given no other information, we can reasonably assume that $A$ and $B$ are independent events. Thus,

$$P(A \cap B) = P(A)P(B) = (.80)(.80) = .64$$

To summarize this section, we note that our interest in conditional probability is motivated by the fact that events are often related. In such cases, we say the events are dependent and the conditional probability formulas in equations (4.7) and (4.8) must be used to compute the event probabilities. If two events are not related they are independent and neither event's probability is affected by whether the other event occurred.

## NOTES AND COMMENTS

Do not confuse the notion of mutually exclusive events with that of independent events. Two events with nonzero probabilities cannot be both mutually exclusive and independent. If one mutually exclusive event is known to occur, the other cannot occur; thus, the probability of the other event occurring is reduced to zero. They are therefore dependent.

## EXERCISES

### Methods

**30.** Suppose that we have two events, $A$ and $B$, with $P(A) = .50$, $P(B) = .60$, and $P(A \cap B) = .40$.

    **a.**  Find $P(A \mid B)$.

    **b.**  Find $P(B \mid A)$.

    **c.**  Are $A$ and $B$ independent? Why or why not?

**31.** Assume that we have two events, $A$ and $B$, that are mutually exclusive. Assume further that we know $P(A) = .30$ and $P(B) = .40$.

    **a.**  What is $P(A \cap B)$?

    **b.**  What is $P(A \mid B)$?

    **c.**  A student in statistics argues that the concepts of mutually exclusive events and independent events are really the same, and that if events are mutually exclusive they must be independent. Do you agree with this statement? Use the probability information in this problem to justify your answer.

    **d.**  What general conclusion would you make about mutually exclusive and independent events given the results of this problem?

## Applications

**32.** A Daytona Beach nightclub has the following data on the age and marital status of 140 customers.

|  |  | Marital Status | |
|---|---|---|---|
|  |  | **Single** | **Married** |
| Age | **Under 30** | 77 | 14 |
|  | **30 or Over** | 28 | 21 |

**a.** Develop a joint probability table for these data.
**b.** Use the marginal probabilities to comment on the age of customers attending the club.
**c.** Use the marginal probabilities to comment on the marital status of customers attending the club.
**d.** What is the probability of finding a customer who is single and under the age of 30?
**e.** If a customer is under 30, what is the probability that he or she is single?
**f.** Is marital status independent of age? Explain, using probabilities.

**33.** In a survey of MBA students, the following data were obtained on "students' first reason for application to the school in which they matriculated."

|  |  | Reason for Application | | | |
|---|---|---|---|---|---|
|  |  | **School Quality** | **School Cost or Convenience** | **Other** | **Totals** |
| Enrollment Status | **Full Time** | 421 | 393 | 76 | 890 |
|  | **Part Time** | 400 | 593 | 46 | 1039 |
|  | **Totals** | 821 | 986 | 122 | 1929 |

**a.** Develop a joint probability table for these data.
**b.** Use the marginal probabilities of school quality, cost/convenience, and other to comment on the most important reason for choosing a school.
**c.** If a student goes full time, what is the probability that school quality is the first reason for choosing a school?
**d.** If a student goes part time, what is the probability that school quality is the first reason for choosing a school?
**e.** Let A denote the event that a student is full time and let B denote the event that the student lists school quality as the first reason for applying. Are events A and B independent? Justify your answer.

**34.** The following table shows the distribution of blood types in the general population (Hoxworth Blood Center, Cincinnati, Ohio).

|  | **A** | **B** | **AB** | **O** |
|---|---|---|---|---|
| **Rh+** | 34% | 9% | 4% | 38% |
| **Rh−** | 6% | 2% | 1% | 6% |

**a.** What is the probability a person will have type O blood?
**b.** What is the probability a person will be Rh−?
**c.** What is the probability a married couple will both be Rh−?
**d.** What is the probability a married couple will both have type AB blood?
**e.** What is the probability a person will be Rh− given she or he has type O blood?
**f.** What is the probability a person will have type B blood given he or she is Rh+?

35. "Since 1950, the January Barometer has predicted the annual course of the stock market with amazing accuracy" (*1998 Stock Trader's Almanac*). Over the 48 years from 1950 through 1997, the stock market has been up in January 31 times; it has been up for the year 36 times; and it has been up for the year and up for January 29 times.
    a. Estimate the probability the stock market will be up in January.
    b. Estimate the probability the stock market will be up for the year.
    c. What is the probability the stock market will be up for the year given it is up in January?
    d. Do the probabilities suggest that the stock market's January performance and its annual performance are independent events? Explain.

36. A study of job satisfaction was conducted for four occupations: cabinetmaker, lawyer, physical therapist, and systems analyst. Job satisfaction was measured on a scale of 0–100. The data obtained are summarized in the following crosstabulation.

| Occupation | Under 50 | 50–59 | 60–69 | 70–79 | 80–89 |
|---|---|---|---|---|---|
| Cabinetmaker | 0 | 2 | 4 | 3 | 1 |
| Lawyer | 6 | 2 | 1 | 1 | 0 |
| Physical Therapist | 0 | 5 | 2 | 1 | 2 |
| Systems Analyst | 2 | 1 | 4 | 3 | 0 |

(Satisfaction Score spans the five columns: Under 50, 50–59, 60–69, 70–79, 80–89)

    a. Develop a joint probability table.
    b. What is the probability one of the participants studied received a satisfaction score in the 80s?
    c. What is the probability of a satisfaction score in the 80s given the study participant was a physical therapist?
    d. What is the probability one of the participants studied was a lawyer?
    e. What is the probability one of the participants was a lawyer and received a score under 50?
    f. What is the probability of receiving a satisfaction score under 50 given a person is a lawyer?
    g. What is the probability of a satisfaction score of 70 or higher?

37. A purchasing agent has placed rush orders for a particular raw material with two different suppliers, A and B. If neither order arrives in four days, the production process must be shut down until at least one of the orders arrives. The probability that supplier A can deliver the material in four days is .55. The probability that supplier B can deliver the material in four days is .35.
    a. What is the probability that both suppliers will deliver the material in four days? Because two separate suppliers are involved, we are willing to assume independence.
    b. What is the probability that at least one supplier will deliver the material in four days?
    c. What is the probability that the production process will be shut down in four days because of a shortage of raw material (that is, both orders are late)?

38. A survey of 1035 workers by the Institute for the Future and the Gallup Organization found that workers are being inundated by messages (*The Cincinnati Enquirer*, November 2, 1998). The study indicated that each worker gets an average of 190 messages per day. The following table shows the breakdown by type of message.

| Source | Daily Messages | Source | Daily Messages |
|---|---|---|---|
| Telephone | 52 | E-mail | 30 |
| Voice mail | 22 | Interoffice mail | 18 |
| U.S. mail | 18 | Fax | 15 |
| Post-it note | 11 | Phone msg. slip | 10 |
| Pager | 4 | Overnight courier | 4 |
| Cellular phone | 3 | U.S. Express mail | 3 |

a. For any particular worker, what is the probability the next message will be on the telephone?

b. For the next two messages, what is the probability the first will be via e-mail and the second will be via fax?

c. What is the probability the next message received will be via telephone call or inter-office mail?

## 4.5 BAYES' THEOREM

In the discussion of conditional probability, we indicated that revising probabilities when new information is obtained is an important phase of probability analysis. Often, we begin the analysis with initial or **prior probability** estimates for specific events of interest. Then, from sources such as a sample, a special report, or a product test, we obtain additional information about the events. Given this new information, we update the prior probability values by calculating revised probabilities, referred to as **posterior probabilities. Bayes' theorem** provides a means for making these probability calculations. The steps in this probability revision process are shown in Figure 4.9.

As an application of Bayes' theorem, consider a manufacturing firm that receives shipments of parts from two different suppliers. Let $A_1$ denote the event that a part is from supplier 1 and $A_2$ denote the event that a part is from supplier 2. Currently, 65% of the parts purchased by the company are from supplier 1 and the remaining 35% are from supplier 2. Hence, if a part is selected at random, we would assign the prior probabilities $P(A_1) = .65$ and $P(A_2) = .35$.

The quality of the purchased parts varies with the source of supply. Historical data suggest that the quality ratings of the two suppliers are as shown in Table 4.6. If we let $G$ denote the event that a part is good and $B$ denote the event that a part is bad, the information in Table 4.6 provides the following conditional probability values.

$$P(G \mid A_1) = .98 \quad P(B \mid A_1) = .02$$
$$P(G \mid A_2) = .95 \quad P(B \mid A_2) = .05$$

The tree diagram in Figure 4.10 depicts the process of the firm receiving a part from one of the two suppliers and then discovering that the part is good or bad as a two-step experiment. We see that four experimental outcomes are possible; two correspond to the part being good and two correspond to the part being bad.

Each of the experimental outcomes is the intersection of two events, so we can use the multiplication rule to compute the probabilities. For instance,

$$P(A_1, G) = P(A_1 \cap G) = P(A_1)P(G \mid A_1)$$

The process of computing these joint probabilities can be depicted in what is called a probability tree (see Figure 4.11). From left to right through the tree, the probabilities

**FIGURE 4.9** PROBABILITY REVISION USING BAYES' THEOREM

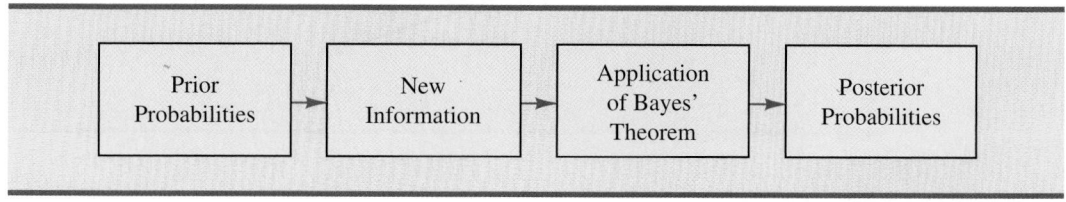

**TABLE 4.6**    HISTORICAL QUALITY LEVELS OF TWO SUPPLIERS

|  | Percentage Good Parts | Percentage Bad Parts |
|---|---|---|
| **Supplier 1** | 98 | 2 |
| **Supplier 2** | 95 | 5 |

**FIGURE 4.10**    TWO-STEP DIAGRAM

Note: Step 1 shows that the part comes from one of two suppliers, and Step 2 shows whether the part is good or bad.

**FIGURE 4.11**    PROBABILITY TREE FOR TWO-SUPPLIER EXAMPLE

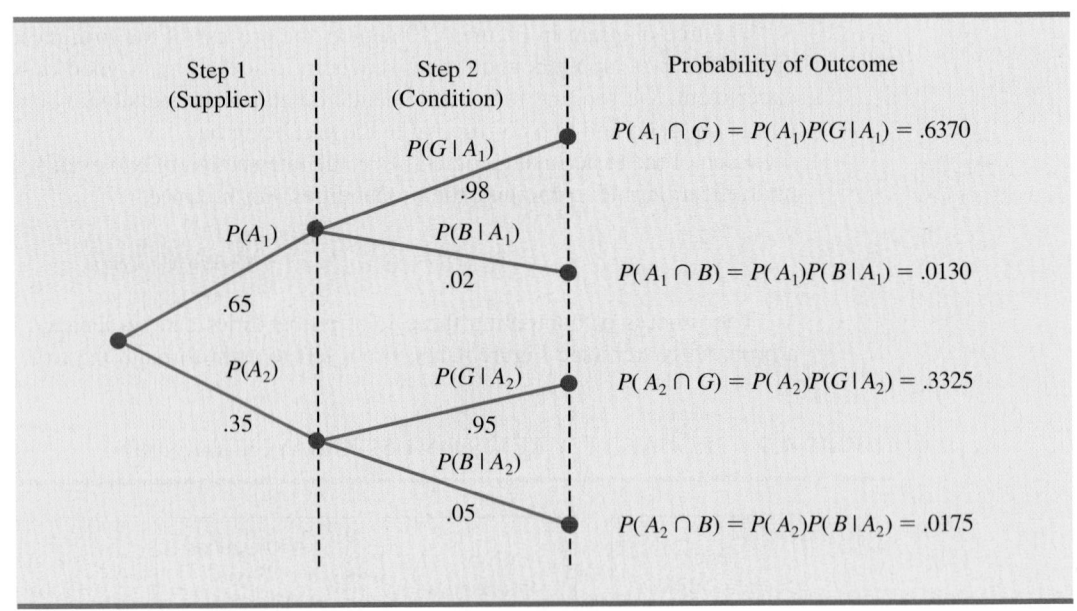

for each branch at step 1 are prior probabilities and the probabilities for each branch at step 2 are conditional probabilities. To find the probabilities of each experimental outcome, we simply multiply the probabilities on the branches leading to the outcome. Each of these joint probabilities is shown in Figure 4.11 along with the known probabilities for each branch.

Suppose now that the parts from the two suppliers are used in the firm's manufacturing process and that a machine breaks down because it attempts to process a bad part. Given the information that the part is bad, what is the probability that it came from supplier 1 and what is the probability that it came from supplier 2? With the information in the probability tree (Figure 4.11), Bayes' theorem can be used to answer these questions.

Letting $B$ denote the event that the part is bad, we are looking for the posterior probabilities $P(A_1 \mid B)$ and $P(A_2 \mid B)$. From the law of conditional probability, we know that

$$P(A_1 \mid B) = \frac{P(A_1 \cap B)}{P(B)} \qquad\qquad (4.14)$$

Referring to the probability tree, we see that

$$P(A_1 \cap B) = P(A_1)P(B \mid A_1) \qquad\qquad (4.15)$$

To find $P(B)$, we note that event $B$ can occur in only two ways: $(A_1 \cap B)$ and $(A_2 \cap B)$. Therefore, we have

$$
\begin{aligned}
P(B) &= P(A_1 \cap B) + P(A_2 \cap B) \\
&= P(A_1)P(B \mid A_1) + P(A_2)P(B \mid A_2)
\end{aligned}
\qquad\qquad (4.16)
$$

Substituting from equations (4.15) and (4.16) into equation (4.14) and writing a similar result for $P(A_2 \mid B)$, we obtain Bayes' theorem for the case of two events.

The Reverend Thomas Bayes (1702–1761), a Presbyterian minister, is credited with the original work leading to the version of Bayes' theorem in use today.

**Bayes' Theorem (Two-Event Case)**

$$P(A_1 \mid B) = \frac{P(A_1)P(B \mid A_1)}{P(A_1)P(B \mid A_1) + P(A_2)P(B \mid A_2)} \qquad\qquad (4.17)$$

$$P(A_2 \mid B) = \frac{P(A_2)P(B \mid A_2)}{P(A_1)P(B \mid A_1) + P(A_2)P(B \mid A_2)} \qquad\qquad (4.18)$$

Using equation (4.17) and the probability values provided in the example, we have

$$
\begin{aligned}
P(A_1 \mid B) &= \frac{P(A_1)P(B \mid A_1)}{P(A_1)P(B \mid A_1) + P(A_2)P(B \mid A_2)} \\[2mm]
&= \frac{(.65)(.02)}{(.65)(.02) + (.35)(.05)} = \frac{.0130}{.0130 + .0175} \\[2mm]
&= \frac{.0130}{.0305} = .4262
\end{aligned}
$$

In addition, using equation (4.18), we find $P(A_2 \mid B)$.

$$P(A_2 \mid B) = \frac{(.35)(.05)}{(.65)(.02) + (.35)(.05)}$$

$$= \frac{.0175}{.0130 + .0175} = \frac{.0175}{.0305} = .5738$$

Note that in this application we started with a probability of .65 that a part selected at random was from supplier 1. However, given information that the part is bad, the probability that the part is from supplier 1 drops to .4262. In fact, if the part is bad, it has better than a 50–50 chance that it came from supplier 2; that is, $P(A_2 \mid B) = .5738$.

Bayes' theorem is applicable when the events for which we want to compute posterior probabilities are mutually exclusive and their union is the entire sample space.* Bayes' theorem can be extended to the case of $n$ mutually exclusive events $A_1, A_2, \ldots, A_n$, whose union is the entire sample space. In such a case, Bayes' theorem for the computation of any posterior probability $P(A_i \mid B)$ has the following form.

### Bayes' Theorem

$$P(A_i \mid B) = \frac{P(A_i)P(B \mid A_i)}{P(A_1)P(B \mid A_1) + P(A_2)P(B \mid A_2) + \cdots + P(A_n)P(B \mid A_n)} \quad \textbf{(4.19)}$$

With prior probabilities $P(A_1), P(A_2), \ldots, P(A_n)$ and the appropriate conditional probabilities $P(B \mid A_1), P(B \mid A_2), \ldots, P(B \mid A_n)$, equation (4.19) can be used to compute the posterior probability of the events $A_1, A_2, \ldots, A_n$.

## Tabular Approach

A tabular approach is helpful in conducting the Bayes' theorem calculations. Such an approach is shown in Table 4.7 for the parts supplier problem. The computations shown there are done in the following steps.

**Step 1.** Prepare the following three columns:
Column 1—The mutually exclusive events $A_i$ for which posterior probabilities are desired.
Column 2—The prior probabilities $P(A_i)$ for the events.
Column 3—The conditional probabilities $P(B \mid A_i)$ of the new information $B$ given each event.

**Step 2.** In column 4, compute the joint probabilities $P(A_i \cap B)$ for each event and the new information $B$ by using the multiplication law. These joint probabilities are found by multiplying the prior probabilities in column 2 by the corresponding conditional probabilities in column 3; that is, $P(A_i \cap B) = P(A_i)P(B \mid A_i)$.

**Step 3.** Sum the joint probabilities in column 4. The sum is the probability of the new information, $P(B)$. Thus we see in Table 4.7 that there is a .0130 probability of a bad part and supplier 1 and a .0175 probability of a bad part and supplier 2. Because these are the only two ways in which a bad part can be obtained, the sum .0130 + .0175 shows an overall probability of .0305 of finding a bad part from the combined shipments of the two suppliers.

---

*If the union of events is the entire sample space, the events are said to be *collectively exhaustive*.

**TABLE 4.7**   SUMMARY OF BAYES' THEOREM CALCULATIONS FOR THE TWO-SUPPLIER PROBLEM

| (1) Events $A_i$ | (2) Prior Probabilities $P(A_i)$ | (3) Conditional Probabilities $P(B \mid A_i)$ | (4) Joint Probabilities $P(A_i \cap B)$ | (5) Posterior Probabilities $P(A_i \mid B)$ |
|---|---|---|---|---|
| $A_1$ | .65 | .02 | .0130 | .0130/.0305 =  .4262 |
| $A_2$ | .35 | .05 | .0175 | .0175/.0305 =  .5738 |
|  | 1.00 |  | $P(B) = .0305$ | 1.0000 |

**Step 4.** In column 5, compute the posterior probabilities using the basic relationship of conditional probability.

$$P(A_i \mid B) = \frac{P(A_i \cap B)}{P(B)}$$

Note that the joint probabilities $P(A_i \cap B)$ are in column 4 and the probability $P(B)$ is the sum of column 4.

## Using Excel to Compute Posterior Probabilities

The tabular approach to Bayes' Theorem can be easily implemented within an Excel worksheet. In this subsection we show how the Bayes' theorem calculations shown in Table 4.7 can be made. Refer to Figure 4.12 as we describe the tasks involved. The formula worksheet is in the background; the value worksheet is in the foreground.

**Enter Data:**   Labels are placed in rows 1 and 2 and the two mutually exclusive events are identified in cells A3:A4. The prior probabilities were entered into cells B3:B4 and the conditional probabilities were entered into cells C3:C4.

**Enter Functions and Formulas:**   The formulas in cells D3:D4 show that the joint probabilities are the product of the prior probabilities in column B and the conditional probabilities in column C. The results, shown in cells D3:D4 of the value worksheet, are the same as those shown in Table 4.7. The sum in cell D5 shows that the probability of finding a bad part is .0305. This probability is the denominator in Bayes' theorem. The formulas in cells E3:E4 provide the posterior probabilities. From the value worksheet we see that they are the same as the posterior probabilities in Table 4.7.

**FIGURE 4.12**   EXCEL WORKSHEET FOR COMPUTING POSTERIOR PROBABILITIES

| | A | B | C | D | E | F |
|---|---|---|---|---|---|---|
| 1 | | Prior | Conditional | Joint | Posterior | |
| 2 | Events | Probabilities | Probabilities | Probabilities | Probabilities | |
| 3 | A1 | 0.65 | 0.02 | =B3*C3 | =D3/$D$5 | |
| 4 | A2 | 0.35 | 0.05 | =B4*C4 | =D4/$D$5 | |
| 5 | | =SUM(B3:B4) | | =SUM(D3:D4) | =SUM(E3:E4) | |
| 6 | | | | | | |

| | A | B | C | D | E | F |
|---|---|---|---|---|---|---|
| 1 | | Prior | Conditional | Joint | Posterior | |
| 2 | Events | Probabilities | Probabilities | Probabilities | Probabilities | |
| 3 | A1 | 0.65 | 0.02 | 0.0130 | 0.4262 | |
| 4 | A2 | 0.35 | 0.05 | 0.0175 | 0.5738 | |
| 5 | | 1 | | 0.0305 | 1.0000 | |
| 6 | | | | | | |

Note that the same worksheet could be used to find the posterior probabilities of the two suppliers given a good part is found. The prior probabilities in cells B3:B4 would not change. But, we would replace the conditional probabilities in cells C3:C4 with the values .98 and .95 respectively. Doing so would provide $P(A_1 \mid G) = .6570$ and $P(A_2 \mid G) = .3430$ in cells E3:E4.

This worksheet can also be modified to handle Bayes' theorem calculations for more than two events. Just add a row for each additional event and move the sum row down.

## NOTES AND COMMENTS

1. Bayes' theorem is used extensively in decision analysis. The prior probabilities are often subjective estimates provided by a decision maker. Sample information is obtained and posterior probabilities are computed for use in choosing the best decision.

2. An event and its complement are mutually exclusive, and their union is the entire sample space. Thus, Bayes' theorem is always applicable for computing posterior probabilities of an event and its complement.

## EXERCISES

### Methods

**39.** The prior probabilities for events $A_1$ and $A_2$ are $P(A_1) = .40$ and $P(A_2) = .60$. It is also known that $P(A_1 \cap A_2) = 0$. Suppose $P(B \mid A_1) = .20$ and $P(B \mid A_2) = .05$.
   **a.** Are $A_1$ and $A_2$ mutually exclusive? Explain.
   **b.** Compute $P(A_1 \cap B)$ and $P(A_2 \cap B)$.
   **c.** Compute $P(B)$.
   **d.** Apply Bayes' theorem to compute $P(A_1 \mid B)$ and $P(A_2 \mid B)$.

**40.** The prior probabilities for events $A_1$, $A_2$, and $A_3$ are $P(A_1) = .20$, $P(A_2) = .50$, and $P(A_3) = .30$. The conditional probabilities of event $B$ given $A_1$, $A_2$, and $A_3$ are $P(B \mid A_1) = .50$, $P(B \mid A_2) = .40$, and $P(B \mid A_3) = .30$.
   **a.** Compute $P(B \cap A_1)$, $P(B \cap A_2)$, and $P(B \cap A_3)$.
   **b.** Apply Bayes' theorem, equation (4.19), to compute the posterior probability $P(A_2 \mid B)$.
   **c.** Use the tabular approach to applying Bayes' theorem to compute $P(A_1 \mid B)$, $P(A_2 \mid B)$, and $P(A_3 \mid B)$.

### Applications

**41.** A consulting firm has submitted a bid for a large research project. The firm's management initially felt they had a 50–50 chance of getting the project. However, the agency to which the bid was submitted has subsequently requested additional information on the bid. Past experience indicates that on 75% of the successful bids and 40% of the unsuccessful bids the agency requested additional information.
   **a.** What is the prior probability of the bid being successful (that is, prior to the request for additional information)?
   **b.** What is the conditional probability of a request for additional information given that the bid will ultimately be successful?
   **c.** Compute a posterior probability that the bid will be successful given that a request for additional information has been received.

**42.** A local bank is reviewing its credit card policy with a view toward recalling some of its credit cards. In the past approximately 5% of cardholders have defaulted and the bank has been unable to collect the outstanding balance. Hence, management has established a prior probability of .05 that any particular cardholder will default. The bank has further found that the probability of missing one or more monthly payments is .20 for customers who do not default. Of course, the probability of missing one or more payments for those who default is 1.

a. Given that a customer has missed a monthly payment, compute the posterior probability that the customer will default.

b. The bank would like to recall its card if the probability that a customer will default is greater than .20. Should the bank recall its card if the customer misses a monthly payment? Why or why not?

43. Small cars get better gas mileage, but they are not as safe as bigger cars. Small cars accounted for 18% of the vehicles on the road, but accidents involving small cars led to 11,898 fatalities during a recent year (*Reader's Digest,* May 2000). The probability of an accident involving a small car leading to a fatality is .128 and the probability of an accident not involving a small car leading to a fatality is .05. Suppose you learn of an accident involving a fatality. What is the probability a small car was involved?

44. A city has a professional basketball team playing at home and a professional hockey team playing away on the same night. A professional basketball team has a .641 probability of winning a home game and a professional hockey team has a .462 probability of winning an away game. Historically, when both teams play on the same night, the chance that the next morning's leading sports story will be about the basketball game is 60% and the chance that it will be about the hockey game is 40%. Suppose that on the morning after these games the newspaper's leading sports story begins with the headline "We Win!!" What is the probability that the story is about the basketball team?

45. *M. D. Computing* (May 1991) describes the use of Bayes' theorem and the use of conditional probability in medical diagnosis. Prior probabilities of diseases are based on the physician's assessment of such things as geographical location, seasonal influence, occurrence of epidemics, and so forth. Assume that a patient is believed to have one of two diseases, denoted $D_1$ and $D_2$ with $P(D_1) = .60$ and $P(D_2) = .40$ and that medical research has determined the probability associated with each symptom that may accompany the diseases. Suppose that, given diseases $D_1$ and $D_2$, the probabilities that the patient will have symptoms $S_1$, $S_2$, or $S_3$ are as follows.

|  |  | Symptoms | | |
| --- | --- | --- | --- | --- |
|  |  | $S_1$ | $S_2$ | $S_3$ |
| Disease | $D_1$ | .15 | .10 | .15 |
|  | $D_2$ | .80 | .15 | .03 |

$P(S_3 \mid D_1)$

After a certain symptom is found to be present, the medical diagnosis may be aided by finding the revised probabilities of each particular disease. Compute the posterior probabilities of each disease given the following medical findings.

a. The patient has symptom $S_1$.

b. The patient has symptom $S_2$.

c. The patient has symptom $S_3$.

d. For the patient with symptom $S_1$ in part (a), suppose we also find symptom $S_2$. What are the revised probabilities of $D_1$ and $D_2$?

## SUMMARY

In this chapter we introduced basic probability concepts and illustrated how probability analysis can be used to provide helpful information for decision making. We described how probability can be interpreted as a numerical measure of the likelihood that an event will occur. In addition, we saw that the probability of an event can be computed either by summing the probabilities of the experimental outcomes (sample points) comprising the event or by using the relationships established by the addition, conditional probability, and multiplication laws of probability. For cases in which additional information is available, we showed how Bayes' theorem can be used to obtain revised or posterior probabilities.

## GLOSSARY

**Probability**   A numerical measure of the likelihood that an event will occur.

**Experiment**   A process that generates well-defined outcomes.

**Sample space**   The set of all experimental outcomes.

**Sample point**   An element of the sample space. A sample point represents an experimental outcome.

**Tree diagram**   A graphical representation helpful in identifying the sample points of an experiment involving multiple steps.

**Basic requirements of probability**   Two requirements that restrict the manner in which probability assignments can be made: (1) for each experimental outcome $E_i$ we must have $0 \leq P(E_i) \leq 1$; (2) considering all experimental outcomes, we must have $P(E_1) + P(E_2) + \cdots + P(E_n) = 1$.

**Classical method**   A method of assigning probabilities that is appropriate when the experimental outcomes are equally likely.

**Relative frequency method**   A method of assigning probabilities that is appropriate when data are available to estimate the proportion of times an experimental outcome will occur in the long run.

**Subjective method**   A method of assigning probabilities on the basis of judgment.

**Event**   A collection of sample points.

**Complement of event $A$**   The event consisting of all sample points that are not in $A$.

**Venn diagram**   A graphical representation for showing symbolically the sample space and operations involving events in which the sample space is represented by a rectangle and events are represented as circles within the sample space.

**Union of events $A$ and $B$**   The event containing all sample points that are in $A$, in $B$, or in both. The union is denoted $A \cup B$.

**Intersection of events $A$ and $B$**   The event containing all sample points that are in both $A$ and $B$. The intersection is denoted $A \cap B$.

**Addition law**   A probability law used to compute the probability of a union of two events, denoted $A$ and $B$. It is $P(A \cup B) = P(A) + P(B) - P(A \cap B)$. For mutually exclusive events, because $P(A \cap B) = 0$, it reduces to $P(A \cup B) = P(A) + P(B)$.

**Mutually exclusive events**   Events that have no sample points in common; that is, $A \cap B$ is empty and $P(A \cap B) = 0$.

**Conditional probability**   The probability of an event given that another event has occurred. The conditional probability of $A$ given $B$ is $P(A \mid B) = P(A \cap B)/P(B)$.

**Joint probability**   The probability of two events both occurring; that is, the probability of the intersection of two events.

**Marginal probability**   The unconditional probabilities appearing in the margins of a joint probability table.

**Independent events**    Two events $A$ and $B$ where $P(A \mid B) = P(A)$ or $P(B \mid A) = P(B)$; that is, the events have no influence on each other.

**Multiplication law**    A probability law used to compute the probability of an intersection of two events, denoted $A$ and $B$. It is $P(A \cap B) = P(B)P(A \mid B)$ or $P(A \cap B) = P(A)P(B \mid A)$. For independent events it reduces to $P(A \cap B) = P(A)P(B)$.

**Prior probabilities**    Initial estimates of the probabilities of events.

**Posterior probabilities**    Revised probabilities of events based on additional information.

**Bayes' theorem**    A method used to compute posterior probabilities.

## KEY FORMULAS

**Counting Rule for Combinations**

$$C_n^N = \binom{N}{n} = \frac{N!}{n!(N-n)!} \tag{4.1}$$

**Counting Rule for Permutations**

$$P_n^N = n!\binom{N}{n} = \frac{N!}{(N-n)!} \tag{4.2}$$

**Computing Probability Using the Complement**

$$P(A) = 1 - P(A^c) \tag{4.5}$$

**Addition Law**

$$P(A \cup B) = P(A) + P(B) - P(A \cap B) \tag{4.6}$$

**Conditional Probability**

$$P(A \mid B) = \frac{P(A \cap B)}{P(B)} \tag{4.7}$$

$$P(B \mid A) = \frac{P(A \cap B)}{P(A)} \tag{4.8}$$

**Multiplication Law**

$$P(A \cap B) = P(B)P(A \mid B) \tag{4.11}$$
$$P(A \cap B) = P(A)P(B \mid A) \tag{4.12}$$

**Multiplication Law for Independent Events**

$$P(A \cap B) = P(A)P(B) \tag{4.13}$$

**Bayes' Theorem**

$$P(A_i \mid B) = \frac{P(A_i)P(B \mid A_i)}{P(A_1)P(B \mid A_1) + P(A_2)P(B \mid A_2) + \cdots + P(A_n)P(B \mid A_n)} \tag{4.19}$$

## SUPPLEMENTARY EXERCISES

**46.** In a *Business Week*/Harris Poll, 1035 adults were asked about their attitudes toward business (*Business Week*, September 11, 2000). One question asked: "How would you rate large U.S. companies on making good products and competing in a global environment?" The responses were: excellent—18%, pretty good—50%, only fair—26%, poor—5%, and don't know/no answer—1%.
   **a.** What is the probability that a respondent rated U.S. companies pretty good or excellent?
   **b.** How many respondents rated U.S. companies poor?
   **c.** How many respondents did not know or did not answer?

**47.** A financial manager has just made two new investments—one in the oil industry and one in municipal bonds. After a one-year period, each of the investments will be classified as either successful or unsuccessful. Consider the making of the two investments as an experiment.
   **a.** How many sample points exist for this experiment?
   **b.** Show a tree diagram and list the sample points.
   **c.** Let $O$ = the event that the oil industry investment is successful and $M$ = the event that the municipal bond investment is successful. List the sample points in $O$ and in $M$.
   **d.** List the sample points in the union of the events ($O \cup M$).
   **e.** List the sample points in the intersection of the events ($O \cap M$).
   **f.** Are events $O$ and $M$ mutually exclusive? Explain.

**48.** A survey of American opinion asked: Are you satisfied or dissatisfied with the state of the U.S. economy today? (*The Wall Street Journal*, June 27, 1997). The following table provides the responses for all adults and the distribution by age groups.

|  | **Satisfied (%)** | **Dissatisfied (%)** | **Other (%)** |
|---|---|---|---|
| **All Adults** | 61 | 37 | 2 |
| **18–34** | 64 | 35 | 1 |
| **35–49** | 58 | 41 | 1 |
| **50–64** | 57 | 40 | 3 |
| **65+** | 70 | 26 | 4 |

   **a.** What is the probability a respondent is satisfied?
   **b.** Which age groups report a higher level of satisfaction than the average for all adults?
   **c.** What is the probability a respondent 65 or over did not indicate they were satisfied?

**49.** A study of 31,000 hospital admissions in New York State was conducted by a Harvard research team led by Paul Weiler (*Business Week*, March 27, 1995). They found that 4% of the admissions led to treatment-caused injuries. One-seventh of these treatment-caused injuries resulted in death, and one-fourth were caused by negligence. Malpractice claims were filed in one out of 7.5 cases involving negligence, and payments were made in one out of every two claims.
   **a.** What is the probability a person admitted to the hospital will suffer a treatment-caused injury due to negligence?
   **b.** What is the probability a person admitted to the hospital will die from a treatment-caused injury?
   **c.** In the case of a negligent treatment-caused injury, what is the probability a malpractice claim will be paid?

**50.** A telephone survey was used to determine viewer response to a new television show. The following data were obtained.

| Rating | Frequency |
|---|---|
| Poor | 4 |
| Below average | 8 |
| Average | 11 |
| Above average | 14 |
| Excellent | 13 |

**a.** What is the probability that a randomly selected viewer will rate the new show as average or better?

**b.** What is the probability that a randomly selected viewer will rate the new show below average or worse?

51. *Business Week* surveyed its subscribers concerning the number of cars they owned or leased. Responses were obtained to three questions: How many cars do you own? How many cars do you lease? How many cars do you have (owned or leased)? Table 4.8 contains the results obtained from 932 households (*Business Week* 1996 Worldwide Subscriber Study). In interpreting the table note that the third row shows that 401 households own 2 cars, 47 households lease 2 cars, and 447 households have 2 cars (owned and/or leased).

    **a.** What is the probability a household leases 1 car?

    **b.** What is the probability a household owns 2 or fewer cars?

    **c.** What is the probability a household has 3 or more cars?

    **d.** What is the probability a household does not own or lease a car?

**TABLE 4.8**    NUMBER OF CARS OWNED OR LEASED, AND TOTAL NUMBER OF CARS PER HOUSEHOLD

| | | Number of Households | |
|---|---|---|---|
| Cars | **Own** | **Lease** | **Have** |
| 0 | 65 | 708 | 19 |
| 1 | 242 | 168 | 168 |
| 2 | 401 | 47 | 447 |
| 3 | 149 | 9 | 186 |
| 4 or more | 75 | 0 | 112 |
| Total | 932 | 932 | 932 |

52. A GMAC MBA new-matriculants survey provided the following data for 2018 students.

| | | Applied to More Than One School | |
|---|---|---|---|
| | | **Yes** | **No** |
| | **23 and under** | 207 | 201 |
| Age | **24–26** | 299 | 379 |
| Group | **27–30** | 185 | 268 |
| | **31–35** | 66 | 193 |
| | **36 and over** | 51 | 169 |

    **a.** For a randomly selected MBA student, prepare a joint probability table for the experiment consisting of observing the student's age and whether the student applied to one or more schools.

    **b.** What is the probability that a randomly selected applicant is 23 or under?

    **c.** What is the probability that a randomly selected applicant is older than 26?

    **d.** What is the probability that a randomly selected applicant applied to more than one school?

53. Refer again to the data from the GMAC new-matriculants survey in Exercise 52.

    **a.** Given that a person applied to more than one school, what is the probability that the person is 24–26 years old?

    **b.** Given that a person is in the 36-and-over age group, what is the probability that the person applied to more than one school?

    **c.** What is the probability that a person is 24–26 years old or applied to more than one school?

    **d.** Suppose a person is known to have applied to only one school. What is the probability that the person is 31 or more years old?

    **e.** Is the number of schools applied to independent of age? Explain.

**54.** An IBD/TIPP poll was conducted to learn about attitudes toward investment and retirement (*Investor's Business Daily*, May 5, 2000). One question asked male and female respondents how important they felt level of of risk was in choosing a retirement investment. The following joint probability table was constructed from the data provided. Important means the respondent said level of risk was either important or very important.

| | Male | Female | Total |
|---|---|---|---|
| **Important** | .22 | .27 | .49 |
| **Not Important** | .28 | .23 | .51 |
| **Total** | .50 | .50 | 1.00 |

    **a.** What is the probability a survey respondent will say level of risk is important?

    **b.** What is the probability a male respondent will say level of risk is important?

    **c.** What is the probability a female respondent will say level of risk is important?

    **d.** Is the level of risk independent of the gender of the respondent? Why or why not?

    **e.** Do male and female attitudes toward risk differ?

**55.** A large consumer goods company has been running a television advertisement for one of its soap products. A survey was conducted. On the basis of this survey, probabilities were assigned to the following events.

$$B = \text{individual purchased the product}$$
$$S = \text{individual recalls seeing the advertisement}$$
$$B \cap S = \text{individual purchased the product and recalls seeing the advertisement}$$

The probabilities assigned were $P(B) = .20$, $P(S) = .40$, and $P(B \cap S) = .12$.

    **a.** What is the probability of an individual's purchasing the product given that the individual recalls seeing the advertisement? Does seeing the advertisement increase the probability that the individual will purchase the product? As a decision maker, would you recommend continuing the advertisement (assuming that the cost is reasonable)?

    **b.** Assume that individuals who do not purchase the company's soap product buy from its competitors. What would be your estimate of the company's market share? Would you expect that continuing the advertisement will increase the company's market share? Why or why not?

    **c.** The company has also tested another advertisement and assigned it values of $P(S) = .30$ and $P(B \cap S) = .10$. What is $P(B \mid S)$ for this other advertisement? Which advertisement seems to have had the bigger effect on customer purchases?

**56.** Cooper Realty is a small real estate company located in Albany, New York, specializing primarily in residential listings. They have recently become interested in determining the likelihood of one or their listings being sold within a certain number of days. An analysis of company sales of 800 homes in previous years produced the following data.

| | | Days Listed Until Sold | | |
|---|---|---|---|---|
| | | Under 30 | 31–90 | Over 90 | Total |
| | **Under $50,000** | 50 | 40 | 10 | 100 |
| | **$50,000–$99,999** | 20 | 150 | 80 | 250 |
| **Initial Asking Price** | **$100,000–$150,000** | 20 | 280 | 100 | 400 |
| | **Over $150,000** | 10 | 30 | 10 | 50 |
| | **Total** | 100 | 500 | 200 | 800 |

  **a.** If $A$ is defined as the event that a home is listed for over 90 days before being sold, estimate the probability of $A$.
  **b.** If $B$ is defined as the event that the initial asking price is under \$50,000, estimate the probability of $B$.
  **c.** What is the probability of $A \cap B$?
  **d.** Assuming that a contract has just been signed to list a home that has an initial asking price of less than \$50,000, what is the probability that the home will take Cooper Realty more than 90 days to sell?
  **e.** Are events $A$ and $B$ independent?

**57.** A company has studied the number of lost-time accidents occurring at its Brownsville, Texas, plant. Historical records show that 6% of the employees had lost-time accidents last year. Management believes that a special safety program will reduce such accidents to 5% during the current year. In addition, it estimates that 15% of employees who had lost-time accidents last year will have a lost-time accident during the current year.
  **a.** What percentage of the employees will have lost-time accidents in both years?
  **b.** What percentage of the employees will have at least one lost-time accident over the two-year period?

**58.** The Dallas IRS auditing staff is concerned with identifying potentially fraudulent tax returns. From past experience they believe that the probability of finding a fraudulent return given that the return contains deductions for contributions exceeding the IRS standard is .20. Given that the deductions for contributions do not exceed the IRS standard, the probability of a fraudulent return decreases to .02. If 8% of all returns exceed the IRS standard for deductions due to contributions, what is the best estimate of the percentage of fraudulent returns?

**59.** An oil company has purchased an option on land in Alaska. Preliminary geologic studies have assigned the following prior probabilities.

$$P(\text{high-quality oil}) = .50$$
$$P(\text{medium-quality oil}) = .20$$
$$P(\text{no oil}) = .30$$

  **a.** What is the probability of finding oil?
  **b.** After 200 feet of drilling on the first well, a soil test is taken. The probabilities of finding the particular type of soil identified by the test follow.

$$P(\text{soil} \mid \text{high-quality oil}) = .20$$
$$P(\text{soil} \mid \text{medium-quality oil}) = .80$$
$$P(\text{soil} \mid \text{no oil}) = .20$$

  How should the firm interpret the soil test? What are the revised probabilities, and what is the new probability of finding oil?

**60.** A Bayesian approach can be used to revise probabilities that a prospect field will produce oil (*Oil & Gas Journal,* January 11, 1988). In one case, geological assessment indicates a 25% chance that the field will produce oil. Further, there is an 80% chance that a particular well will produce oil given that oil is present in the prospect field.
  **a.** Suppose that one well is drilled on the field and it comes up dry. What is the probability that the prospect field will produce oil?
  **b.** If two wells come up dry, what is the probability that the field will produce oil?
  **c.** The oil company would like to keep looking as long as the chances of finding oil are greater than 1%. How many dry wells must be drilled before the field will be abandoned?

**Case Problem · HAMILTON COUNTY JUDGES**

Hamilton County judges try thousands of cases per year. In an overwhelming majority of the cases disposed, the verdict stands as rendered. However, some cases are appealed, and of those appealed, some of the cases are reversed. Kristen DelGuzzi of *The Cincinnati Enquirer* conducted a study of cases handled by Hamilton County judges over the years 1994 through 1996 (*The Cincinnati Enquirer,* January 11, 1998). Shown in Table 4.9 are the results for 182,908 cases handled (disposed) by 38 judges in Common Pleas Court, Domestic Relations Court, and Municipal Court. Two of the judges (Dinkelacker and Hogan) did not serve in the same court for the entire three-year period.

The purpose of the newspaper's study was to evaluate the performance of the judges. Appeals are often the result of mistakes made by judges, and the newspaper wanted to know which judges were doing a good job and which were making too many mistakes. You have been called in to assist in the data analysis. Use your knowledge of probability and conditional probability to help with the ranking of the judges. You also may be able to analyze the likelihood of cases handled by different courts being appealed and reversed.

## Managerial Report

Prepare a report with your rankings of the judges. Also, include an analysis of the likelihood of appeal and case reversal in the three courts. At a minimum, your report should include the following:

1. The probability of cases being appealed and reversed in the three different courts.
2. The probability of a case being appealed for each judge.
3. The probability of a case being reversed for each judge.
4. The probability of reversal given an appeal for each judge.
5. Rank the judges within each court. State the criteria you used and provide a rationale for your choice.

**TABLE 4.9**  TOTAL CASES DISPOSED, APPEALED, AND REVERSED IN HAMILTON
COUNTY COURTS DURING 1994 THROUGH 1996

### Common Pleas Court

| Judge | Total Cases Disposed | Appealed Cases | Reversed Cases |
|---|---|---|---|
| Fred Cartolano | 3037 | 137 | 12 |
| Thomas Crush | 3372 | 119 | 10 |
| Patrick Dinkelacker | 1258 | 44 | 8 |
| Timothy Hogan | 1954 | 60 | 7 |
| Robert Kraft | 3138 | 127 | 7 |
| William Mathews | 2264 | 91 | 18 |
| William Morrissey | 3032 | 121 | 22 |
| Norbert Nadel | 2959 | 131 | 20 |
| Arthur Ney, Jr. | 3219 | 125 | 14 |
| Richard Niehaus | 3353 | 137 | 16 |
| Thomas Nurre | 3000 | 121 | 6 |
| John O'Connor | 2969 | 129 | 12 |
| Robert Ruehlman | 3205 | 145 | 18 |
| J. Howard Sundermann | 955 | 60 | 10 |
| Ann Marie Tracey | 3141 | 127 | 13 |
| Ralph Winkler | 3089 | 88 | 6 |
| Total | 43945 | 1762 | 199 |

### Domestic Relations Court

| Judge | Total Cases Disposed | Appealed Cases | Reversed Cases |
|---|---|---|---|
| Penelope Cunningham | 2729 | 7 | 1 |
| Patrick Dinkelacker | 6001 | 19 | 4 |
| Deborah Gaines | 8799 | 48 | 9 |
| Ronald Panioto | 12970 | 32 | 3 |
| Total | 30499 | 106 | 17 |

### Municipal Court

| Judge | Total Cases Disposed | Appealed Cases | Reversed Cases |
|---|---|---|---|
| Mike Allen | 6149 | 43 | 4 |
| Nadine Allen | 7812 | 34 | 6 |
| Timothy Black | 7954 | 41 | 6 |
| David Davis | 7736 | 43 | 5 |
| Leslie Isaiah Gaines | 5282 | 35 | 13 |
| Karla Grady | 5253 | 6 | 0 |
| Deidra Hair | 2532 | 5 | 0 |
| Dennis Helmick | 7900 | 29 | 5 |
| Timothy Hogan | 2308 | 13 | 2 |
| James Patrick Kenney | 2798 | 6 | 1 |
| Joseph Luebbers | 4698 | 25 | 8 |
| William Mallory | 8277 | 38 | 9 |
| Melba Marsh | 8219 | 34 | 7 |
| Beth Mattingly | 2971 | 13 | 1 |
| Albert Mestemaker | 4975 | 28 | 9 |
| Mark Painter | 2239 | 7 | 3 |
| Jack Rosen | 7790 | 41 | 13 |
| Mark Schweikert | 5403 | 33 | 6 |
| David Stockdale | 5371 | 22 | 4 |
| John A. West | 2797 | 4 | 2 |
| Total | 108464 | 500 | 104 |

# Chapter 5

# DISCRETE PROBABILITY DISTRIBUTIONS

## CONTENTS

## STATISTICS IN PRACTICE

### CITIBANK*
*Long Island City, New York*

Citibank, a division of Citigroup, makes available a wide range of financial services, including checking and savings accounts, loans and mortgages, insurance, and investment services, within the framework of a unique strategy for delivering those services called Citibanking. Citibanking entails a consistent brand identity all over the world, consistent product offerings, and high-level customer service. Citibanking lets you manage your money anytime, anywhere, anyway you choose. Whether you need to save for the future or borrow for today, you can do it all at Citibank.

Citibanking's state-of-the art automatic teller machines (ATMs) located in Citicard Banking Centers (CBCs), let customers do all their banking in one place with the touch of a finger, 24 hours a day, 7 days a week. More than 150 different banking functions from deposits to managing investments can be performed with ease. Citibanking ATMs are so much more than just cash machines that customers today use them for 80% of their transactions.

Each Citibank CBC operates as a waiting line system with randomly arriving customers seeking service at one of the ATMs. If all ATMs are busy, the arriving customers wait in line. Periodic CBC capacity studies are used to analyze customer waiting times and to determine whether additional ATMs are needed.

Data collected by Citibank showed that the random customer arrivals followed a probability distribution known as the Poisson probability distribution. Using the Poisson probability distribution, Citibank can compute probabilities for the number of customers arriving at a CBC during any time period and

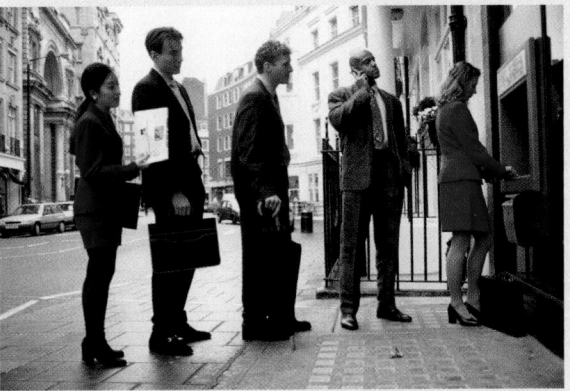

Customers waiting in line at an ATM. © PhotoDisc, Inc.

make decisions concerning the number of ATMs needed. For example, let $x$ = the number of customers arriving during a one-minute period. Assuming that a particular CBC has a mean arrival rate of two customers per minute, the following table shows the probabilities for the number of customers arriving during a one-minute period.

| $x$ | Probability |
|---|---|
| 0 | .1353 |
| 1 | .2707 |
| 2 | .2707 |
| 3 | .1804 |
| 4 | .0902 |
| 5 or more | .0527 |

Discrete probability distributions, such as the one used by Citibank, are the topic of this chapter. In addition to the Poisson probability distribution, you will learn about the binomial and hypergeometric probability distributions and how they can be used to provide helpful probability information.

*The authors are indebted to Ms. Stacey Karter, Citibank, for providing this Statistics in Practice.

In this chapter we continue the study of probability by introducing the concepts of random variables and probability distributions. The focus of this chapter is discrete probability distributions. Three special discrete probability distributions—the binomial, Poisson, and hypergeometric—are covered.

## 5.1    RANDOM VARIABLES

In Chapter 4 we defined the concept of an experiment and its associated experimental outcomes. A random variable provides a means for describing experimental outcomes using numerical values.

Random variables must
assume numerical values.

> **Random Variable**
>
> A **random variable** is a numerical description of the outcome of an experiment.

In effect, a random variable associates a numerical value with each possible experimental outcome. The particular numerical value of the random variable depends on the outcome of the experiment. A random variable can be classified as being either *discrete* or *continuous* depending on the numerical values it assumes.

## Discrete Random Variables

A random variable that may assume either a finite number of values or an infinite sequence of values such as 0, 1, 2, . . . is referred to as a **discrete random variable.** For example, consider the experiment of an accountant taking the certified public accountant (CPA) examination. The examination has four parts. We can define a random variable as $x =$ the number of parts of the CPA examination passed. It is a discrete random variable because it may assume the finite number of values 0, 1, 2, 3, or 4.

As another example of a discrete random variable, consider the experiment of cars arriving at a tollbooth. The random variable of interest is $x =$ the number of cars arriving during a one-day period. The possible values for $x$ come from the sequence of integers 0, 1, 2, and so on. Hence, $x$ is a discrete random variable assuming one of the values in this infinite sequence.

Although many experiments have outcomes that are naturally described by numerical values, others do not. For example, a survey question might ask an individual to recall the message in a recent television commercial. This experiment would have two possible outcomes: the individual cannot recall the message and the individual can recall the message. We can still describe these experimental outcomes numerically by defining the discrete random variable $x$ as follows: let $x = 0$ if the individual cannot recall the message and $x = 1$ if the individual can recall the message. The numerical values for this random variable are arbitrary (we could have used 5 and 10), but they are acceptable in terms of the definition of a random variable—namely, $x$ is a random variable because it provides a numerical description of the outcome of the experiment.

Table 5.1 provides some additional examples of discrete random variables. Note that in each example the discrete random variable assumes a finite number of values or an infinite sequence of values such as 0, 1, 2, . . . . Discrete random variables such as these are discussed in detail in this chapter.

**TABLE 5.1    EXAMPLES OF DISCRETE RANDOM VARIABLES**

| Experiment | Random Variable ($x$) | Possible Values for the Random Variable |
|---|---|---|
| Contact five customers | Number of customers who place an order | 0, 1, 2, 3, 4, 5 |
| Inspect a shipment of 50 radios | Number of defective radios | 0, 1, 2, $\cdots$, 49, 50 |
| Operate a restaurant for one day | Number of customers | 0, 1, 2, 3, $\cdots$ |
| Sell an automobile | Gender of the customer | 0 if male; 1 if female |

## Continuous Random Variables

A random variable that may assume any numerical value in an interval or collection of intervals is called a **continuous random variable.** Experimental outcomes that are based on measurement scales such as time, weight, distance, and temperature can be described by continuous random variables. For example, consider an experiment of monitoring incoming telephone calls to the claims office of a major insurance company. Suppose the random variable of interest is $x =$ the time between consecutive incoming calls in minutes. This random variable may assume any value in the interval $x \geq 0$. Actually, an infinite number of values are possible for $x$, including values such as 1.26 minutes, 2.751 minutes, 4.3333 minutes, and so on. As another example, consider a 90-mile section of interstate highway I-75 north of Atlanta, Georgia. For an emergency ambulance service located in Atlanta, we might define the random variable as $x =$ number of miles to the location of the next traffic accident along this section of I-75. In this case, $x$ would be a continuous random variable assuming any value in the interval $0 \leq x \leq 90$. Additional examples of continuous random variables are listed in Table 5.2. Note that each example describes a random variable that may assume any value in an interval of values. Continuous random variables and their probability distributions will be the topic of Chapter 6.

**TABLE 5.2**    EXAMPLES OF CONTINUOUS RANDOM VARIABLES

| Experiment | Random Variable ($x$) | Possible Values for the Random Variable |
|---|---|---|
| Operate a bank | Time between customer arrivals in minutes | $x \geq 0$ |
| Fill a soft drink can (max = 12.1 ounces) | Number of ounces | $0 \leq x \leq 12.1$ |
| Construct a new library | Percentage of project complete after 6 months | $0 \leq x \leq 100$ |
| Test a new chemical process | Temperature when the desired reaction takes place (min 150° F; max 212° F) | $150 \leq x \leq 212$ |

**NOTES AND COMMENTS**

One way to determine whether a random variable is discrete or continuous is to think of the values of the random variable as points on a line segment. Choose two points representing values of the random variable. If the entire line segment between the two points also represents possible values for the random variable, then the random variable is continuous.

**EXERCISES**

## Methods

1.  Consider the experiment of tossing a coin twice.
    a.   List the experimental outcomes.
    b.   Define a random variable that represents the number of heads occurring on the two tosses.
    c.   Show what value the random variable would assume for each of the experimental outcomes.
    d.   Is this random variable discrete or continuous?

2. Consider the experiment of a worker assembling a product.
   a. Define a random variable that represents the time in minutes required to assemble the product.
   b. What values may the random variable assume?
   c. Is the random variable discrete or continuous?

## Applications

3. Three students have interviews scheduled for summer employment at the Brookwood Institute. In each case the result of the interview will be that a position is either offered or not offered. Experimental outcomes are defined in terms of the results of the three interviews.
   a. List the experimental outcomes.
   b. Define a random variable that represents the number of offers made. Is the random variable discrete or continuous?
   c. Show the value of the random variable for each of the experimental outcomes.

4. Suppose we know home mortgage rates for 12 Florida lending institutions. Assume that the random variable of interest is the number of lending institutions in this group that offers a 30-year fixed rate of 8.5% or less. What values may this random variable assume?

5. To perform a certain type of blood analysis, lab technicians must perform two procedures. The first procedure requires either 1 or 2 separate steps, and the second procedure requires either 1, 2, or 3 steps.
   a. List the experimental outcomes associated with performing the blood analysis.
   b. If the random variable of interest is the total number of steps required to do the complete analysis (both procedures), show what value the random variable will assume for each of the experimental outcomes.

6. Listed is a series of experiments and associated random variables. In each case, identify the values that the random variable can assume and state whether the random variable is discrete or continuous.

| Experiment | Random Variable ($x$) |
|---|---|
| a. Take a 20-question examination | Number of questions answered correctly |
| b. Observe cars arriving at a tollbooth for 1 hour | Number of cars arriving at tollbooth |
| c. Audit 50 tax returns | Number of returns containing errors |
| d. Observe an employee's work | Number of nonproductive hours in an 8-hour workday |
| e. Weigh a shipment of goods | Number of pounds |

## 5.2  DISCRETE PROBABILITY DISTRIBUTIONS

The **probability distribution** for a random variable describes how probabilities are distributed over the values of the random variable. For a discrete random variable $x$, the probability distribution is defined by a **probability function,** denoted by $f(x)$. The probability function provides the probability for each value of the random variable.

As an illustration of a discrete random variable and its probability distribution, consider the sales of automobiles at DiCarlo Motors in Saratoga, New York. Over the past 300 days of operation, sales data show 54 days with no automobiles sold, 117 days with 1 automobile sold, 72 days with 2 automobiles sold, 42 days with 3 automobiles sold, 12 days with 4 automobiles sold, and 3 days with 5 automobiles sold. Suppose we consider the experiment of selecting a day of operation at DiCarlo Motors and define the random variable of interest as $x =$ the number of automobiles sold during a day. From historical data, we know $x$ is a discrete random variable that can assume the values 0, 1, 2, 3, 4, or 5. In probability function notation, $f(0)$ provides the probability of 0 automobiles sold, $f(1)$ provides the probability of 1 automobile sold, and so on. Because historical data show 54 of 300 days with 0 automobiles sold, we assign the value 54/300 = .18 to $f(0)$, indicating that the probability of 0 automobiles being sold during a day is .18. Similarly, because 117 of 300 days had 1 automobile sold, we assign the value 117/300 = .39 to $f(1)$, indicating that the probability of exactly 1 automobile being sold during a day is .39. Continuing in this way for the other values of the random variable, we compute the values for $f(2), f(3), f(4),$ and $f(5)$ as shown in Table 5.3, the probability distribution for the number of automobiles sold during a day at DiCarlo Motors.

A primary advantage of defining a random variable and its probability distribution is that once the probability distribution is known, it is relatively easy to determine the probability of a variety of events that may be of interest to a decision maker. For example, using the probability distribution for DiCarlo Motors as shown in Table 5.3, we see that the most probable number of automobiles sold during a day is 1 with a probability of $f(1) = .39$. In addition, there is an $f(3) + f(4) + f(5) = .14 + .04 + .01 = .19$ probability of selling 3 or more automobiles during a day. These probabilities, plus others the decision maker may ask about, provide information that can help the decision maker understand the process of selling automobiles at DiCarlo Motors.

In the development of a probability function for any discrete random variable, the following two conditions must be satisfied.

These conditions are the analogs to the two basic requirements for assigning probabilities to experimental outcomes presented in Chapter 4.

**Required Conditions for a Discrete Probability Function**

$$f(x) \geq 0 \tag{5.1}$$
$$\Sigma f(x) = 1 \tag{5.2}$$

Table 5.3 shows that the probabilities for the random variable $x$ satisfy equation (5.1); $f(x)$ is greater than or equal to 0 for all values of $x$. In addition, the probabilities sum to 1 so equation (5.2) is satisfied. Thus, the DiCarlo Motors probability function is a valid discrete probability function.

We can also present probability distributions graphically. In Figure 5.1 the values of the random variable $x$ for DiCarlo Motors are shown on the horizontal axis and the probability associated with these values is shown on the vertical axis.

In addition to tables and graphs, a formula that gives the probability function, $f(x)$, for every value of $x$ is often used to describe probability distributions. The simplest example of

**TABLE 5.3**   PROBABILITY DISTRIBUTION FOR THE NUMBER OF AUTOMOBILES
SOLD DURING A DAY AT DICARLO MOTORS

| $x$ | $f(x)$ |
|-----|--------|
| 0 | .18 |
| 1 | .39 |
| 2 | .24 |
| 3 | .14 |
| 4 | .04 |
| 5 | .01 |
| Total | 1.00 |

**FIGURE 5.1**   GRAPHICAL REPRESENTATION OF THE PROBABILITY DISTRIBUTION FOR THE NUMBER OF AUTOMOBILES SOLD DURING A DAY AT DICARLO MOTORS

a discrete probability distribution given by a formula is the **discrete uniform probability distribution.** Its probability function is given.

**Discrete Uniform Probability Function**

$$f(x) = 1/n \tag{5.3}$$

where

$$n = \text{the number of values the random variable may assume}$$

For example, consider the experiment of rolling a die and define the random variable $x$ to be the number of dots on the upward face. There are $n = 6$ possible values for the random variable; $x = 1, 2, 3, 4, 5, 6$. Thus, the probability function for this random variable is

$$f(x) = 1/6 \qquad x = 1, 2, 3, 4, 5, 6$$

The possible values of the random variable and the associated probabilities are shown.

| $x$ | $f(x)$ |
|---|---|
| 1 | 1/6 |
| 2 | 1/6 |
| 3 | 1/6 |
| 4 | 1/6 |
| 5 | 1/6 |
| 6 | 1/6 |

Note that the values of the random variable are equally likely.

As another example, consider the random variable $x$ with the following discrete probability distribution.

| $x$ | $f(x)$ |
|---|---|
| 1 | 1/10 |
| 2 | 2/10 |
| 3 | 3/10 |
| 4 | 4/10 |

This probability distribution can be defined by the formula

$$f(x) = \frac{x}{10} \qquad \text{for } x = 1, 2, 3, \text{ or } 4$$

Evaluating $f(x)$ for a given value of the random variable will provide the associated probability. For example, using the preceding probability function, we see that $f(2) = 2/10$ provides the probability that the random variable assumes a value of 2.

The more widely used discrete probability distributions generally are specified by formulas. Three important cases are the binomial, Poisson, and hypergeometric probability distributions; they are discussed later in the chapter.

## EXERCISES

## Methods

7.  The probability distribution of the random variable $x$ is shown as follows.

| $x$ | $f(x)$ |
|---|---|
| 20 | .20 |
| 25 | .15 |
| 30 | .25 |
| 35 | .40 |

a.  Is it a proper probability distribution? Check to see that equations (5.1) and (5.2) are satisfied.
b.  What is the probability that $x = 30$?
c.  What is the probability that $x$ is less than or equal to 25?
d.  What is the probability that $x$ is greater than 30?

## Applications

8.  The following data were collected by counting the number of operating rooms in use at Tampa General Hospital over a 20-day period: On 3 of the days only 1 operating room was used, on 5 of the days 2 were used, on 8 of the days 3 were used, and on 4 days all 4 of the hospital's operating rooms were used.
a.  Use the relative frequency approach to construct a probability distribution for the number of operating rooms in use on any given day.
b.  Draw a graph of the probability distribution.
c.  Show that your probability distribution satisfies the required conditions for a valid discrete probability distribution.

9. The following data show the number of employees at each of the five executive levels in the federal government (U.S. Office of Personnel Management, *Pay Structure of the Federal Civil Service,* 1996).

| Executive Level | Number of Employees |
|:---:|:---:|
| 1 | 15 |
| 2 | 32 |
| 3 | 84 |
| 4 | 300 |
| 5 | 31 |
| Total | 462 |

Suppose we want to select a sample of executive-level employees for a survey about working conditions. Let $x$ be a random variable indicating the executive level of one employee randomly selected.

   a. Use the data to develop a probability distribution for $x$. Specify the values for the random variable and the corresponding values for the probability function $f(x)$.
   b. Draw a graph of the probability distribution.
   c. Show that the probability distribution satisfies equations (5.1) and (5.2).

10. Table 5.4 shows the percent frequency distributions of job satisfaction scores for a sample of information systems (IS) senior executives and IS middle managers (*Computerworld,* May 26, 1997). The scores range from a low of 1 (very dissatisfied) to a high of 5 (very satisfied).

   a. Develop a probability distribution for the job satisfaction score of a senior executive.
   b. Develop a probability distribution for the job satisfaction score of a middle manager.
   c. What is the probability a senior executive will report a job satisfaction score of 4 or 5?
   d. What is the probability a middle manager is very satisfied?
   e. Compare the overall job satisfaction of senior executives and middle managers.

11. A technician services mailing machines at companies in the Phoenix area. Depending on the type of malfunction, the service call can take 1, 2, 3, or 4 hours. The different types of malfunctions occur at about the same frequency.

   a. Develop a probability distribution for the duration of a service call.
   b. Draw a graph of the probability distribution.
   c. Show that your probability distribution satisfies the conditions required for a discrete probability function.
   d. What is the probability a service call will take 3 hours?
   e. A service call has just come in, but the type of malfunction is unknown. It is 3:00 P.M. and service technicians usually get off at 5:00 P.M. What is the probability the service technician will have to work overtime to fix the machine today?

**TABLE 5.4** PERCENT FREQUENCY DISTRIBUTION OF JOB SATISFACTION SCORES FOR INFORMATION SYSTEMS EXECUTIVES AND MIDDLE MANAGERS

| Job Satisfaction Score | IS Senior Executives (%) | IS Middle Managers (%) |
|:---:|:---:|:---:|
| 1 | 5 | 4 |
| 2 | 9 | 10 |
| 3 | 3 | 12 |
| 4 | 42 | 46 |
| 5 | 41 | 28 |
| Total | 100 | 100 |

**12.** The director of admissions at Lakeville Community College has subjectively assessed a probability distribution for $x$, the number of entering students, as follows.

| $x$ | $f(x)$ |
|------|--------|
| 1000 | .15 |
| 1100 | .20 |
| 1200 | .30 |
| 1300 | .25 |
| 1400 | .10 |

    **a.**  Is this a valid probability distribution?
    **b.**  What is the probability of 1200 or fewer entering students?

**13.** A psychologist has determined that the number of hours required to obtain the trust of a new patient is either 1, 2, or 3. Let $x$ be a random variable indicating the time in hours required to gain the patient's trust. The following probability function has been proposed.

$$f(x) = \frac{x}{6} \qquad \text{for } x = 1, 2, \text{ or } 3$$

    **a.**  Is this a valid probability function? Explain.
    **b.**  What is the probability that it takes exactly 2 hours to gain the patient's trust?
    **c.**  What is the probability that it takes at least 2 hours to gain the patient's trust?

**14.** The following table is a partial probability distribution for the MRA Company's projected profits ($x$ = profit in $1000s) for the first year of operation (the negative value denotes a loss).

| $x$ | $f(x)$ |
|------|--------|
| $-100$ | .10 |
| 0 | .20 |
| 50 | .30 |
| 100 | .25 |
| 150 | .10 |
| 200 | |

    **a.**  What is the proper value for $f(200)$? What is your interpretation of this value?
    **b.**  What is the probability that MRA will be profitable?
    **c.**  What is the probability that MRA will make at least $100,000?

## 5.3   EXPECTED VALUE AND VARIANCE

### Expected Value

The **expected value,** or mean, of a random variable is a measure of the central location for the random variable. The formula for the expected value of a discrete random variable $x$ follows.

*The expected value is a weighted average of the values the random variable may assume. The weights are the probabilities.*

> **Expected Value of a Discrete Random Variable**
>
> $$E(x) = \mu = \Sigma x f(x) \tag{5.4}$$

Both the notations $E(x)$ and $\mu$ are used to denote the expected value of a random variable.

Equation (5.4) shows that to compute the expected value of a discrete random variable, we must multiply each value of the random variable by the corresponding probability $f(x)$ and then add the resulting products. Using the DiCarlo Motors automobile sales example from Section 5.2, we show the calculation of the expected value for the number of automobiles sold during a day in Table 5.5. The sum of the entries in the $xf(x)$ column shows that the expected value is 1.50 automobiles per day. We therefore know that although sales of 0, 1, 2, 3, 4, or 5 automobiles are possible on any one day, over time DiCarlo can anticipate selling an average of 1.50 automobiles per day. Assuming 30 days of operation during a month, we can use the expected value of 1.50 to forecast average monthly sales of $30(1.50) = 45$ automobiles.

*The expected value does not have to be a value the random variable can assume.*

## Variance

Even though the expected value provides the mean value for the random variable, we often need a measure of variability, or dispersion. Just as we used the **variance** in Chapter 3 to summarize the variability in data, we now use variance to summarize the variability in the values of a random variable. The formula for the variance of a discrete random variable follows.

*The variance is a weighted average of the squared deviations of a random variable from its mean. The weights are the probabilities.*

---

**Variance of a Discrete Random Variable**

$$\text{Var}(x) = \sigma^2 = \Sigma(x - \mu)^2 f(x) \tag{5.5}$$

---

As equation (5.5) shows, an essential part of the variance formula is the deviation, $x - \mu$, which measures how far a particular value of the random variable is from the expected value, or mean, $\mu$. In computing the variance of a random variable, the deviations are squared and then weighted by the corresponding value of the probability function. The sum of these weighted squared deviations for all values of the random variable is referred to as the *variance*. The notations $\text{Var}(x)$ and $\sigma^2$ are both used to denote the variance of a random variable.

The calculation of the variance for the probability distribution of the number of automobiles sold during a day at DiCarlo Motors is summarized in Table 5.6. We see that the variance is 1.25. The **standard deviation**, $\sigma$, is defined as the positive square root of the variance. Thus, the standard deviation for the number of automobiles sold during a day is

$$\sigma = \sqrt{1.25} = 1.118$$

**TABLE 5.5** CALCULATION OF THE EXPECTED VALUE FOR THE NUMBER OF AUTOMOBILES SOLD DURING A DAY AT DICARLO MOTORS

| $x$ | $f(x)$ | $xf(x)$ |
|---|---|---|
| 0 | .18 | $0(.18) = $ .00 |
| 1 | .39 | $1(.39) = $ .39 |
| 2 | .24 | $2(.24) = $ .48 |
| 3 | .14 | $3(.14) = $ .42 |
| 4 | .04 | $4(.04) = $ .16 |
| 5 | .01 | $5(.01) = $ .05 |
| | | 1.50 |

$$E(x) = \mu = \Sigma xf(x)$$

**TABLE 5.6**   CALCULATION OF THE VARIANCE FOR THE NUMBER OF AUTOMOBILES
SOLD DURING A DAY AT DICARLO MOTORS

| $x$ | $x - \mu$ | $(x - \mu)^2$ | $f(x)$ | $(x - \mu)^2 f(x)$ |
|---|---|---|---|---|
| 0 | $0 - 1.50 = -1.50$ | 2.25 | .18 | $2.25(.18) = .4050$ |
| 1 | $1 - 1.50 = -.50$ | .25 | .39 | $.25(.39) = .0975$ |
| 2 | $2 - 1.50 = .50$ | .25 | .24 | $.25(.24) = .0600$ |
| 3 | $3 - 1.50 = 1.50$ | 2.25 | .14 | $2.25(.14) = .3150$ |
| 4 | $4 - 1.50 = 2.50$ | 6.25 | .04 | $6.25(.04) = .2500$ |
| 5 | $5 - 1.50 = 3.50$ | 12.25 | .01 | $12.25(.01) = .1225$ |

$$1.2500$$

$$\sigma^2 = \Sigma(x - \mu)^2 f(x)$$

The standard deviation is measured in the same units as the random variable ($\sigma = 1.118$ automobiles) and therefore is often preferred in describing the variability of a random variable. The variance $\sigma^2$ is measured in squared units and is thus more difficult to interpret.

## Using Excel to Compute the Expected Value, Variance, and Standard Deviation

The calculations involved in computing the expected value and variance for a discrete random variable can easily be made in an Excel worksheet. One approach is to enter the formulas necessary to make the calculations in Tables 5.5 and 5.6. An easier way, however, is to make use of Excel's SUMPRODUCT function. In this section we show how to use the SUMPRODUCT function to compute the expected value and variance for daily automobile sales at DiCarlo Motors. Refer to Figure 5.2 as we describe the tasks involved. The formula worksheet is in the background; the value worksheet is in the foreground.

**Enter Data:**   The data needed are the values for the random variable and the corresponding probabilities. Labels, values for the random variable, and the corresponding probabilities are entered in cells A1:B7.

**Enter Functions and Formulas:**   The SUMPRODUCT function multiplies each value in one range by the corresponding value in another range, and sums the products. To use the SUMPRODUCT function to compute the expected value of daily automobile sales at DiCarlo Motors, we entered the following formula into cell B9:

$$=\text{SUMPRODUCT(A2:A7,B2:B7)}$$

Note that the first range, A2:A7, contains the values for the random variable, daily automobile sales. The second range, B2:B7, contains the corresponding probabilities. Thus, the SUMPRODUCT function in cell B9 is computing A2*B2 + A3*B3 + A4*B4 + A5*B5 + A6*B6 + A7*B7; hence, it is applying the formula in equation (5.4) to compute the expected value. The result, shown in cell B9 of the value worksheet, is 1.5.

The formulas in cells C2:C7 are used to compute the squared deviations from the expected value or mean of 1.5 (the mean is in cell B9). The results, shown in the value worksheet, are the same as the results shown in Table 5.6. The formula necessary to compute the variance for daily automobile sales was entered into cell B11. It uses the SUMPRODUCT function to multiply each value in the range C2:C7 by each corresponding value in the range B2:B7, and sums the products. The result, shown in the value worksheet, is 1.25. Because the standard deviation is the square root of the variance, we entered the formula

**FIGURE 5.2** EXCEL WORKSHEET FOR EXPECTED VALUE, VARIANCE, AND STANDARD DEVIATION

| | A | B | C | D |
|---|---|---|---|---|
| 1 | Sales | Probability | Sq Dev from Mean | |
| 2 | 0 | 0.18 | =(A2-$B$9)^2 | |
| 3 | 1 | 0.39 | =(A3-$B$9)^2 | |
| 4 | 2 | 0.24 | =(A4-$B$9)^2 | |
| 5 | 3 | 0.14 | =(A5-$B$9)^2 | |
| 6 | 4 | 0.04 | =(A6-$B$9)^2 | |
| 7 | 5 | 0.01 | =(A7-$B$9)^2 | |
| 8 | | | | |
| 9 | Mean | =SUMPRODUCT(A2:A7,B2:B7) | | |
| 10 | | | | |
| 11 | Variance | =SUMPRODUCT(C2:C7,B2:B7) | | |
| 12 | | | | |
| 13 | Std Deviation | =SQRT(B11) | | |
| 14 | | | | |

| | A | B | C | D |
|---|---|---|---|---|
| 1 | Sales | Probability | Sq Dev from Mean | |
| 2 | 0 | 0.18 | 2.25 | |
| 3 | 1 | 0.39 | 0.25 | |
| 4 | 2 | 0.24 | 0.25 | |
| 5 | 3 | 0.14 | 2.25 | |
| 6 | 4 | 0.04 | 6.25 | |
| 7 | 5 | 0.01 | 12.25 | |
| 8 | | | | |
| 9 | Mean | 1.5 | | |
| 10 | | | | |
| 11 | Variance | 1.25 | | |
| 12 | | | | |
| 13 | Std Deviation | 1.118034 | | |
| 14 | | | | |

=SQRT(B11) into cell B13 to compute the standard deviation for daily automobile sales. The result, shown in the value spreadsheet, is 1.118034.

## EXERCISES

### Methods

**15.** The following table is a probability distribution for the random variable $x$.

| $x$ | $f(x)$ |
|---|---|
| 3 | .25 |
| 6 | .50 |
| 9 | .25 |
| Total | 1.00 |

    **a.** Compute $E(x)$, the expected value of $x$.
    **b.** Compute $\sigma^2$, the variance of $x$.
    **c.** Compute $\sigma$, the standard deviation of $x$.

 **SELF** test

**16.** The following table is a probability distribution for the random variable $y$.

| $y$ | $f(y)$ |
|---|---|
| 2 | .20 |
| 4 | .30 |
| 7 | .40 |
| 8 | .10 |
| Total | 1.00 |

    **a.** Compute $E(y)$.
    **b.** Compute Var($y$) and $\sigma$.

## Applications

**17.** A volunteer ambulance service handles 0 to 5 service calls on any given day. The probability distribution for the number of service calls is as follows.

| Number of Service Calls | Probability |
|:---:|:---:|
| 0 | .10 |
| 1 | .15 |
| 2 | .30 |
| 3 | .20 |
| 4 | .15 |
| 5 | .10 |

**a.** What is the expected number of service calls?
**b.** What is the variance in the number of service calls? What is the standard deviation?

**18.** The *Statistical Abstract* of the United States, 1997, shows that the average number of television sets per household is 2.3. Assume that the probability distribution for the number of television sets per household in New Orleans is as shown in the following table.

| $x$ | $f(x)$ |
|:---:|:---:|
| 0 | .01 |
| 1 | .23 |
| 2 | .41 |
| 3 | .20 |
| 4 | .10 |
| 5 | .05 |

**a.** Compute the expected value of the number of television sets per household and compare it with the average reported in the *Statistical Abstract*.
**b.** What are the variance and standard deviation of the number of television sets per household?

**19.** The actual shooting records of four basketball teams showed the probability of making a 2-point basket was .50 and the probability of making a 3-point basket was .39.
**a.** What is the expected value of a 2-point shot for these teams?
**b.** What is the expected value of a 3-point shot for these teams?
**c.** If the probability of making a 2-point basket is greater than the probability of making a 3-point basket, why do coaches allow some players to shoot the 3-point shot if they have the opportunity? Use expected value to explain your answer.

**20.** The probability distribution for damage claims paid by the Newton Automobile Insurance Company on collision insurance is shown as follows.

| Payment ($) | Probability |
|:---:|:---:|
| 0 | .90 |
| 400 | .04 |
| 1000 | .03 |
| 2000 | .01 |
| 4000 | .01 |
| 6000 | .01 |

**a.** Use the expected collision payment to determine the collision insurance premium that would enable the company to break even.
**b.** The insurance company charges an annual rate of $260 for the collision coverage. What is the expected value of the collision policy for a policyholder? (Hint: It is the expected payments from the company minus the cost of coverage.) Why does the policyholder purchase a collision policy with this expected value?

**21.** Shown are the probability distributions of job satisfaction scores for a sample of information systems (IS) senior executives and IS middle managers (*Computerworld,* May 26, 1997). The scores range from a low of 1 (very dissatisfied) to a high of 5 (very satisfied).

| Job Satisfaction Score | Probability IS Senior Executives | Probability IS Middle Managers |
|:---:|:---:|:---:|
| 1 | .05 | .04 |
| 2 | .09 | .10 |
| 3 | .03 | .12 |
| 4 | .42 | .46 |
| 5 | .41 | .28 |
| Total | 1.00 | 1.00 |

a. What is the expected value of the job satisfaction score for senior executives?
b. What is the expected value of the job satisfaction score for middle managers?
c. Compute the variance of job satisfaction scores for executives and middle managers.
d. Compute the standard deviation of job satisfaction scores for both probability distributions.
e. Compare the overall job satisfaction of senior executives and middle managers.

**22.** The demand for a product of Carolina Industries varies greatly from month to month. The probability distribution in the following table, based on the past two years of data, shows the company's monthly demand.

| Unit Demand | Probability |
|:---:|:---:|
| 300 | .20 |
| 400 | .30 |
| 500 | .35 |
| 600 | .15 |

a. If the company bases monthly orders on the expected value of the monthly demand, what should Carolina's monthly order quantity be for this product?
b. Assume that each unit demanded generates $70 in revenue and that each unit ordered costs $50. How much will the company gain or lose in a month if it places an order based on your answer to part (a) and the actual demand for the item is 300 units?

**23.** According to a survey, 95% of subscribers to *The Wall Street Journal Interactive Edition* have a computer at home. For those households, the probability distributions for the number of laptop and desktop computers are given (*The Wall Street Journal Interactive Edition Subscriber Study,* 1999).

| Number of Computers | Probability Laptop | Desktop |
|:---:|:---:|:---:|
| 0 | .47 | .06 |
| 1 | .45 | .56 |
| 2 | .06 | .28 |
| 3 | .02 | .10 |

a. What is the expected value of the number of computers per household for each type?
b. What is the variance in the number of computers per household for each computer type?
c. Make some comparisons between the number of laptops and the number of desktops owned by the *Journal's* subscribers.

**24.** The J. R. Ryland Computer Company is considering a plant expansion that will enable the company to begin production of a new computer product. The company's president must determine whether to make the expansion a medium- or large-scale project. An uncertainty is the demand for the new product, which for planning purposes may be low demand, medium demand, or high demand. The probability estimates for demand are .20, .50, and .30, respectively. Letting $x$ and $y$ indicate the annual profit in thousands of dollars, the firm's planners have developed the following profit forecasts for the medium- and large-scale expansion projects.

|  |  | Medium-Scale Expansion Profit | | Large-Scale Expansion Profit | |
|---|---|---|---|---|---|
|  |  | $x$ | $f(x)$ | $y$ | $f(y)$ |
|  | **Low** | 50 | .20 | 0 | .20 |
| Demand | **Medium** | 150 | .50 | 100 | .50 |
|  | **High** | 200 | .30 | 300 | .30 |

   **a.** Compute the expected value for the profit associated with the two expansion alternatives. Which decision is preferred for the objective of maximizing the expected profit?

   **b.** Compute the variance for the profit associated with the two expansion alternatives. Which decision is preferred for the objective of minimizing the risk or uncertainty?

## 5.4   BINOMIAL PROBABILITY DISTRIBUTION

The binomial probability distribution is a discrete probability distribution that has many applications. It is associated with a multiple-step experiment that we call the binomial experiment.

### A Binomial Experiment

A **binomial experiment** has the following four properties.

> **Properties of a Binomial Experiment**
>
> 1. The experiment consists of a sequence of $n$ identical trials.
> 2. Two outcomes are possible on each trial. We refer to one as a *success* and the other as a *failure*.
> 3. The probability of a success, denoted by $p$, does not change from trial to trial. Consequently, the probability of a failure, denoted by $1 - p$, does not change from trial to trial.
> 4. The trials are independent.

Jakob Bernoulli (1654–1705), the first of the Bernoulli family of Swiss mathematicians, published a treatise on probability that contained the theory of permutations and combinations, as well as the Binomial Theorem.

    If properties 2, 3, and 4 are present, we say the trials are generated by a Bernoulli process. If, in addition, property 1 is present, we say we have a binomial experiment. Figure 5.3 depicts one possible sequence of outcomes of a binomial experiment involving eight trials. This case presents the possibility of 5 successes and 3 failures.

    In a binomial experiment, our interest is in the *number of successes occurring in the n trials*. If we let $x$ denote the number of successes occurring in the $n$ trials, we see that $x$ can assume the values of 0, 1, 2, 3, . . . , $n$. Because the number of values is finite, $x$ is a *discrete* random variable. The probability distribution associated with this random variable is called the **binomial probability distribution**. For example, consider the experiment of tossing a coin five times and on each toss observing whether the coin lands with a head or a tail on its upward face. Suppose we are interested in counting the number of heads appearing over

**FIGURE 5.3**   DIAGRAM OF AN EIGHT-TRIAL BINOMIAL EXPERIMENT

the five tosses. Does this experiment have the properties of a binomial experiment? What is the random variable of interest? Note that:

1. The experiment consists of five identical trials; each trial involves the tossing of one coin.
2. Two outcomes are possible for each trial: a head or a tail. We can designate head a success and tail a failure.
3. The probability of a head and the probability of a tail are the same for each trial, with $p = .5$ and $1 - p = .5$.
4. The trials or tosses are independent because the outcome on any one trial is not affected by what happens on other trials or tosses.

Thus, the properties of a binomial experiment are satisfied. The random variable of interest is $x = $ the number of heads appearing in the five trials. In this case, $x$ can assume the values of 0, 1, 2, 3, 4, or 5.

As another example, consider an insurance salesperson who visits 10 randomly selected families. The outcome associated with each visit is classified as a success if the family purchases an insurance policy and a failure if the family does not. From past experience, the salesperson knows the probability that a randomly selected family will purchase an insurance policy is .10. Checking the properties of a binomial experiment, we observe that:

1. The experiment consists of 10 identical trials; each trial involves contacting one family.
2. Two outcomes are possible on each trial: the family purchases a policy (success) or the family does not purchase a policy (failure).
3. The probabilities of a purchase and a nonpurchase are assumed to be the same for each sales call, with $p = .10$ and $1 - p = .90$.
4. The trials are independent because the families are randomly selected.

Because the four assumptions are satisfied, this example is a binomial experiment. The random variable of interest is the number of sales obtained in contacting the 10 families. In this case, $x$ can assume the values of 0, 1, 2, 3, 4, 5, 6, 7, 8, 9, and 10.

Property 3 of the binomial experiment is called the *stationarity assumption* and is sometimes confused with property 4, independence of trials. To see how they differ, consider again the case of the salesperson calling on families to sell insurance policies. If, as the day wore on, the salesperson got tired and lost enthusiasm, the probability of success (selling a policy) might drop to .05, for example, by the tenth call. In such a case, property 3 (stationarity) would not be satisfied, and we would not have a binomial experiment. Even if property 4 held—that is, the purchase decisions of each family were made independently—it would not be a binomial experiment if property 3 was not satisfied.

In applications involving binomial experiments, a special mathematical formula, called the **binomial probability function,** can be used to compute the probability of $x$ successes in the *n* trials. Using probability concepts introduced in Chapter 4, we will show in the context of an illustrative problem how the formula can be developed.

## Martin Clothing Store Problem

Let us consider the purchase decisions of the next three customers who enter the Martin Clothing Store. On the basis of past experience, the store manager estimates the probability that any one customer will make a purchase is .30. What is the probability that two of the next three customers will make a purchase?

Using a tree diagram (Figure 5.4), we can see that the experiment of observing the three customers each making a purchase decision has eight possible outcomes. Using *S* to denote success (a purchase) and *F* to denote failure (no purchase), we are interested in experimental outcomes involving two successes in the three trials (purchase decisions). Next, let us verify that the experiment involving the sequence of three purchase decisions can be viewed as a binomial experiment. Checking the four requirements for a binomial experiment, we note that:

1. The experiment can be described as a sequence of three identical trials, one trial for each of the three customers who will enter the store.
2. Two outcomes—the customer makes a purchase (success) or the customer does not make a purchase (failure)—are possible for each trial.
3. The probability that the customer will make a purchase (.30) or will not make a purchase (.70) is assumed to be the same for all customers.
4. The purchase decision of each customer is independent of the decisions of the other customers.

**FIGURE 5.4**   TREE DIAGRAM FOR THE MARTIN CLOTHING STORE PROBLEM

*S* = Purchase
*F* = No purchase
*x* = Number of customers making a purchase

Hence, the properties of a binomial experiment are present.

The number of experimental outcomes resulting in exactly $x$ successes in $n$ trials can be computed from the following formula.*

**Number of Experimental Outcomes Providing Exactly $x$ Successes in $n$ Trials**

$$\binom{n}{x} = \frac{n!}{x!(n-x)!} \qquad (5.6)$$

where

$$n! = n(n-1)(n-2) \cdots (2)(1)$$

and

$$0! = 1$$

Now let us return to the Martin Clothing Store experiment involving three customer purchase decisions. Equation (5.6) can be used to determine the number of experimental outcomes involving two purchases; that is, the number of ways of obtaining $x = 2$ successes in the $n = 3$ trials. From (5.6) we have

$$\binom{n}{x} = \binom{3}{2} = \frac{3!}{2!(3-2)!} = \frac{(3)(2)(1)}{(2)(1)(1)} = \frac{6}{2} = 3$$

Equation (5.6) shows that three of the outcomes yield two successes. From Figure 5.4 we see these three outcomes are denoted by *SSF*, *SFS*, and *FSS*.

Using equation (5.6) to determine how many experimental outcomes have three successes (purchases) in the three trials, we obtain

$$\binom{n}{x} = \binom{3}{3} = \frac{3!}{3!(3-3)!} = \frac{3!}{3!0!} = \frac{(3)(2)(1)}{3(2)(1)(1)} = \frac{6}{6} = 1$$

From Figure 5.4 we see that the one experimental outcome with three successes is identified by *SSS*.

We know that equation (5.6) can be used to determine the number of experimental outcomes that result in $x$ successes. But, if we are to determine the probability of $x$ successes in $n$ trials, we must also know the probability associated with each of these experimental outcomes. Because the trials of a binomial experiment are independent, we can simply multiply the probabilities associated with each trial outcome to find the probability of a particular sequence of successes and failures.

The probability of purchases by the first two customers and no purchase by the third customer (*SSF*) is given by

$$pp(1-p)$$

---

*This formula is introduced in Chapter 4 to determine the number of combinations of $n$ objects selected $x$ at a time. For the binomial experiment, this combinatorial formula provides the number of experimental outcomes (sequences of $n$ trials) resulting in $x$ successes.

With a .30 probability of a purchase on any one trial, the probability of a purchase on the first two trials and no purchase on the third is given by

$$(.30)(.30)(.70) = (.30)^2(.70) = .063$$

Two other sequences of outcomes result in two successes and one failure. The probabilities for all three sequences involving two successes are shown as follows.

| Trial Outcomes | | | Experi-mental Outcome | Probability of Experimental Outcome |
|---|---|---|---|---|
| **1st Customer** | **2nd Customer** | **3rd Customer** | | |
| Purchase | Purchase | No purchase | SSF | $pp(1 - p) = p^2(1 - p)$ $= (.30)^2(.70) = .063$ |
| Purchase | No purchase | Purchase | SFS | $p(1 - p)p = p^2(1 - p)$ $= (.30)^2(.70) = .063$ |
| No purchase | Purchase | Purchase | FSS | $(1 - p)pp = p^2(1 - p)$ $= (.30)^2(.70) = .063$ |

Observe that all three experimental outcomes with two successes have exactly the same probability. This observation holds in general. In any binomial experiment, all sequences of trial outcomes yielding $x$ successes in $n$ trials have the *same probability* of occurrence. The probability of each sequence of trials yielding $x$ successes in $n$ trials follows.

$$\text{Probability of a Particular Sequence of Trial Outcomes} = p^x(1 - p)^{(n-x)} \tag{5.7}$$
with $x$ Successes in $n$ Trials

For the Martin Clothing Store, this formula shows that any experimental outcome with two successes has a probability of $p^2(1 - p)^{(3-2)} = p^2(1 - p)^1 = (.30)^2(.70)^1 = .063$.

Because equation (5.6) shows the number of outcomes in a binomial experiment with $x$ successes and equation (5.7) gives the probability for each sequence involving $x$ successes, we combine equations (5.6) and (5.7) to obtain the following binomial probability function.

**Binomial Probability Function**

$$f(x) = \binom{n}{x} p^x(1 - p)^{(n-x)} \tag{5.8}$$

where

$f(x) =$ the probability of $x$ successes in $n$ trials

$n =$ the number of trials

$\binom{n}{x} = \dfrac{n!}{x!(n - x)!}$

$p =$ the probability of a success on any one trial

$(1 - p) =$ the probability of a failure on any one trial

**TABLE 5.7**   PROBABILITY DISTRIBUTION FOR THE NUMBER OF CUSTOMERS MAKING A PURCHASE

| $x$ | $f(x)$ |
|---|---|
| 0 | $\dfrac{3!}{0!3!}(.30)^0(.70)^3 = .343$ |
| 1 | $\dfrac{3!}{1!2!}(.30)^1(.70)^2 = .441$ |
| 2 | $\dfrac{3!}{2!1!}(.30)^2(.70)^1 = .189$ |
| 3 | $\dfrac{3!}{3!0!}(.30)^3(.70)^0 = \underline{.027}$ |
|   | $1.000$ |

In the Martin Clothing Store example, let us compute the probability that no customer makes a purchase, exactly one customer makes a purchase, exactly two customers make a purchase, and all three customers make a purchase. The calculations are summarized in Table 5.7, which gives the probability distribution of the number of customers making a purchase. Figure 5.5 is a graph of this probability distribution.

The binomial probability function can be applied to *any* binomial experiment. If we are satisfied that a situation has the properties of a binomial experiment and if we know the values of $n, p$, and $(1 - p)$, we can use equation (5.8) to compute the probability of $x$ successes in the $n$ trials.

If we consider variations of the Martin experiment, such as 10 customers rather than three entering the store, the binomial probability function given by equation (5.8) is still ap-

**FIGURE 5.5**   GRAPHICAL REPRESENTATION OF THE PROBABILITY DISTRIBUTION FOR THE NUMBER OF CUSTOMERS MAKING A PURCHASE

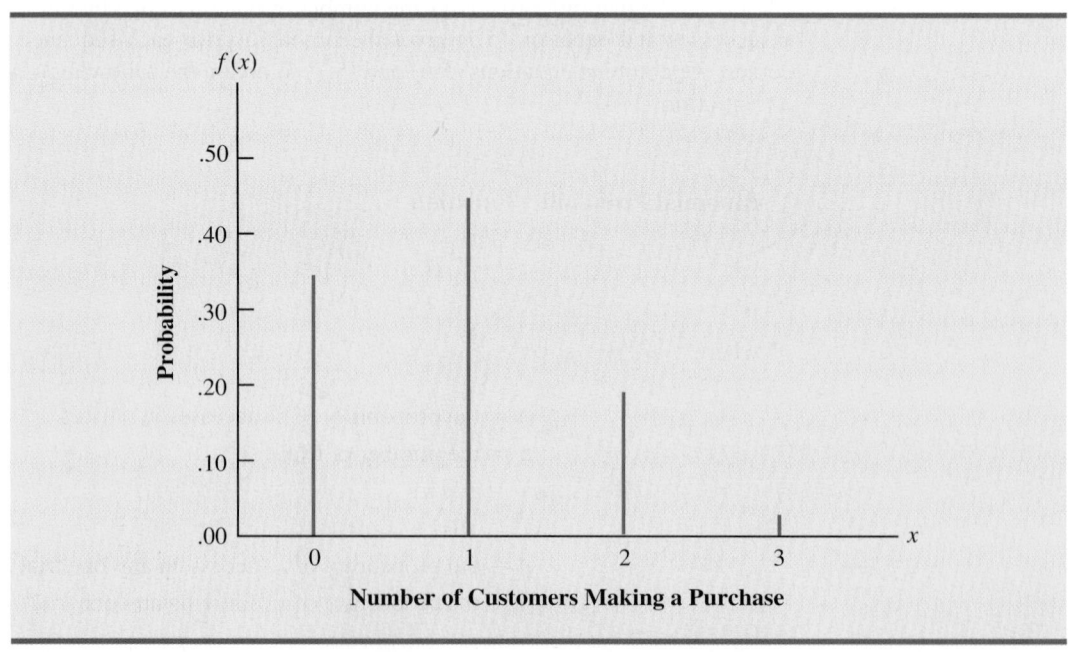

plicable. Suppose we have a binomial experiment with $n = 10$, $x = 4$, and $p = .30$. The probability of making exactly four sales to 10 potential customers entering the store is

$$f(4) = \frac{10!}{4!6!}(.30)^4(.70)^6 = .2001$$

## Using Excel to Compute Binomial Probabilities

For many probability functions that can be specified as formulas, Excel provides functions for computing probabilities and cumulative probabilities. In this section, we show how Excel's BINOMDIST function can be used to compute binomial probabilities and cumulative binomial probabilities. We begin by showing how to compute the binomial probabilities for the Martin Clothing Store example shown in Table 5.7. Refer to Figure 5.6 as we describe the tasks involved. The formula worksheet is in the background; the value worksheet is in the foreground.

**Enter Data:**    In order to compute a binomial probability we must know the number of trials ($n$), the probability of success ($p$), and the value of the random variable ($x$). For the Martin Clothing Store example, the number of trials is 3; this value has been entered into cell D1. The probability of success is .3; this value has been entered into cell D2. Because we want to compute the probability for $x = 0$, 1, 2, and 3, these values were entered into cells B5:B8.

**Enter Functions and Formulas:**    The BINOMDIST function has four arguments: the first is the value of $x$, the second is the value of $n$, the third is the value of $p$, and the fourth is FALSE or TRUE. We choose FALSE for the fourth argument if a probability is desired and TRUE if a cumulative probability is desired. The formula =BINOMDIST(B5,$D$1, $D$2,FALSE) has been entered into cell C5 to compute the probability of 0 successes in 3 trials. Note in the value worksheet that the probability computed for $f(0)$, .343, is the same as that shown in Table 5.7. The formula in cell C5 is copied to cells C6:C8 to compute the probabilities for $x = 1$, 2, and 3 successes, respectively.

We can also compute cumulative probabilities using Excel's BINOMDIST function. To illustrate, let us consider the case of 10 customers entering the Martin Clothing Store and compute the probabilities and cumulative probabilities for the number of customers making a purchase. Recall that the cumulative probability for $x = 1$ is the probability of 1 or

**FIGURE 5.6**    EXCEL WORKSHEET FOR COMPUTING BINOMIAL PROBABILITIES OF NUMBER OF CUSTOMERS MAKING A PURCHASE

| | A | B | C | D | E |
|---|---|---|---|---|---|
| 1 | | | Number of Trials (*n*) | 3 | |
| 2 | | | Probability of Success (*p*) | 0.3 | |
| 3 | | | | | |
| 4 | | *x* | *f(x)* | | |
| 5 | | 0 | =BINOMDIST(B5,$D$1,$D$2,FALSE) | | |
| 6 | | 1 | =BINOMDIST(B6,$D$1,$D$2,FALSE) | | |
| 7 | | 2 | =BINOMDIST(B7,$D$1,$D$2,FALSE) | | |
| 8 | | 3 | =BINOMDIST(B8,$D$1,$D$2,FALSE) | | |
| 9 | | | | | |

| | A | B | C | D | E |
|---|---|---|---|---|---|
| 1 | | Number of Trials (*n*) | | 3 | |
| 2 | | Probability of Success (*p*) | | 0.3 | |
| 3 | | | | | |
| 4 | | *x* | *f(x)* | | |
| 5 | | 0 | 0.343 | | |
| 6 | | 1 | 0.441 | | |
| 7 | | 2 | 0.189 | | |
| 8 | | 3 | 0.027 | | |
| 9 | | | | | |

fewer purchases, the cumulative probability for $x = 2$ is the probability of 2 or fewer purchases, and so on. So, the cumulative probability for $x = 10$ is 1. Refer to Figure 5.7 as we describe the tasks involved in computing these cumulative probabilities. The formula worksheet is in the background; the value worksheet is in the foreground.

**Enter Data:** We have entered the number of trials (10) into cell D1, the probability of success (.3) into cell D2, and the values for the random variable into cells B5:B15.

**Enter Functions and Formulas:** The binomial probabilities for each value of the random variable are computed in column C and the cumulative probabilities are computed in column D. We have entered the formula =BINOMDIST(B5,$D$1,$D$2,FALSE) into cell C5 to compute the probability of 0 successes in 10 trials. Note that we used FALSE as the fourth argument in the BINOMDIST function. The probability (.0282) is shown in cell C5 of the value worksheet. The formula in cell C5 is simply copied to cells C6:C15 to compute the remaining probabilities.

To compute the cumulative probabilities we start by entering the formula =BINOMDIST(B5,$D$1,$D$2,TRUE) into cell D5. Note that we used TRUE as the fourth argument in the BINOMDIST function. The formula in cell D5 is then copied to cells D6:D15 to compute the remaining cumulative probabilities. In cell D5 of the value worksheet we see that the cumulative probability for $x = 0$ is the same as the probability for $x = 0$. Each of the remaining cumulative probabilities is the sum of the previous cumulative probability and the individual probability in column C. For instance, the cumulative probability for $x = 4$ is given by .6496 + .2001 = .8497. Note also that the cumulative probability for $x = 10$ is 1. The cumulative probability of $x = 9$ is also 1 because the probability of $x = 10$ is zero (to 4 decimal places of accuracy).

## Expected Value and Variance for the Binomial Probability Distribution

In Section 5.3 we provided formulas for computing the expected value and variance of a discrete random variable. In the special case where the random variable has a binomial probability distribution with a known number of trials $n$ and a known probability of suc-

**FIGURE 5.7** EXCEL WORKSHEET FOR COMPUTING PROBABILITIES AND CUMULATIVE PROBABILITIES FOR NUMBER OF PURCHASES WITH 10 CUSTOMERS

| | A | B | C | D | E |
|---|---|---|---|---|---|
| 1 | | | Number of Trials (*n*) | 10 | |
| 2 | | | Probability of Success (*p*) | 0.3 | |
| 3 | | | | | |
| 4 | | *x* | *f(x)* | Cum Prob | |
| 5 | | 0 | =BINOMDIST(B5,$D$1,$D$2,FALSE) | =BINOMDIST(B5,$D$1,$D$2,TRUE) | |
| 6 | | 1 | =BINOMDIST(B6,$D$1,$D$2,FALSE) | =BINOMDIST(B6,$D$1,$D$2,TRUE) | |
| 7 | | 2 | =BINOMDIST(B7,$D$1,$D$2,FALSE) | =BINOMDIST(B7,$D$1,$D$2,TRUE) | |
| 8 | | 3 | =BINOMDIST(B8,$D$1,$D$2,FALSE) | =BINOMDIST(B8,$D$1,$D$2,TRUE) | |
| 9 | | 4 | =BINOMDIST(B9,$D$1,$D$2,FALSE) | =BINOMDIST(B9,$D$1,$D$2,TRUE) | |
| 10 | | 5 | =BINOMDIST(B10,$D$1,$D$2,FALSE) | =BINOMDIST(B10,$D$1,$D$2,TRUE) | |
| 11 | | 6 | =BINOMDIST(B11,$D$1,$D$2,FALSE) | =BINOMDIST(B11,$D$1,$D$2,TRUE) | |
| 12 | | 7 | =BINOMDIST(B12,$D$1,$D$2,FALSE) | =BINOMDIST(B12,$D$1,$D$2,TRUE) | |
| 13 | | 8 | =BINOMDIST(B13,$D$1,$D$2,FALSE) | =BINOMDIST(B13,$D$1,$D$2,TRUE) | |
| 14 | | 9 | =BINOMDIST(B14,$D$1,$D$2,FALSE) | =BINOMDIST(B14,$D$1,$D$2,TRUE) | |
| 15 | | 10 | =BINOMDIST(B15,$D$1,$D$2,FALSE) | =BINOMDIST(B15,$D$1,$D$2,TRUE) | |
| 16 | | | | | |

| | A | B | C | D | E |
|---|---|---|---|---|---|
| 1 | | Number of Trials (*n*) | | 10 | |
| 2 | | Probability of Success (*p*) | | 0.3 | |
| 3 | | | | | |
| 4 | | *x* | *f(x)* | Cum Prob | |
| 5 | | 0 | 0.0282 | 0.0282 | |
| 6 | | 1 | 0.1211 | 0.1493 | |
| 7 | | 2 | 0.2335 | 0.3828 | |
| 8 | | 3 | 0.2668 | 0.6496 | |
| 9 | | 4 | 0.2001 | 0.8497 | |
| 10 | | 5 | 0.1029 | 0.9527 | |
| 11 | | 6 | 0.0368 | 0.9894 | |
| 12 | | 7 | 0.0090 | 0.9984 | |
| 13 | | 8 | 0.0014 | 0.9999 | |
| 14 | | 9 | 0.0001 | 1.0000 | |
| 15 | | 10 | 0.0000 | 1.0000 | |
| 16 | | | | | |

cess $p$, the general formulas for the expected value and variance can be simplified. The results follow.

---

**Expected Value and Variance for the Binomial Probability Distribution**

$$E(x) = \mu = np \tag{5.9}$$

$$Var(x) = \sigma^2 = np(1 - p) \tag{5.10}$$

---

For the Martin Clothing Store problem with three customers, we can use equation (5.9) to compute the expected number of customers making a purchase.

$$E(x) = np = 3(.30) = .9$$

Suppose that for the next month the Martin Clothing Store forecasts 1000 customers will enter the store. What is the expected number of customers who will make a purchase? The answer is $\mu = np = (1000)(.3) = 300$. Thus, to increase the expected number of sales, Martin's must induce more customers to enter the store and/or somehow increase the probability that any individual customer will make a purchase after entering.

For the Martin Clothing Store problem with three customers, we see that the variance and standard deviation for the number of customers making a purchase are

The *np* chart and lot acceptance sampling are quality control procedures that are excellent examples of the use of the binomial distribution. These procedures are discussed in Chapter 19, Statistical Methods for Quality Control.

$$\sigma^2 = np(1 - p) = 3(.3)(.7) = .63$$
$$\sigma = \sqrt{.63} = .79$$

For the next 1000 customers entering the store, the variance and standard deviation for the number of customers making a purchase are

$$\sigma^2 = np(1 - p) = 1000(.3)(.7) = 210$$
$$\sigma = \sqrt{210} = 14.49$$

## NOTES AND COMMENTS

Statisticians have developed tables that give probabilities and cumulative probabilities for a binomial random variable. These tables can be found in some statistics textbooks. With modern calculators and the capability of the BINOMDIST function in Microsoft Excel, such tables are unnecessary.

## EXERCISES

### Methods

25. Consider a binomial experiment with two trials and $p = .4$.
    a. Draw a tree diagram showing it as a two-trial experiment (see Figure 5.4).
    b. Compute the probability of one success, $f(1)$.
    c. Compute $f(0)$.
    d. Compute $f(2)$.
    e. Compute the probability of at least one success.
    f. Compute the expected value, variance, and standard deviation.

26. Consider a binomial experiment with $n = 10$ and $p = .10$.
    a. Compute $f(0)$.
    b. Compute $f(2)$.
    c. Compute $P(x \leq 2)$.
    d. Compute $P(x \geq 1)$.
    e. Compute $E(x)$.
    f. Compute $\text{Var}(x)$ and $\sigma$.

27. Consider a binomial experiment with $n = 20$ and $p = .70$.
    a. Compute $f(12)$.
    b. Compute $f(16)$.
    c. Compute $P(x \geq 16)$.
    d. Compute $P(x \leq 15)$.
    e. Compute $E(x)$.
    f. Compute $\text{Var}(x)$ and $\sigma$.

## Applications

28. The 1999 Youth and Money Survey, sponsored by the American Savings Education Council, the Employee Benefit Research Institute, and Matthew Greenwald & Associates, talked to a thousand students ages 16–22 about personal finance. The survey found that 33% of the students have their own credit card.
    a. In a sample of six students, what is the probability that two will have their own credit card?
    b. In a sample of six students, what is the probability that at least two will have their own credit card?
    c. In a sample of 10 students, what is the probability that none will have their own credit card?

29. According to a *Business Week*/Harris Poll of 1035 adults, 40% of those surveyed agreed strongly with the proposition that business has too much power over American life (*Business Week,* September 11, 2000). Assume this percentage is representative of the American population and that a sample of 20 individuals has been taken from a cross-section of the American population to learn about the role of business in their lives. What is the probability that at least five of these individuals will feel that business has too much power over American life?

30. When a new machine is functioning properly, only 3% of the items produced are defective. Assume that we will randomly select two parts produced on the machine and that we are interested in the number of defective parts found.
    a. Describe the conditions under which this situation would be a binomial experiment.
    b. Draw a tree diagram similar to Figure 5.4 showing this problem as a two-trial experiment.
    c. How many experimental outcomes result in exactly one defect being found?
    d. Compute the probabilities associated with finding no defects, exactly one defect, and two defects.

31. Five percent of American truck drivers are women (*Statistical Abstract of the United States,* 1997). Suppose 10 truck drivers are selected randomly to be interviewed about quality of work conditions.
    a. Is the selection of the 10 drivers a binomial experiment? Explain.
    b. What is the probability that two of the drivers will be women?
    c. What is the probability that none will be women?
    d. What is the probability that at least one will be a woman?

32. Military radar and missile detection systems are designed to warn a country against enemy attacks. A reliability question is whether a detection system will be able to identify an attack and issue a warning. Assume that a particular detection system has a .90 probability of detecting a missile attack. Use the binomial probability distribution to answer the following questions.

    **a.** What is the probability that a single detection system will detect an attack?

    **b.** If two detection systems are installed in the same area and operate independently, what is the probability that at least one of the systems will detect the attack?

    **c.** If three systems are installed, what is the probability that at least one of the systems will detect the attack?

    **d.** Would you recommend that multiple detection systems be used? Explain.

**33.** Fifty percent of midsize manufacturers planned to have management representatives visit Canada and Mexico to take advantage of opportunities created by the North American Free Trade Agreement (*Grant Thornton Survey of American Manufacturers,* 1995). An export–import group in Toronto, Canada, has invited 20 U.S. midsize manufacturers to participate in a conference to explore trade opportunities.

    **a.** What is the probability that exactly 12 of these manufacturers will send representatives?

    **b.** What is the probability that no more than five of these manufacturers will send representatives?

    **c.** How many of these manufacturers would you expect to send representatives?

    **d.** What are the variance and standard deviation of the number of manufacturers sending representatives?

**34.** Forty percent of business travelers carry either a cell phone or a laptop (*USA Today,* September 12, 2000). In a sample of 15 business travelers,

    **a.** What is the probability three of the travelers have a cell phone or laptop?

    **b.** What is the probability that 12 of the travelers have neither a cell phone nor a laptop?

    **c.** What is the probability that at least three of the travelers have a cell phone or a laptop?

**35.** A university found that 20% of its students withdraw without completing the introductory statistics course. Assume that 20 students have registered for the course this quarter.

    **a.** What is the probability that two or fewer will withdraw?

    **b.** What is the probability that exactly four will withdraw?

    **c.** What is the probability that more than three will withdraw?

    **d.** What is the expected number of withdrawals?

**36.** For the special case of a binomial random variable, we stated that the variance could be computed using the formula $\sigma^2 = np(1 - p)$. For the Martin Clothing Store problem data in Table 5.7, we found $\sigma^2 = np(1 - p) = .63$. Use the general definition of variance for a discrete random variable, equation (5.5), and the data in Table 5.7 to verify that the variance is in fact .63.

**37.** Twenty-nine percent of lawyers and judges are women (*Statistical Abstract of the United States,* 1997). In a jurisdiction with 30 lawyers and judges, what is the expected number of women? What are the variance and standard deviation?

## 5.5   POISSON PROBABILITY DISTRIBUTION

In this section we consider a discrete random variable that is often useful in estimating the number of occurrences over a specified interval of time or space. For example, the random variable of interest might be the number of arrivals at a car wash in one hour, the number of repairs needed in 10 miles of highway, or the number of leaks in 100 miles of pipeline. If the following two properties are satisfied, the number of occurrences is a random variable described by the **Poisson probability distribution.**

*The Poisson probability distribution is often used to model arrival rates in waiting line situations.*

> **Properties of a Poisson Experiment**
>
>     **1.** The probability of an occurrence is the same for any two intervals of equal length.
>
>     **2.** The occurrence or nonoccurrence in any interval is independent of the occurrence or nonoccurrence in any other interval.

The **Poisson probability function** is defined by equation (5.11).

Siméon Poisson taught mathematics at the Ecole Polytechnique in Paris from 1802 to 1808. In 1837, he published a work entitled, "Researches on the Probability of Criminal and Civil Verdicts," which includes a discussion of what later became known as the Poisson distribution.

**Poisson Probability Function**

$$f(x) = \frac{\mu^x e^{-\mu}}{x!} \qquad\qquad (5.11)$$

where

$$f(x) = \text{the probability of } x \text{ occurrences in an interval}$$
$$\mu = \text{expected value or mean number of occurrences}$$
$$\text{in an interval}$$
$$e = 2.71828$$

Before we consider a specific example to see how the Poisson distribution can be applied, note that the number of occurrences, $x$, has no upper limit. It is a discrete random variable that may assume an infinite sequence of values ($x = 0, 1, 2, \ldots$).

## An Example Involving Time Intervals

Bell Labs has made substantial use of the Poisson distribution in modeling the arrival of phone calls.

Suppose that we are interested in the number of arrivals at the drive-up teller window of a bank during a 15-minute period on weekday mornings. If we can assume that the probability of a car arriving is the same for any two time periods of equal length and that the arrival or nonarrival of a car in any time period is independent of the arrival or nonarrival in any other time period, the Poisson probability function is applicable. Suppose these assumptions are satisfied and an analysis of historical data shows that the average number of cars arriving in a 15-minute period of time is 10; in this case, the following probability function applies.

$$f(x) = \frac{10^x e^{-10}}{x!}$$

The random variable here is $x$ = number of cars arriving in any 15-minute period.

If management wanted to know the probability of exactly five arrivals in 15 minutes, we would set $x = 5$ and thus obtain

$$\begin{array}{c}\text{Probability of Exactly} \\ \text{5 Arrivals in 15 Minutes}\end{array} = f(5) = \frac{10^5 e^{-10}}{5!} = .0378$$

This probability was determined by using a calculator to evaluate the probability function with $\mu = 10$ and $x = 5$. Microsoft Excel also provides a function, called POISSON, for computing Poisson probabilities and cumulative probabilities. This function is easier to use when numerous probabilities and/or cumulative probabilities are desired. We show how to compute these probabilities with Excel at the end of this section.

Our illustration involves a 15-minute period, but other time periods can be used. Suppose we want to compute the probability of one arrival in a three-minute period. Because 10 is the expected number of arrivals in a 15-minute period, we see that 10/15 = 2/3 is the expected number of arrivals in a one-minute period and that (2/3)(3 minutes) = 2 is the expected number of arrivals in a three-minute period. Thus, the probability of $x$ arrivals in a three-minute time period with $\mu = 2$ is given by the following Poisson probability function.

$$f(x) = \frac{2^x e^{-2}}{x!}$$

Suppose now we want to compute the probability of one arrival in a three-minute period.

$$\begin{array}{c} \text{Probability of Exactly} \\ \text{1 Arrival in 3 Minutes} \end{array} = f(1) = \frac{2^1 e^{-2}}{1!} = .2707$$

## An Example Involving Length or Distance Intervals

Let us illustrate an application not involving time intervals in which the Poisson probability distribution is useful. Suppose we are concerned with the occurrence of major defects in a highway one month after resurfacing. We will assume that the probability of a defect is the same for any two highway intervals of equal length and that the occurrence or nonoccurrence of a defect in any one interval is independent of the occurrence or nonoccurrence of a defect in any other interval. Hence, the Poisson probability distribution can be applied.

Suppose we learn that major defects one month after resurfacing occur at the average rate of two per mile. Let us find the probability of no major defects in a particular three-mile section of the highway. Because we are interested in an interval with a length of three miles, $\mu = (2 \text{ defects/mile})(3 \text{ miles}) = 6$ represents the expected number of major defects over the three-mile section of highway. Using equation (5.11), the probability of no major defects is $f(0) = 6^0 e^{-6}/0! = .0025$. Thus, it is unlikely that no major defects will occur in the three-mile section. In fact, this example indicates a $1 - .0025 = .9975$ probability of at least one major defect in the three-mile highway section.

## Using Excel to Compute Poisson Probabilities

The Excel function for computing Poisson probabilities and cumulative probabilities is called POISSON. It works in much the same way as the Excel function for computing binomial probabilities. Here we show how to use it to compute Poisson probabilities and cumulative probabilities. To illustrate, we use the example introduced earlier in this section; cars arrive at a bank drive-up teller window at the mean rate of 10 per 15-minute time interval. Refer to Figure 5.8 as we describe the tasks involved.

**Enter Data:**    In order to compute a Poisson probability we must know the mean number of occurrences ($\mu$) per time period and the number of occurrences for which we want to compute the probability ($x$). For the drive-up teller window example, the occurrences of interest are the arrivals of cars. The mean arrival rate is 10, which has been entered in cell D1. Earlier in this section, we computed the probability of 5 arrivals. But, suppose now we want to compute the probability of zero up through 20 arrivals.* To do so, we enter the values 0, 1, 2, . . . , 20 into cells A4:A24.

**Enter Functions and Formulas:**    The POISSON function has three arguments: the first is the value of $x$, the second is the value of $\mu$, and the third is FALSE or TRUE. We choose FALSE for the third argument if a probability is desired. The formula =POISSON(A4, $D$1,FALSE) has been entered into cell B4 to compute the probability of 0 arrivals in a 15-minute period. See the formula worksheet in the background of Figure 5.8. The value worksheet in the foreground shows that the probability of 0 arrivals is 0.0000. The formula in cell B4 is copied to cells B5:B24 to compute the probabilities for 1 through 20 arrivals.

---

*The Poisson probabilities for $x > 20$ are very close to zero and not shown.

**FIGURE 5.8** EXCEL WORKSHEET FOR COMPUTING POISSON PROBABILITIES

| | A | B | C | D | E |
|---|---|---|---|---|---|
| 1 | | | Mean No. of Occurrences | 10 | |
| 2 | | | | | |
| 3 | No. of Arrivals (x) | Probability f(x) | | | |
| 4 | 0 | =POISSON(A4,$D$1,FALSE) | | | |
| 5 | 1 | =POISSON(A5,$D$1,FALSE) | | | |
| 6 | 2 | =POISSON(A6,$D$1,FALSE) | | | |
| 7 | 3 | =POISSON(A7,$D$1,FALSE) | | | |
| 8 | 4 | =POISSON(A8,$D$1,FALSE) | | | |
| 9 | 5 | =POISSON(A9,$D$1,FALSE) | | | |
| 10 | 6 | =POISSON(A10,$D$1,FALSE) | | | |
| 11 | 7 | =POISSON(A11,$D$1,FALSE) | | | |
| 12 | 8 | =POISSON(A12,$D$1,FALSE) | | | |
| 13 | 9 | =POISSON(A13,$D$1,FALSE) | | | |
| 14 | 10 | =POISSON(A14,$D$1,FALSE) | | | |
| 15 | 11 | =POISSON(A15,$D$1,FALSE) | | | |
| 16 | 12 | =POISSON(A16,$D$1,FALSE) | | | |
| 17 | 13 | =POISSON(A17,$D$1,FALSE) | | | |
| 18 | 14 | =POISSON(A18,$D$1,FALSE) | | | |
| 19 | 15 | =POISSON(A19,$D$1,FALSE) | | | |
| 20 | 16 | =POISSON(A20,$D$1,FALSE) | | | |
| 21 | 17 | =POISSON(A21,$D$1,FALSE) | | | |
| 22 | 18 | =POISSON(A22,$D$1,FALSE) | | | |
| 23 | 19 | =POISSON(A23,$D$1,FALSE) | | | |
| 24 | 20 | =POISSON(A24,$D$1,FALSE) | | | |
| 25 | | | | | |

| | A | B | C | D | E | F | G | H | I |
|---|---|---|---|---|---|---|---|---|---|
| 1 | | Mean No. of Occurrences | | 10 | | | | | |
| 2 | | | | | | | | | |
| 3 | No. of Arrivals (x) | Probability f(x) | | | | | | | |
| 4 | 0 | 0.0000 | | | | | | | |
| 5 | 1 | 0.0005 | | | | | | | |
| 6 | 2 | 0.0023 | | | | | | | |
| 7 | 3 | 0.0076 | | | | | | | |
| 8 | 4 | 0.0189 | | | | | | | |
| 9 | 5 | 0.0378 | | | | | | | |
| 10 | 6 | 0.0631 | | | | | | | |
| 11 | 7 | 0.0901 | | | | | | | |
| 12 | 8 | 0.1126 | | | | | | | |
| 13 | 9 | 0.1251 | | | | | | | |
| 14 | 10 | 0.1251 | | | | | | | |
| 15 | 11 | 0.1137 | | | | | | | |
| 16 | 12 | 0.0948 | | | | | | | |
| 17 | 13 | 0.0729 | | | | | | | |
| 18 | 14 | 0.0521 | | | | | | | |
| 19 | 15 | 0.0347 | | | | | | | |
| 21 | 17 | 0.0128 | | | | | | | |
| 22 | 18 | 0.0071 | | | | | | | |
| 23 | 19 | 0.0037 | | | | | | | |
| 24 | 20 | 0.0019 | | | | | | | |
| 25 | | | | | | | | | |

Poisson Probabilities (chart: Probability vs. No. of Arrivals)

Note, in cell B9 of the value worksheet, that the probability of 5 arrivals is .0378. This result is the same as we calculated earlier in the text.

Notice how easy it was to compute all the probabilities for 0 through 20 arrivals using the Excel function. These calculations would take quite a bit of work using a calculator. We have also used Excel's chart wizard to develop a graph of the Poisson probability distribution of arrivals. See the value worksheet in Figure 5.8. This chart gives a nice graphical presentation of the probabilities for the various number of arrival possibilities in a 15-minute interval. We can quickly see that the most likely number of arrivals is 9 or 10 and that the probabilities fall off rather smoothly for smaller and larger values.

Let us now see how cumulative probabilities are generated using Excel's POISSON function. It is really a simple extension of what we have already done. We will again use the example of arrivals at a drive-up teller window. Refer to Figure 5.9 as we describe the tasks involved.

**Enter Data:** To compute cumulative Poisson probabilities we must provide the mean number of occurrences ($\mu$) per time period and the values of $x$ that we are interested in. The mean arrival rate (10) has been entered into cell D1. Suppose we want to compute the cumulative probabilities for a number of arrivals ranging from zero up through 20. To do so, we enter the values 0, 1, 2, . . . , 20 into cells A4:A24.

**Enter Functions and Formulas:** Refer to the formula worksheet in the background of Figure 5.8. The formulas we enter into cells B4:B24 of Figure 5.9 are the same as in Figure 5.8 with one exception. Instead of FALSE for the third argument we enter the word TRUE to obtain cumulative probabilities. After entering these formulas into cells B4:B24 of the worksheet in Figure 5.9 the cumulative probabilities shown were obtained.

Note, in Figure 5.9, that the probability of 5 or fewer arrivals is .0671 and that the probability of 4 or fewer arrivals is .0293. Thus, the probability of exactly 5 arrivals is the differ-

*Instructions for using the Chart Wizard are in Chapter 2.*

**FIGURE 5.9**    EXCEL WORKSHEET FOR COMPUTING CUMULATIVE POISSON PROBABILITIES

| | A | B | C | D | E |
|---|---|---|---|---|---|
| 1 | | | Mean No. of Occurrences |10 | |
| 2 | | | | | |
| 3 | No. of Arrivals (x) | Probability f(x) | | | |
| 4 | 0 | =POISSON(A4,$D$1,TRUE) | | | |
| 5 | 1 | =POISSON(A5,$D$1,TRUE) | | | |
| 6 | 2 | =POISSON(A6,$D$1,TRUE) | | | |
| 7 | 3 | =POISSON(A7,$D$1,TRUE) | | | |
| 8 | 4 | =POISSON(A8,$D$1,TRUE) | | | |
| 9 | 5 | =POISSON(A9,$D$1,TRUE) | | | |
| 10 | 6 | =POISSON(A10,$D$1,TRUE) | | | |
| 11 | 7 | =POISSON(A11,$D$1,TRUE) | | | |
| 12 | 8 | =POISSON(A12,$D$1,TRUE) | | | |
| 13 | 9 | =POISSON(A13,$D$1,TRUE) | | | |
| 14 | 10 | =POISSON(A14,$D$1,TRUE) | | | |
| 15 | 11 | =POISSON(A15,$D$1,TRUE) | | | |
| 16 | 12 | =POISSON(A16,$D$1,TRUE) | | | |
| 17 | 13 | =POISSON(A17,$D$1,TRUE) | | | |
| 18 | 14 | =POISSON(A18,$D$1,TRUE) | | | |
| 19 | 15 | =POISSON(A19,$D$1,TRUE) | | | |
| 20 | 16 | =POISSON(A20,$D$1,TRUE) | | | |
| 21 | 17 | =POISSON(A21,$D$1,TRUE) | | | |
| 22 | 18 | =POISSON(A22,$D$1,TRUE) | | | |
| 23 | 19 | =POISSON(A23,$D$1,TRUE) | | | |
| 24 | 20 | =POISSON(A24,$D$1,TRUE) | | | |
| 25 | | | | | |

| | A | B | C | D | E |
|---|---|---|---|---|---|
| 1 | Mean No. of Occurrences | | | 10 | |
| 2 | | | | | |
| 3 | Arrivals (x) | Probability f(x) | | | |
| 4 | 0 | 0.0000 | | | |
| 5 | 1 | 0.0005 | | | |
| 6 | 2 | 0.0028 | | | |
| 7 | 3 | 0.0103 | | | |
| 8 | 4 | 0.0293 | | | |
| 9 | 5 | 0.0671 | | | |
| 10 | 6 | 0.1301 | | | |
| 11 | 7 | 0.2202 | | | |
| 12 | 8 | 0.3328 | | | |
| 13 | 9 | 0.4579 | | | |
| 14 | 10 | 0.5830 | | | |
| 15 | 11 | 0.6968 | | | |
| 16 | 12 | 0.7916 | | | |
| 17 | 13 | 0.8645 | | | |
| 18 | 14 | 0.9165 | | | |
| 19 | 15 | 0.9513 | | | |
| 20 | 16 | 0.9730 | | | |
| 21 | 17 | 0.9857 | | | |
| 22 | 18 | 0.9928 | | | |
| 23 | 19 | 0.9965 | | | |
| 24 | 20 | 0.9984 | | | |
| 25 | | | | | |

ence in these two numbers: $f(5) = .0671 - .0293 = .0378$. We computed this probability earlier in this section and in Figure 5.8. Using these cumulative probabilities it is easy to compute the probability that a random variable lies within a certain interval. For instance, suppose we wanted to know the probability of more than 5 and fewer than 16 arrivals. We would just find the cumulative probability of 15 arrivals and subtract from that the cumulative probability for 5 arrivals. Referring to Figure 5.9 to obtain the appropriate probabilities we obtain $.9513 - .0671 = .8842$. With such a high probability, we could conclude that 6 to 15 cars will arrive in most 15-minute intervals. Using the cumulative probability for 20 arrivals, we can also conclude that the probability of more than 20 arrivals in a 15-minute period is $1 - .9984 = .0016$; thus, there is almost no chance of more than 20 cars arriving.

## EXERCISES

## Methods

**38.**    Consider a Poisson probability distribution with $\mu = 3$.
   **a.**    Write the appropriate Poisson probability function.
   **b.**    Compute $f(2)$.
   **c.**    Compute $f(1)$.
   **d.**    Compute $P(x \geq 2)$.

**39.** Consider a Poisson probability distribution with an average number of occurrences per time period of two.
   **a.** Write the appropriate Poisson probability function.
   **b.** What is the average number of occurrences in three time periods?
   **c.** Write the appropriate Poisson probability function to determine the probability of $x$ occurrences in three time periods.
   **d.** Find the probability of two occurrences in one time period.
   **e.** Find the probability of six occurrences in three time periods.
   **f.** Find the probability of five occurrences in two time periods.

## Applications

**40.** Phone calls arrive at the rate of 48 per hour at the reservation desk for Regional Airways.
   **a.** Find the probability of receiving three calls in a five-minute interval of time.
   **b.** Find the probability of receiving exactly 10 calls in 15 minutes.
   **c.** Suppose no calls are currently on hold. If the agent takes five minutes to complete the current call, how many callers do you expect to be waiting by that time? What is the probability that none will be waiting?
   **d.** If no calls are currently being processed, what is the probability that the agent can take three minutes for personal time without being interrupted by a call?

**41.** During the period of time phone-in registrations are being taken at a local university, calls come in at the rate of one every two minutes.
   **a.** What is the expected number of calls in one hour?
   **b.** What is the probability of three calls in five minutes?
   **c.** What is the probability of no calls in a five-minute period?

**42.** The mean number of times per year that *Barron's* subscribers take domestic flights for personal reasons is four (*Barron's* 1995 Primary Reader Survey).
   **a.** What is the probability a subscriber takes two domestic flights for personal reasons in a year?
   **b.** What is the mean number of domestic flights for personal reasons in a 3-month period?
   **c.** What is the probability a subscriber takes one or more domestic flights for personal reasons in a 6-month period?

**43.** Airline passengers arrive randomly and independently at the passenger-screening facility at a major international airport. The mean arrival rate is 10 passengers per minute.
   **a.** What is the probability of no arrivals in a one-minute period?
   **b.** What is the probability that three or fewer passengers arrive in a one-minute period?
   **c.** What is the probability of no arrivals in a 15-second period?
   **d.** What is the probability of at least one arrival in a 15-second period?

**44.** Investment activities for subscribers to *The Wall Street Journal Interactive Edition* show that the average number of security transactions per year is approximately 15 (*The Wall Street Journal* Subscriber Study, 1999). Assume that a particular investor makes transactions at this rate. Furthermore, assume that the probability of a transaction for this investor is the same for any two months and transactions in one month are independent of transactions in any other month. Answer the following questions.
   **a.** What is the mean number of transactions per month?
   **b.** What is the probability of no stock transactions during a month?
   **c.** What is the probability of exactly one stock transaction during a month?
   **d.** What is the probability of more than one stock transaction during a month?

**45.** Each year, 450 accidental deaths due to firearms occur in the 15–24 age group (National Safety Council, *Accident Facts*, 1996).
   **a.** What is the average number of accidental deaths due to firearms per week?
   **b.** What is the probability of no accidental deaths due to firearms in a typical week?
   **c.** What is the probability of two or more accidental deaths due to firearms in a typical day?

## 5.6    HYPERGEOMETRIC PROBABILITY DISTRIBUTION

The hypergeometric probability distribution is closely related to the binomial probability distribution. The key difference between the two probability distributions is that with the hypergeometric distribution, the trials are not independent; and the probability of success changes from trial to trial.

The usual notation in applications of the hypergeometric probability distribution is to let $r$ denote the number of elements in the population of size $N$ that are labeled success and $N - r$ denote the number of elements in the population that are labeled failure. The **hypergeometric probability function** is used to compute the probability that in a random selection of $n$ elements, selected without replacement, we will obtain $x$ elements labeled success and $n - x$ elements labeled failure. For this outcome to occur, we must obtain $x$ successes from the $r$ successes in the population and $n - x$ failures from the $N - r$ failures. The following hypergeometric probability function provides $f(x)$, the probability of obtaining $x$ successes in a sample of size $n$.

**Hypergeometric Probability Function**

$$f(x) = \frac{\binom{r}{x}\binom{N - r}{n - x}}{\binom{N}{n}} \qquad \text{for } 0 \leq x \leq r \qquad\qquad \textbf{(5.12)}$$

where

$$f(x) = \text{probability of } x \text{ successes in } n \text{ trials}$$
$$n = \text{number of trials}$$
$$N = \text{number of elements in the population}$$
$$r = \text{number of elements in the population labeled success}$$

Note that $\binom{N}{n}$ represents the number of ways a sample of size $n$ can be selected from a population of size $N$; $\binom{r}{x}$ represents the number of ways that $x$ successes can be selected from a total of $r$ successes in the population; and $\binom{N - r}{n - x}$ represents the number of ways that $n - x$ failures can be selected from a total of $N - r$ failures in the population.

To illustrate the computations involved in using equation (5.12), let us consider the problem of selecting two people from a five-member committee to send to a Las Vegas convention. Assume that the five-member committee consists of three women and two men. To determine the probability of randomly selecting two women, we can use equation (5.12) with $n = 2$, $N = 5$, $r = 3$, and $x = 2$.

$$f(2) = \frac{\binom{3}{2}\binom{2}{0}}{\binom{5}{2}} = \frac{\left(\dfrac{3!}{2!1!}\right)\left(\dfrac{2!}{2!0!}\right)}{\left(\dfrac{5!}{2!3!}\right)} = \frac{3}{10} = .30$$

Suppose we learn later that three committee members will be allowed to make the trip. If we use $n = 3, N = 5, r = 3$, and $x = 2$, the probability that exactly two of the three members will be women is

$$f(2) = \frac{\binom{3}{2}\binom{2}{1}}{\binom{5}{2}} = \frac{\left(\frac{3!}{2!1!}\right)\left(\frac{2!}{1!1!}\right)}{\left(\frac{5!}{2!3!}\right)} = \frac{6}{10} = .60$$

As another illustration, suppose a population consists of 10 items, four of which are classified as defective and six of which are classified as nondefective. What is the probability that a random selection of three will provide two defective items? For this problem we can think of obtaining a defective item as a "success." Using equation (5.12) with $n = 3$, $N = 10, r = 4$, and $x = 2$, we can compute $f(2)$ as follows.

$$f(2) = \frac{\binom{4}{2}\binom{6}{1}}{\binom{10}{3}} = \frac{\left(\frac{4!}{2!2!}\right)\left(\frac{6!}{1!5!}\right)}{\left(\frac{10!}{3!7!}\right)} = \frac{36}{120} = .30$$

## Using Excel to Compute Hypergeometric Probabilities

The Excel function for computing hypergeometric probabilities is called HYPGEOMDIST. It only computes probabilities; not cumulative probabilities. The HYPGEOMDIST function has four arguments: $x, n, r, N$. It is fairly straightforward to use so we dispense with showing a worksheet figure and just show the formula. Let us reconsider the example of three women and two men on a five-person committee. Two people are to be chosen at random to send to a Las Vegas convention. We want to compute the probability that the two persons chosen are women. In this case, $x = 2, n = 2, r = 3$, and $N = 5$. So the appropriate formula to place in a cell of an Excel worksheet would be =HYPGEOMDIST(2,2,3,5). Placing this formula in a cell of an Excel worksheet provides a hypergeometric probability of .30.

If 3 people are selected to go to Las Vegas, we have $x = 2, n = 3, r = 3$, and $N = 5$. So using the HYPGEOMDIST function to compute the probability of randomly selecting two women, we would enter the following formula into a cell of the worksheet: =HYPGEOMDIST(2,3,3,5). The probability computed is .6.

## EXERCISES

### Methods

**SELF** test

**46.** Suppose $N = 10$ and $r = 3$. Compute the hypergeometric probabilities for the following values of $n$ and $x$.

   **a.** $n = 4, x = 1$.
   **b.** $n = 2, x = 2$.
   **c.** $n = 2, x = 0$.
   **d.** $n = 4, x = 2$.

**47.** Suppose $N = 15$ and $r = 4$. What is the probability of $x = 3$ for $n = 10$?

## Applications

**48.** According to *Beverage Digest,* Coke Classic and Pepsi ranked number one and number two in sales (*The Wall Street Journal Almanac,* 1998). Assume that in a group of 10 individuals, six preferred Coke Classic and four preferred Pepsi. A random sample of three of these individuals is selected.
   **a.** What is the probability that exactly two preferred Coke Classic?
   **b.** What is the probability that the majority (either two or three) preferred Pepsi?

**49.** Blackjack, or twenty-one as it is frequently called, is a popular gambling game played in Las Vegas casinos. A player is dealt two cards. Face cards (jacks, queens, and kings) and tens have a point value of 10. Aces have a point value of 1 or 11. A 52-card deck has 16 cards with a point value of 10 (jacks, queens, kings, and tens) and four aces.
   **a.** What is the probability that both cards dealt are aces or 10-point cards?
   **b.** What is the probability that both of the cards are aces?
   **c.** What is the probability that both of the cards have a point value of 10?
   **d.** A blackjack is a 10-point card and an ace for a value of 21. Use your answers to parts (a), (b), and (c) to determine the probability that a player is dealt blackjack. (Hint: Part (d) is not a hypergeometric problem. Develop your own logical relationship as to how the hypergeometric probabilities from parts (a), (b), and (c) can be combined to answer this question.)

**50.** Axline Computers manufactures personal computers at two plants, one in Texas and the other in Hawaii. The Texas plant has 40 employees; the Hawaii plant has 20. A random sample of 10 employees is to be asked to fill out a benefits questionnaire.
   **a.** What is the probability that none of the employees are at the plant in Hawaii?
   **b.** What is the probability that one of the employees is at the plant in Hawaii?
   **c.** What is the probability that two or more of the employees are at the plant in Hawaii?
   **d.** What is the probability that nine of the employees are at the plant in Texas?

**51.** Of the 25 students (14 boys and 11 girls) in the sixth-grade class at St. Andrew School, 5 students were absent Thursday.
   **a.** What is the probability that two of the absent students were girls?
   **b.** What is the probability that two of the absent students were boys?
   **c.** What is the probability that all of the absent students were boys?
   **d.** What is the probability that none of the absent students were boys?

**52.** A shipment of 10 items has two defective and eight nondefective items. In the inspection of the shipment, a sample of items will be selected and tested. If a defective item is found, the shipment of 10 items will be rejected.
   **a.** If a sample of three items is selected, what is the probability that the shipment will be rejected?
   **b.** If a sample of four items is selected, what is the probability that the shipment will be rejected?
   **c.** If a sample of five items is selected, what is the probability that the shipment will be rejected?
   **d.** If management would like a .90 probability of rejecting a shipment with two defective and eight nondefective items, how large a sample would you recommend?

## SUMMARY

The concept of a random variable was introduced to provide a numerical description of the outcome of an experiment. We saw that the probability distribution for a random variable describes how the probabilities are distributed over the values the random variable can assume. For any discrete random variable $x$, the probability distribution is defined by a probability function, denoted by $f(x)$, which provides the probability associated with each value of the random variable. Once the probability function has been defined, we can compute the expected value, variance and standard deviation for the random variable.

The binomial probability distribution can be used to determine the probability of $x$ successes in $n$ trials whenever the experiment has the following properties:

1. The experiment consists of a sequence of $n$ identical trials.
2. Two outcomes are possible on each trial, one called success and the other failure.
3. The probability of a success $p$ does not change from trial to trial. Consequently, the probability of failure, $1 - p$, does not change from trial to trial.
4. The trials are independent.

When the four properties hold, a binomial probability function can be used to determine the probability of obtaining $x$ successes in $n$ trials. Formulas were also presented for the mean and variance of the binomial probability distribution.

The Poisson probability distribution is used when it is desirable to determine the probability of obtaining $x$ occurrences over an interval of time or space. The following assumptions are necessary for the Poisson distribution to be applicable.

1. The probability of an occurrence of the event is the same for any two intervals of equal length.
2. The occurrence or nonoccurrence of the event in any interval is independent of the occurrence or nonoccurrence of the event in any other interval.

A third discrete probability distribution, the hypergeometric, was introduced in Section 5.6. Like the binomial, it is used to compute the probability of $x$ successes in $n$ trials. But, in contrast to the binomial, the probability of success changes from trial to trial.

## GLOSSARY

**Random variable**   A numerical description of the outcome of an experiment.

**Discrete random variable**   A random variable that may assume either a finite number of values or an infinite sequence of values.

**Continuous random variable**   A random variable that may assume any value in an interval or collection of intervals.

**Probability distribution**   A description of how the probabilities are distributed over the values the random variable can assume.

**Probability function**   A function, denoted by $f(x)$, that provides the probability that $x$ assumes a particular value for a discrete random variable.

**Discrete uniform probability distribution**   A probability distribution for which each possible value of the random variable has the same probability.

**Expected value**   A measure of the mean, or central location, of a random variable.

**Variance**   A measure of the variability, or dispersion, of a random variable.

**Standard deviation**   The positive square root of the variance.

**Binomial experiment**   A probability experiment having the four properties stated at the beginning of Section 5.4.

**Binomial probability distribution**   A probability distribution showing the probability of $x$ successes in $n$ trials of a binomial experiment.

**Binomial probability function**    The function used to compute binomial probabilities.

**Poisson probability distribution**    A probability distribution showing the probability of $x$ occurrences of an event over a specified interval of time or space.

**Poisson probability function**    The function used to compute Poisson probabilities.

**Hypergeometric probability function**    The function used to compute the probability of $x$ successes in $n$ trials when the trials are dependent.

## KEY FORMULAS

**Discrete Uniform Probability Function**

$$f(x) = 1/n \tag{5.3}$$

where $n$ = the number of values the random variable may assume

**Expected Value of a Discrete Random Variable**

$$E(x) = \mu = \Sigma x f(x) \tag{5.4}$$

**Variance of a Discrete Random Variable**

$$\text{Var}(x) = \sigma^2 = \Sigma(x - \mu)^2 f(x) \tag{5.5}$$

**Number of Experimental Outcomes Providing Exactly $x$ Successes in $n$ Trials**

$$\binom{n}{x} = \frac{n!}{x!(n-x)!} \tag{5.6}$$

**Binomial Probability Function**

$$f(x) = \binom{n}{x} p^x (1-p)^{(n-x)} \tag{5.8}$$

**Expected Value for the Binomial Probability Distribution**

$$E(x) = \mu = np \tag{5.9}$$

**Variance for the Binomial Probability Distribution**

$$\text{Var}(x) = \sigma^2 = np(1-p) \tag{5.10}$$

**Poisson Probability Function**

$$f(x) = \frac{\mu^x e^{-\mu}}{x!} \tag{5.11}$$

**Hypergeometric Probability Function**

$$f(x) = \frac{\binom{r}{x}\binom{N-r}{n-x}}{\binom{N}{n}} \qquad \text{for } 0 \leq x \leq r \tag{5.12}$$

## SUPPLEMENTARY EXERCISES

**53.** A *Wall Street Journal*/NBC News poll asked 2004 adults how they felt about their opportunities for career advancement (*The Wall Street Journal,* September 19, 1997). Twenty-three percent indicated they were very satisfied; 38% indicated they were somewhat satisfied; 3% indicated they were not sure; 18% indicated they were somewhat dissatisfied; and 18% indicated they were very dissatisfied. Let $x$ be a random variable representing level of satisfaction. We let $x = 5$ for very satisfied, $x = 4$ for somewhat satisfied, $x = 3$ for not sure, $x = 2$ for somewhat dissatisfied, and $x = 1$ for very dissatisfied.

    **a.** Use the preceding numerical values to develop a probability distribution for level of satisfaction with opportunities for career advancement.

    **b.** Compute the expected level of satisfaction. Does a higher score indicate more or less satisfaction?

    **c.** Compute the variance and standard deviation for the satisfaction scores.

**54.** An opinion survey of 1009 adults was conducted by Louis Harris & Associates, Inc. (*Business Week,* December 29, 1997). Table 5.8 shows the probability distribution of responses to a question concerning the stock market's valuation.

    **a.** Show that the probability distribution in Table 5.8 satisfies the properties of all probability distributions.

    **b.** What are the expected value and variance of the probability distribution of opinions?

    **c.** Comment on whether people think the stock market is overvalued.

**55.** The budgeting process for a midwestern college resulted in expense forecasts for the coming year (in $millions) of $9, $10, $11, $12, and $13. Because the actual expenses are unknown, the following respective probabilities are assigned: .3, .2, .25, .05, and .2.

    **a.** Show the probability distribution for the expense forecast.

    **b.** What is the expected value of the expense forecast for the coming year?

    **c.** What is the variance in the expense forecast for the coming year?

    **d.** If income projections for the year are estimated at $12 million, comment on the financial position of the college.

**56.** Kristen DelGuzzi conducted a study of Hamilton County judges and courts over a three-year period (*The Cincinnati Enquirer,* January 11, 1998). One finding was that 4% of the cases decided in Common Pleas Court were appealed.

    **a.** If 20 cases are heard on a particular day, what is the probability that 3 will be appealed?

    **b.** If 20 cases are heard on a particular day, what is the probability none will be appealed?

    **c.** It is not unusual for 1200 cases to be heard in a month. What is the expected number of appeals?

    **d.** If 1200 cases are heard in a month, what are the variance and standard deviation of the number of appeals?

**TABLE 5.8**    PROBABILITY DISTRIBUTION OF RESPONSES CONCERNING STOCK MARKET'S VALUATION

| Market Valuation | Random Variable ($x$) | Probability $f(x)$ |
|---|---|---|
| Very undervalued | 1 | 0.02 |
| Somewhat undervalued | 2 | 0.06 |
| Fairly valued | 3 | 0.28 |
| Somewhat overvalued | 4 | 0.54 |
| Very overvalued | 5 | 0.10 |

57.  A company is planning to interview Internet users to learn how its proposed web site will be received by different age groups. According to the Bureau of the Census, 40% of individuals aged 18 to 54, and 12% of individuals aged 55 and over use the Internet (*Statistical Abstract of the United States,* 2000).

    **a.**  How many people from the 18–54 age group must be contacted to find an expected number of at least 10 Internet users?

    **b.**  How many people from the age group 55 and over must be contacted to find an expected number of at least 10 Internet users?

    **c.**  If you contact the number of 18- to 54-year-old people suggested in part (a), what is the standard deviation of the number who will be Internet users?

    **d.**  If you contact the number of people aged 55 and older suggested in part (b), what is the standard deviation of the number who will be Internet users?

58.  Many companies use a quality control technique called *acceptance sampling* to monitor incoming shipments of parts, raw materials, and so on. In the electronics industry, component parts are commonly shipped from suppliers in large lots. Inspection of a sample of $n$ components can be viewed as the $n$ trials of a binomial experiment. The outcome for each component tested (trial) will be that the component is classified as good or defective. Reynolds Electronics accepts a lot from a particular supplier if the defective components in the lot do not exceed 1%. Suppose a random sample of five items from a recent shipment has been tested.

    **a.**  Assume that 1% of the shipment is defective. Compute the probability that no items in the sample are defective.

    **b.**  Assume that 1% of the shipment is defective. Compute the probability that exactly one item in the sample is defective.

    **c.**  What is the probability of observing one or more defective items in the sample if 1% of the shipment is defective?

    **d.**  Would you feel comfortable accepting the shipment if one item were found to be defective? Why or why not?

59.  The unemployment rate is 4.1% (*Barron's,* September 4, 2000). Assume that 100 employable people are selected randomly.

    **a.**  What is the expected number of people who are unemployed?

    **b.**  What is the variance and standard deviation of the number of people who are unemployed?

60.  In December 1997, the U.S. Department of Justice issued an injunction against Microsoft Corporation for bundling its Internet Explorer® Web browser with its Windows 95® operating system (*Fortune,* February 2, 1998). Public opinion was divided on whether Microsoft was a monopoly. In a *Fortune* poll, 41% of respondents agreed with the statement, "Microsoft is a monopoly." Suppose a sample of 800 people has been taken.

    **a.**  How many would you expect to agree that Microsoft is a monopoly?

    **b.**  What is the standard deviation of the number of respondents who believe Microsoft is a monopoly?

    **c.**  What is the standard deviation of the number of respondents who do not believe Microsoft is a monopoly?

61.  Cars arrive at a car wash randomly and independently; the probability of an arrival is the same for any two time intervals of equal length. The mean arrival rate is 15 cars per hour. What is the probability that 20 or more cars will arrive during any given hour of operation?

62.  A new automated production process has had an average of 1.5 breakdowns per day. Because of the cost associated with a breakdown, management is concerned about the possibility of having three or more breakdowns during a day. Assume that breakdowns occur randomly, that the probability of a breakdown is the same for any two time intervals of equal length, and that breakdowns in one period are independent of breakdowns in other periods. What is the probability of having three or more breakdowns during a day?

**63.** A regional director responsible for business development in the state of Pennsylvania is concerned about the number of small business failures. If the mean number of small business failures per month is 10, what is the probability that exactly four small businesses will fail during a given month? Assume that the probability of a failure is the same for any two months and that the occurrence or nonoccurrence of a failure in any month is independent of failures in any other month.

**64.** Customer arrivals at a bank are random and independent; the probability of an arrival in any one-minute period is the same as the probability of an arrival in any other one-minute period. Answer the following questions, assuming a mean arrival rate of three customers per minute.

   **a.** What is the probability of exactly three arrivals in a one-minute period?
   **b.** What is the probability of at least three arrivals in a one-minute period?

**65.** A deck of playing cards contains 52 cards, four of which are aces. What is the probability that the deal of a five card hand provides:

   **a.** A pair of aces?
   **b.** Exactly one ace?
   **c.** No aces?
   **d.** At least one ace?

**66.** According to the WTA Tour and ATP Tour, four of the top 10 women tennis players use Wilson rackets (*USA Today,* March 2, 1995). Suppose two of these players have reached the finals of a tournament.

   **a.** What is the probability that exactly one uses a Wilson racket?
   **b.** What is the probability that both use Wilson rackets?
   **c.** What is the probability that neither uses a Wilson racket?

# CONTINUOUS PROBABILITY DISTRIBUTIONS

Chapter 6

## CONTENTS

## STATISTICS IN PRACTICE

### PROCTER & GAMBLE*
*Cincinnati, Ohio*

Procter & Gamble (P&G) is in the consumer products business worldwide. P&G produces and markets such products as detergents, disposable diapers, over-the-counter pharmaceuticals, dentifrices, bar soaps, mouthwashes, and paper towels. It has the leading brand in more categories than any other consumer products company.

As a leader in the application of statistical methods in decision making, P&G employs people with diverse academic backgrounds: engineering, statistics, operations research, and business. The major quantitative technologies for which these people provide support are probabilistic decision and risk analysis, advanced simulation, quality improvement, and quantitative methods (e.g., linear programming, regression analysis, probability analysis).

The Industrial Chemicals Division of P&G is a major supplier of fatty alcohols derived from natural substances such as coconut oil and from petroleum-based derivatives. The division wanted to know the economic risks and opportunities of expanding its fatty-alcohol production facilities, and P&G's experts in probabilistic decision and risk analysis were called in to help. After structuring and modeling the problem, they determined that the key to profitability was the cost difference between the petroleum- and coconut-based raw materials. Future costs were unknown, but the analysts were able to represent them with the following continuous random variables.

$$x = \text{the coconut oil price per pound of fatty alcohol}$$

and

$$y = \text{the petroleum raw material price per pound of fatty alcohol}$$

Because the key to profitability was the difference between these two random variables, a third random

Some of Procter & Gamble's many well-known products.
Photo © Joe Higgins/South-Western.

variable, $d = x - y$, was used in the analysis. Experts were interviewed to determine the probability distribution for $x$ and $y$. In turn, this information was used to develop a probability distribution for the difference in prices $d$. This continuous probability distribution showed a .90 probability that the price difference would be $.0655 or less and a .50 probability that the price difference would be $.035 or less. In addition, there was only a .10 probability that the price difference would be $.0045 or less.[†]

The Industrial Chemicals Division thought that being able to quantify the impact of raw material price differences was key to reaching a consensus. The probabilities obtained were used in a sensitivity analysis of the raw material price difference. The analysis yielded sufficient insight to form the basis for a recommendation to management.

The use of continuous random variables and their probability distributions was helpful to P&G in analyzing the economic risks associated with its fatty-alcohol production. In this chapter, you will gain an understanding of continuous random variables and their probability distributions including one of the most important probability distributions in statistics, the normal distribution.

---

*The authors are indebted to Joel Kahn of Procter & Gamble for providing this Statistics in Practice.

[†]The price differences stated here have been modified to protect proprietary data.

In the preceding chapter we discussed discrete random variables and their probability distributions. In this chapter we turn to the study of continuous random variables. Specifically, we discuss three continuous probability distributions: the uniform, the normal, and the exponential.

A fundamental difference separates discrete and continuous random variables in terms of how probabilities are computed. For a discrete random variable, the probability function $f(x)$ provides the probability that the random variable assumes a particular value. With continuous random variables, the counterpart of the probability function is the **probability density function**, also denoted by $f(x)$. The difference is that the probability density function does not directly provide probabilities. However, the area under the graph of $f(x)$ corresponding to a given interval does provide the probability that the continuous random variable $x$ assumes a value in that interval. So when we compute probabilities for continuous random variables we are computing the probability that the random variable assumes any value in an interval.

One of the implications of the definition of probability for continuous random variables is that the probability of any particular value of the random variable is zero, because the area under the graph of $f(x)$ at any particular point is zero. In Section 6.1 we demonstrate these concepts for a continuous random variable that has a uniform probability distribution.

Much of the chapter is devoted to describing and showing applications of the normal probability distribution. The normal probability distribution is of major importance; it is used extensively in statistical inference. The chapter closes with a discussion of the exponential probability distribution.

## 6.1   UNIFORM PROBABILITY DISTRIBUTION

Consider the random variable $x$ that represents the flight time of an airplane traveling from Chicago to New York. Suppose the flight time can be any value in the interval from 120 minutes to 140 minutes. Because the random variable $x$ can assume any value in that interval, $x$ is a continuous rather than a discrete random variable. Let us assume that sufficient actual flight data are available to conclude that the probability of a flight time within any one-minute interval is the same as the probability of a flight time within any other one-minute interval contained in the larger interval from 120 to 140 minutes. With every one-minute interval being equally likely, the random variable $x$ is said to have a **uniform probability distribution**. The probability density function, which defines the uniform probability distribution for the flight-time random variable, is

> Whenever the probability is proportional to the length of the interval, the random variable is uniformly distributed.

$$f(x) = \begin{cases} 1/20 & \text{for } 120 \leq x \leq 140 \\ 0 & \text{elsewhere} \end{cases}$$

Figure 6.1 is a graph of this probability density function. In general, the uniform probability density function for a random variable $x$ is defined by the following formula.

---

**Uniform Probability Density Function**

$$f(x) = \begin{cases} \dfrac{1}{b-a} & \text{for } a \leq x \leq b \\ 0 & \text{elsewhere} \end{cases} \tag{6.1}$$

---

For the flight-time random variable, $a = 120$ and $b = 140$.

**FIGURE 6.1** UNIFORM PROBABILITY DENSITY FUNCTION FOR FLIGHT TIME

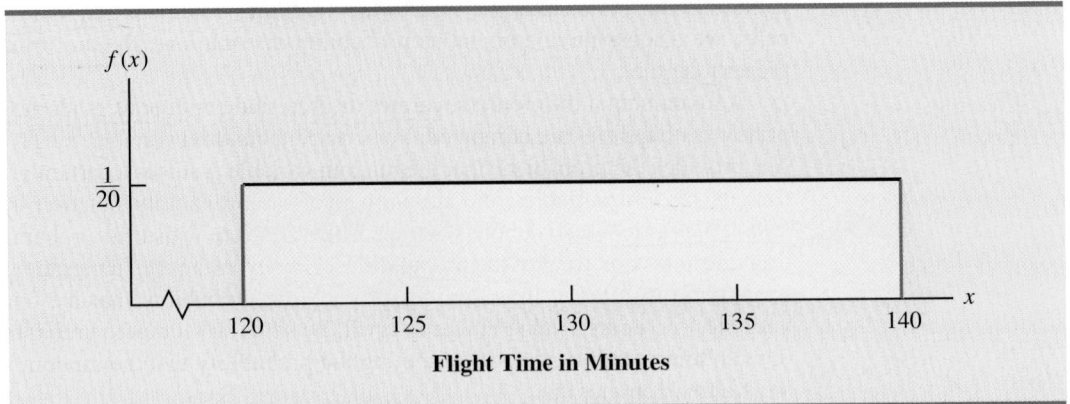

As noted in the introduction, for a continuous random variable, we consider probability only in terms of the likelihood that a random variable assumes a value within a specified interval. In the flight-time example, an acceptable probability question is: What is the probability that the flight time is between 120 and 130 minutes? That is, what is $P(120 \leq x \leq 130)$? Because the flight time must be between 120 and 140 minutes and because the probability is described as being uniform over this interval, we feel comfortable saying $P(120 \leq x \leq 130) = .50$. In the following subsection we show that this probability can be computed as the area under the graph of $f(x)$ from 120 to 130 (see Figure 6.2).

## Area as a Measure of Probability

Let us make an observation about the graph in Figure 6.2. Consider the area under the graph of $f(x)$ in the interval from 120 to 130. The area is rectangular, and the area of a rectangle is simply the width multiplied by the height. With the width of the interval equal to $130 - 120 = 10$ and the height equal to the value of the probability density function $f(x) = 1/20$, we have area = width × height = $10(1/20) = 10/20 = .50$.

What observation can you make about the area under the graph of $f(x)$ and probability? They are identical! Indeed, this observation is valid for all continuous random variables.

**FIGURE 6.2** AREA PROVIDES PROBABILITY OF FLIGHT TIME BETWEEN 120 AND 130 MINUTES

Once a probability density function $f(x)$ has been identified, the probability that $x$ takes a value between some lower value $x_1$ and some higher value $x_2$ can be found by computing the area under the graph of $f(x)$ over the interval from $x_1$ to $x_2$.

Given the uniform probability distribution for flight time and using the interpretation of area as probability, we can answer any number of probability questions about flight times. For example, what is the probability of a flight time between 128 and 136 minutes? The width of the interval is $136 - 128 = 8$. With the uniform height of $f(x) = 1/20$, we see that $P(128 \leq x \leq 136) = 8(1/20) = .40$.

Note that $P(120 \leq x \leq 140) = 20(1/20) = 1$. That is, the total area under the graph of $f(x)$ is equal to 1. This property holds for all continuous probability distributions and is the analog of the condition that the sum of the probabilities must equal 1 for a discrete probability function. For a continuous probability density function, we must also require that $f(x) \geq 0$ for all values of $x$. This requirement is the analog of the requirement that $f(x) \geq 0$ for discrete probability functions.

Two major differences stand out between the treatment of continuous random variables and the treatment of their discrete counterparts.

1.  We no longer talk about the probability of the random variable assuming a particular value. Instead, we talk about the probability of the random variable assuming a value within some given interval.

2.  The probability of the random variable assuming a value within some given interval from $x_1$ to $x_2$ is defined to be the area under the graph of the probability density function between $x_1$ and $x_2$. It implies that the probability of a continuous random variable assuming any particular value exactly is zero, because the area under the graph of $f(x)$ at a single point is zero.

To see that the probability of any single point is 0, refer to Figure 6.2 and compute the probability of a single point, say, $x = 125$. $P(x = 125) = P(125 \leq x \leq 125) = 0(1/20) = 0$.

The calculation of the expected value and variance for a continuous random variable is analogous to that for a discrete random variable. However, because the computational procedure involves integral calculus, we leave the derivation of the appropriate formulas to more advanced texts.

For the uniform continuous probability distribution introduced in this section, the formulas for the expected value and variance are

$$E(x) = \frac{a + b}{2}$$

$$\text{Var}(x) = \frac{(b - a)^2}{12}$$

In these formulas, $a$ is the smallest value and $b$ is the largest value that the random variable may assume.

Applying these formulas to the uniform probability distribution for flight times from Chicago to New York, we obtain

$$E(x) = \frac{(120 + 140)}{2} = 130$$

$$\text{Var}(x) = \frac{(140 - 120)^2}{12} = 33.33$$

The standard deviation of flight times can be found by taking the square root of the variance. Thus, $\sigma = 5.77$ minutes.

## NOTES AND COMMENTS

1. For a continuous random variable the probability of any particular value is zero; thus, $P(a \leq x \leq b) = P(a < x < b)$. This result shows that the probability of a random variable assuming a value in any interval is the same whether or not the endpoints are included.

2. To see more clearly why the height of a probability density function is not a probability, think about a random variable with the following uniform probability distribution.

$$f(x) = \begin{cases} 2 & \text{for } 0 \leq x \leq .5 \\ 0 & \text{elsewhere} \end{cases}$$

The height of the probability density function, $f(x)$, is 2 for values of $x$ between 0 and .5. However, we know probabilities can never be greater than 1. Thus, we see that $f(x)$ cannot be interpreted as the probability of $x$.

## EXERCISES

### Methods

1. The random variable $x$ is known to be uniformly distributed between 1.0 and 1.5.
   a. Show the graph of the probability density function.
   b. Compute $P(x = 1.25)$.
   c. Compute $P(1.0 \leq x \leq 1.25)$.
   d. Compute $P(1.20 < x < 1.5)$.

2. The random variable $x$ is known to be uniformly distributed between 10 and 20.
   a. Show the graph of the probability density function.
   b. Compute $P(x < 15)$.
   c. Compute $P(12 \leq x \leq 18)$.
   d. Compute $E(x)$.
   e. Compute $\text{Var}(x)$.

### Applications

3. Delta Airlines quotes a flight time of 2 hours, 5 minutes for its flights from Cincinnati to Tampa. Suppose we believe that actual flight times are uniformly distributed between 2 hours and 2 hours, 20 minutes.
   a. Show the graph of the probability density function for flight times.
   b. What is the probability that the flight will be no more than five minutes late?
   c. What is the probability that the flight will be more than 10 minutes late?
   d. What is the expected flight time?

4. Most computer languages have a function that can be used to generate random numbers. In Excel, the RAND function can be used to generate random numbers between 0 and 1. If we let $x$ denote a random number generated using RAND, then $x$ is a continuous random variable with the following probability density function.

$$f(x) = \begin{cases} 1 & \text{for } 0 \leq x \leq 1 \\ 0 & \text{elsewhere} \end{cases}$$

   a. Graph the probability density function.
   b. What is the probability of generating a random number between .25 and .75?
   c. What is the probability of generating a random number with a value less than or equal to .30?
   d. What is the probability of generating a random number with a value greater than .60?

5.  The driving distance for the top 60 women golfers on the LPGA tour is between 238.9 and 261.2 yards (*Golfweek,* December 6, 1997). Assume that the driving distance for these women is uniformly distributed over this interval.
    a.  Give a mathematical expression for the probability density function of driving distance.
    b.  What is the probability the driving distance for one of these women is less than 250 yards?
    c.  What is the probability the driving distance for one of these women is at least 255 yards?
    d.  What is the probability the driving distance for one of these women is between 245 and 260 yards?
    e.  How many of these women drive the ball at least 250 yards?

6.  The label on a bottle of liquid detergent shows contents to be 12 ounces per bottle. The production operation fills the bottle uniformly according to the following probability density function.

$$f(x) = \begin{cases} 8 & \text{for } 11.975 \le x \le 12.100 \\ 0 & \text{elsewhere} \end{cases}$$

    a.  What is the probability that a bottle will be filled with between 12 and 12.05 ounces?
    b.  What is the probability that a bottle will be filled with 12.02 or more ounces?
    c.  Quality control accepts a bottle that is filled to within .02 ounces of the number of ounces shown on the container label. What is the probability that a bottle of this liquid detergent will fail to meet the quality control standard?

7.  Suppose we are interested in bidding on a piece of land and we know there is one other bidder.* The seller has announced that the highest bid in excess of $10,000 will be accepted. Assume that the competitor's bid *x* is a random variable that is uniformly distributed between $10,000 and $15,000.
    a.  Suppose you bid $12,000. What is the probability that your bid will be accepted?
    b.  Suppose you bid $14,000. What is the probability that your bid will be accepted?
    c.  What amount should you bid to maximize the probability that you get the property?
    d.  Suppose you know someone who is willing to pay you $16,000 for the property. Would you consider bidding less than the amount in part (c)? Why or why not?

## 6.2   NORMAL PROBABILITY DISTRIBUTION

The most important probability distribution for describing a continuous random variable is the **normal probability distribution**. The normal probability distribution has been used in a wide variety of practical applications in which the random variables are heights and weights of people, test scores, scientific measurements, amounts of rainfall, and so on. It is also widely used in statistical inference, which is the major topic of the remainder of this book. In such applications, the normal probability distribution provides a description of the likely results obtained through sampling.

## Normal Curve

The form, or shape, of the normal probability distribution is illustrated by the bell-shaped curve in Figure 6.3. The probability density function that defines the bell-shaped curve of the normal probability distribution follows.

Abraham de Moivre, a French mathematician, published *The Doctrine of Chances* in 1733. He derived the normal probability distribution.

---

*This exercise is based on a problem suggested to us by Professor Roger Myerson of Northwestern University.

**Normal Probability Density Function**

$$f(x) = \frac{1}{\sigma\sqrt{2\pi}} e^{-(x-\mu)^2/2\sigma^2}$$  (6.2)

where

$\mu$ = mean

$\sigma$ = standard deviation

$\pi$ = 3.14159

$e$ = 2.71828

**FIGURE 6.3**   BELL-SHAPED CURVE FOR THE NORMAL PROBABILITY DISTRIBUTION

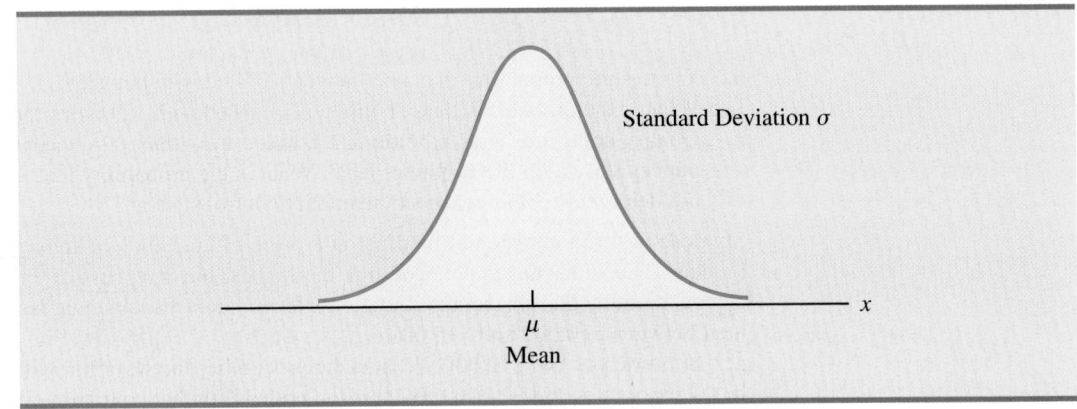

We make several observations about the characteristics of the normal probability distribution.

*The normal curve has two parameters, $\mu$ and $\sigma$. They determine the location and shape of the normal probability distribution.*

1. The entire family of normal probability distributions is differentiated by its mean $\mu$ and its standard deviation $\sigma$.
2. The highest point on the normal curve is at the mean, which is also the median and mode of the distribution.
3. The mean of the distribution can be any numerical value: negative, zero, or positive. Three normal distributions with the same standard deviation but three different means ($-10$, 0, and 20) are shown here.

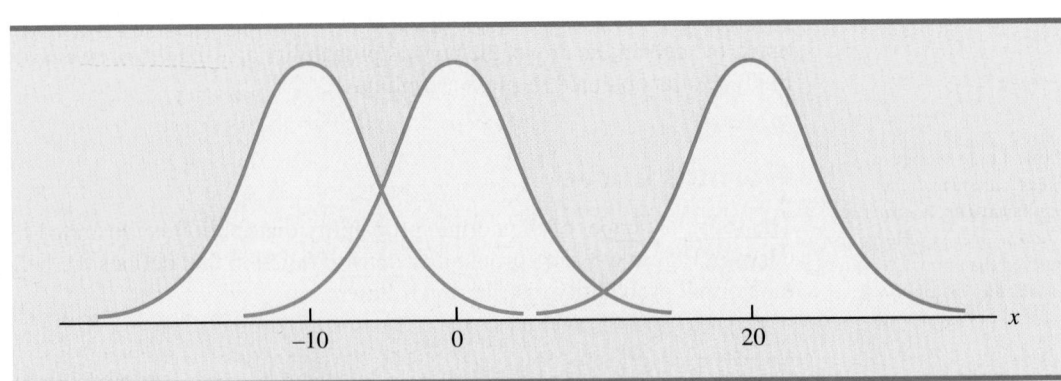

4. The normal probability distribution is symmetric, with the shape of the curve to the left of the mean a mirror image of the shape of the curve to the right of the mean. The tails of the curve extend to infinity in both directions and theoretically never touch the horizontal axis.

5. The standard deviation determines how flat and wide the curve is. Larger values of the standard deviation result in wider, flatter curves, showing more variability in the data. Two normal distributions with the same mean but with different standard deviations are shown here.

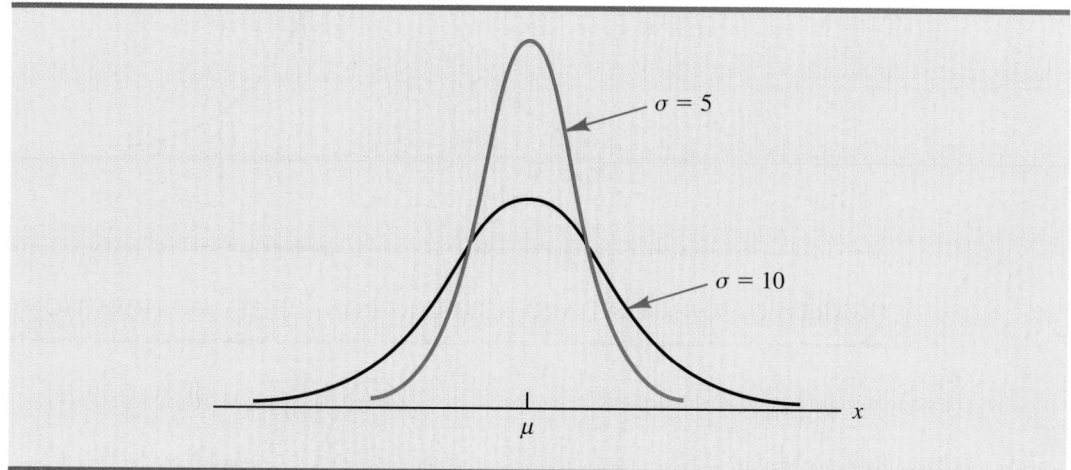

6. Probabilities for the normal random variable are given by areas under the curve. The total area under the curve for the normal probability distribution is 1, which is true for all continuous probability distributions. Because the distribution is symmetric, the total area under the curve to the left of the mean is .50 and the total area under the curve to the right of the mean is .50.

7. The percentage of values in some commonly used intervals are:

   a. 68.26% of the values of a normal random variable are within plus or minus one standard deviation of its mean.

   b. 95.44% of the values of a normal random variable are within plus or minus two standard deviations of its mean.

   c. 99.72% of the values of a normal random variable are within plus or minus three standard deviations of its mean.

   Figure 6.4 shows properties (a), (b), and (c) graphically.

*These percentages are the basis for the empirical rule introduced in Section 3.3.*

## Standard Normal Probability Distribution

A random variable that has a normal distribution with a mean of zero and a standard deviation of one is said to have a **standard normal probability distribution.** The letter $z$ is commonly used to designate this particular normal random variable. Figure 6.5 is the graph of the standard normal probability distribution. It has the same general appearance as other normal distributions, but with the special properties of $\mu = 0$ and $\sigma = 1$.

*For the uniform distribution, the height of the probability density function is constant, so it is easy to compute the area under the curve. For the normal probability density function, the height of the curve varies and calculus is required to compute the areas that represent probability.*

As with other continuous random variables, probability calculations with any normal probability distribution are made by computing areas under the graph of the probability density function. Thus, to find the probability that a normal random variable is within any specific interval, we must compute the area under the normal curve over that interval. For the standard normal probability distribution, areas under the normal curve have been computed and are available in tables that can be used in computing probabilities. Table 6.1 is such a table; it is also available as Table 1 of Appendix B and inside the front cover of this text.

**FIGURE 6.4** AREAS UNDER THE CURVE FOR ANY NORMAL PROBABILITY DISTRIBUTION

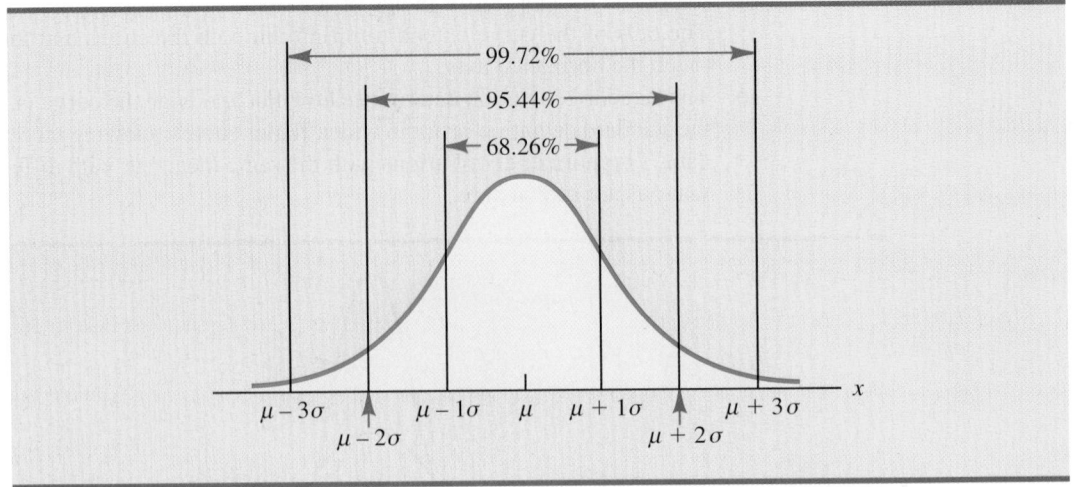

**FIGURE 6.5** THE STANDARD NORMAL PROBABILITY DISTRIBUTION

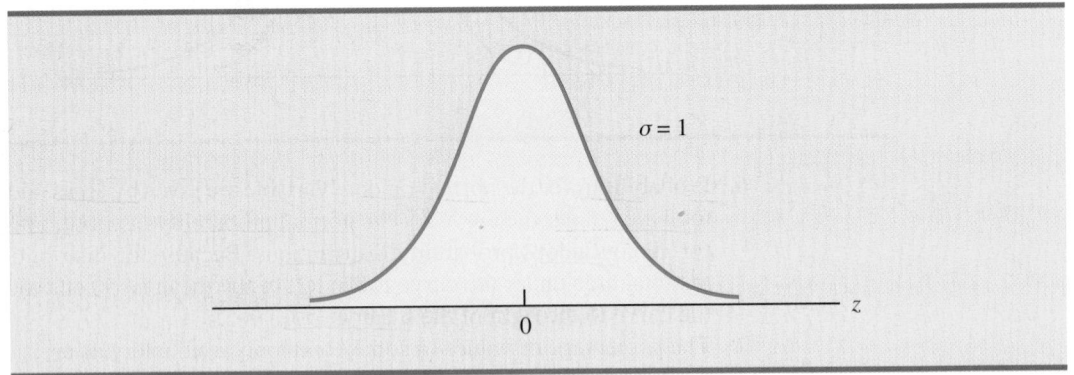

To see how the table of areas under the curve for the standard normal probability distribution (Table 6.1) can be used to find probabilities, let us consider some examples. Later, we will see how this same table can be used to compute probabilities for any normal distribution. To begin, let us see how we can compute the probability that the $z$ value for the standard normal random variable will be less than or equal to 1.00; that is, $P(z \leq 1.00)$. This cumulative probability is represented by the darkly shaded region in the following graph.

Given a $z$ value, we use the standard normal table to find the appropriate probability (an area under the curve).

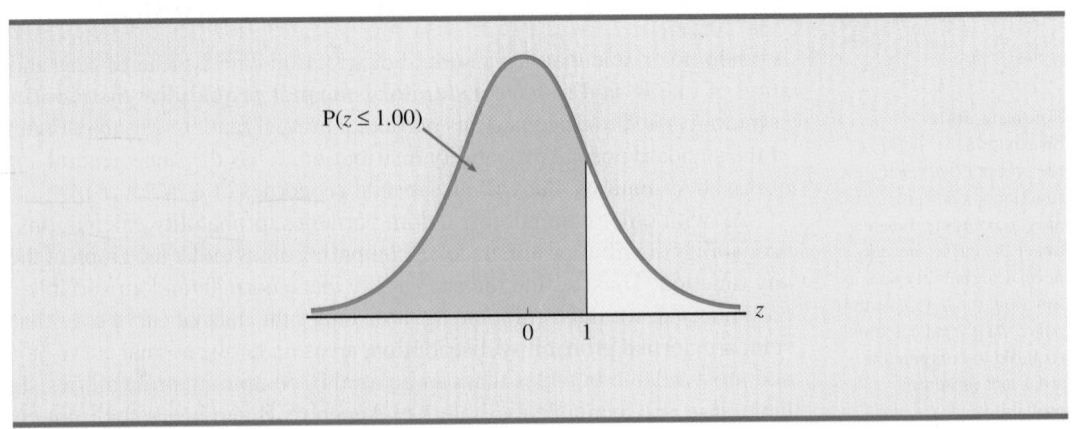

**TABLE 6.1**    CUMULATIVE PROBABILITIES FOR THE STANDARD NORMAL DISTRIBUTION

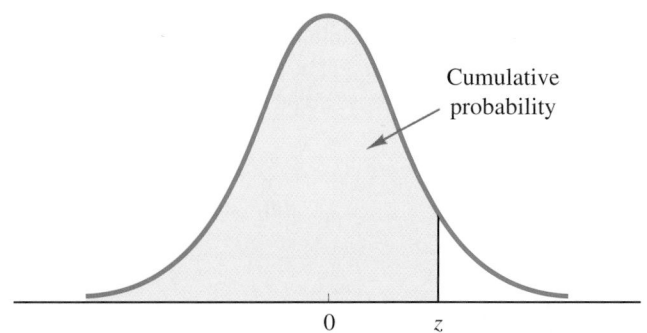

Cumulative probability

0    $z$

| $z$ | .00 | .01 | .02 | .03 | .04 | .05 | .06 | .07 | .08 | .09 |
|---|---|---|---|---|---|---|---|---|---|---|
| .0 | .5000 | .5040 | .5080 | .5120 | .5160 | .5199 | .5239 | .5279 | .5319 | .5359 |
| .1 | .5398 | .5438 | .5478 | .5517 | .5557 | .5596 | .5636 | .5675 | .5714 | .5753 |
| .2 | .5793 | .5832 | .5871 | .5910 | .5948 | .5987 | .6026 | .6064 | .6103 | .6141 |
| .3 | .6179 | .6217 | .6255 | .6293 | .6331 | .6368 | .6406 | .6443 | .6480 | .6517 |
| .4 | .6554 | .6591 | .6628 | .6664 | .6700 | .6736 | .6772 | .6808 | .6844 | .6879 |
| .5 | .6915 | .6950 | .6985 | .7019 | .7054 | .7088 | .7123 | .7157 | .7190 | .7224 |
| .6 | .7257 | .7291 | .7324 | .7357 | .7389 | .7422 | .7454 | .7486 | .7517 | .7549 |
| .7 | .7580 | .7611 | .7642 | .7673 | .7704 | .7734 | .7764 | .7794 | .7823 | .7852 |
| .8 | .7881 | .7910 | .7939 | .7967 | .7995 | .8023 | .8051 | .8078 | .8106 | .8133 |
| .9 | .8159 | .8186 | .8212 | .8238 | .8264 | .8289 | .8315 | .8340 | .8365 | .8389 |
| 1.0 | .8413 | .8438 | .8461 | .8485 | .8508 | .8531 | .8554 | .8577 | .8599 | .8621 |
| 1.1 | .8643 | .8665 | .8686 | .8708 | .8729 | .8749 | .8770 | .8790 | .8810 | .8830 |
| 1.2 | .8849 | .8869 | .8888 | .8907 | .8925 | .8944 | .8962 | .8980 | .8997 | .9015 |
| 1.3 | .9032 | .9049 | .9066 | .9082 | .9099 | .9115 | .9131 | .9147 | .9162 | .9177 |
| 1.4 | .9192 | .9207 | .9222 | .9236 | 9.251 | .9265 | .9279 | .9292 | .9306 | .9319 |
| 1.5 | .9332 | .9345 | .9357 | .9370 | .9382 | .9394 | .9406 | .9418 | .9429 | .9441 |
| 1.6 | .9452 | .9463 | .9474 | .9484 | .9495 | .9505 | .9515 | .9525 | .9535 | .9545 |
| 1.7 | .9554 | .9564 | .9573 | .9582 | .9591 | .9599 | .9608 | .9616 | .9625 | .9633 |
| 1.8 | .9641 | .9649 | .9656 | .9664 | .9671 | .9678 | .9686 | .9693 | .9699 | .9706 |
| 1.9 | .9713 | .9719 | .9726 | .9732 | .9738 | .9744 | .9750 | .9756 | .9761 | .9767 |
| 2.0 | .9772 | .9778 | .9783 | .9788 | .9793 | .9798 | .9803 | .9808 | .9812 | .9817 |
| 2.1 | .9821 | .9826 | .9830 | .9834 | .9838 | .9842 | .9846 | .9850 | .9854 | .9857 |
| 2.2 | .9861 | .9864 | .9868 | .9871 | .9875 | .9878 | .9881 | .9884 | .9887 | .9890 |
| 2.3 | .9893 | .9896 | .9898 | .9901 | .9904 | .9906 | .9909 | .9911 | .9913 | .9913 |
| 2.4 | .9918 | .9920 | .9922 | .9925 | .9927 | .9929 | .9931 | .9932 | .9934 | .9936 |
| 2.5 | .9938 | .9940 | .9941 | .9943 | .9945 | .9946 | .9948 | .9949 | .9951 | .9952 |
| 2.6 | .9953 | .9955 | .9956 | .9957 | .9959 | .9960 | .9961 | .9962 | .9963 | .9964 |
| 2.7 | .9965 | .9966 | .9967 | .9968 | .9969 | .9970 | .9971 | .9972 | .9973 | .9974 |
| 2.8 | .9974 | .9975 | .9976 | .9977 | .9977 | .9978 | .9979 | .9979 | .9980 | .9981 |
| 2.9 | .9981 | .9982 | .9982 | .9983 | .9984 | .9984 | .9985 | .9985 | .9986 | .9986 |
| 3.0 | .9986 | .9987 | .9987 | .9988 | .9988 | .9989 | .9989 | .9989 | .9990 | .9990 |

The probabilities in Table 6.1 are cumulative probabilities so we must find the entry in the table corresponding to $z = 1.00$. First we find 1.0 in the left column of the table and then find .00 in the top row of the table. By looking in the body of the table, we find that the 1.0 row and the .00 column intersect at the value of .8413. Thus, $P(z \leq 1.00) = .8413$. A portion of Table 6.1 showing these steps follows.

| $z$ | .00 | .01 | .02 |
|-----|-----|-----|-----|
| . | | | |
| . | | | |
| . | | | |
| .9 | .8159 | .8186 | .8212 |
| 1.0 | .8413 | .8438 | .8461 |
| 1.1 | .8643 | .8665 | .8686 |
| 1.2 | .8849 | .8869 | .8888 |
| . | | | |
| . | | | |
| . | | | |

$P(z \leq 1.00)$

Now suppose we want to compute the probability that the standard normal random variable will be between .00 and 1.00; that is, $P(.00 \leq z \leq 1.00)$. The darkly shaded region in the following graph shows this area, or probability.

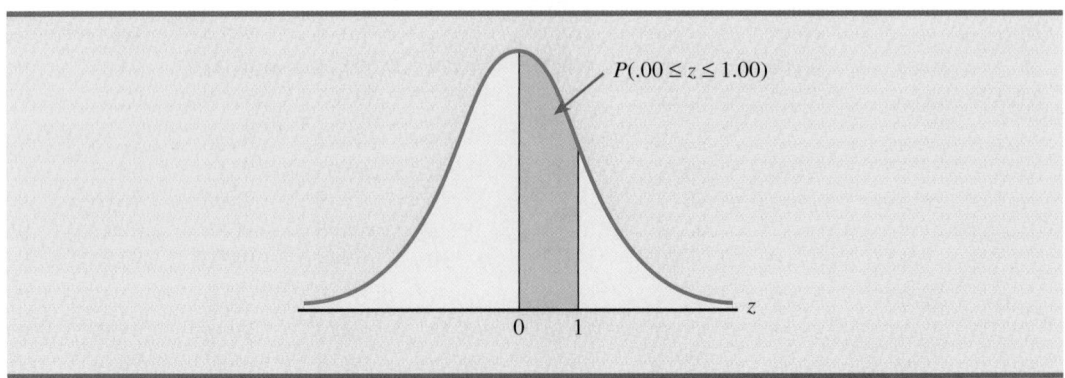

$P(.00 \leq z \leq 1.00)$

We just found $P(z \leq 1.00) = .8413$. To find $P(.00 \leq z \leq 1.00)$, we must now subtract the area under the curve to the left of $z = .00$. This area is .50. Thus, $P(.00 \leq z \leq 1.00) = P(z \leq 1.00) - P(z \leq .00) = .8413 - .5000 = .3413$.

Using the same approach, we can find $P(.00 \leq z \leq 1.25)$. By first locating the 1.2 row and then moving across to the .05 column, we find $P(z \leq 1.25) = .8944$. Subtracting the area under the curve to the left of the mean, we obtain $P(0.00 \leq z \leq 1.25) = P(z \leq 1.25) - P(z \leq 0.00) = .8944 - .5000 = .3944$.

As another example of the use of the table of areas for the standard normal distribution, we compute the probability of obtaining a $z$ value between $z = -1.00$ and $z = 1.00$; that is, $P(-1.00 \leq z \leq 1.00)$. We have already shown that the probability of a $z$ value between

$z = .00$ and $z = 1.00$ is .3413. Now recall that the normal probability distribution is symmetric. Thus, the probability of a $z$ value between $z = .00$ and $z = -1.00$ is the same as the probability of a $z$ value between $z = .00$ and $z = +1.00$. Hence, the probability of a $z$ value between $z = -1.00$ and $z = +1.00$ is

$$P(-1.00 \le z \le .00) + P(.00 \le z \le 1.00) = .3413 + .3413 = .6826$$

This area is shown graphically in the following figure.

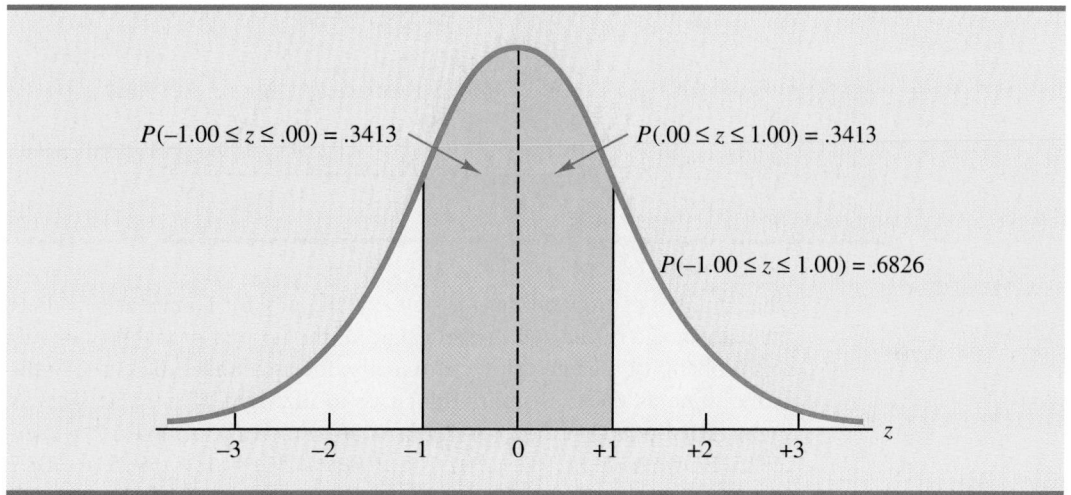

In a similar manner, we can use the values in Table 6.1 to show that the probability of a $z$ value between $-2.00$ and $+2.00$ is $.4772 + .4772 = .9544$ and that the probability of a $z$ value between $-3.00$ and $+3.00$ is $.4986 + .4986 = .9972$. Because we know that the total probability or total area under the curve for any continuous random variable must be 1.0000, the probability .9972 tells us that the value of $z$ will almost always be between $-3.00$ and $+3.00$.

Next, we compute the probability of obtaining a $z$ value of at least 1.58; that is, $P(z \ge 1.58)$. First, we use the $z = 1.5$ row and the .08 column of Table 6.1 to find that $P(z < 1.58) = .9429$. Now, because the total area under the curve equals 1, $P(z \ge 1.58) = 1 - P(z < 1.58) = 1 - .9429 = .0571$. This probability is shown in the following figure.

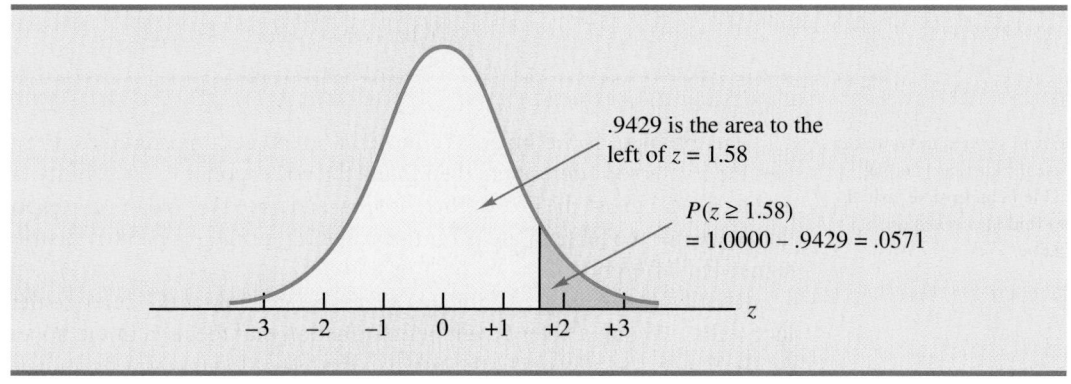

As another illustration, let us compute the probability that the random variable $z$ assumes a value of at most $-.50$; that is, $P(z \le -.50)$. We are interested in the area under the normal curve to the left of $z = -.50$. The following graph shows this area.

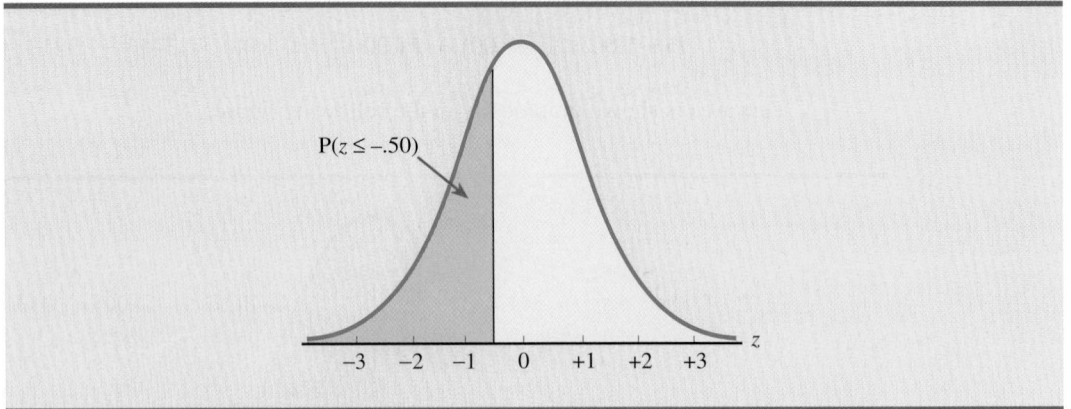

The cumulative probabilities in Table 6.1 are only for nonnegative values of $z$. So we must take advantage of the symmetric nature of the normal probability distribution to compute this probability. Because of the symmetry, the area under the curve to the left of $z = -.50$ is the same as the area under the curve to the right of $z = .50$. That is, $P(z \le -.50) = P(z \ge .50)$. But, $P(z \ge .50) = 1 - P(z \le .50)$. Referring to Table 6.1, we see that $P(z \le .50) = .6915$. So we have $P(z \le -.50) = 1 - P(z \le .50) = 1 - .6915 = .3085$.

As a final illustration, let us find a $z$ value such that the probability of obtaining a larger $z$ value is .10. The following figure shows this situation graphically.

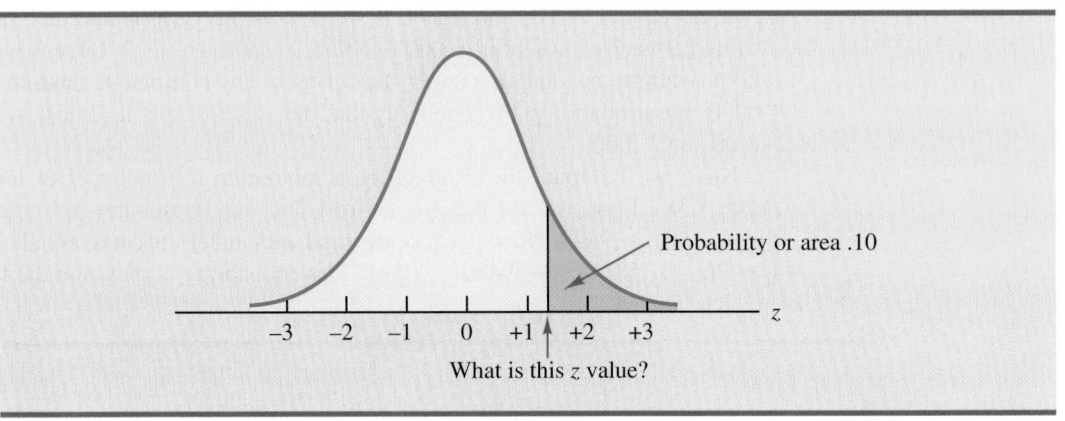

Given a probability, we can use the standard normal table in an inverse fashion to find the corresponding $z$ value.

This problem is the inverse of those in the preceding examples. Previously, we specified the $z$ value of interest and then found the corresponding probability, or area. In this example, we are given the probability, or area, and asked to find the corresponding $z$ value. To do so, we use the table of areas for the standard normal probability distribution (Table 6.1) somewhat differently.

Recall that the body of Table 6.1 gives the area under the curve to the left of a particular $z$ value. We have been given the information that the area in the upper tail of the curve is .10. Hence, the area under the curve to the left of the unknown $z$ value must equal .9000. Scanning the body of the table, we find .8997 as the probability value closest to .9000. The section of the table providing this result follows.

| z | .06 | .07 | .08 | .09 |
|-----|-------|-------|-------|-------|
| . | | | | |
| . | | | | |
| . | | | | |
| 1.0 | .8554 | .8577 | .8599 | .8621 |
| 1.1 | .8770 | .8790 | .8810 | .8830 |
| 1.2 | .8962 | .8980 | .8997 | .9015 |
| 1.3 | .9131 | .9147 | .9162 | .9177 |
| 1.4 | .9279 | .9292 | .9306 | .9319 |
| . | | | | |
| . | | | | |
| . | | | | |

Area value in body
of table closest to .9000

Reading the $z$ value from the left most column and the top row of the table, we find that the corresponding $z$ value is 1.28. Thus, an area of approximately .9000 (actually .8997) will be to the left of $z = 1.28$.* In terms of the question originally asked, there is an approximately .10 probability of a $z$ value larger than 1.28.

The examples illustrate that the table of cumulative probabilities for the standard normal probability distribution can be used to find probabilities associated with values of the standard normal random variable $z$. Two types of questions can be asked. The first type of question specifies a value, or values, for $z$ and asks us to use the table to determine the corresponding areas or probabilities. The second type of question provides an area, or probability, and asks us to use the table to determine the corresponding $z$ value. Thus, we need to be flexible in using the standard normal probability table to answer the desired probability question. In most cases, sketching a graph of the standard normal probability distribution and shading the appropriate area helps to visualize the situation and aids in determining the correct answer.

## Computing Probabilities for Any Normal Probability Distribution

The reason for discussing the standard normal distribution so extensively is that probabilities for all normal distributions are computed by using the standard normal distribution. That is, when we have a normal distribution with any mean $\mu$ and any standard deviation $\sigma$, we answer probability questions about the distribution by first converting to the standard normal distribution. Then we can use Table 6.1 and the appropriate $z$ values to find the desired probabilities. The formula used to convert any normal random variable $x$ with mean $\mu$ and standard deviation $\sigma$ to the standard normal distribution follows.

The formula for the standard normal random variable is similar to the formula we introduced in Chapter 3 for computing $z$ scores for a data set.

**Converting to the Standard Normal Distribution**

$$z = \frac{x - \mu}{\sigma}$$

**(6.3)**

A value of $x$ equal to its mean $\mu$ results in $z = (\mu - \mu)/\sigma = 0$. Thus, we see that a value of $x$ equal to its mean $\mu$ corresponds to a value of $z$ at its mean 0. Now suppose that $x$ is one standard deviation above its mean; that is, $x = \mu + \sigma$. Applying equation (6.3), we see that

---

*We could use interpolation in the body of the table to get a better approximation of the $z$ value that corresponds to an area of .9000. Doing so to provide one more decimal place of accuracy would yield a $z$ value of 1.282. However, in most practical situations, sufficient accuracy is obtained by simply using the table value closest to the desired probability.

the corresponding $z$ value is $z = [(\mu + \sigma) - \mu]/\sigma = \sigma/\sigma = 1$. Thus, an $x$ value that is one standard deviation above its mean corrresponds to $z = 1$. In other words, we can interpret $z$ as the number of standard deviations that the normal random variable $x$ is from its mean $\mu$.

To see how this conversion enables us to compute probabilities for any normal distribution, suppose we have a normal distribution with $\mu = 10$ and $\sigma = 2$. What is the probability that the random variable $x$ is between 10 and 14? Using equation (6.3) we see that at $x = 10$, $z = (x - \mu)/\sigma = (10 - 10)/2 = 0$ and that at $x = 14$, $z = (14 - 10)/2 = 4/2 = 2$. Thus, the answer to our question about the probability of $x$ being between 10 and 14 is given by the equivalent probability that $z$ is between 0 and 2 for the standard normal distribution. In other words, the probability that we are seeking is the probability that the random variable $x$ is between its mean and two standard deviations above the mean. Using $z = 2.00$ and Table 6.1, we see that $P(z \leq 2) = .9772$. And with $P(z \leq 0) = .5000$, we can compute $P(.00 \leq z \leq 2.00) = P(z \leq 2) - P(z \leq 0) = .9772 - .5000 = .4772$. Hence the probability that $x$ is between 10 and 14 is .4772.

## Grear Tire Company Problem

We turn now to an application of the normal probability distribution. Suppose the Grear Tire Company has just developed a new steel-belted radial tire that will be sold through a national chain of discount stores. Because the tire is a new product, Grear's managers believe that the mileage guarantee offered with the tire will be an important factor in the acceptance of the product. Before finalizing the tire mileage guarantee policy, Grear's managers want probability information about $x$ = number of miles the tires will last.

From actual road tests with the tires, Grear's engineering group has estimated that the mean tire mileage is $\mu = 36,500$ miles and that the standard deviation is $\sigma = 5000$. In addition, the data collected indicate that a normal distribution is a reasonable assumption. What percentage of the tires can be expected to last more than 40,000 miles? In other words, what is the probability that the tire mileage, $x$, will exceed 40,000? This question can be answered by finding the area of the darkly shaded region in Figure 6.6.

**FIGURE 6.6**   GREAR TIRE COMPANY MILEAGE DISTRIBUTION

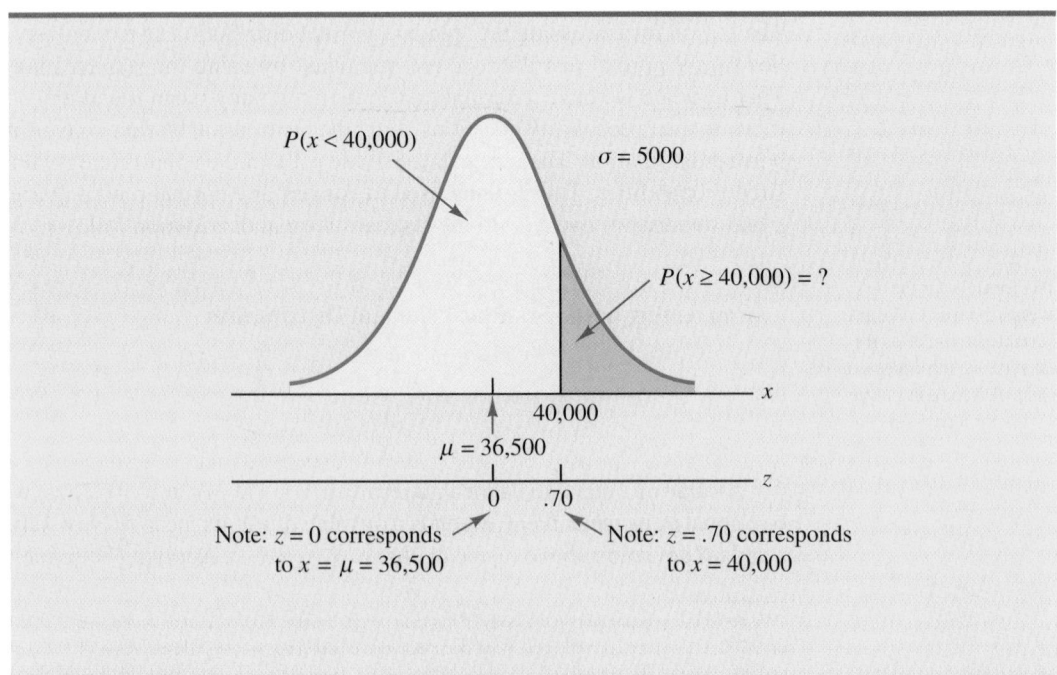

At $x = 40,000$, we have

$$z = \frac{x - \mu}{\sigma} = \frac{40,000 - 36,500}{5000} = \frac{3500}{5000} = .70$$

Refer now to the bottom of Figure 6.6. We see that a value of $x = 40,000$ on the Grear Tire normal distribution corresponds to a value of $z = .70$ on the standard normal distribution. Using Table 6.1, we see that the area under the standard normal curve to the left of $z = .70$ is .7580. Thus, $1.000 - .7580 = .2420$ is the probability that $z$ will exceed .70 and hence $x$ will exceed 40,000. We can conclude that about 24.2% of the tires will exceed 40,000 in mileage.

Let us now assume that Grear is considering a guarantee that will provide a discount on replacement tires if the original tires do not provide the guaranteed mileage. What should the guarantee mileage be if Grear wants no more than 10% of the tires to be eligible for the discount guarantee? This question is interpreted graphically in Figure 6.7.

According to Figure 6.7, the area under the curve to the left of the unknown guarantee mileage must be .10. So, we must first find the $z$-value that cuts off an area of .10 in the left tail of a standard normal distribution. Table 6.1 does not provide negative $z$-values, so we must take advantage of the symmetry of the normal curve and look for the $z$-value that cuts off an area of .10 in the upper tail. The negative of that $z$-value will cut off an area of .10 in the lower tail. The $z$-value that cuts off an area of .10 in the upper tail is the same as the $z$-value that provides a cumulative probability of .90. Looking to Table 6.1 we see that a $z$-value of approximately 1.28 provides a cumulative probability of .90. Therefore, $z = -1.28$ cuts off an area of .10 in the lower tail. Hence, $z = -1.28$ is the value of the standard normal random variable corresponding to the desired mileage guarantee on the Grear Tire normal distribution. To find the value of $x$ corresponding to $z = -1.28$, we have

The guarantee mileage we need to find is 1.28 standard deviations below the mean. Thus, $x = \mu - 1.28\sigma$.

$$z = \frac{x - \mu}{\sigma} = -1.28$$
$$x - \mu = -1.28\sigma$$
$$x = \mu - 1.28\sigma$$

**FIGURE 6.7**  GREAR'S DISCOUNT GUARANTEE

$\sigma = 5000$

10% of tires eligible for discount guarantee

Guarantee mileage = ?    $\mu = 36,500$

$x$

With $\mu = 36{,}500$ and $\sigma = 5000$,

$$x = 36{,}500 - 1.28(5000) = 30{,}100$$

Thus, a guarantee of 30,100 miles will meet the requirement that approximately 10% of the tires will be eligible for the guarantee. Perhaps, with this information, the firm will set its tire mileage guarantee at 30,000 miles.

Again, we see the important role that probability distributions play in providing decision-making information. Namely, once a probability distribution is established for a particular application, it can be used to obtain probability information about the problem. Probability does not make a decision recommendation directly, but it provides information that helps the decision maker better understand the risks and uncertainties associated with the problem. Ultimately, this information may assist the decision maker in reaching a good decision.

With the guarantee set at 30,000 miles, the actual percentage eligible for the guarantee will be 9.68%.

## Using Excel to Compute Normal Probabilities

Excel has two functions for computing probabilities and $z$ values for a standard normal probability distribution: NORMSDIST and NORMSINV. The NORMSDIST function is used to compute the cumulative probability given a $z$ value, and the NORMSINV function is used to compute the $z$ value given a cumulative probability. Two similar functions, NORMDIST and NORMINV, are available for computing the cumulative probability and the $x$ value for any normal distribution. We begin by showing how to use the NORMSDIST and NORMSINV functions.

The NORMSDIST function provides the area under the standard normal curve to the left of a given $z$ value. For nonnegative $z$ values, the NORMSDIST function provides the same cumulative probability we would obtain if we used Table 6.1. Using the NORMSDIST function is just like having the computer look up cumulative normal probabilities for you. But, unlike Table 6.1, the NORMSDIST function provides cumulative probabilities for negative $z$ values as well. The NORMSINV function is the inverse of the NORMSDIST function; it takes a cumulative probability as input and provides the $z$ value corresponding to that cumulative probability.

The letter S that appears in the name of the NORMSDIST and NORMSINV functions reminds us that these functions relate to the standard normal probability distribution.

Let's see how both of these functions work by computing the probabilities and $z$ values obtained earlier in this section using Table 6.1. Refer to Figure 6.8 as we describe the tasks involved. The formula worksheet is in the background; the value worksheet is in the foreground.

**Enter Data:**   No data are entered in the worksheet. We will simply enter the appropriate $z$ values and probabilities directly into the formulas as needed.

**Enter Functions and Formulas:**   The NORMSDIST function has one argument: the $z$ value for which we want to obtain the cumulative probability. To illustrate the use of the NORMSDIST function we have computed the six probabilities shown in cells D3:D8 of Figure 6.8.

To compute the cumulative probability to the left of a given $z$ value (area in lower tail), we simply evaluate NORMSDIST at the $z$ value. For instance, to compute $P(z \leq 1)$ we entered the formula =NORMSDIST(1) into cell D3. The result, .8413, is the same as obtained using Table 6.1. The cumulative probability in cell D8, $P(z \leq -.50)$, is computed in a similar fashion.

To compute the probability of $z$ being in an interval we compute the value of NORMSDIST at the upper endpoint of the interval and subtract the value of NORMSDIST at the lower endpoint of the interval. For instance, to find $P(.00 \leq z \leq 1.00)$, we entered the for-

**FIGURE 6.8**    EXCEL WORKSHEET FOR COMPUTING PROBABILITIES AND $z$ VALUES FOR THE STANDARD NORMAL DISTRIBUTION

| | A | B | C | D | E |
|---|---|---|---|---|---|
| 1 | | | Probabilities: Standard Normal Distribution | | |
| 2 | | | | | |
| 3 | | | $P(z <= 1)$ | =NORMSDIST(1) | |
| 4 | | | $P(0.00 <= z <= 1.00)$ | =NORMSDIST(1)-NORMSDIST(0) | |
| 5 | | | $P(0.00 <= z <= 1.25)$ | =NORMSDIST(1.25)-NORMSDIST(0) | |
| 6 | | | $P(-1.00 <= z <= 1.00)$ | =NORMSDIST(1)-NORMSDIST(-1) | |
| 7 | | | $P(z >= 1.58)$ | =1-NORMSDIST(1.58) | |
| 8 | | | $P(z <= -.50)$ | =NORMSDIST(-0.5) | |
| 9 | | | | | |
| 10 | | | Finding $z$-values Given Probabilities | | |
| 11 | | | | | |
| 12 | | | $z$ value with .10 in upper tail | =NORMSINV(0.9) | |
| 13 | | | $z$ value with .025 in upper tail | =NORMSINV(0.975) | |
| 14 | | | $z$ value with .025 in lower tail | =NORMSINV(0.025) | |
| 15 | | | | | |

| | A | B | C | D | E |
|---|---|---|---|---|---|
| 1 | Probabilities: Standard Normal Distribution | | | | |
| 2 | | | | | |
| 3 | | | $P(z <= 1)$ | 0.8413 | |
| 4 | | | $P(0.00 <= z <= 1.00)$ | 0.3413 | |
| 5 | | | $P(0.00 <= z <= 1.25)$ | 0.3944 | |
| 6 | | | $P(-1.00 <= z <= 1.00)$ | 0.6827 | |
| 7 | | | $P(z >= 1.58)$ | 0.0571 | |
| 8 | | | $P(z <= -.50)$ | 0.3085 | |
| 9 | | | | | |
| 10 | | Finding $z$-values Given Probabilities | | | |
| 11 | | | | | |
| 12 | | | $z$ value with .10 in upper tail | 1.28 | |
| 13 | | | $z$ value with .025 in upper tail | 1.96 | |
| 14 | | | $z$ value with .025 in lower tail | -1.96 | |
| 15 | | | | | |

The probability in cell D6, 0.6827, differs from what we computed earlier (.6826) due to rounding.

mula =NORMSDIST(1)-NORMSDIST(0) into cell D4. The interval probabilities in cells D5 and D6 are computed in a similar fashion.

To compute the probability to the right of a given $z$ value (upper tail area), we must subtract the cumulative probability represented by the area under the curve below the $z$ value (lower tail area) from 1. For example, to compute $P(z \geq 1.58)$ we entered the formula =1-NORMSDIST(1.58) into Cell D7.

To compute the $z$ value for a given cumulative probability (lower tail area), we use the NORMSINV function. To find the $z$ value corresponding to an upper tail probability of .10, we entered the formula =NORMSINV(0.9) into cell D12. Actually, NORMSINV(0.9) gives us the $z$ value providing a cumulative probability (lower tail area) of .9. But, it is also the $z$ value associated with an upper tail area of .10.

Two other $z$ values are computed in Figure 6.8. These $z$ values will be used extensively in succeeding chapters. To compute the $z$ value corresponding to an upper tail probability of .025, we entered the formula =NORMSINV(0.975) into cell D13. To compute the $z$ value corresponding to a lower tail probability of .025, we entered the formula =NORMSINV(0.025) into cell D14. We see that $z = 1.96$ corresponds to an upper tail probability of .025 and $z = -1.96$ corresponds to a lower tail probability of .025.

Let us now turn to the Excel functions for computing cumulative probabilities and $x$ values for any normal distribution. The NORMDIST function provides the area under the normal curve to the left of a given value of the random variable $x$. It provides cumulative probabilities. The NORMINV function is the inverse of the NORMDIST function; it takes a cumulative probability as input and provides the value of $x$ corresponding to that cumulative probability. The NORMDIST and NORMINV functions do the same thing for any normal distribution that the NORMSDIST and NORMSINV functions do for the standard normal distribution.

Let's see how both of these functions work by computing probabilities and $x$ values for the Grear Tire Company example introduced earlier in this section. Recall that the lifetime of a Grear tire has a mean of 36,500 miles and a standard deviation of 5000 miles. Refer to Figure 6.9 as we describe the tasks involved. The formula worksheet is in the background; the value worksheet is in the foreground.

**FIGURE 6.9** EXCEL WORKSHEET FOR COMPUTING PROBABILITIES AND $x$ VALUES FOR THE NORMAL DISTRIBUTION

| | B | C | D | E |
|---|---|---|---|---|
| 1 | | | Probabilities: Normal Distribution | |
| 2 | | | | |
| 3 | | $P(x <= 20000)$ | =NORMDIST(20000,36500,5000,TRUE) | |
| 4 | | $P(20000 <= x <= 40000)$ | =NORMDIST(40000,36500,5000,TRUE)-NORMDIST(20000,36500,5000,TRUE) | |
| 5 | | $P(x >= 40000)$ | =1-NORMDIST(40000,36500,5000,TRUE) | |
| 6 | | | | |
| 7 | | | Finding $x$ values Given Probabilities | |
| 8 | | | | |
| 9 | | $x$ value with .10 in lower tail | =NORMINV(0.1,36500,5000) | |
| 10 | | $x$ value with .025 in upper tail | =NORMINV(0.975,36500,5000) | |
| 11 | | | | |

| | A | B | C | D | E |
|---|---|---|---|---|---|
| 1 | | | Probabilities: Normal Distribution | | |
| 2 | | | | | |
| 3 | | | $P(x <= 20000)$ | 0.0005 | |
| 4 | | | $P(20000 <= x <= 40000)$ | 0.7576 | |
| 5 | | | $P(x >= 40000)$ | 0.2420 | |
| 6 | | | | | |
| 7 | | Finding $x$ values Given Probabilities | | | |
| 8 | | | | | |
| 9 | | | $x$ value with .10 in lower tail | 30092.25 | |
| 10 | | $x$ value with .025 in upper tail | | 46299.81 | |
| 11 | | | | | |

**Enter Data:**    No data are entered in the worksheet. We will simply enter the appropriate $x$ values and probabilities directly into the formulas as needed.

**Enter Functions and Formulas:**    The NORMDIST function has four arguments: (1) the $x$ value we want to compute the cumulative probability for, (2) the mean, (3) the standard deviation, and (4) a value of TRUE or FALSE. For the fourth argument, we enter TRUE if a cumulative probability is desired and we enter FALSE if the height of the curve is desired. Because we will always be using NORMDIST to compute cumulative probabilities, we will always choose TRUE for the fourth argument.

To compute the cumulative probability to the left of a given $x$ value (lower tail area), we simply evaluate NORMDIST at the $x$ value. For instance, to compute the probability that a Grear tire will not last more than 20,000 miles we entered the formula =NORMDIST(20000,36500,5000, TRUE) into cell D3. The value worksheet shows that this cumulative probability is .0005. So, we can conclude that almost all Grear tires will last at least 20,000 miles.

To compute the probability of $x$ being in an interval we compute the value of NORMDIST at the upper endpoint of the interval and subtract the value of NORMDIST at the lower endpoint of the interval. The formula in cell D4 provides the probability that a tire's lifetime is between 20,000 and 40,000 miles, $P(20,000 \leq x \leq 40,000)$. In the value worksheet, we see that this probability is .7576.

To compute the probability to the right of a given $x$ value (upper tail area), we must subtract the cumulative probability represented by the area under the curve below the $x$ value (lower tail area) from 1. The formula in cell D5 computes the probability that a Grear tire will last for at least 40,000 miles. We see that this probability is .2420.

To compute the $x$ value for a given cumulative probability, we use the NORMINV function. The NORMINV function has only three arguments. The first argument is the cumulative probability; the second and third arguments are the mean and standard deviation. For instance, to compute the tire mileage corresponding to a lower tail area of .1 for Grear Tire, we enter the formula =NORMINV(0.1,36500,5000) into cell D9. From the value worksheet, we see that 10% of the Grear tires will not last over 30,092.25 miles.

To compute the minimum tire mileage for the top 2.5% of Grear tires, we want to find the value of $x$ corresponding to an area of .025 in the upper tail. This calculation is the same as finding the $x$ value that provides a cumulative probability of .975. Thus we have entered the formula =NORMINV(0.975,36500,5000) into cell D10 to compute this tire mileage. From the value worksheet, we see that 2.5% of the Grear tires will last at least 46,299.81 miles.

## EXERCISES

### Methods

8. Using Figure 6.4 as a guide, sketch a normal curve for a random variable $x$ that has a mean of $\mu = 100$ and a standard deviation of $\sigma = 10$. Label the horizontal axis with values of 70, 80, 90, 100, 110, 120, and 130.

9. A random variable is normally distributed with a mean of $\mu = 50$ and a standard deviation of $\sigma = 5$.
    a. Sketch a normal curve for the probability density function. Label the horizontal axis with values of 35, 40, 45, 50, 55, 60, and 65. Figure 6.4 shows that the normal curve almost touches the horizontal axis at three standard deviations below and at three standard deviations above the mean (in this case at 35 and 65).
    b. What is the probability the random variable will assume a value between 45 and 55?
    c. What is the probability the random variable will assume a value between 40 and 60?

10. Draw a graph for the standard normal distribution. Label the horizontal axis at values of $-3, -2, -1, 0, 1, 2$, and 3. Then use the table of probabilities for the standard normal distribution to compute the following probabilities.
    a. $P(0 \le z \le 1)$
    b. $P(0 \le z \le 1.5)$
    c. $P(0 < z < 2)$
    d. $P(0 < z < 2.5)$

11. Given that $z$ is a standard normal random variable, compute the following probabilities.
    a. $P(-1 \le z \le 0)$
    b. $P(-1.5 \le z \le 0)$
    c. $P(-2 < z < 0)$
    d. $P(-2.5 \le z \le 0)$
    e. $P(-3 < z \le 0)$

12. Given that $z$ is a standard normal random variable, compute the following probabilities.
    a. $P(0 \le z \le .83)$
    b. $P(-1.57 \le z \le 0)$
    c. $P(z > .44)$
    d. $P(z \ge -.23)$
    e. $P(z < 1.20)$
    f. $P(z \le -.71)$

13. Given that $z$ is a standard normal random variable, compute the following probabilities.

    a. $P(-1.98 \le z \le .49)$
    b. $P(.52 \le z \le 1.22)$
    c. $P(-1.75 \le z \le -1.04)$

14. Given that $z$ is a standard normal random variable, find $z$ for each situation.
    a. The area between 0 and $z$ is .4750.
    b. The area between 0 and $z$ is .2291.
    c. The area to the right of $z$ is .1314.
    d. The area to the left of $z$ is .6700.

**15.** Given that $z$ is a standard normal random variable, find $z$ for each situation.
    **a.** The area to the left of $z$ is .2119.
    **b.** The area between $-z$ and $z$ is .9030.
    **c.** The area between $-z$ and $z$ is .2052.
    **d.** The area to the left of $z$ is .9948.
    **e.** The area to the right of $z$ is .6915.

**16.** Given that $z$ is a standard normal random variable, find $z$ for each situation.
    **a.** The area to the right of $z$ is .01.
    **b.** The area to the right of $z$ is .025.
    **c.** The area to the right of $z$ is .05.
    **d.** The area to the right of $z$ is .10.

## Applications

**17.** The average American male adult is 5 feet 9 inches tall (*Astounding Averages,* 1995). Assume that a normal distribution applies and that the standard deviation is 3 inches in answering the following questions.
    **a.** What is the probability an adult male is taller than 6 feet?
    **b.** What is the probability an adult male is shorter than 5 feet?
    **c.** What is the probability an adult male is between 5 feet 6 inches and 5 feet 10 inches?
    **d.** What is the probability an adult male is no more than 6 feet tall?

**18.** The average time a subscriber spends reading *The Wall Street Journal* is 49 minutes (*The Wall Street Journal* Subscriber Study, 1996). Assume the standard deviation is 16 minutes and that the times are normally distributed.
    **a.** What is the probability a subscriber will spend at least 1 hour reading the *Journal*?
    **b.** What is the probability a subscriber will spend no more than 30 minutes reading the *Journal*?
    **c.** For the 10% who spend the most time reading the *Journal,* how much time do they spend?

**19.** The average amount of precipitation in Dallas, Texas, during the month of April is 3.5 inches (*The World Almanac,* 2000). Assume that a normal distribution applies and that the standard deviation is .8 inches.
    **a.** What percentage of the time does the amount of rainfall in April exceed 5 inches?
    **b.** What percentage of the time is the amount of rainfall in April less than 3 inches?
    **c.** A month is classified as extremely wet if the amount of rainfall is in the upper 10% for that month. How much precipitation must fall before a month of April is classified as extremely wet?

**20.** According to a survey, subscribers to *The Wall Street Journal Interactive Edition* spend an average of 27 hours per week using the computer at work (*WSJ.com* Subscriber Study, 1999). Assume the normal distribution applies and that the standard deviation is 8 hours.
    **a.** What is the probability a randomly selected subscriber spends less than 11 hours using the computer at work?
    **b.** What percentage of the subscribers spends more than 40 hours per week using the computer at work?
    **c.** A person is classified as a heavy user if he or she is in the upper 20% in terms of hours of usage. How many hours must a subscriber use the computer in order to be classified as a heavy user?

**21.** A person must score in the upper 2% of the population on an IQ test to qualify for membership in Mensa, the international high-IQ society (*US Airways Attache,* September 2000). If IQ scores are normally distributed with a mean of 100 and a standard deviation of 15, what score must a person get to qualify for Mensa?

**22.** According to the Bureau of Labor Statistics, the average weekly pay for a U.S. production worker was $441.84 in 1998 (*The World Almanac,* 2000). Assume that available data indicate that wages are normally distributed with a standard deviation of $90.

a. What is the probability that a worker earns between $400 and $500?
b. How much does a production worker have to earn to be in the top 20% of wage earners?
c. For a randomly selected production worker, what is the probability the worker earns less than $250 per week?

23. The time needed to complete a final examination in a particular college course is normally distributed with a mean of 80 minutes and a standard deviation of 10 minutes. Answer the following questions.

a. What is the probability of completing the exam in one hour or less?
b. What is the probability that a student will complete the exam in more than 60 minutes but less than 75 minutes?
c. Assume that the class has 60 students and that the examination period is 90 minutes in length. How many students do you expect will be unable to complete the exam in the allotted time?

24. The daily trading volumes (millions of shares) for stocks traded on the New York Stock Exchange for 12 days in August and September are shown here (*Barron's*, August 7, 2000, September 4, 2000, and September 11, 2000).

|  |  |  |
|---|---|---|
| 917 | 983 | 1,046 |
| 944 | 723 | 783 |
| 813 | 1,057 | 766 |
| 836 | 992 | 973 |

The probability distribution of trading volume is approximately normal.

a. Compute the mean and standard deviation for the daily trading volume to use as estimates of the population mean and standard deviation.
b. What is the probability that on a particular day the trading volume will be less than 800 million shares?
c. What is the probability that trading volume will exceed 1 billion shares?
d. If the exchange wants to issue a press release on the top 5% of trading days, what volume will trigger a release?

25. The average ticket price for a major league baseball game was $11.98 in 1998 (*USA Today*, November 11, 1998). Adding the cost of food, parking, and souvenirs, the average cost for a family of four to attend a game was approximately $110. Assume the normal distribution applies and that the standard deviation is $20.

a. What is the probability a family will spend more than $100?
b. What is the probability a family will spend $90 or less?
c. What is the probability a family will spend between $80 and $130?

## 6.3    EXPONENTIAL PROBABILITY DISTRIBUTION

A continuous probability distribution that is useful in describing the time it takes to complete a task is the **exponential probability distribution.** The exponential random variable can be used to describe such things as the time between arrivals at a car wash, the time required to load a truck, the distance between major defects in a highway, and so on. The exponential probability density function is defined as follows.

> **Exponential Probability Density Function**
>
> $$f(x) = \frac{1}{\mu} e^{-x/\mu} \qquad \text{for } x \geq 0, \mu > 0 \tag{6.4}$$

As an example of the exponential probability distribution, suppose that $x$ = the time it takes to load a truck at the Schips loading dock follows such a distribution. If the mean, or average, time to load a truck is 15 minutes ($\mu = 15$), the appropriate probability density function is

$$f(x) = \frac{1}{15} e^{-x/15}$$

The blue line in Figure 6.10 is the graph of this probability density function.

## Computing Probabilities for the Exponential Distribution

In waiting line applications, the exponential distribution is often used for service time.

As with any continuous probability distribution, the area under the curve corresponding to an interval provides the probability that the random variable assumes a value in that interval. In the Schips loading dock example, the probability that loading a truck will take 6 minutes or less ($x \leq 6$) is defined to be the area under the curve in Figure 6.10 from $x = 0$ to $x = 6$. Similarly, the probability that loading a truck will take 18 minutes or less ($x \leq 18$) is the area under the curve from $x = 0$ to $x = 18$. Note also that the probability that loading a truck will take between 6 minutes and 18 minutes ($6 \leq x \leq 18$) is given by the area under the curve from $x = 6$ to $x = 18$.

To compute exponential probabilities such as those just described, we use the following formula. It provides the cumulative probability of obtaining a value for the exponential random variable of less than or equal to some specific value of $x$, denoted by $x_0$.

**Exponential Distribution: Cumulative Probabilities**

$$P(x \leq x_0) = 1 - e^{-x_0/\mu} \tag{6.5}$$

For the Schips loading dock example, $x$ = loading time and $\mu = 15$. So, we have

$$P(x \leq x_0) = 1 - e^{-x_0/15}$$

**FIGURE 6.10**   EXPONENTIAL PROBABILITY DISTRIBUTION FOR THE SCHIPS LOADING DOCK EXAMPLE

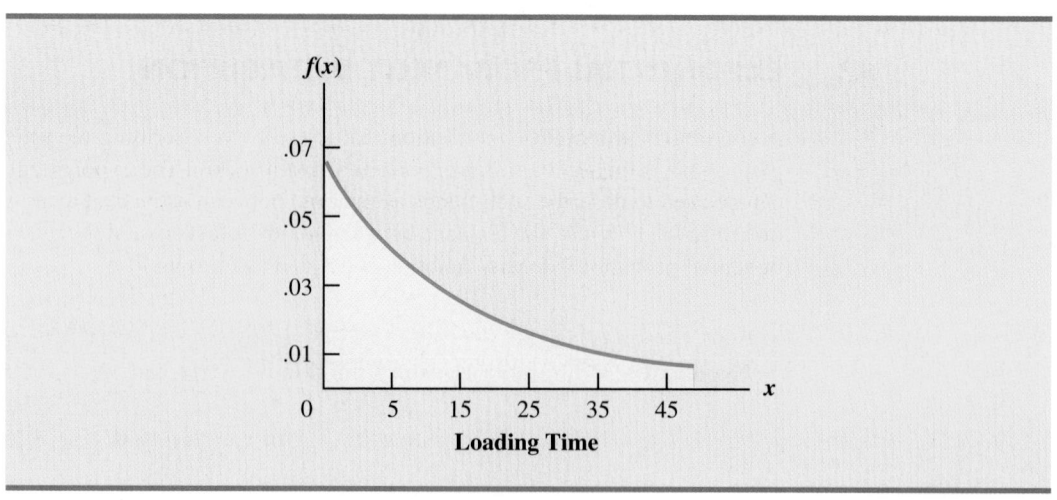

Hence, the probability that loading a truck will take 6 minutes or less is

$$P(x \leq 6) = 1 - e^{-6/15} = .3297$$

Figure 6.11 shows the area or probability for a loading time of 6 minutes or less.

Using equation (6.5), the probability of loading a truck in 18 minutes or less $P(x \leq 18)$ is

$$P(x \leq 18) = 1 - e^{-18/15} = .6988$$

Thus, the probability that loading a truck will take between 6 minutes and 18 minutes is equal to .6988 − .3297 = .3691. Probabilities for any other interval can be computed similarly.

## Relationship Between the Poisson and Exponential Distributions

In Section 5.5 we introduced the Poisson distribution as a discrete probability distribution that is often useful in examining the number of occurrences of an event over a specified interval of time or space. Recall that the Poisson probability function is

$$f(x) = \frac{\mu^x e^{-\mu}}{x!}$$

where

$$\mu = \text{expected value or mean number of}$$
$$\text{occurrences over a specified interval}$$

The continuous exponential probability distribution is related to the discrete Poisson distribution. If the Poisson distribution provides an appropriate description of the number of occurrences per interval, the exponential distribution provides a description of the length of the interval between occurrences.

**FIGURE 6.11**    PROBABILITY OF A LOADING TIME OF SIX MINUTES OR LESS

To illustrate this relationship, suppose the number of cars that arrive at a car wash during one hour is described by a Poisson probability distribution with a mean of 10 cars per hour. The Poisson probability function that gives the probability of $x$ arrivals per hour is

$$f(x) = \frac{10^x e^{-10}}{x!}$$

Because the average number of arrivals is 10 cars per hour, the average time between cars arriving is

$$\frac{1 \text{ hour}}{10 \text{ cars}} = .1 \text{ hour/car}$$

Thus, the corresponding exponential distribution that describes the time between the arrivals has a mean of $\mu = .1$ hour per car; as a result, the appropriate exponential probability density function is

$$f(x) = \frac{1}{.1} e^{-x/.1} = 10 e^{-10x}$$

## Using Excel to Compute Exponential Probabilities

The EXPONDIST function can be used to compute exponential probabilities. We will illustrate by computing probabilities associated with the time it takes to load a truck at the Schips loading dock. This example was introduced at the beginning of this section. Refer to Figure 6.12 as we describe the tasks involved. The formula worksheet is in the background; the value worksheet is in the foreground.

**Enter Data:** No data are entered in the worksheet. We will simply enter the appropriate values for the exponential random variable into the formulas as needed. The random variable is $x =$ loading time.

**Enter Functions and Formulas:** The EXPONDIST function has three arguments: the first is the value of $x$, the second is $1/\mu$, and the third is TRUE or FALSE. We choose TRUE for the third argument if a cumulative probability is desired and FALSE if the height of the probability density function is desired. We will always use TRUE because we will always be computing probabilities.

The first probability we compute is the probability that the loading time is 18 minutes or less. For the Schips problem, $1/\mu = 1/15$, so we enter the formula =EXPONDIST

**FIGURE 6.12** EXCEL WORKSHEET FOR COMPUTING PROBABILITIES FOR THE EXPONENTIAL PROBABILITY DISTRIBUTION

| | A | B | C | D | E |
|---|---|---|---|---|---|
| 1 | | | \multicolumn{2}{l}{Probabilities: Exponential Distribution} | |
| 2 | | | | | |
| 3 | | | $P(x \le 18)$ | =EXPONDIST(18,1/15,TRUE) | |
| 4 | | | $P(6 \le x \le 18)$ | =EXPONDIST(18,1/15,TRUE)-EXPONDIST(6,1/15,TRUE) | |
| 5 | | | $P(x \ge 8)$ | =1-EXPONDIST(8,1/15,TRUE) | |
| 6 | | | | | |

| | A | B | C | D | E |
|---|---|---|---|---|---|
| 1 | Probabilities: Exponential Distribution | | | | |
| 2 | | | | | |
| 3 | | | $P(x \le 18)$ | 0.6988 | |
| 4 | | | $P(6 \le x \le 18)$ | 0.3691 | |
| 5 | | | $P(x \ge 8)$ | 0.5866 | |
| 6 | | | | | |

(18,1/15,TRUE) into cell D3 to compute the desired cumulative probability. From the value worksheet, we see that the probability of loading a truck in 18 minutes or less is .6988.

The second probability we compute is the probability that the loading time is between 6 and 18 minutes. To find this probability we first compute the cumulative probability for the upper endpoint of the time interval and subtract the cumulative probability for the lower endpoint of the interval. The formula we have entered into cell D4 calculates this probability. The value worksheet shows that this probability is .3691.

The last probability we calculate is the probability that the loading time is at least 8 minutes. Because the EXPONDIST function only computes cumulative (lower tail) probabilities, we compute this probability by entering the formula =1-EXPONDIST(8,1/15,TRUE) into cell D5. The value worksheet shows that the probability of a loading time of 8 minutes or more is .5866.

## EXERCISES

## Methods

**26.** Consider the following exponential probability density function.

$$f(x) = \frac{1}{8} e^{-x/8} \qquad \text{for } x \geq 0$$

    **a.** Compute $P(x \leq 6)$.
    **b.** Compute $P(x \leq 4)$.
    **c.** Compute $P(x \geq 6)$.
    **d.** Compute $P(4 \leq x \leq 6)$.

**27.** Consider the following exponential probability density function.

$$f(x) = \frac{1}{3} e^{-x/3} \qquad \text{for } x \geq 0$$

    **a.** Write the formula for $P(x \leq x_0)$.
    **b.** Compute $P(x \leq 2)$.
    **c.** Compute $P(x \geq 3)$.
    **d.** Compute $P(x \leq 5)$.
    **e.** Compute $P(2 \leq x \leq 5)$.

## Applications

**28.** *Internet Magazine* monitors Internet service providers (ISPs) and provides statistics on their performance. The average time to download a web page for free ISPs is approximately 20 seconds for European web pages (*Internet Magazine*, January 2000). Assume the time to download a web page follows an exponential distribution.
    **a.** What is the probability it will take less than 10 seconds to download a web page?
    **b.** What is the probability it will take more than 30 seconds to download a web page?
    **c.** What is the probability it will take between 10 and 30 seconds to download a web page?

**29.** The time between arrivals of vehicles at a particular intersection follows an exponential probability distribution with a mean of 12 seconds.

    **a.** Sketch this exponential probability distribution.
    **b.** What is the probability that the time between vehicle arrivals is 12 seconds or less?
    **c.** What is the probability that the time between vehicle arrivals is 6 seconds or less?
    **d.** What is the probability of 30 or more seconds between vehicle arrivals?

30. The lifetime (hours) of an electronic device is a random variable with the following exponential probability density function.

$$f(x) = \frac{1}{50} e^{-x/50} \qquad \text{for } x \geq 0$$

   a.  What is the mean lifetime of the device?
   b.  What is the probability that the device will fail in the first 25 hours of operation?
   c.  What is the probability that the device will operate 100 or more hours before failure?

31. Sparagowski & Associates conducted a study of service times at the drive-up window of fast-food restaurants. The average time between placing an order and receiving the order at McDonald's restaurants was 2.78 minutes (*The Cincinnati Enquirer,* July 9, 2000). Waiting times, such as these, frequently follow an exponential distribution.
   a.  What is the probability that a customer's service time is less than 2 minutes?
   b.  What is the probability that a customer's service time is more than 5 minutes?
   c.  What is the probability that a customer's service time is more than 2.78 minutes?

32. According to *Barron's 1998 Primary Reader Survey,* the average annual number of investment transactions for a subscriber is 30 (http://www.barronsmag.com, July 28, 2000). Suppose the number of transactions in a year follows the Poisson probability distribution.
   a.  Show the probability distribution for the time between investment transactions.
   b.  What is the probability of no transactions during the month of January for a particular subscriber?
   c.  What is the probability that the next transaction will occur within the next half-month for a particular subscriber?

## SUMMARY

This chapter extended the discussion of probability distributions to the case of continuous random variables. The major conceptual difference between discrete and continuous probability distributions involves the method of computing probabilities. With discrete distributions, the probability function $f(x)$ provides the probability that the random variable $x$ assumes various values. With continuous probability distributions, the probability density function $f(x)$ does not provide probability values directly. Instead, probabilities are given by areas under the curve or graph of the probability density function $f(x)$. Because the area under the curve above a single point is zero, we observe that the probability of any particular value is zero for a continuous random variable.

Three continuous probability distributions—the uniform, normal, and exponential distributions—were treated in detail. The normal probability distribution is used widely in statistical inference and will be used extensively throughout the remainder of the text.

## GLOSSARY

**Probability density function**   A function used to compute probabilities for a continuous random variable. The area under the graph of a probability density function over an interval represents probability.

**Uniform probability distribution**   A continuous probability distribution for which the probability that the random variable will assume a value in any interval is the same for all intervals of equal length.

**Normal probability distribution**    A continuous probability distribution. Its probability density function is bell shaped and determined by its mean $\mu$ and standard deviation $\sigma$.

**Standard normal probability distribution**    A normal distribution with a mean of zero and a standard deviation of one.

**Exponential probability distribution**    A continuous probability distribution that is useful in computing probabilities for the time it takes to complete a task.

## KEY FORMULAS

**Uniform Probability Density Function**

$$f(x) = \begin{cases} \dfrac{1}{b-a} & \text{for } a \leq x \leq b \\ 0 & \text{elsewhere} \end{cases} \tag{6.1}$$

**Normal Probability Density Function**

$$f(x) = \frac{1}{\sigma\sqrt{2\pi}}\, e^{-(x-\mu)^2/2\sigma^2} \tag{6.2}$$

**Converting to the Standard Normal Distribution**

$$z = \frac{x-\mu}{\sigma} \tag{6.3}$$

**Exponential Probability Density Function**

$$f(x) = \frac{1}{\mu}\, e^{-x/\mu} \qquad \text{for } x \geq 0, \mu > 0 \tag{6.4}$$

**Exponential Distribution: Cumulative Probabilities**

$$P(x \leq x_0) = 1 - e^{-x_0/\mu} \tag{6.5}$$

## SUPPLEMENTARY EXERCISES

**33.**  A business executive has been transferred from Chicago to Atlanta and needs to sell her house in Chicago quickly. The executive's employer has offered to buy the house for $210,000, but the offer expires at the end of the week. The executive does not currently have a better offer, but can afford to leave the house on the market for another month. From conversations with her realtor, the executive believes the price she will get by leaving the house on the market for another month is uniformly distributed between $200,000 and $225,000.
 
   **a.**  If she leaves the house on the market for another month, what is the mathematical expression for the probability density function of the sales price?

   **b.**  If she leaves it on the market for another month, what is the probability she will get at least $215,000 for the house?

   **c.**  If she leaves it on the market for another month, what is the probability she will get less than $210,000?

   **d.**  Should the executive leave the house on the market for another month? Why or why not?

**34.** Sixty-eight percent of the debt owed by American families is home mortgage or equity credit (*Federal Reserve Bulletin,* January 1997). The median amount of mortgage debt for families with the head of the household under 35 years old is $63,000. Assume the amount of mortgage debt for this group is normally distributed and the standard deviation is $15,000.
   **a.** What is the mean amount of mortgage debt for this group?
   **b.** How much mortgage debt do the 10% with the smallest debt have?
   **c.** What percent of these families have mortgage debt in excess of $80,000?
   **d.** The upper 5% of mortgage debt is in excess of what amount?

**35.** Motorola used the normal distribution to determine the probability of defects and the number of defects expected in a production process (*APICS—The Performance Advantage,* July 1991). Assume a production process produces units with a mean weight of 10 ounces. Calculate the probability of a defect and the expected number of defects for a 1000-unit production run in the following situations.
   **a.** The process standard deviation is .15, and the process control is set at plus or minus one standard deviation. Units with weights less than 9.85 or greater than 10.15 ounces will be classified as defects.
   **b.** Through process design improvements, the process standard deviation can be reduced to .05. Assume the process control remains the same, with weights less than 9.85 or greater than 10.15 ounces being classified as defects.
   **c.** What is the advantage of reducing process variation thereby setting process control limits at a greater number of standard deviations from the mean?

**36.** The mean hourly operating cost of a US Airways 737 airplane is $2071 (*The Tampa Tribune,* February 17, 1995). Assume that the hourly operating cost for the airplane is normally distributed.
   **a.** If 11% of the hourly operating costs are $1800 or less, what is the standard deviation of hourly operating cost?
   **b.** What is the probability that the hourly operating cost of a US Airways 737 airplane is between $2000 and $2500?
   **c.** What is the hourly operating cost of the 3% of the airplanes that have the lowest operating cost?

**37.** The sales of High-Brite Toothpaste are believed to be approximately normally distributed, with a mean of 10,000 tubes per week and a standard deviation of 1500 tubes per week.
   **a.** What is the probability that more than 12,000 tubes will be sold in any given week?
   **b.** To have a .95 probability that the company will have sufficient stock to cover the weekly demand, how many tubes should be produced?

**38.** Ward Doering Auto Sales is considering offering a special service contract that will cover the total cost of any service work required on leased vehicles. From experience, the company manager estimates that yearly service costs are approximately normally distributed, with a mean of $150 and a standard deviation of $25.
   **a.** If the company offers the service contract to customers for a yearly charge of $200, what is the probability that any one customer's service costs will exceed the contract price of $200?
   **b.** What is Ward's expected profit per service contract?

**39.** The Asian currency crisis of late 1997 and early 1998 was expected to lead to substantial job losses in the United States as inexpensive imports flooded markets. California was expected to be especially hard hit. The Economic Policy Institute estimated that the mean number of job losses in California would be 126,681 (*St. Petersburg Times,* January 24, 1998). Assume the number of jobs lost is normally distributed with a standard deviation of 30,000.
   **a.** What is the probability the number of lost jobs is between 80,000 and 150,000?
   **b.** What is the probability the number of lost jobs will be less than 50,000?
   **c.** What cutoff value will provide a .95 probability that the number of lost jobs will not exceed the value?

**40.** Assume that the test scores from a college admissions test are normally distributed, with a mean of 450 and a standard deviation of 100.
   **a.** What percentage of the people taking the test score between 400 and 500?
   **b.** Suppose someone receives a score of 630. What percentage of the people taking the test score better? What percentage score worse?
   **c.** If a particular university will not admit anyone scoring below 480, what percentage of the persons taking the test would be acceptable to the university?

**41.** According to *Advertising Age,* the average base salary for women working as copywriters in advertising firms is higher than the average base salary for men. The average base salary for women is $67,000 and the average base salary for men is $65,500 (*Working Woman,* July/August 2000). Assume salaries are normally distributed and that the standard deviation is $7000 for both men and women.
   **a.** What is the probability of a woman receiving a salary in excess of $75,000?
   **b.** What is the probability of a man receiving a salary in excess of $75,000?
   **c.** What is the probability of a woman receiving a salary below $50,000?
   **d.** How much would a woman have to make to have a higher salary than 99% of her male counterparts?

**42.** A machine fills containers with a particular product. The standard deviation of filling weights is known from past data to be .6 ounce. If only 2% of the containers hold less than 18 ounces, what is the mean filling weight for the machine? That is, what must $\mu$ equal? Assume the filling weights have a normal distribution.

**43.** The time in minutes for which a student uses a computer terminal at the computer center of a major university follows an exponential probability distribution with a mean of 36 minutes. Assume a student arrives at the terminal just as another student is beginning to work on the terminal.

$\mu = 36$

   **a.** What is the probability that the wait for the second student will be 15 minutes or less?
   **b.** What is the probability that the wait for the second student will be between 15 and 45 minutes?
   **c.** What is the probability that the second student will have to wait an hour or more?

**44.** A new automated production process has been averaging two breakdowns per day, and the number of breakdowns per day follows a Poisson probability distribution.
   **a.** What is the mean time between breakdowns, assuming eight hours of operation per day?
   **b.** Show the exponential probability density function that can be used for the time between breakdowns.
   **c.** What is the probability that the process will run one hour or more before another breakdown?
   **d.** What is the probability that the process can run a full eight-hour shift without a breakdown?

**45.** The time (in minutes) a checkout lane is idle at a supermarket follows an exponential probability distribution with a mean of 1.2 minutes.

$\mu . / . 2$

   **a.** Show the probability density function for this distribution.
   **b.** What is the probability that the next customer will arrive between .5 and 1.0 minute after the lane becomes idle?
   **c.** What is the probability of the checkout lane being idle for more than a minute?

**46.** The time (in minutes) between telephone calls at an insurance claims office has the following exponential probability distribution.

$$f(x) = .50e^{-.50x} \qquad \text{for } x \geq 0$$

   **a.** What is the mean time between telephone calls?
   **b.** What is the probability of having 30 seconds or less between telephone calls?
   **c.** What is the probability of having 1 minute or less between telephone calls?
   **d.** What is the probability of having 5 or more minutes without a telephone call?

# Chapter 7

# SAMPLING AND SAMPLING DISTRIBUTIONS

## CONTENTS

## STATISTICS IN PRACTICE

### MEAD CORPORATION*
*Dayton, Ohio*

Mead Corporation is a diversified paper and forest products company that has more than 16,000 employees. It operates worldwide in 32 countries, with customers located in 98 countries. Mead holds a leading position in paper production, with an annual capacity of 1.8 million tons. The company's products include textbook paper, glossy magazine paper, beverage packaging systems, and office products. Mead's internal consulting group uses sampling to provide a variety of information that enables the company to obtain significant productivity benefits and remain competitive.

For example, Mead maintains large woodland holdings, which provide the trees that are the raw material for many of the company's products. Managers need reliable and accurate information about the timberlands and forests to evaluate the company's ability to meet its future raw material needs. What is the present volume in the forests? What is the past growth of the forests? What is the projected future growth of the forests? With answers to these important questions, Mead's managers can develop plans for the future including long-term planting and harvesting schedules for the trees.

How does Mead obtain the information it needs about its vast forest holdings? Data collected from sample plots throughout the forests are the basis for learning about the population of trees owned by the company. To identify the sample plots, the timberland holdings are first divided into three sections based on location and types of trees. Using maps and random numbers, Mead analysts identify random samples of 1/5 to 1/7 acre plots in each section of the forest. The sample plots are where Mead foresters collect data and learn about the forest population.

*The authors are indebted to Dr. Edward P. Winkofsky of Mead Corporation for providing this Statistics in Practice.

Random sampling of its forest holdings enables Mead Corporation to meet future raw material needs. © Larry Goldstein/Stone.

Foresters throughout the organization participate in the field data collection process. Periodically, two-person teams gather information on each tree in every sample plot. The sample data are entered into the company's continuous forest inventory (CFI) computer system. Reports from the CFI system include a number of frequency distribution summaries containing statistics on types of trees, present forest volume, past forest growth rates, and projected future forest growth and volume. Sampling and the associated statistical summaries of the sample data provide the reports that are essential for the effective management of Mead's forests and timberlands.

In this chapter you will learn about simple random sampling and the sample selection process. In addition, you will learn how statistics such as the sample mean and sample proportion are used to estimate the population mean and population proportion. The important concept of a sampling distribution is also introduced.

In Chapter 1, we defined a *population* and a *sample* as two important aspects of a statistical study. The definitions are restated here.

**1.** A *population* is the set of all the elements of interest in a particular study.
**2.** A *sample* is a subset of the population.

The purpose of *statistical inference* is to develop estimates and test hypotheses about the characteristics of a population using information contained in a sample. Let us begin by citing two situations in which sampling is conducted to give a manager or decision maker information about a population.

1. A tire manufacturer developed a new tire designed to provide an increase in mileage over the firm's current line of tires. To estimate the mean number of miles provided by the new tires, the manufacturer selected a sample of 120 new tires for testing. The test results provided a sample mean of 36,500 miles. Hence, an estimate of the mean tire mileage for the population of new tires was 36,500 miles.

2. Members of a political party were considering supporting a particular candidate for election to the U.S. Senate, and party leaders wanted an estimate of the proportion of registered voters favoring the candidate. The time and cost associated with contacting every individual in the population of registered voters were prohibitive. Hence, a sample of 400 registered voters was selected and 160 of the 400 voters indicated a preference for the candidate. An estimate of the proportion of the population of registered voters favoring the candidate was 160/400 = .40.

The preceding examples show how sampling and the sample results can be used to develop estimates of population characteristics. Note that in the tire mileage example, collecting the data on tire life involves wearing out each tire tested. Clearly it is not feasible to test every tire in the population; a sample is the only realistic way to obtain the desired tire mileage data. In the example involving the election, contacting every registered voter in the population is theoretically possible, but the time and cost in doing so are prohibitive; thus, a sample of registered voters is preferred.

The examples illustrate some of the reasons for using samples. However, it is important to realize that sample results provide only *estimates* of the values of the population characteristics. That is, we do not expect the sample mean of 36,500 miles to exactly equal the mean mileage for all tires in the population, nor do we expect exactly 40% of the population of registered voters to favor the candidate. The reason is simply that the sample contains only a portion of the population. With proper sampling methods, the sample results will provide "good" estimates of the population characteristics. But how good can we expect the sample results to be? Fortunately, statistical procedures are available for answering this question.

In this chapter we show how simple random sampling can be used to select a sample from a population. We then show how data obtained from a simple random sample can be used to compute estimates of a population mean, a population standard deviation, and a population proportion. In addition, we introduce the important concept of a sampling distribution. As we show, knowledge of the appropriate sampling distribution is what enables us to make statements about the goodness of the sample results. The last section discusses some alternatives to simple random sampling that are often employed in practice.

> A sample mean provides an estimate of a population mean, and a sample proportion provides an estimate of a population proportion. With estimates such as these, some sampling error can be expected. A key point in this chapter is that statistical methods can be used to make probability statements about the size of the sampling error.

## 7.1   THE ELECTRONICS ASSOCIATES SAMPLING PROBLEM

The director of personnel for Electronics Associates, Inc. (EAI), has been assigned the task of developing a profile of the company's 2500 managers. The characteristics to be identified include the mean annual salary for the managers and the proportion of managers having completed the company's management training program.

Using the 2500 managers as the population for this study, we can find the annual salary and the training program status for each individual by referring to the firm's personnel records. The data file containing this information for all 2500 managers in the population is on the disk at the back of the book.

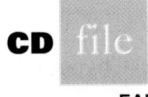

CD file

**EAI**

Using the EAI data set and the formulas presented in Chapter 3, we computed the population mean and the population standard deviation for the annual salary data.

$$\text{Population mean:} \quad \mu = \$51{,}800$$
$$\text{Population standard deviation:} \quad \sigma = \$4000$$

The data for the training program status show that 1500 of the 2500 managers have completed the training program. Letting $p$ denote the proportion of the population having completed the training program, we see that $p = 1500/2500 = .60$.

A **parameter** is a numerical measure of a population characteristic. The population mean annual salary ($\mu = \$51{,}800$), the population standard deviation of annual salary ($\sigma = \$4000$), and the population proportion having completed the training program ($p = .60$) are parameters of the population of EAI managers.

Now, suppose that the necessary information on all the EAI managers was not readily available in the company's database. Employee records for recent hires might not be on the computer. Perhaps only the salary information (and not the training program status) is in the employee's record. Or, maybe the employee records at some locations are on the computer, but records at other locations are not. For whatever reason, it is often the case that it is not possible, or is perhaps too costly, to collect and process information on all elements of a population. In such cases, information from a sample can often be used to develop estimates of the population parameters of interest.

The question we now consider is how the firm's director of personnel can obtain estimates of the population parameters of interest by using a sample of managers rather than all 2500 managers in the population. A sample of 30 managers will be used. Clearly, the time and the cost of developing a profile would be substantially less for 30 managers than for the entire population. If the personnel director could be assured that a sample of 30 managers would provide adequate information about the population of 2500 managers, working with a sample would be preferable to working with the entire population. Let us explore the possibility of using a sample for the EAI study by first considering how we can identify a sample of 30 managers.

*Often the cost of collecting information from a sample is substantially less than from a population, especially when personal interviews must be conducted to collect the information.*

## 7.2   SIMPLE RANDOM SAMPLING

Several methods can be used to select a sample from a population; one of the most common is **simple random sampling**. The definition of a simple random sample and the process of selecting a simple random sample depend on whether the population is *finite* or *infinite*. Because the EAI sampling problem involves a finite population of 2500 managers, we first consider sampling from a finite population.

### Sampling from a Finite Population

A simple random sample of size $n$ from a finite population of size $N$ is defined as follows.

**Simple Random Sample (Finite Population)**

A simple random sample of size $n$ from a finite population of size $N$ is a sample selected such that each possible sample of size $n$ has the same probability of being selected.

One procedure for selecting a simple random sample from a finite population is to choose the elements for the sample one at a time in such a way that each of the elements remaining in the population has the same probability of being selected. Sampling $n$ elements in this way will satisfy the definition of a simple random sample from a finite population.

To select a simple random sample from the finite population of EAI managers, one approach is to first assign each of the 2500 EAI managers a number. For instance, we can number them from 1 to 2500 in the order that their names appear in EAI personnel files. Next, we refer to the table of random numbers shown in Table 7.1.[1] Referring to the first row of the table, each digit, 6, 3, 2, . . . , is a random digit having an equal chance of occurring. Because the largest number in the population list of EAI managers, 2500, has four digits, we will select random numbers from the table in sets or groups of four digits. We may start anywhere in the table and move systematically in a direction of our choice. We choose to use the first row of Table 7.1 and move from left to right. The four-digit random numbers are

*The random numbers are shown in groups of 5 for readability.*

| 6327 | 1599 | 8671 | 7445 | 1102 | 1514 | 1807 |

Because the numbers in the table are random, these four-digit numbers are equally probable or equally likely.

We can now use these four-digit random numbers to give each manager in the population an equal chance of being included in the random sample. The first number, 6327, is greater than 2500. It does not correspond to one of the numbered managers in the population, and hence is discarded. The second number, 1599, is between 1 and 2500. Thus the

**TABLE 7.1**   RANDOM NUMBERS

| | | | | | | | | | |
|---|---|---|---|---|---|---|---|---|---|
| 63271 | 59986 | 71744 | 51102 | 15141 | 80714 | 58683 | 93108 | 13554 | 79945 |
| 88547 | 09896 | 95436 | 79115 | 08303 | 01041 | 20030 | 63754 | 08459 | 28364 |
| 55957 | 57243 | 83865 | 09911 | 19761 | 66535 | 40102 | 26646 | 60147 | 15702 |
| 46276 | 87453 | 44790 | 67122 | 45573 | 84358 | 21625 | 16999 | 13385 | 22782 |
| 55363 | 07449 | 34835 | 15290 | 76616 | 67191 | 12777 | 21861 | 68689 | 03263 |
| 69393 | 92785 | 49902 | 58447 | 42048 | 30378 | 87618 | 26933 | 40640 | 16281 |
| 13186 | 29431 | 88190 | 04588 | 38733 | 81290 | 89541 | 70290 | 40113 | 08243 |
| 17726 | 28652 | 56836 | 78351 | 47327 | 18518 | 92222 | 55201 | 27340 | 10493 |
| 36520 | 64465 | 05550 | 30157 | 82242 | 29520 | 69753 | 72602 | 23756 | 54935 |
| 81628 | 36100 | 39254 | 56835 | 37636 | 02421 | 98063 | 89641 | 64953 | 99337 |
| 84649 | 48968 | 75215 | 75498 | 49539 | 74240 | 03466 | 49292 | 36401 | 45525 |
| 63291 | 11618 | 12613 | 75055 | 43915 | 26488 | 41116 | 64531 | 56827 | 30825 |
| 70502 | 53225 | 03655 | 05915 | 37140 | 57051 | 48393 | 91322 | 25653 | 06543 |
| 06426 | 24771 | 59935 | 49801 | 11082 | 66762 | 94477 | 02494 | 88215 | 27191 |
| 20711 | 55609 | 29430 | 70165 | 45406 | 78484 | 31639 | 52009 | 18873 | 96927 |
| 41990 | 70538 | 77191 | 25860 | 55204 | 73417 | 83920 | 69468 | 74972 | 38712 |
| 72452 | 36618 | 76298 | 26678 | 89334 | 33938 | 95567 | 29380 | 75906 | 91807 |
| 37042 | 40318 | 57099 | 10528 | 09925 | 89773 | 41335 | 96244 | 29002 | 46453 |
| 53766 | 52875 | 15987 | 46962 | 67342 | 77592 | 57651 | 95508 | 80033 | 69828 |
| 90585 | 58955 | 53122 | 16025 | 84299 | 53310 | 67380 | 84249 | 25348 | 04332 |
| 32001 | 96293 | 37203 | 64516 | 51530 | 37069 | 40261 | 61374 | 05815 | 06714 |
| 62606 | 64324 | 46354 | 72157 | 67248 | 20135 | 49804 | 09226 | 64419 | 29457 |
| 10078 | 28073 | 85389 | 50324 | 14500 | 15562 | 64165 | 06125 | 71353 | 77669 |
| 91561 | 46145 | 24177 | 15294 | 10061 | 98124 | 75732 | 00815 | 83452 | 97355 |
| 13091 | 98112 | 53959 | 79607 | 52244 | 63303 | 10413 | 63839 | 74762 | 50289 |

---

[1]Tables of random numbers are available in a variety of handbooks such as The Rand Corporation's *A Million Random Digits with 100,000 Normal Deviates* (New York: The Free Press, 1983).

first manager selected for the random sample is number 1599 in the list of EAI managers. Continuing this process, we ignore the numbers 8671 and 7445 before identifying manager numbers 1102, 1514, and 1807 to be included in the random sample. This process continues until the simple random sample of 30 EAI managers has been obtained.

In implementing this simple random sample selection process, it is possible that a random number used previously may appear again in the table before the sample of 30 EAI managers has been selected. Because we do not want to select a manager more than one time, any previously used random numbers are ignored because the corresponding manager is already included in the sample. Selecting a sample in this manner is referred to as **sampling without replacement.** If we had selected the sample such that previously used random numbers were acceptable and specific managers could be included in the sample two or more times, we would be **sampling with replacement.** Sampling without replacement is the procedure used most often, so when we refer to simple random sampling, we will assume that the sampling is without replacement.

We will now consider another approach to selecting a simple random sample using random numbers; although this approach often takes longer to do by hand, it is efficient when using a computer to implement the procedure. We first assign a random number to each of the 2500 EAI managers. Then, we select the 30 managers with the smallest random numbers as the simple random sample. Because each of the 2500 managers has the same probability of being assigned one of the 30 smallest random numbers, this procedure provides a simple random sample of 30 EAI managers. Using this approach, we do not have to worry about any managers being included twice.[2] We now describe how this approach is implemented using Excel.

## Using Excel to Select a Simple Random Sample

Excel can be used to select a simple random sample without replacement. The method for doing so is based on random numbers generated by Excel's RAND function. The RAND function generates random numbers in the interval from 0 to 1. Because the numbers generated are random, any number in the interval is equally likely; the random numbers are actually values of a uniformly distributed random variable.

To select a simple random sample of 30 EAI managers without replacement from the population of 2500 EAI managers, we begin by generating 2500 random numbers, one for each manager in the population. Then we choose the 30 managers corresponding to the 30 smallest random numbers as our sample. Refer to Figure 7.1 as we describe the steps involved.

**Enter Data:**   The first three columns of the worksheet in the background show the annual salary data and training program status for the first 30 managers in the population of 2500 EAI managers. (The actual worksheet contains all 2500 managers.)

**Enter Functions and Formulas:**   In the background worksheet, the label **Random Numbers** has been entered into cell D1 and the formula =RAND() has been entered into cells D2:D2501 to generate a random number between 0 and 1 for each of the 2500 EAI managers. The random number generated for the first manager is 0.613872, the random number generated for the second manager is 0.473204, and so on.

**Apply Tools:**   All that remains is to find the managers associated with the 30 smallest random numbers. To do so we sort the data in columns A through D into ascending order by the random numbers in column D.

    **Step 1.**  Select cells A2:D2501
    **Step 2.**  Select the **Data** pull-down menu
    **Step 3.**  Choose the **Sort** option

---

[2]It is possible for a tie to occur for the 30th smallest random number. But, the tie can be broken by including tied managers in the sample in the order in which they appear in the list of managers.

**FIGURE 7.1**    USING EXCEL TO SELECT A SIMPLE RANDOM SAMPLE WITHOUT REPLACEMENT

Background worksheet:

| | Manager | Annual Salary | Training Program | Random Numbers |
|---|---|---|---|---|
| 1 | Manager | Annual Salary | Training Program | Random Numbers |
| 2 | 1 | 55769.50 | No | 0.613872 |
| 3 | 2 | 50823.00 | Yes | 0.473204 |
| 4 | 3 | 48408.20 | No | 0.549011 |
| 5 | 4 | 49787.50 | No | 0.047482 |
| 6 | 5 | 52801.60 | Yes | 0.531085 |
| 7 | 6 | 51767.70 | No | 0.994296 |
| 8 | 7 | 58346.60 | Yes | 0.189065 |
| 9 | 8 | 46670.20 | No | 0.020714 |
| 10 | 9 | 50246.80 | Yes | 0.647318 |
| 11 | 10 | 51255.00 | No | 0.524341 |
| 12 | 11 | 52546.60 | No | 0.764998 |
| 13 | 12 | 49512.50 | Yes | 0.255244 |
| 14 | 13 | 51753.00 | Yes | 0.010923 |
| 15 | 14 | 53547.10 | No | 0.238003 |
| 16 | 15 | 48052.20 | No | 0.635675 |
| 17 | 16 | 44652.50 | Yes | 0.177294 |
| 18 | 17 | 51764.90 | Yes | 0.415097 |
| 19 | 18 | 45187.80 | Yes | 0.883440 |
| 20 | 19 | 49867.50 | Yes | 0.476824 |
| 21 | 20 | 53706.30 | Yes | 0.101065 |
| 22 | 21 | 52039.50 | Yes | 0.775323 |
| 23 | 22 | 52973.60 | No | 0.011729 |
| 24 | 23 | 53372.50 | No | 0.762026 |
| 25 | 24 | 54592.00 | Yes | 0.066344 |
| 26 | 25 | 55738.10 | Yes | 0.776766 |
| 27 | 26 | 52975.10 | Yes | 0.828493 |
| 28 | 27 | 52386.20 | Yes | 0.841532 |
| 29 | 28 | 51051.60 | Yes | 0.899427 |
| 30 | 29 | 52095.60 | Yes | 0.486284 |
| 31 | 30 | 44956.50 | No | 0.264628 |
| 32 | | | | |

The formula in cells D2:D2501 is =RAND().

Note: Rows 32–2501 are not shown.

Foreground worksheet:

| | Manager | Annual Salary | Training Program | Random Numbers |
|---|---|---|---|---|
| 1 | Manager | Annual Salary | Training Program | Random Numbers |
| 2 | 812 | 49094.30 | Yes | 0.000193 |
| 3 | 1411 | 53263.90 | Yes | 0.000484 |
| 4 | 1795 | 49643.50 | Yes | 0.002641 |
| 5 | 2095 | 49894.90 | Yes | 0.002763 |
| 6 | 1235 | 47621.60 | No | 0.002940 |
| 7 | 744 | 55924.00 | Yes | 0.002977 |
| 8 | 470 | 49092.30 | Yes | 0.003182 |
| 9 | 1606 | 51404.40 | Yes | 0.003448 |
| 10 | 1744 | 50957.70 | Yes | 0.004203 |
| 11 | 179 | 55109.70 | Yes | 0.005293 |
| 12 | 1387 | 45922.60 | Yes | 0.005709 |
| 13 | 1782 | 57268.40 | No | 0.005729 |
| 14 | 1006 | 55688.80 | Yes | 0.005796 |
| 15 | 278 | 51564.70 | No | 0.005966 |
| 16 | 1850 | 56188.20 | No | 0.006250 |
| 17 | 844 | 51766.00 | Yes | 0.006708 |
| 18 | 2028 | 52541.30 | No | 0.007767 |
| 19 | 1654 | 44980.00 | Yes | 0.008095 |
| 20 | 444 | 51932.60 | Yes | 0.009686 |
| 21 | 556 | 52973.00 | Yes | 0.009711 |
| 22 | 2449 | 45120.90 | Yes | 0.010595 |
| 23 | 13 | 51753.00 | Yes | 0.010923 |
| 24 | 2187 | 54391.80 | No | 0.011364 |
| 25 | 1633 | 50164.20 | No | 0.011603 |
| 26 | 22 | 52973.60 | No | 0.011729 |
| 27 | 1530 | 50241.30 | No | 0.013570 |
| 28 | 820 | 52793.90 | No | 0.013669 |
| 29 | 1258 | 50979.40 | Yes | 0.014042 |
| 30 | 2349 | 55860.90 | Yes | 0.014532 |
| 31 | 1698 | 57309.10 | No | 0.014539 |
| 32 | | | | |

**Step 4.** When the **Sort** dialog box appears
Choose **Random Numbers** in the **Sort by** text box
Choose **Ascending**
Click **OK**

After completing these steps we obtain the worksheet shown in the foreground of Figure 7.1.[3] The managers listed in rows 2–31 are the ones corresponding to the smallest 30

---

[3]Prior to sorting we turned off the automatic recalculation option for the worksheet. To turn off the automatic recalculation option select **Tools,** choose **Options,** select the **Calculation** tab, and in the calculation section select **Manual.** If we had not turned off automatic recalculation, the random numbers in column D of the foreground figure would not have appeared in ascending order. In other words, if the automatic recalculation option is not turned off when the sort operation takes place, Excel will do a recalculation and a new set of random numbers will be generated. However, the new random numbers will

random numbers that were generated. Hence, this group of 30 managers is a simple random sample. Note that the random numbers shown in the foreground of Figure 7.1 are in ascending order, and that the managers are not in their original order. For instance, manager 812 in the population is associated with the smallest random number and is the first element in the sample, and manager 13 in the population (see row 14 of the background worksheet) has been included as the 22nd observation in the sample (row 23 of the foreground worksheet).

## Sampling from an Infinite Population

In practice, a population being studied is usually considered infinite if it involves an ongoing process that makes listing or counting every element in the population impossible.

Many sampling situations in business and economics involve finite populations, but in some situations the population is either infinite or so large that for practical purposes it must be treated as infinite. In sampling from an infinite population, we must use a new definition of a simple random sample. In addition, because the elements in an infinite population cannot be listed and numbered, we must use a different process for selecting the sample.

Suppose we want to estimate the average time between placing an order and receiving food for customers at a fast-food restaurant during the 11:30 A.M. to 1:30 P.M. lunch period. If we consider the population as being all possible customer visits, we see that it would not be feasible to specify a finite limit on the number of possible visits or to list the possible visitors. In fact, if we define the population as being all customer visits that could conceivably occur during the lunch period, we can consider the population as being infinite. Our task is to select a simple random sample of $n$ customers from this population. The definition of a simple random sample from an infinite population follows.

> ### Simple Random Sample (Infinite Population)
>
> A simple random sample from an infinite population is a sample selected such that the following conditions are satisfied.
>
> 1. Each element selected comes from the same population.
> 2. Each element is selected independently.

For infinite populations, a sample selection procedure must be specially devised to select the items independently and thus avoid a selection bias that gives higher selection probabilities to certain types of elements.

For the problem of selecting a simple random sample of customer visits at a fast-food restaurant, the first condition in the definition is satisfied by any customer visit occurring during the 11:30 A.M. to 1:30 P.M. lunch period while the restaurant is operating with its regular staff under "normal" operating conditions. The second condition is satisfied by ensuring that the selection of a particular customer does not influence the selection of any other customer. That is, the customers are selected independently.

A well-known fast-food restaurant has implemented a simple random sampling procedure for just such a situation. The sampling procedure is based on the fact that some customers present discount coupons for special prices on sandwiches, drinks, french fries, and so on. Whenever a customer presents a discount coupon, the next customer served is selected for the sample. Because the customers present discount coupons randomly and independently, the firm is satisfied that the sampling plan satisfies the two conditions in the definition of a simple random sample from an infinite population. We note that the customers presenting the coupons were not selected for the sample because their purchase behavior may not be the same as the rest of the customers.

---

not affect the choice of managers included in the sample because the sort will be based on the original random numbers. The reason we turned off the automatic recalculation was so we could show, in column D of the foreground figure, that the random sample was, indeed, associated with the 30 smallest random numbers.

## NOTES AND COMMENTS

1. Excel has a sampling tool that can be accessed by selecting the **Tools** pull-down menu and choosing the **Data Analysis** option. It selects a simple random sample with replacement. However, as we stated previously, in most practical applications sampling without replacement is the desired procedure.

2. Finite populations are often defined by lists such as organization membership rosters, student enrollment records, credit card account lists, inventory product numbers, and so on. Infinite populations are often defined by an ongoing process whereby the elements of the population consist of items generated as though the process would operate indefinitely under the same conditions. In such cases, it is impossible to obtain a list of all elements in the population. For ex-

ample, populations consisting of all possible parts to be manufactured, all possible customer visits, all possible bank transactions, and so on are classified as infinite populations.

3. The number of different simple random samples of size $n$ that can be selected from a finite population of size $N$ is

$$\frac{N!}{n!(N - n)!}$$

In this formula, $N!$ and $n!$ are the factorial computations discussed in Chapter 4. For the EAI problem with $N = 2500$ and $n = 30$, this expression can be used to show that there is approximately $2.75 \times 10^{69}$ different simple random samples of 30 EAI managers.

## EXERCISES

### Methods

1. Consider a finite population with five elements labeled A, B, C, D, and E. Ten possible simple random samples of size two can be selected.
   a. List the 10 possible samples. Hint: Two are AB and AC.
   b. Using simple random sampling, what is the probability that each sample of size two is selected?
   c. Assign the number 1 to A, the number 2 to B, and so on. List the simple random sample of size two that will be selected by using the random digits 8 0 5 7 5 3 2.

2. Assume a finite population has 350 elements. Use the last three digits of each of the following five-digit random numbers. Move from left to right to determine the first four elements of a simple random sample.

   98601   73022   83448   02147   34229   27553   84147   93289   14209

### Applications

3. *Fortune* publishes data on sales, profits, assets, stockholders' equity, market value, and earnings per share for the 500 largest U.S. industrial corporations (The *Fortune* 500, 2000). Assume that you want to select a simple random sample of 10 corporations from the *Fortune* 500 list. Use the last three digits in column 9 of Table 7.1, beginning with 554. Read down the column and identify the numbers of the 10 corporations that would be selected.

4. Ten companies with widely held stocks are shown here (*USA Today*, September 6, 2000).

   | | |
   |---|---|
   | AT&T | IBM |
   | America Online | Johnson & Johnson |
   | Cisco Systems | Microsoft |
   | General Electric | Motorola |
   | Intel | Pfizer |

   a. Assume that a random sample of five of these companies will be selected for an in-depth study of common business practices in large corporations. Beginning with the first random digit in Table 7.1 and reading down the column, use the single-digit random numbers to sequentially select a simple random sample of five companies to be used in the study.

**b.** Assign one of the first 10 random digits in column one of Table 7.1 to each of the companies. Select a simple random sample of five companies by choosing the ones with the smallest random numbers.

**c.** According to the third point in Notes and Comments, how many different simple random samples of size five can be selected from the list of 10 companies?

**d.** Use Excel to select a simple random sample of five companies.

5. A student government organization is interested in estimating the proportion of students who favor a mandatory "pass-fail" grading policy for elective courses. A list of names and addresses of the 645 students enrolled during the current quarter is available from the registrar's office.

**a.** Using three-digit random numbers in row 10 of Table 7.1 and moving across the row from left to right, identify the first 10 students who would be selected using simple random sampling. The three-digit random numbers begin with 816, 283, and 610.

**b.** Describe how Excel could be used to select a simple random sample of 50 students.

6. The *County and City Data Book,* published by the Bureau of the Census, lists information on 3139 counties throughout the United States. Assume that a national study will collect data from 30 randomly selected counties. Use four-digit random numbers from the last column of Table 7.1 to identify the numbers corresponding to the first five counties selected for the sample. Ignore the first digits and begin with the four-digit random numbers 9945, 8364, 5702, and so on.

7. In this section we showed how Excel can be used to select a simple random sample of 30 EAI managers. Use this procedure to select a simple random sample of 50 EAI managers.

**EAI**

8. The following table provides the NCAA football top 25 teams at the beginning of the 2000 season (*Sports Illustrated,* August 14, 2000).

**Football**

| | |
|---|---|
| 1. Nebraska | 14. Tennessee |
| 2. Florida State | 15. TCU |
| 3. Alabama | 16. Purdue |
| 4. Michigan | 17. Mississippi |
| 5. Wisconsin | 18. USC |
| 6. Kansas State | 19. Penn State |
| 7. Georgia | 20. Southern Miss |
| 8. Clemson | 21. Illinois |
| 9. Texas | 22. Ohio State |
| 10. Miami | 23. Oklahoma |
| 11. Florida | 24. Colorado State |
| 12. Virginia Tech | 25. Colorado |
| 13. Washington | |

**a.** Use the ninth column of the random numbers in Table 7.1 beginning with 13554, to select a simple random sample of six football teams. Begin with 13 and use the first two digits in each row of the ninth column for your selection process. Using this sequential one-at-a-time procedure, how many random numbers were needed and which six teams were selected?

**b.** Use the Excel procedure of selecting the six teams with the smallest random numbers. How many random numbers were needed and which six teams were selected?

9. *Business Week* provided performance data and annual ratings for 895 mutual funds (*Business Week,* February 3, 1997). Assume that a simple random sample of 12 of the 895 mutual funds will be selected for a follow-up study on the performance of mutual funds. Use the fourth column of the random numbers in Table 7.1, beginning with 51102, to select the simple random sample of 12 mutual funds. Begin with mutual fund 511 and use the first three digits in each row of the fourth column for your selection process. What are the numbers of the 12 mutual funds in the simple random sample?

**10.** Indicate whether the following populations should be considered finite or infinite.

    **a.** All registered voters in the state of California.

    **b.** All television sets that could be produced by the Allentown, Pennsylvania, plant of the TV-M Company.

    **c.** All orders that could be processed by a mail-order firm.

    **d.** All emergency telephone calls that could come into a local police station.

    **e.** All components that Fibercon, Inc., produced on the second shift on May 17.

## 7.3   POINT ESTIMATION

Now that we have described how to select a simple random sample, let us return to the EAI problem. A simple random sample of 30 managers has been selected (see Figure 7.1) and the corresponding data on annual salary and management training program participation are as shown in Table 7.2. The notation $x_1, x_2,$ and so on is used to denote the annual salary of the first manager in the sample, the annual salary of the second manager in the sample, and so on. Participation in the management training program is indicated by Yes in the management training program column.

To estimate the value of a population parameter, we compute a corresponding characteristic of the sample, referred to as a **sample statistic**. For example, to estimate the population mean $\mu$ and the population standard deviation $\sigma$ for the annual salary of EAI managers, we simply use the data in Table 7.2 to calculate the corresponding sample statistics: the sample mean $\bar{x}$ and the sample standard deviation $s$. Using the formulas for a sample mean and a sample standard deviation presented in Chapter 3, the sample mean is

$$\bar{x} = \frac{\Sigma x_i}{n} = \frac{1,554,420}{30} = \$51,814.00$$

and the sample standard deviation is

$$s = \sqrt{\frac{\Sigma(x_i - \bar{x})^2}{n - 1}} = \sqrt{\frac{325,009,260}{29}} = \$3347.72$$

In addition, by computing the proportion of managers in the sample who responded Yes, we can estimate the proportion of managers in the population who have completed the management training program. Table 7.2 shows that 19 of the 30 managers in the sample have completed the training program. Thus, the sample proportion, denoted by $\bar{p}$, is given by

$$\bar{p} = \frac{19}{30} = .63$$

This value is used as an estimate of the population proportion $p$.

By making the preceding computations, we have performed the statistical procedure called point estimation. In point estimation we use the data from the sample to compute the value of a sample statistic that serves as an estimate of a population parameter. Using the terminology of point estimation, we refer to $\bar{x}$ as the **point estimator** of the population mean $\mu$, $s$ as the point estimator of the population standard deviation $\sigma$, and $\bar{p}$ as the point estimator of the population proportion $p$. The actual numerical value obtained for $\bar{x}$, $s$, or $\bar{p}$ in a particular sample is called the **point estimate** of the parameter. Thus, for the sample of 30 EAI managers, \$51,814.00 is the point estimate of $\mu$, \$3347.72 is the point estimate of $\sigma$, and .63 is the point estimate of $p$. Table 7.3 summarizes the sample results and compares the point estimates to the actual values of the population parameters.

**TABLE 7.2**  ANNUAL SALARY AND TRAINING PROGRAM STATUS FOR A SIMPLE RANDOM SAMPLE OF 30 EAI MANAGERS

| Annual Salary ($) | Management Training Program? | Annual Salary ($) | Management Training Program? |
|---|---|---|---|
| $x_1 = 49{,}094.30$ | Yes | $x_{16} = 51{,}766.00$ | Yes |
| $x_2 = 53{,}263.90$ | Yes | $x_{17} = 52{,}541.30$ | No |
| $x_3 = 49{,}643.50$ | Yes | $x_{18} = 44{,}980.00$ | Yes |
| $x_4 = 49{,}894.90$ | Yes | $x_{19} = 51{,}932.60$ | Yes |
| $x_5 = 47{,}621.60$ | No | $x_{20} = 52{,}973.00$ | Yes |
| $x_6 = 55{,}924.00$ | Yes | $x_{21} = 45{,}120.90$ | Yes |
| $x_7 = 49{,}092.30$ | Yes | $x_{22} = 51{,}753.00$ | Yes |
| $x_8 = 51{,}404.40$ | Yes | $x_{23} = 54{,}391.80$ | No |
| $x_9 = 50{,}957.70$ | Yes | $x_{24} = 50{,}164.20$ | No |
| $x_{10} = 55{,}109.70$ | Yes | $x_{25} = 52{,}973.60$ | No |
| $x_{11} = 45{,}922.60$ | Yes | $x_{26} = 50{,}241.30$ | No |
| $x_{12} = 57{,}268.40$ | No | $x_{27} = 52{,}793.90$ | No |
| $x_{13} = 55{,}688.80$ | Yes | $x_{28} = 50{,}979.40$ | Yes |
| $x_{14} = 51{,}564.70$ | No | $x_{29} = 55{,}860.90$ | Yes |
| $x_{15} = 56{,}188.20$ | No | $x_{30} = 57{,}309.10$ | No |

**CD** file

**EAI**

Sampling error is the result of using a subset of the population (the sample), and not the entire population to develop estimates.

As Table 7.3 shows, none of the point estimates are exactly equal to the corresponding population parameters. This variation is to be expected because only a sample and not a census of the entire population is being used to develop the estimate. The absolute value of the difference between an unbiased point estimate and the corresponding population parameter is called the sampling error.[4] For a sample mean, sample standard deviation, and sample proportion, the sampling errors are $|\bar{x} - \mu|$, $|s - \sigma|$, and $|\bar{p} - p|$, respectively. Thus, for the EAI sample, the sampling errors are $|\$51{,}814 - \$51{,}800| = \$14$ for the sample mean, $|\$3347.72 - \$4000.00| = \$652.28$ for the sample standard deviation, and $|.63 - .60| = .03$ for the sample proportion.

**TABLE 7.3**  SUMMARY OF POINT ESTIMATES OBTAINED FROM A SIMPLE RANDOM SAMPLE OF 30 EAI MANAGERS

| Population Parameter | Parameter Value | Point Estimator | Point Estimate |
|---|---|---|---|
| $\mu$ = Population mean annual salary | $51,800.00 | $\bar{x}$ = Sample mean annual salary | $51,814.00 |
| $\sigma$ = Population standard deviation for annual salary | $4000.00 | $s$ = Sample standard deviation for annual salary | $3347.72 |
| $p$ = Population proportion having completed the management training program | .60 | $\bar{p}$ = Sample proportion having completed the management training program | .63 |

---

[4]Technically the difference between the point estimate and the population parameter is called *sampling error* only when the point estimator is unbiased. A point estimator is unbiased if the mean of its sampling distribution (see Sections 7.4–7.6) is equal to the population parameter being estimated. The point estimators ($\bar{x}$, $s$, and $\bar{p}$) used here are unbiased.

We were able to compute the sampling errors here because the population parameters were known. However, in an actual sampling application we will not be able to calculate the sampling error exactly because the value of the population parameter will not be known. We will show how statisticians analyze the sample data in order to make probability statements about the size of the sampling error.

## NOTES AND COMMENTS

In our discussion of point estimators, we use $\bar{x}$ to denote a sample mean and $\bar{p}$ to denote a sample proportion. Our use of $\bar{p}$ is based on the fact that the sample proportion is also a *sample mean*. Suppose that in a sample of size $n$ with data values $x_1$, $x_2, \ldots, x_n$, we let $x_i = 1$ when a characteristic of interest is present for the $i$th observation and $x_i = 0$ when the characteristic is not present. Then the sample proportion is computed by $\Sigma x_i/n$, which is the formula for a sample mean. We also like the consistency of using the bar over the letter to remind the reader that the sample proportion $\bar{p}$ estimates the population proportion just as the sample mean $\bar{x}$ estimates the population mean. Some texts use $\hat{p}$ instead of $\bar{p}$ to denote the sample proportion.

## EXERCISES

### Methods

**11.** The following data are from a simple random sample.

$$5 \quad 8 \quad 10 \quad 7 \quad 10 \quad 14$$

    **a.** What is the point estimate of the population mean?
    **b.** What is the point estimate of the population standard deviation?

**12.** A survey question for a sample of 150 individuals yielded 75 Yes responses, 55 No responses, and 20 No Opinions.
    **a.** What is the point estimate of the proportion in the population who respond Yes?
    **b.** What is the point estimate of the proportion in the population who respond No?

### Applications

**13.** A simple random sample of five months of sales data provided the following information:

| Month: | 1 | 2 | 3 | 4 | 5 |
|---|---|---|---|---|---|
| Units Sold: | 94 | 100 | 85 | 94 | 92 |

    **a.** What is the point estimate of the population mean number of units sold per month?
    **b.** What is the point estimate of the population standard deviation?

**14.** A sample of 784 children ages 9 to 14 were asked about cash provided by their parents (*Consumer Reports,* January 1997). The responses were as follows.

| Source of Cash | Frequency |
|---|---|
| Allowance only | 149 |
| Handouts & chores plus an allowance | 219 |
| Handouts & chores but no allowance | 251 |
| Nothing | 165 |
| Total | 784 |

    **a.** What is the point estimate of the proportion of children who receive an allowance as their only source of cash?

b.    What is the point estimate of the proportion of children who receive cash as handouts and for chores, but nothing in the form of an allowance?

c.    Considering all sources, what is the point estimate of the proportion of children who receive at least some cash from their parents?

15.    *Appliance Magazine* provided estimates of the life expectancy of household appliances (*USA Today,* September 5, 2000). A simple random sample of 10 VCRs shows the following useful life in years.

6.5    8.0    6.2    7.4    7.0    8.4    9.5    4.6    5.0    7.4

a.    What is the point estimate of the population mean life expectancy for VCRs?

b.    What is the point estimate of the population standard deviation for life expectancy of VCRs?

16.    The U.S. Department of Transportation reports statistics on how frequently major airline flights arrive at or before their scheduled arrival times (*Associated Press,* September 2000). Assume that the estimated proportion of flights arriving on time for an airline is based on a sample of 1400 flights. If 1117 of the flights arrive on time, what is the point estimate of the proportion of all flights that arrive on time?

17.    A Louis Harris poll used a survey of 1008 adults to learn how people feel about the economy (*Business Week,* August 7, 2000). Responses were as follow:

595 adults    The economy is growing.
332 adults    The economy is staying about the same.
81 adults    The economy is shrinking.

Develop the point estimate of the following population parameters.

a.    The proportion of all adults who feel the economy is growing.

b.    The proportion of all adults who feel the economy is staying about the same.

c.    The proportion of all adults who feel the economy is shrinking.

18.    In this section we showed how a simple random sample of 30 EAI managers can be used to develop point estimates of the population mean annual salary, the population standard deviation for annual salary, and the population proportion having completed the management training program.

a.    Use Excel to select a simple random sample of 50 EAI managers.

b.    Develop a point estimate of the mean annual salary.

c.    Develop a point estimate of the population standard deviation for annual salary.

d.    Develop a point estimate of the population proportion having completed the management training program.

## 7.4    INTRODUCTION TO SAMPLING DISTRIBUTIONS

In the preceding section we used a simple random sample of 30 EAI managers to develop point estimates of the mean and standard deviation of annual salary for the population of all EAI managers as well as the proportion of the managers in the population who have completed the company's management training program. Suppose we select another simple random sample of 30 EAI managers, and an analysis of the data from the second sample provides the following information.

$$\text{Sample Mean } \bar{x} = \$52,669.70$$
$$\text{Sample Standard Deviation } s = \$4239.07$$
$$\text{Sample Proportion } \bar{p} = .70$$

**TABLE 7.4**     VALUES OF $\bar{x}$, $s$, AND $\bar{p}$ FROM 500 SIMPLE RANDOM SAMPLES OF 30 EAI MANAGERS

| Sample Number | Sample Mean ($\bar{x}$) | Sample Standard Deviation ($s$) | Sample Proportion ($\bar{p}$) |
|---|---|---|---|
| 1 | 51,814.00 | 3,347.72 | .63 |
| 2 | 52,669.70 | 4,239.07 | .70 |
| 3 | 51,780.30 | 4,433.43 | .67 |
| 4 | 51,587.90 | 3,985.32 | .53 |
| . | . | . | . |
| . | . | . | . |
| . | . | . | . |
| 500 | 51,752.00 | 3,857.82 | .50 |

These results show that different values of $\bar{x}$, $s$, and $\bar{p}$ have been obtained with the second sample. In general, a second simple random sample will not contain the same elements as the first. Let us imagine carrying out the same process of selecting a new simple random sample of 30 managers over and over again, each time computing values of $\bar{x}$, $s$, and $\bar{p}$. In this way we could begin to identify the variety of values that these point estimators can have. To illustrate, we repeated the simple random sampling process for the EAI problem until we obtained 500 samples of 30 managers each and the corresponding $\bar{x}$, $s$, and $\bar{p}$ values. A portion of the results is shown in Table 7.4. Table 7.5 gives the frequency and relative frequency distributions for the 500 $\bar{x}$ values. Figure 7.2 is the relative frequency histogram for the $\bar{x}$ values.

Recall that in Chapter 5 we defined a random variable as a numerical description of the outcome of an experiment. If we consider the process of selecting a simple random sample as an experiment, the sample mean $\bar{x}$ is a numerical description of the outcome of the experiment. Thus, the sample mean $\bar{x}$ is a random variable. Just like other random variables, $\bar{x}$ has a mean or expected value, a variance, and a probability distribution. Because the various possible values of $\bar{x}$ are the result of different simple random samples, the probability

> The concept of a sampling distribution is one of the most important topics in this chapter. The ability to understand the material in subsequent chapters depends heavily on the ability to understand and use the sampling distributions presented in this chapter.

**TABLE 7.5**     FREQUENCY DISTRIBUTION OF $\bar{x}$ FROM 500 SIMPLE RANDOM SAMPLES OF 300 EAI MANAGERS

| Mean Annual Salary ($) | Frequency | Relative Frequency |
|---|---|---|
| 49,500.00–49,999.99 | 2 | .004 |
| 50,000.00–50,499.99 | 16 | .032 |
| 50,500.00–50,999.99 | 52 | .104 |
| 51,000.00–51,499.99 | 101 | .202 |
| 51,500.00–51,999.99 | 133 | .266 |
| 52,000.00–52,499.99 | 110 | .220 |
| 52,500.00–52,999.99 | 54 | .108 |
| 53,000.00–53,499.99 | 26 | .052 |
| 53,500.00–53,999.99 | 6 | .012 |
| Totals | 500 | 1.000 |

**FIGURE 7.2**  RELATIVE FREQUENCY HISTOGRAM OF $\bar{x}$ VALUES FROM 500 SIMPLE RANDOM SAMPLES OF SIZE 30 EACH

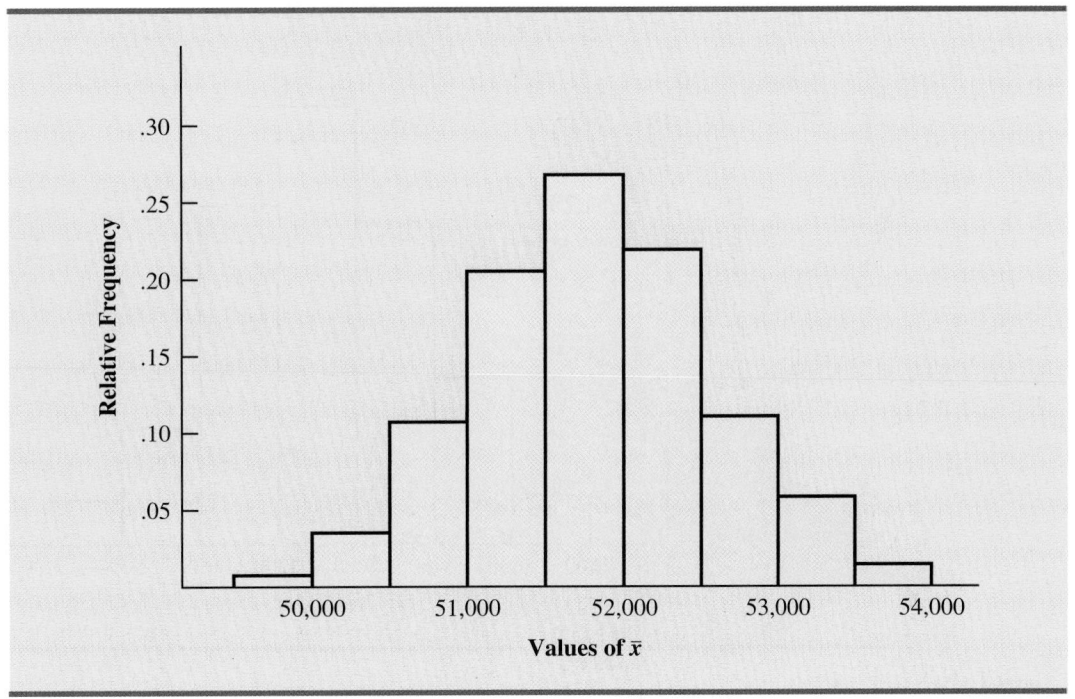

distribution of $\bar{x}$ is called the *sampling distribution* of $\bar{x}$. Knowledge of this sampling distribution and its properties will enable us to make probability statements about how close the sample mean $\bar{x}$ is to the population mean $\mu$.

Let us consider Figure 7.2. We would need to enumerate every possible sample of 30 managers and compute each sample mean to completely determine the sampling distribution of $\bar{x}$. However, the histogram of 500 $\bar{x}$ values gives an approximation of this sampling distribution. From the approximation we observe the bell-shaped appearance of the distribution. We note that the estimate of the population mean provided by $\bar{x}$ varies quite a bit. But we also note that the largest concentration of the $\bar{x}$ values and the mean of the 500 $\bar{x}$ values is near the population mean $\mu = \$51,800$. We will describe the properties of the sampling distribution of $\bar{x}$ more fully in the next section.

The 500 values of the sample standard deviation $s$ and the 500 values of the sample proportion $\bar{p}$ are summarized by the relative frequency histograms in Figures 7.3 and 7.4. As in the case of $\bar{x}$, both $s$ and $\bar{p}$ are random variables that provide numerical descriptions of the outcome of a simple random sample. If every possible sample of size 30 were selected from the population and if a value of $s$ and a value of $\bar{p}$ were computed for each sample, the resulting probability distributions would be called the sampling distribution of $s$ and the sampling distribution of $\bar{p}$, respectively. The relative frequency histograms of the 500 sample values, Figures 7.3 and 7.4, provide an approximation of these two sampling distributions.

In practice, we select only one simple random sample from the population. We repeated the sampling process 500 times in this section simply to illustrate that many different samples are possible and that the different samples generate a variety of values for the sample statistics $\bar{x}$, $s$, and $\bar{p}$. The probability distribution of any particular sample statistic is called the **sampling distribution** of the statistic. In Section 7.5 we show the

**FIGURE 7.3** RELATIVE FREQUENCY HISTOGRAM OF *s* VALUES FROM 500 SIMPLE RANDOM SAMPLES OF SIZE 30 EACH

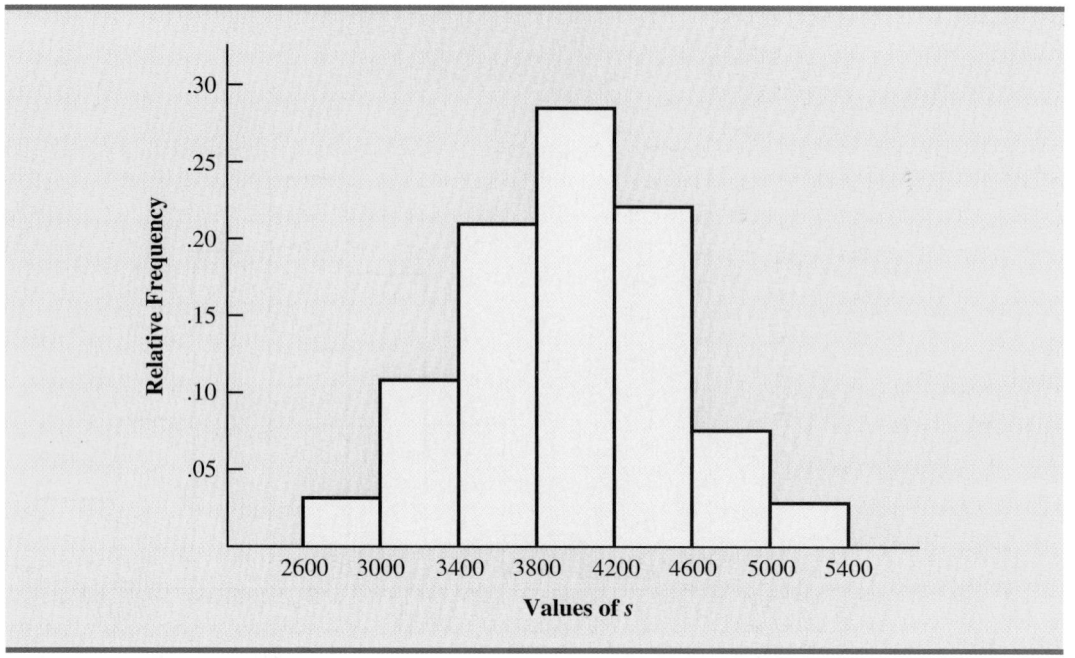

**FIGURE 7.4** RELATIVE FREQUENCY HISTOGRAM OF $\bar{p}$ VALUES FROM 500 SIMPLE RANDOM SAMPLES OF SIZE 30 EACH

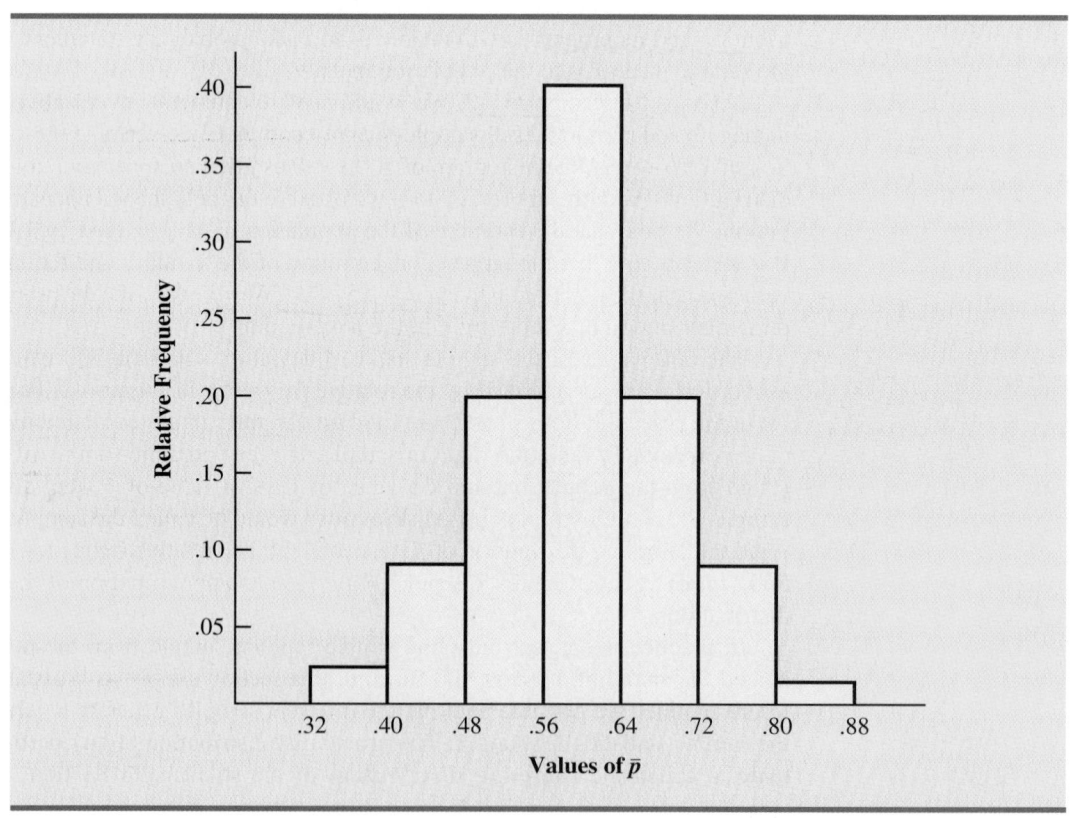

characteristics of the sampling distribution of $\bar{x}$. In Section 7.6 we show the characteristics of the sampling distribution of $\bar{p}$.

## 7.5   SAMPLING DISTRIBUTION OF $\bar{x}$

One of the most common statistical procedures is the use of a sample mean $\bar{x}$ to make inferences about a population mean $\mu$. This process is shown in Figure 7.5. If the process were repeated, we could anticipate obtaining a different value for the sample mean $\bar{x}$ each time. The probability distribution for all possible values of the sample mean $\bar{x}$ is called the sampling distribution of the sample mean $\bar{x}$.

> **Sampling Distribution of $\bar{x}$**
>
> The sampling distribution of $\bar{x}$ is the probability distribution of all possible values of the sample mean, $\bar{x}$.

The purpose of this section is to describe the properties of the sampling distribution of $\bar{x}$, including the expected value or mean of $\bar{x}$, the standard deviation of $\bar{x}$, and the shape or form of the sampling distribution itself. As we shall see, knowledge of the sampling distribution of $\bar{x}$ will enable us to make probability statements about the sampling error involved when $\bar{x}$ is used to estimate $\mu$. Let us begin by considering the mean of all possible $\bar{x}$ values, which is referred to as the expected value of $\bar{x}$.

### Expected Value of $\bar{x}$

In the EAI sampling problem we saw that different simple random samples result in a variety of values for the sample mean $\bar{x}$. Because many different values of the random variable $\bar{x}$ are possible, we are often interested in the mean of all possible values of $\bar{x}$ that can be generated by the various simple random samples. The mean of the $\bar{x}$ random variable is the expected value of $\bar{x}$. Let $E(\bar{x})$ represent the expected value of $\bar{x}$ and $\mu$ represent the mean of

**FIGURE 7.5**    THE STATISTICAL PROCESS OF USING A SAMPLE MEAN TO MAKE INFERENCES ABOUT A POPULATION MEAN

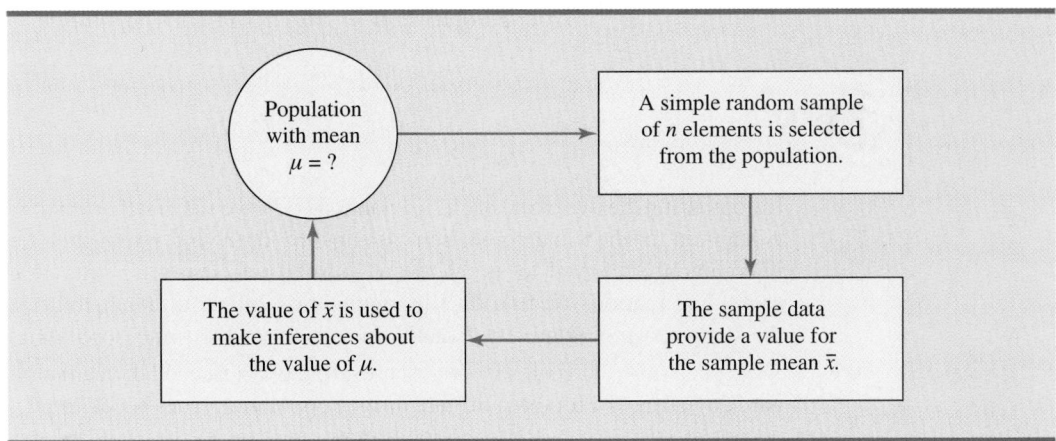

the population from which we are sampling. It can be shown that with simple random sampling, $E(\bar{x})$ and $\mu$ are equal.

---

**Expected Value of $\bar{x}$**

$$E(\bar{x}) = \mu \tag{7.1}$$

where

$$E(\bar{x}) = \text{the expected value of } \bar{x}$$
$$\mu = \text{the population mean}$$

---

*The expected value of $\bar{x}$ equals the mean of the population from which the sample is drawn.*

This result shows that with simple random sampling, the expected value or mean of $\bar{x}$ is equal to the mean of the population from which we are sampling. In Section 7.1 we saw that the mean annual salary for the population of EAI managers is $\mu = \$51,800$. Thus, according to equation (7.1), the mean of all possible sample means for the EAI study is also $51,800.

When the expected value of a point estimator is equal to the population parameter, we say the point estimator is unbiased. Thus, equation (7.1) shows that $\bar{x}$ is an unbiased estimator of the population mean $\mu$. **Unbiasdness** is a desirable property of point estimators.

## Standard Deviation of $\bar{x}$

Let us define the standard deviation of the sampling distribution of $\bar{x}$. We will use the following notation.

$$\sigma_{\bar{x}} = \text{the standard deviation of the sampling distribution of } \bar{x}$$
$$\sigma = \text{the standard deviation of the population}$$
$$n = \text{the sample size}$$
$$N = \text{the population size}$$

It can be shown that with simple random sampling, the standard deviation of $\bar{x}$ depends on whether the population is finite or infinite. The two formulas for the standard deviation of $\bar{x}$ follow.

---

**Standard Deviation of $\bar{x}$**

$$\text{Finite Population} \qquad\qquad \text{Infinite Population}$$

$$\sigma_{\bar{x}} = \sqrt{\frac{N-n}{N-1}}\left(\frac{\sigma}{\sqrt{n}}\right) \qquad\qquad \sigma_{\bar{x}} = \frac{\sigma}{\sqrt{n}} \tag{7.2}$$

---

In comparing the two expressions in equation (7.2), we see that the factor $\sqrt{(N-n)/(N-1)}$ is required for the finite population case but not for the infinite population case. This factor is commonly referred to as the **finite population correction factor.** In many practical sampling situations, we find that the population involved, although finite, is "large," whereas the sample size is relatively "small." In such cases the finite population correction factor $\sqrt{(N-n)/(N-1)}$ is close to 1. As a result, the difference between the values of the standard deviation of $\bar{x}$ for the finite and infinite population cases becomes negligible. When this occurs, $\sigma_{\bar{x}} = \sigma/\sqrt{n}$ becomes a good approximation to the standard deviation of $\bar{x}$ even though the population is finite. This observation leads to the following general guideline or rule of thumb for computing the standard deviation of $\bar{x}$.

**Use the Following Formula to Calculate the Standard Deviation of $\bar{x}$**

$$\sigma_{\bar{x}} = \frac{\sigma}{\sqrt{n}} \tag{7.3}$$

whenever

1. The population is infinite; or
2. The population is finite *and* the sample size is less than or equal to 5% of the population size; that is, $n/N \le .05$.

Problem 21 shows that when $n/N \le .05$, the finite population correction factor has little effect on the value of $\sigma_{\bar{x}}$.

In cases where $n/N > .05$, the finite population version of equation (7.2) should be used in the computation of $\sigma_{\bar{x}}$. Unless otherwise noted, throughout the text we will assume that the population size is "large," $n/N \le .05$, and equation (7.3) can be used to compute $\sigma_{\bar{x}}$.

Now let us return to the EAI study and determine the standard deviation of all possible sample means that can be generated with samples of 30 EAI managers. In Section 7.1 we saw that the population standard deviation for the annual salary data is $\sigma = 4000$. In this case the population is finite, with $N = 2500$. However, with a sample size of 30, we have $n/N = 30/2500 = .012$. Following the rule of thumb given in equation (7.3), we can ignore the finite population correction factor and use equation (7.3) to compute the standard deviation of $\bar{x}$.

$$\sigma_{\bar{x}} = \frac{\sigma}{\sqrt{n}} = \frac{4000}{\sqrt{30}} = 730.30$$

The standard error is, itself, a standard deviation. Standard error is a term used for the standard deviation of a point estimator.

Later we will see that the value of $\sigma_{\bar{x}}$ is helpful in determining how far the sample mean may be from the population mean. Because of the role that $\sigma_{\bar{x}}$ plays in computing possible sampling errors, $\sigma_{\bar{x}}$ is referred to as the **standard error of the mean.**

## Central Limit Theorem

The final step in identifying the characteristics of the sampling distribution of $\bar{x}$ is to determine the form of the probability distribution of $\bar{x}$. We consider two cases: one in which the population distribution is unknown and one in which the population distribution is known to be normally distributed.

When the population distribution is unknown, we rely on one of the most important theorems in statistics—the **central limit theorem.** A statement of the central limit theorem as it applies to the sampling distribution of $\bar{x}$ follows.

**Central Limit Theorem**

In selecting simple random samples of size $n$ from a population, the sampling distribution of the sample mean $\bar{x}$ can be approximated by a *normal probability distribution* as the sample size becomes large.

Figure 7.6 shows how the central limit theorem works for three different populations; each column refers to one of the populations. The top panel shows the probability distributions for

**FIGURE 7.6** ILLUSTRATION OF THE CENTRAL LIMIT THEOREM FOR THREE
POPULATIONS

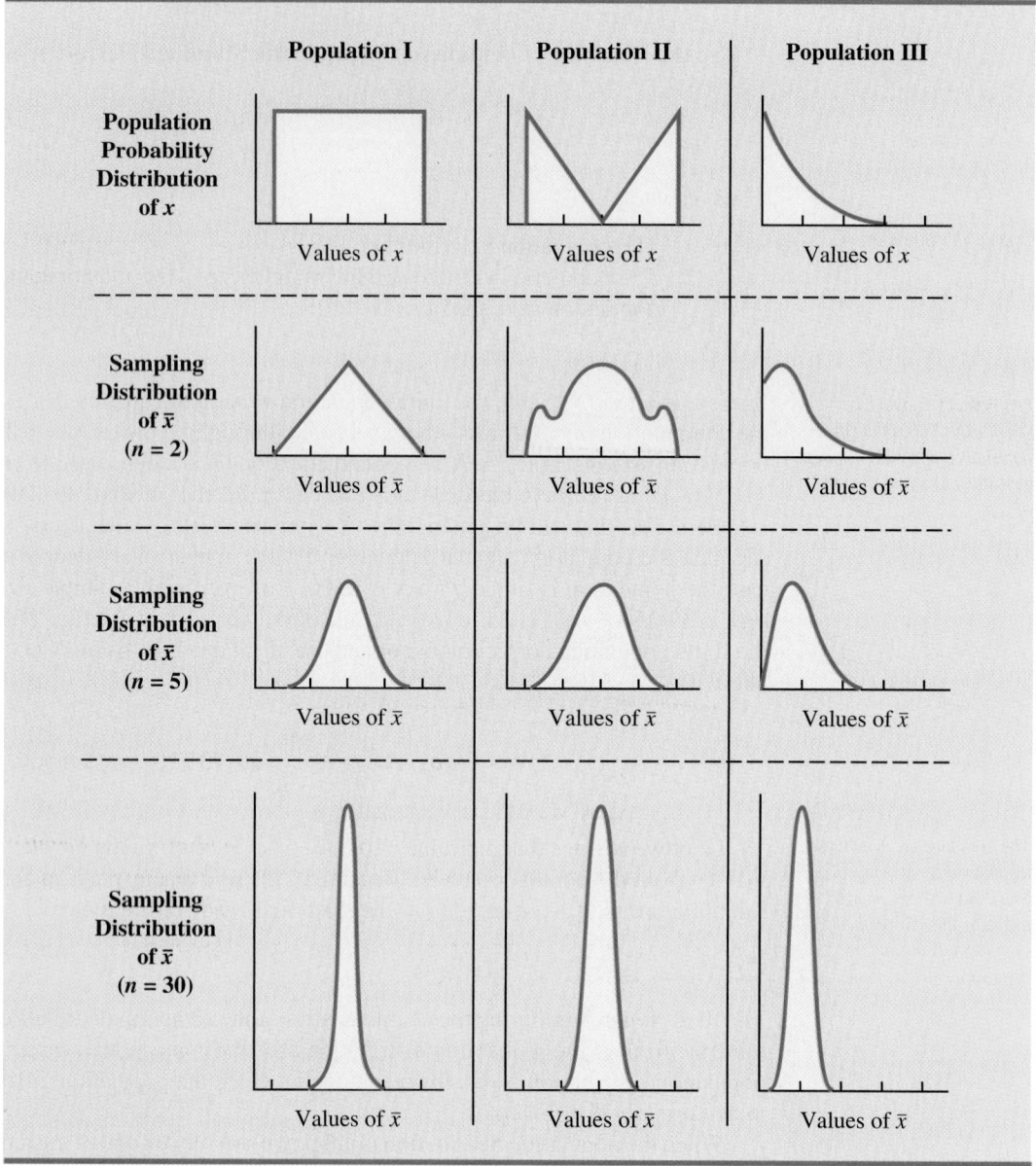

the populations. In each case the population clearly is not normal. However, note what begins to happen to the sampling distribution of $\bar{x}$ as the sample size is increased. When the samples are of size two (see the second panel), we see that the sampling distribution of $\bar{x}$ begins to take on an appearance different from that of the population distribution. For samples of size five, we see all three sampling distributions beginning to take on a bell-shaped appearance. Finally, the samples of size 30 show all three sampling distributions to be approximately normal. Thus, for sufficiently large samples, the sampling distribution of $\bar{x}$ can be approximated by a normal probability distribution. However, how large must the sample size be before we can assume that the central limit theorem applies? General statistical practice is to assume that for most applications, the sampling distribution of $\bar{x}$ can be approximated by a normal probability distribution whenever the sample size is 30 or more. In effect, a sample size of 30 or more is assumed to satisfy the large-sample condition of the central limit theorem. This observation is so important that we restate it.

> The sampling distribution of $\bar{x}$ can be approximated by a normal probability distribution whenever the sample size is large. The large-sample condition can be assumed for simple random samples of size 30 or more.

The central limit theorem applies to any population. Thus, when the sample size is large, it can be used to describe the sampling distribution of $\bar{x}$ even when the population distribution is unknown.

The central limit theorem is the key to identifying the appropriate form of the sampling distribution of $\bar{x}$ whenever the population distribution is unknown. However, we may encounter some sampling situations in which the population is assumed or believed to have a normal probability distribution. When this condition occurs, the following result identifies the form of the sampling distribution of $\bar{x}$.

> Whenever the population has a normal probability distribution, the sampling distribution of $\bar{x}$ has a normal probability distribution for any sample size.

In summary, if we use a large ($n \geq 30$) simple random sample, the central limit theorem enables us to conclude that the sampling distribution of $\bar{x}$ can be approximated by a normal probability distribution. When the simple random sample is small ($n < 30$), the sampling distribution of $\bar{x}$ can be considered normal only if we are willing to assume that the population has a normal probability distribution.

## Sampling Distribution of $\bar{x}$ for the EAI Problem

For the EAI study we have shown that $E(\bar{x}) = 51{,}800$ and $\sigma_{\bar{x}} = 730.30$. Because we are using a simple random sample of 30 managers, the central limit theorem enables us to conclude that the sampling distribution of $\bar{x}$ is approximately normal as shown in Figure 7.7.

**FIGURE 7.7**    SAMPLING DISTRIBUTION OF $\bar{x}$ FOR A SIMPLE RANDOM SAMPLE
OF 30 EAI MANAGERS

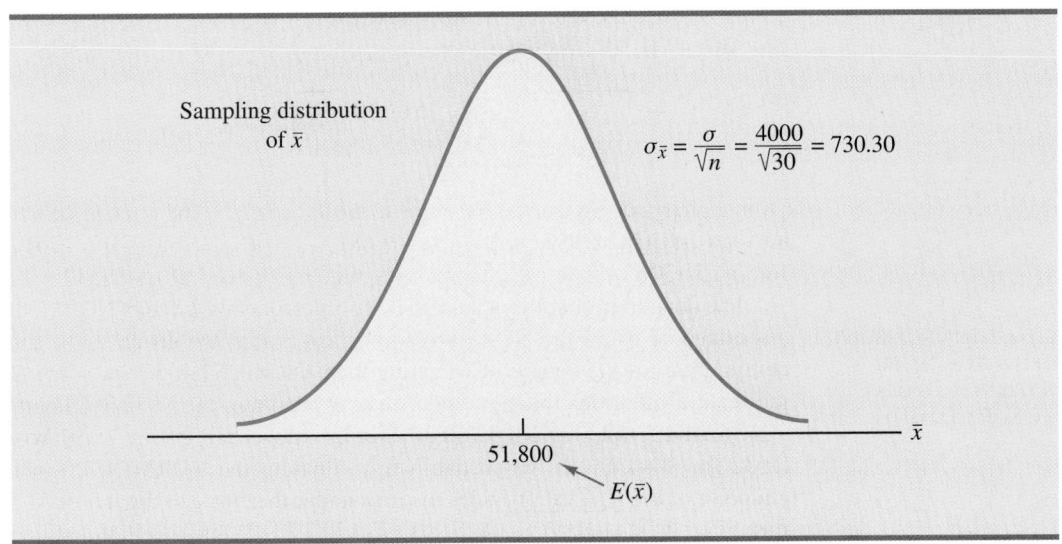

Sampling distribution
of $\bar{x}$

$$\sigma_{\bar{x}} = \frac{\sigma}{\sqrt{n}} = \frac{4000}{\sqrt{30}} = 730.30$$

51,800

$E(\bar{x})$

$\bar{x}$

## Practical Value of the Sampling Distribution of $\bar{x}$

Whenever a simple random sample is selected and the value of the sample mean $\bar{x}$ is used to estimate the value of the population mean $\mu$, we cannot expect the sample mean to exactly equal the population mean. As stated earlier, the absolute value of the difference between the value of the sample mean $\bar{x}$ and the value of the population mean $\mu$, $|\bar{x} - \mu|$, is called the sampling error. The practical reason we are interested in the sampling distribution of $\bar{x}$ is that it can be used to provide probability information about the size of the sampling error. To demonstrate this use, let us return to the EAI problem.

Suppose the personnel director believes the sample mean will be an acceptable estimate of the population mean if the sample mean is within $500 of the population mean. However, it is not possible to guarantee that the sample mean will be within $500 of the population mean. Indeed, Table 7.5 and Figure 7.2 show that some of the 500 sample means differed by more than $2000 from the population mean. So we must think of the personnel director's request in probability terms. That is, the personnel director is concerned with the following question: What is the probability that the sample mean computed using a simple random sample of 30 EAI managers will be within $500 of the population mean?

Since we have identified the properties of the sampling distribution of $\bar{x}$ (see Figure 7.7), we will use this distribution to answer the probability question. Refer to the sampling distribution of $\bar{x}$ shown again in Figure 7.8. The personnel director is asking about the probability that the sample mean is between $51,300 and $52,300. If the value of the sample mean $\bar{x}$ is in this interval, the value of $\bar{x}$ will be within $500 of the population mean. The appropriate probability is given by the shaded area of the sampling distribution shown in Figure 7.8. Because the sampling distribution is normal we can compute this probability using the table for the standard normal probability distribution. We first calculate the $z$-value at the upper endpoint of the interval (52,300) and use the table to find the area under the curve to the left of that point (left tail area). Then we compute the $z$-value at the lower endpoint of the interval (51,300) and use the table to find the area under the curve to the left of that point (another left tail area). Subtracting the second tail area from the first gives us the desired probability.

At $\bar{x} = 52,300$, we have

$$z = \frac{52,300 - 51,800}{730.30} = .68$$

Referring to the standard normal probability distribution table, we find a cumulative probability (area to the left of $z = .68$) of .7517.

At $\bar{x} = 51,300$, we have

$$z = \frac{51,300 - 51,800}{730.30} = -.68$$

By symmetry, the area under the curve to the left of $z = -.68$ is the same as the area under the curve to the right of $z = .68$. So $P(z \le -.68) = 1 - P(z \le .68) = 1 - .7517 = .2483$. Therefore, $P(51,300 \le z \le 52,300) = P(z \le .68) - P(z \le -.68) = .7517 - .2483 = .5034$.

The desired probability can also be computed using Excel's NORMDIST function. The advantage of using the NORMDIST function is that we do not have to make a separate computation of the $z$ value. Evaluating the NORMDIST function at the upper endpoint of the interval provides the area under the curve to the left of 52,300. Entering the formula =NORMDIST(52300,51800,730.30,TRUE) into a cell of an Excel worksheet provides .7532 for this cumulative probability. Evaluating the NORMDIST function at the lower endpoint of the interval provides the area under the curve to the left of 51,300. Entering the formula =NORMDIST(51300,51800,730.30,TRUE) into a cell of an Excel worksheet pro-

*Using Excel's NORMDIST function is easier and provides more accurate results than the tables.*

**FIGURE 7.8** PROBABILITY OF A SAMPLE MEAN BEING WITHIN $500 OF THE POPULATION MEAN WHEN A SIMPLE RANDOM SAMPLE OF 30 EAI MANAGERS IS USED

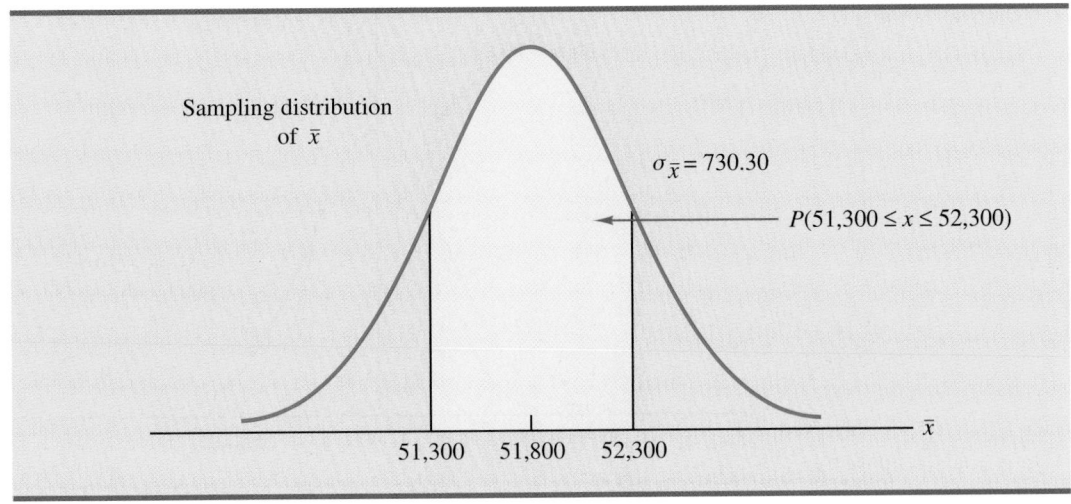

vides .2468 for this cumulative probability. The probability of $\bar{x}$ being in the interval from 51,300 to 52,300 is then given by .7532 − .2468 = .5064. We note that this result is slightly different from the probability obtained using the tables, because in using the normal tables we rounded to 2 decimal places of accuracy when computing the $z$ value. The result obtained using NORMDIST is thus more accurate.

The preceding computations show that a simple random sample of 30 EAI managers has a .5064 probability of providing a sample mean $\bar{x}$ that is within $500 of the population mean. Thus, there is a 1 − .5064 = .4934 probability that the sample mean will miss the population mean by more than $500. In other words, a simple random sample of 30 EAI managers has roughly a 50-50 chance of providing a sample mean within the allowable $500. Perhaps a larger sample size should be considered. Let us explore this possibility by considering the relationship between the sample size and the sampling distribution of $\bar{x}$.

> The sampling distribution of $\bar{x}$ can be used to provide probability information about how close the sample mean of $\bar{x}$ is to the population mean $\mu$.

## Relationship Between the Sample Size and the Sampling Distribution of $\bar{x}$

Suppose that in the EAI sampling problem we select a simple random sample of 100 EAI managers instead of the 30 originally considered. Intuitively, it would seem that with more data provided by the larger sample size, the sample mean based on $n = 100$ should provide a better estimate of the population mean than the sample mean based on $n = 30$. To see how much better, let us consider the relationship between the sample size and the sampling distribution of $\bar{x}$.

First note that $E(\bar{x}) = \mu$ regardless of the sample size. Thus, the mean of all possible values of $\bar{x}$ is equal to the population mean $\mu$ regardless of the sample size $n$. However, note that the standard error of the mean, $\sigma_{\bar{x}} = \sigma/\sqrt{n}$, is related to the square root of the sample size. Specifically, whenever the sample size is increased, the standard error of the mean $\sigma_{\bar{x}}$ is decreased. With $n = 30$, the standard error of the mean for the EAI problem is 730.30. However, with the increase in the sample size to $n = 100$, the standard error of the mean is decreased to

$$\sigma_{\bar{x}} = \frac{\sigma}{\sqrt{n}} = \frac{4000}{\sqrt{100}} = 400$$

**FIGURE 7.9**     COMPARISON OF THE SAMPLING DISTRIBUTIONS OF $\bar{x}$ FOR SIMPLE RANDOM SAMPLES OF $n = 30$ AND $n = 100$ EAI MANAGERS

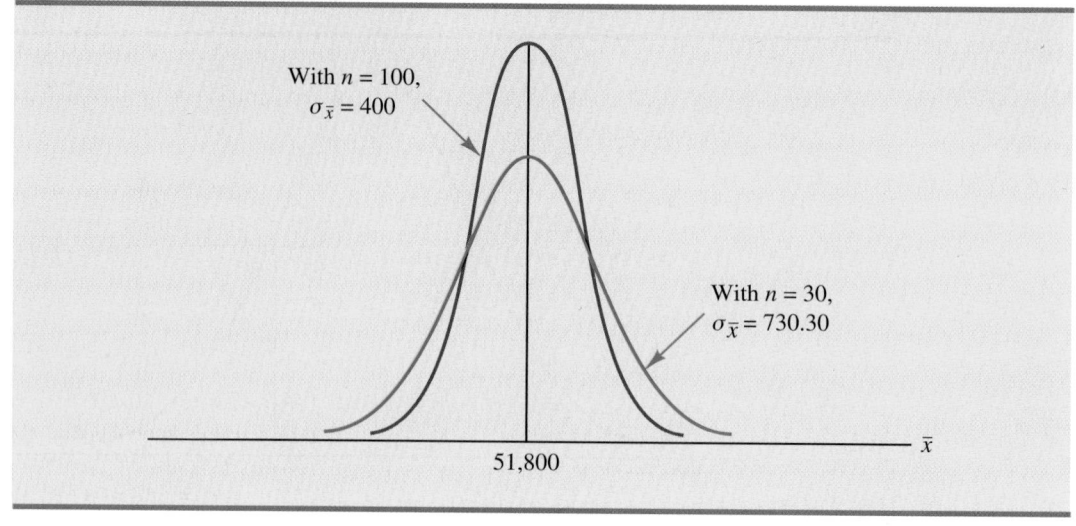

The sampling distributions of $\bar{x}$ with $n = 30$ and $n = 100$ are shown in Figure 7.9. Because the sampling distribution with $n = 100$ has a smaller standard error, the values of $\bar{x}$ have less variation and tend to be closer to the population mean than the values of $\bar{x}$ with $n = 30$.

We can use the sampling distribution of $\bar{x}$ for the case with $n = 100$ to compute the probability that a simple random sample of 100 EAI managers will provide a sample mean that is within \$500 of the population mean. In this case the sampling distribution is normal with a mean of 51,800 and a standard deviation of 400 (see Figure 7.10). Again, we could compute the appropriate $z$ values and use the standard normal probability distribution table to make this probability calculation. However, Excel's NORMDIST function is easier to use and provides more accurate results. Entering the formula $=\text{NORMDIST}(52300,51800,400,$

**FIGURE 7.10**     PROBABILITY OF A SAMPLE MEAN BEING WITHIN \$500 OF THE POPULATION MEAN WHEN A SIMPLE RANDOM SAMPLE OF 100 EAI MANAGERS IS USED

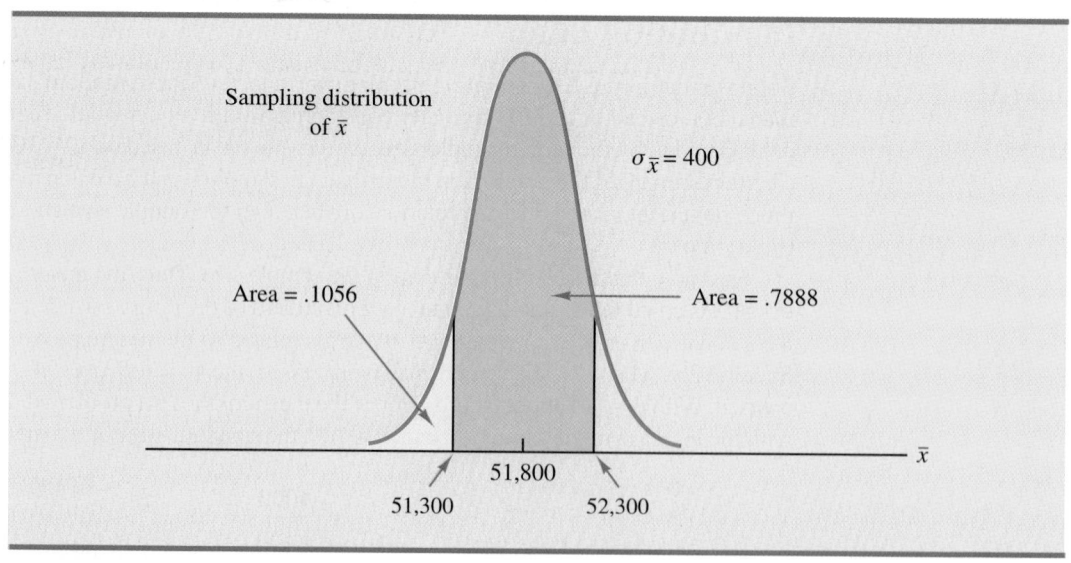

TRUE) into a cell of an Excel worksheet will provide the cumulative probability corresponding to $\bar{x} = 52,300$. The value provided by Excel is .8944. Entering the formula =NORMDIST(51300,51800,400,TRUE) into a cell of an Excel worksheet will provide the cumulative probability corresponding to $\bar{x} = 51,300$. The value provided by Excel is .1056. Thus, the probability of $\bar{x}$ being in the interval from 51,300 to 52,300 is given by .8944 − .1056 = .7888. By increasing the sample size from 30 to 100 EAI managers, we have increased the probability of obtaining a sample mean within $500 of the population mean from .5064 to .7888.

The important point in this discussion is that as the sample size is increased, the standard error of the mean is decreased. As a result, a larger sample size will provide a higher probability that the sample mean is within a specified distance of the population mean.

## NOTES AND COMMENTS

1. In presenting the sampling distribution of $\bar{x}$ for the EAI problem, we took advantage of the fact that the population mean $\mu = 51,800$ and the population standard deviation $\sigma = 4000$ were known. However, usually the values of the population mean $\mu$ and the population standard deviation $\sigma$ that are needed to determine the sampling distribution of $\bar{x}$ will be unknown. In Chapter 8 we will show how the sample mean $\bar{x}$ and the sample standard deviation $s$ are used when $\mu$ and $\sigma$ are unknown.

2. The theoretical proof of the central limit theorem requires independent observations in the sample. This condition is met for infinite populations and for finite populations where sampling is done with replacement. Although the central limit theorem does not directly address sampling without replacement from finite populations, general statistical practice has been to apply the findings of the central limit theorem in this situation when the population size is large.

## EXERCISES

### Methods

19. A population has a mean of 200 and a standard deviation of 50. Suppose a simple random sample of size 100 is selected and $\bar{x}$ is used to estimate $\mu$.
    a.   What is the probability that the sample mean will be within ±5 of the population mean?
    b.   What is the probability that the sample mean will be within ±10 of the population mean?

20. Assume the population standard deviation is $\sigma = 25$. Compute the standard error of the mean, $\sigma_{\bar{x}}$, for sample sizes of 50, 100, 150, and 200. What can you say about the size of the standard error of the mean as the sample size is increased?

21. Suppose a simple random sample of size 50 is selected from a population with $\sigma = 10$. Find the value of the standard error of the mean in each of the following cases (use the finite population correction factor if appropriate).
    a.   The population size is infinite.
    b.   The population size is $N = 50,000$.
    c.   The population size is $N = 5000$.
    d.   The population size is $N = 500$.

22. A population has a mean of 400 and a standard deviation of 50. The probability distribution of the population is unknown.
    a.   A researcher will use simple random samples of either 10, 20, 30, or 40 items to collect data about the population. With which of these sample-size alternatives will we be able to use a normal probability distribution to describe the sampling distribution of $\bar{x}$? Explain.
    b.   Show the sampling distribution of $\bar{x}$ for the instances in which the normal probability distribution is appropriate.

**23.** A large population has a mean of 100 and a standard deviation of 16. What is the probability that a sample mean will be within ±2 of the population mean for each of the following sample sizes?

    **a.** $n = 50$

    **b.** $n = 100$

    **c.** $n = 200$

    **d.** $n = 400$

    **e.** What is the advantage of a larger sample size?

## Applications

**24.** Refer to the EAI sampling problem. Suppose a simple random sample of 60 managers is used.

    **a.** Sketch the sampling distribution of $\bar{x}$ when simple random samples of size 60 are used.

    **b.** What happens to the sampling distribution of $\bar{x}$ if simple random samples of size 120 are used?

    **c.** What general statement can you make about what happens to the sampling distribution of $\bar{x}$ as the sample size is increased? Does this generalization seem logical? Explain.

**25.** In the EAI sampling problem (see Figure 7.8), we showed that for $n = 30$, there was .5064 probability of obtaining a sample mean within ±$500 of the population mean.

    **a.** What is the probability that $\bar{x}$ is within $500 of the population mean if a sample of size 60 is used?

    **b.** Answer part (a) for a sample of size 120.

**26.** The mean price per gallon of regular gasoline sold in the United States is $1.20 (*The Energy Information Administration,* March 3, 1997). Assume the population mean price per gallon is $\mu = 1.20$, and the population standard deviation is $\sigma = .10$. Suppose that a random sample of 50 gasoline stations will be selected, and a sample mean price per gallon will be computed for data collected from the 50 gasoline stations.

    **a.** Show the sampling distribution of the sample mean $\bar{x}$ where $\bar{x}$ is the sample mean price per gallon for the 50 gasoline stations.

    **b.** What is the probability that the simple random sample will provide a sample mean within 2 cents or .02 of the population mean?

    **c.** What is the probability that the simple random sample will provide a sample mean within 1 cent or .01 of the population mean?

**27.** The College Board American College Testing Program reported a population mean SAT score of $\mu = 1017$ (*The New York Times,* 2000 Almanac). Assume that the population standard deviation is $\sigma = 100$.

    **a.** What is the probability that a random sample of 75 students will provide a sample mean SAT score within 10 of the population mean?

    **b.** What is the probability that a random sample of 75 students will provide a sample mean SAT score within 20 of the population mean?

**28.** The mean annual starting salary for marketing majors is $34,000 (*Time,* May 8, 2000). Assume that for the population of graduates with a marketing major, the mean annual starting salary is $\mu = 34,000$, and the standard deviation is $\sigma = 2000$.

    **a.** What is the probability that a simple random sample of marketing majors will have a sample mean within ±$250 of the population mean for each of the following sample sizes: 30, 50, 100, 200, and 400?

    **b.** What is the advantage of a larger sample size when attempting to estimate the population mean?

**29.** The mean monthly rental for a two-bedroom apartment in Atlanta is $982 (*Elle,* September 1998). Assume that the population mean is $982 and the population standard deviation is $210.

**a.** What is the probability that a simple random sample of 40 two-bedroom apartments will provide a sample mean monthly rental within ±$100 of the population mean?

**b.** What is the probability that a simple random sample of 40 two-bedroom apartments will provide a sample mean monthly rental within ±$25 of the population mean?

**c.** Discuss the results in parts (a) and (b).

**30.** The population mean for the price of a new one-family home is $166,500 (U.S. Bureau of the Census, *New One-Family Houses Sold,* 1997). Assume that the population standard deviation is $42,000 and that a sample of 100 new one-family homes will be selected.

**a.** Show the sampling distribution of the sample mean price for new homes based on the sample of 100.

**b.** What is the probability that the sample mean for the 100 new homes will be within $10,000 of the population mean?

**c.** Repeat part (b) for values of $5000, $2500, and $1000.

**d.** To estimate the population mean price to within ±$2500 or ±$1000, what would you recommend?

**31.** *Business Week* reports that its subscribers who plan to purchase a new vehicle plan to spend a mean of $27,100 (*Business Week,* Subscriber Profile, 1996). Assume that the new vehicle price for the population of *Business Week* subscribers has a mean of $\mu = \$27,100$ and a standard deviation of $\sigma = \$5200$.

**a.** What is the probability that the mean new vehicle price for a sample of 30 subscribers is within $1000 of the population mean?

**b.** What is the probability that the mean new vehicle price for a sample of 50 subscribers is within $1000 of the population mean?

**c.** What is the probability that the mean new vehicle price for a sample of 100 subscribers is within $1000 of the population mean?

**d.** Would you recommend a sample size of 30, 50, or 100 if it is desired to have at least a .90 probability that the sample mean is within $1000 of the population mean?

**32.** To estimate the mean age for a population of 4000 employees, a simple random sample of 40 employees is selected.

**a.** Would you use the finite population correction factor in calculating the standard error of the mean? Explain.

**b.** If the population standard deviation is $\sigma = 8.2$ years, compute the standard error both with and without using the finite population correction factor. What is the rationale for ignoring the finite population correction factor whenever $n/N \leq .05$?

**c.** What is the probability that the sample mean age of the employees will be within ±2 years of the population mean age?

## 7.6 SAMPLING DISTRIBUTION OF $\bar{p}$

In many situations in business and economics, we use the sample proportion $\bar{p}$ to make statistical inferences about the population proportion $p$. This process is depicted in Figure 7.11. On each repetition of the process, we can anticipate obtaining a different value for the sample proportion $\bar{p}$. The probability distribution for all possible values of the sample proportion $\bar{p}$ is called the sampling distribution of the sample proportion $\bar{p}$.

**Sampling Distribution of $\bar{p}$**

The sampling distribution of $\bar{p}$ is the probability distribution of all possible values of the sample proportion $\bar{p}$.

**FIGURE 7.11**   THE STATISTICAL PROCESS OF USING A SAMPLE PROPORTION
TO MAKE INFERENCES ABOUT A POPULATION PROPORTION

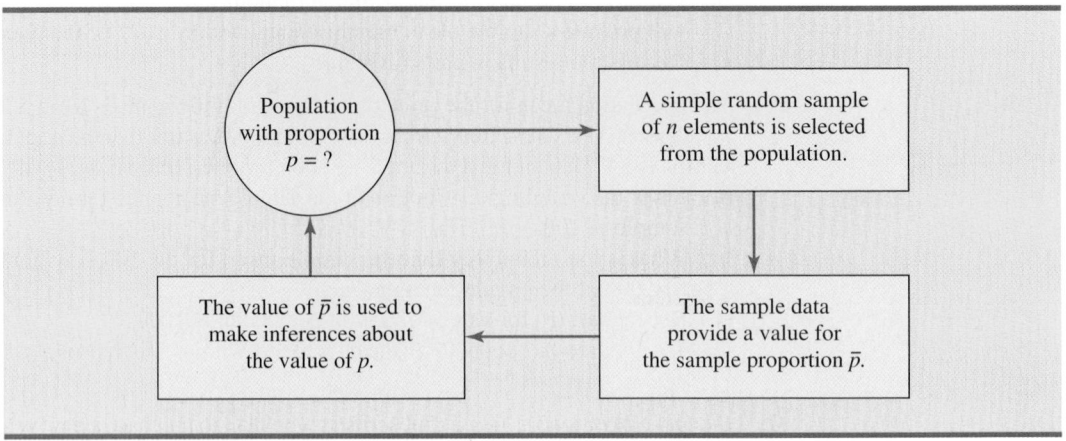

To determine how close the sample proportion $\bar{p}$ is to the population proportion $p$, we
need to understand the properties of the sampling distribution of $\bar{p}$: the expected value of $\bar{p}$,
the standard deviation of $\bar{p}$, and the shape or form of the sampling distribution of $\bar{p}$.

## Expected Value of $\bar{p}$

The expected value of $\bar{p}$, denoted $E(\bar{p})$, is the mean of all possible values of $\bar{p}$. Equation
(7.4) shows that the mean of all possible $\bar{p}$ values is equal to the population proportion $p$.
Thus, the point estimator $\bar{p}$ is an unbiased estimate of the population proportion, $p$.

**Expected Value of $\bar{p}$**

$$E(\bar{p}) = p \qquad \qquad \textbf{(7.4)}$$

where

$$E(\bar{p}) = \text{the expected value of } \bar{p}$$
$$p = \text{the population proportion}$$

Recall that in Section 7.1 we noted that $p = .60$ for the EAI population, where $p$ is the proportion of the population of managers who had participated in the company's management
training program. Equation (7.4) shows that the expected value of $\bar{p}$ for the EAI sampling
problem is .60.

## Standard Deviation of $\bar{p}$

The standard deviation of $\bar{p}$, denoted $\sigma_{\bar{p}}$, is referred to as the *standard error of the proportion.* Just as we found for the sample mean $\bar{x}$, the standard deviation of $\bar{p}$ depends on
whether the population is finite or infinite. The two expressions for computing the standard
deviation of $\bar{p}$ follow.

> ### Standard Deviation of $\bar{p}$
>
> | *Finite Population* | *Infinite Population* |
> |:---:|:---:|
> | $\sigma_{\bar{p}} = \sqrt{\dfrac{N-n}{N-1}}\sqrt{\dfrac{p(1-p)}{n}}$ | $\sigma_{\bar{p}} = \sqrt{\dfrac{p(1-p)}{n}} \qquad \textbf{(7.5)}$ |

Comparing the two expressions in equation (7.5), we see that the only difference is the use of the finite population correction factor $\sqrt{(N-n)/(N-1)}$.

As was the case with the sample mean $\bar{x}$, the difference between the values obtained using the expressions for the finite population and the infinite population becomes negligible if the size of the finite population is large in comparison to the sample size. We follow the same rule of thumb that we recommended for the sample mean. That is, if the population is finite with $n/N \le .05$, we will use $\sigma_{\bar{p}} = \sqrt{p(1-p)/n}$. However, if the population is finite and if $n/N > .05$, the finite population correction factor should be used, as shown in equation (7.5). Again, unless specifically noted, throughout the text we will assume that the population size is large in relation to the sample size and thus the finite population correction factor is unnecessary.

For the EAI study we know that the population proportion of managers who have participated in the management training program is $p = .60$. With $n/N = 30/2500 = .012$, we can ignore the finite population correction factor when we compute the standard deviation of $\bar{p}$. For the simple random sample of 30 managers, $\sigma_{\bar{p}}$ is

$$\sigma_{\bar{p}} = \sqrt{\frac{p(1-p)}{n}} = \sqrt{\frac{.60(1-.60)}{30}} = .0894$$

## Form of the Sampling Distribution of $\bar{p}$

Now that we know the mean and standard deviation of $\bar{p}$, we want to consider the form of the sampling distribution of $\bar{p}$. Applying the central limit theorem as it relates to $\bar{p}$ produces the following result.

> The sampling distribution of $\bar{p}$ can be approximated by a normal probability distribution whenever the sample size is large.

These criteria are slightly different from the $n \ge 30$ criteria we used for the large sample case for $\bar{x}$. The reason is that small values of $p$ or $(1-p)$ can cause the sampling distribution to be skewed even with $n \ge 30$.

With $\bar{p}$, the sample size can be considered large whenever the following two conditions are satisfied.

$$np \ge 5$$
$$n(1-p) \ge 5$$

Recall that for the EAI sampling problem we know that the population proportion of managers who have participated in the training program is $p = .60$. With a simple random sample of size 30, we have $np = 30(.60) = 18$ and $n(1-p) = 30(.40) = 12$. Thus, the sampling distribution of $\bar{p}$ can be approximated by a normal probability distribution as shown in Figure 7.12.

**FIGURE 7.12** SAMPLING DISTRIBUTION OF $\bar{p}$ FOR THE PROPORTION OF EAI MANAGERS WHO HAVE PARTICIPATED IN THE MANAGEMENT TRAINING PROGRAM

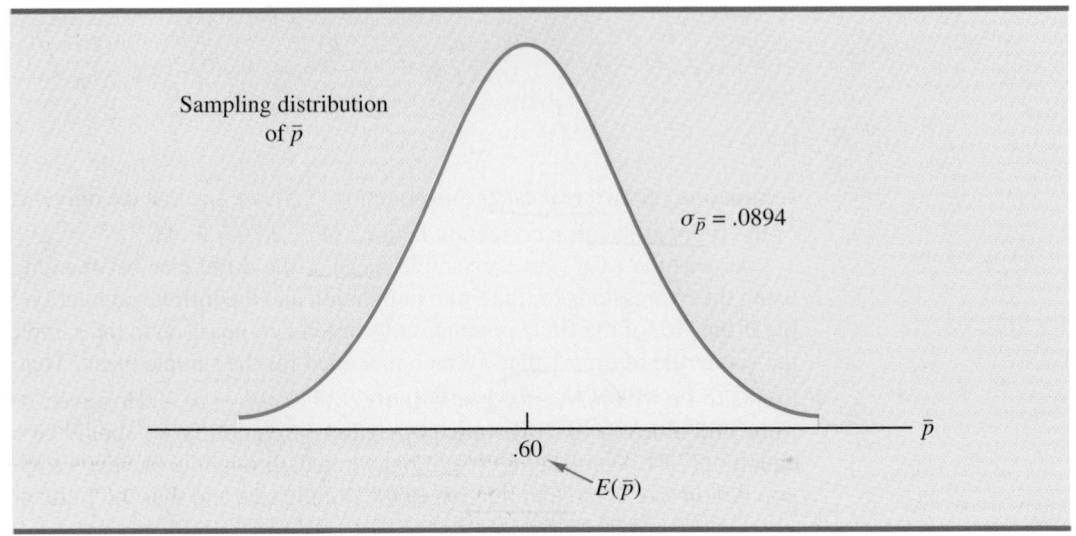

## Practical Value of the Sampling Distribution of $\bar{p}$

Whenever a simple random sample is selected and the value of the sample proportion $\bar{p}$ is used to estimate the value of the population proportion $p$, we anticipate some sampling error. In this case, the sampling error is the absolute value of the difference between the value of the sample proportion $\bar{p}$ and the value of the population proportion $p$. The practical value of the sampling distribution of $\bar{p}$ is that it can be used to provide probability information about the sampling error.

Suppose, in the EAI problem, the personnel director wants to know the probability of obtaining a value of $\bar{p}$ that is within .05 of the population proportion of EAI managers who have participated in the training program. That is, what is the probability of obtaining a sample with a sample proportion $\bar{p}$ between .55 and .65? The dark-blue shaded area in Figure 7.13

**FIGURE 7.13** SAMPLING DISTRIBUTION OF $\bar{p}$ FOR THE EAI SAMPLING PROBLEM

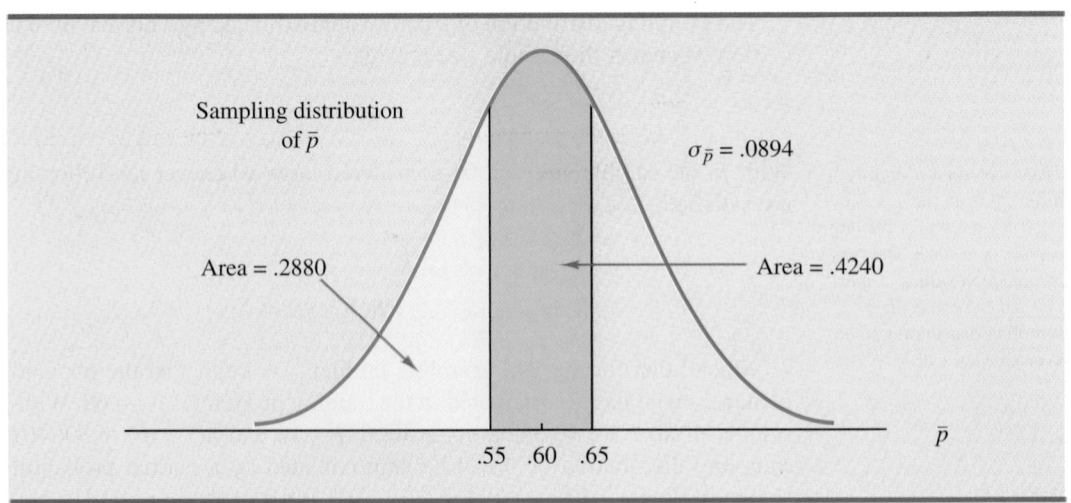

shows this probability. Using the fact that the sampling distribution of $\bar{p}$ can be approximated by a normal probability distribution with a mean of .60 and a standard error of $\sigma_{\bar{p}} = .0894$, we can use Excel's NORMDIST function to make this calculation. Entering the formula =NORMDIST(.65,.60,.0894,TRUE) into a cell of an Excel worksheet will provide the cumulative probability corresponding to $\bar{p} = .65$. The value provided by Excel is .7120. Entering the formula =NORMDIST(.55,.60,.0894,TRUE) into a cell of an Excel worksheet will provide the cumulative probability corresponding to $\bar{p} = .55$. The value provided by Excel is .2880. Thus, the probability of $\bar{p}$ being in the interval from .55 to .65 is given by .7120 − .2880 = .4240.

If we consider increasing the sample size to $n = 100$, the standard error of the proportion becomes

$$\sigma_{\bar{p}} = \sqrt{\frac{.60(1 - .60)}{100}} = .0490$$

With a sample size of 100 EAI managers, the probability of the sample proportion having a value within .05 of the population proportion can now be computed. Because the sampling distribution is approximately normal, with mean .60 and standard deviation .0490, we can use Excel's NORMDIST function to make this calculation. Entering the formula =NORMDIST(.65,.60,.0490,TRUE) into a cell of an Excel worksheet will provide the cumulative probability corresponding to $\bar{p} = .65$. The value provided by Excel is .8462. Entering the formula =NORMDIST(.55,.60,.0490,TRUE) into a cell of an Excel worksheet will provide the cumulative probability corresponding to $\bar{p} = .55$. The value provided by Excel is .1538. Thus, the probability of $\bar{p}$ being in the interval from .55 to .65 is given by .8462 − .1538 = .6924.

## EXERCISES

## Methods

33. A simple random sample of size 100 is selected from a population with $p = .40$.
    a. What is the expected value of $\bar{p}$?
    b. What is the standard deviation of $\bar{p}$?
    c. Show the sampling distribution of $\bar{p}$.
    d. What does the sampling distribution of $\bar{p}$ show?

34. A population proportion is .40. A simple random sample of size 200 will be taken and the sample proportion $\bar{p}$ will be used to estimate the population proportion.
    a. What is the probability that the sample proportion will be within ±.03 of the population proportion?
    b. What is the probability that the sample proportion will be within ±.05 of the population proportion?

35. Assume that the population proportion is .55. Compute the standard error of the proportion, $\sigma_{\bar{p}}$, for sample sizes of 100, 200, 500, and 1000. What can you say about the size of the standard error of the proportion as the sample size is increased?

36. The population proportion is .30. What is the probability that a sample proportion will be within ±.04 of the population proportion for each of the following sample sizes?
    a. $n = 100$
    b. $n = 200$
    c. $n = 500$
    d. $n = 1000$
    e. What is the advantage of a larger sample size?

## Applications

37. The president of Doerman Distributors, Inc., believes that 30% of the firm's orders come from first-time customers. A simple random sample of 100 orders will be used to estimate the proportion of first-time customers.
    a. Assume that the president is correct and $p = .30$. What is the sampling distribution of $\bar{p}$ for this study?
    b. What is the probability that the sample proportion $\bar{p}$ will be between .20 and .40?
    c. What is the probability that the sample proportion will be within $\pm.05$ of the population proportion $p = .30$?

38. The Grocery Manufacturers of America reported that 76% of consumers read the ingredients listed on a product's label. Assume the population proportion is $p = .76$ and a sample of 400 consumers is selected from the population.
    a. Show the sampling distribution of the sample proportion $\bar{p}$ where $\bar{p}$ is the proportion of the sampled consumers who read the ingredients listed on a product's label.
    b. What is the probability that the sample proportion will be within $\pm.03$ of the population proportion?
    c. Answer part (b) for a sample of 750 consumers.

39. *Time*/CNN voter polls monitored public opinion for the presidential candidates during the 2000 presidential election campaign. One *Time*/CNN poll conducted by Yankelovich Partners, Inc., used a sample of 589 likely voters (*Time,* June 26, 2000). Assume the population proportion for a presidential candidate is $p = .50$. Let $\bar{p}$ be the sample proportion of likely voters favoring the presidential candidate.
    a. Show the sampling distribution of $\bar{p}$.
    b. What is the probability the *Time*/CNN poll will provide a sample proportion within $\pm.04$ of the population proportion?
    c. What is the probability the *Time*/CNN poll will provide a sample proportion within $\pm.03$ of the population proportion?
    d. What is the probability the *Time*/CNN poll will provide a sample proportion within $\pm.02$ of the population proportion?

40. Even though most people believe breakfast is the most important meal of the day, 25% of adults skip breakfast (*U.S. News & World Report,* November 10, 1997). Assume the population proportion is $p = .25$, and $\bar{p}$ is the sample proportion of adults who skip breakfast based on a sample of 200 adults.
    a. Show the sampling distribution of $\bar{p}$.
    b. What is the probability that the sample proportion will be within $\pm.03$ of the population proportion?
    c. What is the probability that the sample proportion will be within $\pm.05$ of the population proportion?

41. The Institute for Women's Policy Research reported that women constitute 37% of all union members. Suppose the population proportion of women who are union members is $p = .37$, and a simple random sample of 1000 union members is selected.
    a. Show the sampling distribution of $\bar{p}$, the proportion of women in the sample.
    b. What is the probability that the sample proportion will be within $\pm.03$ of the population proportion?
    c. Answer part (b) for a simple random sample of 500.

42. Assume that 15% of the parts produced in an assembly line operation are defective, but that the firm's production manager is not aware of this situation. Assume further that 50 parts are tested by the quality assurance department to determine the quality of the assembly operation. Let $\bar{p}$ be the sample proportion found defective by the quality assurance test.
    a. Show the sampling distribution for $\bar{p}$.
    b. What is the probability that the sample proportion will be within $\pm.03$ of the population proportion that is defective?

c.   If the test shows $\bar{p} = .10$ or more, the assembly line operation will be shut down to check for the cause of the defects. What is the probability that the sample of 50 parts will lead to the conclusion that the assembly line should be shut down?

43.   The Food Marketing Institute shows that 17% of households spend more than $100 per week on groceries. Assume the population proportion is $p = .17$ and a simple random sample of 800 households will be selected from the population.

a.   Show the sampling distribution of $\bar{p}$, the sample proportion of households spending more than $100 per week on groceries.

b.   What is the probability that the sample proportion will be within $\pm.02$ of the population proportion?

c.   Answer part (b) for a sample of 1600 households.

## 7.7   OTHER SAMPLING METHODS

This section provides a brief introduction to sampling methods other than simple random sampling.

We have described the simple random sampling procedure and discussed the properties of the sampling distributions of $\bar{x}$ and $\bar{p}$ when simple random sampling is used. However, simple random sampling is not the only sampling method available. Such methods as stratified random sampling, cluster sampling, and systematic sampling are alternatives that in some situations have advantages over simple random sampling. In this section we briefly introduce some of these alternative sampling methods.

### Stratified Random Sampling

In **stratified random sampling,** the elements in the population are first divided into groups called *strata,* such that each element in the population belongs to one and only one stratum. The basis for forming the strata, such as department, location, age, industry type, and so on, is at the discretion of the designer of the sample. However, the best results are obtained when the elements within each stratum are as much alike (homogeneous) as possible. Figure 7.14 is a diagram of a population divided into $H$ strata.

After the strata are formed, a simple random sample is taken from each stratum. Formulas are available for combining the results for the individual stratum samples into one estimate of the population parameter of interest. The value of stratified random sampling depends on how homogeneous the elements are within the strata. If elements within strata are alike, the strata will have low variances. Thus relatively small sample sizes can be used to obtain good estimates of the strata characteristics. If strata are homogeneous, the stratified random sampling procedure will provide results just as precise as those of simple random sampling by using a smaller total sample size.

Stratified random sampling works best when the variance among elements in each stratum is relatively small.

**FIGURE 7.14**   DIAGRAM FOR STRATIFIED RANDOM SAMPLING

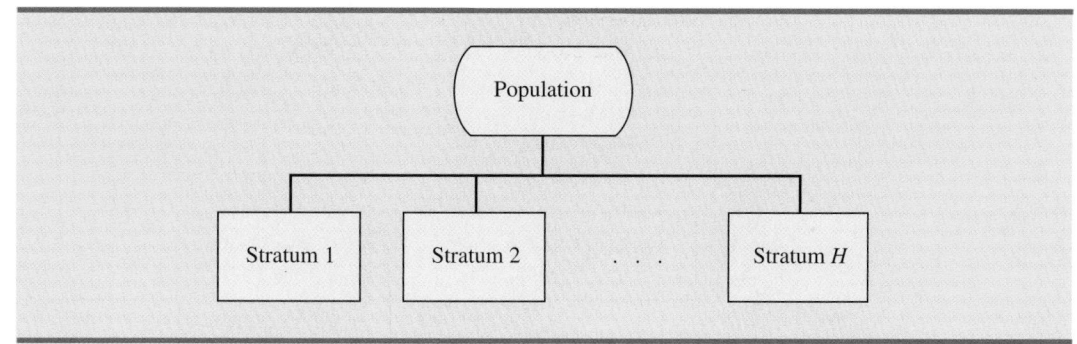

## Cluster Sampling

Cluster sampling works best when each cluster provides a small-scale representation of the population.

In **cluster sampling**, the elements in the population are first divided into separate groups of elements called clusters. Each element of the population belongs to one and only one cluster (see Figure 7.15). A simple random sample of the clusters is then taken. All elements within each sampled cluster form the sample. Cluster sampling tends to provide the best results when the elements within the clusters are not alike (heterogeneous). In the ideal case, each cluster is a representative small-scale version of the entire population. The value of cluster sampling depends on how representative each cluster is of the entire population. If all clusters are alike in this regard, sampling a small number of clusters will provide good estimates of the population parameters.

One of the primary applications of cluster sampling is area sampling, where clusters are city blocks or other well-defined areas. Cluster sampling generally requires a larger total sample size than either simple random sampling or stratified random sampling. However, it can result in cost savings because of the fact that when an interviewer is sent to a sampled cluster (e.g., a city-block location), many sample observations can be obtained in a relatively short time. Hence, a larger sample size may be obtainable with a significantly lower total cost.

## Systematic Sampling

In some sampling situations, especially those with large populations, it is time-consuming to select a simple random sample by first finding a random number and then counting or searching through the list of the population until the corresponding element is found. An alternative to simple random sampling is **systematic sampling.** For example, if a sample size of 50 is desired from a population containing 5000 elements, we will sample one element for every $5000/50 = 100$ elements in the population. A systematic sample for this case involves selecting randomly one of the first 100 elements from the population list. Other sample elements are identified by starting with the first sampled element and then selecting every 100th element that follows in the population list. In effect, the sample of 50 is identified by moving systematically through the population and identifying every 100th element after the first randomly selected element. The sample of 50 usually will be easier to identify in this way than it would be if simple random sampling were used. Because the first element selected is a random choice, a systematic sample is usually assumed to have the properties of a simple random sample. This assumption is especially applicable when the list of elements in the population is a random ordering of the elements in the population (e.g., a telephone book).

## Convenience Sampling

The sampling methods discussed thus far are referred to as *probability sampling* techniques. Elements selected from the population have a known probability of being included in the sample. The advantage of probability sampling is that the sampling distribution of the ap-

**FIGURE 7.15**   DIAGRAM FOR CLUSTER SAMPLING

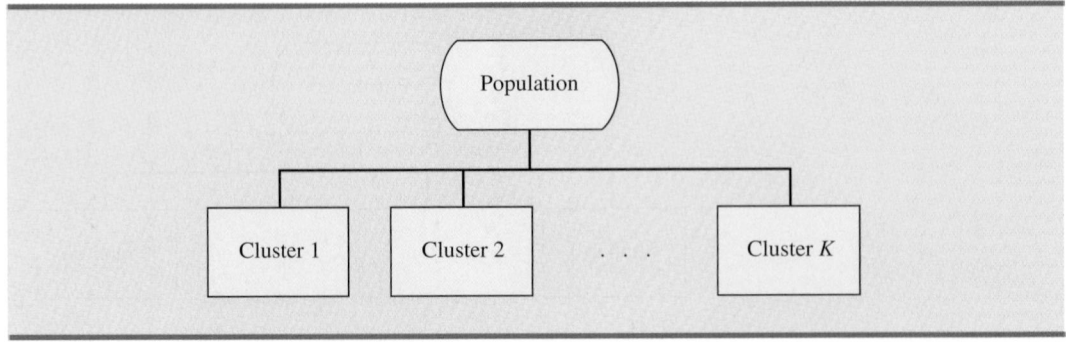

propriate sample statistic generally can be identified. Formulas such as the ones for simple random sampling presented in this chapter can be used to determine the properties of the sampling distribution. Then the sampling distribution can be used to make probability statements about the sampling error associated with the results.

Convenience sampling is a *nonprobability sampling* technique. As the name implies, the sample is identified primarily by convenience. Elements are included in the sample without prespecified or known probabilities of being selected. For example, a professor conducting research at a university may use student volunteers to constitute a sample simply because they are readily available and will participate as subjects for little or no cost. Similarly, an inspector may sample a shipment of oranges by selecting oranges haphazardly from among several crates. Labeling each orange and using a probability method of sampling would be impractical. Samples such as wildlife captures and volunteer panels for consumer research are also convenience samples.

Convenience samples have the advantage of relatively easy sample selection and data collection; however, it is impossible to evaluate the "goodness" of the sample in terms of its representativeness of the population. A convenience sample may provide good results or it may not; no statistically justified procedure allows a probability analysis and inference about the quality of the sample results. Sometimes researchers apply statistical methods designed for probability samples to a convenience sample, arguing that the convenience sample can be treated as though it were a probability sample. However, this argument cannot be supported, and we should be cautious in interpreting the results of convenience samples that are used to make inferences about populations.

## Judgment Sampling

One additional nonprobability sampling technique is judgment sampling. In this approach, the person most knowledgeable on the subject of the study selects elements of the population that he or she feels are most representative of the population. Often this method is a relatively easy way of selecting a sample. For example, a reporter may sample two or three senators, judging that those senators reflect the general opinion of all senators. However, the quality of the sample results depends on the judgment of the person selecting the sample. Again, great caution is warranted in drawing conclusions based on judgment samples used to make inferences about populations.

### NOTES AND COMMENTS

We recommend using probability sampling methods: simple random sampling, stratified random sampling, cluster sampling, or systematic sampling. For these methods, formulas are available for evaluating the "goodness" of the sample results in terms of the closeness of the results to the population characteristics being estimated. An evaluation of the goodness cannot be made with convenience or judgment sampling. Thus, great care should be used in interpreting the results when nonprobability sampling methods are used.

### SUMMARY

In this chapter we presented the concepts of simple random sampling and sampling distributions. We demonstrated how a simple random sample can be selected and how the data collected for the sample can be used to develop point estimates of population parameters. Because different simple random samples provide a variety of different values for the point estimators, point estimators such as $\bar{x}$ and $\bar{p}$ are random variables. The probability distribution of such a random variable is called a sampling distribution. In particular, we described the sampling distributions of the sample mean $\bar{x}$ and the sample proportion $\bar{p}$.

In considering the characteristics of the sampling distributions of $\bar{x}$ and $\bar{p}$, we stated that $E(\bar{x}) = \mu$ and $E(\bar{p}) = p$. These results allow us to conclude that they are unbiased point estimators. After developing the standard deviation or standard error formulas for these estimators, we showed how the central limit theorem provided the basis for using a normal probability distribution to approximate these sampling distributions in the large-sample case. Rules of thumb were given for determining when large-sample conditions were satisfied. Other sampling methods including stratified random sampling, cluster sampling, systematic sampling, convenience sampling, and judgment sampling were discussed.

## GLOSSARY

**Parameter**  A numerical measure of a population characteristic, such as a population mean $\mu$, a population standard deviation $\sigma$, a population proportion $p$, and so on.

**Simple random sampling**  Finite population: a sample selected such that each possible sample of size $n$ has the same probability of being selected. Infinite population: a sample selected such that each element comes from the same population and the elements are selected independently.

**Sampling without replacement**  Once an element has been included in the sample, it is removed from the population and cannot be selected a second time.

**Sampling with replacement**  Once an element has been included in the sample, it is returned to the population. A previously selected element can be selected again and therefore may appear in the sample more than once.

**Sample statistic**  A sample characteristic, such as a sample mean $\bar{x}$, a sample standard deviation $s$, a sample proportion $\bar{p}$, and so on. The value of the sample statistic is used to estimate the value of the population parameter.

**Point estimator**  The sample statistic, such as $\bar{x}$, $s$, or $\bar{p}$, that provides the point estimate of the population parameter.

**Point estimate**  A single numerical value used as an estimate of a population parameter.

**Sampling error**  The absolute value of the difference between an unbiased point estimator and the corresponding population parameter. For a sample mean, sample standard deviation, and sample proportion, the sampling errors are $|\bar{x} - \mu|$, $|s - \sigma|$, and $|\bar{p} - p|$, respectively.

**Sampling distribution**  A probability distribution consisting of all possible values of a sample statistic.

**Unbiasedness**  A property of a point estimator. If the expected value of a point estimator is equal to the population parameter it estimates, then the point estimator is unbiased.

**Finite population correction factor**  The term $\sqrt{(N - n)/(N - 1)}$ that is used in the formulas for $\sigma_{\bar{x}}$ and $\sigma_{\bar{p}}$ whenever a finite population, rather than an infinite population, is being sampled. The generally accepted rule of thumb is to ignore the finite population correction factor whenever $n/N \leq .05$.

**Standard error**  The standard deviation of a point estimator.

**Central limit theorem**  A theorem that enables one to use the normal probability distribution to approximate the sampling distribution of $\bar{x}$ and $\bar{p}$ whenever the sample size is large.

**Stratified random sampling**   A probability sampling method in which the population is first divided into strata and a simple random sample is then taken from each stratum.

**Cluster sampling**   A probability sampling method in which the population is first divided into clusters and then a simple random sample of the clusters is taken.

**Systematic sampling**   A probability sampling method in which we randomly select one of the first $k$ elements and then select every $k$th element thereafter.

**Convenience sampling**   A nonprobability method of sampling whereby elements are selected for the sample on the basis of convenience.

**Judgment sampling**   A nonprobability method of sampling whereby elements are selected for the sample based on the judgment of the person doing the study.

## KEY FORMULAS

**Expected Value of $\bar{x}$**

$$E(\bar{x}) = \mu \tag{7.1}$$

**Standard Deviation of $\bar{x}$**

*Finite Population*          *Infinite Population*

$$\sigma_{\bar{x}} = \sqrt{\frac{N-n}{N-1}}\left(\frac{\sigma}{\sqrt{n}}\right) \qquad\qquad \sigma_{\bar{x}} = \frac{\sigma}{\sqrt{n}} \tag{7.2}$$

**Expected Value of $\bar{p}$**

$$E(\bar{p}) = p \tag{7.4}$$

**Standard Deviation of $\bar{p}$**

*Finite Population*          *Infinite Population*

$$\sigma_{\bar{p}} = \sqrt{\frac{N-n}{N-1}}\sqrt{\frac{p(1-p)}{n}} \qquad\qquad \sigma_{\bar{p}} = \sqrt{\frac{p(1-p)}{n}} \tag{7.5}$$

## SUPPLEMENTARY EXERCISES

**44.** *Business Week's* Corporate Scoreboard provides quarterly data on sales, profits, net income, return on equity, price/earnings ratio, and earning per share for 899 companies (*Business Week,* August 14, 2000). The companies can be numbered 1 to 899 in the order they appear on the Corporate Scoreboard list. Begin at the bottom of the second column of random digits in Table 7.1. Ignoring the first two digits in each group and using the three-digit random numbers beginning with 112, read *up* the column to identify the first eight companies to be included in a simple random sample.

**45.** The mean television viewing time for teens is 3 hours per day (*Barron's,* November 8, 1999). Assume the population mean is $\mu = 3$ and the population standard deviation is $\sigma = 1.2$ hours. Suppose a sample of 50 teens will be used to monitor television viewing time. Let $\bar{x}$ denote the sample mean viewing time.
  **a.** Show the sampling distribution of $\bar{x}$.
  **b.** What is the probability the sample mean will be within $\pm.25$ hours of the population mean?

**46.** The mean travel time to work for individuals in Chicago is 31.5 minutes (*1998 Information Please Almanac*). Assume the population mean is $\mu = 31.5$ minutes and the population standard deviation is $\sigma = 12$ minutes. A sample of 50 Chicago residents is selected.

   **a.** Show the sampling distribution of $\bar{x}$ where $\bar{x}$ is the sample mean travel time to work for the 50 Chicago residents.

   **b.** What is the probability that the sample mean will be within $\pm 1$ minute of the population mean?

   **c.** What is the probability that the sample mean will be within $\pm 3$ minutes of the population mean?

**47.** The U.S. Bureau of Labor Statistics reported the mean hourly wage rate for individuals in executive, administrative, and managerial occupations is $24.07 (*The Wall Street Journal Almanac 1998*). Assume the population mean is $\mu = \$24.07$ and the population standard deviation is $\sigma = \$4.80$. A sample of 120 individuals in executive, administrative, and managerial occupations will be selected.

   **a.** What is the probability that the sample mean will be within $\pm\$0.50$ of the population mean?

   **b.** What is the probability that the sample mean will be within $\pm\$1.00$ of the population mean?

**48.** According to *USA Today* (April 11, 1995), the mean number of days per year that business travelers are on the road for business is 115. The standard deviation is 60 days per year. Assume that these results apply to the population of business travelers and that a sample of 50 business travelers will be selected from the population.

   **a.** What is the value of the standard error of the mean?

   **b.** What is the probability that the sample mean will be more than 115 days per year?

   **c.** What is the probability that the sample mean will be within $\pm 5$ days of the population mean?

   **d.** How would the probability change in part (c) if the sample size were increased to 100?

**49.** Three firms have inventories that differ in size. Firm A has an inventory of 2000 items, firm B has an inventory of 5000 items, and firm C has an inventory of 10,000 items. The population standard deviation for the cost of the items in each firm's inventory is $\sigma = 144$. A statistical consultant recommends that each firm take a sample of 50 items from its inventory to provide statistically valid estimates of the average cost per item. Managers of the small firm state that because it has the smallest population, it should be able to obtain the data from a much smaller sample than that required by the larger firms. However, the consultant states that to obtain the same standard error and thus the same precision in the sample results, all firms should use the same sample size regardless of population size.

   **a.** Using the finite population correction factor, compute the standard error for each of the three firms given a sample of size 50.

   **b.** What is the probability that for each firm the sample mean $\bar{x}$ will be within $\pm 25$ of the population mean $\mu$?

**50.** A researcher reports survey results by stating that the standard error of the mean is 20. The population standard deviation is 500.

   **a.** How large was the sample used in this survey?

   **b.** What is the probability that the point estimate was within $\pm 25$ of the population mean?

**51.** A production process is checked periodically by a quality control inspector. The inspector selects simple random samples of 30 finished products and computes the sample mean product weights $\bar{x}$. If test results over a long period of time show that 5% of the $\bar{x}$ values are over 2.1 pounds and 5% are under 1.9 pounds, what are the mean and the standard deviation for the population of products produced with this process?

**52.** What is the most important factor for business travelers when they are staying in a hotel? According to *USA Today*, 74% of business travelers state that having a smoke-free room is the most important factor (USA Today, April 11, 1995). Assume that the population proportion is $p = .74$ and that a sample of 200 business travelers will be selected.

    **a.** Show the sampling distribution of $\bar{p}$, the sample proportion of business travelers stating that a smoke-free room is the most important factor when staying in a hotel.

    **b.** What is the probability that the sample proportion will be within $\pm.04$ of the population proportion?

    **c.** What is the probability that the sample proportion will be within $\pm.02$ of the population proportion?

**53.** A market research firm conducts telephone surveys with a 40% historical response rate. What is the probability that in a new sample of 400 telephone numbers, at least 150 individuals will cooperate and respond to the questions? In other words, what is the probability that the sample proportion will be at least $150/400 = .375$?

**54.** According to ORC International, 71% of Internet users connect their computers to the Internet by normal telephone lines (*USA Today*, January 18, 2000). Assume a population proportion $p = .71$.

    **a.** What is the probability that a sample proportion from a simple random sample of 350 Internet users will be within $\pm.05$ of the population proportion?

    **b.** What is the probability that a sample proportion from a simple random sample of 350 Internet users will be .75 or greater?

**55.** The proportion of individuals insured by the All-Driver Automobile Insurance Company who have received at least one traffic ticket during a five-year period is .15.

    **a.** Show the sampling distribution of $\bar{p}$ if a random sample of 150 insured individuals is used to estimate the proportion having received at least one ticket.

    **b.** What is the probability that the sample proportion will be within $\pm.03$ of the population proportion?

**56.** Lori Jeffrey is a successful sales representative for a major publisher of college textbooks. Historically, Lori obtains a book adoption on 25% of her sales calls. Viewing her sales calls for one month as a sample of all possible sales calls, assume that a statistical analysis of the data yields a standard error of the proportion of .0625.

    **a.** How large was the sample used in this analysis? That is, how many sales calls did Lori make during the month?

    **b.** Let $\bar{p}$ indicate the sample proportion of book adoptions obtained during the month. Show the sampling distribution of $\bar{p}$.

    **c.** Using the sampling distribution of $\bar{p}$, compute the probability that Lori will obtain book adoptions on 30% or more of her sales calls during a one-month period.

# Chapter 8

# INTERVAL ESTIMATION

**CONTENTS**

## STATISTICS IN PRACTICE

### DOLLAR GENERAL CORPORATION*
*Goodlettsville, Tennessee*

Dollar General Corporation was founded in 1939 as a dry goods wholesale company. After World War II, the company began opening retail locations in rural south-central Kentucky. Today Dollar General Corporation operates more than 4300 stores across the middle and southeastern United States. Emphasizing small-store convenience, Dollar General markets health and beauty aids, cleaning supplies, housewares, stationery, apparel, shoes, and domestic items at everyday low prices.

Being in an inventory-intense business with more than 20,000 products, Dollar General made the decision to adopt the LIFO (last-in, first-out) method of inventory valuation. This method matches current costs against current revenues, which minimizes the effect of radical price changes on profit and loss results. In addition, the LIFO method reduces net income and thereby income taxes during periods of inflation. LIFO also brings disposable cash generated from sales in line with income and allows for the replacement of inventory at current costs.

Accounting practices require that a LIFO index be established for inventory under the LIFO method of valuation. For example, a LIFO index of 1.028 indicates that the company's inventory value at current costs reflects a 2.8% increase due to inflation over the most recent one-year period.

The establishment of a LIFO index requires that the year-end inventory count for each product be valued at the current year-end cost and at the preceding year-end cost. To avoid counting the inventory of every product in more than 4300 retail locations, a random sample of 800 products is selected from 100 retail locations and three warehouses. Physical inven-

This store in Bedford, Indiana, is one of more than 4300 Dollar General Stores. © Darren Wright/South-Western.

tories for the sampled products are taken at the end of the year. Accounting personnel then provide the current-year and preceding-year costs needed to construct the LIFO index.

For a recent year, the LIFO index was 1.030. However, because this index is a sample estimate of the population's LIFO index, a statement about the precision of the estimate was required. On the basis of the sample results and a 95% confidence level, the margin of error was computed to be .006. Thus, the interval from 1.024 to 1.036 provides the 95% confidence interval estimate of the population LIFO index. This precision was judged to be good.

In this chapter you will learn how to compute the margin of error associated with a sample mean and a sample proportion. Then, you will learn how to use this information to construct and interpret confidence interval estimates of a population mean and a population proportion. You will also learn how to determine the sample size needed to ensure that the margin of error will be within acceptable limits.

*The authors are indebted to Robert S. Knaul, Controller, Dollar General Corporation, for providing this Statistics in Practice.

In Chapter 7 we stated that a point estimator is a sample statistic used to estimate a population parameter. For instance, the sample mean $\bar{x}$ is a point estimator of the population mean $\mu$, and the sample proportion $\bar{p}$ is a point estimator of the population proportion $p$. Because a point estimator does not provide information about how close the estimate is to the population parameter, statisticians usually prefer to construct an **interval estimate** by subtracting and adding a value, called the **margin of error,** to a point estimate.

$$\text{Point Estimate} \pm \text{Margin of Error}$$

The focus in this chapter will be on developing interval estimates for a population mean $\mu$ and a population proportion $p$. Thus, an interval estimate of the population mean is

$$\bar{x} \pm \text{Margin of Error}$$

and an interval estimate of a population proportion is

$$\bar{p} \pm \text{Margin of Error}$$

The inclusion of the margin of error term in an interval estimate provides a measure of the precision associated with the estimate. As we shall see, much of the work in constructing an interval estimate is in determining a value for the margin of error that will provide the desired precision. The sampling distribution of $\bar{x}$ and the sampling distribution of $\bar{p}$ presented in Chapter 7 play important roles in this regard.

## 8.1 INTERVAL ESTIMATION OF A POPULATION MEAN: LARGE-SAMPLE CASE

In this section we show how a simple random sample can be used to develop an interval estimate of a population mean in the large-sample case ($n \geq 30$). We begin with a situation in which the population standard deviation $\sigma$ can be assumed *known*. We then consider the case where it cannot be; in this case $\sigma$ is estimated by the sample standard deviation $s$.

### CJW Problem

The development of an interval estimate of a population mean can be illustrated by considering the monthly customer service survey conducted by CJW, Inc. CJW provides a web site for accepting customer orders and providing follow-up service over the Internet. The company prides itself on providing easy online ordering, timely delivery, and prompt response to customer inquiries. Good customer service is critical to the ongoing success of the company.

CJW's quality assurance team uses a customer survey to measure satisfaction with its web site and online customer service. Each month, a questionnaire is sent to a random sample of customers who have placed an order or requested service during the previous month. Customers are asked to rate their satisfaction with such things as ease of placing orders, timely delivery, accurate order filling, and technical advice. Each customer's questionnaire is summarized by an overall satisfaction score $x$ that ranges from 0 (worst possible score) to 100 (best possible score). A sample mean customer satisfaction score $\bar{x}$ is then computed.

The sample mean satisfaction score is used as a point estimate of the mean satisfaction score $\mu$ for the population of all CJW customers for the month. With this timely measure of customer service, CJW can promptly take corrective action if a low customer satisfaction score is obtained. The company has been conducting this satisfaction survey for a number of months and has consistently obtained an estimate near 20 for the standard deviation of satisfaction scores; they now assume a known value of $\sigma = 20$ for the population standard deviation.

During the month of May, the quality assurance team has surveyed 100 customers, and a sample mean satisfaction score of $\bar{x} = 82$ has been obtained. This sample mean satisfaction score provides a point estimate of the population mean satisfaction score for the month of May. In the discussion that follows, we will show how to compute a margin of error for this estimate and hence develop an interval estimate.

**Margin of Error and the Interval Estimate**    As previously stated, CJW assumes that the population standard deviation of customer satisfaction scores is $\sigma = 20$. With a sample size of $n = 100$, the central limit theorem, introduced in Chapter 7, enables us to conclude that the sampling distribution of $\bar{x}$ can be approximated by a normal probability distribution with an unknown mean of $\mu$ and a standard error of $\sigma_{\bar{x}} = \sigma/\sqrt{n} = 20/\sqrt{100} = 2$. The sampling distribution of $\bar{x}$ is shown in Figure 8.1. It shows how the values of $\bar{x}$ are distributed around $\mu$, and hence provides information about the possible difference between $\bar{x}$ and $\mu$. As noted in Chapter 7 the absolute value of the difference between the sample mean and the population mean, denoted $|\bar{x} - \mu|$, is called the **sampling error.**

Using the table of areas for the standard normal probability distribution, we find that 95% of the values of any normally distributed random variable are within $\pm1.96$ standard deviations of the mean. Because the sampling distribution of $\bar{x}$ can be approximated by a normal probability distribution, 95% of all $\bar{x}$ values must be within $\pm1.96$ standard errors of the population mean $\mu$. In the CJW case, $1.96\,\sigma_{\bar{x}} = 1.96(2) = 3.92$, so we know that 95% of the sample means that could be obtained using a sample of size $n = 100$ must be within $\pm3.92$ of the population mean.

The location of the sample means that differ from $\mu$ by 3.92 or less is shown in Figure 8.2. Note that if a sample mean is in the region denoted "95% of all $\bar{x}$ values," it provides a sampling error of 3.92 or less. However, if a sample mean is in either the lower tail or the upper tail of the distribution, the sampling error, $|\bar{x} - \mu|$, will be greater than 3.92. Therefore we can make the following probability statement about the sampling error for the CJW problem.

> There is a .95 probability that the sample mean will provide a sampling error of 3.92 or less.

This probability statement about the sampling error is a **precision statement** telling CJW about the likely size of the sampling error when a simple random sample of 100 customers is used to estimate the population mean satisfaction score.

An interval estimate for a population mean, $\mu$, is of the form:

$$\bar{x} \pm \text{Margin of Error} \tag{8.1}$$

If we select $1.96\sigma_{\bar{x}} = 1.96(2) = 3.92$ as the margin of error in the CJW case, we can then construct an interval estimate of the population mean satisfaction score $\mu$ by subtracting 3.92 from $\bar{x}$ and adding 3.92 to $\bar{x}$; that is, we compute $\bar{x} \pm 3.92$. It follows from the precision statement above, that there is .95 probability that this interval estimate will contain the population mean $\mu$. For the month of May, a sample of 100 customers provided a sample mean satisfaction score of $\bar{x} = 82$. With $\bar{x} = 82$ and a margin of error of 3.92, the interval

*The standard error is the standard deviation of the sampling distribution. The standard deviation of $x$ is $\sigma$, and the standard deviation of $\bar{x}$ is the standard error $\sigma_{\bar{x}} = \sigma/\sqrt{n}$.*

**FIGURE 8.1**    SAMPLING DISTRIBUTION OF THE SAMPLE MEAN SATISFACTION SCORE FOR SIMPLE RANDOM SAMPLES OF 100 CUSTOMERS

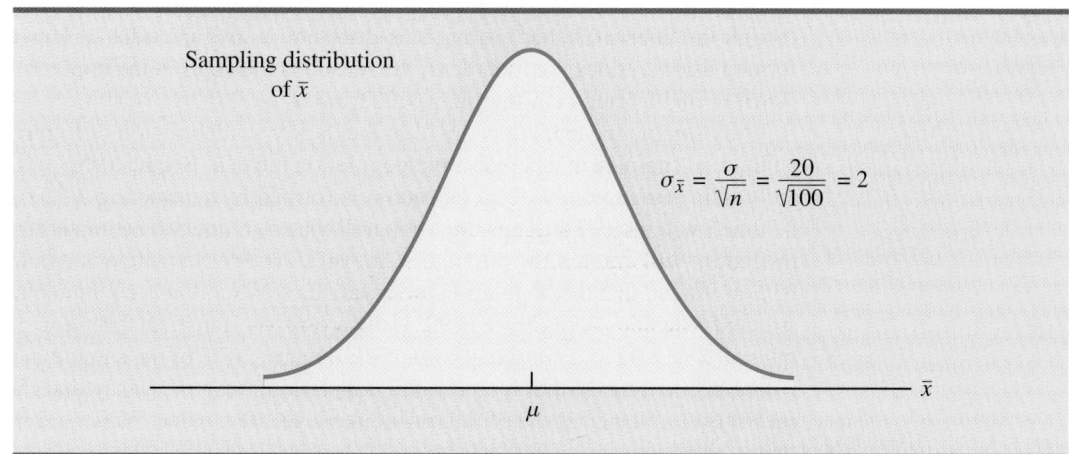

**FIGURE 8.2**    SAMPLING DISTRIBUTION OF $\bar{x}$ SHOWING THE LOCATION OF SAMPLE MEANS THAT PROVIDE A SAMPLING ERROR OF 3.92 OR LESS

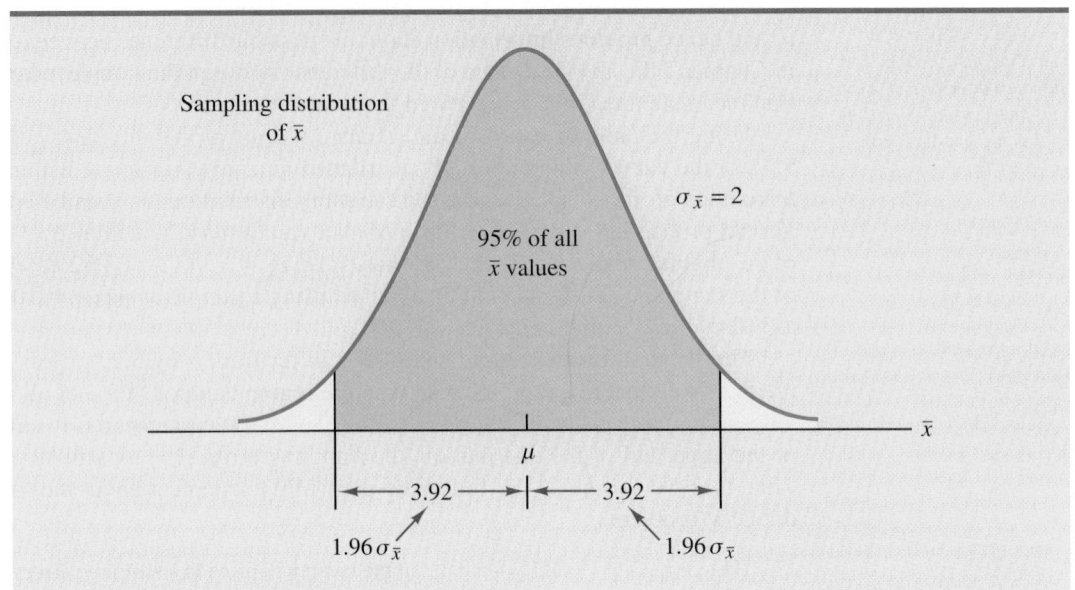

estimate of the population mean satisfaction score is $82 \pm 3.92$, or $82 - 3.92 = 78.08$ to $82 + 3.92 = 85.92$.

## Large-Sample Case with $\sigma$ Assumed Known

We have developed an interval estimate for the population mean satisfaction score for the CJW problem. Let us now develop a general procedure for interval estimates in the large-sample case ($n \geq 30$) when $\sigma$ is assumed known.

In actual practice, only one sample is selected to develop an interval estimate. But, in order to show how to correctly interpret the interval estimate of $\mu$, let us return to the CJW example and suppose that three *different* random samples of 100 customers were taken. We will refer to the value of the first sample mean as $\bar{x}_1$, the value of the second sample mean as $\bar{x}_2$, and the value of the third sample mean as $\bar{x}_3$. Figure 8.3 shows the resulting interval estimates. We have obtained three different interval estimates, but each has the same margin of error (3.92).

As Figure 8.3 shows, the interval formed using $\bar{x}_1$ includes the population mean $\mu$. Although the interval formed using $\bar{x}_2$ is different, it also includes $\mu$. However, the interval formed using $\bar{x}_3$ does not include $\mu$; the reason is that $\bar{x}_3$ is in the upper tail of the sampling distribution of $\bar{x}$ and is farther than 3.92 from $\mu$.

Any sample mean, $\bar{x}$, that is within the darkly shaded region of Figure 8.3 will provide an interval estimate that contains the population mean $\mu$. Because 95% of the sample means are within this region, 95% of all intervals formed by subtracting 3.92 from $\bar{x}$ and adding 3.92 to $\bar{x}$ will include $\mu$. Thus, the probability that an interval estimate generated using this procedure will contain the population mean, $\mu$, is .95. Statisticians would say that we are 95% confident that the population mean satisfaction score $\mu$ is contained in an interval constructed from $\bar{x} - 3.92$ to $\bar{x} + 3.92$. Using common statistical terminology, we refer to the interval $\bar{x} \pm 3.92$ as a *confidence interval*. Because 95% of the sample means will result in a confidence interval that includes the population mean $\mu$, we say that the **confidence interval** is established at the 95% **confidence level**. The value .95 is referred to as the *confidence coefficient*.

**FIGURE 8.3**    INTERVALS FORMED FROM SELECTED SAMPLE MEANS AT LOCATIONS $\bar{x}_1$, $\bar{x}_2$, AND $\bar{x}_3$

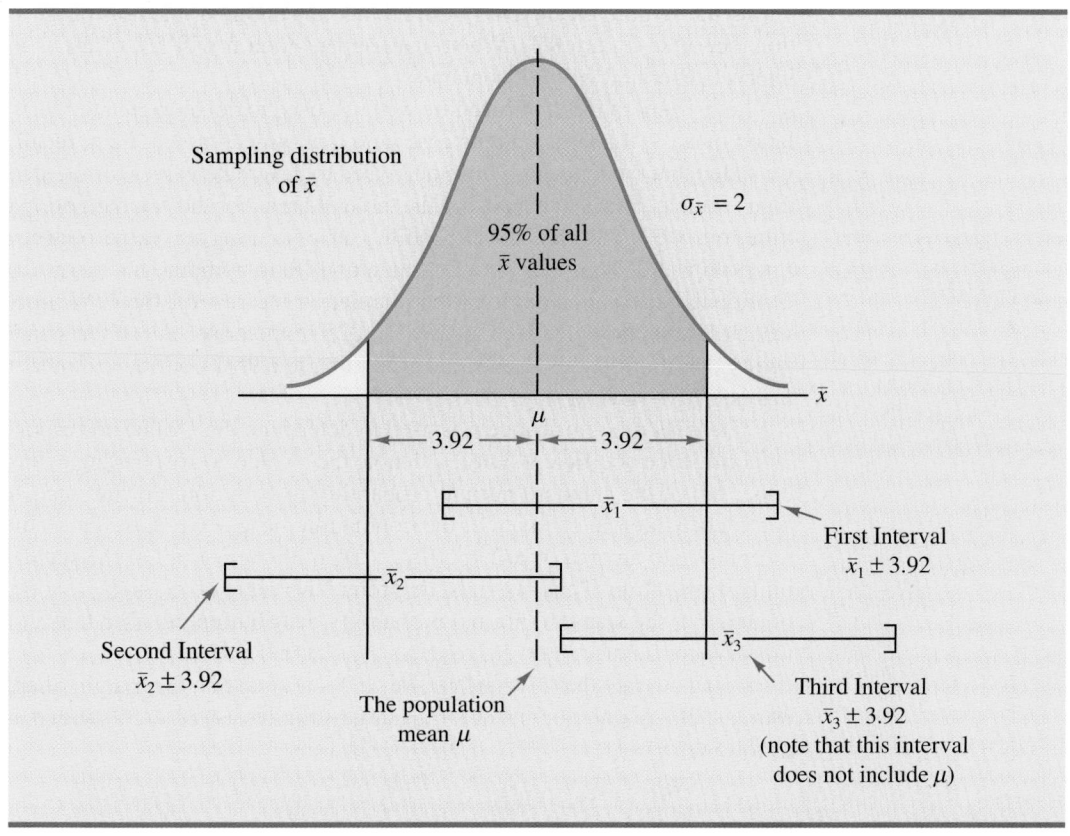

Although a 95% confidence level is frequently used in developing an interval estimate, other confidence levels such as 90% and 99% can be used. For instance, using the standard normal probability distribution table, we find that 90% of the $\bar{x}$ values are within $\pm 1.645$ standard deviations of $\mu$. Thus, if we choose a margin of error of $1.645\sigma_{\bar{x}}$, we can conclude that 90% of the interval estimates generated of the form $\bar{x} \pm 1.645\sigma_{\bar{x}}$ will contain the population mean. Thus, an interval of the form $\bar{x} \pm 1.645\sigma_{\bar{x}}$ is a 90% confidence interval. In CJW's case $\sigma_{\bar{x}} = 2$, so the margin of error for a 90% confidence interval would be $1.645(2) = 3.29$, and a 90% confidence interval would be given by $\bar{x} \pm 3.29$. Similarly, because 99% of the $\bar{x}$ values are within 2.576 standard deviations[1] of $\mu$, a 99% confidence interval would be constructed by choosing a margin of error of $2.576\sigma_{\bar{x}}$. In CJW's case, $2.576\sigma_{\bar{x}} = 2.576(2) = 5.15$. Hence, a 99% confidence interval estimate of $\mu$ is $\bar{x} \pm 5.15$.

Another term sometimes associated with an interval estimate is the **level of significance.** The level of significance associated with an interval estimate is denoted by the Greek letter $\alpha$. The level of significance and the confidence coefficient are related as follows:

$$\alpha = \text{Level of Significance} = 1 - \text{Confidence Coefficient}$$

The level of significance is the probability of erroneously concluding that a confidence interval generated using the procedure we have described will contain $\mu$. For example, the

2.57

[1]The standard normal probability table provides $z$ values with two decimal places. However, for the common confidence levels of 90%, 95%, and 99%, it is common practice to use three decimal places of accuracy for the three values (1.645, 1.960, and 2.576).

level of significance corresponding to a .95 confidence coefficient is $\alpha = 1 - .95 = .05$. In CJW's case, the level of significance ($\alpha = .05$) is the probability of drawing a sample, computing the sample mean, and finding that $\bar{x}$ lies in one of the tails of the sampling distribution (see $\bar{x}_3$ in Figure 8.3). When that happens (and it will 5% of the time), the confidence interval generated will not contain $\mu$.

Let us generalize the procedure we have used to develop an interval estimate of a population mean in the large-sample case with $\sigma$ assumed known. First, recall that in Chapter 6 we stated that the letter $z$ is commonly used to designate values for the standard normal random variable. For instance, using the table of areas for the standard normal probability distribution, we know that the probability of obtaining a $z$ value between $z = -1.96$ and $z = 1.96$ is .95. Thus, we used a $z$ value of 1.96 to compute the margin of error for a 95% confidence interval estimate of the population mean $\mu$ for the CJW problem. Because a $z$ value of 1.96 corresponds to an area of .025 in the upper tail of the standard normal probability distribution, the $z$ value corresponding to a 95% confidence interval is denoted $z_{.025}$; that is, $z_{.025} = 1.96$.

The level of significance $\alpha$ is used to determine the $z$ value corresponding to a particular confidence coefficient. Let $z_{\alpha/2}$ denote the $z$ value corresponding to an area of $\alpha/2$ in the upper tail of the standard normal probability distribution. For instance, to develop a 90% confidence interval estimate of the population mean $\mu$ we must determine the $z$ value corresponding to an area of $\alpha/2 = .10/2 = .05$ in the upper tail of the standard normal probability distribution. Thus, we must determine the value of $z_{\alpha/2} = z_{.10/2} = z_{.05}$. Using the table of areas for the standard normal probability distribution, we find that $z_{.05} = 1.645$. Hence, the 90% confidence interval is $\bar{x} \pm z_{\alpha/2}\sigma_{\bar{x}} = \bar{x} \pm 1.645\sigma_{\bar{x}}$.

Using the fact that $\sigma_{\bar{x}} = \sigma/\sqrt{n}$, we can now state that the margin of error for an interval estimate of a population mean for the large-sample case ($n \geq 30$) with $\sigma$ assumed known is as follows:

$$z_{\alpha/2}\frac{\sigma}{\sqrt{n}}$$

Thus, the appropriate interval estimate is

**Interval Estimate of a Population Mean: Large-Sample Case ($n \geq 30$) with $\sigma$ Assumed Known**

$$\bar{x} \pm z_{\alpha/2}\frac{\sigma}{\sqrt{n}} \tag{8.2}$$

where $1 - \alpha$ is the confidence coefficient and $z_{\alpha/2}$ is the $z$ value providing an area of $\alpha/2$ in the upper tail of the standard normal probability distribution.

The values of $z_{\alpha/2}$ and the margins of error for the most commonly used confidence levels are given in Table 8.1.

## Large-Sample Case with $\sigma$ Estimated by $s$

A difficulty in using expression (8.2) to compute an interval estimate is that in most applications the value of the population standard deviation $\sigma$ is unknown. In the large-sample case ($n \geq 30$), we simply use the value of the sample standard deviation, $s$, as the point es-

**TABLE 8.1**    VALUES OF $z_{\alpha/2}$ AND MARGINS OF ERROR FOR THE MOST COMMONLY USED CONFIDENCE LEVELS

| Confidence Level | $\alpha$ | $\alpha/2$ | $z_{\alpha/2}$ | Margin of Error |
|---|---|---|---|---|
| 90% | .10 | .05 | 1.645 | $1.645\sigma_{\bar{x}}$ |
| 95% | .05 | .025 | 1.960 | $1.960\sigma_{\bar{x}}$ |
| 99% | .01 | .005 | 2.576 | $2.576\sigma_{\bar{x}}$ |

timate of the population standard deviation $\sigma$ in computing the margin of error. The following interval estimate is obtained.[2]

> **Interval Estimate of a Population Mean: Large-Sample Case ($n = 30$) with $\sigma$ Estimated by $s$**
>
> $$\bar{x} \pm z_{\alpha/2}\frac{s}{\sqrt{n}} \qquad (8.3)$$
>
> where $s$ is the sample standard deviation, $1 - \alpha$ is the confidence coefficient, and $z_{\alpha/2}$ is the $z$ value providing an area of $\alpha/2$ in the upper tail of the standard normal probability distribution.

To illustrate this interval estimation procedure, let us consider a sampling study designed to estimate the credit card debt of U.S. households. A sample of 85 households provided the credit card balances shown in Table 8.2. With $n = 85$, we have the large-sample case. And, with no prior information about the standard deviation of credit card balances, we will use the sample standard deviation $s$ as an estimate of $\sigma$. Thus, it is appropriate to use expression (8.3) to develop an interval estimate. Let us develop a 95% confidence interval estimate of the population mean credit card balance per household.

**TABLE 8.2**    CREDIT CARD BALANCES FOR A SAMPLE OF 85 HOUSEHOLDS

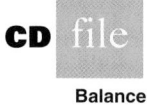

**Balance**

| | | | | | |
|---|---|---|---|---|---|
| 9619 | 5994 | 3344 | 7888 | 7581 | 9980 |
| 5364 | 4652 | 13627 | 3091 | 12545 | 8718 |
| 8348 | 5376 | 968 | 943 | 7959 | 8452 |
| 7348 | 5998 | 4714 | 8762 | 2563 | 4935 |
| 381 | 7530 | 4334 | 1407 | 6787 | 5938 |
| 2998 | 3678 | 4911 | 6644 | 5071 | 5266 |
| 1686 | 3581 | 1920 | 7644 | 9536 | 10658 |
| 1962 | 5625 | 3780 | 11169 | 4459 | 3910 |
| 4920 | 5619 | 3478 | 7979 | 8047 | 7503 |
| 5047 | 9032 | 6185 | 3258 | 8083 | 1582 |
| 6921 | 13236 | 1141 | 8660 | 2153 | |
| 5759 | 4447 | 7577 | 7511 | 8003 | |
| 8047 | 609 | 4667 | 14442 | 6795 | |
| 3924 | 414 | 5219 | 4447 | 5915 | |
| 3470 | 7636 | 6416 | 6550 | 7164 | |

---

[2]The theoretical justification for this interval estimate is that the large-sample case allows us to conclude both that $\bar{x}$ is normally distributed and that $s$ is a good approximation of $\sigma$.

Using the data in Table 8.2, we find $\bar{x} = \$5900$ and $s = \$3058$. At 95% confidence, $z_{\alpha/2} = z_{.025} = 1.96$. With a sample size of $n = 85$, expression (8.3) provides the following interval estimate:

$$5900 \pm 1.96 \frac{3058}{\sqrt{85}}$$

$$5900 \pm 650.11$$

Rounding to the nearest dollar, the margin of error is $650 and the 95% confidence interval estimate of the population mean is $5900 - 650 = 5250$ to $5900 + 650 = 6550$. Thus, we can be 95% confident that the population mean credit card balance for all U.S. households is between $5250 and $6550.

## Using Excel to Construct a Confidence Interval: Large-Sample Case

We will use the credit card balance data in Table 8.2 to illustrate how Excel can be used to construct confidence intervals for the population mean in the large sample case. Because $\sigma$ is unknown, $s$ and the sample size $n$ are used to estimate the standard error. The margin of error is computed as the product of the $z$ value and the estimated standard error. Then by subtracting and adding the margin of error to the point estimate (the sample mean) we obtain the confidence interval. Refer to Figure 8.4 as we describe the tasks involved. The formula worksheet is in the background; the value worksheet is in the foreground.

**Enter Data:** A label and the credit card balances for the 85 households have been entered into cells A1:A86.

**Enter Functions and Formulas:** The descriptive statistics we need are provided in cells D4:D6. Excel's COUNT, AVERAGE, and STDEV functions have been used to compute the sample size, sample mean, and sample standard deviation for the data in cells A2:A86. The value worksheet shows $n = 85$, $\bar{x} = 5900$, and $s = 3058$.

Cells D8:D10 are used to compute the appropriate $z$ value. The confidence coefficient has been entered into cell D8 and the level of significance ($\alpha$) has been computed in cell D9 by entering the formula =1-D8. The $z$ value corresponding to an upper tail area of $\alpha/2$ has been computed in cell D10 by using the NORMSINV function. Recall from Chapter 6 that the form of the NORMSINV function is =NORMSINV (cumulative probability). We use a cumulative probability as input, and the function provides the corresponding $z$ value. If we want an area of $\alpha/2$ in the upper tail, the appropriate cumulative probability is $1 - \alpha/2$. Thus, we have entered the formula =NORMSINV(1-D9/2) into cell D10. The value worksheet shows that the $z$ value obtained is $z_{.025} = 1.960$.

Cells D12:D13 provide the estimate of the standard error and the margin of error. In cell D12, we have entered the formula =D6/SQRT(D4) to estimate the standard error of the mean. The formula =D10*D12 has been entered into cell D13 to compute the margin of error associated with a 95% confidence interval. The resulting value of 650 is the margin of error associated with the interval estimate of the population mean household credit card balance.

Cells D15:D17 provide the point estimate and the lower and upper limits for the confidence interval. Because the point estimate is just the sample mean, the formula =D5 has been entered into cell D15. To compute the lower limit of the 95% confidence interval, $\bar{x} - $ (margin of error), we entered the formula =D15-D13 into cell D16. To compute the upper limit of the 95% confidence interval, $\bar{x} + $ (margin of error), we entered the formula

**FIGURE 8.4**    EXCEL WORKSHEET FOR 95% CONFIDENCE INTERVAL ESTIMATE OF THE POPULATION MEAN HOUSEHOLD CREDIT CARD BALANCE

| | A | B | C | D | E |
|---|---|---|---|---|---|
| 1 | Balance | | Interval Estimate of a Population Mean | | |
| 2 | 9619 | | Using the Standard Normal Distribution (z) | | |
| 3 | 5364 | | | | |
| 4 | 8348 | | Sample Size | =COUNT(A2:A86) | |
| 5 | 7348 | | Mean | =AVERAGE(A2:A86) | |
| 6 | 381 | | Standard Deviation | =STDEV(A2:A86) | |
| 7 | 2998 | | | | |
| 8 | 1686 | | Confidence Coefficient | 0.95 | |
| 9 | 1962 | | Level of Significance (alpha) | =1-D8 | |
| 10 | 4920 | | z Value | =NORMSINV(1-D9/2) | |
| 11 | 5047 | | | | |
| 12 | 6921 | | Standard Error | =D6/SQRT(D4) | |
| 13 | 5759 | | Margin of Error | =D10*D12 | |
| 14 | 8047 | | | | |
| 15 | 3924 | | Point Estimate | =D5 | |
| 16 | 3470 | | Lower Limit | =D15-D13 | |
| 17 | 5994 | | Upper Limit | =D15+D13 | |
| 18 | 4652 | | | | |
| 84 | 3910 | | | | |
| 85 | 7503 | | | | |
| 86 | 1582 | | | | |
| 87 | | | | | |

| | A | B | C | D | E | F | G |
|---|---|---|---|---|---|---|---|
| 1 | Balance | | Interval Estimate of a Population Mean | | | | |
| 2 | 9619 | | Using the Standard Normal Distribution (z) | | | | |
| 3 | 5364 | | | | | | |
| 4 | 8348 | | Sample Size | 85 | | | |
| 5 | 7348 | | Mean | 5900 | | | |
| 6 | 381 | | Standard Deviation | 3058 | | | |
| 7 | 2998 | | | | | | |
| 8 | 1686 | | Confidence Coefficient | 0.95 | | | |
| 9 | 1962 | | Level of Significance (alpha) | 0.05 | | | |
| 10 | 4920 | | z Value | 1.960 | | | |
| 11 | 5047 | | | | | | |
| 12 | 6921 | | Standard Error | 331.69 | | | |
| 13 | 5759 | | Margin of Error | 650 | | | |
| 14 | 8047 | | | | | | |
| 15 | 3924 | | Point Estimate | 5900 | | | |
| 16 | 3470 | | Lower Limit | 5250 | | | |
| 17 | 5994 | | Upper Limit | 6550 | | | |
| 18 | 4652 | | | | | | |
| 84 | 3910 | | | | | | |
| 85 | 7503 | | | | | | |
| 86 | 1582 | | | | | | |
| 87 | | | | | | | |

Note: Rows 19–83 are hidden.

This and future worksheets in this chapter can be used as templates for interval estimation problems.

=D15+D13 into cell D17. The value worksheet shows a lower limit of 5250 and an upper limit of 6550. In other words, the 95% confidence interval for the population mean is from $5250 to $6550.

We note that once a worksheet has been set up to compute a confidence interval other confidence intervals can easily be computed. For instance, a 90% confidence interval can be computed by simply changing the confidence coefficient in cell D8 to .90. Doing so, we would obtain a 90% confidence interval of $5354 to $6446. As expected the 90% confidence interval is slightly narrower than the 95% confidence interval.

The credit card balance problem we have just worked with is one in which $s$ is used as an estimate of $\sigma$. To use this worksheet as a template for another problem of this type, we must first enter the new problem data in column A. Then the ranges for the formulas in the descriptive statistics cells (D4:D6) would be revised to correspond to the new data. After doing so, the point estimate and a 95% confidence interval will be displayed in cells D15:D17. If a confidence interval with a different confidence coefficient is desired, we simply change the value in cell D8.

This worksheet can also be used as a template for large-sample interval estimation when $\sigma$ is assumed known. In this type of situation, we would just type the value of the assumed standard deviation in cell D6 and proceed as before. Students can also use this worksheet as a template for text exercises in which the sample mean, the sample standard deviation, and the sample size are given. In this type of situation we simply replace the formulas in cells D4:D6 with the given values for the sample size, the sample mean, and the sample standard deviation.

## NOTES AND COMMENTS

1. In developing an interval estimate of the population mean, we specify the desired confidence coefficient $(1 - \alpha)$ before selecting the sample. Thus, prior to selecting the sample, we conclude that there is a $1 - \alpha$ probability that the confidence interval we eventually compute will contain the population mean $\mu$ and an $\alpha$ probability that it will not. However, once the sample is taken, the sample mean $\bar{x}$ is computed, and the particular interval estimate is determined, the resulting interval may or may not contain $\mu$. If $1 - \alpha$ is reasonably large, we can be confident that the resulting interval will contain $\mu$ because we know that if we use this procedure repeatedly, $100(1 - \alpha)$ percent of all possible intervals developed in this way will contain $\mu$.

2. In practical applications, the population standard deviation $\sigma$ is rarely known, and $s$ is used to estimate $\sigma$. However, in some cases it makes sense to assume a known value of $\sigma$. For instance, in quality control applications the variance of an in-control process can often be assumed known. And, in situations where a substantial amount of historical data is available (e.g., standardized test scores), it is often reasonable to use the standard deviation for the historical data as a known value of $\sigma$.

3. The sample size $n$ appears in the denominator of the interval estimation expressions (8.2) and (8.3). Thus, if a particular sample size provides too wide an interval to be of any practical use, we may want to consider increasing the sample size. With $n$ in the denominator, a larger sample size will provide a smaller margin of error, a narrower interval, and greater precision. The procedure for determining the size of a simple random sample necessary to obtain a desired precision is discussed in Section 8.3.

## EXERCISES

### Methods

1. A simple random sample of 40 items resulted in a sample mean of 25. The population standard deviation is $\sigma = 5$.
   a. What is the standard error of the mean, $\sigma_{\bar{x}}$?
   b. At 95% confidence, what is the margin of error?

**SELF** test
2. A simple random sample of 50 items resulted in a sample mean of 32 and a sample standard deviation of 6.
   a. Provide a 90% confidence interval for the population mean.
   b. Provide a 95% confidence interval for the population mean.
   c. Provide a 99% confidence interval for the population mean.

3. A sample of 60 items resulted in a sample mean of 80 and a sample standard deviation of 15.
   a. Compute the 95% confidence interval for the population mean.
   b. Assume that the same sample mean and sample standard deviation were obtained from a sample of 120 items. Provide a 95% confidence interval for the population mean.
   c. What is the effect of a larger sample size on the interval estimate of a population mean?

4. A 95% confidence interval for a population mean was reported to be 122 to 130. If the sample mean is 126 and the sample standard deviation is 16.07, what sample size was used in this study?

### Applications

**SELF** test
5. In an effort to estimate the mean amount spent per customer for dinner at a major Atlanta restaurant, data were collected for a sample of 49 customers.
   a. Assume a population standard deviation of $5. What is the standard error of the mean?
   b. At a 95% confidence level, what is the margin of error?
   c. If the sample mean is $34.80, what is the 95% confidence interval for the population mean?

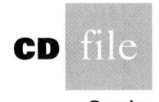

Service

**6.** Mean weekly earnings of individuals working in various industries were reported in *The New York Times 1998 Almanac.* The mean weekly earnings for individuals in the service industry was $369. Suppose that a follow-up study of 250 service employees resulted in the weekly salaries contained in the data set Service.
   **a.** Use the sample data to develop a point estimate of the mean weekly salary for the population of service employees.
   **b.** What is the sample standard deviation?
   **c.** Develop a 95% confidence interval estimate of the mean weekly salary for the population of service employees.

**7.** The mean undergraduate grade point average (GPA) for students admitted to the top graduate business schools was 3.37 (*Best Graduate Schools, U.S. News and World Report,* 2001 Edition). Assume this estimate was based on a sample of 120 students admitted to the top schools. Using past years' data, the population standard deviation can be assumed known with $\sigma = .28$. What is the 95% confidence interval estimate of the mean undergraduate GPA for students admitted to the top graduate business schools?

**8.** The National Association of Independent Colleges and Universities reported that students graduating from public colleges and universities have an average debt of $12,000 upon graduation (*Kiplinger's Personal Finance Magazine,* November 1998). Assume that this average or mean amount is based on a sample of 245 students and that, based on past studies, the population standard deviation for the debt upon graduation is $2200.
   **a.** Develop a 90% confidence interval estimate of the population mean.
   **b.** Develop a 95% confidence interval estimate of the population mean.
   **c.** Develop a 99% confidence interval estimate of the population mean.
   **d.** Discuss what happens to the width of the confidence interval as the confidence level is increased. Does this result seem reasonable? Explain.

Workers

**9.** A summary of the mean hourly pay for production workers was reported in *The Wall Street Journal,* November 25, 1997. A sample of 60 hourly pay rates for production workers is contained in the data set Workers.
   **a.** Use the Workers data set to develop a point estimate of the hourly pay rate for the population of production workers.
   **b.** What is the sample standard deviation?
   **c.** What is the 95% confidence interval for the mean hourly pay rate for the population of production workers.

**10.** Nielsen Media Research reports the household mean television viewing time during the 8 P.M. to 11 P.M. time period is 7.75 hours per week (*The World Almanac 2000*). Assuming a sample size of 180 households and a sample standard deviation of 3.45 hours, what is the 95% confidence interval estimate of the mean television viewing time per week during the 8 P.M. to 11 P.M. time period?

**11.** The International Air Transport Association surveys business travelers to develop quality ratings for transatlantic gateway airports. The maximum possible rating is 10. Suppose a simple random sample of 50 business travelers is selected and each traveler is asked to provide a rating for the Miami International Airport. The ratings obtained from the sample of 50 follow.

Miami

| 6 | 4 | 6 | 8 | 7 | 7 | 6 | 3 | 3 | 8 | 10 | 4 | 8 |
| 7 | 8 | 7 | 5 | 9 | 5 | 8 | 4 | 3 | 8 | 5 | 5 | 4 |
| 4 | 4 | 8 | 4 | 5 | 6 | 2 | 5 | 9 | 9 | 8 | 4 | 8 |
| 9 | 9 | 5 | 9 | 7 | 8 | 3 | 10 | 8 | 9 | 6 | | |

Develop a 95% confidence interval estimate of the population mean rating for Miami.

**12.** Thirty fast-food restaurants including Wendy's, McDonald's, and Burger King were visited during the summer of 2000 (*The Cincinnati Enquirer,* July 9, 2000). During each visit, the customer went to the drive-through window and ordered a basic meal such as a "combo" meal or a sandwich, fries, and shake. The elapsed time between a customer pulling up to the message board and receiving a filled order was recorded. The times in minutes for 30 visits are as follow:

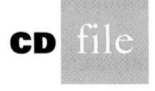

**FastFood**

| 0.9 | 1.0 | 1.2 | 2.2 | 1.9 | 3.6 | 2.8 | 5.2 | 1.8 | 2.1 |
| 6.8 | 1.3 | 3.0 | 4.5 | 2.8 | 2.3 | 2.7 | 5.7 | 4.8 | 3.5 |
| 2.6 | 3.3 | 5.0 | 4.0 | 7.2 | 9.1 | 2.8 | 3.6 | 7.3 | 9.0 |

a. Provide a point estimate of the population mean drive-through time at fast-food restaurants.
b. At 95% confidence, what is the margin of error?
c. Develop a 95% confidence interval estimate of the population mean.

## 8.2 INTERVAL ESTIMATION OF A POPULATION MEAN: SMALL-SAMPLE CASE

*The methodology presented in this section is based on the assumption that the population has a normal probability distribution.*

The sampling distribution of $\bar{x}$ depends on the probability distribution of the population from which the sample was drawn. In the large sample case ($n \geq 30$) the central limit theorem allows us to conclude that the sampling distribution is approximately normal and the methodology of section 8.1 is applicable. In the small-sample case ($n < 30$), we cannot draw such a conclusion.

If the population has a normal probability distribution, the methodology presented in this section can be used to develop a confidence interval for a population mean in the small-sample case. However, if the assumption of a normal probability distribution for the population is not appropriate, the only alternative is to increase the sample size to $n \geq 30$ and rely on the large-sample interval estimation procedures given by expressions (8.2) and (8.3).

### Small-Sample Case with $\sigma$ Assumed Known

We begin by making the assumption that the population has a normal distribution and that the population standard deviation $\sigma$ is assumed known. Under these conditions, and regardless of the sample size, the sampling distribution of $\bar{x}$ is exactly normal with mean $\mu$ and standard deviation $\sigma_{\bar{x}} = \sigma/\sqrt{n}$. Thus, given that the sampling distribution of $\bar{x}$ is a normal distribution, the small-sample interval estimation procedure with $\sigma$ assumed known is identical to the large-sample interval estimation procedure presented in Section 8.1.

---

**Interval Estimate of a Population Mean: Small-Sample Case ($n < 30$) with $\sigma$ Assumed Known**

*When using Excel to develop an interval estimate using expression (8.4), the worksheet in Figure 8.4 can be used as a template*

Assumption: The population has a normal distribution.

$$\bar{x} \pm z_{\alpha/2} \frac{\sigma}{\sqrt{n}} \qquad \textbf{(8.4)}$$

where $(1 - \alpha)$ is the confidence coefficient and $z_{\alpha/2}$ is the $z$-value providing an area $\alpha/2$ in the upper tail of the standard normal probability distribution

---

With $\sigma$ assumed known and $z_{\alpha/2}$ selected based on the desired confidence level, the selection of a sample of size $n$ and the computation of the sample mean $\bar{x}$ will provide the information necessary to use expression (8.4) to compute the margin of error and the interval estimate of the population mean. Because this computation is identical to the computations made in Section 8.1, we shall not present a new numerical example here.

## Small-Sample Case with $\sigma$ Estimated by $s$

We start by again making the assumption that the population has a normal distribution. If the situation provides no basis for assuming that the population standard deviation $\sigma$ is known, the sample standard deviation $s$ is used to estimate $\sigma$. Under these conditions, the interval estimation procedure is based on a probability distribution known as the *t distribution.*

William Sealy Gosset, writing under the name "Student," developed the *t* distribution. Gosset, an Oxford graduate in mathematics, worked for the Guinness Brewery in Dublin, Ireland. He developed a new small-sample theory of statistics while doing work involving temperature experiments in the brewery.

The *t* distribution is a family of similar probability distributions, with each individual *t* distribution's shape depending on a parameter known as the **degrees of freedom.** The *t* distribution with one degree of freedom is unique, as is the *t* distribution with two degrees of freedom, with three degrees of freedom, and so on. As the number of degrees of freedom increases, the difference between the *t* distribution and the standard normal probability distribution becomes smaller and smaller. Figure 8.5 shows *t* distributions with 10 and 20 degrees of freedom and their relationship to the standard normal probability distribution. Note that a *t* distribution with more degrees of freedom has less variability and more closely resembles the standard normal probability distribution. The means of both the standard normal and the *t* distributions are zero.

We will place a subscript on *t* to indicate the area in the upper tail of the *t* distribution. For example, just as we used $z_{.025}$ to indicate the $z$ value providing a .025 area in the upper tail of a standard normal probability distribution, we will use $t_{.025}$ to indicate a .025 area in the upper tail of a *t* distribution. In general, we will use the notation $t_{\alpha/2}$ to represent a *t* value with an area of $\alpha/2$ in the upper tail of the *t* distribution. See Figure 8.6.

Table 8.3 is a table for the *t* distribution. This table is also shown inside the front cover of the text. Note, for example, that for a *t* distribution with 10 degrees of freedom, $t_{.025} = 2.228$. Similarly, for a *t* distribution with 20 degrees of freedom, $t_{.025} = 2.086$. As the degrees of freedom continue to increase, $t_{.025}$ approaches $z_{.025} = 1.96$.

Now that we have an idea of what the *t* distribution is, let us see how it is used to develop an interval estimate of a population mean. Assume that the population has a normal probability distribution and that the sample standard deviation $s$ is used to estimate the population standard deviation $\sigma$. With a confidence coefficient of $1 - \alpha$,

**FIGURE 8.5**    COMPARISON OF THE STANDARD NORMAL DISTRIBUTION WITH *t* DISTRIBUTIONS HAVING 10 AND 20 DEGREES OF FREEDOM

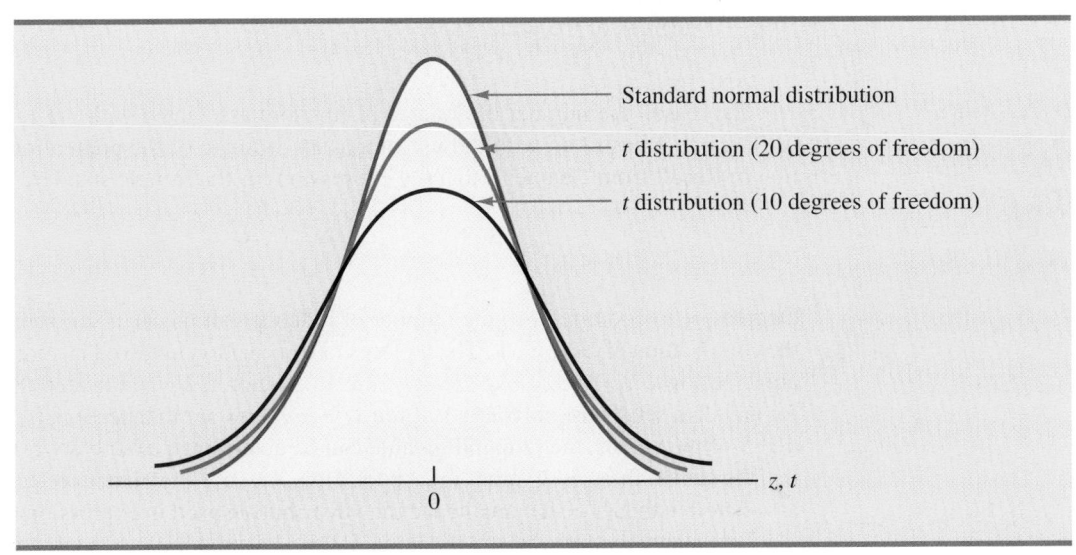

**FIGURE 8.6**   $t$ DISTRIBUTION WITH AN AREA OR PROBABILITY OF $\alpha/2$ IN THE UPPER TAIL

the margin of error is given by $t_{\alpha/2}\dfrac{s}{\sqrt{n}}$ and the interval estimation procedure is given by expression (8.5).

---

**Interval Estimate of a Population Mean: Small-Sample Case ($n < 30$) with $\sigma$ Estimated by $s$**

Assumption: The population has a normal distribution.

$$\bar{x} \pm t_{\alpha/2}\frac{s}{\sqrt{n}} \tag{8.5}$$

where $s$ is the sample standard deviation, $(1 - \alpha)$ is the confidence coefficient, and $t_{\alpha/2}$ is the $t$ value providing an area of $\alpha/2$ in the upper tail of the $t$ distribution with $n - 1$ degrees of freedom.

---

The reason the number of degrees of freedom associated with the $t$ value in equation (8.5) is $n - 1$ has to do with the use of $s$ as an estimate of the population standard deviation $\sigma$. Recall from Chapter 3 that the expression for the sample standard deviation is

$$s = \sqrt{\frac{\Sigma(x_i - \bar{x})^2}{n - 1}}$$

Degrees of freedom refer to the number of independent pieces of information that go into the computation of $\Sigma(x_i - \bar{x})^2$. The $n$ pieces of information involved in computing $\Sigma(x_i - \bar{x})^2$ are as follows: $x_1 - \bar{x}, x_2 - \bar{x}, \ldots, x_n - \bar{x}$. In Section 3.2 we indicated that $\Sigma(x_i - \bar{x}) = 0$ for any data set. Thus, only $n - 1$ of the $x_i - \bar{x}$ values are independent; that is, if we know $n - 1$ of the values, the remaining value can be determined exactly by using the condition that the sum of the $x_i - \bar{x}$ values must be 0. Thus, $n - 1$ is the number of degrees of freedom associated with $\Sigma(x_i - \bar{x})^2$ and hence the $t$ distribution used in expression (8.5).

Let us demonstrate the small-sample interval estimation procedure by considering the training program evaluation conducted by Scheer Industries. Scheer's director of manufacturing is interested in a computer-assisted program that can be used to train the firm's

**TABLE 8.3**    *t* DISTRIBUTION TABLE FOR AREAS IN THE UPPER TAIL.
EXAMPLE: WITH 10 DEGREES OF FREEDOM, $t_{.025} = 2.228$

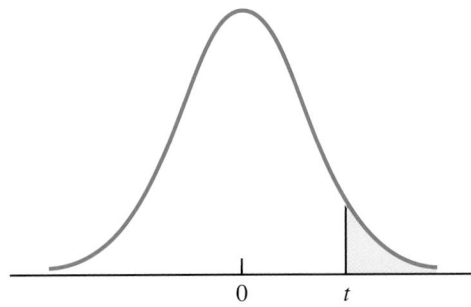

As the degrees of freedom increase, the *t* distribution approaches the standard normal distribution. In fact, standard normal distribution *z* values can be found in the infinite degrees of freedom row of this *t* distribution table.

| Degrees of Freedom | Upper-Tail Area (Shaded) | | | | |
|---|---|---|---|---|---|
| | **.10** | **.05** | **.025** | **.01** | **.005** |
| 1 | 3.078 | 6.314 | 12.706 | 31.821 | 63.657 |
| 2 | 1.886 | 2.920 | 4.303 | 6.965 | 9.925 |
| 3 | 1.638 | 2.353 | 3.182 | 4.541 | 5.841 |
| 4 | 1.533 | 2.132 | 2.776 | 3.747 | 4.604 |
| 5 | 1.476 | 2.015 | 2.571 | 3.365 | 4.032 |
| 6 | 1.440 | 1.943 | 2.447 | 3.143 | 3.707 |
| 7 | 1.415 | 1.895 | 2.365 | 2.998 | 3.499 |
| 8 | 1.397 | 1.860 | 2.306 | 2.896 | 3.355 |
| 9 | 1.383 | 1.833 | 2.262 | 2.821 | 3.250 |
| 10 | 1.372 | 1.812 | **2.228** | 2.764 | 3.169 |
| 11 | 1.363 | 1.796 | 2.201 | 2.718 | 3.106 |
| 12 | 1.356 | 1.782 | 2.179 | 2.681 | 3.055 |
| 13 | 1.350 | 1.771 | 2.160 | 2.650 | 3.012 |
| 14 | 1.345 | 1.761 | 2.145 | 2.624 | 2.977 |
| 15 | 1.341 | 1.753 | 2.131 | 2.602 | 2.947 |
| 16 | 1.337 | 1.746 | 2.120 | 2.583 | 2.921 |
| 17 | 1.333 | 1.740 | 2.110 | 2.567 | 2.898 |
| 18 | 1.330 | 1.734 | 2.101 | 2.552 | 2.878 |
| 19 | 1.328 | 1.729 | 2.093 | 2.539 | 2.861 |
| 20 | 1.325 | 1.725 | 2.086 | 2.528 | 2.845 |
| 21 | 1.323 | 1.721 | 2.080 | 2.518 | 2.831 |
| 22 | 1.321 | 1.717 | 2.074 | 2.508 | 2.819 |
| 23 | 1.319 | 1.714 | 2.069 | 2.500 | 2.807 |
| 24 | 1.318 | 1.711 | 2.064 | 2.492 | 2.797 |
| 25 | 1.316 | 1.708 | 2.060 | 2.485 | 2.787 |
| 26 | 1.315 | 1.706 | 2.056 | 2.479 | 2.779 |
| 27 | 1.314 | 1.703 | 2.052 | 2.473 | 2.771 |
| 28 | 1.313 | 1.701 | 2.048 | 2.467 | 2.763 |
| 29 | 1.311 | 1.699 | 2.045 | 2.462 | 2.756 |
| 30 | 1.310 | 1.697 | 2.042 | 2.457 | 2.750 |
| 40 | 1.303 | 1.684 | 2.021 | 2.423 | 2.704 |
| 60 | 1.296 | 1.671 | 2.000 | 2.390 | 2.660 |
| 120 | 1.289 | 1.658 | 1.980 | 2.358 | 2.617 |
| ∞ | 1.282 | 1.645 | 1.960 | 2.326 | 2.576 |

maintenance employees for machine-repair operations. The expectation is that the computer-assisted method will reduce the time needed to train employees. To evaluate the training method, the director of manufacturing has requested an estimate of the mean training time required for the computer-assisted program.

Suppose management has agreed to train 15 employees with the new approach. The data on training days required for each employee in the sample are listed in Table 8.4. The sample mean and sample standard deviation for these data follow.

$$\bar{x} = \frac{\Sigma x_i}{n} = \frac{808}{15} = 53.87 \text{ days}$$

$$s = \sqrt{\frac{\Sigma(x_i - \bar{x})^2}{n - 1}} = \sqrt{\frac{651.73}{14}} = 6.82 \text{ days}$$

The point estimate of the mean training time for the population of employees is 53.87 days. We can obtain information about the precision of this estimate by computing the margin of error and developing an interval estimate of the population mean. Because the population standard deviation is unknown, we will use the sample standard deviation $s = 6.82$ days. With the small sample size, $n = 15$, we will use expression (8.5) to develop an interval estimate of the population mean at 95% confidence. With the assumption that the population of training times has a normal probability distribution, the $t$ distribution with $n - 1 = 14$ degrees of freedom is the appropriate probability distribution for the interval estimation procedure. We see from Table 8.3 that with 14 degrees of freedom, $t_{\alpha/2} = t_{.025} = 2.145$. Using expression (8.5), we have

> *The t distribution is based on the assumption that the population has a normal probability distribution. However, confidence intervals based on the t distribution can be used as long as the population distribution is approximately normal.*

$$\bar{x} \pm t_{.025}\frac{s}{\sqrt{n}}$$

$$53.87 \pm 2.145\left(\frac{6.82}{\sqrt{15}}\right)$$

$$53.87 \pm 3.78$$

Thus, the margin of error is 3.78, and the 95% confidence interval estimate of the population mean training time is 50.09 days to 57.65 days.

### Using Excel to Construct a Confidence Interval: With $\sigma$ Estimated by $s$

Excel can be used to construct a 95% confidence interval for the population mean training time at Scheer Industries. Excel's TINV function is used to compute the appropriate $t$ value. Because $\sigma$ is unknown, $s$ and the sample size $n$ are used to estimate the standard error. The

**TABLE 8.4**  TRAINING TIME IN DAYS FOR THE COMPUTER-ASSISTED TRAINING PROGRAM AT SCHEER INDUSTRIES

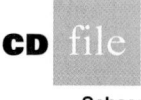

**CD file**

**Scheer**

| Employee | Time | Employee | Time | Employee | Time |
|----------|------|----------|------|----------|------|
| 1 | 52 | 6 | 59 | 11 | 54 |
| 2 | 44 | 7 | 50 | 12 | 58 |
| 3 | 55 | 8 | 54 | 13 | 60 |
| 4 | 44 | 9 | 62 | 14 | 62 |
| 5 | 45 | 10 | 46 | 15 | 63 |

margin of error is computed as the product of the *t* value and the estimated standard error. Then by subtracting and adding the margin of error to the point estimate (the sample mean) we obtain the confidence interval. Refer to Figure 8.7 as we describe the tasks involved. The formula worksheet is in the background; the value worksheet is in the foreground.

**Enter Data:**    A label and the training time data for the 15 employees have been entered into cells A1:A16.

**Enter Functions and Formulas:**    The descriptive statistics we need are provided in cells D4:D6. Excel's COUNT, AVERAGE, and STDEV functions have been used to compute the sample size, sample mean, and sample standard deviation for the data in cells A2:A16. The value worksheet shows $n = 15$, $\bar{x} = 53.87$, and $s = 6.82$.

Cells D8:D11 are used to compute the appropriate *t* value. The confidence coefficient (.95) has been entered into cell D8 and the level of significance ($\alpha$) has been computed in cell D9 by entering the formula =1-D8. We have entered the formula =D4-1 into cell D10 to compute the degrees of freedom as the (sample size) $- 1$. Next, the *t* value corresponding to an upper tail area of $\alpha/2$, $t_{\alpha/2}$, is computed by using the TINV function. The form of the TINV function is TINV(level of significance, degrees of freedom). Because the level of significance ($\alpha$) is in cell D9 and the degrees of freedom ($n - 1$) are in cell D10, the formula =TINV(D9, D10) has been entered into cell D11. The value worksheet shows that $t_{.025} = 2.145$.

Cells D13:D14 provide the estimate of the standard error and the margin of error. In cell D13, we have entered the formula =D6/SQRT(D4) to estimate the standard error of the mean. The formula =D11*D13 has been entered into cell D14 to compute the margin of error associated with a 95% confidence interval. The resulting value of 3.78 is the margin of error associated with the 95% interval estimate of the population mean training time for Scheer Industries employees.

Cells D16:D18 provide the point estimate and the lower and upper limits for the confidence interval. Because the point estimate is just the sample mean, the formula =D5 has

**FIGURE 8.7**    EXCEL WORKSHEET FOR SCHEER INDUSTRIES

been entered into cell D16. To compute the lower limit of the 95% confidence interval, $\bar{x}$ − (margin of error), we entered the formula =D16-D14 into cell D17. To compute the upper limit of the 95% confidence interval, $\bar{x}$ + (margin of error), we entered the formula =D16+D14 into cell D18. The value worksheet shows a lower limit of 50.09 and an upper limit of 57.65. In other words the 95% confidence interval for the population mean training time is 50.09 to 57.65 days.

The worksheet in Figure 8.7 can be used as a template for developing confidence intervals in the small sample ($n < 30$) case when $s$ is used to estimate $\sigma$. The Scheer Industries problem is one in which $s$ is used as an estimate of $\sigma$. To use this worksheet as a template for another problem of this type, we must first enter the new problem data in column A. Then the ranges for the formulas in the descriptive statistics cells (D4:D6) would be revised to correspond to the new data. After doing so, the point estimate and a 95% confidence interval will be displayed in cells D16:D18. If a confidence interval with a different confidence coefficient is desired, we simply change the value in cell D8.

## The Role of the Population Distribution

As we close this section, let us point out that an important consideration in developing an interval estimate of a population mean is determining what is known about the population distribution. The large-sample interval estimation procedures in Section 8.1 make no assumption about the population distribution and can be applied to a population having any distribution. The interval estimation procedures in Section 8.2 are based on the assumption that the population has a normal distribution and can be applied to a population having a normal, or near-normal distribution.

In practice, if the sample size is large ($n \geq 30$) and the form of the population distribution is unknown, we rely on the procedures in Section 8.1. In this case, an interval estimate of population mean can be constructed as follows:

$\sigma$ assumed known

$$\bar{x} \pm z_{\alpha/2} \frac{\sigma}{\sqrt{n}} \tag{8.2}$$

$\sigma$ estimated by $s$

$$\bar{x} \pm z_{\alpha/2} \frac{s}{\sqrt{n}} \tag{8.3}$$

Most importantly, the large-sample theory supports the use of expressions (8.2) and (8.3) for a population having any distribution.

If the population has a normal distribution, the procedures in Section 8.2 apply. In this case we can develop an interval estimate of a population mean as follows:

$\sigma$ assumed known

$$\bar{x} \pm z_{\alpha/2} \frac{\sigma}{\sqrt{n}} \tag{8.4}$$

$\sigma$ estimated by $s$

$$\bar{x} \pm t_{\alpha/2} \frac{s}{\sqrt{n}} \tag{8.5}$$

In fact, if the population has a normal distribution, expressions (8.4) and (8.5) can be used to develop an interval estimate of a population mean in both the large-sample and small-sample cases.

In most practical applications, the form of the population distribution is unknown. Because expressions (8.2) and (8.3) apply to a population with any distribution, we make no assumption about the form of the population distribution and use (8.2) or (8.3) provided the sample size is large ($n \geq 30$). Thus, the only time it is necessary to address the assumption that the population has a normal distribution and consider using expressions (8.4) or (8.5) is when the sample size is small ($n < 30$). Figure 8.8 summarizes the interval-estimation procedures we have covered and provides a practical guide for computing an interval estimate of a population mean.

Excel can be used to implement the interval estimation procedures summarized in Figure 8.8. For the intervals involving a $z_{\alpha/2}$ value, the worksheet in Figure 8.4 can be used as a template. For the intervals involving a $t_{\alpha/2}$ value, the worksheet in Figure 8.7 can be used as a template.

**FIGURE 8.8**    SUMMARY OF INTERVAL ESTIMATION PROCEDURES FOR A POPULATION MEAN

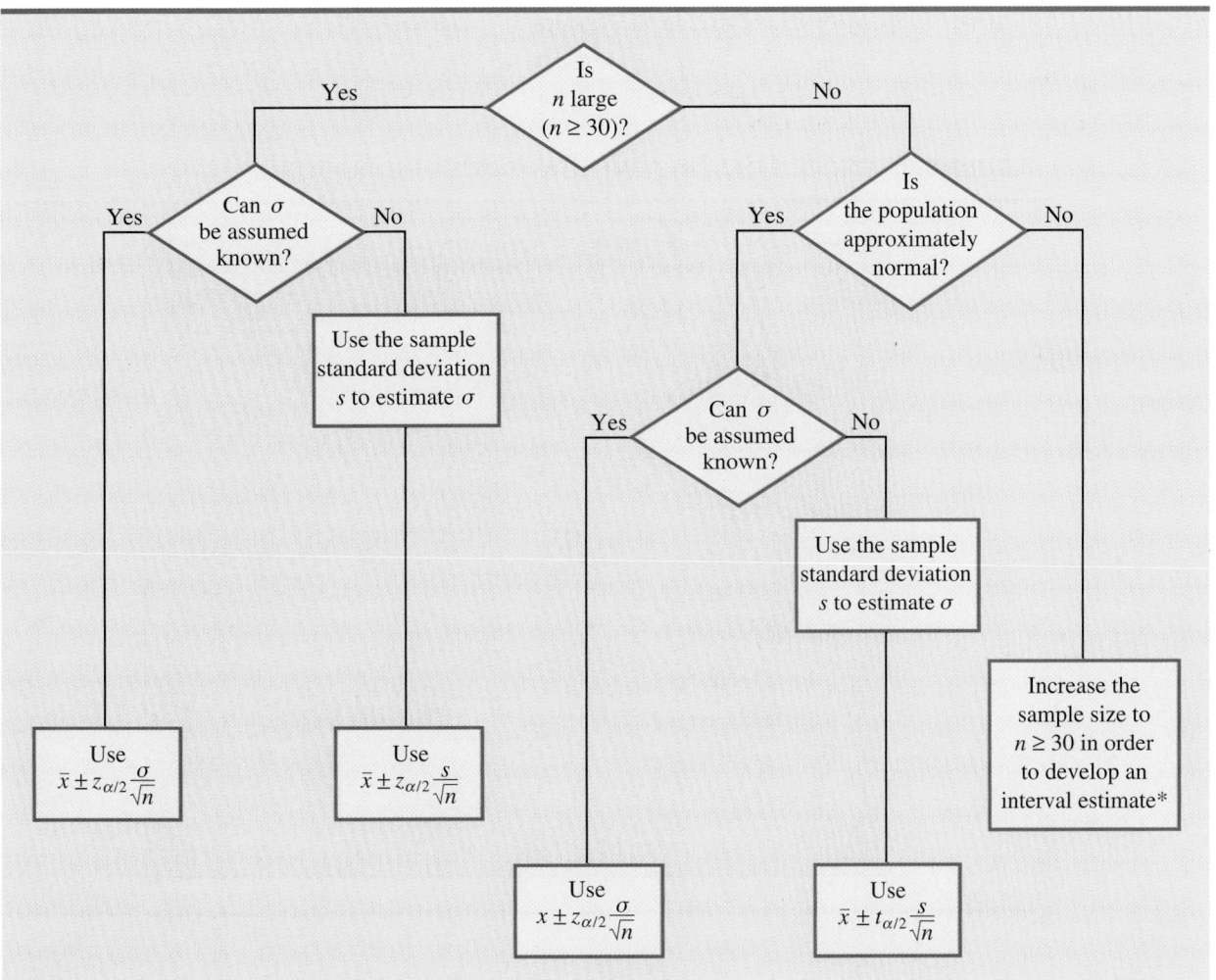

*Sometimes methods from nonparametric statistics can be used in the small-sample case to develop confidence intervals.

## NOTES AND COMMENTS

1. To develop an interval estimate of $\mu$ in the small-sample case, the population must have a normal or approximately normal probability distribution. In Chapter 12 we present a goodness of fit test, and in Chapter 14 we discuss the use of normal probability plots to determine whether a population follows a normal probability distribution. Determining normality for the small-sample case is difficult, and all that can usually be done is to apply good judgment. If in your judgment the population is roughly mound shaped and approximately symmetric, then the normality assumption and the use of the $t$ distribution are appropriate.

2. Excel's descriptive statistics tool (see Chapter 3) can also be used to compute the margin of error when the $t$ distribution is used for a confidence interval estimate of a population mean. For instance, suppose we wanted to compute descriptive statistics and the margin of error for a 95% confidence interval for the Scheer Industries training time data. Starting with a worksheet containing the data in column A of Figure 8.7, select the **Tools** pull-down menu, choose the **Data Analysis** option, and then choose **Descriptive Statistics** from the list of analysis tools. When the descriptive statistics dialog box appears, complete it as shown in Figure 8.9. Note that we have provided the usual information needed to compute descriptive statistics plus we have checked the **Confidence Level for Mean:** box and entered **95** as the confidence level. After clicking **OK,** the information shown in Figure 8.10 will be generated. Note that the margin of error is contained in cell D16. Using the margin of error and the sample mean in cell D3 it is easy to now compute the confidence interval.

**FIGURE 8.9**    EXCEL'S DESCRIPTIVE STATISTICS DIALOG BOX

**FIGURE 8.10**   DESCRIPTIVE STATISTICS AND MARGIN OF ERROR FOR SCHEER INDUSTRIES

| | A | B | C | D | E | F | G |
|---|---|---|---|---|---|---|---|
| 1 | Training Time | | *Training Time* | | | | |
| 2 | 52 | | | | | | |
| 3 | 44 | | Mean | 53.86667 | | | |
| 4 | 55 | | Standard Error | 1.761673 | | | |
| 5 | 44 | | Median | 54 | | | |
| 6 | 45 | | Mode | 44 | | | |
| 7 | 59 | | Standard Deviation | 6.822931 | | | |
| 8 | 50 | | Sample Variance | 46.55238 | | | |
| 9 | 54 | | Kurtosis | -1.37004 | | | |
| 10 | 62 | | Skewness | -0.23179 | | | |
| 11 | 46 | | Range | 19 | | | |
| 12 | 54 | | Minimum | 44 | | | |
| 13 | 58 | | Maximum | 63 | | | |
| 14 | 60 | | Sum | 808 | | | |
| 15 | 62 | | Count | 15 | | The value of the margin of error appears in cell D16. | |
| 16 | 63 | | Confidence Level(95.0%) | 3.778416 | | | |
| 17 | | | | | | | |
| 18 | | | | | | | |

## EXERCISES

## Methods

13. For a $t$ distribution with 12 degrees of freedom, find the area, or probability, that is in each region.
    a. To the left of 1.782.
    b. To the right of $-1.356$.
    c. To the right of 2.681.
    d. To the left of $-1.782$.
    e. Between $-2.179$ and $+2.179$.
    f. Between $-1.356$ and $+1.782$.

14. Find the $t$ value(s) for each of the following examples.
    a. Upper tail area of .05 with 18 degrees of freedom.
    b. Lower tail area of .10 with 22 degrees of freedom.
    c. Upper tail area of .01 with 5 degrees of freedom.
    d. 90% of the area is between these two $t$ values with 14 degrees of freedom.
    e. 95% of the area is between these two $t$ values with 28 degrees of freedom.

15. The following data have been collected for a sample from a normal population: 10, 8, 12, 15, 13, 11, 6, 5.
    a. What is the point estimate of the population mean?
    b. What is the point estimate of the population standard deviation?
    c. What is the 95% confidence interval for the population mean?

16. A simple random sample of 20 observations from a normal population resulted in a sample mean of 17.25 and a sample standard deviation of 3.3.
    a. Develop a 90% confidence interval for the population mean.
    b. Develop a 95% confidence interval for the population mean.
    c. Develop a 99% confidence interval for the population mean.

# Applications

**17.** In the testing of a new production method, 18 employees were selected randomly and asked to try the new method. The sample mean production rate for the 18 employees was 80 parts per hour and the sample standard deviation was 10 parts per hour. Provide 90% and 95% confidence intervals for the population mean production rate for the new method, assuming the population has a normal probability distribution.

**18.** A *USA Today* study of rental car gasoline prices found the following prices per gallon at 12 major airports (*USA Today,* April 4, 2000).

1.58   1.53   1.60   1.55   1.80   1.75   1.58   1.62   1.69   1.21   1.50   1.55

  **a.** What is the point estimate of the population mean price per gallon?
  **b.** What is the point estimate of the population standard deviation?
  **c.** Assuming the population follows a normal distribution, develop a 95% confidence interval estimate of the population mean rental car price per gallon.

**CD** file

**TVtime**

**19.** The American Association of Advertising Agencies records data on nonprogram minutes on half-hour, prime-time television shows. Representative data in minutes for a sample of 20 prime-time shows on major networks at 8:30 P.M. follows.

$\bar{x} = 6.5$

$\sigma = 3.07$

| | | |
|---|---|---|
| 6.0 | 6.6 | 5.8 |
| 7.0 | 6.3 | 6.2 |
| 7.2 | 5.7 | 6.4 |
| 7.0 | 6.5 | 6.2 |
| 6.0 | 6.5 | 7.2 |
| 7.3 | 7.6 | 6.8 |
| 6.0 | 6.2 | |

Provide a point estimate and a 95% confidence interval for the mean number of nonprogram minutes on half-hour, prime-time television shows at 8:30 P.M. Assume the population has a normal distribution.

**20.** Sales personnel for Skillings Distributors are required to submit weekly reports listing the customer contacts made during the week. A sample of 61 weekly contact reports showed a mean of 22.4 customer contacts per week for the sales personnel. The sample standard deviation was 5 contacts.
  **a.** Use the large-sample case [expression (8.3)] to develop a 95% confidence interval for the mean number of weekly customer contacts for the population of sales personnel.
  **b.** Assume that the population of weekly contact data has a normal distribution. Use the *t* distribution with 60 degrees of freedom to develop a 95% confidence interval for the mean number of weekly customer contacts.
  **c.** Compare your answers for parts (a) and (b). Comment on why in the large-sample case it is permissible to develop interval estimates using the procedure in part (a) even though the *t* distribution may also be applicable.

**21.** Due to constituents' complaints to their representatives about rising prescription drug prices, the U.S. Congress considered laws that would force pharmaceutical companies to offer prescription discounts to senior citizens. The House Government Reform Committee provided data on the prescription cost for some of the most widely used drugs (*Newsweek,* May 8, 2000). Assume the following data show a sample of the prescription cost (in dollars) for Zocor, a drug used to lower cholesterol.

$n = 8$

$\bar{x} = 108$

$\sigma = 7.7$

110      112      115      99      100      98      104      126

Assuming a normally distributed population, develop a 95% confidence interval estimate of the population mean cost for a prescription of Zocor.

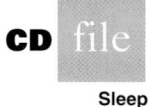

**CD file**

**Sleep**

22. The number of hours Americans sleep each night varies considerably with 12% of the population sleeping less than six hours to 3% sleeping more than eight hours (*The Macmillan Visual Almanac,* 1996). The following sample of 25 individuals reports the hours of sleep per night.

| | | | | |
|---|---|---|---|---|
| 6.9 | 7.6 | 6.5 | 6.2 | 5.3 |
| 7.8 | 7.0 | 5.5 | 7.6 | 6.7 |
| 7.3 | 6.6 | 7.1 | 6.9 | 6.0 |
| 6.8 | 6.5 | 7.2 | 5.8 | 8.6 |
| 7.6 | 7.1 | 6.0 | 7.2 | 7.7 |

   a. What is the point estimate of the population mean number of hours of sleep each night?
   b. Assuming that the population has a normal distribution, develop a 95% confidence interval for the population mean number of hours of sleep each night.

## 8.3    DETERMINING THE SAMPLE SIZE

In the large-sample case with $\sigma$ known, the quantity $z_{\alpha/2} (\sigma/\sqrt{n})$ is the margin of error for an interval estimate with a confidence coefficient of $1 - \alpha$. The values of $z_{\alpha/2}$, $\sigma$, and the sample size $n$ combine to determine the margin of error. Given values for $z_{\alpha/2}$ and $\sigma$, we can determine the sample size $n$ needed to provide any desired margin of error. Development of the formula used to compute the required sample size $n$ follows.

Let $E$ = the desired margin of error

$$E = z_{\alpha/2} \frac{\sigma}{\sqrt{n}}$$

Solving for $\sqrt{n}$, we have

$$\sqrt{n} = \frac{z_{\alpha/2}\sigma}{E}$$

*If a desired margin of error $E$ is selected prior to sampling, the procedures in this section can be used to determine the sample size necessary to satisfy the margin of error requirement.*

Squaring both sides of this equation, we obtain the following expression for the sample size.

**Sample Size for an Interval Estimate of a Population Mean**

$$n = \frac{(z_{\alpha/2})^2\sigma^2}{E^2} \tag{8.6}$$

This sample size will provide the desired margin of error at the chosen confidence level.

In equation (8.6) $E$ is the margin of error that the user is willing to accept, and the value of $z_{\alpha/2}$ follows directly from the confidence level to be used in developing the interval estimate. Although user preference must be considered, 95% confidence is the most frequently chosen value ($z_{.025} = 1.96$).

*A planning value for the population standard deviation $\sigma$ must be specified before the sample size can be determined. Three methods of obtaining a planning value for $\sigma$ are discussed here.*

Finally, equation (8.6) requires a value for the population standard deviation $\sigma$. In most cases, $\sigma$ will be unknown. However, we can still use equation (8.6) if we have a preliminary or *planning value* for $\sigma$. In practice, one of the following procedures can be used.

1. Use the sample standard deviation from a previous sample of the same or similar units.
2. Use a pilot study to select a preliminary sample. The sample standard deviation from the preliminary sample can be used as the planning value for $\sigma$.

3. Use judgment or a "best guess" for the value of $\sigma$. For example, we might begin by estimating the largest and smallest data values in the population. The difference between the largest and smallest values provides an estimate of the range for the data. Finally, the range divided by four is often suggested as a rough approximation of the standard deviation and thus an acceptable planning value for $\sigma$.

Let us demonstrate the use of equation (8.6) to determine the sample size by considering the following example. A previous study that investigated the cost of renting automobiles in the United States found that the cost of renting a medium-sized automobile ranged from $36 per day in Oakland, California, to $73.50 per day in Hartford, Connecticut (*USA Today*, October 16, 1998). Suppose that the organization that conducted this study would like to conduct a new study in order to estimate the current population mean daily rental cost for a medium-sized automobile in the United States. In designing the new study, let us also suppose that the project director has specified that the population mean daily rental cost should be estimated with a margin of error of $2 and a 95% level of confidence.

The project director has specified a desired margin of error of $E = 2$ and the 95% level of confidence indicates $z_{.025} = 1.96$. Thus, we only need a planning value for the population standard deviation $\sigma$ in order to compute the required sample size. At this point, an analyst reviewed the sample data from the previous study and found that the sample standard deviation for the daily rental cost was $9.65. Using this value as the planning value for $\sigma$, we have

Equation (8.6) provides the minimum sample size needed to satisfy the desired margin of error requirement. If the computed sample size is not integer, rounding up to the next integer value will provide a margin of error slightly smaller than required.

$$n = \frac{(z_{\alpha/2})^2\sigma^2}{E^2} = \frac{(1.96)^2(9.65)^2}{2^2} = 89.43$$

Thus, the sample size for the new study needs to be at least 89.43 medium-sized automobile rentals in order to satisfy the project director's $2 margin-of-error requirement. In cases where the computed $n$ is not an integer, we round up to the next integer value; hence, the recommended sample size is 90 medium-sized automobile rentals.

## EXERCISES

### Methods

**23.** How large a sample should be selected to provide a 95% confidence interval with a margin of error of 5? Assume that the population standard deviation is 25.

**24.** The range for a set of data is estimated to be 36.
   a. What is the planning value for the population standard deviation?
   b. Using a 95% confidence level, how large a sample should be used to provide a margin of error of 3?
   c. Using a 95% confidence level, how large a sample should be used to provide a margin of error of 2?

### Applications

**25.** Refer to the Scheer Industries example in Section 8.2. Use $\sigma = 6.82$ as a planning value for the population standard deviation.
   a. Assuming a 95% confidence level, what sample size would be required to obtain a margin of error of 1.5 days?
   b. If the precision statement was made with a 90% confidence level, what sample size would be required to obtain a margin of error of 2 days?

**26.** *Bride's* magazine reported that the mean cost of a wedding is $19,000 (*USA Today,* April 17, 2000). Assume that the population standard deviation is $9,400. *Bride's* plans to use an annual survey to monitor the cost of a wedding. Use 95% confidence.
   **a.** What is the recommended sample size if the desired margin of error is $1000?
   **b.** What is the recommended sample size if the desired margin of error is $500?
   **c.** What is the recommended sample size if the desired margin of error is $200?

**27.** Annual starting salaries for college graduates with business administration degrees are believed to have a standard deviation of approximately $2000. Assume that a 95% confidence interval estimate of the mean annual starting salary is desired. How large a sample should be taken if the margin of error is
   $\sigma = \$2000$
   **a.** $500?
   **b.** $200?
   **c.** $100?

**28.** RealFacts, a real estate research firm, provides monthly mean apartment rental costs for Los Angeles County (*Los Angeles Times,* August 1, 1999). Assume the population standard deviation of rental cost is $220 and that the desired margin of error is $50.
   **a.** What is the recommended sample size for a 90% confidence interval estimate of the population mean rental cost?
   **b.** What is the recommended sample size for a 95% confidence interval?
   **c.** What is the recommended sample size for a 99% confidence interval?
   **d.** If the desired margin of error is fixed, what happens to the sample size as the confidence level is increased?

**29.** The travel-to-work time for residents of the 15 largest cities in the United States is reported in the *1998 Information Please Almanac.* Suppose that a preliminary simple random sample of residents of San Francisco is used to develop a planning value of 6.25 minutes for the population standard deviation.

   **a.** If we want to estimate the population mean travel-to-work time for San Francisco residents with a margin of error of 2 minutes, what sample size should be used? Assume a 95% confidence level.
   **b.** If we want to estimate the population mean travel-to-work time for San Francisco residents with a margin of error of 1 minute, what sample size should be used? Assume 95% confidence level.

**30.** The sample standard deviation of P/E ratios for stocks listed on the New York Stock Exchange is $s = 7.8$ (*The Wall Street Journal,* January 20, 2000). Assume that we are now interested in estimating the population mean P/E ratio for all stocks listed on the New York Stock Exchange. How many stocks should be included in the sample if we want a margin of error of 2? Use a 95% confidence level.

## 8.4   INTERVAL ESTIMATION OF A POPULATION PROPORTION

In Chapter 7 we showed that a sample proportion $\bar{p}$ is used as an estimator of a population proportion $p$ and that for large samples the sampling probability distribution of $\bar{p}$ can be approximated by a normal probability distribution, as shown in Figure 8.11. Recall that the use of the normal distribution as an approximation of the sampling distribution of $\bar{p}$ is based on the condition that both $np$ and $n(1 - p)$ are 5 or more. We will be using the sampling distribution of $\bar{p}$ to make probability statements about the sampling error whenever a sample proportion $\bar{p}$ is used to estimate a population proportion $p$. In this case, the sampling error is defined as the absolute value of the difference between $\bar{p}$ and $p$, written $|\bar{p} - p|$.

When the sample size is large enough to assume the sampling distribution of $\bar{p}$ is normal, the following statement can be made about the sampling error.

There is a $1 - \alpha$ probability that the value of the sample proportion will provide a sampling error of $z_{\alpha/2}\sigma_{\bar{p}}$ or less.

**FIGURE 8.11**    NORMAL APPROXIMATION OF THE SAMPLING DISTRIBUTION OF $\bar{p}$
WHEN $np \geq 5$ AND $n(1 - p) \geq 5$

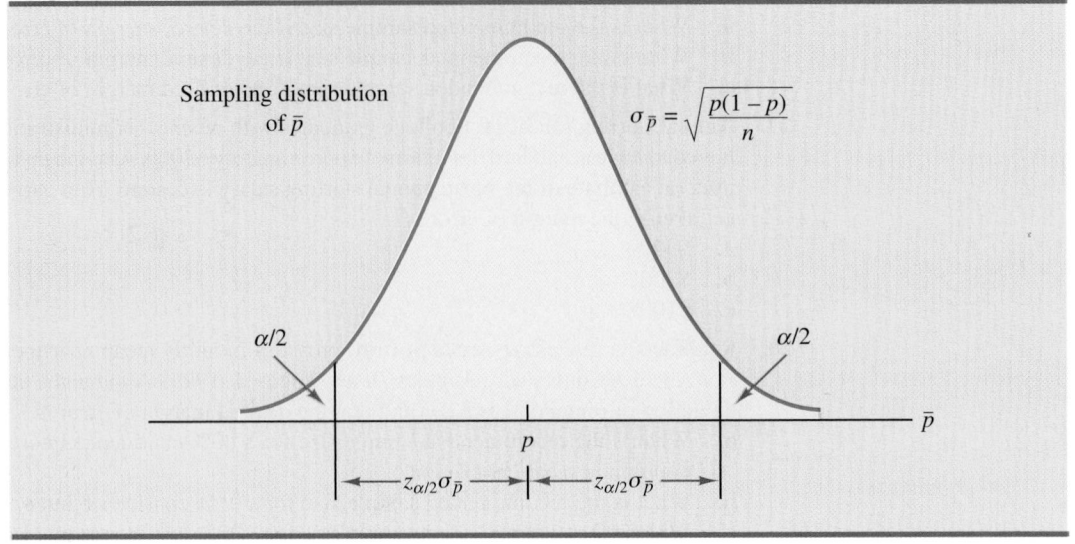

Hence, for a proportion, the quantity $z_{\alpha/2}\sigma_{\bar{p}}$ is the margin of error.

Once we know the margin of error, $z_{\alpha/2}\sigma_{\bar{p}}$, we can subtract and add this value to $\bar{p}$ to obtain an interval estimate of the population proportion. Such an interval estimate is given by

$$\bar{p} \pm z_{\alpha/2}\sigma_{\bar{p}} \tag{8.7}$$

where $1 - \alpha$ is the confidence coefficient. Because $\sigma_{\bar{p}} = \sqrt{p(1 - p)/n}$, we can rewrite (8.7) as

$$\bar{p} \pm z_{\alpha/2}\sqrt{\frac{p(1 - p)}{n}} \tag{8.8}$$

To use expression (8.8) to develop an interval estimate of a population proportion $p$, the value of $p$ would have to be known. But, the value of $p$ is what we are trying to estimate, so we simply substitute the sample proportion $\bar{p}$ for $p$. The resulting general expression for a confidence interval estimate of a population proportion follows.[3]

**Interval Estimate of a Population Proportion**

$$\bar{p} \pm z_{\alpha/2}\sqrt{\frac{\bar{p}(1 - \bar{p})}{n}} \tag{8.9}$$

where $1 - \alpha$ is the confidence coefficient and $z_{\alpha/2}$ is the $z$ value providing an area of $\alpha/2$ in the upper tail of the standard normal probability distribution.

---

[3]An unbiased estimate of $\sigma_{\bar{p}}^2$ is $\bar{p}(1 - \bar{p})/(n - 1)$, which suggests that $\sqrt{\bar{p}(1 - \bar{p})/(n - 1)}$ should be used in place of $\sqrt{\bar{p}(1 - \bar{p})/n}$ in expression (8.9). However, the bias introduced by using $n$ in the denominator does not cause any difficulty because a large sample is generally used in making estimates about population proportions. In such cases the numerical difference between the results obtained by using $n$ and those obtained by using $n - 1$ is negligible.

Let us use the following example to illustrate the computation of the margin of error and an interval estimate for a population proportion. In 1997, Ferrell Calvillo Communications conducted a national survey of 902 women golfers to learn how women golfers view themselves as being treated at golf courses in the United States (*USA Today,* June 3, 1997). The survey found that 397 of the women golfers were satisfied with the availability of tee times. Thus, a point estimate of the proportion of the population of women golfers who are satisfied with the availability of tee times is 397/902 = .4401. Using expression (8.9) and a 95% confidence level, we have

$$\bar{p} \pm z_{\alpha/2} \sqrt{\frac{\bar{p}(1-\bar{p})}{n}}$$

$$.4401 \pm 1.96 \sqrt{\frac{.4401(1-.4401)}{902}}$$

$$.4401 \pm .0324$$

Thus, at 95% confidence, the margin of error is .0324 and the interval estimate of the population proportion is .4077 to .4725. Using percentages, the survey results enable us to state with 95% confidence that between 40.77% and 47.25% of all women golfers are satisfied with the availability of tee times.

## Using Excel to Construct a Confidence Interval

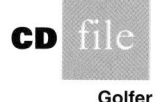

**Golfer**

Excel can be used to construct an interval estimate of the population proportion of women golfers who are satisfied with the availability of tee times. Suppose that the responses in the Ferrell Calvillo survey had been recorded as a Yes or No for each woman surveyed. Refer to Figure 8.12 as we describe the tasks involved in constructing a 95% confidence interval. The formula worksheet is in the background; the value worksheet is in the foreground.

**Enter Data:**  A label and the Yes-No data for the 902 women golfers have been entered into cells A1:A903.

**Enter Functions and Formulas:**  The descriptive statistics we need are provided in cells D3:D6. Because Excel's COUNT function only works with numerical data, we used the COUNTA function in cell D3 to compute the sample size. The response for which we want to develop an interval estimate, Yes or No, is entered into cell D4. Figure 8.12 shows that Yes has been entered into cell D4, indicating that we want to develop an interval estimate of the population proportion of women golfers who are satisfied with the availability of tee times. If we had wanted to develop an interval estimate of the population proportion of women golfers who are not satisfied with the availability of tee times, we would have entered No in cell D4. With Yes entered in cell D4, the COUNTIF function in cell D5 counts the number of Yes responses in the sample. The sample proportion is then computed in cell D6 by dividing the number of Yes responses in cell D5 by the sample size in cell D3.

Cells D8:D10 are used to compute the appropriate $z$ value. The confidence coefficient (0.95) has been entered into cell D8 and the level of significance ($\alpha$) has been computed in cell D9 by entering the formula =1-D8. The $z$ value corresponding to an upper tail area of $\alpha/2$ has been computed by entering the formula =NORMSINV(1-D9/2) into cell D10. The value worksheet shows that $z_{.025} = 1.960$.

Cells D12:D13 provide the estimate of the standard error and the margin of error. In cell D12, we have entered the formula =SQRT(D6*(1-D6)/D3) to compute the standard error using the sample proportion and the sample size as inputs. The formula =D10*D12 has been entered into cell D13 to compute the margin of error.

**FIGURE 8.12** EXCEL WORKSHEET FOR THE SURVEY OF WOMEN GOLFERS

| | A | B | C | D | E |
|---|---|---|---|---|---|
| 1 | Response | | Interval Estimate of a Population Proportion | | |
| 2 | Yes | | | | |
| 3 | No | | Sample Size | =COUNTA(A2:A903) | |
| 4 | Yes | | Response of Interest | Yes | |
| 5 | Yes | | Count for Response | =COUNTIF(A2:A903,D4) | |
| 6 | No | | Sample Proportion | =D5/D3 | |
| 7 | No | | | | |
| 8 | No | | Confidence Coefficient | 0.95 | |
| 9 | Yes | | Level of Significance (alpha) | =1-D8 | |
| 10 | Yes | | z Value | =NORMSINV(1-D9/2) | |
| 11 | Yes | | | | |
| 12 | No | | Standard Error | =SQRT(D6*(1-D6)/D3) | |
| 13 | No | | Margin of Error | =D10*D12 | |
| 14 | Yes | | | | |
| 15 | No | | Point Estimate | =D6 | |
| 16 | No | | Lower Limit | =D15-D13 | |
| 17 | Yes | | Upper Limit | =D15+D13 | |
| 18 | No | | | | |
| 901 | Yes | | | | |
| 902 | No | | | | |
| 903 | Yes | | | | |
| 904 | | | | | |

Note: Rows 19–900 are hidden.

| | A | B | C | D | E | F | G |
|---|---|---|---|---|---|---|---|
| 1 | Response | | Interval Estimate of a Population Proportion | | | | |
| 2 | Yes | | | | | | |
| 3 | No | | Sample Size | 902 | Enter Yes as the | | |
| 4 | Yes | | Response of Interest | Yes | Response of Interest | | |
| 5 | Yes | | Count for Response | 397 | | | |
| 6 | No | | Sample Proportion | 0.4401 | | | |
| 7 | No | | | | | | |
| 8 | No | | Confidence Coefficient | 0.95 | | | |
| 9 | Yes | | Level of Significance (alpha) | 0.05 | | | |
| 10 | Yes | | z Value | 1.960 | | | |
| 11 | Yes | | | | | | |
| 12 | No | | Standard Error | 0.0165 | | | |
| 13 | No | | Margin of Error | 0.0324 | | | |
| 14 | Yes | | | | | | |
| 15 | No | | Point Estimate | 0.4401 | | | |
| 16 | No | | Lower Limit | 0.4077 | | | |
| 17 | Yes | | Upper Limit | 0.4725 | | | |
| 18 | No | | | | | | |
| 901 | Yes | | | | | | |
| 902 | No | | | | | | |
| 903 | Yes | | | | | | |
| 904 | | | | | | | |

Cells D15:D17 provide the point estimate and the lower and upper limits for a confidence interval. The point estimate in cell D15 is the sample proportion. The lower and upper limits in cells D16 and D17 are obtained by subtracting and adding the margin of error to the point estimate. We note that the 95% confidence interval for the proportion of women golfers who are satisfied with the availability of tee times is .4077 to .4725.

The worksheet in Figure 8.12 can be used as a template for developing confidence intervals about a population proportion $p$. To use this worksheet for another problem of this type, we must first enter the new problem data in column A. The response of interest would then be typed in cell D4 and the ranges for the formulas in cells D3 and D5 would be revised to correspond to the new data. After doing so, the point estimate and a 95% confidence interval will be displayed in cells D15:D17. If a confidence interval with a different confidence coefficient is desired, we simply change the value in cell D8.

## Determining the Sample Size

Let us consider the question of how large the sample size should be to obtain an estimate of a population proportion at a specified level of precision. The rationale for the sample size determination in developing interval estimates of $p$ is similar to the rationale used in Section 8.3 to determine the sample size for estimating a population mean.

Previously in this section we pointed out that the margin of error associated with an estimate of a population proportion is $z_{\alpha/2}\sigma_{\bar{p}}$. With $\sigma_{\bar{p}} = \sqrt{p(1-p)/n}$ the size of the margin of error is based on the values of $z_{\alpha/2}$, the population proportion $p$, and the sample size $n$. For a confidence coefficient of $1 - \alpha$, $z_{\alpha/2}$ is known. Then, for a specified value of the population proportion $p$, the size of the margin of error is determined by the sample size $n$. Larger sample sizes provide a smaller margin of error and better precision.

Let $E$ = the desired margin of error

$$E = z_{\alpha/2}\sqrt{\frac{p(1-p)}{n}}$$

Solving this equation for $n$ provides the following formula for the sample size.

**Sample Size for an Interval Estimate of a Population Proportion**

$$n = \frac{(z_{\alpha/2})^2 p(1-p)}{E^2} \qquad\qquad \textbf{(8.10)}$$

In the left margin: Because the population proportion $p$ is what we are attempting to estimate from the sample, a planning value for $p$ must be available in order to use equation (8.10). Four ways to obtain this planning value are provided here.

In equation (8.10), an acceptable size for the desired margin of error is usually specified by the user; in most cases, $E = .10$ or less is chosen. User preference also determines the confidence level and thus the corresponding value of $z_{\alpha/2}$. Finally, because the value of $p$ will not be known in practice, use of equation (8.10) requires a planning value for the population proportion $p$. The planning value can be chosen by one of the following procedures.

1.  Use the sample proportion from a previous sample of the same or similar units.
2.  Use a pilot study to select a preliminary sample. The sample proportion from this sample can be used as the planning value for $p$.
3.  Use judgment or a "best guess" for the value of $p$.
4.  If none of the preceding alternatives apply, use a planning value of $p = .50$.

Let us return to the Ferrell Calvillo Communications survey of women golfers and assume that the company is interested in conducting a new survey to estimate the current proportion of the population of women golfers who are satisfied with the availability of tee times. How large should the sample be if the survey director wants the new study to be able to estimate the population proportion with a margin of error of .025 at a 95% confidence level? With $E = .025$ and $z_{\alpha/2} = 1.96$, we need a planning value of $p$ to answer the sample size question. Using the 1997 survey result of $\bar{p} = .4401$ as the planning value for $p$, equation (8.10) shows that

$$n = \frac{(z_{\alpha/2})^2 p(1-p)}{E^2} = \frac{(1.96)^2(.4401)(1-.4401)}{(.025)^2} = 1514.5861$$

Thus, the sample size must be at least 1514.5861 women golfers to satisfy the margin of error requirement. Rounding up to the next integer value indicates that a sample of 1515 women golfers is recommended.

The fourth alternative suggested for selecting a planning value for $p$ is to use $p = .50$. This value of $p$ is frequently used when no other information is available. To understand why, note that the numerator of equation (8.10) shows that the sample size is proportional to the quantity $p(1-p)$. A larger value for the quantity $p(1-p)$ will result in a larger sample size. Table 8.5 gives some possible values of $p(1-p)$. Note that the largest value of $p(1-p)$ occurs when $p = .50$. Thus, any uncertainty about an appropriate planning value for $p$ can be eased by using $p = .50$ because it provides the largest sample size recommendation. In effect, we are being on the safe or conservative side in recommending the largest possible sample size. If the proportion turns out to be different from the .50 planning value, the precision statement will be better than anticipated. Thus, in using $p = .50$, we are guaranteeing that the sample size will be sufficient to obtain the desired margin of error.

In the left margin: Surveys that ask many questions about proportions are often designed by using a planning value of $p = .50$ for the sample size computation. Using this planning value gives a sample size that guarantees that all estimates of proportions will meet their margin of error requirements.

**TABLE 8.5**     SOME POSSIBLE VALUES FOR $p(1 - p)$

| $p$ | $p(1 - p)$ | |
|---|---|---|
| .10 | $(.10)(.90) = .09$ | |
| .30 | $(.30)(.70) = .21$ | |
| .40 | $(.40)(.60) = .24$ | |
| .50 | $(.50)(.50) = .25$ | ⟵ Largest value for $p(1 - p)$ |
| .60 | $(.60)(.40) = .24$ | |
| .70 | $(.70)(.30) = .21$ | |
| .90 | $(.90)(.10) = .09$ | |

In the survey of women golfers example, a planning value of $p = .50$ would have provided the sample size

$$n = \frac{(z_{\alpha/2})^2 p(1 - p)}{E^2} = \frac{(1.96)^2(.50)(1 - .50)}{(.025)^2} = 1536.64$$

Thus a slightly larger sample size of 1537 women golfers is recommended.

## NOTES AND COMMENTS

The margin of error for estimating a population proportion is almost always .10 or less. In national public opinion polls conducted by organizations such as Gallup and Harris, a .03 or .04 margin of error is generally reported. With such margins of error [$E$ in equation (8.10)] the sample size formula will almost always provide a sample size that is large enough to satisfy the large sample requirements of $np \geq 5$ and $n(1 - p) \geq 5$.

## EXERCISES

### Methods

**SELF** test

**31.** A simple random sample of 400 individuals provided 100 Yes responses.
   a. What is the point estimate of the proportion of the population who would provide Yes responses?
   b. What is the standard error of the proportion, $\sigma_{\bar{p}}$?
   c. Compute the 95% confidence interval for the population proportion.

**32.** A simple random sample of 800 elements generates a sample proportion $\bar{p} = .70$.
   a. Provide a 90% confidence interval for the population proportion.
   b. Provide a 95% confidence interval for the population proportion.

**33.** In a survey, the planning value for the population proportion $p$ is .35. How large a sample should be taken to provide a 95% confidence interval with a margin of error of .05?

**34.** Using a 95% confidence level, how large a sample should be taken to obtain a margin of error for the estimation of a population proportion of .03? Assume that past data are not available for developing a planning value for $p$.

## Applications

**35.** A *Time*/CNN poll asked 814 adults to respond to a series of questions about their feelings toward the state of affairs within the United States. A total of 562 adults responded Yes to the question: Do you feel things are going well in the United States these days? (*Time*, August 11, 1997).

    **a.** What is the point estimate of the proportion of the adult population who feel things are going well in the United States?

    **b.** At a 90% confidence level, what is the margin of error?

    **c.** What is the 90% confidence interval for the proportion of the adult population who feel things are going well in the United States?

**36.** A survey by the Society for Human Resource Management asked 346 job seekers why employees change jobs so frequently (*The Wall Street Journal*, March 28, 2000). The answer selected most (152 times) was "higher compensation elsewhere."

    **a.** What is the point estimate of the proportion of job seekers who would select "higher compensation elsewhere" as the reason for changing jobs?

    **b.** What is the 95% confidence interval estimate of the population proportion?

**CD** file

**Attitude**

$n = 650$

**37.** A survey by Wirthlin Worldwide collected data on attitudes toward the quality of customer service in retail stores. The percentage of Americans who believe that customer service is better today than it was two years ago was reported (*USA Today*, January 20, 1998). Suppose that a sample of 650 adults resulted in the data contained in the data set Attitude. A response of Yes indicates that the individual surveyed believes that customer service is better today than it was two years ago. Develop a 95% confidence interval for the proportion of the population of adults who believe that customer service is better today than it was two years ago.

**38.** Audience profile data collected at the ESPN SportsZone web site showed that 26% of the users were women (*USA Today*, January 21, 1998). Assume that this percentage was based on a sample of 400 users.

    **a.** At the 95% confidence level, what is the margin of error associated with the estimated proportion of users who are women?

    **b.** What is the 95% confidence interval for the population proportion of ESPN SportsZone web site users who are women?

    **c.** How large a sample should be taken if the desired margin of error is .03?

**39.** An Employee Benefit Research Institute survey explored the reasons small employers offer a retirement plan to their employees (*USA Today*, April 4, 2000). The reason "competitive advantage in recruitment/retention" was mentioned 33% of the time.

    **a.** What sample size is recommended if a survey goal is to estimate the proportion of small employers who offer a retirement plan primarily for "competitive advantage in recruitment/retention" with a margin of error of .03. Use 95% confidence.

    **b.** Repeat part (a) using 99% confidence.

**40.** An Associated Press poll of 1018 adults found 255 adults planned to spend less money on gifts during the 1998 holiday season compared to the previous year (ICR Media survey, November 13–17, 1998).

    **a.** What is the point estimate of the proportion of all adults who planned to spend less money on gifts during the 1998 holiday season?

    **b.** At the 95% confidence level, what is the margin of error associated with this estimate?

**41.** An American Express retail survey found that 16% of U.S. consumers had used the Internet to buy gifts during the 1999 holiday season (*USA Today*, January 18, 2000). If 1285 customers participated in the survey, what is the margin of error and what is the interval estimate of the population proportion of customers using the Internet to buy gifts? Use 95% confidence.

$206.$

$1285$

$$\frac{.16\,(.84)}{1285}$$

**42.** A *USA Today*/CNN/Gallup poll for the 2000 presidential campaign sampled 491 potential voters in June (*USA Today,* June 9, 2000). A primary purpose of the poll was to obtain an estimate of the proportion of potential voters who favor each candidate.

Closer to the November election, better precision and smaller margins of error are desired. Assume a planning value for the population proportion of $p = .50$ and that a 95% confidence level is desired. Determine the recommended sample size for each of the following surveys.

| Survey | Margin of Error |
|---|---|
| September | .04 |
| October | .03 |
| Early November | .02 |
| Pre-Election Day | .01 |

**43.** The League of American Theatres and Producers uses an ongoing audience tracking survey that provides up-to-date information about Broadway theater audiences (*Playbill,* Winter 1997). Every week, the League distributes a one-page survey on random theater seats at a rotation roster of Broadway shows. The survey questionnaire takes only five minutes to complete and enables audiences to communicate their views about the theater industry.

**a.** How large a sample should be taken if the desired margin of error on any population proportion is .04? Use a 95% confidence level and a planning value of $p = .50$.

**b.** Assume that the sample size recommended in part (a) is implemented and that during one week 445 theatergoers indicated that they do not live in New York City. What is the point estimate of the proportion of Broadway audiences that do not live in New York City?

**c.** Using the data in part (b), what is the 95% confidence interval for the population proportion of Broadway audiences that do not live in New York City?

# SUMMARY

In this chapter we presented methods for developing a confidence interval for a population mean $\mu$ and a population proportion $p$. The purpose of developing a confidence interval is to give the user a better understanding of the margin of error that may be present. A wide confidence interval indicates poor precision; in such cases, the sample size can be increased to reduce the width of the confidence interval and improve the precision of the estimate.

The expression used to compute an interval estimate of a population mean depends on whether the sample size is large ($n \geq 30$) or small ($n < 30$); whether the population standard deviation can be assumed known or is estimated using the sample standard deviation; and in some cases whether the form of the population is a normal or approximately normal probability distribution. If the sample size is large, no assumption is required about the distribution of the population, and $z_{\alpha/2}$ is used in the computation of the interval estimate. If the sample size is small, the population must have a normal, or approximately normal, probability distribution in order to develop an interval estimate of $\mu$. For a normal probability distribution, $z_{\alpha/2}$ is used in the computation of the interval estimate when $\sigma$ is assumed known, whereas $t_{\alpha/2}$ is used when $\sigma$ is estimated by the sample standard deviation $s$. Finally, if the sample size is small and the assumption of a normally distributed population is inappropriate, we recommend increasing the sample size to $n \geq 30$ to develop a large-sample interval estimate of the population mean.

In practice, the sample sizes required for interval estimates of a population proportion are generally large. Hence, we only provided the large-sample interval estimation formulas for a population proportion where both $np \geq 5$ and $n(1 - p) \geq 5$. In addition, we showed how to determine the sample size so that interval estimates of $\mu$ and $p$ would have a desired margin of error.

We showed how to implement all of the interval estimation procedures using an Excel worksheet. The worksheet in Figure 8.4 can be used as a template to develop interval estimates of a population mean involving a $z_{\alpha/2}$ value and the worksheet in Figure 8.7 can be used as a template for interval estimates of a population mean involving a $t_{\alpha/2}$ value. The worksheet in Figure 8.12 can be used as a template for using Excel to develop interval estimates of a population proportion.

## GLOSSARY

**Interval estimate**   An estimate of a population parameter that provides an interval believed to contain the value of the parameter. It is of the form: Point Estimator $\pm$ Margin of Error.

**Margin of error**   The $\pm$ value added to and subtracted from a point estimate in order to develop a confidence interval.

**Sampling error**   The absolute value of the difference between an unbiased point estimator, such as the sample mean $\bar{x}$, and the population parameter it estimates, such as the population mean $\mu$. In the case of a population mean, the sampling error is $|\bar{x} - \mu|$. In the case of a population proportion, the sampling error is $|\bar{p} - p|$.

**Precision statement**   A probability statement about the size of the sampling error.

**Confidence level**   The confidence associated with an interval estimate. For example, if an interval estimation procedure provides intervals such that 95% of the intervals formed using the procedure will include the population parameter, the interval estimate is said to be constructed at the 95% confidence level.

**Level of significance**   The probability that an interval estimation procedure will generate an interval that does not contain the population parameter.

**$t$ distribution**   A family of probability distributions that can be used to develop interval estimates of a population mean whenever the population standard deviation is estimated by the sample standard deviation and the population has a normal or near-normal probability distribution.

**Degrees of freedom**   A parameter of the $t$ distribution. When the $t$ distribution is used in the computation of an interval estimate of a population mean, the appropriate $t$ distribution has $n - 1$ degrees of freedom, where $n$ is the size of the simple random sample.

## KEY FORMULAS

**General Form of Interval Estimate**

$$\bar{x} \pm \text{Margin of Error} \tag{8.1}$$

**Interval Estimate of a Population Mean: Large-Sample Case ($n \geq 30$) with $\sigma$ Assumed Known**

$$\bar{x} \pm z_{\alpha/2} \frac{\sigma}{\sqrt{n}} \tag{8.2}$$

**Interval Estimate of a Population Mean: Large-Sample Case ($n \geq 30$) with $\sigma$ Estimated by $s$**

$$\bar{x} \pm z_{\alpha/2} \frac{s}{\sqrt{n}} \tag{8.3}$$

**Interval Estimate of a Population Mean: Small-Sample Case ($n < 30$) with $\sigma$ Assumed Known**

$$\bar{x} \pm z_{\alpha/2} \frac{\sigma}{\sqrt{n}} \tag{8.4}$$

**Interval Estimate of a Population Mean: Small-Sample Case ($n < 30$) with $\sigma$ Estimated by $s$**

$$\bar{x} \pm t_{\alpha/2} \frac{s}{\sqrt{n}} \qquad (8.5)$$

**Sample Size for an Interval Estimate of a Population Mean**

$$n = \frac{(z_{\alpha/2})^2 \sigma^2}{E^2} \qquad (8.6)$$

**Interval Estimate of a Population Proportion**

$$\bar{p} \pm z_{\alpha/2} \sqrt{\frac{\bar{p}(1 - \bar{p})}{n}} \qquad (8.9)$$

**Sample Size for an Interval Estimate of a Population Proportion**

$$n = \frac{(z_{\alpha/2})^2 p(1 - p)}{E^2} \qquad (8.10)$$

## SUPPLEMENTARY EXERCISES

**44.** A survey of first-time home buyers found that the mean of annual household income was $50,000 (*CNBC.com,* July 11, 2000). Assume the survey used a sample of 400 first-time home buyers and that the sample standard deviation in income was $20,500.
  **a.** Using 95% confidence, what is the margin of error for this study?
  **b.** Develop a 95% confidence interval for the population mean annual household income for first-time home buyers.

**45.** A survey conducted by the American Automobile Association showed that a family of four spends an average of $215.60 per day while on vacation. Suppose a sample of 64 families of four vacationing at Niagara Falls resulted in the daily expenditures contained in the data set Vacation.
  **a.** Develop a 95% confidence interval estimate of the mean amount spent per day by a family of four visiting Niagara Falls.
  **b.** Using the confidence interval from part (a), does it appear that the population mean amount spent per day by families visiting Niagara Falls is different from the mean reported by the American Automobile Association? Explain.

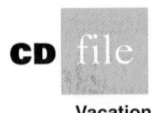
**Vacation**

**46.** A survey by Accountemps asked a sample of 200 executives to provide data on the number of minutes per day office workers waste trying to locate mislabeled, misfiled, or misplaced items (*Astounding Averages,* by D. D. Dauphinais and K. Droste, 1995). Data consistent with this survey are contained in the data set ActTemps.
  **a.** Use ActTemps to develop a point estimate of the number of minutes per day office workers waste trying to locate mislabeled, misfiled, or misplaced items.
  **b.** What is the sample standard deviation?
  **c.** What is the 95% confidence interval for the mean number of minutes wasted per day?

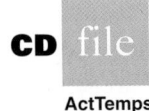
**ActTemps**

**47.** Arthur D. Little, Inc., estimates that approximately 70% of mail received by a household is advertisements (*Time,* July 14, 1997). A sample of 20 households shows the following data for the number of advertisements received and the total number of pieces of mail received during one week.

**Mail**

| Household | Advertisements | Total Mail | Household | Advertisements | Total Mail |
|-----------|----------------|------------|-----------|----------------|------------|
| 1 | 24 | 35 | 4 | 9 | 12 |
| 2 | 9 | 14 | 5 | 15 | 28 |
| 3 | 18 | 30 | 6 | 23 | 33 |

| Household | Advertisements | Total Mail | Household | Advertisements | Total Mail |
|-----------|----------------|------------|-----------|----------------|------------|
| 7 | 13 | 20 | 14 | 17 | 22 |
| 8 | 17 | 20 | 15 | 21 | 24 |
| 9 | 20 | 23 | 16 | 21 | 33 |
| 10 | 20 | 25 | 17 | 15 | 25 |
| 11 | 13 | 19 | 18 | 15 | 24 |
| 12 | 16 | 28 | 19 | 18 | 24 |
| 13 | 20 | 27 | 20 | 12 | 16 |

a. What is the point estimate of the mean number of advertisements received per week? What is the 95% confidence interval for the population mean?

b. What is the point estimate of the mean number of pieces of mail received per week? What is the 95% confidence interval for the population mean?

c. Use the point estimates in parts (a) and (b). Are these estimates in agreement with the statement that approximately 70% of mailings are advertisements?

48. The Money & Investing section of *The Wall Street Journal* contains a summary of daily investment performance for stock exchanges, overseas markets, options, commodities, futures, and so on. In the New York Stock Exchange section, information is provided on each stock's 52-week high price per share, 52-week low price per share, dividend rate, yield, P/E ratio, daily volume, daily high price per share, daily low price per share, closing price per share, and daily net change. The P/E (price/earnings) ratio for each stock is determined by dividing the price of a share of stock by the earnings per share reported by the company for the most recent four quarters. A sample of 10 stocks taken from *The Wall Street Journal* (September 29, 2000) provided the following data on P/E ratios: 5, 7, 9, 10, 14, 23, 20, 15, 3, 26.

a. What is the point estimate of the mean P/E ratio for the population of all stocks listed on the New York Stock Exchange?

b. What is the point estimate of the standard deviation of the P/E ratios for the population of all stocks listed on the New York Stock Exchange?

c. At 95% confidence, what is the interval estimate of the mean P/E ratio for the population of all stocks listed on the New York Stock Exchange? Assume that the population has a normal distribution.

d. Comment on the precision of the results.

49. Many Americans who work in large offices also work at home or in the office on weekends (*USA Today*, June 18, 1997). How large a sample should be taken to estimate the population mean amount of time worked on weekends with a margin of error of 10 minutes. Use a 95% confidence level and assume that the planning value for the population standard deviation is 45 minutes.

50. Mileage tests are conducted for a particular model of automobile. If the desired precision is a 98% confidence interval with a margin of error of one mile per gallon, how many automobiles should be used in the test? Assume that preliminary mileage tests indicate the standard deviation to be 2.6 miles per gallon.

51. In developing patient appointment schedules, a medical center wants an estimate of the mean time that a staff member spends with each patient. How large a sample should be taken if the margin of error is to be 2 minutes at a 95% level of confidence? How large a sample should be taken for a 99% level of confidence? Use a planning value for the population standard deviation of 8 minutes.

52. Annual salary plus bonus data for chief executive officers are presented in the *Business Week* 47th Annual Pay Survey (*Business Week*, April 21, 1997). A preliminary sample showed that the standard deviation is $675 with data provided in thousands of dollars. How many chief executive officers should be in a sample if we want to estimate the population mean annual salary plus bonus with a margin of error of $100,000? (Note: The margin of error would be $E = 100$ because the data are in thousands of dollars.) Use a 95% confidence interval.

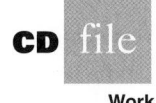

**Work**

**53.** The National Center for Education Statistics conducted a survey to determine the percentage of college students who work to pay for tuition and living expenses (*The Tampa Tribune,* January 22, 1997). The data set Work provides results consistent with the survey for a sample of 450 college students. A response of Yes indicates that the student works to pay for tuition and living expenses.

    **a.** Provide a 95% confidence interval for the population proportion of college students who work to pay for tuition and living expenses.

    **b.** Provide a 99% confidence interval for the population proportion of college students who work to pay for tuition and living expenses.

    **c.** What happens to the margin of error as the confidence is increased from 95% to 99%?

**54.** A *USA Today*/CNN Gallup survey of 369 working parents found 200 who said they spend too little time with their children because of work commitments (*USA Today,* April 10, 1995).

    **a.** What is the point estimate of the proportion of the population of working parents who feel they spend too little time with their children because of work commitments?

    **b.** At a 95% confidence level, what is the margin of error?

    **c.** What is the 95% confidence interval estimate of the population proportion of working parents who feel they spend too little time with their children because of work commitments?

**55.** A *Time*/CNN poll of 1400 American adults asked, "Where would you rather go in your spare time?" The top response by 504 adults was a shopping mall.

    **a.** What is the point estimate of the proportion of adults who would prefer going to a shopping mall in their spare time?

    **b.** At a 95% confidence level, what is the margin of error associated with this estimate?

**56.** A well-known bank credit card firm is interested in estimating the proportion of credit cardholders who carry a nonzero balance at the end of the month and incur an interest charge. Assume that the desired margin of error is .03 at a 98% confidence level.

    **a.** How large a sample should be selected if it is anticipated that roughly 70% of the firm's cardholders carry a nonzero balance at the end of the month?

    **b.** How large a sample should be selected if no planning value for the population proportion could be specified?

**57.** In a survey, 200 people were asked to identify their major source of news information; 110 stated that their major source was television news.

    **a.** Construct a 95% confidence interval for the proportion of people in the population who consider television their major source of news information.

    **b.** How large a sample would be necessary to estimate the population proportion with a margin of error of .05 at a 95% confidence level?

**58.** A Roper Starch survey asked employees ages 18 to 29 if they would prefer better health insurance or a raise in salary (*USA Today,* September 5, 2000). Answer the following questions assuming 340 of 500 employees said they would prefer better health insurance over a raise.

    **a.** What is the point estimate of the proportion of employees ages 18 to 29 who would prefer better health insurance?

    **b.** What is the 95% confidence interval estimate of the population proportion?

**59.** The *1997 Statistical Abstract of the United States* reports the percentage of people 18 years of age and older who smoke. Suppose that a study is being designed to collect new data on smokers and nonsmokers. The best preliminary estimate of the population proportion who smoke is .30.

    **a.** How large a sample should be taken to estimate the proportion of smokers in the population with a margin of error of .02? Use a 95% confidence level.

    **b.** Assume that the study uses your sample size recommendation in part (a) and finds 520 smokers. What is the point estimate of the proportion of smokers in the population?

    **c.** What is the 95% confidence interval for the proportion of smokers in the population?

**60.** Although airline schedules and cost are important factors for business travelers when choosing an airline carrier, a *USA Today* survey found that business travelers list an airline's frequent flyer program as the most important factor (*USA Today*, April 11, 1995). From a sample of $n = 1993$ business travelers who responded to the survey, 618 listed a frequent flyer program as the most important factor.

   **a.** What is the point estimate of the proportion of the population of business travelers who believe a frequent flyer program is the most important factor when choosing an airline carrier?

   **b.** Develop a 95% confidence interval estimate of the population proportion.

   **c.** How large a sample would be required to report the margin of error of .01 at a 95% confidence level? Would you recommend that *USA Today* attempt to provide this degree of precision? Why or why not?

## Case Problem 1    BOCK INVESTMENT SERVICES

Lisa Rae Bock started Bock Investment Services (BIS) in 1994 with the goal of making BIS the leading money market advisory service in South Carolina. To provide better service for her present clients and to attract new clients, she has developed a weekly newsletter. Lisa has been considering adding a new feature to the newsletter that will report the results of a weekly telephone survey of fund managers. To investigate the feasibility of offering this service, and to determine what type of information to include in the newsletter, Lisa selected a simple random sample of 45 money market funds. A portion of the data obtained is shown in Table 8.6, which reports fund assets and 7-day and 30-day yields. Before calling the money market fund managers to obtain additional data, Lisa decided to do some preliminary analysis of the data already collected.

### Managerial Report

   **1.** Use appropriate descriptive statistics to summarize the data on assets and yields for the money market funds.

   **2.** Develop a 95% confidence interval estimate of the mean assets, mean 7-day yield, and mean 30-day yield for the population of money market funds. Provide a managerial interpretation of each interval estimate.

   **3.** Discuss the implications of your findings in terms of how Lisa could use this type of information in preparing her weekly newsletter.

   **4.** What other information would you recommend that Lisa gather to provide the most useful information to her clients?

## Case Problem 2    GULF REAL ESTATE PROPERTIES

Gulf Real Estate Properties, Inc., is a real estate firm located in Southwest Florida. The company, which advertises itself as "expert in the real estate market," monitors condominium sales by collecting data on location, list price, sale price, and number of days it takes to sell each unit. Each condominium is classified as *Gulf View* if it is located directly on the Gulf of Mexico or *No Gulf View* if it is located on the bay or a golf course, near but not on the Gulf. Sample data from the multiple listing service in Naples, Florida, provided recent sales data for 40 Gulf View condominiums and 18 No Gulf-View condominiums.* The data are shown in Table 8.7. Prices are in thousands of dollars.

---

*Data based on condominium sales reported in the Naples MLS (Coldwell Banker, June 2000).

**TABLE 8.6**   DATA FOR BOCK INVESTMENT SERVICES CASE PROBLEM

CD file

**Bock**

| Money Market Fund | Assets (millions $) | 7-day Yield (%) | 30-day Yield (%) |
|---|---|---|---|
| Amcore | 103.9 | 4.10 | 4.08 |
| Alger | 156.7 | 4.79 | 4.73 |
| Arch MM/Trust | 496.5 | 4.17 | 4.13 |
| BT Instit Treas | 197.8 | 4.37 | 4.32 |
| Benchmark Div | 2755.4 | 4.54 | 4.47 |
| Bradford | 707.6 | 3.88 | 3.83 |
| Capital Cash | 1.7 | 4.29 | 4.22 |
| Cash Mgt Trust | 2707.8 | 4.14 | 4.04 |
| Composite | 122.8 | 4.03 | 3.91 |
| Cowen Standby | 694.7 | 4.25 | 4.19 |
| Cortland | 217.3 | 3.57 | 3.51 |
| Declaration | 38.4 | 2.67 | 2.61 |
| Dreyfus | 4832.8 | 4.01 | 3.89 |
| Elfun | 81.7 | 4.51 | 4.41 |
| FFB Cash | 506.2 | 4.17 | 4.11 |
| Federated Master | 738.7 | 4.41 | 4.34 |
| Fidelity Cash | 13272.8 | 4.51 | 4.42 |
| Flex-fund | 172.8 | 4.60 | 4.48 |
| Fortis | 105.6 | 3.87 | 3.85 |
| Franklin Money | 996.8 | 3.97 | 3.92 |
| Freedom Cash | 1079.0 | 4.07 | 4.01 |
| Galaxy Money | 801.4 | 4.11 | 3.96 |
| Government Cash | 409.4 | 3.83 | 3.82 |
| Hanover Cash | 794.3 | 4.32 | 4.23 |
| Heritage Cash | 1008.3 | 4.08 | 4.00 |
| Infinity/Alpha | 53.6 | 3.99 | 3.91 |
| John Hancock | 226.4 | 3.93 | 3.87 |
| Landmark Funds | 481.3 | 4.28 | 4.26 |
| Liquid Cash | 388.9 | 4.61 | 4.64 |
| MarketWatch | 10.6 | 4.13 | 4.05 |
| Merrill Lynch Money | 27005.6 | 4.24 | 4.18 |
| NCC Funds | 113.4 | 4.22 | 4.20 |
| Nationwide | 517.3 | 4.22 | 4.14 |
| Overland | 291.5 | 4.26 | 4.17 |
| Pierpont Money | 1991.7 | 4.50 | 4.40 |
| Portico Money | 161.6 | 4.28 | 4.20 |
| Prudential MoneyMart | 6835.1 | 4.20 | 4.16 |
| Reserve Primary | 1408.8 | 3.91 | 3.86 |
| Schwab Money | 10531.0 | 4.16 | 4.07 |
| Smith Barney Cash | 2947.6 | 4.16 | 4.12 |
| Stagecoach | 1502.2 | 4.18 | 4.13 |
| Strong Money | 470.2 | 4.37 | 4.29 |
| Transamerica Cash | 175.5 | 4.20 | 4.19 |
| United Cash | 323.7 | 3.96 | 3.89 |
| Woodward Money | 1330.0 | 4.24 | 4.21 |

*Source: Barron's,* October 3, 1994.

**TABLE 8.7**    SALES DATA FOR GULF REAL ESTATE PROPERTIES

| Gulf View Condominiums | | | No Gulf View Condominiums | | |
|---|---|---|---|---|---|
| **List Price** | **Sale Price** | **Days to Sell** | **List Price** | **Sale Price** | **Days to Sell** |
| 495.0 | 475.0 | 130 | 217.0 | 217.0 | 182 |
| 379.0 | 350.0 | 71 | 148.0 | 135.5 | 338 |
| 529.0 | 519.0 | 85 | 186.5 | 179.0 | 122 |
| 552.5 | 534.5 | 95 | 239.0 | 230.0 | 150 |
| 334.9 | 334.9 | 119 | 279.0 | 267.5 | 169 |
| 550.0 | 505.0 | 92 | 215.0 | 214.0 | 58 |
| 169.9 | 165.0 | 197 | 279.0 | 259.0 | 110 |
| 210.0 | 210.0 | 56 | 179.9 | 176.5 | 130 |
| 975.0 | 945.0 | 73 | 149.9 | 144.9 | 149 |
| 314.0 | 314.0 | 126 | 235.0 | 230.0 | 114 |
| 315.0 | 305.0 | 88 | 199.8 | 192.0 | 120 |
| 885.0 | 800.0 | 282 | 210.0 | 195.0 | 61 |
| 975.0 | 975.0 | 100 | 226.0 | 212.0 | 146 |
| 469.0 | 445.0 | 56 | 149.9 | 146.5 | 137 |
| 329.0 | 305.0 | 49 | 160.0 | 160.0 | 281 |
| 365.0 | 330.0 | 48 | 322.0 | 292.5 | 63 |
| 332.0 | 312.0 | 88 | 187.5 | 179.0 | 48 |
| 520.0 | 495.0 | 161 | 247.0 | 227.0 | 52 |
| 425.0 | 405.0 | 149 | | | |
| 675.0 | 669.0 | 142 | | | |
| 409.0 | 400.0 | 28 | | | |
| 649.0 | 649.0 | 29 | | | |
| 319.0 | 305.0 | 140 | | | |
| 425.0 | 410.0 | 85 | | | |
| 359.0 | 340.0 | 107 | | | |
| 469.0 | 449.0 | 72 | | | |
| 895.0 | 875.0 | 129 | | | |
| 439.0 | 430.0 | 160 | | | |
| 435.0 | 400.0 | 206 | | | |
| 235.0 | 227.0 | 91 | | | |
| 638.0 | 618.0 | 100 | | | |
| 629.0 | 600.0 | 97 | | | |
| 329.0 | 309.0 | 114 | | | |
| 595.0 | 555.0 | 45 | | | |
| 339.0 | 315.0 | 150 | | | |
| 215.0 | 200.0 | 48 | | | |
| 395.0 | 375.0 | 135 | | | |
| 449.0 | 425.0 | 53 | | | |
| 499.0 | 465.0 | 86 | | | |
| 439.0 | 428.5 | 158 | | | |

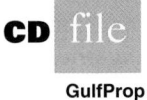

**CD** file

**GulfProp**

## Managerial Report

1. Use appropriate descriptive statistics to summarize each of the three variables for the 40 Gulf View condominiums.
2. Use appropriate descriptive statistics to summarize each of the three variables for the 18 No Gulf View condominiums.
3. Compare your summary results. Discuss any specific statistical results that would help a real estate agent understand the condominium market.

4. Develop a 95% confidence interval estimate for the mean sales price and mean number of days to sell a Gulf View condominium. Interpret your results.
5. Develop a 95% confidence interval estimate for the mean sales price and mean number of days to sell a No Gulf View condominium. Interpret your results.
6. Assume the branch manager has requested estimates of the mean selling price of Gulf View condominiums with a margin of error of $40,000 and the mean selling price of No Gulf View condominiums with a margin of error of $15,000. Using 95% confidence, how large should the sample sizes be?
7. Gulf Real Estate Properties has just signed contracts for two new listings: a Gulf View condominium with a list price of $589,000 and a No Gulf View condominium with a list price of $285,000. What is your estimate of the final selling price and number of days required to sell each of these units?

## Case Problem 3   METROPOLITAN RESEARCH, INC.

Metropolitan Research, Inc., is a consumer research organization that conducts surveys designed to evaluate a wide variety of products and services available to consumers. In one particular study, Metropolitan was interested in learning about consumer satisfaction with the performance of automobiles produced by a major Detroit manufacturer. A questionnaire sent to owners of one of the manufacturer's full-sized cars revealed several complaints about early transmission problems. To learn more about the transmission failures, Metropolitan used a sample of actual transmission repairs provided by a transmission repair firm in the Detroit area. The following data show the actual number of miles that 50 vehicles had been driven at the time of transmission failure.

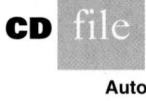

Auto

| | | | | | | | |
|---|---|---|---|---|---|---|---|
| 85,092 | 32,609 | 59,465 | 77,437 | 32,534 | 64,090 | 32,464 | 59,902 |
| 39,323 | 89,641 | 94,219 | 116,803 | 92,857 | 63,436 | 65,605 | 85,861 |
| 64,342 | 61,978 | 67,998 | 59,817 | 101,769 | 95,774 | 121,352 | 69,568 |
| 74,276 | 66,998 | 40,001 | 72,069 | 25,066 | 77,098 | 69,922 | 35,662 |
| 74,425 | 67,202 | 118,444 | 53,500 | 79,294 | 64,544 | 86,813 | 116,269 |
| 37,831 | 89,341 | 73,341 | 85,288 | 138,114 | 53,402 | 85,586 | 82,256 |
| 77,539 | 88,798 | | | | | | |

## Managerial Report

1. Use appropriate descriptive statistics to summarize the transmission failure data.
2. Develop a 95% confidence interval for the mean number of miles driven until transmission failure for the population of automobiles that have had transmission failure. Provide a managerial interpretation of the interval estimate.
3. Discuss the implications of your statistical finding in terms of the belief that some owners of the automobiles have experienced early transmission failures.
4. How many repair records should be sampled if the research firm wants the population mean number of miles driven until transmission failure to be estimated with a margin of error of 5000 miles? Use a 95% confidence level.
5. What other information would you like to gather to evaluate the transmission failure problem more fully?

# HYPOTHESIS TESTING

**CONTENTS**

Chapter 9

## STATISTICS IN PRACTICE

### HARRIS CORPORATION*
*Melbourne, Florida*

Harris Corporation is a communications equipment company that provides products and services for worldwide markets including wireless, broadcast, government, and network support systems. The company has sales and service facilities in more than 80 countries. Many of the Harris products require medium- to high-volume production operations, including printed circuit assembly, final product assembly, and testing.

Harris Corporation used hypothesis testing to solve a problem in the soldering process for one of its circuit boards. © CORBIS.

One of the company's high-volume products has an assembly called an RF deck. Each RF deck consists of 16 electronic components soldered to a machined casting that forms the plated surface of the deck. During a manufacturing run, a problem developed in the soldering process; the flow of solder onto the deck did not meet the quality criteria established for the product. After considering a variety of factors that might affect the soldering process, an engineer made the preliminary determination that the soldering problem was most likely due to defective platings.

The engineer wondered whether the proportion of defective platings in the Harris inventory exceeded that set by the supplier's design specifications. With $p$ indicating the proportion of defective platings in the Harris inventory and $p_0$ indicating the proportion of defective platings set by the supplier's design specifications, the following hypotheses were formulated.

$$H_0: p \leq p_0$$
$$H_a: p > p_0$$

$H_0$ indicates that the Harris inventory has a defective plating proportion less than or equal to that set by the design specifications. Such a proportion would be judged acceptable, and the engineer would need to look for other causes of the soldering problem. How-

ever, $H_a$ indicates that the Harris inventory has a defective plating proportion greater than that set by the design specifications. In that case, excessive defective platings may well be the cause of the soldering problem and action should be taken to determine why the defective proportion in inventory is so high.

Tests made on a sample of platings from the Harris inventory resulted in the rejection of $H_0$. The conclusion was that $H_a$ was true and that the proportion of defective platings in inventory exceeded that set by the supplier's design specifications. Further investigation of the inventory storage area led to the conclusion that the underlying problem was shelf contamination during storage. By altering the storage environment, the engineer was able to solve the problem.

In this chapter you will learn how to formulate hypotheses about a population mean and a population proportion. Through the analysis of sample data, you will be able to determine whether a hypothesis should or should not be rejected. Appropriate conclusions and actions will be demonstrated for testing research hypotheses, testing the validity of a claim, and decision making.

---

*The authors are indebted to Richard A. Marshall of the Harris Corporation for providing this Statistics in Practice.

In Chapters 7 and 8 we showed how a sample could be used to develop point and interval estimates of population parameters. In this chapter we continue the discussion of statistical inference by showing how *hypothesis testing* can be used to determine whether a statement about the value of a population parameter should or should not be rejected.

In hypothesis testing we begin by making a tentative assumption about a population parameter. This tentative assumption is called the **null hypothesis** and is denoted by $H_0$. We then define another hypothesis, called the **alternative hypothesis,** which is the opposite of what is stated in the null hypothesis. The alternative hypothesis is denoted by $H_a$. The hypothesis testing procedure involves using data from a sample to test the two competing statements indicated by $H_0$ and $H_a$.

The purpose of this chapter is to show how hypothesis tests can be conducted about a population mean and a population proportion. We begin by providing examples that illustrate approaches to developing null and alternative hypotheses.

## 9.1   DEVELOPING NULL AND ALTERNATIVE HYPOTHESES

*Learning to formulate hypotheses correctly will take practice. Expect some initial confusion over the proper choice of hypotheses $H_0$ and $H_a$. The examples in this section show a variety of forms for $H_0$ and $H_a$ depending upon the application.*

In some applications it may not be obvious how the null and alternative hypotheses should be formulated. Care must be taken to be sure the hypotheses are structured appropriately and that the hypothesis testing conclusion provides the information the researcher or decision maker wants. Guidelines for establishing the null and alternative hypotheses will be given for three types of situations in which hypothesis testing procedures are commonly employed.

### Testing Research Hypotheses

Consider a particular automobile model that currently attains an average fuel efficiency of 24 miles per gallon. A product research group has developed a new fuel injection system specifically designed to increase the miles-per-gallon rating. To evaluate the new system, several will be manufactured, installed in automobiles, and subjected to research-controlled driving tests. Here the product research group is looking for evidence to conclude that the new system *increases* the mean miles-per-gallon rating. In this case, the research hypothesis is that the new fuel injection system will provide a mean miles-per-gallon rating exceeding 24; that is, $\mu > 24$. As a general guideline, a research hypothesis should be stated as the *alternative hypothesis*. Hence, the appropriate null and alternative hypotheses for the study are:

$$H_0: \mu \leq 24$$
$$H_a: \mu > 24$$

*Hypothesis testing is proof by contradiction. Thus, the research hypothesis is the alternative hypothesis. The conclusion that the research hypothesis is true can be made if the sample data contradicts the null hypothesis.*

If the sample results indicate that $H_0$ cannot be rejected, researchers cannot conclude that the new fuel injection system is better. Perhaps more research and subsequent testing should be conducted. However, if the sample results indicate that $H_0$ can be rejected, researchers can make the inference that $H_a: \mu > 24$ is true. With this conclusion, the researchers have the statistical support necessary to state that the new system increases the mean number of miles per gallon. Action to begin production with the new fuel injection system may be undertaken.

In research studies such as these, the null and alternative hypotheses should be formulated so that the rejection of $H_0$ supports the conclusion and action being sought. The research hypothesis therefore should be expressed as the alternative hypothesis.

### Testing the Validity of a Claim

As an illustration of testing the validity of a claim, consider the situation of a manufacturer of soft drinks who states that two-liter containers of its products have an average of at least 67.6 fluid ounces. A sample of two-liter containers will be selected, and the contents will be measured to test the manufacturer's claim. In this type of hypothesis testing situation, we generally assume that the manufacturer's claim is true unless the sample evidence is contradictory. Using this approach for the soft-drink example, we would state the null and alternative hypotheses as follows.

$$H_0: \mu \geq 67.6$$
$$H_a: \mu < 67.6$$

If the sample results indicate $H_0$ cannot be rejected, the manufacturer's claim will not be challenged. However, if the sample results indicate $H_0$ can be rejected, the inference will be made that $H_a$: $\mu < 67.6$ is true. With this conclusion, statistical evidence indicates that the manufacturer's claim is incorrect and that the soft drink containers are being filled with a mean less than the claimed 67.6 ounces. Appropriate action against the manufacturer may be considered.

> A manufacturer's claim is usually given the benefit of the doubt and stated as the null hypothesis. The conclusion that the claim is false can be made if the null hypothesis is rejected.

In any situation that involves testing the validity of a claim, the null hypothesis is generally based on the assumption that the claim is true. The alternative hypothesis is then formulated so that rejection of $H_0$ will provide statistical evidence that the stated assumption is incorrect. Action to correct the claim should be considered whenever $H_0$ is rejected.

## Testing in Decision-Making Situations

In testing research hypotheses or testing the validity of a claim, action is taken if $H_0$ is rejected. In many instances, however, action must be taken both when $H_0$ cannot be rejected and when $H_0$ can be rejected. In general, this type of situation occurs when a decision maker must choose between two courses of action, one associated with the null hypothesis and another associated with the alternative hypothesis. For example, on the basis of a sample of parts from a shipment that has just been received, a quality control inspector must decide whether to accept the shipment or to return the shipment to the supplier because it does not meet specifications. Assume that specifications for a particular part require a mean length of two inches per part. If the mean length is greater or less than the 2-inch standard, the parts will cause quality problems in the assembly operation. In this case, the null and alternative hypotheses would be formulated as follows.

$$H_0: \mu = 2$$
$$H_a: \mu \neq 2$$

If the sample results indicate $H_0$ cannot be rejected, the quality control inspector will have no reason to doubt that the shipment meets specifications, and the shipment will be accepted. However, if the sample results indicate $H_0$ should be rejected, the conclusion will be that the parts do not meet specifications. In this case, the quality control inspector will have sufficient evidence to return the shipment to the supplier. Thus, we see that for these types of situations, action is taken both when $H_0$ cannot be rejected and when $H_0$ can be rejected.

## Summary of Forms for Null and Alternative Hypotheses

Let $\mu_0$ denote the specific numerical value being considered in the null and alternative hypotheses. In general, a hypothesis test about the values of a population mean $\mu$ takes one of the following three forms.

> The three possible forms of hypotheses $H_0$ and $H_a$ are shown here. Note that the equality always appears in the null hypothesis $H_0$.

$$
\begin{array}{ccc}
H_0: \mu \geq \mu_0 & H_0: \mu \leq \mu_0 & H_0: \mu = \mu_0 \\
H_a: \mu < \mu_0 & H_a: \mu > \mu_0 & H_a: \mu \neq \mu_0
\end{array}
$$

In many situations, the choice of $H_0$ and $H_a$ is not obvious and judgment is necessary to select the proper form. However, as the preceding forms show, the equality part of the expression (either $\geq$, $\leq$, or $=$) *always* appears in the null hypothesis. In selecting the proper form of $H_0$ and $H_a$, keep in mind that the alternative hypothesis is what the test is attempting to establish. Hence, asking whether the user is looking for evidence to support $\mu < \mu_0$, $\mu > \mu_0$, or $\mu \neq \mu_0$ will help determine $H_a$. The following exercises are designed to provide practice in choosing the proper form for a hypothesis test.

## EXERCISES

**1.** The manager of the Danvers-Hilton Resort Hotel has stated that the mean guest bill for a weekend is $600 or less. A member of the hotel's accounting staff has noticed that the total charges for guest bills have been increasing in recent months. The accountant will use a sample of weekend guest bills to test the manager's claim.

$\overline{x} = 600$

    **a.** Which form of the hypotheses should be used to test the manager's claim? Explain.

$$H_0: \mu \geq 600 \qquad H_0: \mu \leq 600 \qquad H_0: \mu = 600$$
$$H_a: \mu < 600 \qquad H_a: \mu > 600 \qquad H_a: \mu \neq 600$$

    **b.** What conclusion is appropriate when $H_0$ cannot be rejected?
    **c.** What conclusion is appropriate when $H_0$ can be rejected?

**2.** The manager of an automobile dealership is considering a new bonus plan designed to increase sales volume. Currently, the mean sales volume is 14 automobiles per month. The manager wants to conduct a research study to see whether the new bonus plan increases sales volume. To collect data on the plan, a sample of sales personnel will be allowed to sell under the new bonus plan for a 1-month period.

    **a.** Develop the null and alternative hypotheses that are most appropriate for this research situation.
    **b.** Comment on the conclusion when $H_0$ cannot be rejected.
    **c.** Comment on the conclusion when $H_0$ can be rejected.

**3.** A production line operation is designed to fill cartons with laundry detergent to a mean weight of 32 ounces. A sample of cartons is periodically selected and weighed to determine whether underfilling or overfilling is occurring. If the sample data lead to a conclusion of underfilling or overfilling, the production line will be shut down and adjusted to obtain proper filling.

$\overline{x} = 32$

    **a.** Formulate the null and alternative hypotheses that will help in deciding whether to shut down and adjust the production line.
    **b.** Comment on the conclusion and the decision when $H_0$ cannot be rejected.
    **c.** Comment on the conclusion and the decision when $H_0$ can be rejected.

**4.** Because of high production-changeover time and costs, a director of manufacturing must convince management that a proposed manufacturing method reduces costs before the new method can be implemented. The current production method operates with a mean cost of $220 per hour. A research study is to be conducted in which the cost of the new method will be measured over a sample production period.

    **a.** Develop the null and alternative hypotheses that are most appropriate for this study.
    **b.** Comment on the conclusion when $H_0$ cannot be rejected.
    **c.** Comment on the conclusion when $H_0$ can be rejected.

## 9.2 TYPE I AND TYPE II ERRORS

The null and alternative hypotheses are competing statements about the population. Either the null hypothesis $H_0$ is true or the alternative hypothesis $H_a$ is true, but not both. Ideally the hypothesis testing procedure should lead to the acceptance of $H_0$ when $H_0$ is true and the rejection of $H_0$ when $H_a$ is true. Unfortunately, the correct conclusions are not always possible. Because hypothesis tests are based on sample information, we must allow for the possibility of errors. Table 9.1 illustrates the two kinds of errors that can be made in hypothesis testing.

    The first row of Table 9.1 shows what can happen when the conclusion is to accept $H_0$. If $H_0$ is true, this conclusion is correct. However, if $H_a$ is true, we have made a **Type II error;**

**TABLE 9.1**     ERRORS AND CORRECT CONCLUSIONS IN HYPOTHESIS TESTING

|  |  | Population Condition | |
|---|---|---|---|
|  |  | $H_0$ True | $H_a$ True |
| Conclusion | Accept $H_0$ | Correct Conclusion | Type II Error |
|  | Reject $H_0$ | Type I Error | Correct Conclusion |

that is, we have accepted $H_0$ when it is false. The second row of Table 9.1 shows what can happen when the conclusion is to reject $H_0$. If $H_0$ is true, we have made a **Type I error**; that is, we have rejected $H_0$ when it is true. However, if $H_a$ is true, rejecting $H_0$ is correct.

Recall the hypothesis testing illustration discussed in Section 9.1 in which an automobile product research group had developed a new fuel injection system designed to increase the miles-per-gallon rating of a particular automobile. With the current model obtaining an average of 24 miles per gallon, the hypothesis test was formulated as follows.

$$H_0: \mu \leq 24$$
$$H_a: \mu > 24$$

The alternative hypothesis, $H_a: \mu > 24$, indicates that the researchers are looking for sample evidence that will support the conclusion that the population mean miles per gallon is greater than 24.

In this application, the Type I error of rejecting $H_0$ when it is true corresponds to the researchers claiming that the new fuel injection system improves the miles-per-gallon rating ($\mu > 24$) when in fact the new fuel injection system is not any better than the current system. In contrast, the Type II error of accepting $H_0$ when it is false corresponds to the researchers concluding that the new fuel injection system is not any better than the current system ($\mu \leq 24$) when in fact the new fuel injection system improves the miles-per-gallon rating.

In practice, the person conducting the hypothesis test specifies the maximum allowable probability of making a Type I error, called the **level of significance** for the test. The level of significance is denoted $\alpha$. Common choices for the level of significance are $\alpha = .05$ and $\alpha = .01$. Referring to the second row of Table 9.1, note that the conclusion to *reject $H_0$* indicates that either a Type I error or a correct conclusion has been made. Thus, if the probability of making a Type I error is controlled for by selecting a small value for the level of significance, we have a high degree of confidence that the conclusion to reject $H_0$ is correct. In such cases, we have statistical support for concluding that $H_0$ is false and $H_a$ is true. Any action suggested by the alternative hypothesis $H_a$ is appropriate.

Although most applications of hypothesis testing control for the probability of making a Type I error, they do not always control for the probability of making a Type II error. Hence, if we decide to accept $H_0$, we cannot determine how confident we can be with that decision. Because of the uncertainty associated with making a Type II error, statisticians often recommend that we use the statement "do not reject $H_0$" instead of "accept $H_0$." Using the statement "do not reject $H_0$" carries the recommendation to withhold both judgment and action. In effect, by never directly accepting $H_0$, the statistician avoids the risk of making a Type II error. Whenever the probability of making a Type II error has not been determined and controlled, we will not make the conclusion to accept $H_0$. In such cases, only two conclusions are possible: *do not reject $H_0$* or *reject $H_0$*.

If the sample data are consistent with the null hypothesis $H_0$, we will follow the practice of concluding "*do not reject $H_0$*." This conclusion is preferred over "*accept $H_0$*," when we have not controlled for the probability of making a Type II error.

Controlling for a Type II error in hypothesis testing is not common, but it can be done. In fact, in Sections 9.7 and 9.8, we will illustrate procedures for determining and controlling the probability of making a Type II error. If proper controls have been established for this error, action based on an "accept $H_0$" conclusion can be appropriate.

## NOTES AND COMMENTS

Many applications of hypothesis testing have a decision-making goal. The conclusion *reject $H_0$* provides the statistical support to conclude that $H_a$ is true and to take whatever action is appropriate. The statement "do not reject $H_0$", although inconclusive, often forces managers to behave as though $H_0$ is true. In this case, managers need to be aware of the fact that such action may result in a Type II error.

## EXERCISES

5. Americans spend an average of 8.6 minutes per day reading newspapers (*USA Today*, April 10, 1995). A researcher believes that individuals in management positions spend more than the national average time per day reading newspapers. A sample of individuals in management positions will be selected by the researcher. Data on newspaper reading times will be used to test the following null and alternative hypotheses.

$$H_0: \mu \leq 8.6$$
$$H_a: \mu > 8.6$$

   a. What is the Type I error in this situation? What are the consequences of making this error?
   b. What is the Type II error in this situation? What are the consequences of making this error?

6. The label on a 3-quart carton of orange juice claims that the orange juice contains an average of 1 gram of fat or less. Answer the following questions for a hypothesis test that could be used to test the claim on the label.
   a. Develop the appropriate null and alternative hypotheses.
   b. What is the Type I error in this situation? What are the consequences of making this error?
   c. What is the Type II error in this situation? What are the consequences of making this error?

7. Carpetland salespersons have had sales averaging $8000 per week. Steve Contois, the firm's vice president, has proposed a compensation plan with new selling incentives. Steve hopes that the results of a trial selling period will enable him to conclude that the compensation plan increases the average sales per salesperson.
   a. Develop the appropriate null and alternative hypotheses.
   b. What is the Type I error in this situation? What are the consequences of making this error?
   c. What is the Type II error in this situation? What are the consequences of making this error?

8. Suppose a new production method will be implemented if a hypothesis test supports the conclusion that the new method reduces the mean operating cost per hour.
   a. State the appropriate null and alternative hypotheses if the mean cost for the current production method is $220 per hour.
   b. What is the Type I error in this situation? What are the consequences of making this error?
   c. What is the Type II error in this situation? What are the consequences of making this error?

## 9.3  ONE-TAILED TESTS ABOUT A POPULATION MEAN: LARGE-SAMPLE CASE

The Federal Trade Commission (FTC) periodically conducts studies designed to test the claims manufacturers make about their products. For example, the label on a large can of Hilltop Coffee states that the can contains at least 3 pounds of coffee. Suppose we want to check this claim by using hypothesis testing.

The first step is to develop the null and alternative hypotheses. We begin by tentatively assuming that the manufacturer's claim is correct. If the population of coffee cans has a mean weight of 3 or more pounds per can, Hilltop's claim about its product is correct. However, if the population of coffee cans has a mean weight less than 3 pounds per can, Hilltop's claim is incorrect.

With $\mu$ denoting the mean weight of cans for the population, the null and the alternative hypotheses are as follows.

$$H_0: \mu \geq 3$$
$$H_a: \mu < 3$$

If the sample data indicate that $H_0$ cannot be rejected, the statistical evidence does not support the conclusion that a label violation has occurred. Hence, no action would be taken against Hilltop. However, if sample data indicate that $H_0$ can be rejected, we will conclude that the alternative hypothesis, $H_a: \mu < 3$, is true. In that case, a conclusion of underfilling and a charge of a label violation would be justified.

Suppose a random sample of 36 cans of coffee is selected. Note that if the mean filling weight, $\bar{x}$, for the sample of 36 cans is less than 3 pounds, the sample results will begin to cast doubt on the null hypothesis $H_0: \mu \geq 3$. But how much less than 3 pounds must $\bar{x}$ be before we would be willing to risk making a Type I error and falsely accuse the company of a label violation?

To answer this question, let us tentatively assume that the null hypothesis is true with $\mu = 3$. From the study of sampling distributions in Chapter 7, we know that whenever the sample size is large ($n \geq 30$), the sampling distribution of $\bar{x}$ can be approximated by a normal probability distribution. Figure 9.1 shows the sampling distribution of $\bar{x}$ when the null hypothesis is true at $\mu = 3$.

The value of $z = (\bar{x} - 3)/\sigma_{\bar{x}}$ is the number of standard errors $\bar{x}$ is from $\mu = 3$. For hypothesis tests about a population mean, we will use $z$ as a **test statistic** to determine whether

**FIGURE 9.1**   SAMPLING DISTRIBUTION OF $\bar{x}$ FOR THE HILLTOP COFFEE STUDY WHEN THE NULL HYPOTHESIS IS TRUE ($\mu = 3$)

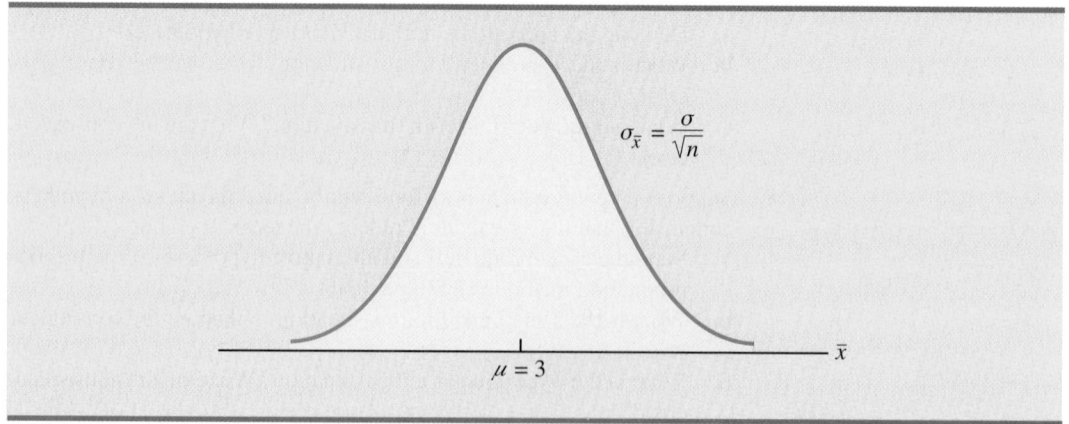

Recall that the standard
error is the name used for
the standard deviation of a
sampling distribution.

$\bar{x}$ deviates enough from $\mu = 3$ to justify rejecting the null hypothesis. Note that a value of $z = -1$ means that $\bar{x}$ is 1 standard error below $\mu = 3$, a value of $z = -2$ means that $\bar{x}$ is 2 standard errors below $\mu = 3$, and so on. Obtaining a value of $z < -3$ is unlikely if the null hypothesis is true. The key question is: How small must the test statistic $z$ be before we have enough evidence to reject the null hypothesis?

Figure 9.2 shows that the probability of observing a value for $\bar{x}$ of more than 1.645 standard errors below the mean of $\mu = 3$ is .05. Hence, if we were to reject the null hypothesis whenever the value of the test statistic $z = (\bar{x} - 3)/\sigma_{\bar{x}}$ is less than $-1.645$, the probability of making a Type I error would be .05. If the FTC considered .05 to be an acceptable probability of making a Type I error, we would reject the null hypothesis whenever the test statistic indicates that the sample mean is more than 1.645 standard errors below $\mu = 3$. Thus, we would reject $H_0$ if $z < -1.645$.

The methodology of hypothesis testing requires that we specify the maximum allowable probability of a Type I error. As noted in the preceding section, this maximum probability is called the level of significance ($\alpha$) for the test; it represents the probability of making a Type I error when the null hypothesis is true as an equality. The manager must specify the level of significance. If the cost of making a Type I error is high, a small value should be chosen for the level of significance. If the cost is not high, a larger value may be appropriate.

In the Hilltop Coffee study, the director of the FTC's testing program has made the following statement: "If the company is meeting its weight specifications exactly ($\mu = 3$), I would like a 99% chance of not taking any action against the company. While I do not want to accuse the company wrongly of underfilling its product, I am willing to risk a 1% chance of making this error."

From the director's statement, the maximum probability of a Type I error is .01. Hence, the level of significance for the hypothesis test is $\alpha = .01$. Figure 9.3 shows the sampling distributions of both $\bar{x}$ and $z = (\bar{x} - \mu)/\sigma_{\bar{x}}$ for the Hilltop Coffee example. Note that when the null hypothesis is true at $\mu = 3$, the probability is .01 that $\bar{x}$ is more than 2.33 standard errors below the mean of 3. Therefore, we establish the following rejection rule.

$$\text{Reject } H_0 \text{ if } z = \frac{\bar{x} - \mu}{\sigma_{\bar{x}}} < -2.33$$

If the value of $\bar{x}$ is such that the test statistic $z$ is in the **rejection region,** we reject $H_0$ and conclude that $H_a$ is true. If the value of $\bar{x}$ is such that the test statistic $z$ is not in the rejection

**FIGURE 9.2**    PROBABILITY THAT $\bar{x}$ IS MORE THAN 1.645 STANDARD ERRORS BELOW
THE MEAN OF $\mu = 3$

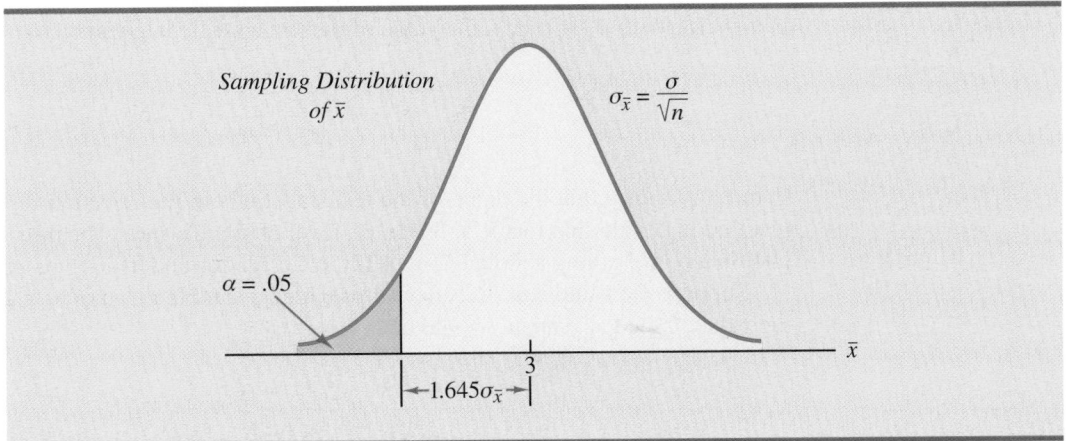

**FIGURE 9.3**   HILLTOP COFFEE REJECTION RULE HAS A LEVEL OF SIGNIFICANCE
OF $\alpha = .01$

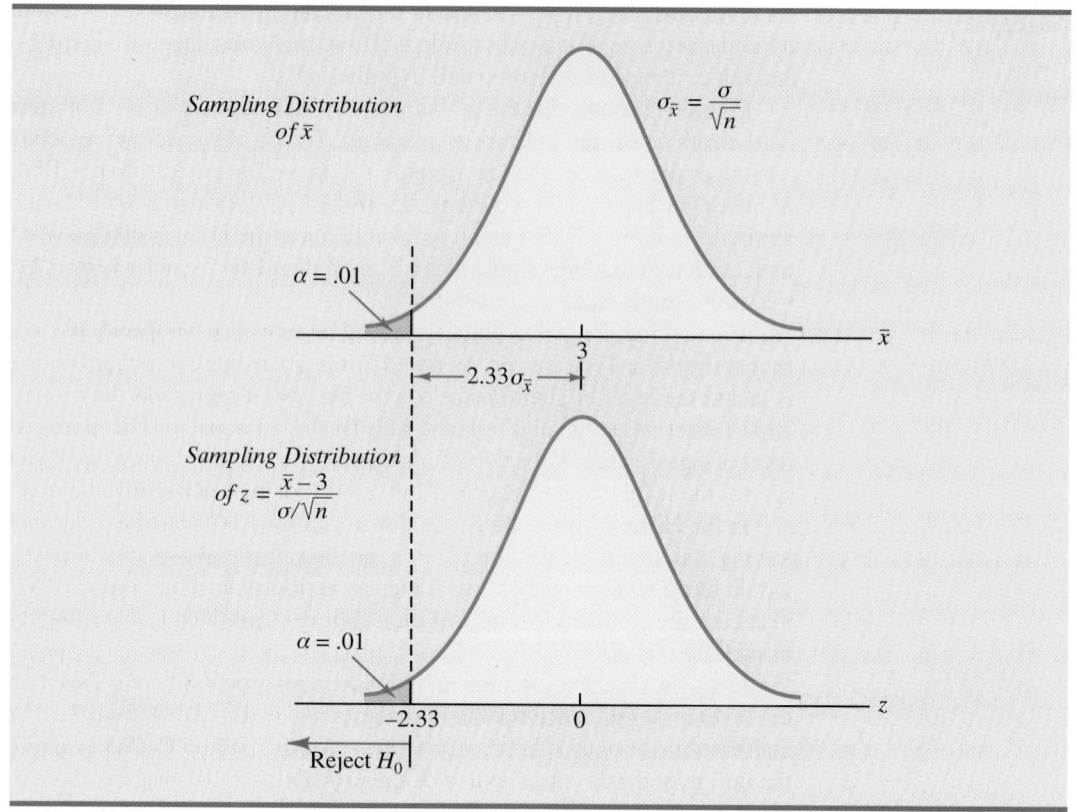

region, we cannot reject $H_0$. Note that the rejection region in Figure 9.3 is in only one tail of the sampling distribution. In such cases, we say the test is a **one-tailed hypothesis test.**

## One-Tailed Tests: Large-Sample Case with $\sigma$ Assumed Known

We will use the Hilltop Coffee study to show how to conduct a hypothesis test in the large-sample case with $\sigma$ assumed known. Suppose a sample of 36 cans provides a mean of $\bar{x} = 2.92$ pounds and we know from previous studies that the population standard deviation is $\sigma = .18$. With $\sigma_{\bar{x}} = \sigma/\sqrt{n}$, the value of the test statistic is given by

$$z = \frac{\bar{x} - \mu}{\sigma/\sqrt{n}} = \frac{2.92 - 3}{.18/\sqrt{36}} = -2.67$$

Figure 9.4 shows that the value of the test statistic is in the rejection region. We are now justified in concluding that $\mu < 3$ at a .01 level of significance. The director has statistical justification for taking action against Hilltop Coffee for underfilling its product.

Suppose the sample of 36 cans had provided a sample mean of $\bar{x} = 2.97$. In this case, the value of the test statistic would be

$$z = \frac{\bar{x} - 3}{\sigma/\sqrt{n}} = \frac{2.97 - 3}{.18/\sqrt{36}} = -1.00$$

**FIGURE 9.4**   VALUE OF THE TEST STATISTIC FOR $\bar{x} = 2.92$ IS IN THE REJECTION
REGION

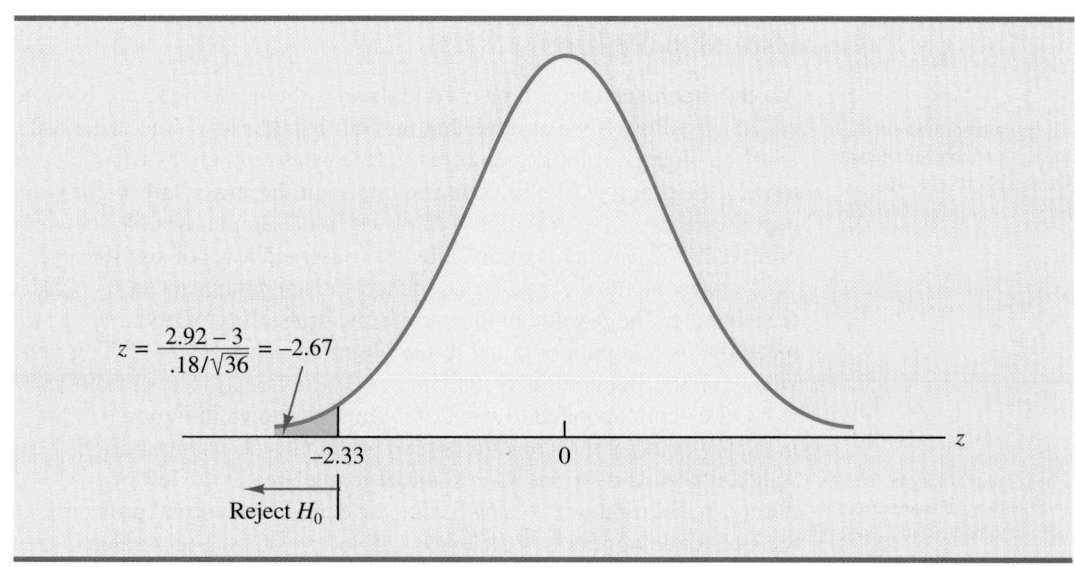

Because $z = -1.00$ is greater than $-2.33$, the value of the test statistic is not in the rejection region (see Figure 9.5). Hence we cannot reject the null hypothesis. Thus, with a sample mean of $\bar{x} = 2.97$, the statistical evidence is not sufficient to take action against Hilltop Coffee.

The value $z = -2.33$ establishes the boundary of the rejection region and is called the **critical value.** In establishing the critical value, we tentatively assume the null hypothesis is true. For Hilltop Coffee, the null hypothesis is true whenever $\mu \geq 3$; however, we considered only the case when $\mu = 3$. What about the case when $\mu > 3$? If $\mu > 3$, the probability of making a Type I error will be less than it is when $\mu = 3$; that is, we are even less likely to find a value of the test statistic that is in the rejection region. Because the

**FIGURE 9.5**   VALUE FOR THE TEST STATISTIC FOR $\bar{x} = 2.97$ IS NOT IN THE
REJECTION REGION

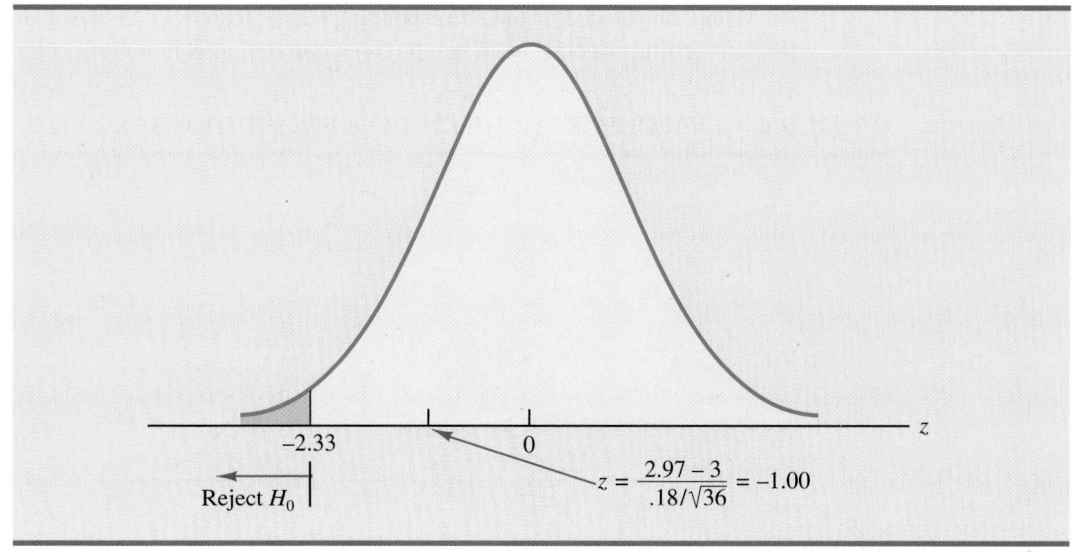

objective of the hypothesis testing procedure is to control for the maximum probability of making a Type I error, the critical value for the test is established by assuming $\mu = 3$.

## Use of *p*-Values

The *p*-value provides a measure of how significant the sample results are.

Another approach that can be used to decide whether to reject $H_0$ is based on a probability called a *p*-**value.** If we assume that the null hypothesis is true, the *p*-value is the probability of obtaining a sample result that is at least as unlikely as what is observed. In the Hilltop Coffee example, the rejection region is in the lower tail; the *p*-value for a lower-tail hypothesis test is the probability of observing a sample mean less than or equal to what is observed. The *p*-value is often called the observed level of significance.

Let us compute the *p*-value associated with the sample mean $\bar{x} = 2.92$ in the Hilltop Coffee example. The *p*-value in this case is the probability of obtaining a value for the sample mean that is less than or equal to the observed value of $\bar{x} = 2.92$, given the hypothesized value for the population mean of $\mu = 3$. Previously we showed that the test statistic $z = -2.67$ corresponded to $\bar{x} = 2.92$. Thus, as shown in Figure 9.6, the *p*-value is the area in the lower tail of the standard normal probability distribution for $z = -2.67$. Because the standard normal distribution is symmetric, the area to the left of $z = -2.67$ is the same as the area to the right of $z = 2.67$. Using the cumulative normal probability table, we find that the area to the right of $z = 2.67$ is $1 - .9962 = .0038$. The *p*-value is therefore .0038. This *p*-value shows a small probability of obtaining a sample mean as small as $\bar{x} = 2.92$ when sampling from a population with $\mu = 3$.

The *p*-value for a one-tailed test is always the area from the test statistic toward the rejection tail of the distribution. With a lower-tailed test, it is the cumulative probability to the left of the test statistic.

The *p*-value can be used to make the decision in a hypothesis test by noting that if the *p*-value is *less than the level of significance* $\alpha$, the value of the test statistic is in the rejection region. Similarly, if the *p*-value is *greater than or equal to* $\alpha$, the value of the test statistic is not in the rejection region. For the Hilltop Coffee example, the fact that the *p*-value of .0038 is less than the level of significance, $\alpha = .01$, indicates that the null hypothesis should be rejected. Given the level of significance $\alpha$, the decision of whether to reject $H_0$ can be made as follows.

> ### *p*-Value Criterion for Hypothesis Testing
>
> Reject $H_0$ if *p*-value $< \alpha$

Using the *p*-value or the corresponding test statistic will always provide the same hypothesis testing conclusion. When the rejection region is in the lower tail of the sampling

**FIGURE 9.6**   *p*-VALUE FOR THE HILLTOP COFFEE STUDY WHEN $\bar{x} = 2.92$ AND $z = -2.67$

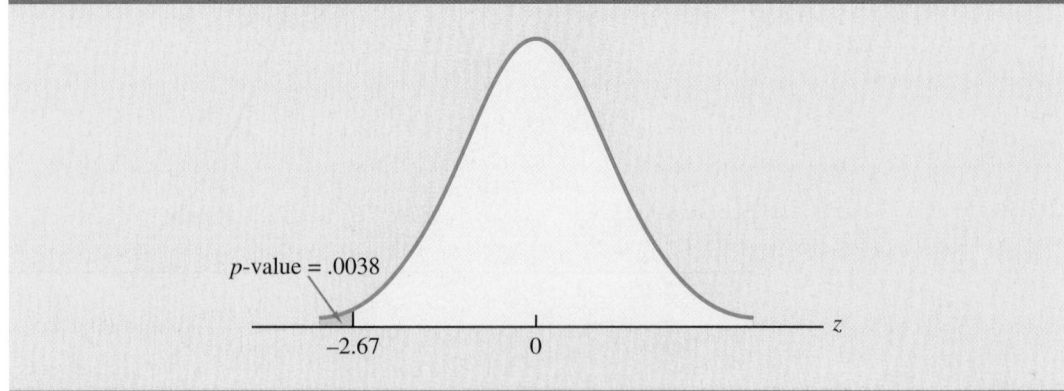

Sometimes a researcher may simply report the p-value for a particular sample result. The user of the research findings can select any level of significance, $\alpha$, he or she is willing to tolerate. Depending on that choice, some may reject $H_0$; others may not.

distribution, the p-value is the area under the curve less than or equal to the test statistic (a cumulative probability). When the rejection region is in the upper tail of the sampling distribution, the p-value is the area under the curve greater than or equal to the test statistic. For continuous sampling distributions, the p-value for an upper-tail rejection region is 1 minus the p-value for a lower-tail rejection region.

A small p-value indicates a sample result that is unusual given the assumption that $H_0$ is true. Small p-values lead to rejection of $H_0$, whereas large p-values indicate that the null hypothesis cannot be rejected.

## Steps of Hypothesis Testing

In conducting the Hilltop Coffee hypothesis test, we carried out the steps that can be used for any hypothesis test. In the summary that follows, note that either the test statistic or the p-value may be used to draw the hypothesis testing conclusion.

---

**Steps of Hypothesis Testing**

1. Develop the null and alternative hypotheses.
2. Specify the level of significance $\alpha$.
3. Select the test statistic that will be used to test the hypothesis.

**Using the Test Statistic:**

4. Use the level of significance to determine the critical value(s) for the test statistic and state the rejection rule for $H_0$.
5. Collect the sample data and compute the value of the test statistic.
6. Use the value of the test statistic and the rejection rule to determine whether to reject $H_0$.

**Using the p-Value:**

4. Collect the sample data and compute the value of the test statistic.
5. Use the value of the test statistic to compute the p-value.
6. Reject $H_0$ if p-value $< \alpha$.

---

## One-Tailed Tests: Large-Sample Case with $\sigma$ Estimated by $s$

In the Hilltop Coffee study the test statistic used to make the hypothesis-testing decision was

$$z = \frac{\bar{x} - \mu_0}{\sigma/\sqrt{n}} \tag{9.1}$$

To compute the value of $z$ corresponding to a particular sample mean $\bar{x}$, we had to know the value of the population standard deviation. A difficulty in using equation (9.1) is that in most applications the population standard deviation $\sigma$ is unknown. In the large-sample case ($n \geq 30$), we simply use the value of the sample standard deviation, $s$, as the point estimate of the population standard deviation $\sigma$ in computing the test statistic. The following test statistic is obtained.

$$z = \frac{\bar{x} - \mu_0}{s/\sqrt{n}} \tag{9.2}$$

As an illustration of this hypothesis testing procedure, let us consider a problem facing ComSpeed, Inc., a firm that provides high-speed Internet access throughout the Northeast. As a marketing strategy, management is considering opening kiosks in shopping malls to attract new customers. Before committing to this strategy, ComSpeed has decided to try it for one weekend at a sample of 30 shopping malls. For each mall, the random variable of interest is the number of people who sign up for the ComSpeed service. To justify the cost incurred for leasing space and hiring additional employees, management has decided that the mean number of customers who sign up at each mall must be greater than 100. If the sample results enable management to conclude that the population mean is greater than 100, ComSpeed plans to start using this approach at each of the malls in their service area.

Let us see how a hypothesis test can be conducted to determine whether ComSpeed should expand the mall kiosk strategy to its entire service area. For the population of all shopping malls, $\mu$ is the mean number of customers who sign up for the ComSpeed service. Because ComSpeed wants to take action if the mean number of customers is greater than 100, the appropriate null and alternative hypotheses for the study are:

$$H_0: \mu \le 100$$
$$H_a: \mu > 100$$

Suppose the maximum probability of a Type I error that management is willing to accept is .05. Hence, the level of significance for the hypothesis test is $\alpha = .05$.

With $n = 30$ (large-sample case) and the value of the population standard deviation $\sigma$ unknown, equation (9.2) can be used to compute the value of the test statistic $z$. Because the alternative hypothesis is greater than ($>$), the rejection region is placed in the upper tail of the sampling distribution. The key question is: How large must the test statistic $z$ be before we have enough evidence to reject the null hypothesis? Using the standard normal probability distribution, we know that the $z$ value corresponding to an upper-tail probability of .05 is $z = 1.645$. Therefore, we establish the following rejection rule.

$$\text{Reject } H_0 \text{ if } z = \frac{\bar{x} - \mu}{s/\sqrt{n}} > 1.645$$

Figure 9.7 shows the sampling distribution of $z$ and the rejection region for the ComSpeed problem.

**FIGURE 9.7**    REJECTION REGION FOR THE COMSPEED UPPER-TAIL HYPOTHESIS TEST

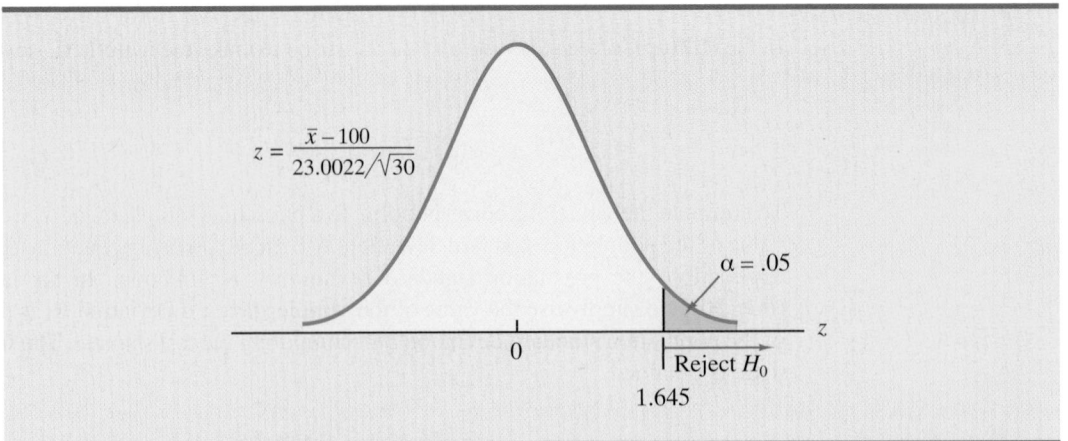

The data obtained for the sample of 30 malls are shown in Table 9.2. The sample mean is $\bar{x} = 109$, and the sample standard deviation is $s = 23.0022$. Thus, the value of the test statistic is given by

$$z = \frac{\bar{x} - \mu}{s/\sqrt{n}} = \frac{109 - 100}{23.0022/\sqrt{30}} = 2.1431$$

Because the value of the test statistic ($z = 2.1431$) is greater than the critical value (1.645), at the .05 level of significance we can reject the null hypothesis and conclude that the mean number of customers that sign up for the ComSpeed service is greater than 100. Management of ComSpeed has statistical justification for opening kiosks in all the shopping malls in their service area.

The $p$-value approach can also be used to make the hypothesis testing decision for ComSpeed. The $p$-value in this case is the probability of obtaining a value for the sample mean that is greater than or equal to the observed value of $\bar{x} = 109$, given the hypothesized value for the population mean of $\mu = 100$. Previously, we showed that the test statistic is $z = 2.1431$. Thus, the $p$-value is the area in the upper tail of the standard normal probability distribution for $z = 2.1431$. Using the cumulative normal probability table, we find that the area to the right of $z = 2.14$ is $1 - .9838 = .0162$. Thus, the $p$-value is .0162. Recall that when using the $p$-value approach to hypothesis testing, the decision of whether to reject $H_0$ at the level of significance $\alpha$ is made as follows:

$$\text{Reject } H_0 \text{ if } p\text{-value} < \alpha$$

Most computer software packages provide the $p$-value for the user. This allows the user to draw a hypothesis test conclusion using his/her own choice of $\alpha$.

Thus, for the ComSpeed study, we reject $H_0$ at the .05 level of significance because the $p$-value $= .0162$ is less than $\alpha = .05$; as a result, we can conclude that the mean number of customers that sign up for the ComSpeed service is greater than 100.

## Using Excel to Conduct a One-Tailed Hypothesis Test

Excel can be used to conduct a hypothesis test for the ComSpeed study. We show how to compute the $p$-value. The user can then choose $\alpha$ and draw a conclusion. Refer to Figure 9.8 as we describe the tasks involved. The formula worksheet is in the background; the value worksheet is in the foreground.

**TABLE 9.2**   COMSPEED DATA FOR A SAMPLE OF 30 MALLS

CD file

ComSpeed

| Mall | Number of Customers | Mall | Number of Customers | Mall | Number of Customers |
|------|------|------|------|------|------|
| 1 | 86 | 11 | 97 | 21 | 118 |
| 2 | 97 | 12 | 79 | 22 | 124 |
| 3 | 159 | 13 | 103 | 23 | 125 |
| 4 | 92 | 14 | 104 | 24 | 129 |
| 5 | 146 | 15 | 104 | 25 | 132 |
| 6 | 138 | 16 | 105 | 26 | 98 |
| 7 | 101 | 17 | 105 | 27 | 88 |
| 8 | 87 | 18 | 102 | 28 | 68 |
| 9 | 151 | 19 | 112 | 29 | 135 |
| 10 | 69 | 20 | 116 | 30 | 100 |

**FIGURE 9.8**    EXCEL WORKSHEET FOR COMSPEED ONE-TAILED HYPOTHESIS TEST

| | A | B | C | D | E | F |
|---|---|---|---|---|---|---|
| 1 | Customers | | Hypothesis Test about a Population Mean | | | |
| 2 | 86 | | Using the Standard Normal Distribution (z) | | | |
| 3 | 97 | | | | | |
| 4 | 159 | | Sample Size | =COUNT(A2:A31) | | |
| 5 | 92 | | Mean | =AVERAGE(A2:A31) | | |
| 6 | 146 | | Standard Deviation | =STDEV(A2:A31) | | |
| 7 | 138 | | | | | |
| 8 | 101 | | Hypothesized value | 100 | | |
| 9 | 87 | | | | | |
| 10 | 151 | | Standard Error | =D6/SQRT(D4) | | |
| 11 | 69 | | Test Statistic | =(D5-D8)/D10 | | |
| 12 | 97 | | | | | |
| 13 | 79 | | $p$-value | =1-NORMSDIST(D11) | | |
| 14 | 103 | | | | | |
| 15 | 104 | | | | | |
| 16 | 104 | | | | | |
| 17 | 105 | | | | | |
| 29 | 68 | | | | | |
| 30 | 135 | | | | | |
| 31 | 100 | | | | | |
| 32 | | | | | | |

| | A | B | C | D | E | F | G | H |
|---|---|---|---|---|---|---|---|---|
| 1 | Customers | | Hypothesis Test about a Population Mean | | | | | |
| 2 | 86 | | Using the Standard Normal Distribution (z) | | | | | |
| 3 | 97 | | | | | | | |
| 4 | 159 | | Sample Size | 30 | | | | |
| 5 | 92 | | Mean | 109 | | | | |
| 6 | 146 | | Standard Deviation | 23.0022 | | | | |
| 7 | 138 | | | | | | | |
| 8 | 101 | | Hypothesized value | 100 | | | | |
| 9 | 87 | | | | | | | |
| 10 | 151 | | Standard Error | 4.1996 | | | | |
| 11 | 69 | | Test Statistic | 2.1431 | | $z = \dfrac{\bar{x}-\mu}{s/\sqrt{n}} = \dfrac{109-100}{4.1996}$ | | |
| 12 | 97 | | | | | | | |
| 13 | 79 | | $p$-value | 0.0161 | | | | |
| 14 | 103 | | | | | | | |
| 15 | 104 | | | | | | | |
| 16 | 104 | | | | | | | |
| 17 | 105 | | | | | | | |
| 29 | 68 | | | | | | | |
| 30 | 135 | | | | | | | |
| 31 | 100 | | | | | | | |
| 32 | | | | | | | | |

Note: Rows 18–28 are hidden.

**Enter Data:**    Column A shows the number of people who signed up for the ComSpeed service at each of the 30 malls.

**Enter Functions and Formulas:**    The descriptive statistics needed are provided in cells D4:D6. Excel's COUNT, AVERAGE, and STDEV functions are used to compute the sample size, sample mean, and sample standard deviation respectively.

The hypothesized value of the population mean (100) was entered into cell D8. Using the sample standard deviation as an estimate of the population standard deviation, an estimate of the standard error was obtained in cell D10 by dividing the sample standard deviation in cell D6 by the square root of the sample size in cell D4. The formula =(D5-D8)/D10 was entered into cell D11 to compute the test statistic $z$ (2.1431). Finally, the NORMSDIST function was used in cell D13 to compute the $p$-value corresponding to $z = 2.1431$. Because it is an upper-tail test, we use 1-NORMSDIST(D11) to find the area in the upper tail as the $p$-value; the result is .0161.

We can reject $H_0$ at the .05 level of significance because the $p$-value = .0161 is less than the level of significance. We conclude that the mean number of customers who sign up for the ComSpeed service is greater than 100.

In the ComSpeed problem, the alternative hypothesis is $H_a$: $\mu > 100$. Thus, the rejection region is located in the upper tail of the sampling distribution of $\bar{x}$. In the Hilltop Coffee study the alternative hypothesis was $H_a$: $\mu < 3$, and thus the rejection region was located in the lower tail of the sampling distribution. To use the Excel procedure that we have just described for hypothesis tests in which the rejection region is in the lower tail, we will modify the ComSpeed worksheet in Figure 9.8 by computing two $p$-values: a $p$-value (Lower Tail) and a $p$-value (Upper Tail). If the hypothesis test we are conducting has a rejection region in the lower tail, we compare the $p$-value (Lower Tail) to $\alpha$ to make the rejection decision. If the hypothesis test we are conducting has a rejection region in the upper tail, we compare the $p$-value (Upper Tail) to $\alpha$ to make the rejection decision.

The worksheet in Figure 9.9 shows the extension we have described. Cell D13 provides the $p$-value for a lower-tail test using the ComSpeed data, and cell D14 provides the $p$-value for an upper-tail test using the ComSpeed data. In the background worksheet we see that the formula in cell D13 is =NORMSDIST(D11), and the formula in cell D14 is =1-NORMSDIST(D11). As in Figure 9.8, the $p$-value for the upper-tail test (cell D14) is .0161. The $p$-value for the lower-tail test (cell D13) is .9839. For a given value of the test statistic, the $p$-value for the upper-tail test is just one minus the $p$-value for a lower-tail test. The cell formulas required for both the lower and upper tail cases are summarized here:

|  | Rejection Region in Lower Tail | Rejection Region in Upper Tail |
|---|---|---|
| $p$-value | =NORMSDIST(D11) | =1-NORMSDIST(D11) |

The worksheet in Figure 9.9 can be used as a template for one-tailed hypothesis tests of a population mean in the large-sample case. To use it for a different data set, one would need to insert the new data in column A, modify the ranges for the descriptive statistics in cells D4:D6, and place the hypothesized value for $\mu_0$ into cell D8. The $p$-value corresponding to a lower-tail hypothesis test is computed in cell D13, and the $p$-value corresponding to an upper-tail hypothesis test is computed in cell D14. For a hypothesis test with the rejection region in the lower tail, the $p$-value in cell D13 can be compared with $\alpha$ to make the rejection decision. For a hypothesis test with the rejection region in the upper tail, the $p$-value in cell D14 can be compared with $\alpha$ to make the rejection decision.

This worksheet will also work as a template for exercises in which $n$, $\bar{x}$, and $s$ or $\sigma$ are given. Just ignore the data section in column A and type the known values for the descriptive statistics in cells D4:D6. Then type the appropriate hypothesized value for $\mu_0$ into cell D8. The $p$-values corresponding to lower- and upper-tail hypothesis tests will then appear in cells D13 and D14.

**FIGURE 9.9**   MODIFIED WORKSHEET FOR COMSPEED ONE-TAILED HYPOTHESIS TEST

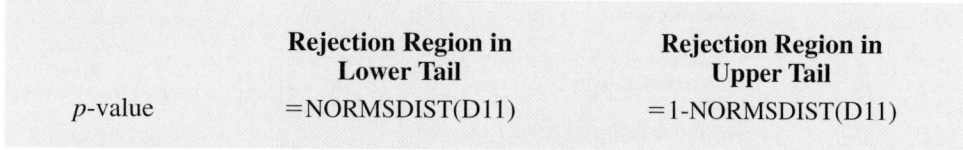

| | A | B | C | D | E | F |
|---|---|---|---|---|---|---|
| 1 | Customers | | Hypothesis Test about a Population Mean | | | |
| 2 | 86 | | Using the Standard Normal Distribution (z) | | | |
| 3 | 97 | | | | | |
| 4 | 159 | | Sample Size | =COUNT(A2:A31) | | |
| 5 | 92 | | Mean | =AVERAGE(A2:A31) | | |
| 6 | 146 | | Standard Deviation | =STDEV(A2:A31) | | |
| 7 | 138 | | | | | |
| 8 | 101 | | Hypothesized value | 100 | | |
| 9 | 87 | | | | | |
| 10 | 151 | | Standard Error | =D6/SQRT(D4) | | |
| 11 | 69 | | Test Statistic | =(D5-D8)/D10 | | |
| 12 | 97 | | | | | |
| 13 | 79 | | $p$-value (Lower Tail) | =NORMSDIST(D11) | | |
| 14 | 103 | | $p$-value (Upper Tail) | =1-NORMSDIST(D11) | | |
| 15 | 104 | | | | | |
| 16 | 104 | | | | | |
| 17 | 105 | | | | | |
| 29 | 68 | | | | | |
| 30 | 135 | | | | | |
| 31 | 100 | | | | | |
| 32 | | | | | | |

Note: Rows 18–28 are hidden.

| | A | B | C | D | E | F | G |
|---|---|---|---|---|---|---|---|
| 1 | Customers | | Hypothesis Test about a Population Mean | | | | |
| 2 | 86 | | Using the Standard Normal Distribution (z) | | | | |
| 3 | 97 | | | | | | |
| 4 | 159 | | Sample Size | 30 | | | |
| 5 | 92 | | Mean | 109 | | | |
| 6 | 146 | | Standard Deviation | 23.0022 | | | |
| 7 | 138 | | | | | | |
| 8 | 101 | | Hypothesized value | 100 | | | |
| 9 | 87 | | | | | | |
| 10 | 151 | | Standard Error | 4.1996 | | | |
| 11 | 69 | | Test Statistic | 2.1431 | | | |
| 12 | 97 | | | | | | |
| 13 | 79 | | $p$-value (Lower Tail) | 0.9839 | | | |
| 14 | 103 | | $p$-value (Upper Tail) | 0.0161 | | | |
| 15 | 104 | | | | | | |
| 16 | 104 | | | | | | |
| 17 | 105 | | | | | | |
| 29 | 68 | | | | | | |
| 30 | 135 | | | | | | |
| 31 | 100 | | | | | | |
| 32 | | | | | | | |

**FIGURE 9.10** WORKSHEET FOR HILLTOP COFFEE ONE-TAILED HYPOTHESIS TEST

| | A | B | C | D | E | F |
|---|---|---|---|---|---|---|
| 1 | Customers | | Hypothesis Test about a Population Mean | | | |
| 2 | 86 | | Using the Standard Normal Distribution (z) | | | |
| 3 | 97 | | | | | |
| 4 | 159 | | Sample Size | 36 | | |
| 5 | 92 | | Mean | 2.92 | | |
| 6 | 146 | | Standard Deviation | 0.18 | | |
| 7 | 138 | | | | | |
| 8 | 101 | | Hypothesized value | 3 | | |
| 9 | 87 | | | | | |
| 10 | 151 | | Standard Error | =D6/SQRT(D4) | | |
| 11 | 69 | | Test Statistic | =(D5-D8)/D10 | | |
| 12 | 97 | | | | | |
| 13 | 79 | | *p*-value (Lower Tail) | =NORMSDIST(D11) | | |
| 14 | 103 | | *p*-value (Upper Tail) | =1-NORMSDIST(D11) | | |
| 15 | 104 | | | | | |
| 16 | 104 | | | | | |
| 17 | 105 | | | | | |
| 29 | 68 | | | | | |
| 30 | 135 | | | | | |
| 31 | 100 | | | | | |
| 32 | | | | | | |

| | A | B | C | D | E | F | G |
|---|---|---|---|---|---|---|---|
| 1 | Customers | | Hypothesis Test about a Population Mean | | | | |
| 2 | 86 | | Using the Standard Normal Distribution (z) | | | | |
| 3 | 97 | | | | | | |
| 4 | 159 | | Sample Size | 36 | | | |
| 5 | 92 | | Mean | 2.92 | | | |
| 6 | 146 | | Standard Deviation | 0.1800 | | | |
| 7 | 138 | | | | | | |
| 8 | 101 | | Hypothesized value | 3 | | | |
| 9 | 87 | | | | | | |
| 10 | 151 | | Standard Error | 0.0300 | | | |
| 11 | 69 | | Test Statistic | -2.6667 | | | |
| 12 | 97 | | | | | | |
| 13 | 79 | | *p*-value (Lower Tail) | 0.0038 | | | |
| 14 | 103 | | *p*-value (Upper Tail) | 0.9962 | | | |
| 15 | 104 | | | | | | |
| 16 | 104 | | | | | | |
| 17 | 105 | | | | | | |
| 29 | 68 | | | | | | |
| 30 | 135 | | | | | | |
| 31 | 100 | | | | | | |
| 32 | | | | | | | |

Note: Rows 18–28 are hidden.

To illustrate, suppose that we wanted to use the worksheet in Figure 9.9 as a template for the Hilltop Coffee hypothesis test. The sample size was $n = 36$, the sample mean was $\bar{x} = 2.92$, and the population standard deviation was assumed known with $\sigma = .18$. The hypothesized value was $\mu_0 = 3$. Figure 9.10 shows the worksheet obtained by entering these values in the appropriate cells of the worksheet in Figure 9.9. Note in the background worksheet that the formulas in cells D4:D6 have been replaced with numerical values and the hypothesized value in cell D8 has been changed to 3. The values of the standard error and the test statistic are .03 and $-2.6667$ (the same values calculated earlier). Because the Hilltop Coffee hypothesis test has a rejection region in the lower tail, the $p$-value in cell D13 (.0038) is the one we want to use. Thus, for $\alpha = .01$, we would reject the null hypothesis.

## Summary: One-Tailed Tests About a Population Mean

Let us generalize the hypothesis testing procedure for one-tailed tests about a population mean. We consider the large-sample case ($n \geq 30$) in which the central limit theorem enables us to assume that the sampling distribution of $\bar{x}$ can be approximated by a normal probability distribution. In the large-sample case with $\sigma$ unknown, we simply substitute the sample standard deviation $s$ for $\sigma$ in computing the test statistic.

The general form of a lower-tail test, where $\mu_0$ is a stated value for the population mean, follows.

In most applications the sample standard deviation $s$ is used in the computation of the test statistic because the population standard deviation $\sigma$ is unknown

**One-Tailed Test: Large-Sample Case ($n \geq 30$) with the Rejection Region in the Lower Tail**

$$H_0: \mu \geq \mu_0$$
$$H_a: \mu < \mu_0$$

**Test Statistic: $\sigma$ Assumed Known**

$$z = \frac{\bar{x} - \mu_0}{\sigma/\sqrt{n}} \qquad \text{(9.1)}$$

**Test Statistic: $\sigma$ Estimated by $s$**

$$z = \frac{\bar{x} - \mu_0}{s/\sqrt{n}} \qquad \text{(9.2)}$$

**Rejection Rule**

Using Test Statistic:   Reject $H_0$ if $z < -z_\alpha$
Using $p$-Value:        Reject $H_0$ if $p$-value $< \alpha$

The general form of the upper-tail test, where $\mu_0$ is a stated value for the population mean, follows.

**One-Tailed Test: Large-Sample Case ($n \geq 30$) with the Rejection Region in the Upper Tail**

$$H_0\!: \mu \leq \mu_0$$
$$H_a\!: \mu > \mu_0$$

**Test Statistic: $\sigma$ Assumed Known**

$$z = \frac{\bar{x} - \mu_0}{\sigma/\sqrt{n}} \qquad \text{(9.1)}$$

**Test Statistic: $\sigma$ Estimated by $s$**

$$z = \frac{\bar{x} - \mu_0}{s/\sqrt{n}} \qquad \text{(9.2)}$$

**Rejection Rule**

Using Test Statistic:   Reject $H_0$ if $z > z_\alpha$
Using $p$-Value:        Reject $H_0$ if $p$-value $< \alpha$

## NOTES AND COMMENTS

The $p$-value, the observed level of significance, is a measure of the likelihood of the sample results when the null hypothesis is assumed to be true. The smaller the $p$-value, the less likely it is that the sample results came from a population where the null hypothesis is true.

## EXERCISES

*Note to Student:* Some of the hypothesis testing exercises that follow will ask you to compare the value of the test statistic to the critical value and other exercises will ask you to compare the *p*-value to $\alpha$. Both methods will provide the same hypothesis testing conclusion. We have provided exercises with both methods so that you have practice using both. In an actual application, you may select either method based on personal preference.

## Methods

**9.** Consider the following hypothesis test.

$$H_0: \mu \geq 10$$
$$H_a: \mu < 10$$

A sample with $n = 50$ provides a sample mean of 9.46 and sample standard deviation of 2.

  **a.** At $\alpha = .05$, what is the critical value for $z$? What is the rejection rule?

  **b.** Compute the value of the test statistic $z$. What is your conclusion?

**10.** Consider the following hypothesis test.

$$H_0: \mu \leq 15$$
$$H_a: \mu > 15$$

A sample size of 40 provides a sample mean of 16.5 and sample standard deviation of 7.

  **a.** At $\alpha = .02$, what is the critical value for $z$, and what is the rejection rule?

  **b.** Compute the value of the test statistic $z$.

  **c.** What is the *p*-value?

  **d.** What is your conclusion?

**11.** Consider the following hypothesis test.

$$H_0: \mu \geq 25$$
$$H_a: \mu < 25$$

A sample of 100 is used, and the population standard deviation is 12. Provide the value of the test statistic $z$ and your conclusion for each of the following sample results. Use $\alpha = .05$.

  **a.** $\bar{x} = 22.0$

  **b.** $\bar{x} = 24.0$

  **c.** $\bar{x} = 23.5$

  **d.** $\bar{x} = 22.8$

**12.** Consider the following hypothesis test.

$$H_0: \mu \leq 5$$
$$H_a: \mu > 5$$

Assume the following test statistics. Compute the corresponding *p*-values and make the appropriate conclusions based on $\alpha = .05$.

  **a.** $z = 1.82$

  **b.** $z = .45$

  **c.** $z = 1.50$

  **d.** $z = 3.30$

  **e.** $z = -1.00$

## Applications

**13.** Individuals filing federal income tax returns prior to March 31 had an average refund of $1056. Consider the population of "last-minute" filers who mail their returns during the last five days of the income tax period (typically April 10 to April 15).

  a. A researcher suggests that one of the reasons individuals wait until the last five days to file their returns is that on average those individuals have a lower refund than early filers. Develop appropriate hypotheses such that rejection of $H_0$ will support the researcher's contention.

  b. Using $\alpha = .05$, what is the critical value for the test statistic, and what is the rejection rule?

  c. For a sample of 400 individuals who filed a return between April 10 and April 15, the sample mean refund was $910 and the sample standard deviation was $1600. Compute the value of the test statistic.

  d. What is your conclusion?

  e. What is the $p$-value for the test?

**14.** A Nielsen survey estimated the mean number of hours of television viewing per household at 7.25 hours per day (*New York Daily News,* November 2, 1997). Assume that the Nielsen survey involved 200 households and that the sample standard deviation was 2.5 hours per day. Ten years ago the population mean number of hours of television viewing per household was reported to be 6.70 hours. Letting $\mu$ = the population mean number of hours of television viewing per household in 1997, test the hypotheses $H_0$: $\mu \leq 6.70$ and $H_a$: $\mu > 6.70$. Use $\alpha = .01$.

  a. What is the critical value of the test statistic, and what is the rejection rule?

  b. Compute the value of the test statistic.

  c. What is your conclusion?

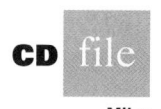

**Auto**

$n = 100$

$\bar{x} = 10,192$

**15.** According to the National Automobile Dealers Association, the mean price for used cars is $10,192. A manager of a Kansas City used car dealership selected a sample of 100 recent used car sales at the dealership. The sample data are contained in the data set Auto. Letting $\mu$ denote the population mean price for used cars at the Kansas City dealership, test $H_0$: $\mu \geq 10,192$ and $H_a$: $\mu < 10,192$ at a .05 level of significance.

  a. What is the hypothesis testing conclusion?

  b. What is the $p$-value?

  c. What information does the hypothesis test result provide for the manager of the Kansas City dealership? What follow-up action might the manager want to consider?

**Miles**

**16.** New tires manufactured by a company in Findlay, Ohio, are designed to provide a mean of at least 28,000 miles. Tests with 30 randomly selected tires resulted in the data set Miles. Using a .05 level of significance, test whether the data provide sufficient evidence to reject the claim of a mean of at least 28,000 miles. What is the $p$-value?

$\bar{x} = 13$

$n = 145$

$\sigma = 9.2$

$\bar{x} = 10.8$

$\alpha = .01$

**17.** Media Metrix, Inc., tracks Internet users in seven countries: Australia, Great Britain, Canada, France, Germany, Japan, and the United States. According to recent measurement figures, American home users rank first in Internet usage with a mean of 13 hours per month (*The Washington Post,* August 4, 2000). Assume that in a follow-up study involving a sample of 145 Canadian Internet users, the sample mean was 10.8 hours per month and the sample standard deviation was 9.2 hours.

  a. Formulate the null and alternative hypotheses that can be used to determine whether the sample data support the conclusion that Canadian Internet users have a population mean less than the U.S. mean of 13 hours per month.

  b. Using $\alpha = .01$, what is the critical value for the test statistic? State the rejection rule.

  c. What is the value of the test statistic?

  d. What is your conclusion?

144 degrees of freed

**18.** A Channel One Network study reported that teens spend a mean of $5.72 per visit to fast-food restaurants such as McDonald's, Burger King, and Wendy's (*USA Today,* October 5, 1998). In a follow-up study, a sample of 102 teen visits to fast-food restaurants in Chicago found a sample mean of $5.98 and a sample standard deviation of $1.24.

   **a.** Formulate the null and alternative hypotheses that can be used to determine whether the sample data support the conclusion that teens in Chicago have a population mean expenditure of more than $5.72 per visit to fast-food restaurants.

   **b.** What is the value of the test statistic?

   **c.** What is the $p$-value?

   **d.** Using $\alpha = .05$, what is your conclusion?

## 9.4 TWO-TAILED TESTS ABOUT A POPULATION MEAN: LARGE-SAMPLE CASE

Two-tailed hypothesis tests differ from one-tailed tests in that the rejection region is divided between the lower and the upper tails of the sampling distribution. Let us introduce an example to show how and why two-tailed tests are conducted.

The United States Golf Association (USGA) has established rules that manufacturers of golf equipment must meet if their products are to be acceptable for use in USGA events. One of the rules for the manufacture of golf balls states: "A brand of golf ball, when tested on apparatus approved by the USGA on the outdoor range at the USGA Headquarters . . . shall not cover an average distance in carry and roll exceeding 280 yards." Suppose Superflight, Inc., has recently developed a high-technology manufacturing method that can produce golf balls having an average distance in carry and roll of 280 yards.

Superflight realizes, however, that if the new manufacturing process goes out of adjustment, the process may produce balls for which the average distance is either less than 280 yards or greater than 280 yards. In the former case, sales may decline as a result of marketing an inferior product, and in the latter case the golf balls may be rejected by the USGA.

Superflight's management has instituted a quality control program to monitor the manufacturing process. Periodically, a hypothesis test will be used to help determine whether the manufacturing process is operating correctly. In formulating the null and alternative hypotheses, we will begin by assuming that the manufacturing process is functioning correctly, with the golf balls having the desired mean distance of 280 yards. The null and alternative hypotheses are as follow:

$$H_0: \mu = 280$$
$$H_a: \mu \neq 280$$

If the sample data indicate that $H_0$ cannot be rejected, no action will be taken to adjust the manufacturing process. However, if the sample data indicate that $H_0$ should be rejected, we can conclude that the golf balls do not have the desired mean distance of 280 yards; in this case corrective action should be taken to return the manufacturing process to its desired state.

The quality control team has selected $\alpha = .05$ as the level of significance for the hypothesis test. With a sample size of at least 36 golf balls used each time the quality control test is performed, we have a large-sample case. As a result the test statistic is

*If $\sigma$ is unknown, we use $s$ to estimate $\sigma$.*

$$z = \frac{\bar{x} - \mu_0}{\sigma/\sqrt{n}}$$

As usual, we make the tentative assumption that the null hypothesis is true. We want to reject $H_0: \mu = 280$ when the test statistic $z$ indicates that the sample mean distance $\bar{x}$ is significantly less than 280 yards or significantly greater than 280 yards. Thus, $H_0$ may be rejected for values of $z$ in either the lower tail or upper tail of the sampling distribution. Therefore, the test is called a **two-tailed hypothesis test.**

Figure 9.11 shows the sampling distribution of $z$ with the two-tailed rejection region for $\alpha = .05$. With two-tailed hypothesis tests, we will always determine the rejection region by placing an area or probability of $\alpha/2$ in each tail of the distribution. The values of $z$ that provide an area of .025 in each tail can be found from the cumulative normal probability table. We see in Figure 9.11 that $-z_{.025} = -1.96$ identifies an area of .025 in the lower tail and $z_{.025} = +1.96$ identifies an area of .025 in the upper tail. Referring to Figure 9.11, we can establish the following rejection rule.

$$\text{Reject } H_0 \text{ if } z < -1.96 \text{ or if } z > 1.96$$

Suppose that a simple random sample of 36 golf balls provided the data in Table 9.3. For these data we obtained a sample mean of $\bar{x} = 278.5$ yards and a sample standard deviation of $s = 12$ yards. Using $\mu_0 = 280$ from the null hypothesis and the sample standard deviation of $s = 12$ as an estimate of the population standard deviation $\sigma$, the value of the test statistic is

$$z = \frac{\bar{x} - \mu_0}{s/\sqrt{n}} = \frac{278.5 - 280}{12/\sqrt{36}} = -.75$$

According to the rejection rule, $H_0$ cannot be rejected. The sample results provide no reason to doubt the assumption that the manufacturing process is producing golf balls with a population mean distance of 280 yards.

## p-Values for Two-Tailed Tests

Let us compute the $p$-value for the Superflight golf ball example. The sample mean of $\bar{x} = 278.5$ has a corresponding $z$ value of $-.75$. Because the standard normal probability distribution is symmetric, the area to the left of $z = -.75$ is the same as the area to the right of

**FIGURE 9.11    REJECTION REGION FOR THE TWO-TAILED HYPOTHESIS TEST FOR SUPERFLIGHT, INC.**

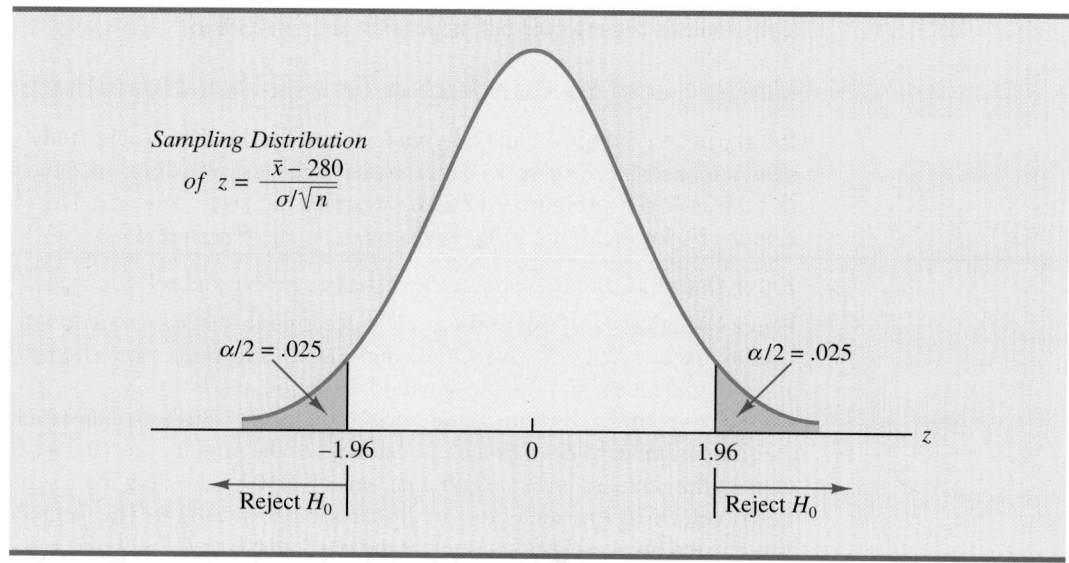

**TABLE 9.3**     DISTANCE DATA FOR SIMPLE RANDOM SAMPLE OF 36 SUPERFLIGHT
GOLF BALLS

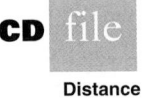

**CD** file

**Distance**

| Ball | Yards | Ball | Yards | Ball | Yards |
|------|-------|------|-------|------|-------|
| 1 | 269 | 13 | 296 | 25 | 272 |
| 2 | 300 | 14 | 265 | 26 | 285 |
| 3 | 268 | 15 | 271 | 27 | 293 |
| 4 | 278 | 16 | 279 | 28 | 281 |
| 5 | 282 | 17 | 284 | 29 | 269 |
| 6 | 263 | 18 | 260 | 30 | 299 |
| 7 | 301 | 19 | 275 | 31 | 263 |
| 8 | 295 | 20 | 282 | 32 | 264 |
| 9 | 288 | 21 | 260 | 33 | 273 |
| 10 | 278 | 22 | 266 | 34 | 291 |
| 11 | 276 | 23 | 270 | 35 | 274 |
| 12 | 286 | 24 | 293 | 36 | 277 |

$z = .75$. Using the cumulative normal probability table, we find that the area to the right of $z = .75$ is $1 - .7734 = .2266$. Thus, the area in the lower tail is .2266. Looking at Figure 9.11, we see that the lower-tail portion of the rejection region has an area or probability of $\alpha/2 = .05/2 = .025$. Thus, with $.2266 > .025$, the test statistic is not in the rejection region, and the null hypothesis cannot be rejected.

In a two-tailed test, the *p*-value is found by doubling the area in the tail. The doubling of the area is done so that the *p*-value can be compared directly to $\alpha$. As a result the same rejection rule can be used for both one-tailed and two-tailed tests.

One question remains: What value should we report as the *p*-value for the two-tailed test? At first glance, you may be inclined to say the *p*-value is .2266. If that is your choice, you will have to remember two different rules: one for the one-tailed test, which is to reject $H_0$ if the *p*-value $< \alpha$, and another for the two-tailed test, which is to reject $H_0$ if the *p*-value $< \alpha/2$. Alternatively, suppose we define the *p*-value for a two-tailed test as *double* the area found in the tail of the sampling distribution. Thus, for the Superflight example, we would define the *p*-value to be $2(.2266) = .4532$. The advantage of this definition of the *p*-value for a two-tailed test is that the *p*-value can be compared directly to the level of significance $\alpha$. Hence, with $.4532 > .05$, we see that the null hypothesis cannot be rejected. By remembering that the *p*-value for a two-tailed test is simply double the area found in the tail of the sampling distribution, the previous rule to reject $H_0$ if the *p*-value $< \alpha$ can be used for all hypothesis tests (lower-tail, upper-tail, and two-tailed).

## Using Excel to Conduct a Two-Tailed Hypothesis Test

Excel can be used to conduct a hypothesis test for the Superflight study. The worksheet is similar to the one in Figure 9.10 for the one-tailed test. We simply add the *p*-value for a two-tailed test. Refer to Figure 9.12 as we describe the tasks involved. The formula worksheet is in the background; the value worksheet is in the foreground.

**Enter Data:**    Column A shows the distance in carry and roll for each of the 36 balls.

**Enter Functions and Formulas:**    The descriptive statistics needed are provided in cells D4:D6. Excel's COUNT, AVERAGE, and STDEV functions are used to compute the sample size, sample mean, and sample standard deviation, respectively.

The hypothesized value of the population mean (280) was entered into cell D8. Using the sample standard deviation as an estimate of the population standard deviation, an estimate of the standard error was obtained in cell D10 by dividing the sample standard deviation in cell D6 by the square root of the sample size in cell D4. The formula =(D5-D8)/D10 was entered into cell D11 to compute the test statistic $z$ ($-.7499$).

**FIGURE 9.12**    EXCEL WORKSHEET FOR THE SUPERFLIGHT TWO-TAILED HYPOTHESIS TEST

Note: Rows 17–33 are hidden.

We then use the test statistic to compute the $p$-value. The formula =NORMSDIST(D11) was entered into cell D13 to compute the $p$-value corresponding to a hypothesis test with the rejection region in the lower tail. Then, the formula =1-NORMSDIST(D11) was entered into cell D14 to compute the $p$-value corresponding to a hypothesis test with the rejection region in the upper tail. Finally, the $p$-value corresponding to a two-tailed hypothesis test is then computed in cell D15 as 2 times the minimum of the $p$-values in cell D13 and D14; the result is $p$-value (Two Tail) = .4533. We cannot reject $H_0$ at the .05 level of significance because the $p$-value (Two Tail) = .4533 is greater than $\alpha$ = .05. Thus, the quality control manager has no reason to doubt the assumption that the manufacturing process is producing golf balls with a population mean distance of 280 yards.

## Summary: Two-Tailed Tests About a Population Mean

Let $\mu_0$ represent the value of the population mean in the hypotheses. The general form of the two-tailed hypothesis test about a population mean follows.

**Two-Tailed Test: Large-Sample Case ($n \geq 30$)**

$$H_0: \mu = \mu_0$$
$$H_a: \mu \neq \mu_0$$

**Test Statistic: $\sigma$ Assumed Known**

$$z = \frac{\bar{x} - \mu_0}{\sigma/\sqrt{n}} \tag{9.1}$$

**Test Statistic: $\sigma$ Estimated by $s$**

$$z = \frac{\bar{x} - \mu_0}{s/\sqrt{n}} \tag{9.2}$$

**Rejection Rule**

Using Test Statistic:    Reject $H_0$ if $z < -z_{\alpha/2}$ or if $z > z_{\alpha/2}$

Using $p$-Value:    Reject $H_0$ if $p$-value $< \alpha$

$$\left.\vphantom{\begin{matrix}a\\b\end{matrix}}\right\}\tag{9.3}$$

## Relationship Between Interval Estimation and Hypothesis Testing

In Chapter 8 we showed how to develop a confidence interval estimate of a population mean. In the large-sample case, the confidence interval estimate of a population mean corresponding to a $1 - \alpha$ confidence coefficient is given by

$$\bar{x} \pm z_{\alpha/2} \frac{\sigma}{\sqrt{n}} \tag{9.4}$$

when $\sigma$ is assumed known and

$$\bar{x} \pm z_{\alpha/2} \frac{s}{\sqrt{n}} \tag{9.5}$$

when $\sigma$ is estimated by $s$.

Conducting a hypothesis test requires us first to make an assumption about the value of a population parameter. In the case of the population mean, the two-tailed hypothesis test has the form

$$H_0: \mu = \mu_0$$
$$H_a: \mu \neq \mu_0$$

where $\mu_0$ is the hypothesized value for the population mean. Using the rejection rule provided by expression (9.3), we see that the region over which we do not reject $H_0$ includes all values of the sample mean $\bar{x}$ that are within $-z_{\alpha/2}$ and $+z_{\alpha/2}$ standard errors of $\mu_0$. Thus, the do-not-reject region for the sample mean $\bar{x}$ in a two-tailed hypothesis test is given by

$$\mu_0 \pm z_{\alpha/2} \frac{\sigma}{\sqrt{n}} \tag{9.6}$$

when $\sigma$ is assumed known and

$$\mu_0 \pm z_{\alpha/2} \frac{s}{\sqrt{n}} \tag{9.7}$$

when $\sigma$ is estimated by $s$.

A close look at expressions (9.4) and (9.6) provides insight about the relationship between the estimation and hypothesis testing approaches to statistical inference. Note in particular that both procedures require the computation of the values $z_{\alpha/2}$ and $\sigma/\sqrt{n}$. Focusing on $\alpha$, we see that a confidence coefficient of $(1 - \alpha)$ for interval estimation corresponds to a level of significance of $\alpha$ in hypothesis testing. For example, a 95% confidence interval corresponds to a .05 level of significance for hypothesis testing. Furthermore, expressions (9.4) and (9.6) show that because $z_{\alpha/2}(\sigma/\sqrt{n})$ is the plus or minus value for both expressions, if $\bar{x}$ is in the do-not-reject region defined by expression (9.6), the hypothesized value $\mu_0$ will be in the confidence interval defined by expression (9.4). Conversely, if the hypothesized value $\mu_0$ is in the confidence interval defined by expression (9.4), the sample mean $\bar{x}$ will be in the do-not-reject region for the hypothesis $H_0: \mu = \mu_0$ as defined by expression (9.6). These observations lead to the following procedure for using confidence interval results to draw hypothesis testing conclusions.

---

**A Confidence Interval Approach to Hypothesis Testing: Large-Sample Case**

Form of Hypotheses:

For a two-tailed hypothesis test, the null hypothesis can be rejected if the confidence interval for the population mean does not include $\mu_0$.

$$H_0: \mu = \mu_0$$
$$H_a: \mu \neq \mu_0$$

1. Select a simple random sample from the population and use the value of the sample mean $\bar{x}$ to develop the confidence interval for the population mean $\mu$. If $\sigma$ is assumed known, compute the interval estimate using

$$\bar{x} \pm z_{\alpha/2} \frac{\sigma}{\sqrt{n}}$$

If $\sigma$ is estimated by $s$, compute the interval estimate using

$$\bar{x} \pm z_{\alpha/2} \frac{s}{\sqrt{n}}$$

2. If the confidence interval contains the hypothesized value $\mu_0$, do not reject $H_0$. Otherwise, reject $H_0$.

---

Let us return to the Superflight golf ball study and the following two-tailed test.

$$H_0: \mu = 280$$
$$H_a: \mu \neq 280$$

To test this hypothesis with a level of significance of $\alpha = .05$, we sampled 36 golf balls and found a sample mean of $\bar{x} = 278.5$ yards and a sample standard deviation of $s = 12$ yards. Using these results with $z_{.025} = 1.96$, we find that the 95% confidence interval estimate of the population mean becomes

$$\bar{x} \pm z_{.025} \frac{s}{\sqrt{n}}$$

$$278.5 \pm 1.96 \frac{12}{\sqrt{36}}$$

$$278.5 \pm 3.92$$

or

$$274.58 \text{ to } 282.42$$

This finding enables the quality control manager to conclude with 95% confidence that the mean distance for the population of golf balls is between 274.58 and 282.42 yards. Because the hypothesized value for the population mean, $\mu_0 = 280$, is in this interval, the hypothesis testing conclusion is that the null hypothesis, $H_0: \mu = 280$, cannot be rejected.

Note that this discussion and example pertain to two-tailed hypothesis tests about a population mean. However, the same confidence interval and hypothesis testing relationship exists for other two-tailed tests about population parameters. In addition, the relationship can be extended to make one-tailed tests about population parameters. Doing so, however, requires the development of one-sided confidence intervals.

## NOTES AND COMMENTS

1. The $p$-value depends only on the sample outcome. However, it is necessary to know whether the hypothesis test being conducted is one-tailed or two-tailed. Given the value of $\bar{x}$ in a sample, the $p$-value for a two-tailed test will always be *twice* the area in the tail of the sampling distribution.

2. The interval estimation approach to hypothesis testing helps to highlight the role of the sample size. From expression (9.4) we can see that larger sample sizes lead to narrower confidence intervals. Thus, for a given level of significance $\alpha$, a larger sample is less likely to lead to an interval containing $\mu_0$ when the null hypothesis is false. That is, the larger sample size will provide a higher probability of rejecting $H_0$ when $H_0$ is false.

## EXERCISES

### Methods

19. Consider the following hypothesis test.

$$H_0: \mu = 10$$
$$H_a: \mu \neq 10$$

A sample of 36 provides a sample mean of 11 and sample standard deviation of 2.5.
   a. At $\alpha = .05$, what is the rejection rule?
   b. Compute the value of the test statistic $z$. What is your conclusion?

20. Consider the following hypothesis test.

$$H_0: \mu = 15$$
$$H_a: \mu \neq 15$$

A sample of 50 gives a sample mean of 14.2 and sample standard deviation of 5.
   a. At $\alpha = .02$, what is the rejection rule?
   b. Compute the value of the test statistic $z$.
   c. What is the $p$-value?
   d. What is your conclusion?

21. Consider the following hypothesis test.

$$H_0: \mu = 25$$
$$H_a: \mu \neq 25$$

A sample of 80 is used and the population standard deviation is 10. Use $\alpha = .05$. Compute the value of the test statistic $z$ and specify your conclusion for each of the following sample results.

  **a.**   $\bar{x} = 22.0$
  **b.**   $\bar{x} = 27.0$
  **c.**   $\bar{x} = 23.5$
  **d.**   $\bar{x} = 28.0$

**22.**  Consider the following hypothesis test.

$$H_0: \mu = 5$$
$$H_a: \mu \neq 5$$

Assume the following test statistics. Compute the corresponding $p$-values and specify your conclusions based on $\alpha = .05$.

  **a.**   $z = 1.80$
  **b.**   $z = -.45$
  **c.**   $z = 2.05$
  **d.**   $z = -3.50$
  **e.**   $z = -1.00$

## Applications

**23.**  The mean length of a work week for the population of workers is 39.2 hours (*Investor's Business Daily,* September 11, 2000). Assume a follow-up sample of 112 workers showed a sample mean of 38.5 hours and a sample standard deviation of 4.8 hours. Test the hypotheses: $H_0: \mu = 39.2$ and $H_a: \mu \neq 39.2$, with $\alpha = .05$.
  **a.**   What are the critical values for the test statistic, and what is the rejection rule for $H_0$?
  **b.**   What is the value of the test statistic?
  **c.**   Can the null hypothesis be rejected? What is your conclusion?
  **d.**   What is the $p$-value?

**24.**  CNN and ActMedia provided a television channel that showed news, features, and ads, and was targeted to individuals waiting in grocery checkout lines. The television programs were designed with an 8-minute cycle on the assumption that the population mean time a shopper stands in line at a grocery store checkout is 8 minutes. (*Astounding Averages,* 1995). A sample of 120 shoppers at a major grocery store showed a sample mean waiting time of 7.5 minutes with a sample standard deviation of 3.2 minutes.
  **a.**   Test $H_0: \mu = 8$ and $H_a: \mu \neq 8$. Use a .05 level of significance. Does the population mean waiting time at the grocery store differ from the 8-minute waiting time assumption?
  **b.**   What is the $p$-value for the test?

**25.**  A production line operates with a mean filling weight of 16 ounces per container. Either overfilling or underfilling is a serious problem, and the production line should be shut down if either occurs. From past data, $\sigma$ is known to be .8 ounces. A quality control inspector samples 30 items every 2 hours and at that time makes the decision of whether to shut the line down for adjustment.
  **a.**   With a .05 level of significance, what is the rejection rule?
  **b.**   If a sample mean of $\bar{x} = 16.32$ ounces were found, what action would you recommend?
  **c.**   If $\bar{x} = 15.82$ ounces, what action would you recommend?
  **d.**   What is the $p$-value for parts (b) and (c)?

**26.**  An automobile assembly line operation has a scheduled mean completion time of 2.2 minutes. Because of the effect of completion time on both preceding and subsequent assembly operations, it is important to maintain the 2.2-minute mean completion time. A random sample of 45 assemblies resulted in the completion times shown in the data set Assembly. Use a .02 level of significance and test whether the operation is meeting its 2.2-minute mean completion time.

**27.** Historically, evening long-distance phone calls from a particular city have averaged 15.2 minutes per call. In a random sample of 35 calls, the sample mean time was 14.3 minutes per call, with a sample standard deviation of 5 minutes. Use this sample information to test for any change in the mean duration of long-distance phone calls. Use a .05 level of significance. What is the *p*-value?

**28.** A Gallup survey found the mean charitable contribution on federal tax returns was $1075 (*USA Today,* April 10, 2000). Assume a sample of April 2001 tax returns will be used to conduct a hypothesis test designed to determine whether any change has occurred in the mean charitable contributions.

**a.** Formulate the null and alternative hypotheses.
**b.** Assume that a sample of 200 tax returns has a sample mean of $1160 and a sample standard deviation of $840. What is the value of the test statistic?
**c.** What is the *p*-value?
**d.** Using $\alpha = .05$, what is your conclusion?

## 9.5 TESTS ABOUT A POPULATION MEAN: SMALL-SAMPLE CASE

The procedures for hypothesis tests about a population mean discussed in Sections 9.3 and 9.4 were based on the central limit theorem and large-sample theory. In this section, we consider tests about a population mean using a small sample ($n < 30$). In this case the sampling distribution of $\bar{x}$ depends on the distribution of the population. In fact, the hypothesis testing procedures for the small-sample case require the assumption that the population has a normal probability distribution. If this assumption is appropriate, the methodology presented in this section can be used. However, if this assumption is not appropriate, the best alternative is to increase the sample size to $n > 30$ and rely on the large-sample hypothesis testing procedures presented in Sections 9.3 and 9.4.

> The methodology presented in this section is based on the assumption that the population has a normal distribution.

Let us first consider the situation where the sample size is small ($n < 30$), the population is assumed to have a normal distribution, and based on historical data, theoretical or other reasons, the population standard deviation $\sigma$ is assumed known. Under these conditions, and regardless of the sample size, the sampling distribution of $\bar{x}$ is exactly normal with mean $\mu$ and standard deviation $\sigma_{\bar{x}} = \sigma/\sqrt{n}$. Thus, given the sampling distribution of $\bar{x}$ is a normal distribution and $\sigma$ is assumed known, the small-sample hypothesis testing procedures are identical to the large-sample hypothesis testing procedures presented in Sections 9.3 and 9.4. In this case, the test statistic is

$$z = \frac{\bar{x} - \mu_0}{\sigma/\sqrt{n}} \tag{9.7}$$

Because the hypothesis testing computations are identical to the computations made previously, we shall not present a new numerical example at this time.

> The small-sample hypothesis testing procedure with $\sigma$ estimated by $s$ is based on the same theory used for the small-sample interval estimation procedure with $\sigma$ estimated by $s$ presented in Section 8.2. Both use a normal population assumption and the $t$ distribution.

Next, consider the situation in which the sample size is small ($n < 30$), the population is assumed to have a normal distribution, and the population standard deviation $\sigma$ is estimated by the sample standard deviation $s$. In this case, the $t$ distribution can be used to make inferences about the value of the population mean. The test statistic is

$$t = \frac{\bar{x} - \mu_0}{s/\sqrt{n}} \tag{9.8}$$

This test statistic has a $t$ distribution with $n - 1$ degrees of freedom.

Let us consider an example of a one-tailed hypothesis test about a population mean for the small-sample case. The International Air Transport Association surveys business trav-

**Heathrow**

elers to develop ratings of transatlantic gateway airports. The maximum possible rating is 10. A magazine devoted to business travel has decided to classify airports according to the rating they receive. Airports that have a population mean rating of 7 or more will be designated as providing superior service. Suppose a simple random sample of 12 business travelers have been asked to rate London's Heathrow airport, and that the 12 ratings obtained are 7, 8, 10, 8, 6, 9, 6, 7, 7, 8, 9, and 8. The sample mean is $\bar{x} = 7.75$ and the sample standard deviation is $s = 1.2154$. Assuming that the population of ratings can be approximated by a normal probability distribution, should Heathrow be designated as providing superior service?

Using a .05 level of significance, we need a test to determine whether the population mean rating for the Heathrow airport is greater than 7. The null and alternative hypotheses follow.

$$H_0: \mu \leq 7$$
$$H_a: \mu > 7$$

The Heathrow airport will be designated as providing superior service if the sample data provides sufficient evidence to conclude that $H_0$ can be rejected, indicating that the population mean rating is greater than 7.

The rejection region is in the upper tail of the sampling distribution. With $n - 1 = 12 - 1 = 11$ degrees of freedom, Table 2 of Appendix B shows that the critical value is $t_{.05} = 1.796$. Thus, the rejection rule is

$$\text{Reject } H_0 \text{ if } t > 1.796$$

Using equation (9.8) with $\bar{x} = 7.75$ and $s = 1.2154$, we have the following value for the test statistic.

$$t = \frac{\bar{x} - \mu_0}{s/\sqrt{n}} = \frac{7.75 - 7}{1.2154/\sqrt{12}} = 2.1376$$

Because 2.1376 is greater than 1.796, the null hypothesis is rejected. At the .05 level of significance, we can conclude that the population mean rating for the Heathrow airport is greater than 7. Thus, Heathrow can be designated as providing superior service. Figure 9.13 shows that the value of the test statistic is in the rejection region.

In the Heathrow Airport study, the rejection region was located in the upper tail of the sampling distribution. The general form of an upper-tail test about a population mean for the small-sample case is the same as in the large-sample case. With $\mu_0$ denoting the stated value for the population mean, we would state the null and alternative hypotheses as follows:

$$H_0: \mu \leq \mu_0$$
$$H_a: \mu > \mu_0$$

The test statistic is

$$t = \frac{\bar{x} - \mu_0}{s/\sqrt{n}}$$

and the rejection rule at a level of significance $\alpha$ is

$$\text{Reject } H_0 \text{ if } t > t_\alpha$$

**FIGURE 9.13**     VALUE OF THE TEST STATISTIC ($t = 2.1376$) FOR THE HEATHROW AIRPORT HYPOTHESIS TEST IS IN THE REJECTION REGION

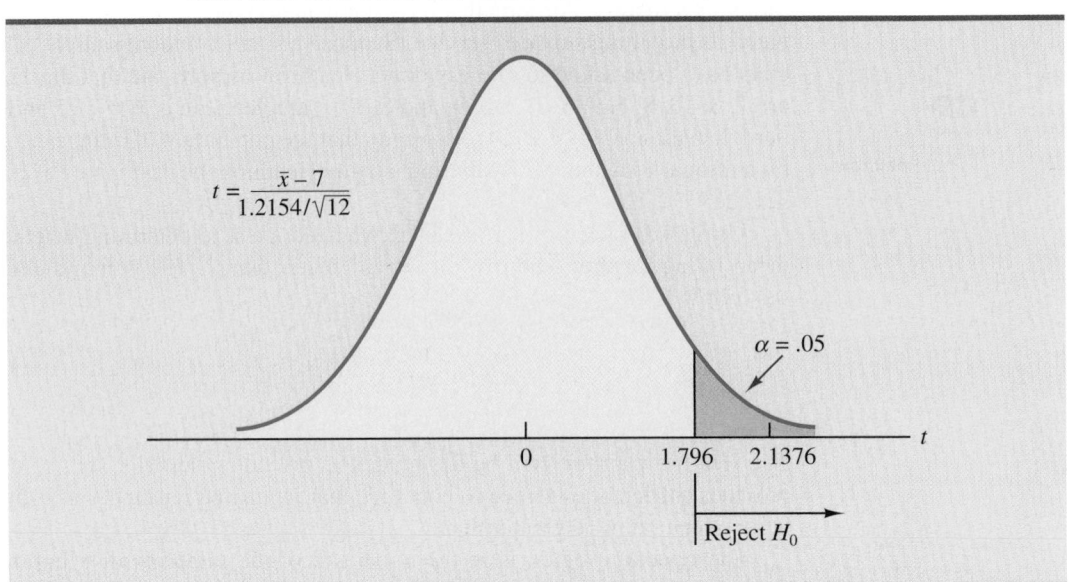

A second form of the one-tailed test for the small-sample case rejects the null hypothesis when the test statistic is in the lower tail of the sampling distribution. In this case, the general form of the test is as follows:

$$H_0: \mu \geq \mu_0$$
$$H_a: \mu < \mu_0$$

The test statistic for the upper-tail case is the same as for the lower-tail case, given by equation (9.8). The only change is that the rejection rule now becomes

$$\text{Reject } H_0 \text{ if } t < t_\alpha$$

## *p*-Values and the *t* Distribution

Let us consider the *p*-value for the Heathrow airport hypothesis test. The usual rule applies: If the *p*-value is less than the level of significance $\alpha$, the null hypothesis can be rejected. Unfortunately, the format of the *t* distribution table provided in most statistics textbooks does not have sufficient detail to determine the exact *p*-value for the test. However, we can still use the *t* distribution table to narrow the range of possible values. For example, the *t* distribution used in the Heathrow airport hypothesis test has 11 degrees of freedom. Referring to Table 2 of Appendix B, we see that row 11 provides the following information about a *t* distribution with 11 degrees of freedom.

*The p-values are difficult to obtain directly from a table of the t distribution. Generally, the best that can be done with the table is to specify a range for the p-value such as between .05 and .025. With Excel we can compute the exact p-value.*

| Area in Upper Tail | .10 | .05 | .025 | .01 | .005 |
|---|---|---|---|---|---|
| *t* Value | 1.363 | 1.796 | 2.201 | 2.718 | 3.106 |

The computed test statistic for the hypothesis test was $t = 2.1376$. The *p*-value is the area in the tail corresponding to $t = 2.1376$. From the preceding information, we see that 2.1376 is between 1.796 and 2.201. Thus, although we cannot determine the exact $p$-value associated with $t = 2.1376$, we do know that the $p$-value must be between .05 and .025. With a level of significance of $\alpha = .05$, we know that the $p$-value must be less than .05; thus, the null hypothesis is rejected.

## Using Excel to Conduct a One-Tailed Hypothesis Test: Small-Sample Case

Excel can be used to conduct one-tailed hypothesis tests for the small-sample case. The procedure is similar to that used in the large-sample case. The only difference is the function used to compute the $p$-value. Recall that in the large-sample case, the test statistic $z$ has a standard normal probability distribution. Thus, the NORMSDIST function was used to compute the $p$-value. However, because the test statistic in the small-sample case has a $t$ distribution, we must use the TDIST function to compute the $p$-value.

The general form of the TDIST function is as follows:

$$\text{TDIST(test statistic,degrees of freedom,tails)}$$

Only nonnegative values are allowed for the test statistic argument. If the value of tails is 1, the function returns the area in the upper tail of the $t$ distribution corresponding to the value of the test statistic. In the Heathrow Airport study we found a value for the test statistic of $t = 2.1376$. If we enter the function =TDIST(2.1376,11,1) into an Excel worksheet, the value obtained will be .0279. Thus, .0279 is the probability of obtaining a $t$ value of 2.1376 or greater for a $t$ distribution with 11 degrees of freedom. Thus, .0279 is the $p$-value for the Heathrow Airport upper-tail hypothesis test.

As already noted, the TDIST function will not allow negative values for the test statistic argument. We know that the $p$-value for a lower-tail hypothesis test is the cumulative probability associated with the value of the test statistic; that is, the $p$-value is the area under the curve for the $t$ distribution to the left of the value of the test statistic. We also know that the $p$-value for an upper-tail hypothesis test is the area under the curve to the right of the value of the test statistic. So, as with hypothesis tests involving the normal probability distribution, the $p$-value for an upper-tail test involving the $t$ distribution is one minus the $p$-value for a lower-tail test. These points are the keys to how we compute $p$-values for the $t$ distribution. We first find the value of the test statistic. To determine the $p$-value for a lower-tail test, we compute the area under the curve in the lower tail. Then, we subtract the $p$-value we computed for a lower-tail test from one to obtain the $p$-value for an upper-tail test. Finally, the $p$-value for a two-tailed test is just 2 times the smaller of the two tail areas, in other words, the $p$-value for a two-tailed test is just two times the minimum of the two one-tailed $p$-values.

Let us develop a general formula for using the TDIST function to compute lower-tail areas. It involves using Excel's IF function to first determine whether the value of the test statistic is positive or negative. If the test statistic is negative, we use TDIST in one way to compute the $p$-value. If the test statistic is nonnegative, we use TDIST in another way to compute the $p$-value. The general form of the IF function for computing lower-tail $p$-values for the $t$ distribution is IF(test statistic $< 0$,formula1,formula2). If the test statistic is negative, formula1 is used to compute the $p$-value. If the test statistic is nonnegative, formula2 is used to compute the $p$-value.

$$\text{formula1} = \text{TDIST(-test statistic, degrees of freedom, 1)}$$
$$\text{formula2} = 1-\text{TDIST(test statistic, degrees of freedom, 1)}$$

As noted, once $p$-value (Lower Tail) has been computed, $p$-value (Upper Tail) can be easily computed by subtracting $p$-value (Lower Tail) from 1.

*We show an example of a two-tailed test in the next subsection.*

Let us now construct an Excel worksheet to conduct the upper-tail hypothesis test for the Heathrow Airport rating study. Refer to Figure 9.14 as we describe the tasks involved. The formula worksheet is in the background; the value worksheet is in the foreground.

**Enter Data:**  Column A shows the rating provided by each of the 12 travelers.

**Enter Functions and Formulas:**  The descriptive statistics needed are provided in cells D4:D6. Excel's COUNT, AVERAGE, and STDEV functions are used to obtain the sample size, sample mean, and sample standard deviation.

The hypothesized value of the population mean (7) was entered into cell D8. Using the sample standard deviation as an estimate of the population standard deviation, an estimate of the standard error was obtained in cell D10 by dividing the sample standard deviation in cell D6 by the square root of the sample size in cell D4. The formula =(D5-D8)/D10 was entered into cell D11 to compute the test statistic $t$ (2.1376). The degrees of freedom are computed in cell D12 as the sample size in cell D4 minus 1.

To compute the $p$-value for a lower-tail test, we entered the formula

$$=\text{IF}(D11<0,\text{TDIST}(-D11,D12,1),1-\text{TDIST}(D11,D12,1))$$

into cell D14. The $p$-value for an upper-tail test is then computed in cell D15 as 1 minus the $p$-value for the lower-tail test. Finally, the $p$-value for a two-tailed test is computed in cell D16 as 2 times the minimum of the two one-tailed $p$-values.

In the Heathrow Airport study we want to conduct an upper-tail hypothesis test, so we want to compare the $p$-value (Upper Tail) with the level of significance. Because the $p$-value (Upper Tail) = .0279 in cell D15 is less than $\alpha$ = .05, we reject the null hypothesis and conclude that the mean rating for the Heathrow airport is greater than 7.

The worksheet developed in Figure 9.14 can be used for any hypothesis test involving the $t$ distribution. If a lower-tail test is required, compare the $p$-value (Lower Tail) with $\alpha$ to make the rejection decision. If an upper-tail test is required, compare the $p$-value (Upper Tail) with $\alpha$ to make the rejection decision. And, if a two-tailed test is required, compare the $p$-value (Two Tail) with $\alpha$ to make the rejection decision. Let us now see an example involving a two-tailed hypothesis test.

**FIGURE 9.14**    EXCEL WORKSHEET FOR THE HEATHROW AIRPORT HYPOTHESIS TEST

## Two-Tailed Test

As an example of a two-tailed hypothesis test about a population mean using a small sample, consider the following production problem. A production process is designed to fill containers with a mean filling weight of $\mu = 16$ ounces. If the process underfills containers, the consumer will not receive the amount of product indicated on the container label. If the process overfills containers, the firm loses money because more product is placed in a container than is required. To monitor the process, quality assurance personnel periodically select a simple random sample of eight containers and test the following two-tailed hypotheses.

$$H_0: \mu = 16$$
$$H_a: \mu \neq 16$$

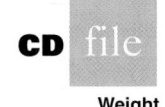

**Weight**

If $H_0$ is rejected, the production process will be stopped and the mechanism for regulating filling weights will be readjusted to ensure a mean filling weight of 16 ounces. Suppose a sample yields data values of 16.02, 16.22, 15.82, 15.92, 16.22, 16.32, 16.12, and 15.92 ounces. The sample mean is $\bar{x} = 16.07$, and the sample standard deviation is .1773. Assume that the population of filling weights is normally distributed. At the .05 level of significance, what action should be taken?

With a two-tailed test and a level of significance of $\alpha = .05$, the value of $-t_{.025}$ and the value of $t_{.025}$ are the critical values for the test. Using the table for the $t$ distribution, we find that with $n - 1 = 8 - 1 = 7$ degrees of freedom, $-t_{.025} = -2.365$ and $t_{.025} = +2.365$. Thus, the rejection rule is

$$\text{Reject } H_0 \text{ if } t < -2.365 \text{ or if } t > 2.365$$

Using $\bar{x} = 16.07$ and $s = .1773$, we have

$$t = \frac{\bar{x} - \mu_0}{s/\sqrt{n}} = \frac{16.07 - 16}{.1773/\sqrt{8}} = 1.117$$

Because $t = 1.117$ is not in the rejection region, the null hypothesis cannot be rejected. The evidence is not sufficient to stop the production process.

Using Table 2 of Appendix B and the row for seven degrees of freedom, we see that the computed $t$ value of 1.117 has an upper tail area of *more than* .10. Although the format of the $t$ distribution table prevents us from being more specific, we can at least conclude that the two-tailed $p$-value is greater than $2(.10) = .20$. Because this value is greater than the .05 level of significance, we see that the $p$-value leads to the same conclusion; that is, do not reject $H_0$.

## Using Excel to Conduct a Two-Tailed Hypothesis Test: Small-Sample Case

Excel can be used to conduct the two-tailed hypothesis test for the container filling production problem. Refer to Figure 9.15 as we describe the tasks involved. The formula worksheet is in the background; the value worksheet is in the foreground.

**Enter Data:**   Column A shows the weight in ounces for each of the eight containers.

**Enter Functions and Formulas:**   The descriptive statistics needed are provided in cells D4:D6. Excel's COUNT, AVERAGE, and STDEV functions are used to obtain the sample size, sample mean, and sample standard deviation.

**FIGURE 9.15     EXCEL WORKSHEET FOR THE CONTAINER-FILLING HYPOTHESIS TEST**

The hypothesized value of the population mean (16) was entered into cell D8. Using the sample standard deviation as an estimate of the population standard deviation, an estimate of the standard error was obtained in cell D10 by dividing the sample standard deviation in cell D6 by the square root of the sample size in cell D4. The formula $=(D5 - D8)/D10$ was entered into cell D11 to compute the test statistic $t$ (1.1168). The degrees of freedom are computed in cell D12 as the sample size in cell D4 minus 1.

To compute the $p$-value (Lower Tail), we entered the formula

$$=IF(D11<0,TDIST(-D11,D12,1),1-TDIST(D11,D12,1))$$

into cell D14. Then, the $p$-value (Upper Tail) is computed in cell D15 as $1 - p$-value (Lower Tail). Finally, the $p$-value (Two Tail) is computed in cell D16 as 2 times the minimum of the two one-tailed $p$-values.

In the container-filling study we want to conduct a two-tailed hypothesis test, so we want to compare the two-tailed $p$-value with the level of significance. Because the $p$-value (Two Tail) = .3009 in cell D16 is greater than $\alpha = .05$, we cannot reject the null hypothesis. We conclude that the sample data do not provide sufficient evidence to stop the production process.

## EXERCISES

### Methods

**29.**   Consider the following hypothesis test.

$$H_0: \mu \leq 10$$
$$H_a: \mu > 10$$

A sample of 16 items provides a sample mean of 11 and sample standard deviation of 3.
  **a.**   With $\alpha = .05$, what is the rejection rule?
  **b.**   Compute the value of the test statistic $t$. What is your conclusion?

**30.** Consider the following hypothesis test.

$$H_0: \mu = 20$$
$$H_a: \mu \neq 20$$

Data from a sample of six items are 18, 20, 16, 19, 17, 18.
   **a.** Compute the sample mean.
   **b.** Compute the sample standard deviation.
   **c.** With $\alpha = .05$, what is the rejection rule?
   **d.** Compute the value of the test statistic $t$.
   **e.** What is your conclusion?

**31.** Consider the following hypothesis test.

$$H_0: \mu \geq 15$$
$$H_a: \mu < 15$$

A sample of size 22 is used, and the sample standard deviation is 8. Use $\alpha = .05$. Provide the value of the test statistic $t$ and your conclusion for each of the following sample results.
   **a.** $\bar{x} = 13.0$
   **b.** $\bar{x} = 11.5$
   **c.** $\bar{x} = 15.0$
   **d.** $\bar{x} = 19.0$

**32.** Consider the following hypothesis test.

$$H_0: \mu \leq 50$$
$$H_a: \mu > 50$$

Assume a sample of 16 items provides the following test statistics. What can you say about the $p$-values in each case? What are your conclusions based on $\alpha = .05$?
   **a.** $t = 2.602$
   **b.** $t = 1.341$
   **c.** $t = 1.960$
   **d.** $t = 1.055$
   **e.** $t = 3.261$

## Applications

**33.** The population mean earnings per share for financial services corporations including American Express, E*Trade Group, Goldman Sachs, and Merrill Lynch was $3 (*Business Week*, August 14, 2000). In 2001, a sample of 10 financial services corporations provided the following earnings per share data:

| 1.92 | 2.16 | 3.63 | 3.16 | 4.02 | 3.14 | 2.20 | 2.34 | 3.05 | 2.38 |
|------|------|------|------|------|------|------|------|------|------|

   **a.** Formulate the null and alternative hypotheses that can be used to determine whether population mean earnings per share in 2001 differs from the $3 per share reported in 2000.
   **b.** Using $\alpha = .05$, what are the critical values for the test statistic, and what is the rejection rule?
   **c.** Compute the sample mean.
   **d.** Compute the sample standard deviation.
   **e.** Compute the value of the test statistic.
   **f.** What is your conclusion?
   **g.** What is the $p$-value?

**DailyExp**

**34.** The average U.S. household spends $90 per day (*American Demographics,* August 1997). Suppose a sample of 25 households in Corning, New York, resulted in the data set DailyExp.

    **a.** Test $H_0$: $\mu = 90$ and $H_a$: $\mu \neq 90$ to see whether the population mean in Corning, New York, differs from the U.S. mean. Use a .05 level of significance. What is your conclusion?

    **b.** What is the *p*-value?

**35.** On the average, a stay-at-home mom with a husband and two children is estimated to work 55 hours or less per week on household-related activities. The hours worked during a week for a sample of eight stay-at-home moms are 58, 52, 64, 63, 59, 62, 62, and 55.

    **a.** Use $\alpha = .05$ to test $H_0$: $\mu \leq 55$, $H_a$: $\mu > 55$. What is your conclusion about the mean number of hours worked per week?

    **b.** What is the *p*-value?

**36.** The cost of a one-carat VS2 clarity, H color diamond from the Diamond Source USA is $4000 (www.diasource.com, July 2000). A midwestern jeweler makes calls to contacts in the diamond district of New York City to see whether the mean price of similar diamonds differs from $4000. The jeweler collects cost data from 14 New York City contacts.

    **a.** Formulate the null and alternative hypotheses that can be used to determine whether the mean price in New York City differs from $4000.

    **b.** Using $\alpha = .05$, what are the critical values for the test, and what is the rejection rule?

    **c.** Assume the sample of 14 New York City contacts provides a sample mean price of $4120 and a sample standard deviation of $275. Compute the value of the test statistic.

    **d.** What is your conclusion?

    **e.** What is the *p*-value?

**37.** Callaway Golf Company's new forged titanium ERC driver has been described as "illegal" because it promised driving distances that exceeded the USGA's standard. *Golf Digest* compared actual driving distances with the ERC driver and a USGA-approved driver with a population mean driving distance of 280 yards. Using nine test drives, the mean driving distance by the ERC driver was 286.9 yards. (*Golf Digest,* May 12, 2000). Answer the following questions assuming a population standard deviation driving distance of 10 yards.

    **a.** Formulate the null and alternative hypotheses that can be used to determine whether the new ERC driver has a population mean driving distance greater than 280 yards.

    **b.** On average, how many yards farther did the golf ball travel with the ERC driver?

    **c.** Using $\alpha = .05$, what is the critical value for the test statistic, and what is the rejection rule?

    **d.** Compute the value of the test statistic.

    **e.** What is your conclusion?

    **f.** What is the *p*-value?

**38.** Joan's Nursery specializes in custom-designed landscaping for residential areas. The estimated labor cost associated with a particular landscaping proposal is based on the number of plantings of trees, shrubs, and so on to be used for the project. For cost-estimating purposes, managers use 2 hours of labor time for the planting of a medium-sized tree. Actual times from a sample of 10 plantings during the past month follow (times in hours).

| 1.9 | 1.7 | 2.8 | 2.4 | 2.6 | 2.5 | 2.8 | 3.2 | 1.6 | 2.5 |
|-----|-----|-----|-----|-----|-----|-----|-----|-----|-----|

Using a .05 level of significance, test whether the mean tree-planting time exceeds 2 hours. What is your conclusion, and what recommendations would you consider making to the managers?

## 9.6    TESTS ABOUT A POPULATION PROPORTION

With $p$ denoting the population proportion and $p_0$ denoting a particular hypothesized value for the population proportion, the three forms for a hypothesis test about a population proportion are as follows.

$$H_0: p \geq p_0 \qquad H_0: p \leq p_0 \qquad H_0: p = p_0$$
$$H_a: p < p_0 \qquad H_a: p > p_0 \qquad H_a: p \neq p_0$$

The first two forms are one-tailed tests, whereas the third form is a two-tailed test. The specific form used depends on the application.

Hypothesis tests about a population proportion are based on the difference between the sample proportion $\bar{p}$ and the hypothesized population proportion $p_0$. The methods used to conduct the tests are similar to the procedures used for hypothesis tests about a population mean. The only difference is that we use the sample proportion $\bar{p}$ and its standard error $\sigma_{\bar{p}}$ in developing the test statistic. We begin by formulating null and alternative hypotheses about the value of the population proportion. Then, using the value of the sample proportion $\bar{p}$ and its standard error $\sigma_{\bar{p}}$, we compute a value for the test statistic $z$. Comparing the value of the test statistic to the critical value enables us to determine whether the null hypothesis should be rejected. We can also determine whether the null hypothesis should be rejected using the $p$-value approach; that is, we reject $H_0$ if the $p$-value $< \alpha$.

Let us illustrate hypothesis testing for a population proportion by considering the situation faced by Pine Creek golf course. Over the past few months, 20% of the players at Pine Creek have been women. In an effort to increase the proportion of women playing, Pine Creek is now using a special promotion to attract women golfers. After one week, a random sample of 400 players showed 300 men and 100 women. Course managers would like to determine whether the data support the conclusion that the population proportion of women playing at Pine Creek has increased.

To determine whether the effect of the promotion has been to increase the population proportion of women golfers, we state the following null and alternative hypotheses.

$$H_0: p \leq .20$$
$$H_a: p > .20$$

As usual, we begin the hypothesis testing procedure by assuming that $H_0$ is true with $p = .20$. Using the sample proportion $\bar{p}$ to estimate $p$, we next consider the sampling distribution of $\bar{p}$. From Chapter 7, we know that the mean of the sampling distribution of $\bar{p}$ is $p = .20$, and the standard deviation of $\bar{p}$ (the standard error) is given by

$$\sigma_{\bar{p}} = \sqrt{\frac{p(1-p)}{n}}$$

With the assumed value of $p = .20$ and a sample size of $n = 400$, the standard error of $\bar{p}$ is

$$\sigma_{\bar{p}} = \sqrt{\frac{.20(1 - .20)}{400}} = .02$$

In Chapter 7 we saw that the sampling distribution of $\bar{p}$ can be approximated by a normal probability distribution if both $np$ and $n(1 - p)$ are greater than or equal to 5. In the Pine Creek case, $np = 400(.20) = 80$ and $n(1 - p) = 400(.80) = 320$; thus, the normal probability distribution approximation is appropriate. The sampling distribution of $\bar{p}$ is shown in Figure 9.16.

**FIGURE 9.16** SAMPLING DISTRIBUTION OF $\bar{p}$ FOR THE PROPORTION OF WOMEN GOLFERS AT PINE CREEK GOLF COURSE

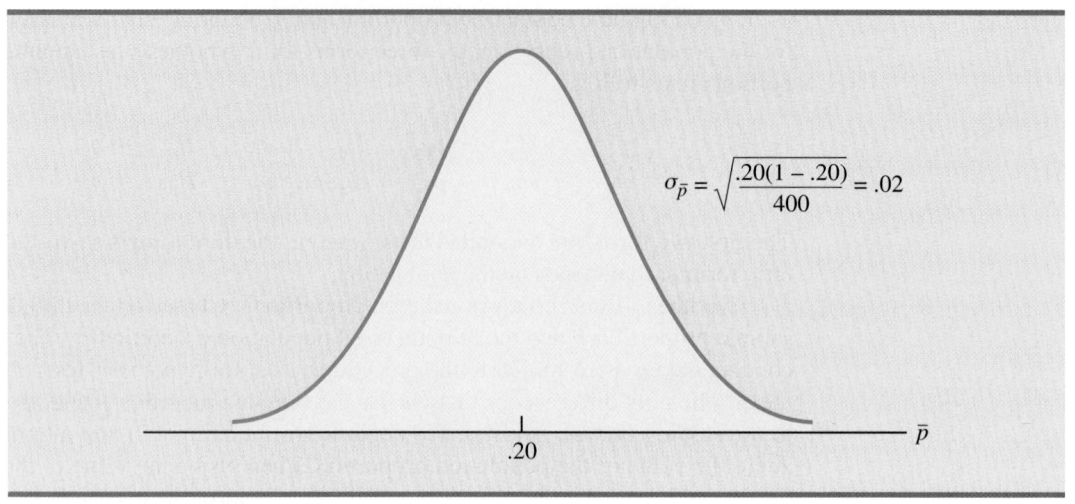

Because the sampling distribution of $\bar{p}$ is approximately normal, the following test statistic can be used.

**Test Statistic for Hypothesis Tests About a Population Proportion**

In hypothesis testing, a value of the population proportion, $p_0$, is assumed in $H_0$. Therefore, when $H_0$ is true, $\sigma_{\bar{p}}$ can be computed by using $p_0$ as shown in equation (9.10). The sample proportion, $\bar{p}$, is not used in the computation of $\sigma_{\bar{p}}$.

$$z = \frac{\bar{p} - p_0}{\sigma_{\bar{p}}} \tag{9.9}$$

where

$$\sigma_{\bar{p}} = \sqrt{\frac{p_0(1 - p_0)}{n}} \tag{9.10}$$

Suppose that $\alpha = .05$ has been selected as the level of significance for the test. With $z_{.05} = 1.645$, the upper-tail rejection region for the hypothesis test (see Figure 9.17) provides the following rejection rule.

$$\text{Reject } H_0 \text{ if } z > 1.645$$

Because 100 of the 400 players during the promotion were women, we obtain $\bar{p} = 100/400 = .25$. With $\sigma_{\bar{p}} = .02$, the value of the test statistic is

$$z = \frac{\bar{p} - p_0}{\sigma_{\bar{p}}} = \frac{.25 - .20}{.02} = 2.5$$

Because $z = 2.5 > 1.645$, we can reject $H_0$. The Pine Creek managers can conclude that the population proportion of women players has increased.

The $p$-value approach can also be used to determine whether the null hypothesis should be rejected. Using the cumulative normal probability table, we find that the area to the right of $z = 2.5$ is $1 - .9938 = .0062$. Thus, the $p$-value for the test is .0062. Because the $p$-value is less than $\alpha$, the null hypothesis can be rejected.

**FIGURE 9.17**    REJECTION REGION FOR THE PINE CREEK GOLF COURSE
HYPOTHESIS TEST

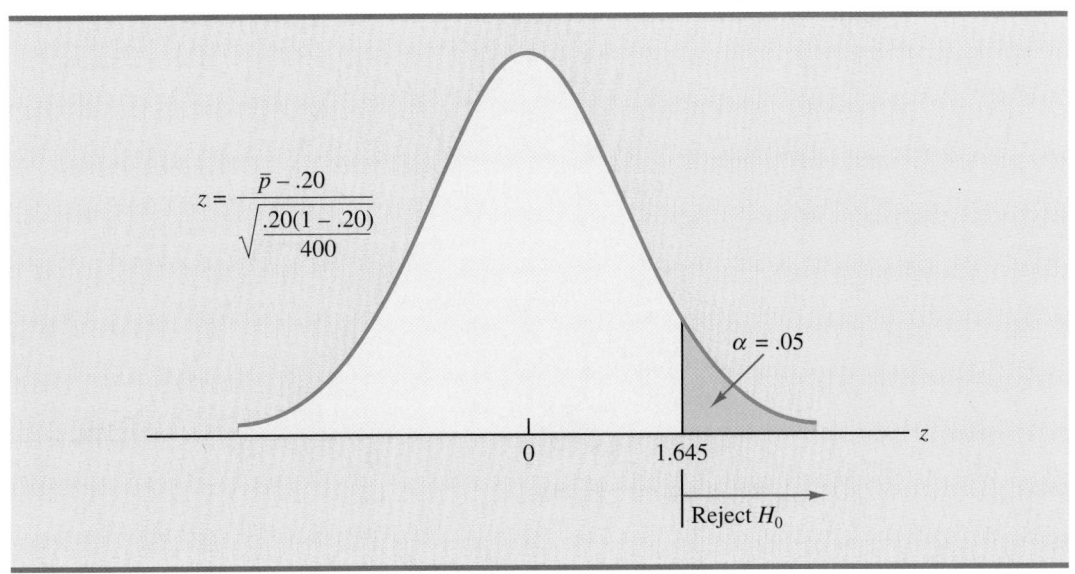

We see that hypothesis tests about a population proportion and a population mean are similar; the primary difference is that the test statistic is based on the sampling distribution of $\bar{x}$ when the hypothesis test involves a population mean and on the sampling distribution of $\bar{p}$ when the hypothesis test involves a population proportion. The tentative assumption that the null hypothesis is true, the use of the level of significance to establish the critical value, and the comparison of the test statistic to the critical value are identical in the two testing procedures. Figure 9.18 summarizes the decision rules for hypothesis tests about a population proportion. We assume the large-sample case, $np \geq 5$ and $n(1 - p) \geq 5$, where the normal probability distribution can be used to approximate the sampling distribution of $\bar{p}$.

## Using Excel to Conduct Hypothesis Tests About a Population Proportion

As we stated in the preceding paragraph, the primary difference between hypothesis tests about a population proportion and a population mean is that the test statistic is based on the sampling distribution of $\bar{x}$ when the hypothesis test involves a population mean and on the sampling distribution of $\bar{p}$ when the hypothesis test involves a population proportion. But, in the large-sample case, both the sampling distribution of $\bar{x}$ and the sampling distribution of $\bar{p}$ can be approximated by a normal probability distribution. Thus, although different formulas are used to compute the test statistic needed to make the hypothesis testing decision, the computations of the critical value and the $p$-value for the tests are identical. We will illustrate the procedure by showing how Excel can be used to conduct the hypothesis test for the Pine Creek golf course study. Refer to Figure 9.19 as we describe the tasks involved. The value worksheet is in the foreground; the formula worksheet is in the background.

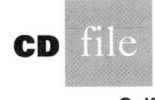

**Golf**

**Enter Data:**    Column A identifies the gender of each golfer in the sample of size 400.

**Enter Functions and Formulas:**    The descriptive statistics needed are provided in cells D4:D7. Because the data are not numeric, Excel's COUNTA function, not the COUNT function, is used in cell D4 to determine the sample size. We have typed Female in cell D5 to identify the response for which we wish to compute a proportion. The COUNTIF function is then used in cell D6 to determine the number of responses of the type identified in

**FIGURE 9.18** SUMMARY OF REJECTION RULES FOR HYPOTHESIS TESTS ABOUT A POPULATION PROPORTION

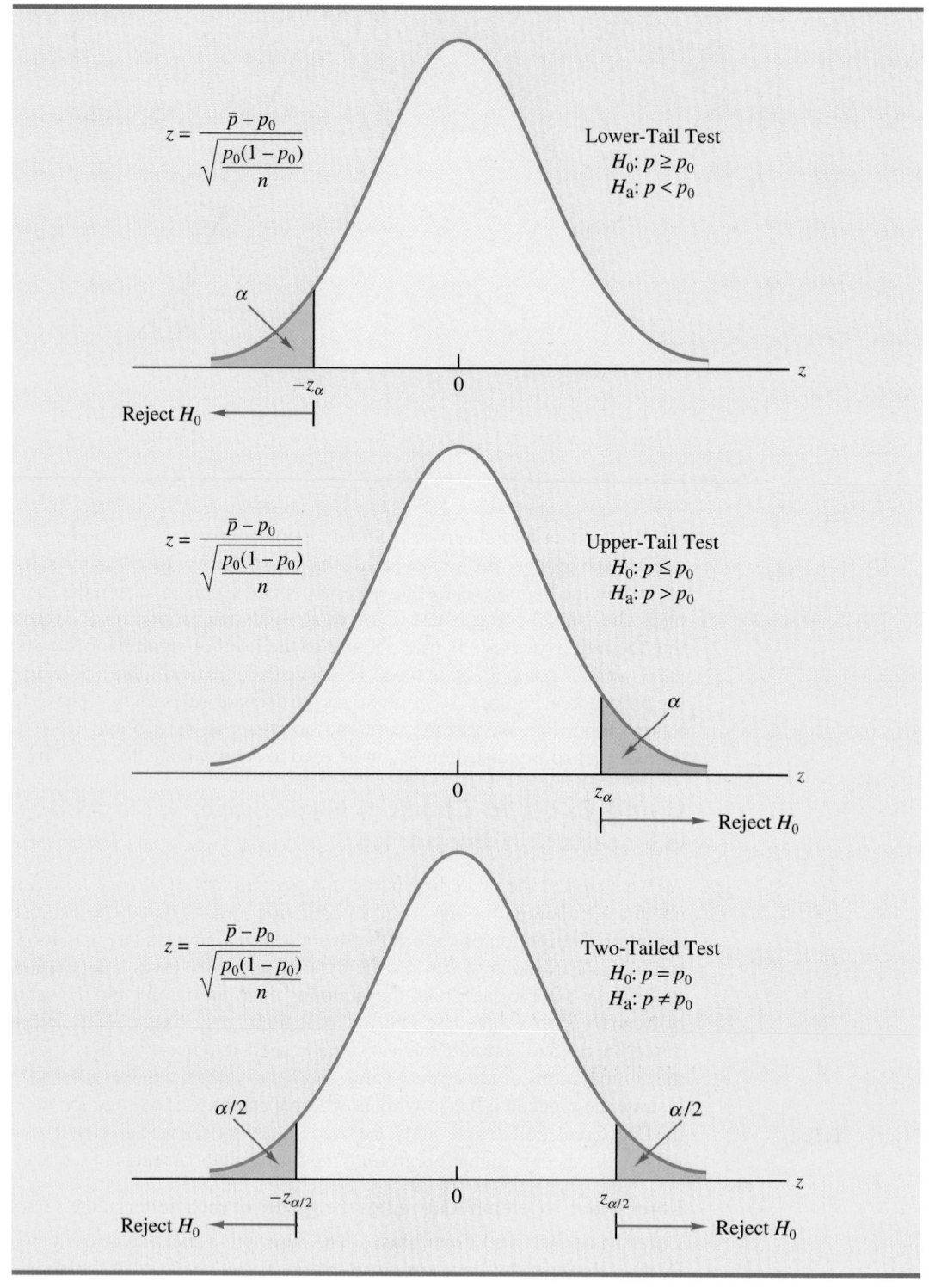

**FIGURE 9.19    EXCEL WORKSHEET FOR PINE CREEK GOLF COURSE HYPOTHESIS TEST**

Note: Rows 18–398 are hidden.

cell D5. The sample proportion is then computed in cell D7 by dividing the response count by the sample size.

The hypothesized value of the population proportion (.2) was entered into cell D9. An estimate of the standard error was obtained in cell D11 by entering the formula =SQRT(D9*(1-D9)/D4). The formula =(D7-D9)/D11 was entered into cell D12 to compute the test statistic $z$ (2.5). Finally, the NORMSDIST function was used in cells D14 and D15 to compute the lower-tail and upper-tail $p$-values, respectively. Although we didn't need it for this application, the two-tailed $p$-value is also computed in cell D16 as 2 times the minimum of the one-tailed $p$-values.

The Pine Creek hypothesis test has an upper-tail rejection region, so the $p$-value we want to use is found in cell D15 ($p$-value (Upper Tail) = .0062). At the $\alpha = .05$ level of significance we reject the null hypothesis that the population proportion is .20 or less. Indeed, with this $p$-value we would have rejected the null hypothesis for any level of significance greater than .0062.

The worksheet in Figure 9.19 can be used as a template for hypothesis tests about a population proportion in the large-sample case. Just enter the appropriate data in column A, adjust the ranges for the formulas in cells D4 and D6, type the appropriate response in cell D5, and enter the hypothesized value in cell D9. The standard error, the test statistic, and the three $p$-values will then appear. Depending on the form of the hypothesis test (lower-tail, upper-tail, or two-tailed), we can then choose the appropriate $p$-value to make the rejection decision.

## NOTES AND COMMENTS

We have not shown the procedure for small-sample hypothesis tests involving population proportions. In the small-sample case, the sampling distribution of $\bar{p}$ follows the binomial distribution and hence the nor-mal approximation is not applicable. More advanced texts show how hypothesis tests are conducted for this situation. However, in practice large samples are almost always used to estimate a population proportion.

## EXERCISES

### Methods

**39.** Consider the following hypothesis test.

$$H_0: p \leq .50$$
$$H_a: p > .50$$

A sample of 200 items provided a sample proportion $\bar{p} = .57$.
   **a.** At $\alpha = .05$, what is the rejection rule?
   **b.** Compute the value of the test statistic $z$. What is your conclusion?

**40.** Consider the following hypothesis test.

$$H_0: p = .20$$
$$H_a: p \neq .20$$

A sample of 400 items provided a sample proportion of $\bar{p} = .175$.
   **a.** At $\alpha = .05$, what is the rejection rule?
   **b.** Compute the value of the test statistic $z$.
   **c.** What is the $p$-value?
   **d.** What is your conclusion?

**41.** Consider the following hypothesis test.

$$H_0: p \geq .75$$
$$H_a: p < .75$$

A sample of 300 items is selected. Use $\alpha = .05$. Provide the value of the test statistic $z$, the $p$-value, and your conclusion for each of the following sample results.
   **a.** $\bar{p} = .68$
   **b.** $\bar{p} = .72$
   **c.** $\bar{p} = .70$
   **d.** $\bar{p} = .77$

### Applications

**42.** The Heldrich Center for Workforce Development found that 40% of Internet users received more than 10 e-mail messages per day (*USA Today,* May 7, 2000). In 2001, a similar study on the use of e-mail was repeated. The purpose of the study was to see whether use of e-mail had increased.
   **a.** Formulate the null and alternative hypotheses to determine whether an *increase* had occurred in the proportion of Internet users receiving more than 10 e-mails message per day.
   **b.** Using $\alpha = .05$, what is the critical value for the test, and what is the rejection rule?
   **c.** If a sample of 420 Internet users found 188 receiving more than 10 e-mail messages per day, what is the sample proportion, and what is the value of the test statistic?
   **d.** What is your conclusion?

**43.** A study by *Consumer Reports* showed that 64% of supermarket shoppers believed supermarket brands to be as good as national name brands in terms of product quality. To investigate whether this result applies to its own product, the manufacturer of a national name-brand ketchup product asked 100 supermarket shoppers whether they believed the supermarket brand of ketchup was as good as the national name-brand ketchup. Use the fact that 52 of the shoppers in the sample indicated that the supermarket brand was as good as the national name brand to test $H_0$: $p \geq .64$ and $H_a$: $p < .64$. Use a .05 level of significance. What is your conclusion?

**44.** Burger King sponsored what it believed to be the biggest product giveaway in fast-food history when it initiated "FreeFryDay" on Friday, January 2, 1998. Anyone who stopped at one of Burger King's 7400 restaurants received a small order of the new Burger King fries free of charge. A national taste test comparing the new Burger King fries to McDonald's fries was the basis for the launch of the Burger King promotion. Of the 500 customers who participated in the taste test, 285 expressed a taste preference for the Burger King fries (*USA Today,* December 10, 1997). Let $p$ = the population proportion that favors the Burger King fries. Consider the following hypothesis test:

$$H_0: p \leq .50$$
$$H_a: p > .50$$

   **a.** What is the point estimate of the population proportion that favors the Burger King fries?
   **b.** What is your conclusion? Use a .01 level of significance.
   **c.** Do you believe that the national taste test statistics helped Burger King's management decide to implement the "FreeFryDay" campaign? Discuss.

**Students**

**45.** A magazine claims that 25% of its readers are college students. A random sample of 200 readers resulted in the data set Students. A response of Yes indicates that the reader is a college student. Use a .10 level of significance to test $H_0$: $p = .25$ and $H_a$: $p \neq .25$. What is the $p$-value?

$n = 200$

$.5987$

**46.** Shell Oil office workers were asked which work schedule appealed most: working five 8-hour days or four 10-hour days (*USA Today,* September 11, 2000). Let $p$ equal the proportion of office workers preferring the schedule with four 10-hour days. Test the hypotheses $H_0$: $p = .50$ and $H_a$: $p \neq .50$ at $\alpha = .01$. A sample of 105 office workers showed that 67 prefer the four 10-hour day schedule.
   **a.** What is the sample proportion preferring four 10-hour days?
   **b.** What is the value of the test statistic?
   **c.** What is the $p$-value?
   **d.** What is your conclusion? Is a statistically significant preference indicated between the two alternatives?

**47.** Drugstore.com was the first e-commerce company to offer Internet drugstore retailing. Drugstore.com customers could buy health, beauty, personal care, wellness, and pharmaceutical replenishment products over the Internet. At the end of 10 months of operation, the company reported that 44% of orders were from repeat customers (*Drugstore.com Annual Report,* January 2, 2000). Assume that Drugstore.com will use a sample of customer orders each quarter to determine whether the proportion of orders from repeat customers has changed from the initial $p = .44$.
   **a.** Formulate the null and alternative hypotheses.
   **b.** During the first quarter, a sample of 500 orders showed 205 repeat customers. What is the $p$-value? What is your conclusion using $\alpha = .05$?   $.41$
   **c.** During the second quarter, a sample of 500 orders showed 245 repeat customers. What is the $p$-value? What is your conclusion using $\alpha = .05$?   $.49$

$44\%$

$2.43$

$\dfrac{205}{500} \times \dfrac{}{100}$

$500 x = 20500$

$.41$

**48.** Microsoft Outlook is believed to be the most widely used e-mail manager. A Microsoft executive claims that Microsoft Outlook is used by at least 75% of Internet users. A Merrill Lynch study reported 72% use Microsoft Outlook (CNBC, June 2000). Test the following hypotheses: $H_0$: $p \geq .75$, $H_a$: $p < 75$ at $\alpha = .05$.
   **a.** Assuming the Merrill Lynch sample size was 300 users, compute the value of the test statistic.
   **b.** What is the $p$-value?
   **c.** Should the executive's claim of at least 75% be rejected?

**49.** Based on rates of errors, third base is the most difficult position to play in professional baseball. Considering all third basemen, an error occurs on 4.7% of fielding chances (*ESPN The Magazine,* July 12, 1999). A sample of games played by all-star third baseman Brooks Robinson showed that he had 35 errors in 1182 fielding chances. Does the sample support the conclusion that Brooks Robinson makes fewer errors than the typical third baseman? Use $\alpha = .01$.

a. What are the appropriate null and alternative hypotheses?
b. What is the sample proportion error percentage for Brooks Robinson?
c. Compute the value of the test statistic.
d. What is the *p*-value?
e. What is your conclusion?

## 9.7 HYPOTHESIS TESTING AND DECISION MAKING

In Section 9.1 we noted three types of situations in which hypothesis testing is used:

1. Testing research hypotheses.
2. Testing the validity of a claim.
3. Testing in decision-making situations.

In the first two situations, action is taken only when the null hypothesis $H_0$ is rejected and hence the alternative hypothesis $H_a$ is concluded to be true. In the third situation—decision making—it is necessary to take action when the null hypothesis is not rejected as well as when it is rejected.

The hypothesis testing procedures presented thus far have limited applicability in a decision-making situation because it is not considered appropriate to accept $H_0$ and take action based on the conclusion that $H_0$ is true. The reason for not taking action when the test results indicate *do not reject $H_0$* is that the decision to accept $H_0$ exposes the decision maker to the risk of making a Type II error; that is, accepting $H_0$ when it is false. With the hypothesis testing procedures described in the preceding sections, the probability of a Type I error is controlled by establishing a level of significance for the test. However, the probability of making the Type II error is not controlled.

Clearly, in certain decision-making situations the decision maker may want—and in some cases may be forced—to take action with both the conclusion *do not reject $H_0$* and the conclusion *reject $H_0$*. A good illustration of this situation is lot acceptance sampling, a topic we will discuss in greater depth in Chapter 19. For example, a quality control manager must decide to accept a shipment of batteries from a supplier or to return the shipment because of poor quality. Assume that design specifications require batteries from the supplier to have a mean useful life of at least 120 hours. To evaluate the quality of an incoming shipment, a sample of 36 batteries will be selected and tested. On the basis of the sample, a decision must be made to accept the shipment of batteries or to return it to the supplier because of poor quality. Let $\mu$ denote the mean number of hours of useful life for batteries in the shipment. The null and alternative hypotheses about the population mean follow.

$$H_0: \mu \geq 120$$
$$H_a: \mu < 120$$

If $H_0$ is rejected, the alternative hypothesis is concluded to be true. This conclusion indicates that the appropriate decision is to return the shipment to the supplier. However, if $H_0$ is not rejected, the decision maker will make the decision to use the batteries. Thus, without directly concluding that $H_0$ is true, but merely by not rejecting it, the decision maker will have made the decision to accept the shipment as being of satisfactory quality.

    In such decision-making situations, it is recommended that the hypothesis testing procedure be extended to include consideration of the probability of making a Type II error. Because a decision will be made and action taken when we do not reject $H_0$, knowledge of the probability of making a Type II error will be helpful. In Sections 9.8 and 9.9 we explain how to compute the probability of making a Type II error and how the sample size can be adjusted to help control the probability of making a Type II error.

## 9.8    CALCULATING THE PROBABILITY OF TYPE II ERRORS

In this section we show how to calculate the probability of making a Type II error for a hypothesis test about a population mean. We illustrate the procedure by using the lot-acceptance example described in Section 9.7. The null and alternative hypotheses about the mean number of hours of useful life for a shipment of batteries are $H_0: \mu \geq 120$ and $H_a: \mu < 120$. If $H_0$ is rejected, the decision will be to return the shipment to the supplier because the mean hours of useful life are less than the specified 120 hours. If $H_0$ is not rejected, the decision will be to accept the shipment and use the batteries.

    Suppose a level of significance of $\alpha = .05$ is used to conduct the hypothesis test. The test statistic is

$$z = \frac{\bar{x} - \mu}{\sigma/\sqrt{n}} = \frac{\bar{x} - 120}{\sigma/\sqrt{n}}$$

With $z_{.05} = 1.645$, the rejection rule for the lower-tail test is

$$\text{Reject } H_0 \text{ if } z < -1.645$$

Suppose a sample of 36 batteries will be selected and we know from previous shipments that the standard deviation for the population is $\sigma = 12$ hours. The rejection rule indicates that we will reject $H_0$ when

$$z = \frac{\bar{x} - 120}{12/\sqrt{36}} < -1.645$$

Solving for $\bar{x}$ in the preceding expression indicates that we will reject $H_0$ whenever

$$\bar{x} < 120 - 1.645\left(\frac{12}{\sqrt{36}}\right) = 116.71$$

Rejecting $H_0$ when $\bar{x} < 116.71$ means that we will make the decision to accept the shipment whenever

$$\bar{x} \geq 116.71$$

With this information, we are ready to compute probabilities associated with making a Type II error. First, recall that we make a Type II error whenever the true shipment mean is less than 120 hours and we make the decision to accept $H_0: \mu \geq 120$. Hence, to compute the probability of making a Type II error, we must select a particular value of $\mu$ less than 120 hours. For example, suppose the shipment is considered to be of poor quality if the batteries have a mean life of $\mu = 112$ hours. If $\mu = 112$ is really true, what is the probability of accepting $H_0: \mu \geq 120$ and hence committing a Type II error? Note that this probability is the probability that the sample mean $\bar{x}$ is greater than or equal to 116.71 when $\mu = 112$.

Figure 9.20 shows the sampling distribution of $\bar{x}$ when the mean is $\mu = 112$. The shaded area in the upper tail gives the probability of obtaining $\bar{x} \geq 116.71$. Using the standard normal probability distribution calculation based on Figure 9.20, we see that

$$z = \frac{\bar{x} - \mu}{\sigma/\sqrt{n}} = \frac{116.71 - 112}{12/\sqrt{36}} = 2.36$$

The standard normal probability distribution table shows that with $z = 2.36$, the area in the upper tail is $1.000 - .9909 = .0091$. Thus, the probability of making a Type II error when $\mu = 112$ is .0091. Denoting the probability of making a Type II error as $\beta$, we see that when $\mu = 112$, $\beta = .0091$.

We can repeat these calculations for other values of $\mu$ less than 120. Doing so will show a different probability of making a Type II error for each chosen value of $\mu$. For example, suppose the shipment of batteries really has a mean useful life of $\mu = 115$ hours. Because we will accept $H_0$ whenever $\bar{x} \geq 116.71$, the $z$ value for $\mu = 115$ is given by

$$z = \frac{\bar{x} - \mu}{\sigma/\sqrt{n}} = \frac{116.71 - 115}{12/\sqrt{36}} = .86$$

From the standard normal probability distribution table, we find that the area in the upper tail of the standard normal probability distribution for $z = .86$ is $1.0000 - .8051 = .1949$. Thus, the probability of making a Type II error when the true mean is $\mu = 115$ is $\beta = .1949$.

As Table 9.4 shows, the probability of a Type II error depends on the value of the population mean $\mu$. For values of $\mu$ near $\mu_0$, the probability of making the Type II error can be high.

In Table 9.4 we show the probability of making a Type II error for a variety of values of $\mu$ less than 120. Note that as $\mu$ increases toward 120, the probability of making a Type II error increases toward an upper bound of .95. However, as $\mu$ decreases to values farther below 120, the probability of making a Type II error diminishes. This pattern is what we should expect. When the true population mean $\mu$ is close to the null hypothesis value of $\mu = 120$, the probability is high that we will make a Type II error. However, when the true population mean $\mu$ is far below the null hypothesis value of $\mu = 120$, the probability is low that we will make a Type II error.

**FIGURE 9.20** PROBABILITY OF A TYPE II ERROR WHEN $\mu = 112$

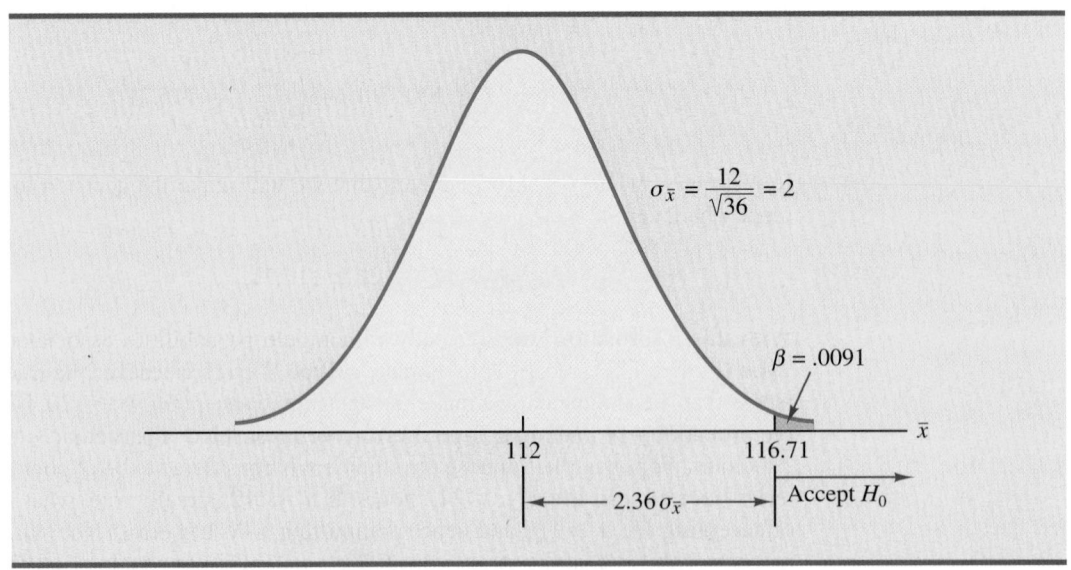

**TABLE 9.4**   PROBABILITY OF MAKING A TYPE II ERROR FOR THE LOT ACCEPTANCE
HYPOTHESIS TEST

| True Population Mean $\mu$ | $z = \dfrac{116.71 - \mu}{12/\sqrt{36}}$ | Probability of a Type II Error ($\beta$) | Power $(1 - \beta)$ |
|---|---|---|---|
| 112 | 2.36 | .0091 | .9909 |
| 114 | 1.36 | .0869 | .9131 |
| 115 | .86 | .1949 | .8051 |
| 116.71 | .00 | .5000 | .5000 |
| 117 | −.15 | .5596 | .4404 |
| 118 | −.65 | .7422 | .2578 |
| 119.999 | −1.645 | .9500 | .0500 |

The probability of correctly rejecting $H_0$ when it is false is called the **power** of the test. For any particular value of $\mu$, the power is $1 - \beta$. That is, the probability of correctly rejecting the null hypothesis is 1 minus the probability of making a Type II error. Values of power are listed in Table 9.4. On the basis of these values, the power associated with each value of $\mu$ is shown graphically in Figure 9.21. Such a graph is called a **power curve.** Note that the power curve extends over the values of $\mu$ for which the null hypothesis is false. The height of the power curve at any value of $\mu$ indicates the probability of correctly rejecting $H_0$ when $H_0$ is false.*

In summary, the following step-by-step procedure can be used to compute the probability of making a Type II error in hypothesis tests about a population mean.

1. Formulate the null and alternative hypotheses.
2. Use the level of significance $\alpha$ to establish a rejection rule based on the test statistic.

**FIGURE 9.21**   POWER CURVE FOR THE LOT ACCEPTANCE HYPOTHESIS TEST

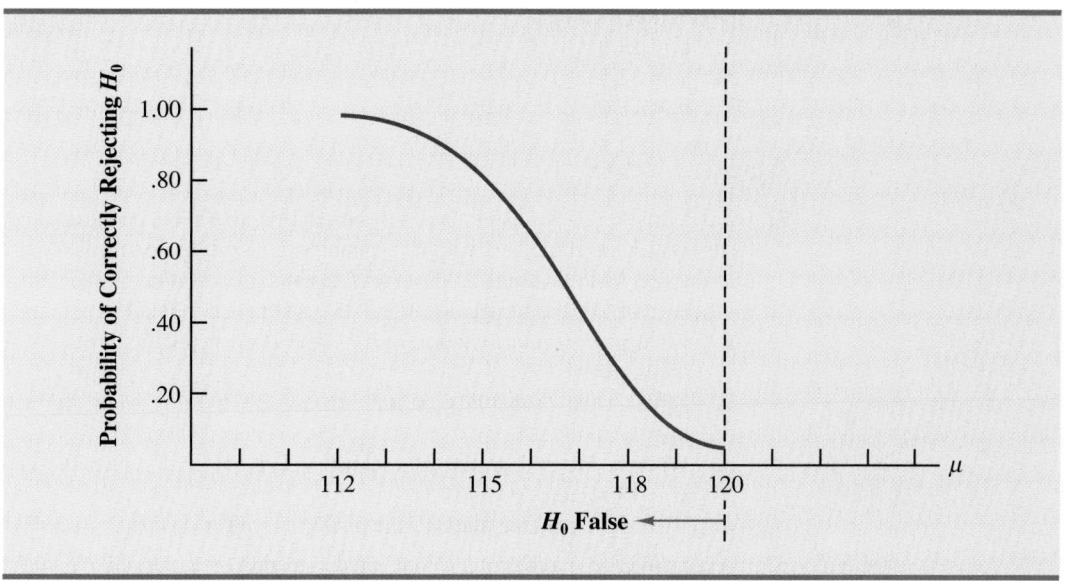

---

*Another graph, called the *operating characteristic curve,* is sometimes used to provide information about the probability of making a Type II error. The operating characteristic curve shows the probability of accepting $H_0$ and thus provides $\beta$ for the values of $\mu$ where the null hypothesis is false. The probability of making a Type II error can be read directly from this graph.

3. Using the rejection rule, solve for the value of the sample mean that identifies the rejection region for the test.
4. Use the results from step 3 to state the values of the sample mean that lead to the acceptance of $H_0$. This defines the acceptance region for the test.
5. Select a particular value of $\mu$ satisfying the alternative hypothesis. Using the acceptance region from step 4, compute the probability that the sample mean will be in the acceptance region. This probability is the probability of making a Type II error at the chosen value of $\mu$.

## EXERCISES

## Methods

**50.** Consider the following hypothesis test.

$$H_0: \mu \geq 10$$
$$H_a: \mu < 10$$

The sample size is 120 and the population standard deviation is 5. Use $\alpha = .05$.
  **a.** If the population mean is 9, what is the probability that the sample mean leads to the conclusion *do not reject $H_0$*?
  **b.** What type of error would be made if the actual population mean is 9 and we conclude that $H_0: \mu \geq 10$ is true?
  **c.** What is the probability of making a Type II error if the actual population mean is 8?

**51.** Consider the following hypothesis test.

$$H_0: \mu = 20$$
$$H_a: \mu \neq 20$$

A sample of 200 items will be taken, and the population standard deviation is assumed known at $\sigma = 10$. Use $\alpha = .05$. Compute the probability of making a Type II error if the population mean is:
  **a.** $\mu = 18.0$
  **b.** $\mu = 22.5$
  **c.** $\mu = 21.0$

## Applications

**52.** Fowle Marketing Research, Inc., bases its charges to a client on the assumption that telephone surveys can be completed within 15 minutes or less. If more time is required, a premium rate is charged. With a sample of 35 surveys, a standard deviation of 4 minutes, and a level of significance of .01, the sample mean will be used to test the null hypothesis $H_0: \mu \leq 15$.
  **a.** What is your interpretation of the Type II error for this problem? What is its impact on the firm?
  **b.** What is the probability of making a Type II error when the actual mean time is $\mu = 17$ minutes?
  **c.** What is the probability of making a Type II error when the actual mean time is $\mu = 18$ minutes?
  **d.** Sketch the general shape of the power curve for this test.

**53.** A consumer research group is interested in testing an automobile manufacturer's claim that a new economy model will travel at least 25 miles per gallon of gasoline ($H_0: \mu \geq 25$).
  **a.** With a .02 level of significance and a sample of 30 cars, what is the rejection rule based on the value of $\bar{x}$ for the test to determine whether the manufacturer's claim should be rejected? Assume that $\sigma$ is three miles per gallon.

**b.** What is the probability of committing a Type II error if the actual mileage is 23 miles per gallon?

**c.** What is the probability of committing a Type II error if the actual mileage is 24 miles per gallon?

**d.** What is the probability of committing a Type II error if the actual mileage is 25.5 miles per gallon?

**54.** *Young Adult* magazine states the following hypotheses about the mean age of its subscribers.

$$H_0: \mu = 28$$
$$H_a: \mu \neq 28$$

**a.** What would it mean to make a Type II error in this situation?

**b.** The population standard deviation is assumed known at $\sigma = 6$ years and the sample size is 100. With $\alpha = .05$, what is the probability of accepting $H_0$ for $\mu$ equal to 26, 27, 29, and 30?

**c.** What is the power at $\mu = 26$? What does this tell you?

**55.** A production line operation is tested for filling-weight accuracy using the following hypotheses.

| **Hypothesis** | **Conclusion and Action** |
|---|---|
| $H_0: \mu = 16$ | Filling okay; keep running |
| $H_a: \mu \neq 16$ | Filling off standard; stop and adjust machine |

The sample size is 30 and the population standard deviation is $\sigma = .8$. Use $\alpha = .05$.

**a.** What would a Type II error mean in this situation?

**b.** What is the probability of making a Type II error when the machine is overfilling by .5 ounces?

**c.** What is the power of the statistical test when the machine is overfilling by .5 ounces?

**d.** Show the power curve for this hypothesis test. What information does it contain for the production manager?

**56.** Refer to Exercise 52. Assume the firm selects a sample of 50 surveys and repeat parts (b) and (c). What observation can you make about how increasing the sample size affects the probability of making a Type II error?

**57.** Sparr Investments, Inc., specializes in tax-deferred investment opportunities for its clients. Recently Sparr has offered a payroll deduction investment program for the employees of a particular company. Sparr estimates that the employees are currently averaging $100 or less per month in tax-deferred investments. A sample of 40 employees will be used to test Sparr's hypothesis about the current level of investment activity among the population of employees. Assume the employee monthly tax-deferred investment amounts have a standard deviation of $75 and that a .05 level of significance will be used for the hypothesis test.

**a.** What is the Type II error in this situation?

**b.** What is the probability of making a Type II error if the actual mean employee monthly investment is $120?

**c.** What is the probability of making a Type II error if the actual mean employee monthly investment is $130?

**d.** Assume a sample size of 80 employees is used and repeat parts (b) and (c).

## 9.9 DETERMINING THE SAMPLE SIZE FOR A HYPOTHESIS TEST ABOUT A POPULATION MEAN

Assume that a hypothesis test is to be conducted about the value of a population mean. The level of significance specified by the user determines the probability of making a Type I error. By controlling the sample size, the user can also control the probability of making a

Type II error. Let us show how a sample size can be determined to control the probability of making both types of errors for the following one-tailed test about a population mean.

$$H_0: \mu \geq \mu_0$$
$$H_a: \mu < \mu_0$$

where $\mu_0$ is the hypothesized value for the population mean.

The upper part of Figure 9.22 is the sampling distribution of $\bar{x}$ when $H_0$ is true and $\mu = \mu_0$. Let $c$ denote the critical value such that $\bar{x} < c$ determines the rejection region for the test. With $z_\alpha$ indicating the $z$ value corresponding to an area of $\alpha$ in the tail of the standard normal probability distribution, we compute $c$ by using the following formula.

$$c = \mu_0 - z_\alpha \frac{\sigma}{\sqrt{n}} \tag{9.11}$$

Now consider the sampling distribution in the lower part of Figure 9.22. Specifically, we have selected a value of the population mean, denoted by $\mu_a$, that corresponds to the case when $H_0$ is false and $H_a$ is true with $\mu_a < \mu_0$. Let us assume that the user specifies the probability of a Type II error that can be tolerated if the true population mean is $\mu_a$. This probability is shown as $\beta$ in Figure 9.22. With $z_\beta$ indicating the $z$ value corresponding to an

**FIGURE 9.22** DETERMINING THE SAMPLE SIZE FOR SPECIFIED LEVELS OF THE TYPE I ($\alpha$) AND TYPE II ($\beta$) ERRORS

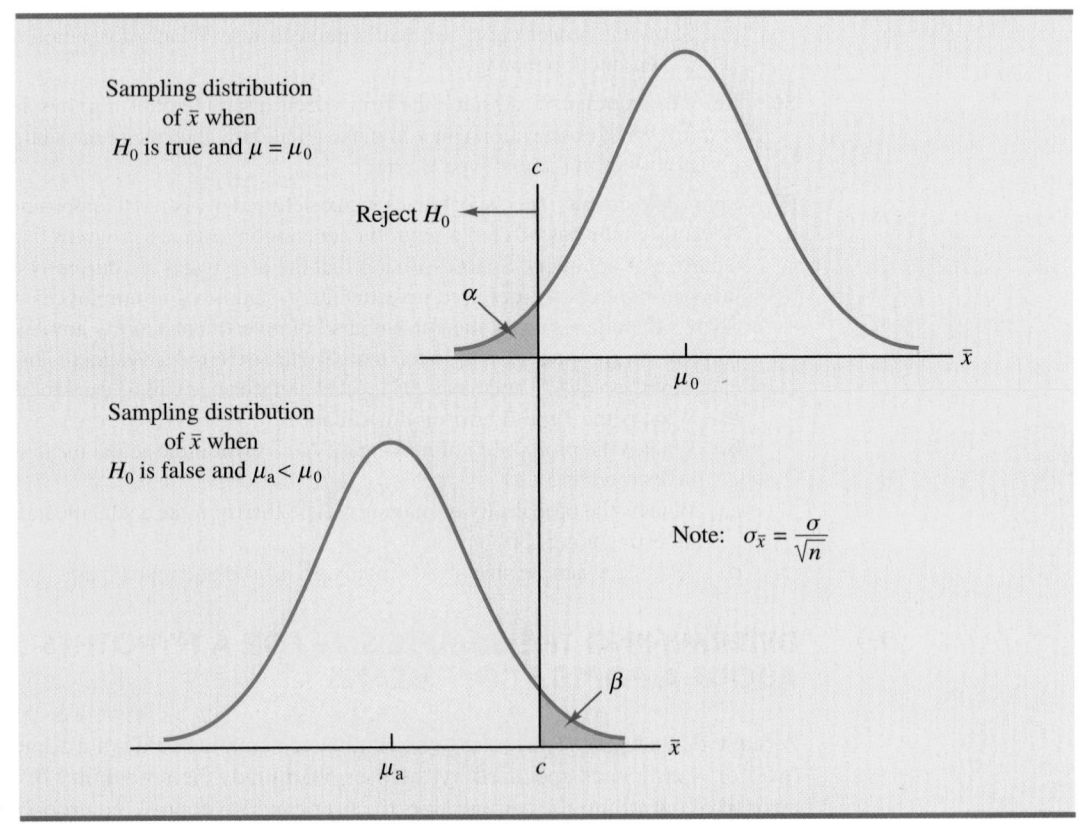

area of $\beta$ in the tail of the standard normal probability distribution, we compute the critical value $c$ by the following formula.

$$c = \mu_a + z_\beta \frac{\sigma}{\sqrt{n}} \qquad (9.12)$$

Because (9.11) and (9.12) are both expressions for $c$, we know they must be equal and thus the following expression must be true.

$$\mu_0 - z_\alpha \frac{\sigma}{\sqrt{n}} = \mu_a + z_\beta \frac{\sigma}{\sqrt{n}}$$

To determine the required sample size, we first solve for the $\sqrt{n}$ as follows.

$$\mu_0 - \mu_a = z_\alpha \frac{\sigma}{\sqrt{n}} + z_\beta \frac{\sigma}{\sqrt{n}}$$

$$\mu_0 - \mu_a = \frac{(z_\alpha + z_\beta)\sigma}{\sqrt{n}}$$

and

$$\sqrt{n} = \frac{(z_\alpha + z_\beta)\sigma}{(\mu_0 - \mu_a)}$$

Squaring both sides of the expression provides the following sample size formula for a one-tailed hypothesis test about a population mean.

---

### Recommended Sample Size for a One-Tailed Hypothesis Test About a Population Mean

For a two-tailed test about a population mean, the recommended sample size can be computed by substituting $z_{\alpha/2}$ for $z_\alpha$ in (9.13).

$$n = \frac{(z_\alpha + z_\beta)^2 \sigma^2}{(\mu_0 - \mu_a)^2} \qquad (9.13)$$

where

$z_\alpha = z$ value providing an area of $\alpha$ in the tail of a standard normal distribution
$z_\beta = z$ value providing an area of $\beta$ in the tail of a standard normal distribution
$\sigma = $ the population standard deviation
$\mu_0 = $ the value of the population mean in the null hypothesis
$\mu_a = $ the value of the population mean used for the Type II error

*Note:* In a two-tailed hypothesis test, use (9.13) with $z_{\alpha/2}$ replacing $z_\alpha$.

---

Although the logic of equation (9.13) was developed for the hypothesis test shown in Figure 9.22, it holds for any one-tailed test about a population mean. Note that in a two-tailed hypothesis test about a population mean, $z_{\alpha/2}$ is used instead of $z_\alpha$ in equation (9.13).

Let us return to the lot acceptance example from Sections 9.7 and 9.8. The design specification for the shipment of batteries indicated a mean useful life of at least 120 hours.

Shipments were rejected if $H_0$: $\mu \geq 120$ was rejected. Let us assume that the quality control manager makes the following statements about the allowable probabilities for the Type I and Type II errors.

> Type I error statement: If the mean life of the batteries in the shipment is $\mu = 120$, I am willing to risk an $\alpha = .05$ probability of rejecting the shipment.

> Type II error statement: If the mean life of the batteries in the shipment is five hours under the specification (i.e., $\mu = 115$), I am willing to risk a $\beta = .10$ probability of accepting the shipment.

These statements are based on the judgment of the manager. Someone else might specify different restrictions on the probabilities. However, statements about the allowable probabilities of both errors must be made before the sample size can be determined.

In the example, $\alpha = .05$ and $\beta = .10$. Using the standard normal probability distribution, we have $z_{.05} = 1.645$ and $z_{.10} = 1.28$. From the statements about the error probabilities, we note that $\mu_0 = 120$ and $\mu_a = 115$. Finally, the population standard deviation was assumed known at $\sigma = 12$. By using equation (9.13), we find that the recommended sample size for the lot acceptance example is

$$n = \frac{(1.645 + 1.28)^2(12)^2}{(120 - 115)^2} = 49.3$$

Rounding up, the recommended sample size is 50.

Because both the Type I and Type II error probabilities have been controlled at allowable levels with $n = 50$, the quality control manager is now justified in using the accept $H_0$ and reject $H_0$ statements for the hypothesis test. The accompanying inferences of $H_0$ true or $H_a$ true are made with known and allowable probabilities of error.

We can make three observations about the relationship among $\alpha$, $\beta$, and the sample size $n$.

1. Once two of the three values are known, the other can be computed.
2. For a given level of significance $\alpha$, increasing the sample size will reduce $\beta$.
3. For a given sample size, decreasing $\alpha$ will increase $\beta$, whereas increasing $\alpha$ will decrease $\beta$.

The third observation should be kept in mind when the probability of a Type II error is not being controlled. It suggests that one should not choose unnecessarily small values for the level of significance $\alpha$. For a given sample size, choosing a smaller level of significance means more exposure to a Type II error. Inexperienced users of hypothesis testing often think that smaller values of $\alpha$ are always better. They are better if we are concerned only about making a Type I error. However, smaller values of $\alpha$ have the disadvantage of increasing the probability of making a Type II error.

## EXERCISES

### Methods

**SELF** test

58. Consider the following hypothesis test.

$$H_0: \mu \geq 10$$
$$H_a: \mu < 10$$

The sample size is 120 and the population standard deviation is assumed known at $\sigma = 5$. Use $\alpha = .05$. If the actual population mean is 9, the probability of a Type II error is .2912. Suppose the researcher wants to reduce the probability of a Type II error to .10 when the actual population mean is 9. What sample size is recommended?

**59.** Consider the following hypothesis test.

$$H_0: \mu = 20$$
$$H_a: \mu \neq 20$$

The population standard deviation is 10. Use $\alpha = .05$. How large a sample should be taken if the researcher is willing to accept a .05 probability of making a Type II error when the actual population mean is 22?

## Applications

**60.** Suppose the project director for the Hilltop Coffee study (see Section 9.3) had asked for a .10 probability of claiming that Hilltop was not in violation when it really was underfilling by 1 ounce ($\mu_a = 2.9375$ pounds). What sample size would have been recommended?

**61.** A special industrial battery must have a life of at least 400 hours. A hypothesis test is to be conducted with a .02 level of significance. If the batteries from a particular production run have an actual mean use life of 385 hours, the production manager wants a sampling procedure that only 10% of the time would show erroneously that the batch is acceptable. What sample size is recommended for the hypothesis test? Use 30 hours as an estimate of the population standard deviation.

**62.** *Young Adult* magazine states the following hypotheses about the mean age of its subscribers.

$$H_0: \mu = 28$$
$$H_a: \mu \neq 28$$

If the manager conducting the test will permit a .15 probability of making a Type II error when the true mean age is 29, what sample size should be selected? Assume $\sigma = 6$ and a .05 level of significance.

**63.** An automobile mileage study tested the following hypotheses.

| **Hypothesis** | **Conclusion** |
| --- | --- |
| $H_0: \mu \geq 25$ mpg | Manufacturer's claim supported |
| $H_a: \mu < 25$ mpg | Manufacturer's claim rejected; average mileage per gallon less than stated |

For $\sigma = 3$ and a .02 level of significance, what sample size would be recommended if the researcher wants an 80% chance of detecting that $\mu$ is less than 25 miles per gallon when it is actually 24 miles per gallon?

## SUMMARY

Hypothesis testing is a statistical procedure that uses sample data to determine whether a statement about the value of a population parameter should be rejected. The hypotheses, which come from a variety of sources, are two competing statements about a population parameter: a null hypothesis $H_0$ and an alternative hypothesis $H_a$. In some applications it is not obvious how the null and alternative hypotheses should be formulated. We suggested guidelines for developing hypotheses in three types of situations.

**1.** Testing research hypotheses: The research hypothesis should be formulated as the alternative hypothesis. The null hypothesis is based on an established theory or the statement that the research treatment will have no effect. Whenever the sample data contradict the null hypothesis, the null hypothesis is rejected. In this case, the alternative or research hypothesis is concluded to be true.

2. Testing the validity of a claim: Generally, the claim made is chosen as the null hypothesis; the challenge to the claim is chosen as the alternative hypothesis. Action against the claim will be taken whenever the sample data contradict the null hypothesis. When that occurs, the challenge implied by the alternative hypothesis is concluded to be true.

3. Testing in decision-making situations: Often a decision maker must choose between two courses of action, one associated with the null hypothesis and one associated with the alternative hypothesis.

Figure 9.23 summarizes the test statistics used in hypothesis tests about a population mean and provides a practical guide for selecting the hypothesis testing procedure. The figure shows that the test statistic depends on whether the sample size is large, whether the population standard deviation is assumed known, and in some cases whether the population has a normal or approximately normal probability distribution. If the sample size is large, ($n \geq 30$), the $z$ test statistic is used to conduct the hypothesis test. If the sample size is small, ($n < 30$), the population must have a normal or approximately normal probability distribution to conduct a hypothesis test about the value of $\mu$. If that is the case, the $z$ test statistic is used if $\sigma$ is assumed known, whereas the $t$ test statistic is used if $\sigma$ is

**FIGURE 9.23** SUMMARY OF THE TEST STATISTICS TO BE USED IN A HYPOTHESIS TEST ABOUT A POPULATION MEAN

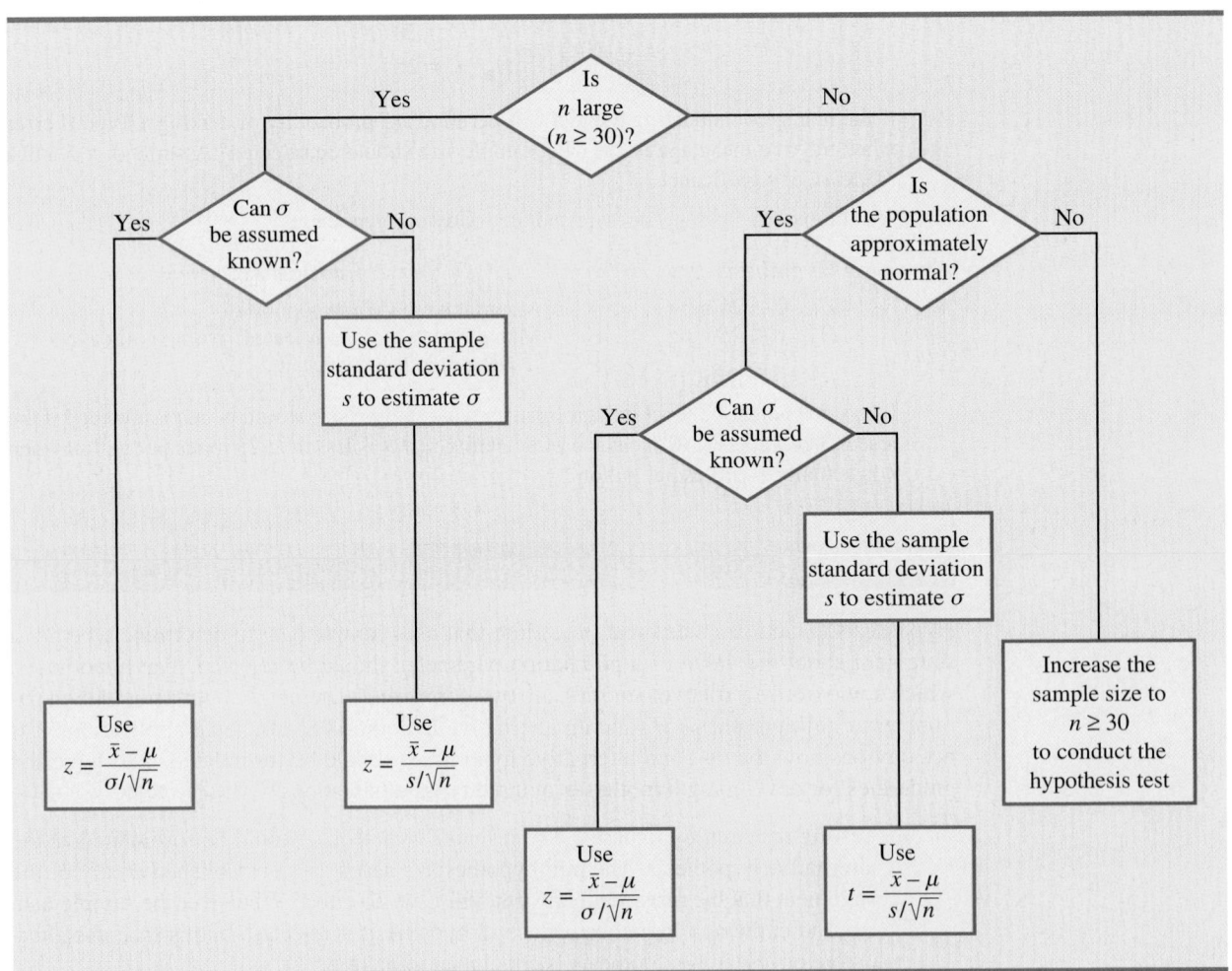

estimated by the sample standard deviation $s$. Finally, note that if the sample size is small and the assumption of a normal probability distribution for the population is inappropriate, we recommend increasing the sample size to $n \geq 30$ to test the hypothesis about a population mean.

Hypothesis tests about a population proportion were developed for the large-sample case where both $np \geq 5$ and $n(1 - p) \geq 5$. The test statistic used is

$$z = \frac{\bar{p} - p_0}{\sqrt{\dfrac{p_0(1 - p_0)}{n}}}$$

The rejection rule for all the hypothesis testing procedures involves comparing the value of the test statistic with a critical value. For lower-tail tests, the null hypothesis is rejected if the value of the test statistic is less than the critical value. For upper-tail tests, the null hypothesis is rejected if the test statistic is greater than the critical value. For two-tailed tests, the null hypothesis is rejected for values of the test statistic in either tail of the sampling distribution.

We also saw that $p$-values could be used for hypothesis testing. The $p$-value is the probability, when the null hypothesis is true, of obtaining a sample result that is at least as unlikely as what is observed. When $p$-values are used to conduct a hypothesis test, the rejection rule calls for rejecting the null hypothesis whenever the $p$-value is less than $\alpha$. The $p$-value is often called the observed level of significance. The $p$-value for a lower-tail test is the area under the curve to the left of the test statistic, and the $p$-value for an upper-tail test is the area under the curve to the right of the test statistic. The $p$-value for a two-tailed test is twice the minimum of the one-tailed $p$-values.

We showed how to implement the hypothesis testing procedures presented using Excel. The worksheet in Figure 9.12 can be used for any hypothesis test about a population mean involving the test statistic $z$ from a normal probability distribution. The worksheet in Figure 9.14 can be used as a template for any hypothesis test about a population mean using a $t$-test. And, the worksheet in Figure 9.19 can be used for hypothesis tests about a population proportion.

## GLOSSARY

**Null hypothesis**    The hypothesis tentatively assumed true in the hypothesis testing procedure.

**Alternative hypothesis**    The hypothesis concluded to be true if the null hypothesis is rejected.

**Type I error**    The error of rejecting $H_0$ when it is true.

**Type II error**    The error of accepting $H_0$ when it is false.

**Level of significance**    The maximum allowable probability of a Type I error.

**Test statistic**    A statistic whose value is used to determine whether the null hypothesis can be rejected.

**Rejection region**    The range of values for the test statistic that will lead to rejection of the null hypothesis.

**One-tailed hypothesis test**    A hypothesis test in which rejection of the null hypothesis occurs for values of the test statistic in one tail of the sampling distribution.

**Critical value**    A value that is compared with the test statistic to determine whether $H_0$ should be rejected.

**p-value**    The probability, when the null hypothesis is true, of obtaining a sample result that is at least as unlikely as what is observed. It is often called the observed level of significance.

**Two-tailed hypothesis test**    A hypothesis test in which rejection of the null hypothesis occurs for values of the test statistic in either tail of the sampling distribution.

**Power**    The probability of correctly rejecting $H_0$ when it is false.

**Power curve**    A graph of the probability of rejecting $H_0$ for all possible values of the population parameter not satisfying the null hypothesis. The power curve provides the probability of correctly rejecting the null hypothesis.

## KEY FORMULAS

**Test Statistics for a Large-Sample ($n \geq 30$) Hypothesis Test About a Population Mean**

$\sigma$ assumed known

$$z = \frac{\bar{x} - \mu_0}{\sigma/\sqrt{n}} \qquad (9.1)$$

$\sigma$ estimated by $s$

$$z = \frac{\bar{x} - \mu_0}{s/\sqrt{n}} \qquad (9.2)$$

**Test Statistics for a Small-Sample ($n < 30$) Hypothesis Test About a Population Mean**

$\sigma$ assumed known

$$z = \frac{\bar{x} - \mu_0}{\sigma/\sqrt{n}} \qquad (9.7)$$

$\sigma$ estimated by $s$

$$t = \frac{\bar{x} - \mu_0}{s/\sqrt{n}} \qquad (9.8)$$

**Test Statistic for Hypothesis Tests About a Population Proportion**

$$z = \frac{\bar{p} - p_0}{\sigma_{\bar{p}}} \qquad (9.9)$$

where

$$\sigma_{\bar{p}} = \sqrt{\frac{p_0(1 - p_0)}{n}} \qquad (9.10)$$

**Sample Size for a One-Tailed Hypothesis Test About a Population Mean**

$$n = \frac{(z_\alpha + z_\beta)^2 \sigma^2}{(\mu_0 - \mu_a)^2} \qquad (9.13)$$

In a two-tailed test, replace $z_\alpha$ with $z_{\alpha/2}$.

## SUPPLEMENTARY EXERCISES

**64.**  The population mean annual salary for public school teachers in the state of New York is $45,250. The mean annual salary of public school teachers in New York City is $47,000 (*Time,* April 3, 2000). Assume the New York City results are based on a sample of 95 teachers and the sample standard deviation was $6,300.

 **a.**  Formulate the null and alternative hypotheses that can be used to determine whether the sample data support the conclusion that public school teachers in New York City have a higher mean annual salary than the public school teachers in the state of New York.

 **b.**  What is the value of the test statistic?

 **c.**  What is the $p$-value?

 **d.**  Using $\alpha = .01$, what is your conclusion?

**65.** The Buick Lesabre is listed as having a highway fuel efficiency average of 30 miles per gallon (U.S. Dept. of Energy, Model Year 2001, Fuel Economy Guide). A consumer interest group conducts automobile mileage tests seeking statistical evidence to show that automobile manufacturers overstate the miles per gallon ratings for particular models. In the case of the Buick Lesabre, hypotheses for the test would be stated $H_0: \mu \geq 30$ and $H_a: \mu < 30$. In a sample of 50 mileage tests with Buick Lesabre, the consumer interest group finds a sample mean highway mileage rating of 29.5 miles per gallon and a sample standard deviation of 1.8 miles per gallon. What conclusion should be drawn from the sample results? Use a .01 level of significance.

**66.** The chamber of commerce of a Florida Gulf Coast community advertises that area residential property is available at a mean cost of $25,000 or less per lot. Using a .05 level of significance, test the validity of this claim. Suppose a sample of 32 properties provided a sample mean of $26,000 per lot and a sample standard deviation of $2500. What is the $p$-value?

**67.** A bath soap manufacturing process is designed to produce a mean of 120 bars of soap per batch. Quantities over or under the standard are undesirable. A sample of 10 batches shows the following numbers of bars of soap. The population is assumed to be normal.

| 108 | 118 | 120 | 122 | 119 | 113 | 124 | 122 | 120 | 123 |
|-----|-----|-----|-----|-----|-----|-----|-----|-----|-----|

Using a .05 level of significance, test to see whether the sample results indicate that the manufacturing process is functioning properly.

**68.** The monthly rent for a two-bedroom apartment in a particular city is reported to average $550. Suppose we want to test $H_0: \mu = 550$ versus $H_a: \mu \neq 550$. A sample of 36 two-bedroom apartments is selected. The sample mean is $\bar{x} = \$562$ and the sample standard deviation is $s = \$40$.
   **a.** Conduct this hypothesis test with a .05 level of significance.
   **b.** Compute the $p$-value.
   **c.** Use the sample results to construct a 95% confidence interval for the population mean. What hypothesis testing conclusion would you draw from the confidence interval result?

**69.** In making bids on building projects, Sonneborn Builders, Inc., assumes construction workers are idle no more than 15% of the time. Hence, for a normal 8-hour shift, the mean idle time per worker should be 72 minutes or less per day. A sample of 30 construction workers resulted in the idle times shown in the data set IdleTime. Suppose a hypothesis test is to be designed to test the validity of the company's assumption.
   **a.** What is the $p$-value associated with the sample result?
   **b.** Using a .05 level of significance and the $p$-value approach, test $H_0: \mu \leq 72$. What is your conclusion?

**70.** The Immigration and Naturalization service reported that 79% of foreign travelers visiting the United States stated that the primary purpose of their visit was to enjoy a vacation. In a follow-up study conducted in 2001, suppose a sample of 500 foreign visitors is selected and that 360 say that their primary reason for visiting the United States is to enjoy a vacation. Is the proportion of foreign travelers vacationing in the United States in 2001 less than the proportion previously reported? Support your conclusion with a statistical test using a .05 level of significance.

**71.** In a comprehensive study of workplace communications conducted by Pitney Bowes, 72% of the workers surveyed said they regularly work with coworkers who are not in the office, which made face-to-face meetings or voice-to-voice phone conversations more difficult to schedule and conduct (*ORMS Today,* August 1998). A related study of 400 workers was conducted at Trident Manufacturing. The data collected are shown in the data set CoWorker. A response of Yes indicates that the worker regularly works with coworkers not in the office. Conduct a statistical test to determine whether the proportion of workers who regularly work with coworkers not in the office is greater at Trident Manufacturing than the percentage reported by Pitney Bowes. Use a .05 level of significance.

**72.** The Gallup Organization conducted a survey of 1350 people for the National Occupational Information Coordinating Committee, a panel Congress created to improve the use of job information. A research question related to the study was: Do individuals hold jobs that they had planned to hold or do they hold jobs for such reasons as chance or lack of choice? Let $p$ indicate the population proportion of individuals who hold jobs that they had planned to hold.

    **a.** If the hypotheses are stated $H_0$: $p \geq .50$ and $H_a$: $p < .50$, discuss the research hypothesis $H_a$ in terms of what the researcher is investigating.

    **b.** The Gallup poll found that 41% of the respondents hold jobs they planned to hold. What is your conclusion at a .01 level of significance? Discuss.

**73.** A well-known doctor hypothesized that 75% of women wear shoes that are too small. A study of 356 women by the American Orthopedic Foot and Ankle Society found 313 women who wore shoes that were at least one size too small. Test $H_0$: $p = .75$ and $H_a$: $p \neq .75$ at $\alpha = .01$. What is your conclusion?

**74.** An airline promotion to business travelers was based on the assumption that approximately two-thirds of business travelers use a laptop computer on overnight business trips. Test this assumption by testing the hypotheses $H_0$: $p = .67$ and $H_a$: $p \neq .67$ at $\alpha = .05$. Use the sample results from an American Express online survey, which found 355 of 546 business travelers use a laptop computer on overnight business trips (*The Cincinnati Enquirer,* August 31, 1998).

    **a.** What is the sample proportion?

    **b.** Compute the value of the test statistic.

    **c.** What is the $p$-value?

    **d.** Can the claim of two-thirds be rejected? Discuss.

**75.** The Department of Transportation reported Amtrack trains had a 78% on-time arrival record over the previous 12 months (*USA Today,* November 23, 1998). Assume that in 2001, a study found 330 of 400 Amtrack trains arrived on time. Does the sample indicate the Amtrack arrival rate has changed? Test $H_0$: $p = .78$ and $H_a$: $p \neq .78$ at $\alpha = .05$.

    **a.** What is the sample proportion of Amtrack trains arriving on time?

    **b.** Compute the value of the test statistic.

    **c.** What is the $p$-value?

    **d.** What is your conclusion?

**76.** Environmental health indicators include air quality, water quality, and food quality. Twenty-five years ago, 47% of U.S. food samples contained pesticide residues (*U.S. News & World Report,* April 17, 2000). In a recent study, 44 of 125 food samples contained pesticide residues. Test the hypotheses: $H_0$: $p \geq .47$ and $H_a$: $p < .47$.

    **a.** What is the sample proportion?

    **b.** Compute the value of the test statistic.

    **c.** What is the $p$-value?

    **d.** Using $\alpha = .01$, what is your conclusion?

**77.** In making bids on building projects, Sonneborn Builders, Inc., assumes construction workers are idle no more than 15% of the time. Hence, for a normal 8-hour shift, the mean idle time per worker should be 72 minutes or less per day. A sample of 30 construction workers had a mean idle time of 80 minutes per day. The sample standard deviation was 20 minutes. Suppose a hypothesis test is to be designed to test the validity of the company's assumption.

    **a.** What is the $p$-value associated with the sample result?

    **b.** What is your conclusion?

**78.** Refer again to Exercise 77.

    **a.** What is the probability of making a Type II error when the population mean idle time is 80 minutes?

    **b.** What is the probability of making a Type II error when the population mean idle time is 75 minutes?

    **c.** What is the probability of making a Type II error when the population mean idle time is 70 minutes?

    **d.** Sketch the power curve for this problem.

**79.** A federal funding program is available to low-income neighborhoods. To qualify for the funding a neighborhood must have a mean household income of less than $15,000 per year. Neighborhoods with mean annual household income of $15,000 or more do not qualify. Funding decisions are based on a sample of residents in the neighborhood. A hypothesis test with a .02 level of significance is conducted. If the funding guidelines call for a maximum probability of .05 of not funding a neighborhood with a mean annual household income of $14,000, what sample size should be used in the funding decision study? Use $\sigma = \$4000$ as a planning value.

**80.** $H_0: \mu = 120$ and $H_a: \mu \neq 120$ are used to test whether a bath soap production process is meeting the standard output of 120 bars per batch. Use a .05 level of significance for the test and a planning value of 5 for the standard deviation.

    **a.** If the mean output drops to 117 bars per batch, the firm wants to have a 98% chance of concluding that the standard production output is not being met. How large a sample should be selected?

    **b.** With your sample size from part (a), what is the probability of concluding that the process is operating satisfactorily for each of the following actual mean outputs: 117, 118, 119, 121, 122, and 123 bars per batch? That is, what is the probability of a Type II error in each case?

## Case Problem 1   UNEMPLOYMENT STUDY

Each month the U.S. Bureau of Labor Statistics publishes a variety of unemployment statistics, including the number of individuals who are unemployed and the mean length of time the individuals have been unemployed. For November 1998, the Bureau of Labor Statistics reported that the national mean length of time of unemployment was 14.6 weeks.

**BLS**

The mayor of Philadelphia has requested a study on the status of unemployment in the Philadelphia area. A sample of 50 unemployed residents of Philadelphia included data on the age and the number of weeks without a job. The data collected in November 1998 are available in the data set BLS.

### Managerial Report

1. Use descriptive statistics to summarize the data.
2. Develop a 95% confidence interval estimate of the mean age of unemployed individuals in Philadelphia.
3. Conduct a hypothesis test to determine whether the mean duration of unemployment in Philadelphia is greater than the national mean duration of 14.6 weeks. Use a .01 level of significance. What is your conclusion?
4. Is there a relationship between the age of an unemployed individual and the number of weeks of unemployment? Explain.

## Case Problem 2   QUALITY ASSOCIATES, INC.

Quality Associates, Inc., is a consulting firm that advises its clients about sampling and statistical procedures that can be used to control manufacturing processes. In one particular application, a client provided Quality Associates with a sample of 800 observations that were taken during a time in which the client's process was operating satisfactorily. The sample standard deviation for these data was .21; hence, the population standard deviation was assumed to be .21. Quality Associates then suggested that random samples of size 30 be taken periodically to monitor the process on an ongoing basis. By analyzing the new samples, the client could quickly learn whether the process was operating satisfactorily. When the process was not operating satisfactorily, corrective action could be taken to eliminate the problem. The design specification indicated the mean for the process should be 12. The hypothesis test suggested by Quality Associates follows.

$$H_0: \mu = 12$$
$$H_a: \mu \neq 12$$

Corrective action will be taken any time $H_0$ is rejected.

The following four samples were collected during the first day of operation of the new statistical process control procedure. These data are available in the data set Quality.

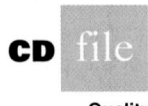

**Quality**

| Sample 1 | Sample 2 | Sample 3 | Sample 4 |
|----------|----------|----------|----------|
| 11.55 | 11.62 | 11.91 | 12.02 |
| 11.62 | 11.69 | 11.36 | 12.02 |
| 11.52 | 11.59 | 11.75 | 12.05 |
| 11.75 | 11.82 | 11.95 | 12.18 |
| 11.90 | 11.97 | 12.14 | 12.11 |
| 11.64 | 11.71 | 11.72 | 12.07 |
| 11.80 | 11.87 | 11.61 | 12.05 |
| 12.03 | 12.10 | 11.85 | 11.64 |
| 11.94 | 12.01 | 12.16 | 12.39 |
| 11.92 | 11.99 | 11.91 | 11.65 |
| 12.13 | 12.20 | 12.12 | 12.11 |
| 12.09 | 12.16 | 11.61 | 11.90 |
| 11.93 | 12.00 | 12.21 | 12.22 |
| 12.21 | 12.28 | 11.56 | 11.88 |
| 12.32 | 12.39 | 11.95 | 12.03 |
| 11.93 | 12.00 | 12.01 | 12.35 |
| 11.85 | 11.92 | 12.06 | 12.09 |
| 11.76 | 11.83 | 11.76 | 11.77 |
| 12.16 | 12.23 | 11.82 | 12.20 |
| 11.77 | 11.84 | 12.12 | 11.79 |
| 12.00 | 12.07 | 11.60 | 12.30 |
| 12.04 | 12.11 | 11.95 | 12.27 |
| 11.98 | 12.05 | 11.96 | 12.29 |
| 12.30 | 12.37 | 12.22 | 12.47 |
| 12.18 | 12.25 | 11.75 | 12.03 |
| 11.97 | 12.04 | 11.96 | 12.17 |
| 12.17 | 12.24 | 11.95 | 11.94 |
| 11.85 | 11.92 | 11.89 | 11.97 |
| 12.30 | 12.37 | 11.88 | 12.23 |
| 12.15 | 12.22 | 11.93 | 12.25 |

## Managerial Report

1. Conduct the hypothesis test for each sample at the .01 level of significance and determine what action, if any, should be taken. Provide the test statistic and $p$-value for each test.
2. Consider the standard deviation for each of the four samples. Does the assumption of .21 for the population standard deviation appear reasonable?
3. Compute limits for the sample mean $\bar{x}$ around $\mu = 12$ such that, as long as a new sample mean is within those limits, the process will be considered to be operating satisfactorily. If $\bar{x}$ exceeds the upper limit or if $\bar{x}$ is below the lower limit, corrective action will be taken. These limits are referred to as upper and lower control limits for quality control purposes.
4. Discuss the implications of changing the level of significance to a larger value. What mistake or error could increase if the level of significance were changed?

# STATISTICAL INFERENCES ABOUT MEANS AND PROPORTIONS FOR TWO POPULATIONS

**Chapter 10**

### CONTENTS

## STATISTICS IN PRACTICE

### FISONS CORPORATION*
*Rochester, New York*

Fisons Corporation, Rochester, New York, is a unit of Fisons Plc., UK. Fisons opened its U.S. operations in 1966.

Fisons' Pharmaceutical Division uses extensive statistical procedures to test and develop new drugs. The testing process in the pharmaceutical industry usually consists of three stages: (1) preclinical testing, (2) testing for long-term usage and safety, and (3) clinical efficacy testing. At each successive stage, the chance that a drug will pass the rigorous tests decreases; however, the cost of further testing increases dramatically. Industry surveys indicate that on average the research and development for one new drug costs $250 million and takes 12 years. Hence, it is important to eliminate unsuccessful new drugs in the early stages of the testing process, as well as identify promising ones for further testing.

Statistics plays a major role in pharmaceutical research, where government regulations are stringent and rigorously enforced. In preclinical testing, a two- or three-population statistical study typically is used to determine whether a new drug should continue to be studied in the long-term usage and safety program. The populations may consist of one using the new drug, one used as a control, and one using a standard drug. The preclinical testing process begins when a new drug is sent to the pharmacology group for evaluation of efficacy—the capacity of the drug to produce the desired effects. As part of the process, a statistician is asked to design an experiment that can be used to test the new drug. The design must specify the sample size and the statistical methods of analysis. In a two-population study, one sample is used to obtain data on the efficacy of the new drug (population 1) and a second sample is used to obtain data on the efficacy of a standard drug (population 2). Depending on the intended use, the new and standard drugs are tested in such disciplines as neurology, cardiology, and immunology. In most studies, the statistical method involves hypothesis

Statistical methods are used to test and develop new drugs.
© Mark Richards/PhotoEdit, Inc.

testing for the difference between the means of the population using the new drug and the population using the standard drug. If a new drug lacks efficacy or produces undesirable effects in comparison with the standard drug, the new drug is withdrawn from further testing. Only new drugs that show promising comparisons with standard drugs are forwarded to the long-term usage and safety testing program.

Further data collection and multipopulation studies are conducted in the long-term usage and safety testing program and in the clinical testing programs. The Food and Drug Administration (FDA) requires that statistical methods be defined prior to such testing to avoid data-related biases. In addition, to avoid human biases, some of the clinical trials are double or triple blind. That is, neither the subject nor the investigator knows what drug is administered to whom. If the new drug meets all requirements in relation to the standard drug, a new drug application is filed with the FDA. The application is rigorously scrutinized by statisticians and scientists at the agency.

In this chapter you will learn how to construct interval estimates and make hypothesis tests about means and proportions with two populations. Techniques will be presented for analyzing independent random samples as well as matched samples.

*The authors are indebted to Dr. M. C. Trivedi for providing this Statistics in Practice.

In Chapters 8 and 9 we showed how to develop interval estimates and conduct hypothesis tests for situations involving one population mean. In this chapter we continue our discussion of statistical inference by showing how interval estimates and hypothesis tests can be developed for situations involving two populations. For example, we may want to develop an interval estimate of the difference between the mean starting salary for a population of men and the mean starting salary for a population of women. We will begin our discussion by showing how an interval estimate of the difference between the means of two populations can be developed for a sampling study conducted by Greystone Department Stores, Inc. As usual, when a new procedure is introduced, we also show how it can be implemented using Excel.

## 10.1    ESTIMATION OF THE DIFFERENCE BETWEEN THE MEANS OF TWO POPULATIONS: INDEPENDENT SAMPLES

Greystone Department Stores, Inc., operates two stores in Buffalo, New York; one is in the inner city and the other is in a suburban shopping center. The regional manager has noticed that products that sell well in one store do not always sell well in the other. The manager believes this situation may be attributable to differences in customer demographics at the two locations. Customers differ in age, education, income, and so on. Suppose the manager has asked us to investigate the difference between the mean ages of the customers who shop at the two stores.

Let us define population 1 as all customers who shop at the inner-city store and population 2 as all customers who shop at the suburban store.

$\mu_1$ = mean of population 1 (i.e., the mean age of all customers who shop at the inner-city store)

$\mu_2$ = mean of population 2 (i.e., the mean age of all customers who shop at the suburban store)

The difference between the two population means is $\mu_1 - \mu_2$.

To estimate $\mu_1 - \mu_2$, we will select a simple random sample of $n_1$ customers from population 1 and a simple random sample of $n_2$ customers from population 2. Because the simple random sample of $n_1$ customers is selected independently of the simple random sample of $n_2$ customers, we have the case of **independent simple random samples.**

$\bar{x}_1$ = sample mean age for the simple random sample of $n_1$ inner-city customers

$\bar{x}_2$ = sample mean age for the simple random sample of $n_2$ suburban customers

Because $\bar{x}_1$ is a point estimator of $\mu_1$ and $\bar{x}_2$ is a point estimator of $\mu_2$, the point estimator of the difference between the two population means is expressed as follows.

> **Point Estimator of the Difference Between the Means of Two Populations**
>
> $$\bar{x}_1 - \bar{x}_2 \tag{10.1}$$

Thus, we see that the point estimator of the difference between the two population means is the difference between the sample means of the two independent simple random samples. Figure 10.1 provides an overview of the process used to estimate the difference between two population means based on two independent simple random samples.

To estimate the difference between the mean ages of the two populations of Greystone Department Store customers, a simple random sample of 36 inner-city customers and a simple random sample of 49 suburban customers were selected. The data obtained are shown in Table 10.1; summary statistics are given in Table 10.2. Using expression (10.1),

**FIGURE 10.1** ESTIMATING THE DIFFERENCE BETWEEN THE MEANS
OF TWO POPULATIONS

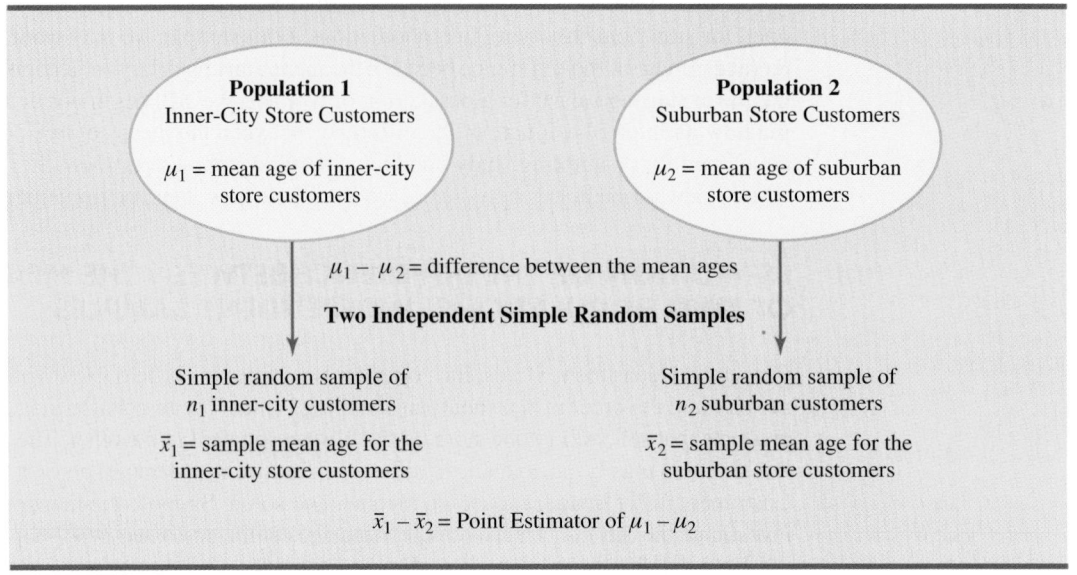

**TABLE 10.1** DATA SET FOR THE GREYSTONE DEPARTMENT STORES STUDY

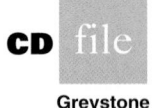

**Greystone**

| Inner-City Customers | | | | Suburban Customers | | | | |
|---|---|---|---|---|---|---|---|---|
| 39 | 35 | 43 | 34 | 28 | 33 | 46 | 39 | 25 |
| 44 | 41 | 21 | 39 | 36 | 40 | 43 | 38 | 47 |
| 28 | 41 | 34 | 52 | 41 | 50 | 38 | 46 | 35 |
| 20 | 49 | 37 | 26 | 14 | 13 | 18 | 37 | 24 |
| 39 | 45 | 45 | 48 | 39 | 35 | 22 | 16 | 17 |
| 42 | 57 | 46 | 58 | 57 | 40 | 34 | 35 | 19 |
| 37 | 43 | 41 | | 36 | 35 | 40 | 29 | 45 |
| 37 | 41 | 53 | | 36 | 41 | 39 | 37 | 23 |
| 34 | 45 | 42 | | 38 | 29 | 35 | 36 | 54 |
| 38 | 44 | 22 | | 36 | 42 | 44 | 35 | |

**TABLE 10.2** SAMPLE STATISTICS FOR GREYSTONE DEPARTMENT STORES

| Store | Number of Customers Sampled | Sample Mean Age | Sample Standard Deviation |
|---|---|---|---|
| Inner City | $n_1 = 36$ | $\bar{x}_1 = 40$ years | $s_1 = 9$ years |
| Suburban | $n_2 = 49$ | $\bar{x}_2 = 35$ years | $s_2 = 10$ years |

we find that a point estimate of the difference between the mean ages of the two populations is $\bar{x}_1 - \bar{x}_2 = 40 - 35 = 5$ years. Thus, we are led to believe that the customers
at the inner-city store have a mean age 5 years greater than the mean age of the suburban
store customers. However, as with all point estimates, we know that 5 years is only one of
many possible estimates of the difference between the mean ages of the two populations. If
Greystone selected another simple random sample of 36 inner-city customers and another
simple random sample of 49 suburban customers, the difference between the two new

sample means would probably not equal 5 years. The sampling distribution of $\bar{x}_1 - \bar{x}_2$ is the probability distribution of the difference in sample means for all possible sets of two independent simple random samples.

## Sampling Distribution of $\bar{x}_1 - \bar{x}_2$

We can use the sampling distribution of $\bar{x}_1 - \bar{x}_2$ to develop an interval estimate of the difference between the two population means in much the same way as we used the sampling distribution of $\bar{x}$ for interval estimation with a single population mean. The sampling distribution of $\bar{x}_1 - \bar{x}_2$ has the following properties.

---

**Sampling Distribution of $\bar{x}_1 - \bar{x}_2$**

The standard deviation of the sampling distribution of $\bar{x}_1 - \bar{x}_2$ is also referred to as the standard error of the point estimator $\bar{x}_1 - \bar{x}_2$.

$$\text{Expected Value:} \quad E(\bar{x}_1 - \bar{x}_2) = \mu_1 - \mu_2 \tag{10.2}$$

$$\text{Standard Deviation:} \quad \sigma_{\bar{x}_1 - \bar{x}_2} = \sqrt{\frac{\sigma_1^2}{n_1} + \frac{\sigma_2^2}{n_2}} \tag{10.3}$$

where

$\sigma_1 = $ standard deviation of population 1

$\sigma_2 = $ standard deviation of population 2

$n_1 = $ sample size for the simple random sample
        from population 1

$n_2 = $ sample size for the simple random sample
        from population 2

Distribution form: If the sample sizes are both *large* ($n_1 \geq 30$) and $n_2 \geq 30$), the sampling distribution of $\bar{x}_1 - \bar{x}_2$ can be approximated by a normal probability distribution.

---

Figure 10.2 shows the sampling distribution of $\bar{x}_1 - \bar{x}_2$ and its relationship to the individual sampling distributions of $\bar{x}_1$ and $\bar{x}_2$.

Let us now develop an interval estimate of the difference between the means of two populations. We consider two cases, one in which the sample sizes are large ($n_1 \geq 30$ and $n_2 \geq 30$) and another in which one or both sample sizes are small ($n_1 < 30$ and/or $n_2 < 30$). We consider the large-sample case first.

## Large-Sample Case

In the large-sample case, the central limit theorem is applicable and thus the sampling distribution of $\bar{x}_1 - \bar{x}_2$ can be approximated by a normal probability distribution. With this approximation we can use the following expression to develop an interval estimate of the difference between the means of the two populations.

---

**Interval Estimate of the Difference Between the Means of Two Populations: Large-Sample Case ($n_1 \geq 30$ and $n_2 \geq 30$) with $\sigma_1$ and $\sigma_2$ Assumed Known**

$$\bar{x}_1 - \bar{x}_2 \pm z_{\alpha/2} \sigma_{\bar{x}_1 - \bar{x}_2} \tag{10.4}$$

where $1 - \alpha$ is the confidence coefficient.

---

**FIGURE 10.2**   SAMPLING DISTRIBUTION OF $\bar{x}_1 - \bar{x}_2$ AND ITS RELATIONSHIP TO THE INDIVIDUAL SAMPLING DISTRIBUTION OF $\bar{x}_1$ AND $\bar{x}_2$

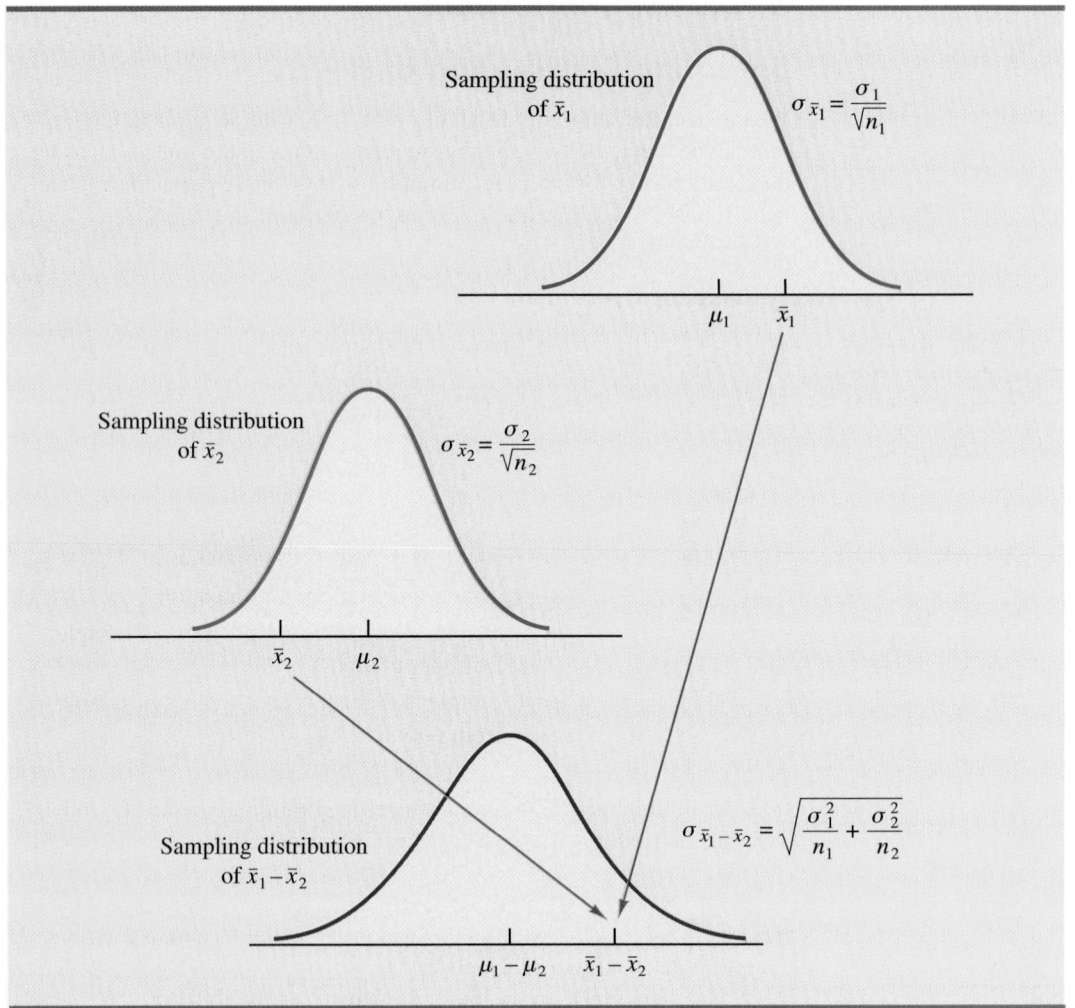

Note that to use expression (10.4) to develop an interval estimate of the difference between the means of two populations, we must know the value of $\sigma_{\bar{x}_1 - \bar{x}_2}$, the standard error of the point estimator $\bar{x}_1 - \bar{x}_2$. However, equation (10.3) shows that the value of $\sigma_{\bar{x}_1 - \bar{x}_2}$ depends on the values of $\sigma_1$ and $\sigma_2$, the standard deviations of each of the populations. When the population standard deviations are unknown, we can use the sample standard deviations as estimates of the population standard deviations and estimate $\sigma_{\bar{x}_1 - \bar{x}_2}$ as follows.

**Point Estimator of $\sigma_{\bar{x}_1 - \bar{x}_2}$**

$$s_{\bar{x}_1 - \bar{x}_2} = \sqrt{\frac{s_1^2}{n_1} + \frac{s_2^2}{n_2}} \qquad (10.5)$$

In the large-sample case, we can use the point estimator of $\sigma_{\bar{x}_1 - \bar{x}_2}$ to develop the following confidence interval estimate of the difference between the two population means.

> **Interval Estimate of the Difference Between the Means of Two Populations:**
> **Large-Sample Case ($n_1 \geq 30$ and $n_2 \geq 30$) with $\sigma_1$ and $\sigma_2$ Estimated by $s_1$ and $s_2$**
>
> $$\bar{x}_1 - \bar{x}_2 \pm z_{\alpha/2} s_{\bar{x}_1 - \bar{x}_2} \tag{10.6}$$
>
> where $1 - \alpha$ is the confidence coefficient.

Let us use expression (10.6) to develop a confidence interval estimate of the difference between the mean ages of the two customer populations in the Greystone Department Store study. Recall that the sample mean age and sample standard deviation for the simple random sample of 36 inner-city customers are $\bar{x}_1 = 40$ years and $s_1 = 9$ years, respectively; the sample mean and sample standard deviation for the simple random sample of 49 suburban customers are $\bar{x}_2 = 35$ years and $s_2 = 10$ years, respectively. Using equation (10.5) to estimate $\sigma_{\bar{x}_1 - \bar{x}_2}$ we have

$$s_{\bar{x}_1 - \bar{x}_2} = \sqrt{\frac{(9)^2}{36} + \frac{(10)^2}{49}} = 2.07$$

With $z_{\alpha/2} = z_{.025} = 1.96$, expression (10.6) provides the following 95% confidence interval.

$$5 \pm (1.96)(2.07)$$

or

$$5 \pm 4.06$$

Thus, at a 95% level of confidence, the margin of error is 4.06 years and the interval estimate of the difference between the mean ages of the two Greystone populations is .94 years to 9.06 years.

## Using Excel: Large-Sample Case

Excel can be used to develop an interval estimate of the difference between the population means in the Greystone Department Stores study. Except for the fact that we are working with two samples, the procedure is similar to the approach used to develop an interval estimate for a single population mean described in Chapter 8. Refer to Figure 10.3 as we describe the tasks involved. The formula worksheet is in the background; the value worksheet is in the foreground.

**Enter Data:**   Column A contains the age data for the simple random sample of 36 inner-city customers, and column B contains the age data for the simple random sample of 49 suburban customers.

**Enter Functions and Formulas:**   The descriptive statistics needed are provided in cells E5:F7. The confidence coefficient was entered into cell E9 (.95) and the corresponding level of significance was computed in cell E10. In cell E11 we used the NORMSINV function to compute the $z$ value needed for the interval estimate.

Using the two sample standard deviations and sample sizes, a point estimate of $\sigma_{\bar{x}_1 - \bar{x}_2}$, the standard error of the point estimator $\bar{x}_1 - \bar{x}_2$, was computed by entering the following formula into cell E13:

$$=\text{SQRT(E7^2/E5+F7^2/F5)}$$

**FIGURE 10.3** EXCEL WORKSHEET FOR THE GREYSTONE DEPARTMENT STORES STUDY

| | A | B | C | D | E | F | G |
|---|---|---|---|---|---|---|---|
| 1 | Inner City | Suburban | | Interval Estimate: Difference in Population Means | | | |
| 2 | 39 | 28 | | Using the Standard Normal Distribution (z) | | | |
| 3 | 44 | 36 | | | | | |
| 4 | 28 | 41 | | | Inner City | Suburban | |
| 5 | 20 | 14 | | Sample Size | =COUNT(A2:A37) | =COUNT(B2:B50) | |
| 6 | 39 | 39 | | Mean | =AVERAGE(A2:A37) | =AVERAGE(B2:B50) | |
| 7 | 42 | 57 | | Standard Deviation | =STDEV(A2:A37) | =STDEV(B2:B50) | |
| 8 | 37 | 36 | | | | | |
| 9 | 37 | 36 | | Confidence Coefficient | 0.95 | | |
| 10 | 34 | 38 | | Level of Significance (alpha) | =1-E9 | | |
| 11 | 38 | 36 | | z Value | =NORMSINV(1-E10/2) | | |
| 12 | 35 | 33 | | | | | |
| 13 | 41 | 40 | | Standard Error | =SQRT(E7^2/E5+F7^2/F5) | | |
| 14 | 41 | 50 | | Margin of Error | =E11*E13 | | |
| 15 | 49 | 13 | | | | | |
| 16 | 45 | 35 | | Point Estimate of Difference | =E6-F6 | | |
| 17 | 57 | 40 | | Lower Limit | =E16-E14 | | |
| 18 | 43 | 35 | | Upper Limit | =E16+E14 | | |
| 36 | 48 | 16 | | | | | |
| 37 | 58 | 35 | | | | | |
| 49 | | 23 | | | | | |
| 50 | | 54 | | | | | |
| 51 | | | | | | | |

| | A | B | C | D | E | F | G | H |
|---|---|---|---|---|---|---|---|---|
| 1 | Inner City | Suburban | | Interval Estimate: Difference in Population Means | | | | |
| 2 | 39 | 28 | | Using the Standard Normal Distribution (z) | | | | |
| 3 | 44 | 36 | | | | | | |
| 4 | 28 | 41 | | | | Inner City | Suburban | |
| 5 | 20 | 14 | | Sample Size | | 36 | 49 | |
| 6 | 39 | 39 | | Mean | | 40 | 35 | |
| 7 | 42 | 57 | | Standard Deviation | | 9.00 | 10 | |
| 8 | 37 | 36 | | | | | | |
| 9 | 37 | 36 | | Confidence Coefficient | | 0.95 | | |
| 10 | 34 | 38 | | Level of Significance (alpha) | | 0.05 | | |
| 11 | 38 | 36 | | z Value | | 1.960 | | |
| 12 | 35 | 33 | | | | | | |
| 13 | 41 | 40 | | Standard Error | | 2.07 | | |
| 14 | 41 | 50 | | Margin of Error | | 4.06 | | |
| 15 | 49 | 13 | | | | | | |
| 16 | 45 | 35 | | Point Estimate of Difference | | 5 | | |
| 17 | 57 | 40 | | Lower Limit | | 0.94 | | |
| 18 | 43 | 35 | | Upper Limit | | 9.06 | | |
| 36 | 48 | 16 | | | | | | |
| 37 | 58 | 35 | | | | | | |
| 49 | | 23 | | | | | | |
| 50 | | 54 | | | | | | |
| 51 | | | | | | | | |

Note: Rows 19–35 and 38–48 are hidden.

This cell formula is the Excel equivalent of equation (10.5). The margin of error was computed in cell E14 by multiplying the $z$ value times the standard error.

In cell E16 the difference in the sample means was used to compute the point estimate of the difference in the two population means. The lower limit of the confidence interval was computed in cell E17 (.94) and the upper limit was computed in cell E18 (9.06); thus, the 95% confidence interval estimate of the difference in the two population means is .94 to 9.06.

## Small-Sample Case

Let us now consider the interval estimation procedure for the difference between the means of two populations whenever one or both sample sizes are less than 30—that is, $n_1 < 30$ and/or $n_2 < 30$, which will be referred to as the small-sample case.

In Chapter 8, we presented the small-sample interval estimation procedures for a population mean. Recall that the small-sample case required the assumption that the population has a normal probability distribution. If the population standard deviation $\sigma$ can be assumed known, the standard normal distribution $z$ is used to develop the interval estimate. However, if the population standard deviation $\sigma$ is estimated by the sample standard deviation $s$, the $t$ distribution is used to develop the interval estimate.

In developing a small-sample interval estimate of the difference between two population means, we make the assumption that both populations have a normal probability distribution. If the population standard deviations $\sigma_1$ and $\sigma_2$ are assumed known, the large-sample interval estimation procedure provided by expression (10.4) can be used for the small-sample case. However, if the population standard deviations $\sigma_1$ and $\sigma_2$ are estimated by the sample standard deviations $s_1$ and $s_2$, the $t$ distribution is required to develop a small-sample interval estimate of the difference between two population means. The details of this procedure and an example follow. We begin by making the following assumptions:

When $\sigma_1$ and $\sigma_2$ are estimated by $s_1$ and $s_2$, the $t$ distribution is used to develop the small-sample interval estimate of the difference between two population means.

**1.** Both populations have normal probability distributions.
**2.** The variances of the populations are equal ($\sigma_1^2 = \sigma_2^2 = \sigma^2$).

Given these assumptions, the sampling distribution of $\bar{x}_1 - \bar{x}_2$ is normally distributed regardless of the sample sizes. The expected value of $\bar{x}_1 - \bar{x}_2$ is $\mu_1 - \mu_2$. Because of the equal variances assumption, equation (10.3) can be written

If the sample sizes are equal, the procedure in this section provides acceptable results even if the population variances are not equal. Thus, whenever possible, a researcher should use equal sample sizes.

$$\sigma_{\bar{x}_1-\bar{x}_2} = \sqrt{\frac{\sigma^2}{n_1} + \frac{\sigma^2}{n_2}} = \sqrt{\sigma^2\left(\frac{1}{n_1} + \frac{1}{n_2}\right)} \tag{10.7}$$

The sampling distribution of $\bar{x}_1 - \bar{x}_2$ is shown in Figure 10.4.

Because equation (10.7) is based on the assumption that $\sigma_1^2 = \sigma_2^2 = \sigma^2$, we do not need separate estimates of $\sigma_1^2$ and $\sigma_2^2$. In fact, we can combine the data from the two samples to provide the best single estimate of $\sigma^2$. The process of combining the results of two independent simple random samples to provide one estimate of $\sigma^2$ is referred to as *pooling*. The **pooled variance** estimator of $\sigma^2$, denoted by $s^2$, is a weighted average of the two sample variances $s_1^2$ and $s_2^2$. The formula for the pooled estimator of $\sigma^2$ follows.

A pooled variance estimator of $\sigma^2$ is a weighted average of the two sample variances and will always be a value between $s_1^2$ and $s_2^2$.

**Pooled Variance Estimator of $\sigma^2$**

$$s^2 = \frac{(n_1 - 1)s_1^2 + (n_2 - 1)s_2^2}{n_1 + n_2 - 2} \tag{10.8}$$

With $s^2$ as the pooled estimator of $\sigma^2$, we can substitute $s^2$ into equation (10.7) to obtain the following estimator of $\sigma_{\bar{x}_1-\bar{x}_2}$.

**Point Estimator of $\sigma_{\bar{x}_1-\bar{x}_2}$ When $\sigma_1^2 = \sigma_2^2 = \sigma^2$**

$$s_{\bar{x}_1-\bar{x}_2} = \sqrt{s^2\left(\frac{1}{n_1} + \frac{1}{n_2}\right)} \tag{10.9}$$

**FIGURE 10.4**   SAMPLING DISTRIBUTION OF $\bar{x}_1 - \bar{x}_2$ WHEN THE POPULATIONS HAVE NORMAL DISTRIBUTIONS WITH EQUAL VARIANCES

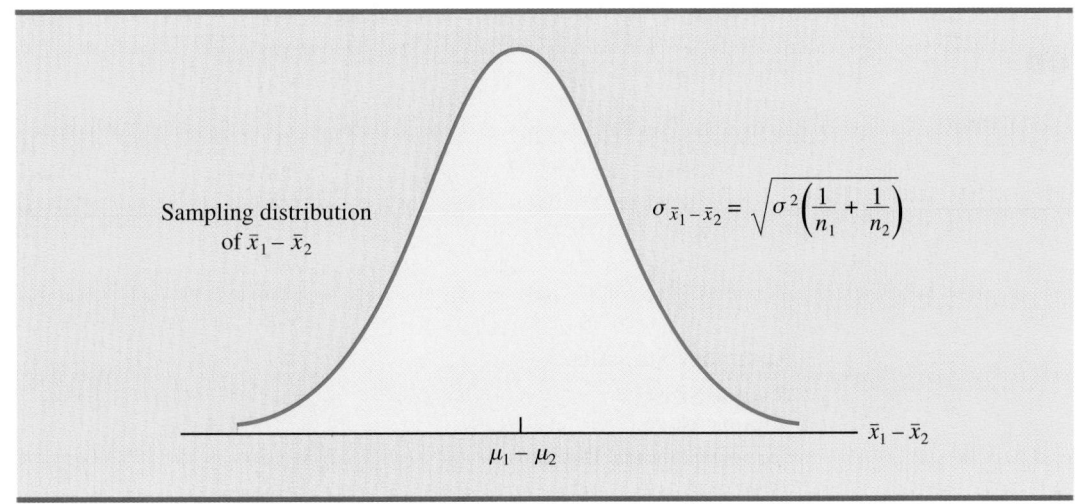

Sampling distribution of $\bar{x}_1 - \bar{x}_2$

$$\sigma_{\bar{x}_1-\bar{x}_2} = \sqrt{\sigma^2\left(\frac{1}{n_1} + \frac{1}{n_2}\right)}$$

$\mu_1 - \mu_2$

$\bar{x}_1 - \bar{x}_2$

The $t$ distribution can now be used to compute an interval estimate of the difference between the means of the two populations. Because $n_1 - 1$ degrees of freedom are associated with the sample from population 1 and $n_2 - 1$ degrees of freedom are associated with the sample from population 2, the $t$ distribution will have $n_1 + n_2 - 2$ degrees of freedom. The interval estimation procedure follows.

**Interval Estimate of the Difference Between the Means of Two Populations: Small-Sample Case ($n_1 < 30$ and/or $n_2 < 30$) with $\sigma_1$ and $\sigma_2$ Estimated by $s_1$ and $s_2$**

$$\bar{x}_1 - \bar{x}_2 \pm t_{\alpha/2} s_{\bar{x}_1 - \bar{x}_2} \tag{10.10}$$

where the $t$ value is based on a $t$ distribution with $n_1 + n_2 - 2$ degrees of freedom and where $1 - \alpha$ is the confidence coefficient.

Let us demonstrate the interval estimation procedure for a sampling study conducted by the Clearview National Bank. Independent random samples of checking account balances for 12 customers at the Cherry Grove branch and 10 customers at the Beechmont Branch were selected. The data obtained and summary statistics are shown in Table 10.3.

Let us use these sample results to develop a 90% confidence interval for the difference between the mean checking account balances at the two branch banks. Suppose that checking account balances are normally distributed at both branches and that the variances of checking account balances at the branches are equal. Using equation (10.8), the pooled estimate of the population variance becomes

$$s^2 = \frac{(n_1 - 1)s_1^2 + (n_2 - 1)s_2^2}{n_1 + n_2 - 2} = \frac{(11)(150)^2 + (9)(120)^2}{12 + 10 - 2} = 18,855$$

**TABLE 10.3**   CHECKING ACCOUNT BALANCE DATA AND SUMMARY STATISTICS FOR THE CLEARVIEW NATIONAL BANK STUDY

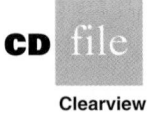

**CD** file

**Clearview**

| | **Cherry Grove** | **Beechmont** |
|---|---|---|
| | 1208 | 1081 |
| | 983 | 971 |
| | 1037 | 1032 |
| | 836 | 886 |
| | 978 | 958 |
| | 915 | 1043 |
| | 996 | 734 |
| | 699 | 747 |
| | 1223 | 906 |
| | 1085 | 842 |
| | 1119 | |
| | 921 | |
| **Summary Statistics** | | |
| Sample Size | $n_1 = 12$ | $n_2 = 10$ |
| Sample Mean | $\bar{x}_1 = 1000$ | $\bar{x}_2 = 920$ |
| Sample Standard Deviation | $s_1 = 150$ | $s_2 = 120$ |

Using equation (10.9), the corresponding estimate of $\sigma_{\bar{x}_1 - \bar{x}_2}$ is

$$s_{\bar{x}_1 - \bar{x}_2} = \sqrt{s^2 \left( \frac{1}{n_1} + \frac{1}{n_2} \right)} = \sqrt{18,855 \left( \frac{1}{12} + \frac{1}{10} \right)} = 58.79$$

The appropriate $t$ distribution for the interval estimation procedure has $n_1 + n_2 - 2 = 12 + 10 - 2 = 20$ degrees of freedom. With $\alpha = .10$, $t_{\alpha/2} = t_{.05} = 1.725$. Thus, using equation (10.10), the interval estimate is

$$\bar{x}_1 - \bar{x}_2 \pm t_{.05}\, s_{\bar{x}_1 - \bar{x}_2}$$
$$1000 - 920 \pm (1.725)(58.79)$$
$$80 \pm 101.41$$

At a 90% confidence level, the margin of error is $101.41 and the interval estimate of the difference between the mean account balances at the two branch banks is $-$21.41 to $181.41. The fact that the interval includes a negative range of values indicates that the actual difference between the two means, $\mu_1 - \mu_2$, may be negative. Thus, $\mu_2$ could actually be larger than $\mu_1$, indicating that the population mean balance could be greater for the Beechmont branch even though the results show a greater sample mean balance at the Cherry Grove branch. The fact that the confidence interval contains the value 0 can be interpreted as indicating that we do not have sufficient evidence to conclude that the population mean account balances differ between the two branches.

## Using Excel: Small-Sample Case

Excel can be used to develop an interval estimate of the difference between the population means at the two branches of the Clearview National Bank. Refer to Figure 10.5 as we describe the tasks involved. The formula worksheet is in the background; the value worksheet is in the foreground.

**Enter Data:** Column A contains the data for the simple random sample of 12 Cherry Grove customers, and column B contains the data for the simple random sample of 10 Beechmont customers.

**Enter Functions and Formulas:** The descriptive statistics needed to compute the interval estimate are provided in cells E5:F7. The confidence coefficient was entered into cell E9 (.90) and the corresponding level of significance was computed in cell E10. The degrees of freedom were computed in cell E11, and the TINV function was used in cell E12 to compute the $t$ value needed to develop the interval estimate.

Using the two sample standard deviations and sample sizes, the pooled variance estimate of the population variance was computed by entering the following formula into cell E14:

$$=((E5-1)*E7^2+(F5-1)*F7^2)/E11$$

This cell formula is the Excel equivalent of equation (10.8).

A point estimate of $\sigma_{\bar{x}_1 - \bar{x}_2}$, the standard error of the point estimator $\bar{x}_1 - \bar{x}_2$, was computed by entering the following formula into cell E15:

$$=SQRT(E14*(1/E5+1/F5))$$

This cell formula is the Excel equivalent of equation (10.9). The margin of error was computed in cell E16 by multiplying the $t$ value times the standard error.

In cell E18 the difference in the sample means was used to compute the point estimate of the difference in the two population means. The lower limit of the confidence interval was computed

**FIGURE 10.5   EXCEL WORKSHEET FOR THE CLEARVIEW NATIONAL BANK STUDY**

| | A | B | C | D | E | F | G |
|---|---|---|---|---|---|---|---|
| 1 | Cherry Grove | Beechmont | | Interval Estimate: Difference in Population Means | | | |
| 2 | 1208 | 1081 | | Using the t Distribution | | | |
| 3 | 983 | 971 | | | | | |
| 4 | 1037 | 1032 | | | Cherry Grove | Beechmont | |
| 5 | 836 | 886 | | Sample Size | =COUNT(A2:A13) | =COUNT(B2:B11) | |
| 6 | 978 | 958 | | Mean | =AVERAGE(A2:A13) | =AVERAGE(B2:B11) | |
| 7 | 915 | 1043 | | Standard Deviation | =STDEV(A2:A13) | =STDEV(B2:B11) | |
| 8 | 996 | 734 | | | | | |
| 9 | 699 | 747 | | Confidence Coefficient | 0.9 | | |
| 10 | 1223 | 906 | | Level of Significance (alpha) | =1-E9 | | |
| 11 | 1085 | 842 | | Degrees of Freedom | =E5+F5-2 | | |
| 12 | 1119 | | | t Value | =TINV(E10,E11) | | |
| 13 | 921 | | | | | | |
| 14 | | | | Pooled Estimate of Variance | =((E5-1)*E7^2+(F5-1)*F7^2)/E11 | | |
| 15 | | | | Standard Error | =SQRT(E14*(1/E5+1/F5)) | | |
| 16 | | | | Margin of Error | =E12*E15 | | |
| 17 | | | | | | | |
| 18 | | | | Point Estimate of Difference | =E6-F6 | | |
| 19 | | | | Lower Limit | =E18-E16 | | |
| 20 | | | | Upper Limit | =E18+E16 | | |
| 21 | | | | | | | |

| | A | B | C | D | E | F |
|---|---|---|---|---|---|---|
| 1 | Cherry Grove | Beechmont | | Interval Estimate: Difference in Population Means | | |
| 2 | 1208 | 1081 | | Using the t Distribution | | |
| 3 | 983 | 971 | | | | |
| 4 | 1037 | 1032 | | | Cherry Grove | Beechmont |
| 5 | 836 | 886 | | Sample Size | 12 | 10 |
| 6 | 978 | 958 | | Mean | 1000 | 920 |
| 7 | 915 | 1043 | | Standard Deviation | 150 | 120 |
| 8 | 996 | 734 | | | | |
| 9 | 699 | 747 | | Confidence Coefficient | 0.9 | |
| 10 | 1223 | 906 | | Level of Significance (alpha) | 0.1 | |
| 11 | 1085 | 842 | | Degrees of Freedom | 20 | |
| 12 | 1119 | | | t Value | 1.725 | |
| 13 | 921 | | | | | |
| 14 | | | | Pooled Estimate of Variance | 18855 | |
| 15 | | | | Standard Error | 58.79 | |
| 16 | | | | Margin of Error | 101.40 | |
| 17 | | | | | | |
| 18 | | | | Point Estimate of Difference | 80 | |
| 19 | | | | Lower Limit | -21.40 | |
| 20 | | | | Upper Limit | 181.40 | |
| 21 | | | | | | |

in cell E19 ($-21.40$) and the upper limit was computed in cell E20 (181.40). The 90% confidence interval estimate of the difference in the two population means is $-21.40$ to 181.40.[1]

## NOTES AND COMMENTS

1. The use of the $t$ distribution in the small-sample case is based on the assumptions that both populations have normal probability distributions and $\sigma_1^2 = \sigma_2^2$. Fortunately, this procedure is a *robust* statistical procedure, meaning that it is relatively insensitive to these assumptions. For instance, if $\sigma_1^2 \neq \sigma_2^2$ the procedure provides acceptable results if $n_1$ and $n_2$ are approximately equal.

2. The $t$ distribution is not restricted to the small-sample situation; it is applicable whenever both populations are normally distributed and the variances of the populations are equal. However, equations (10.4) and (10.6) show how to determine an interval estimate of the difference between the means of two populations when the sample sizes are large. Thus, in the large-sample case, use of the $t$ distribution and its corresponding normality assumption is not required. We therefore do not refer to the $t$ distribution until we have a small-sample case.

## EXERCISES

### Methods

1. Consider the following results for two independent random samples taken from two populations.

| Sample 1 | Sample 2 |
|---|---|
| $n_1 = 50$ | $n_2 = 35$ |
| $\bar{x}_1 = 13.6$ | $\bar{x}_2 = 11.6$ |
| $s_1 = 2.2$ | $s_2 = 3.0$ |

---

[1]This interval differs by .01 from the interval obtained earlier ($-21.41$ to 181.41), because the $t$ value generated by Excel has more decimal places of accuracy than the $t$ value from the table (1.725).

    **a.**    What is the point estimate of the difference between the two population means?

    **b.**    Provide a 90% confidence interval for the difference between the two population means.

    **c.**    Provide a 95% confidence interval for the difference between the two population means.

**2.**  Consider the following results for two independent random samples taken from two populations.

| Sample 1 | Sample 2 |
|---|---|
| $n_1 = 10$ | $n_2 = 8$ |
| $\bar{x}_1 = 22.5$ | $\bar{x}_2 = 20.1$ |
| $s_1 = 2.5$ | $s_2 = 2.0$ |

    **a.**    What is the point estimate of the difference between the two population means?

    **b.**    What is the pooled estimate of the population variance?

    **c.**    Develop a 95% confidence interval for the difference between the two population means.

**3.**  Consider the following data for two independent random samples taken from two populations.

| Sample 1 | | Sample 2 | |
|---|---|---|---|
| 10 | 7 | 8 | 7 |
| 12 | 7 | 8 | 4 |
| 9 | 9 | 6 | 9 |

    **a.**    Compute the two sample means.

    **b.**    Compute the two sample standard deviations.

    **c.**    What is the point estimate of the difference between the two population means?

    **d.**    What is the pooled estimate of the population variance?

    **e.**    Develop a 95% confidence interval for the difference between the two population means.

## Applications

**4.**  Gasoline prices increased substantially from 1999 to 2000. The American Automobile Association provided information on the mean cost per gallon for self-serve regular unleaded gasoline over the 2 years (*AAA Going Places,* May/June 2000). Assume the following results were obtained from independent samples of locations throughout the country.

| 2000 Cost | 1999 Cost |
|---|---|
| $\bar{x}_1 = \$1.58$ | $\bar{x}_2 = \$0.98$ |
| $s_1 = \$0.12$ | $s_2 = \$0.08$ |
| $n_1 = 50$ | $n_2 = 42$ |

    **a.**    What is the point estimate of the increase in the mean cost per gallon from 1999 to 2000?

    **b.**    What is the 95% confidence interval estimate of the increase in the mean cost per gallon from 1999 to 2000?

**Miles**

**5.**  Data gathered by the U.S. Department of Transportation show the number of miles that residents of the 75 largest metropolitan areas travel per day in a car. Suppose that a simple random sample of 50 Buffalo residents and an independent simple random sample of 100 Boston residents resulted in the miles traveled data shown in the data set named Miles.

    **a.**    What is the point estimate of the difference between the mean number of miles that Buffalo residents travel per day and the mean number of miles that Boston residents travel per day?

    **b.**    What is the 95% confidence interval for the difference between the two population means?

6. The International Air Transport Association surveyed business travelers to determine ratings of various international airports. The maximum possible rating score was 10. Suppose 50 business travelers were asked to rate the Miami airport, and 50 other business travelers were asked to rate the Los Angeles airport. The rating scores follow.

**Airport**

**Miami**

| | | | | | | | | | | | | |
|---|---|---|---|---|---|---|---|---|---|---|---|---|
| 6 | 4 | 6 | 8 | 7 | 7 | 6 | 3 | 3 | 8 | 10 | 4 | 8 |
| 7 | 8 | 7 | 5 | 9 | 5 | 8 | 4 | 3 | 8 | 5 | 5 | 4 |
| 4 | 4 | 8 | 4 | 5 | 6 | 2 | 5 | 9 | 9 | 8 | 4 | 8 |
| 9 | 9 | 5 | 9 | 7 | 8 | 3 | 10 | 8 | 9 | 6 | | |

**Los Angeles**

| | | | | | | | | | | | | |
|---|---|---|---|---|---|---|---|---|---|---|---|---|
| 10 | 9 | 6 | 7 | 8 | 7 | 9 | 8 | 10 | 7 | 6 | 5 | 7 |
| 3 | 5 | 6 | 8 | 7 | 10 | 8 | 4 | 7 | 8 | 6 | 9 | 9 |
| 5 | 3 | 1 | 8 | 9 | 6 | 8 | 5 | 4 | 6 | 10 | 9 | 8 |
| 3 | 2 | 7 | 9 | 5 | 3 | 10 | 3 | 5 | 10 | 8 | | |

Develop a 95% confidence interval estimate of the difference between the mean ratings of the Miami and Los Angeles airports.

7. A Cornell University study of wage differentials between men and women reported that one of the reasons wages for men are higher than wages for women is that men tend to have more years of work experience than women (*Business Week,* August 28, 2000). Assume the following sample summaries show the years of experience for each group.

| **Men** | **Women** |
|---|---|
| $\bar{x}_1 = 14.9$ years | $\bar{x}_2 = 10.3$ years |
| $s_1 = 5.2$ years | $s_2 = 3.8$ years |
| $n_1 = 100$ | $n_2 = 85$ |

a. What is the point estimate of the difference between the two population means?
b. At 95% confidence, what is the margin of error?
c. What is the 95% confidence interval estimate of the difference between the two population means?

8. An urban planning group is interested in estimating the difference between the mean household incomes for two neighborhoods in a large metropolitan area. Independent random samples of households in the neighborhoods provided the following results.

| **Neighborhood 1** | **Neighborhood 2** |
|---|---|
| $n_1 = 8$ | $n_2 = 12$ |
| $\bar{x}_1 = \$45,700$ | $\bar{x}_2 = \$44,500$ |
| $s_1 = \$700$ | $s_2 = \$850$ |

a. Develop a point estimate of the difference between the mean incomes in the two neighborhoods.
b. Develop a 95% confidence interval for the difference between the mean incomes in the two neighborhoods.
c. What assumptions were made to compute the interval estimates in part (b)?

9. The National Association of Home Builders provided data on the cost of the most popular home remodeling projects (*USA Today,* June 17, 1997). Sample data on cost (in thousands of dollars) for two types of remodeling projects are as follows.

| **Kitchen** | **Master Bedroom** |
|---|---|
| 25.2 | 18.0 |
| 17.4 | 22.9 |
| 22.8 | 26.4 |
| 21.9 | 24.8 |
| 19.7 | 26.9 |

| Kitchen | Master Bedroom |
|---------|----------------|
| 23.0 | 17.8 |
| 19.7 | 24.6 |
| 16.9 | 21.0 |
| 21.8 | |
| 23.6 | |

**a.** Develop a point estimate of the difference between the population mean remodeling costs for the two types of projects.

**b.** Develop a 90% confidence interval for the difference between the two population means.

**10.** Suppose independent random samples of 15 unionized women and 20 nonunionized women in manufacturing have been selected and the following hourly wage rates are found.

**CD** file

Union

**Union Workers**

| 22.40 | 18.90 | 16.70 | 14.05 | 16.20 | 20.00 | 16.10 | 16.30 | 19.10 |
|-------|-------|-------|-------|-------|-------|-------|-------|-------|
| 16.50 | 18.50 | 19.80 | 17.00 | 14.30 | 17.20 | | | |

**Nonunion Workers**

| 17.60 | 14.40 | 16.60 | 15.00 | 17.65 | 15.00 | 17.55 | 13.30 | 11.20 |
|-------|-------|-------|-------|-------|-------|-------|-------|-------|
| 15.90 | 19.20 | 11.85 | 16.65 | 15.20 | 15.30 | 17.00 | 15.10 | 14.30 |
| 13.90 | 14.50 | | | | | | | |

**a.** What is the point estimate of the difference between the hourly wages for the two populations?

**b.** What is the pooled estimate of the population variance?

**c.** Develop a 95% confidence interval estimate of the difference between the two population means.

**d.** Does there appear to be any difference in the mean wage rate for these two groups? Explain.

## 10.2   HYPOTHESIS TESTS ABOUT THE DIFFERENCE BETWEEN THE MEANS OF TWO POPULATIONS: INDEPENDENT SAMPLES

In this section we present procedures that can be used to test hypotheses about the difference between the means of two populations. The methodology is again divided into large-sample ($n_1 \geq 30$, $n_2 \geq 30$) and small-sample ($n_1 < 30$ and/or $n_2 < 30$) cases.

### Large-Sample Case

As part of a study to evaluate differences in educational quality between two training centers, a standardized examination is given to individuals who are trained at the two centers. The examination scores are a major factor in assessing quality differences between the centers. The population means for the two centers are as follows.

$$\mu_1 = \text{the mean examination score for all}$$
$$\text{individuals trained at center A}$$

$$\mu_2 = \text{the mean examination score for all}$$
$$\text{individuals trained at center B}$$

We begin with the tentative assumption that no difference exists in the training quality provided at the two centers. Hence, in terms of the mean examination scores, the null hypothesis is that $\mu_1 - \mu_2 = 0$. If sample evidence leads to the rejection of this hypothesis, we will conclude that the mean examination scores differ for the two populations. This conclusion indicates a quality differential between the two centers and that a follow-up study investigating the reasons for the differential may be warranted. The null and alternative hypotheses are written as follows.

$$H_0: \mu_1 - \mu_2 = 0$$
$$H_a: \mu_1 - \mu_2 \neq 0$$

Following the hypothesis testing procedure from Chapter 9, we make the tentative assumption that $H_0$ is true. Using the difference between the sample means as the point estimator of the difference between the population means, we base the hypothesis test on the sampling distribution of $\bar{x}_1 - \bar{x}_2$ when $H_0$ is true. For the large-sample case, this distribution is as shown in Figure 10.6. Because the sampling distribution of $\bar{x}_1 - \bar{x}_2$ can be approximated by a normal probability distribution, the following test statistic is used.

$$z = \frac{(\bar{x}_1 - \bar{x}_2) - (\mu_1 - \mu_2)}{\sqrt{\sigma_1^2/n_1 + \sigma_2^2/n_2}} \tag{10.11}$$

Whenever $n_1 \geq 30$, $n_2 \geq 30$, and $\sigma_1^2$ and $\sigma_2^2$ are unknown, we will use $s_1^2$ and $s_2^2$ as estimates of $\sigma_1^2$ and $\sigma_2^2$ to compute the test statistic.

The value of $z$ given by equation (10.11) can be interpreted as the number of standard errors $\bar{x}_1 - \bar{x}_2$ is from the value of $\mu_1 - \mu_2$ specified in $H_0$. For $\alpha = .05$ and thus $z_{\alpha/2} = z_{.025} = 1.96$, the rejection region for the two-tailed hypothesis test is shown in Figure 10.7. The rejection rule is as follows:

Using test statistic: Reject $H_0$ if $z < -1.96$ or if $z > +1.96$
Using $p$-value: Reject $H_0$ if $p$-value $< .05$

Suppose that independent random samples of individuals trained at the two centers provide the examination scores in Table 10.4; summary statistics are given in Table 10.5. Using

**FIGURE 10.6**   SAMPLING DISTRIBUTION OF $\bar{x}_1 - \bar{x}_2$

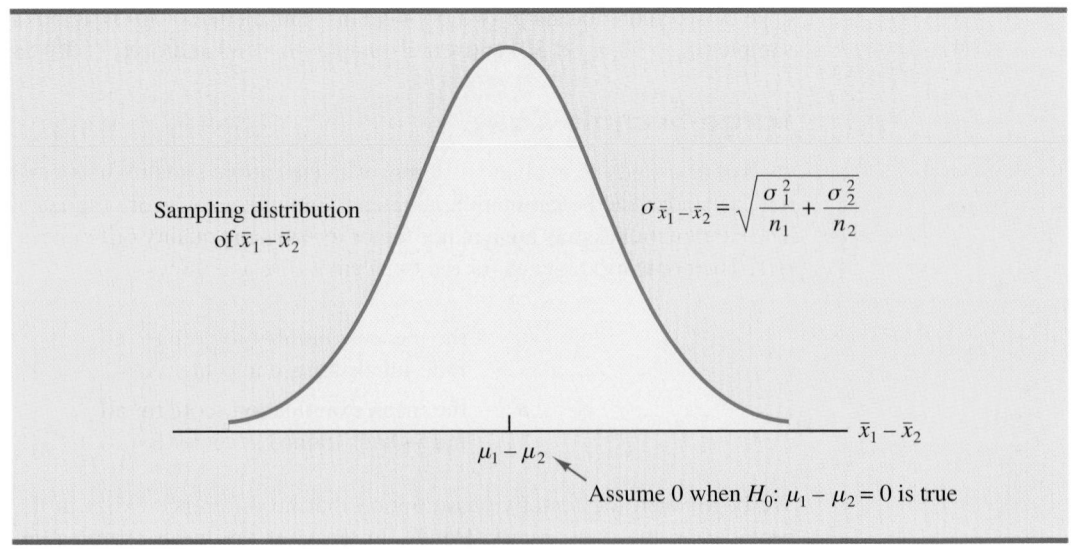

**FIGURE 10.7**   REJECTION REGION FOR THE TWO-TAILED HYPOTHESIS TEST WITH $\alpha = .05$

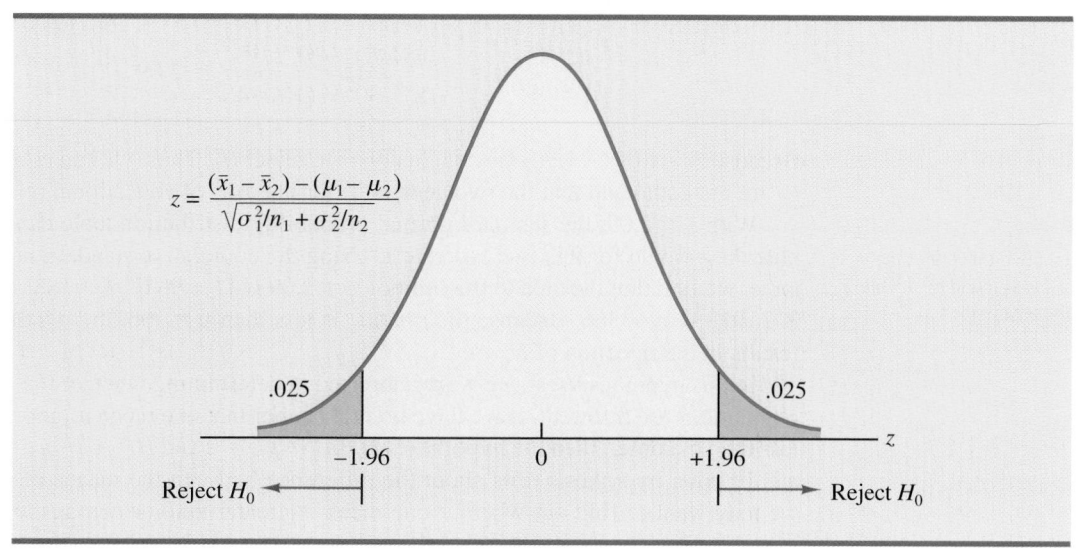

$$z = \frac{(\bar{x}_1 - \bar{x}_2) - (\mu_1 - \mu_2)}{\sqrt{\sigma_1^2/n_1 + \sigma_2^2/n_2}}$$

.025                    .025

−1.96          0          +1.96          z

Reject $H_0$ ◄─────┤                    ├─────► Reject $H_0$

**TABLE 10.4**   EXAMINATION SCORE DATA

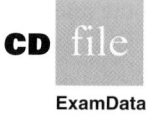

**ExamData**

| Training Center A | | | Training Center B | | | |
|---|---|---|---|---|---|---|
| 97 | 83 | 91 | 64 | 66 | 91 | 84 |
| 90 | 84 | 87 | 85 | 83 | 78 | 85 |
| 94 | 76 | 73 | 72 | 74 | 87 | 85 |
| 79 | 82 | 92 | 64 | 70 | 93 | 84 |
| 78 | 85 | 64 | 74 | 82 | 89 | 59 |
| 87 | 85 | 74 | 93 | 82 | 79 | 62 |
| 83 | 91 | 88 | 70 | 75 | 84 | 91 |
| 89 | 72 | 88 | 79 | 78 | 65 | 83 |
| 76 | 86 | 74 | 79 | 99 | 78 | 80 |
| 84 | 70 | 73 | 75 | 57 | 66 | 76 |

**TABLE 10.5**   DESCRIPTIVE STATISTICS FOR TWO INDEPENDENT SAMPLES OF EXAMINATION SCORES

| Training Center A | Training Center B |
|---|---|
| $n_1 = 30$ | $n_2 = 40$ |
| $\bar{x}_1 = 82.5$ | $\bar{x}_2 = 78$ |
| $s_1 = 8$ | $s_2 = 10$ |

$s_1^2$ and $s_2^2$ to estimate $\sigma_1^2$ and $\sigma_2^2$, we find that the test statistic $z$ given by equation (10.11) for the null hypothesis $H_0: \mu_1 - \mu_2 = 0$ becomes

$$z = \frac{(82.5 - 78) - 0}{\sqrt{(8)^2/30 + (10)^2/40}} = 2.09$$

Because $z = 2.09 > 1.96$, the conclusion is to reject $H_0$. Thus, we can conclude that $\mu_1$ and $\mu_2$ are not equal and that the two centers differ in terms of educational quality.

In a two-tailed test, the *p*-value is found by doubling the area in the tail.

With $z = 2.09$, the standard normal probability distribution table can be used to compute the *p*-value for this two-tailed test. Using the cumulative standard normal probability table, we find that the area to the right of $z = 2.09$ is $1 - .9817 = .0183$. Thus, the *p*-value is $2(.0183) = .0366$. Because the *p*-value is less than $\alpha = .05$, the *p*-value approach also results in the rejection of $H_0$.

In this hypothesis test, we were interested in determining whether the means of the two populations are different. If we have no prior belief that one mean might be greater than or less than the other, then the hypotheses $H_0: \mu_1 - \mu_2 = 0$ and $H_a: \mu_1 - \mu_2 \neq 0$ are appropriate. In other hypothesis tests about the difference between the means of two populations, we may want to find out whether one mean is greater than or perhaps less than the other mean. In these cases, a one-tailed hypothesis test would be appropriate. The two forms of a one-tailed hypothesis test about the difference between two population means follow.

$$H_0: \mu_1 - \mu_2 \leq 0 \qquad H_0: \mu_1 - \mu_2 \geq 0$$
$$H_a: \mu_1 - \mu_2 > 0 \qquad H_a: \mu_1 - \mu_2 < 0$$

In the large-sample case, these hypotheses are tested by using the test statistic $z$ given by equation (10.11). The rejection region for the first test is in the upper tail and the rejection region for the second test is in the lower tail.

## Using Excel: Large-Sample Case

Excel's z-Test: Two Sample for Means tool can be used to conduct a hypothesis test about the difference between the population means in the training center study. Refer to the Excel worksheet shown in Figure 10.8 and the dialog box in Figure 10.9 as we describe the tasks involved. Only two formulas are used, so we will not show the formula worksheet in the background.

**Enter Data:**   Column A contains the examination score data for the simple random sample of 30 individuals trained at center A, and column B contains the examination score data for the simple random sample of 40 individuals trained at center B.

**Enter Functions and Formulas:**   To use Excel's z-Test: Two Sample for Means tool we must first compute the sample variance for both samples. To compute the sample variance for the 30 individuals trained at center A, we entered the formula =VAR(A2:A31) into cell E2. Then, to compute the sample variance for the 40 individuals trained at center B we entered the formula =VAR(B2:B41) into cell F2. The value worksheet shows that the sample variance for center A is 64.0517 and that the sample variance for center B is 100.

**Apply Tools:**   The following steps describe how to use Excel's z-Test: Two Sample for Means tool to conduct the hypothesis test about the difference between the population means in the training center study.

**Step 1.** Select the **Tools** pull-down menu
**Step 2.** Choose the **Data Analysis** option
**Step 3.** Choose **z-Test: Two Sample for Means** from the list of Analysis Tools

**FIGURE 10.8    EXCEL WORKSHEET FOR THE TRAINING CENTER STUDY**

| | A | B | C | D | E | F | G | H | I |
|---|---|---|---|---|---|---|---|---|---|
| 1 | Center A | Center B | | | Center A | Center B | | | |
| 2 | 97 | 64 | | Sample Variance | 64.0517 | 100 | Formula: =VAR(B2:B41) | | |
| 3 | 90 | 85 | | | | | | | |
| 4 | 94 | 72 | | z-Test: Two Sample for Means | | | | | |
| 5 | 79 | 64 | | | | | Formula: =VAR(A2:A31) | | |
| 6 | 78 | 74 | | | Center A | Center B | | | |
| 7 | 87 | 93 | | Mean | 82.5 | 78 | | | |
| 8 | 83 | 70 | | Known Variance | 64.0517 | 100 | | | |
| 9 | 89 | 79 | | Observations | 30 | 40 | | | |
| 10 | 76 | 79 | | Hypothesized Mean Difference | 0 | | | | |
| 11 | 84 | 75 | | z | 2.09 | | | | |
| 12 | 83 | 66 | | P(Z<=z) one-tail | 0.0183 | | | | |
| 13 | 84 | 83 | | z Critical one-tail | 1.645 | | | | |
| 14 | 76 | 74 | | P(Z<=z) two-tail | 0.0366 | | | | |
| 15 | 82 | 70 | | z Critical two-tail | 1.960 | | | | |
| 16 | 85 | 82 | | | | | | | |
| 17 | 85 | 82 | | | | | | | |
| 29 | 88 | 65 | | | | | | | |
| 30 | 74 | 78 | | | | | | | |
| 31 | 73 | 66 | | | | | | | |
| 32 | | 84 | | | | | | | |
| 40 | | 80 | | | | | | | |
| 41 | | 76 | | | | | | | |
| 42 | | | | | | | | | |

Note: Rows 18–28 and 33–39 are hidden.

**FIGURE 10.9    DIALOG BOX FOR EXCEL'S z-TEST: TWO SAMPLE FOR MEANS**

**Step 4.** When the **z-Test: Two Sample for Means** dialog box appears (see Figure 10.9):
   Enter A1:A31 in the **Variable 1 Range** box
   Enter B1:B41 in the **Variable 2 Range** box
   Enter 0 in the **Hypothesized Mean Difference** box
   Enter 64.0517 in the **Variable 1 Variance (known)**[2] box
   Enter 100 in the **Variable 2 Variance (known)** box
   Select **Labels**
   Enter .05 in the **Alpha** box
   Select **Output Range**
   Enter D4 in the **Output Range** box (to identify the upper left corner of the section of the worksheet where the output will appear)
   Click **OK**

Descriptive statistics for the two samples are shown in cells E7:F9. The value of the test statistic, 2.09, is shown in cell E11 of the value worksheet. The critical value 1.96, labeled *z Critical two-tail,* is shown in cell E15. Because $z = 2.09$ is in the rejection region, we can conclude that the population means are not equal. Alternatively, we can use the *p*-value to make the hypothesis testing decision. The *p*-value for the test, labeled $P(Z <= z)$ *two-tail,* is shown in cell E14. Because the *p*-value, 0.0366, is less than the level of significance, $\alpha = .05$, we have sufficient statistical evidence to reject the null hypothesis and conclude that the population means are not equal.

The same procedure can also be used to conduct one-tailed hypothesis tests. The value of the test statistic $z$ is identical to the two-tailed case. The only changes required to make the hypothesis testing decision are that we need to use the critical value for a one-tailed test, labeled z Critical one-tail (see Cell E13), or the *p*-value for a one-tailed test, labeled $P(Z <= z)$ one-tail (see Cell E12).

Excel's z-Test: Two Sample For Means tool assumes a known variance for each population. But, as we have shown, it can also be used when $s_1^2$ and $s_2^2$ are substituted for $\sigma_1^2$ and $\sigma_2^2$ in the large-sample case. The small-sample case is discussed next.

## Small-Sample Case

For the small-sample case, the use of the *t* distribution is based on the assumption that both populations have normal distributions and that the population variances are equal.

Let us now consider hypothesis tests about the difference between the means of two populations for the small-sample case; that is, where $n_1 < 30$ and/or $n_2 < 30$. The procedure we will use is based on the *t* distribution with $n_1 + n_2 - 2$ degrees of freedom. As discussed in Section 10.1, assumptions are made that both populations have normal probability distributions and that the variances of the populations are equal.

The problem situation that we will use to illustrate the small-sample case involves a new computer software package that has been developed to help systems analysts reduce the time required to design, develop, and implement an information system. To evaluate the benefits of the new software package, a random sample of 24 systems analysts is selected. Each analyst is given specifications for a hypothetical information system. Then 12 of the analysts are instructed to produce the information system by using current technology. The other 12 analysts are trained in the use of the new software package and then instructed to use it to produce the information system.

In this study, one population consists of systems analysts using the current technology and the other consists of systems analysts using the new software package. In terms

---

[2]Excel is asking for a known variance ($\sigma_1^2$) here. But, in the large-sample case, we can substitute $s_1^2$. Note, however, that Excel will not accept a reference to cell E2 here. The same is true for the variance of variable 2 on the next line.

of the time required to complete the information system design project, the population means are as follow.

$\mu_1 =$ the mean project completion time for all systems analysts using the current technology

$\mu_2 =$ the mean project completion time for all systems analysts using the new software package

The researcher in charge of the new software evaluation project hopes to show that the new software package will provide a shorter mean project completion time. Thus, the researcher is looking for evidence to conclude that $\mu_2$ is less than $\mu_1$; in this case, the difference between the two population means, $\mu_1 - \mu_2$, will be greater than zero. The research hypothesis $\mu_1 - \mu_2 > 0$ is stated as the alternative hypothesis.

$$H_0: \mu_1 - \mu_2 \leq 0$$
$$H_a: \mu_1 - \mu_2 > 0$$

The researcher is looking for evidence to reject $H_0$ and conclude that the new software package provides a smaller mean completion time.

Suppose that the 24 analysts complete the study with the results shown in Table 10.6. Under the assumption that the variances of the populations are equal, equation (10.8) is used to compute the pooled estimate of $\sigma^2$.

$$s^2 = \frac{(n_1 - 1)s_1^2 + (n_2 - 1)s_2^2}{n_1 + n_2 - 2} = \frac{11(40)^2 + 11(44)^2}{12 + 12 - 2} = 1768$$

The test statistic for the small-sample case is

$$t = \frac{(\bar{x}_1 - \bar{x}_2) - (\mu_1 - \mu_2)}{\sqrt{s^2 \left( \frac{1}{n_1} + \frac{1}{n_2} \right)}} \qquad \textbf{(10.12)}$$

In the case of two independent random samples of sizes $n_1$ and $n_2$, the $t$ distribution will have $n_1 + n_2 - 2$ degrees of freedom. For $\alpha = .05$, the $t$ distribution table shows that with $12 + 12 - 2 = 22$ degrees of freedom, the critical value is $t_{.05} = 1.717$. Thus, the rejection region for the one-tailed test is as follows:

Using test statistic: Reject $H_0$ if $t > 1.717$
Using $p$-value: Reject $H_0$ if $p$-value $< .05$

The sample data and equation (10.12) provide the following value for the test statistic.

$$t = \frac{(325 - 288) - 0}{\sqrt{1768 \left( \frac{1}{12} + \frac{1}{12} \right)}} = 2.16$$

Checking the rejection region, we see that $t = 2.16 > 1.717$ allows the rejection of $H_0$ at the .05 level of significance. Thus, the sample results enable the researcher to conclude that $\mu_1 - \mu_2 > 0$ and that the new software package provides a smaller mean completion time.

**TABLE 10.6**   COMPLETION TIME DATA AND SUMMARY STATISTICS
FOR THE SOFTWARE TESTING STUDY

**Software**

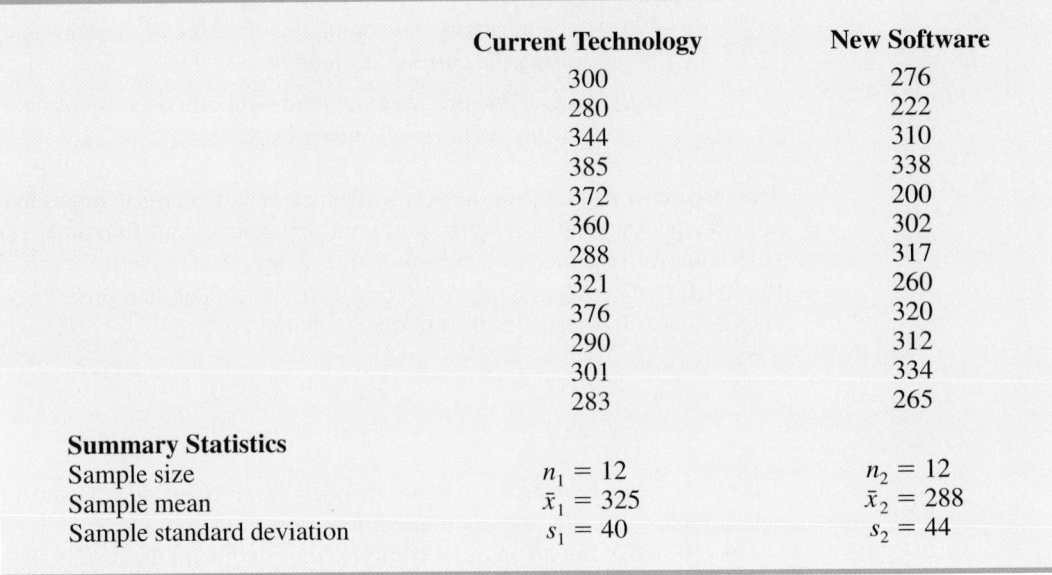

|  | Current Technology | New Software |
|---|---|---|
|  | 300 | 276 |
|  | 280 | 222 |
|  | 344 | 310 |
|  | 385 | 338 |
|  | 372 | 200 |
|  | 360 | 302 |
|  | 288 | 317 |
|  | 321 | 260 |
|  | 376 | 320 |
|  | 290 | 312 |
|  | 301 | 334 |
|  | 283 | 265 |
| **Summary Statistics** | | |
| Sample size | $n_1 = 12$ | $n_2 = 12$ |
| Sample mean | $\bar{x}_1 = 325$ | $\bar{x}_2 = 288$ |
| Sample standard deviation | $s_1 = 40$ | $s_2 = 44$ |

## Using Excel: Small-Sample Case

Excel's t-Test: Two Sample Assuming Equal Variances tool can be used to conduct a hypothesis test about the difference between the population means for the software training study. Refer to the Excel worksheet shown in Figure 10.10 and the dialog box in Figure 10.11 as we describe the tasks involved. No functions or formulas are used so no background worksheet is shown.

**Enter Data:**   Column A contains the completion time data for the simple random sample of 12 projects completed using the current technology, and column B contains the completion time data for the simple random sample of 12 projects completed using the new software package.

**Apply Tools:**   The following steps describe how to use Excel's t-Test: Two Sample Assuming Equal Variances tool.

> **Step 1.** Select the **Tools** pull-down menu
> **Step 2.** Choose the **Data Analysis** option
> **Step 3.** Choose **t-Test: Two-Sample Assuming Equal Variances** from the list of Analysis Tools
> **Step 4.** When the t-Test: Two-Sample Assuming Equal Variances dialog box appears (see Figure 10.11):
> Enter A1:A13 in the **Variable 1 Range** box
> Enter B1:B13 in the **Variable 2 Range** box
> Enter 0 in the **Hypothesized Mean Difference** box
> Select **Labels**
> Enter .05 in the **Alpha** box
> Select **Output Range**
> Enter D1 in the **Output Range** box (to identify the upper left corner of the section of the worksheet where the output will appear)
> Click **OK**

**FIGURE 10.10**    EXCEL WORKSHEET FOR THE SOFTWARE TRAINING STUDY

| | A | B | C | D | E | F | G |
|---|---|---|---|---|---|---|---|
| 1 | **Current** | **New** | | t-Test: Two-Sample Assuming Equal Variances | | | |
| 2 | 300 | 276 | | | | | |
| 3 | 280 | 222 | | | *Current* | *New* | |
| 4 | 344 | 310 | | Mean | 325 | 288 | |
| 5 | 385 | 338 | | Variance | 1600 | 1936 | |
| 6 | 372 | 200 | | Observations | 12 | 12 | |
| 7 | 360 | 302 | | Pooled Variance | 1768 | | |
| 8 | 288 | 317 | | Hypothesized Mean Difference | 0 | | |
| 9 | 321 | 260 | | df | 22 | | |
| 10 | 376 | 320 | | t Stat | 2.16 | | |
| 11 | 290 | 312 | | P(T<=t) one-tail | 0.0212 | | |
| 12 | 301 | 334 | | t Critical one-tail | 1.717 | | |
| 13 | 283 | 265 | | P(T<=t) two-tail | 0.0423 | | |
| 14 | | | | t Critical two-tail | 2.074 | | |
| 15 | | | | | | | |

Descriptive statistics for the completion times using the two software packages are shown in cells E4:F6 and the pooled variance estimate is shown in cell E7.

The value of the test statistic, $t = 2.16$, is shown in cell E10. The critical value 1.717, labeled t Critical one-tail, is shown in cell E12. Because $t = 2.16$ is in the rejection region ($2.16 > 1.717$), we can conclude that the new software package provides a smaller mean completion time. Alternatively, we can use the $p$-value to make the hypothesis testing decision. The $p$-value for the test, labeled P(T $<=$ t) one-tail, is shown in cell E11. Because the $p$-value, 0.0212, is less than the level of significance, $\alpha = .05$, we have sufficient statistical evidence to reject the null hypothesis and conclude that the new software package provides a smaller mean completion time.

**FIGURE 10.11**    DIALOG BOX FOR EXCEL'S t-TEST: TWO-SAMPLE ASSUMING EQUAL VARIANCES

The same procedure can also be used to conduct two-tailed hypothesis tests in the small-sample case. The value of the test statistic $t$ is identical to the one-tailed case. The only changes required to make the hypothesis testing decision are that we need to use the critical value for a two-tailed test, labeled t Critical two-tail (see Cell E14), and the $p$-value for a two-tailed test, labeled P(T $<=$ t) two-tail (see Cell E13).

## NOTES AND COMMENTS

In hypothesis tests about the difference between the means of two populations, the null hypothesis almost always contains the assumption of no difference between the means. Hence, the following null hypotheses are possible choices.

$$H_0: \mu_1 - \mu_2 = 0$$
$$H_0: \mu_1 - \mu_2 \leq 0$$
$$H_0: \mu_1 - \mu_2 \geq 0$$

In some instances, we may want to determine whether there is a nonzero difference $D_0$ between the population means. The specific value chosen for $D_0$ depends on the application under study. However, in this case, the null hypothesis may be one of the following forms.

$$H_0: \mu_1 - \mu_2 = D_0$$
$$H_0: \mu_1 - \mu_2 \leq D_0$$
$$H_0: \mu_1 - \mu_2 \geq D_0$$

The hypothesis testing computations remain the same with the exception that $D_0$ is used for the value of $\mu_1 - \mu_2$ in equations (10.11) and (10.12).

## EXERCISES

### Methods

11. Consider the following hypothesis test.

$$H_0: \mu_1 - \mu_2 \leq 0$$
$$H_a: \mu_1 - \mu_2 > 0$$

The following results are for two independent samples taken from the two populations.

| Sample 1 | Sample 2 |
|---|---|
| $n_1 = 40$ | $n_2 = 50$ |
| $\bar{x}_1 = 25.2$ | $\bar{x}_2 = 22.8$ |
| $s_1 = 5.2$ | $s_2 = 6.0$ |

a. With $\alpha = .05$, what is your hypothesis testing conclusion?
b. What is the $p$-value?

12. Consider the following hypothesis test.

$$H_0: \mu_1 - \mu_2 = 0$$
$$H_a: \mu_1 - \mu_2 \neq 0$$

The following results are for two independent samples taken from the two populations.

| Sample 1 | Sample 2 |
|---|---|
| $n_1 = 80$ | $n_2 = 70$ |
| $\bar{x}_1 = 104$ | $\bar{x}_2 = 106$ |
| $s_1 = 8.4$ | $s_2 = 7.6$ |

a. With $\alpha = .05$, what is your hypothesis testing conclusion?
b. What is the $p$-value?

**13.**   Consider the following hypothesis test.

$$H_0: \mu_1 - \mu_2 = 0$$
$$H_a: \mu_1 - \mu_2 \neq 0$$

The following results are for two independent samples taken from the two populations. With $\alpha = .05$, what is your hypothesis testing conclusion?

| Sample 1 | Sample 2 |
|----------|----------|
| $n_1 = 8$ | $n_2 = 7$ |
| $\bar{x}_1 = 1.4$ | $\bar{x}_2 = 1.0$ |
| $s_1 = 0.4$ | $s_2 = 0.6$ |

## Applications

**14.**   Coastal areas of the United States, including Cape Cod, the Outer Banks, the Carolinas, and the Gulf Coast, had relatively high population growth rates during the 1990s. Data were collected on residents living in the coastal communities as well as on residents living in noncoastal areas throughout the United States (*USA Today*, July 21, 2000). Assume that the following sample results were obtained on the ages of individuals in the two populations:

| Coastal Areas | Noncoastal Areas |
|---------------|------------------|
| $\bar{x}_1 = 39.3$ years | $\bar{x}_2 = 35.4$ years |
| $s_1 = 16.8$ years | $s_2 = 15.2$ years |
| $n_1 = 150$ | $n_2 = 175$ |

Conduct a hypothesis test to determine if the mean ages of the two populations are different. Use $\alpha = .05$.
**a.**   Formulate the null and alternative hypotheses.
**b.**   What is the rejection rule?
**c.**   What is the value of the test statistic?
**d.**   What is your conclusion?
**e.**   What is the *p*-value?

**15.**   Refer to Exercise 6 in which two independent random samples of business travelers rated the Miami and Los Angeles airports. The data for this problem are in the data set Airport. Is the population mean rating for the Los Angeles airport greater than the population mean rating for the Miami airport? Support your conclusion with a statistical test using a .05 level of significance.

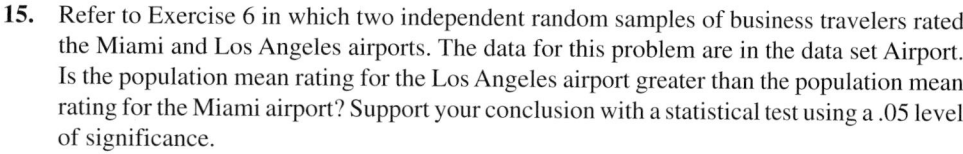

**16.**   The Greystone Department Store study in Section 10.1 supplied the following data on customer ages from independent random samples taken at two store locations (see Table 10.2).

| Inner-City Store | Suburban Store |
|------------------|----------------|
| $n_1 = 36$ | $n_2 = 49$ |
| $\bar{x}_1 = 40$ years | $\bar{x}_2 = 35$ years |
| $s_1 = 9$ years | $s_2 = 10$ years |

For $\alpha = .05$, test $H_0: \mu_1 - \mu_2 = 0$ against the alternative $H_a: \mu_1 - \mu_2 \neq 0$. What is your conclusion about the mean ages of the populations of customers at the two stores?

17. A firm is studying the delivery times of two raw material suppliers. The firm is basically satisfied with supplier A and is prepared to stay with that supplier if the mean delivery time is the same as or less than that of supplier B. However, if the firm finds that the mean delivery time of supplier B is less than that of supplier A, it will begin making raw material purchases from supplier B.
    a. What are the null and alternative hypotheses for this situation?
    b. Assume that independent samples show the following delivery time characteristics for the two suppliers.

| Supplier A | Supplier B |
|---|---|
| $n_1 = 50$ | $n_2 = 30$ |
| $\bar{x}_1 = 14$ days | $\bar{x}_2 = 12.5$ days |
| $s_1 = 3$ days | $s_2 = 2$ days |

With $\alpha = .05$, what is your conclusion for the hypotheses from part (a)? What action do you recommend in terms of supplier selection?

18. In a wage discrimination case involving male and female employees, independent samples of 44 male and 32 female employees with 5 years' experience or more provided the data shown in the data set Wages. The null hypothesis is that male employees have a mean hourly wage less than or equal to that of the female employees. Rejection of $H_0$ leads to the conclusion that male employees have a mean hourly wage exceeding that of the female employees. Test the hypothesis with $\alpha = .01$. Does wage discrimination appear to be present in this case?

19. Starting annual salaries for individuals entering the public accounting and financial planning professions were presented in *Fortune*, June 26, 1995. The starting salaries for a sample of 12 public accountants and a sample of 14 financial planners follow, with data in thousands of dollars.

| Public Accountant | Financial Planner |
|---|---|
| 30.6 | 31.6 |
| 31.2 | 26.6 |
| 28.9 | 25.5 |
| 35.2 | 25.0 |
| 25.1 | 25.9 |
| 33.2 | 32.9 |
| 31.3 | 26.9 |
| 35.3 | 25.8 |
| 31.0 | 27.5 |
| 30.1 | 29.6 |
| 29.9 | 23.9 |
| 24.4 | 26.9 |
|  | 24.4 |
|  | 25.5 |

    a. Using $\alpha = .05$, test for any difference between the population mean starting annual salaries for the two professions. What is your conclusion?
    b. What is the point estimate of the difference between the two population means? Which profession has the higher mean annual starting salary?

20. Arnold Palmer and Tiger Woods are two of the best golfers ever to play the game. The question was raised as to how these two golfers would have compared if both were playing at the top of their game. The following sample data show the results of 18-hole scores during a PGA tournament competition. Palmer's scores are from his 1960 season, while Wood's scores are from his 1999 season (*Golf Magazine*, February 2000).

| Palmer, 1960 | Woods, 1999 |
|---|---|
| $\bar{x}_1 = 69.95$ | $\bar{x}_2 = 69.56$ |
| $n_1 = 112$ | $n_2 = 84$ |

Use the sample results to test the hypothesis of no difference between the population mean 18-hole scores for the two golfers.

**a.**   Assuming a population standard deviation of 2.5 for both golfers, what is the value of the test statistic?

**b.**   What is the $p$-value?

**c.**   Using $\alpha = .01$, what is your conclusion?

21.   The mean time to locate flight information on Internet web sites of the major airline companies is generally 2 to 3 minutes (*USA Today,* September 11, 2000). Sample results representative of the times for Delta Airlines and Northwest Airlines are as follows:

| **Delta** | **Northwest** |
|---|---|
| $\bar{x}_1 = 2.5$ minutes | $\bar{x}_2 = 2.1$ minutes |
| $s_1 = .8$ minutes | $s_2 = 1.1$ minutes |
| $n_1 = 22$ | $n_2 = 20$ |

**a.**   Formulate the hypotheses if the purpose is to test for a significant difference between the mean times for the two airlines.

**b.**   Using $\alpha = .05$, what is the rejection rule?

**c.**   Compute the value of the test statistic.

**d.**   What is your conclusion?

**e.**   What is the $p$-value?

22.   Periodically, Merrill Lynch customers are asked to evaluate Merrill Lynch financial consultants and services (2000 Merrill Lynch Client Satisfaction Survey). Higher ratings on the client satisfaction survey indicate better service with 7 as the maximum service rating. Independent samples of service ratings for two financial consultants are summarized here. Consultant A has 10 years of experience while consultant B has 1 year of experience. Using $\alpha = .05$, test to see whether the consultant with the more experience has the higher population mean service rating.

| **Consultant A** | **Consultant B** |
|---|---|
| $\bar{x}_1 = 6.82$ | $\bar{x}_2 = 6.25$ |
| $s_1 = .64$ | $s_2 = .75$ |
| $n_1 = 16$ | $n_2 = 10$ |

**a.**   Formulate the null and alternative hypotheses.

**b.**   What is your hypothesis testing decision?

## 10.3   INFERENCES ABOUT THE DIFFERENCE BETWEEN THE MEANS OF TWO POPULATIONS: MATCHED SAMPLES

Suppose a manufacturing company is considering two methods by which employees can perform a production task. To maximize production output, the company wants to identify the method with the shortest mean completion time. Let $\mu_1$ denote the mean completion time for production method 1 and $\mu_2$ denote the mean completion time for production method 2. With no preliminary indication of the preferred production method, we begin by tentatively assuming that the two production methods have the same mean completion time. Thus, the null hypothesis is $H_0: \mu_1 - \mu_2 = 0$. If this hypothesis is rejected, we can conclude that the mean completion times differ. In this case, the method providing the shorter mean completion time would be recommended. The null and alternative hypotheses are written as follows.

$$H_0: \mu_1 - \mu_2 = 0$$
$$H_a: \mu_1 - \mu_2 \neq 0$$

In choosing the sampling procedure that will be used to collect production time data and test the hypotheses, we consider two alternative designs. One is based on **independent samples,** and the other is based on **matched samples.**

1. *Independent sample design:* A simple random sample of workers is selected and each worker in the sample uses method 1. A second independent simple random sample of workers is selected and each worker in this sample uses method 2. The test of the difference between means is based on the procedures in Section 10.2.
2. *Matched sample design:* One simple random sample of workers is selected. Each worker first uses one method and then uses the other method. The order of the two methods is assigned randomly to the workers, with some workers performing method 1 first and others performing method 2 first. Each worker provides a pair of completion time values, one value for method 1 and another value for method 2.

In the matched sample design the two production methods are tested under similar conditions (i.e., with the same workers); hence this design often leads to a smaller sampling error than the independent sample design. The primary reason is that in a matched sample design, variation between workers is eliminated as a source of sampling error.

Let us demonstrate the analysis of a matched sample design by using it to test the difference between the two production methods. A random sample of six workers is used. The data on completion times for the six workers are given in Table 10.7. Note that each worker provides a pair of completion time values, one for each production method. Also note that the last column contains the difference in completion times $d_i$ for each worker in the sample.

The key to the analysis of the matched sample data is to realize that we consider only the column of differences. We therefore have six values (.6, −.2, .5, .3, .0, and .6) that will be used to analyze the difference between the means of the two production methods.

Let $\mu_d$ = the mean of the *difference* values for the population of workers. With this notation, the null and alternative hypotheses are rewritten as follows.

$$H_0: \mu_d = 0$$
$$H_a: \mu_d \neq 0$$

If $H_0$ can be rejected, we can conclude that the mean completion times differ.

**TABLE 10.7**   TASK COMPLETION TIMES FOR A MATCHED SAMPLE DESIGN

| Worker | Completion Time for Method 1 (minutes) | Completion Time for Method 2 (minutes) | Difference in Completion Times ($d_i$) |
|---|---|---|---|
| 1 | 6.0 | 5.4 | .6 |
| 2 | 5.0 | 5.2 | −.2 |
| 3 | 7.0 | 6.5 | .5 |
| 4 | 6.2 | 5.9 | .3 |
| 5 | 6.0 | 6.0 | .0 |
| 6 | 6.4 | 5.8 | .6 |

**CD** file

**Matched**

The *d* notation is a reminder that the matched sample provides *difference* data. The sample mean and sample standard deviation for the six difference values in Table 10.7 follow.

Other than the use of the *d* notation, the formulas for the sample mean and sample standard deviation are the same as those used in Chapter 3.

$$\bar{d} = \frac{\Sigma d_i}{n} = \frac{1.8}{6} = .30$$

$$s_d = \sqrt{\frac{\Sigma(d_i - \bar{d})^2}{n - 1}} = \sqrt{\frac{.56}{5}} = .3347$$

In Chapter 9 we stated that if the population can be assumed to be normally distributed, the *t* distribution with $n - 1$ degrees of freedom can be used to test the null hypothesis about a population mean. Assuming that the population of difference data is normally distributed, the test statistic becomes

$$t = \frac{\bar{d} - \mu_d}{s_d/\sqrt{n}} \tag{10.13}$$

With $\alpha = .05$ and $n - 1 = 5$ degrees of freedom ($t_{.025} = 2.571$), the rejection rule for the two-tailed test is as follows:

Using test statistic: Reject $H_0$ if $t < -2.571$ or if $t > 2.571$

Using *p*-value: Reject $H_0$ if *p*-value $< .05$

With $\bar{d} = .30$, $s_d = .3347$, and $n = 6$, the value of the test statistic for the null hypothesis $H_0: \mu_d = 0$ is

$$t = \frac{\bar{d} - \mu_d}{s_d/\sqrt{n}} = \frac{.30 - 0}{.3347/\sqrt{6}} = 2.20$$

Because $t = 2.20$ is not in the rejection region, the sample data do not provide sufficient evidence to conclude that the mean completion times differ.

For 5 degrees of freedom, the *t* distribution table shows that $t = 2.20$ is between $t_{.025} = 2.571$ and $t_{.05} = 2.015$. Thus, the one-tailed area associated with $t = 2.20$ is between .025 and .05. For a two-tailed test, we know the *p*-value is between $2(.025) = .05$ and $2(.05) = .10$. Because this *p*-value is greater than $\alpha = .05$, $H_0$ is not rejected. In the next subsection we will show that using Excel provides the exact *p*-value $= .0795$.

We can obtain an interval estimate of the difference between the two population means by applying the single population methodology of Chapter 8 to the difference data. The calculation follows.

Once the difference data have been computed, the *t* distribution interval estimation procedure for matched samples is the same as for the one-population procedure described in Chapters 8 and 9.

$$\bar{d} \pm t_{\alpha/2} \frac{s_d}{\sqrt{n}}$$

$$0.3 \pm 2.571 \left( \frac{.3347}{\sqrt{6}} \right)$$

$$0.3 \pm .35$$

Thus, the 95% confidence interval for the difference between the mean completion times of the two production methods is $-.05$ minutes to .65 minutes. Note that because the confidence interval includes the value of zero, it confirms our hypothesis testing decision above; that is, the sample data do not provide sufficient evidence to reject $H_0$.

**FIGURE 10.12**   EXCEL WORKSHEET FOR THE MATCHED SAMPLES STUDY

| | A | B | C | D | E | F | G | H |
|---|---|---|---|---|---|---|---|---|
| 1 | Worker | Method 1 | Method 2 | | t-Test: Paired Two Sample for Means | | | |
| 2 | 1 | 6 | 5.4 | | | | | |
| 3 | 2 | 5 | 5.2 | | | Method 1 | Method 2 | |
| 4 | 3 | 7 | 6.5 | | Mean | 6.1 | 5.8 | |
| 5 | 4 | 6.2 | 5.9 | | Variance | 0.428 | 0.212 | |
| 6 | 5 | 6 | 6 | | Observations | 6 | 6 | |
| 7 | 6 | 6.4 | 5.8 | | Pearson Correlation | 0.8764 | | |
| 8 | | | | | Hypothesized Mean Difference | 0 | | |
| 9 | | | | | df | 5 | | |
| 10 | | | | | t Stat | 2.196 | | |
| 11 | | | | | P(T<=t) one-tail | 0.0398 | | |
| 12 | | | | | t Critical one-tail | 2.015 | | |
| 13 | | | | | P(T<=t) two-tail | 0.0795 | | |
| 14 | | | | | t Critical two-tail | 2.571 | | |
| 15 | | | | | | | | |

**FIGURE 10.13**   DIALOG BOX FOR EXCEL'S t-TEST: PAIRED TWO SAMPLE FOR MEANS

## Using Excel

Excel's t-Test: Paired Two Sample for Means tool can be used to conduct a hypothesis test about the difference between the population means for the two production methods. Refer to the Excel worksheet shown in Figure 10.12 and the dialog box in Figure 10.13 as we describe the tasks involved.

**Enter Data:**   Column A is used to identify each of the six workers who participated in the study. Column B contains the completion time data for each worker using method 1, and column C contains the completion time data for each worker using method 2.

**Apply Tools:**   The following steps describe how to use Excel's t-Test: Paired Two Sample for Means tool to conduct the hypothesis test about the difference between the means of the two production methods

> **Step 1.** Select the **Tools** pull-down menu
> **Step 2.** Choose the **Data Analysis** option
> **Step 3.** Choose **t-Test: Paired Two Sample for Means** from the list of Analysis Tools
> **Step 4.** When the t-Test: Paired Two Sample for Means dialog box appears (see Figure 10.13):
>> Enter B1:B7 in the **Variable 1 Range** box
>> Enter C1:C7 in the **Variable 2 Range** box
>> Enter 0 in the **Hypothesized Mean Difference** box
>> Select **Labels**
>> Enter .05 in the **Alpha** box
>> Select **Output Range**
>> Enter E1 in the **Output Range** box (to identify the upper left corner of the section of the worksheet where the output will appear)
>> Click **OK**

The value of the test statistic, $t = 2.196$, is shown in cell F10. The critical value 2.571, labeled t Critical two-tail, is shown in cell F14. Because $t = 2.196$ is not in the rejection region ($2.196 \leq 2.571$), the sample data do not provide sufficient evidence to reject $H_0$. Alternatively, we can use the $p$-value to make the hypothesis testing decision. The $p$-value for the test, labeled P(T <= t) two-tail, is shown in cell F13. Because the $p$-value, 0.0795, is greater than the level of significance, $\alpha = .05$, we cannot reject the null hypothesis that the mean completion times are equal.

The same procedure can also be used to conduct one-tailed hypothesis tests. The value of the test statistic $t$ is identical to the two-tailed case. The only changes required to make the hypothesis testing decision are that we need to use the critical value for a one-tailed test, labeled t Critical one-tail (see cell F12), and the $p$-value for a one-tailed test, labeled P(T <= t) one-tail (see cell F11).

## NOTES AND COMMENTS

1. In the example presented in this section, workers performed the production task with first one method and then the other method. This example illustrates a matched sample design in which each sampled element (worker) provides a pair of data values. It is also possible to use different but "similar" elements to provide the pair of data values. For example, a worker at one location could be matched with a similar worker at another location (similarity based on age, education, sex, experience, etc.). The pairs of workers would provide the difference data that could be used in the matched sample analysis.

2. Because a matched sample procedure for inferences about two population means generally provides better precision than the independent sample approach, it is the recommended design. However, in some applications the matching cannot be achieved, or perhaps the time and cost associated with matching are excessive. In such cases, the independent sample design should be used.

3. The example presented in this section had a sample size of six workers and thus was a small-sample case. The $t$ distribution was used in both the hypothesis test and interval estimation computations. If the sample size is large ($n \geq 30$), use of the $t$ distribution is unnecessary; in such cases, statistical inferences can be based on the $z$ values of the standard normal probability distribution.

## EXERCISES

## Methods

**23.** Consider the following hypothesis test.

$$H_0: \mu_d \leq 0$$
$$H_a: \mu_d > 0$$

The following data are from matched samples taken from two populations.

|  | Population | |
| :---: | :---: | :---: |
| Element | 1 | 2 |
| 1 | 21 | 20 |
| 2 | 28 | 26 |
| 3 | 18 | 18 |
| 4 | 20 | 20 |
| 5 | 26 | 24 |

    **a.** Compute the difference value for each element.
    **b.** Compute $\bar{d}$.
    **c.** Compute the standard deviation $s_d$.
    **d.** Test the hypothesis using $\alpha = .05$. What is your conclusion?

**24.** The following data are from matched samples taken from two populations.

|  | Population | |
| :---: | :---: | :---: |
| Element | 1 | 2 |
| 1 | 11 | 8 |
| 2 | 7 | 8 |
| 3 | 9 | 6 |
| 4 | 12 | 7 |
| 5 | 13 | 10 |
| 6 | 15 | 15 |
| 7 | 15 | 14 |

    **a.** Compute the difference value for each element.
    **b.** Compute $\bar{d}$.
    **c.** Compute the standard deviation $s_d$.
    **d.** What is the point estimate of the difference between the two population means?
    **e.** Provide a 95% confidence interval for the difference between the two population means.

## Applications

**25.** A market research firm used a sample of individuals to rate the purchase potential of a particular product before and after the individuals saw a new television commercial about the product. The purchase potential ratings were based on a 0 to 10 scale, with higher values indicating a higher purchase potential. The null hypothesis stated that the mean rating "after" would be less than or equal to the mean rating "before." Rejection of this hypothesis would show that the commercial improved the mean purchase potential rating. Use $\alpha = .05$ and the following data to test the hypothesis and comment on the value of the commercial.

|  | **Purchase Rating** |  |  | **Purchase Rating** |  |
| Individual | After | Before | Individual | After | Before |
| --- | --- | --- | --- | --- | --- |
| 1 | 6 | 5 | 5 | 3 | 5 |
| 2 | 6 | 4 | 6 | 9 | 8 |
| 3 | 7 | 7 | 7 | 7 | 5 |
| 4 | 4 | 3 | 8 | 6 | 6 |

**26.** A sample of 10 international telephone calls provided the Sprint and WorldCom calling rates per minute for calls from the United States (*World Traveler,* July 2000).

**Traveler**

| Country | Sprint | WorldCom |
| --- | --- | --- |
| Australia | .46 | .26 |
| Belgium | .69 | .40 |
| Brazil | .92 | .53 |
| Colombia | .55 | .53 |
| Denmark | .50 | .26 |
| France | .46 | .26 |
| Germany | .46 | .26 |
| Hong Kong | .92 | .40 |
| Japan | .69 | .40 |
| United Kingdom | .46 | .26 |

Provide a 95% confidence interval estimate of the difference between the two population means.

**27.** The cost of transportation from the airport to the downtown area depends on the method of transportation. One-way costs for taxi and shuttle bus transportation for a sample of 10 major cities follow. Provide a 95% confidence interval for the mean cost increase associated with taxi transportation.

| City | Taxi ($) | Shuttle Bus ($) | City | Taxi ($) | Shuttle Bus ($) |
| --- | --- | --- | --- | --- | --- |
| Atlanta | 15.00 | 7.00 | Minneapolis | 16.50 | 7.50 |
| Chicago | 22.00 | 12.50 | New Orleans | 18.00 | 7.00 |
| Denver | 11.00 | 5.00 | New York (LaGuardia) | 16.00 | 8.50 |
| Houston | 15.00 | 4.50 | Philadelphia | 20.00 | 8.00 |
| Los Angeles | 26.00 | 11.00 | Washington, D.C. | 10.00 | 5.00 |

**28.** Rental car gasoline prices per gallon were sampled at eight major airports. Data for Hertz and National car rental companies follow (*USA Today,* April 4, 2000).

| Airport | Hertz | National |
| --- | --- | --- |
| Boston Logan | 1.55 | 1.56 |
| Chicago O'Hare | 1.62 | 1.59 |
| Los Angeles | 1.72 | 1.78 |
| Miami | 1.65 | 1.49 |
| New York (JFK) | 1.72 | 1.51 |
| New York (LaGuardia) | 1.67 | 1.50 |
| Orange County, CA | 1.68 | 1.77 |
| Washington (Dulles) | 1.52 | 1.41 |

Use $\alpha = .05$ to test the hypothesis of no difference between the population mean prices per gallon for the two companies.

**29.** A survey was made of Book-of-the-Month-Club members to ascertain whether members spend more time watching television than they do reading. Assume a sample of 15 respondents provided the following data on weekly hours of television watching and weekly hours of reading. Using a .05 level of significance, can you conclude that Book-of-the-Month-Club members spend more hours per week watching television than reading?

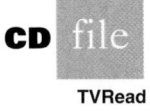

**CD** file

**TVRead**

| Respondent | Television | Reading | Respondent | Television | Reading |
|------------|-----------|---------|------------|-----------|---------|
| 1 | 10 | 6 | 9 | 4 | 7 |
| 2 | 14 | 16 | 10 | 8 | 8 |
| 3 | 16 | 8 | 11 | 16 | 5 |
| 4 | 18 | 10 | 12 | 5 | 10 |
| 5 | 15 | 10 | 13 | 8 | 3 |
| 6 | 14 | 8 | 14 | 19 | 10 |
| 7 | 10 | 14 | 15 | 11 | 6 |
| 8 | 12 | 14 | | | |

**30.** A manufacturer produces both a deluxe and a standard model of an automatic sander designed for home use. Selling prices obtained from a sample of retail outlets follow.

| | Model Price ($) | | | Model Price ($) | |
|--------------|--------|----------|--------------|--------|----------|
| Retail Outlet | Deluxe | Standard | Retail Outlet | Deluxe | Standard |
| 1 | 39 | 27 | 5 | 40 | 30 |
| 2 | 39 | 28 | 6 | 39 | 34 |
| 3 | 45 | 35 | 7 | 35 | 29 |
| 4 | 38 | 30 | | | |

**a.** The manufacturer's suggested retail prices for the two models show a $10 price differential. Using a .05 level of significance, test that the mean difference between the prices of the two models is $10.

**b.** What is the 95% confidence interval for the difference between the mean prices of the two models?

**31.** The 1997 price/earnings ratios and estimated 1998 price/earnings ratios for a sample of 12 stocks are shown here (*Kiplinger's Personal Finance Magazine*, November 1997).

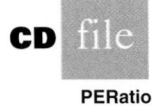

**CD** file

**PERatio**

| Stock | 1997 P/E Ratio | Est. 1998 P/E Ratio |
|-------|---------------|---------------------|
| Coca-Cola | 40 | 32 |
| Walt Disney | 33 | 23 |
| Du Pont | 24 | 16 |
| Eastman Kodak | 21 | 13 |
| General Electric | 30 | 23 |
| General Mills | 25 | 19 |
| IBM | 19 | 14 |
| Merck | 29 | 21 |
| McDonald's | 20 | 17 |
| Motorola | 35 | 20 |
| Philip Morris | 17 | 13 |
| Xerox | 20 | 17 |

**a.** Use $\alpha = .05$ and test for any change in the population mean price/earnings ratios for the two-year period.

**b.** Provide a 95% confidence interval for the change in the population mean price/earnings ratios for the two-year period. What is your conclusion?

## 10.4   INFERENCES ABOUT THE DIFFERENCE BETWEEN THE PROPORTIONS OF TWO POPULATIONS

Let us begin with an example involving a tax preparation firm that is interested in comparing the quality of work at two of its regional offices. By randomly selecting samples of tax returns prepared at each office and having the sample returns verified for accuracy, the firm will be able to estimate the proportion of erroneous returns prepared at each office. Of particular interest is the difference between these proportions. Let

The methods of this section are appropriate for independent random samples from two populations.

$$p_1 = \text{proportion of erroneous returns for population 1 (office 1)}$$
$$p_2 = \text{proportion of erroneous returns for population 2 (office 2)}$$
$$\bar{p}_1 = \text{sample proportion for a simple random sample from population 1}$$
$$\bar{p}_2 = \text{sample proportion for a simple random sample from population 2}$$

The difference between the two population proportions is $p_1 - p_2$. The point estimator of $p_1 - p_2$ is the difference between the two sample proportions.

---

**Point Estimator of the Difference Between the Proportions of Two Populations**

$$\bar{p}_1 - \bar{p}_2 \qquad\qquad \textbf{(10.14)}$$

---

## Sampling Distribution of $\bar{p}_1 - \bar{p}_2$

In the study of the difference between two population proportions, $\bar{p}_1 - \bar{p}_2$ is the point estimator of interest. As we have seen in several preceding cases, the sampling distribution of a point estimator provides the basis for developing interval estimates and in testing hypotheses about parameters of interest. The properties of the sampling distribution of $\bar{p}_1 - \bar{p}_2$ follow.

---

**Sampling Distribution of $\bar{p}_1 - \bar{p}_2$**

$$\text{Expected Value: } E(\bar{p}_1 - \bar{p}_2) = p_1 - p_2 \qquad \textbf{(10.15)}$$

The standard deviation of the sampling distribution of $\bar{p}_1 - \bar{p}_2$ is also referred to as the standard error of the point estimator $\bar{p}_1 - \bar{p}_2$.

$$\text{Standard Deviation: } \sigma_{\bar{p}_1 - \bar{p}_2} = \sqrt{\frac{p_1(1 - p_1)}{n_1} + \frac{p_2(1 - p_2)}{n_2}} \qquad \textbf{(10.16)}$$

where

$$n_1 = \text{sample size for the simple random sample from population 1}$$
$$n_2 = \text{sample size for the simple random sample from population 2}$$

Distribution form: If the sample sizes are large—i.e., $n_1 p_1$, $n_1(1 - p_1)$, $n_2 p_2$, and $n_2(1 - p_2)$ are all greater than or equal to 5—the sampling distribution of $\bar{p}_1 - \bar{p}_2$ can be approximated by a normal probability distribution.

---

Figure 10.14 shows the sampling distribution of $\bar{p}_1 - \bar{p}_2$.

**FIGURE 10.14** SAMPLING DISTRIBUTION OF $\bar{p}_1 - \bar{p}_2$

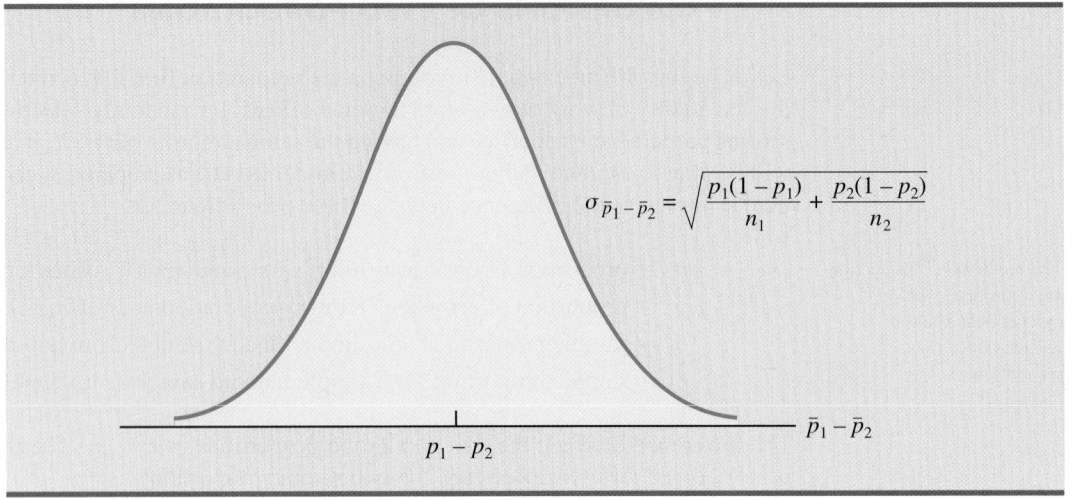

$$\sigma_{\bar{p}_1-\bar{p}_2} = \sqrt{\frac{p_1(1-p_1)}{n_1} + \frac{p_2(1-p_2)}{n_2}}$$

$\bar{p}_1 - \bar{p}_2$

$p_1 - p_2$

## Interval Estimation of $p_1 - p_2$

Suppose that independent simple random samples of tax returns from the two offices provide the following information.

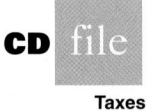

**Taxes**

| Office 1 | Office 2 |
|---|---|
| $n_1 = 250$ | $n_2 = 300$ |
| Number of returns with errors $= 35$ | Number of returns with errors $= 27$ |

The sample proportions for the two offices are as follows:

$$\bar{p}_1 = \frac{35}{250} = .14$$

$$\bar{p}_2 = \frac{27}{300} = .09$$

The point estimate of the difference between the proportions of erroneous tax returns for the two populations is $\bar{p}_1 - \bar{p}_2 = .14 - .09 = .05$. Thus, we estimate that office 1 has a .05 greater error rate than office 2.

Before developing a confidence interval for the difference between population proportions, we must estimate $\sigma_{\bar{p}_1-\bar{p}_2}$. Note that equation (10.16) cannot be used directly because $p_1$ and $p_2$ will not be known in practice. The approach taken is to substitute $\bar{p}_1$ as an estimator of $p_1$ and $\bar{p}_2$ as an estimator of $p_2$ in equation (10.16). Doing so provides the point estimator of $\sigma_{\bar{p}_1-\bar{p}_2}$ given by equation (10.17).

$s_{\bar{p}_1-\bar{p}_2}$ is the point estimator of $\sigma_{\bar{p}_1-\bar{p}_2}$, the standard error of the point estimator $\bar{p}_1 - \bar{p}_2$.

**Point Estimator of $\sigma_{\bar{p}_1-\bar{p}_2}$**

$$s_{\bar{p}_1-\bar{p}_2} = \sqrt{\frac{\bar{p}_1(1-\bar{p}_1)}{n_1} + \frac{\bar{p}_2(1-\bar{p}_2)}{n_2}} \qquad \textbf{(10.17)}$$

Using equation (10.17), the following expression provides an interval estimate of the difference between the proportions of the two populations in the large-sample case.

The use of $z_{\alpha/2}$ in equation (10.18) is due to the fact that we can assume a normal sampling distribution for $\bar{p}_1 - \bar{p}_2$ in the large-sample case.

> **Interval Estimate of the Difference Between the Proportions of Two Populations: Large-Sample Case with $n_1p_1, n_1(1 - p_1), n_2p_2,$ and $n_2(1 - p_2) \geq 5$**
>
> $$\bar{p}_1 - \bar{p}_2 \pm z_{\alpha/2}s_{\bar{p}_1-\bar{p}_2} \qquad \textbf{(10.18)}$$
>
> where $1 - \alpha$ is the confidence coefficient.

Let us now use equation (10.18) to develop an interval estimate of the difference between the proportions for the two tax preparation offices in our example. Using equation (10.17), we find

$$s_{\bar{p}_1-\bar{p}_2} = \sqrt{\frac{.14(.86)}{250} + \frac{.09(.91)}{300}} = .0275$$

With a 90% confidence interval, we have $z_{\alpha/2} = z_{.05} = 1.645$, and a margin of error of $1.645(.0275) = .0452$. Rounding the margin of error to three decimal places, the interval estimate is

$$(.14 - .09) \pm 1.645(.0275) = .05 \pm .045$$

Hence, the 90% confidence interval for the difference in error rates at the two offices is .005 to .095.

## Using Excel to Develop an Interval Estimate of $p_1 - p_2$

Excel can be used to develop an interval estimate of the difference between the proportions of erroneous tax returns at the two offices of the tax preparation firm. Refer to Figure 10.15 as we describe the tasks involved. The formula worksheet is in the background; the value worksheet is in the foreground.

**Enter Data:**   Columns A and B contain Yes or No labels that indicate which of the tax returns from each office have an error.

**Enter Functions and Formulas:**   The descriptive statistics needed to compute the interval estimate are provided in cells E5:F8. Note that Excel's COUNTA function is used in cells E5 and F5 to count the number of observations for each of the samples. The value worksheet indicates 250 returns in the sample from office 1 and 300 returns in the sample from office 2. In cells E6 and F6, we have typed Yes to indicate the response of interest. Excel's COUNTIF function is used in cells E7 and F7 to count the number of erroneous returns from each office. Formulas were then entered into cells E8 and F8 to compute the sample proportions. The confidence coefficient was entered into cell E10 (.9) and the corresponding level of significance was computed in cell E11. In cell E12 we used the NORMSINV function to compute the z value needed to develop the interval estimate.

Using the two sample proportions and sample sizes, a point estimate of $\sigma_{\bar{p}_1-\bar{p}_2}$, the standard error of the point estimator $\bar{p}_1 - \bar{p}_2$, was computed by entering the following formula into cell E14

The formula in cell E14 provides a point estimate of $\sigma_{\bar{p}_1-\bar{p}_2}$, the standard error of the point estimator $\bar{p}_1 - \bar{p}_2$.

$$=\text{SQRT}(\text{E8}*(1-\text{E8})/\text{E5}+\text{F8}*(1-\text{F8})/\text{F5})$$

This cell formula is the Excel equivalent of equation (10.17). The margin of error was computed in cell E15 by multiplying the z value times the standard error.

The point estimate of the difference in the two population proportions was computed by entering the formula =E8-F8 into cell E17; the result, shown in the value worksheet, is

**FIGURE 10.15**  EXCEL WORKSHEET FOR INTERVAL ESTIMATE OF DIFFERENCES
IN POPULATION PROPORTIONS

| | A | B | C | D | E | F | G |
|---|---|---|---|---|---|---|---|
| 1 | Return? | | | Interval Estimate: Difference in Population Proportions | | | |
| 2 | Office 1 | Office 2 | | Using the Standard Normal Distribution (z) | | | |
| 3 | No | Yes | | | | | |
| 4 | No | No | | | Office 1 | Office 2 | |
| 5 | No | No | | Sample Size | =COUNTA(A3:A252) | =COUNTA(B3:B302) | |
| 6 | Yes | No | | Response of Interest | Yes | Yes | |
| 7 | No | No | | Count for Response | =COUNTIF(A3:A252,E6) | =COUNTIF(B3:B302,F6) | |
| 8 | No | No | | Sample Proportion | =E7/E5 | =F7/F5 | |
| 9 | No | No | | | | | |
| 10 | Yes | No | | Confidence Coefficient | 0.9 | | |
| 11 | No | No | | Level of Significance (alpha) | =1-E10 | | |
| 12 | No | No | | z Value | =NORMSINV(1-E11/2) | | |
| 13 | No | No | | | | | |
| 14 | No | Yes | | Standard Error | =SQRT(E8*(1-E8)/E5+F8*(1-F8)/F5) | | |
| 15 | No | Yes | | Margin of Error | =E12*E14 | | |
| 16 | No | No | | | | | |
| 17 | No | No | | Point Estimate of Difference | =E8-F8 | | |
| 18 | Yes | No | | Lower Limit | =E17-E15 | | |
| 19 | No | No | | Upper Limit | =E17+E15 | | |
| 250 | Yes | No | | | | | |
| 251 | No | No | | | | | |
| 252 | No | No | | | | | |
| 301 | | No | | | | | |
| 302 | | No | | | | | |
| 303 | | | | | | | |

Note: Rows 20–249 and
253–300 are hidden.

| | A | B | C | D | E | F | G | H | I |
|---|---|---|---|---|---|---|---|---|---|
| 1 | Erroneous Return? | | | Interval Estimate: Difference in Population Proportions | | | | | |
| 2 | Office 1 | Office 2 | | Using the Standard Normal Distribution (z) | | | | | |
| 3 | No | Yes | | | | | | | |
| 4 | No | No | | | | Office 1 | Office | | |
| 5 | No | No | | Sample Size | | 250 | 300 | | |
| 6 | Yes | No | | Response of Interest | | Yes | Yes | | |
| 7 | No | No | | Count for Response | | 35 | 27 | | |
| 8 | No | No | | Sample Proportion | | 0.14 | 0.09 | | |
| 9 | No | No | | | | | | | |
| 10 | Yes | No | | Confidence Coefficient | | 0.9 | | | |
| 11 | No | No | | Level of Significance (alpha) | | 0.1 | | | |
| 12 | No | No | | z Value | | 1.645 | | | |
| 13 | No | No | | | | | | | |
| 14 | No | Yes | | Standard Error | | 0.0275 | | | |
| 15 | No | Yes | | Margin of Error | | 0.0452 | | | |
| 16 | No | No | | | | | | | |
| 17 | No | No | | Point Estimate of Difference | | 0.05 | | | |
| 18 | Yes | No | | Lower Limit | | 0.0048 | | | |
| 19 | No | No | | Upper Limit | | 0.0952 | | | |
| 250 | Yes | No | | | | | | | |
| 251 | No | No | | | | | | | |
| 252 | No | No | | | | | | | |
| 301 | | No | | | | | | | |
| 302 | | No | | | | | | | |
| 303 | | | | | | | | | |

0.05. To compute the lower limit of the confidence interval, the formula =E17-E15 was entered into cell E18. The upper limit of the confidence interval was computed by entering the formula =E17+E15 into cell E19. The 90% confidence interval estimate of the difference in the two population proportions is .0048 to .0952.

## Hypotheses Tests About $p_1 - p_2$

As an example of a hypothesis test concerning the difference between two population proportions, let us reconsider the example concerning the error rates at two offices of the tax preparation firm. Suppose the firm had simply been interested in whether the two offices experienced a significant difference in error rates. The appropriate null and alternative hypotheses are

$$H_0: p_1 - p_2 = 0$$
$$H_a: p_1 - p_2 \neq 0$$

Figure 10.16 shows the sampling distribution of $\bar{p}_1 - \bar{p}_2$. If $H_0$ is true, there is no difference between the population proportions and $p_1 - p_2 = 0$. In the large-sample case, the sampling distribution is approximately normal and the test statistic for the difference between two population proportions is

$$z = \frac{(\bar{p}_1 - \bar{p}_2) - (p_1 - p_2)}{\sigma_{\bar{p}_1 - \bar{p}_2}} \qquad (10.19)$$

Using $\alpha = .10$ and $z_{\alpha/2} = z_{.05} = 1.645$, the rejection rule is as follows:

Using test statistic: Reject $H_0$ if $z < -1.645$ or if $z > 1.645$
Using p-value: Reject $H_0$ if p-value $< .10$

The computation of $z$ in equation (10.19) requires a value for $\sigma_{\bar{p}_1 - \bar{p}_2}$, the standard error of the point estimator $\bar{p}_1 - \bar{p}_2$. As in the case of interval estimation, it will be necessary to estimate $\sigma_{\bar{p}_1 - \bar{p}_2}$ because $p_1$ and $p_2$ will not be known in practice. But for the special case of a null hypothesis stating no difference in the proportions ($H_0: p_1 = p_2 = 0$), we do not use equation (10.17). This case has only one population proportion; that is, $p_1 = p_2 = p$— and we can combine or *pool* the two sample proportions to provide one estimate of $p$ given by $\bar{p}$.

$$\bar{p} = \frac{n_1 \bar{p}_1 + n_2 \bar{p}_2}{n_1 + n_2} \qquad (10.20)$$

With $\bar{p}$ used in place of both $\bar{p}_1$ and $\bar{p}_2$, equation (10.17) is revised to

$$s_{\bar{p}_1 - \bar{p}_2} = \sqrt{\bar{p}(1 - \bar{p})\left(\frac{1}{n_1} + \frac{1}{n_2}\right)} \qquad (10.21)$$

**FIGURE 10.16**   SAMPLING DISTRIBUTION OF $\bar{p}_1 - \bar{p}_2$

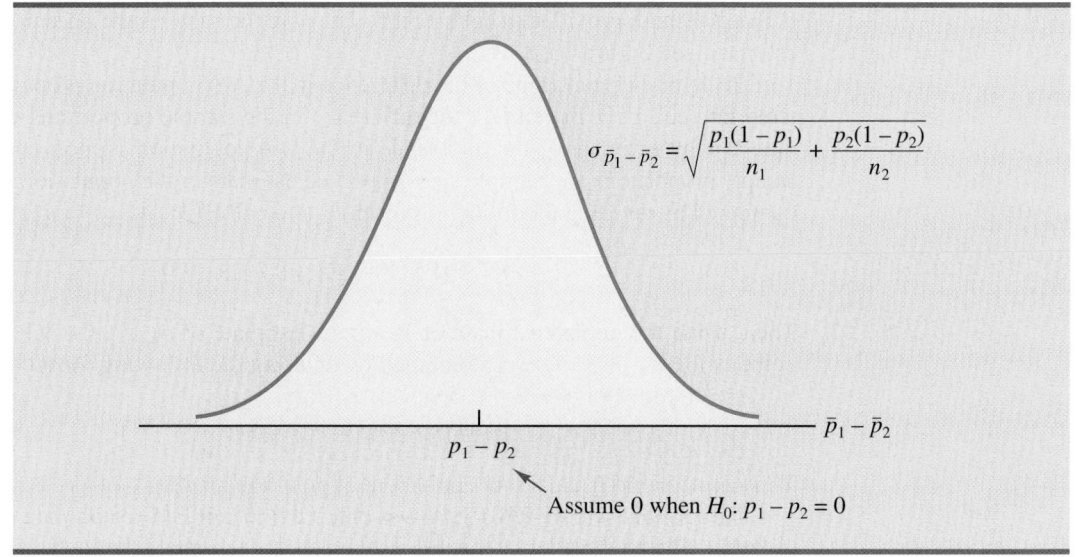

Using equations (10.20) and (10.21), we can now proceed with a hypothesis test for the tax preparation firm example.

$$\bar{p} = \frac{250(.14) + 300(.09)}{550} = \frac{62}{550} = .113$$

$$s_{\bar{p}_1 - \bar{p}_2} = \sqrt{(.113)(.887)\left(\frac{1}{250} + \frac{1}{300}\right)} = .0271$$

The value of the test statistic is

$$z = \frac{(\bar{p}_1 - \bar{p}_2) - (p_1 - p_2)}{s_{\bar{p}_1 - \bar{p}_2}} = \frac{(.14 - .09) - 0}{.0271} = 1.85$$

Because $1.85 > 1.645$, at the .10 level of significance the null hypothesis is rejected. The sample evidence indicates a difference between the error proportions at the two offices.

The $p$-value approach can also be used to make the hypothesis testing decision for the tax preparation firm example. The table for the standard normal probability distribution shows that the area in the upper tail of the standard normal probability distribution for $z = 1.85$ is $1 - .9678 = .0322$. Because it is a two-tailed hypothesis test, the $p$-value is found by doubling the area in the tail. Thus, the $p$-value is $2(.0322) = .0644$. With $.0644 < \alpha = .10$, the null hypothesis is rejected.

As we saw with hypothesis tests about differences between two population means, one-tailed tests can also be developed for the difference between two population proportions. The one-tailed rejection regions are established in a manner similar to the one-tailed hypothesis testing procedures for a single population proportion.

## Using Excel to Conduct a Hypothesis Test About $p_1 - p_2$

Excel can be used to conduct a hypothesis test about the difference between the proportions of erroneous tax returns at the two offices of the tax preparation firm. Refer to Figure 10.17 as we describe the tasks involved. The formula worksheet is in the background; the value worksheet is in the foreground.

**Enter Data:** Columns A and B contain Yes or No labels that indicate which of the tax returns from each office have errors.

**Enter Functions and Formulas:** The descriptive statistics needed to perform the hypothesis test are provided in cells E5:F8. They are the same as the ones used for an interval estimate (see Figure 10.15).

The hypothesized value of the difference in the two population proportions (0) was entered into cell E10. In cell E11 the difference in the sample proportions was used to compute a point estimate of the difference in the two population proportions. Using the two sample proportions and sample sizes, a pooled estimate of the population proportion $p$ was computed by entering the following formula into cell E13:

$$=(E5*E8+F5*F8)/(E5+F5)$$

Then, using the pooled estimate of $p$, a point estimate of $\sigma_{\bar{p}_1 - \bar{p}_2}$, the standard error of the point estimator $\bar{p}_1 - \bar{p}_2$, was computed by entering the following formula into cell E14:

$$=SQRT(E13*(1-E13)*(1/E5+1/F5)$$

This cell formula is the Excel equivalent of equation (10.21)

The formula $=(E11-E10)/E14$ was entered into cell E15 to compute the test statistic $z$ (1.8462). The NORMSDIST function is then used to compute the $p$-value (Lower Tail) and

**FIGURE 10.17**    EXCEL WORKSHEET FOR HYPOTHESIS TEST OF DIFFERENCE
IN POPULATION PROPORTIONS

Note: Rows 20–249 and
253–300 are hidden.

The $p$-value here (.0649)
differs from the one we
found using the normal
tables (.0644) due to
rounding.

the $p$-value (Upper Tail) in cells E17 and E18. The $p$-value (Two Tail) is computed in cell
E19 as twice the minimum of the two one-tailed $p$-values. The value worksheet shows that
$p$-value (Two Tail) = .0649. Because the $p$-value = .0649 is less than the level of significance, $\alpha = .10$, we have sufficient evidence to reject the null hypothesis and conclude that
the population proportions are not equal.

This worksheet can be used as a template for hypothesis testing problems involving a
difference in population proportions. The new data can be entered into columns A and B.
The ranges for the new data and the response of interest need to be revised in cells E5:F7,
and the appropriate hypothesized value needs to be entered into cell E10. The remainder of
the worksheet will then be updated as needed to conduct the hypothesis test.

To use this worksheet for exercises in which the sample statistics are given, just type in
the given values for cells E5:F5 and E7:F8. The appropriate hypothesized value can then
be entered into cell E10. The remainder of the worksheet will then be updated as needed to
conduct the hypothesis test.

## EXERCISES

### Methods

**32.**    Consider the following results for two independent samples taken from two populations.

| Sample 1 | Sample 2 |
|---|---|
| $n_1 = 400$ | $n_2 = 300$ |
| $\bar{p}_1 = .48$ | $\bar{p}_2 = .36$ |

    **a.**    What is the point estimate of the difference between the two population proportions?

    **b.**    Develop a 90% confidence interval for the difference between the two population
proportions.

    c.  Develop a 95% confidence interval for the difference between the two population proportions.

**33.** Consider the following hypothesis test:

$$H_0: p_1 - p_2 \leq 0$$
$$H_a: p_1 - p_2 > 0$$

The following results are for two independent samples taken from the two populations.

| Sample 1 | Sample 2 |
|---|---|
| $n_1 = 200$ | $n_2 = 300$ |
| $\bar{p}_1 = .22$ | $\bar{p}_2 = .16$ |

    a.  Using $\alpha = .05$, what is your hypothesis testing conclusion?
    b.  What is the $p$-value?

## Applications

**34.** A *Business Week*/Harris survey asked senior executives at large corporations their opinions about the economic outlook for the future (*Business Week,* June 16, 1997). One question was "Do you think that there will be an increase in the number of full-time employees at your company over the next 12 months?" In May 1997, 220 of 400 executives answered yes, while in December 1996, 192 of 400 executives had answered yes. Provide a 95% confidence interval estimate for the difference between the proportions at the two points in time. What is your interpretation of the interval estimate?

**35.** A CNN/*USA Today* poll evaluated the popularity of major league baseball after the Mark McGwire and Sammy Sosa record-setting home-run chase during the 1998 season. A sample of 1082 found 682 people responding yes to the question "Are you a fan of major league baseball?" (*USA Today,* September 17, 1998). During the baseball strike of April 1995, a sample of 1008 found only 413 people responding yes to the same question.
    a.  Use the sample proportions to estimate the fan support for major league baseball in 1998 and in 1995. What is the point estimate of the increase in major league baseball fan support from the strike in 1995 to the McGwire/Sosa home-run chase of 1998?
    b.  Develop a 95% confidence interval estimate of the increase in fan support.

**36.** The women and family issues committee of the American Institute of Certified Public Accountants (AICPA) mailed surveys asking about family-friendly policies and women's upward mobility to 5300 firms of all sizes (excluding sole practitioners). Of the 1710 responses, 57% were from firms with five or fewer AICPA members, 26% were from firms with six to 10 members, 9% were from firms with 11 to 20 members, and 8% were from firms with more than 20 members. For the firms with fewer than five AICPA members, 58% of the hires within the previous three years were women and 42% were men. In contrast, firms with more than 20 AICPA members hired 43% women and 57% men (*Journal of Accountancy,* October 1994). Develop a 95% confidence interval estimate of the difference between the proportion of women hired by firms with fewer than five AICPA members and the proportion of women hired by firms with more than 20 AICPA members.

**37.** *Fortune* enlisted Yankelovich Partners to poll 600 adults on their ideas about marriage, divorce, and the contribution of the corporate wife to her executive husband (*Fortune,* February 2, 1998). In response to the statement, "In a divorce in a long-term marriage where the husband works outside the home and the wife is not employed for pay, the wife should be entitled to half the assets accumulated during the marriage," 279 of 300 women agreed and 255 of 300 men agreed.
    a.  What are the sample proportions for the two populations, women and men?
    b.  Test the hypothesis $H_0: p_1 - p_2 = 0$, using $\alpha = .05$. What is your conclusion?
    c.  Provide a 95% confidence interval for the difference between the population proportions.

**38.** A sample of 1545 men and an independent sample of 1691 women were used to compare the amount of housework done by women and men in dual-earner marriages. The study showed that 67.5% of the men felt the division of housework was fair and 60.8% of the women felt the division of housework was fair (*American Journal of Sociology,* September 1994). Is the proportion of men who felt the division of housework was fair greater than the proportion of women who felt the division of housework was fair? Support your conclusion with a statistical test using a .05 level of significance.

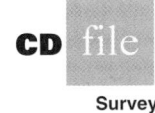

**Survey**

**39.** A survey firm conducts door-to-door surveys on a variety of issues. Some individuals co-operate with the interviewer and complete the interview questionnaire, and others do not. A recent survey of 200 men and 300 women resulted in the data set Survey. A response of Yes means that the resopndent completed the questionnaire.

    **a.** Using $\alpha = .05$, test the hypothesis that the response rate is the same for both men and women.

    **b.** Compute a 95% confidence interval for the difference between the proportions of men and women who completed the questionnaire.

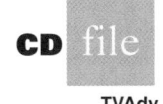

**TVAdv**

**40.** In a test of the quality of two television commercials, each commercial was shown in a separate test area six times over a 1-week period. The following week a telephone survey was conducted to identify individuals who had seen the commercials. The individuals who had seen the commercials were asked to state the primary message in the commercials. The results obtained for 150 individuals who saw commercial A and 200 individuals who saw commercial B are in the data set TVAdv. A response of Yes indicates that the individual recalled the primary message.

    **a.** Using $\alpha = .05$, test the hypothesis of no difference in the recall proportions for the two commercials.

    **b.** Compute a 95% confidence interval for the difference between the recall proportions for the two populations.

**41.** The stock market declined in early 2000 with many stocks dropping below their 1997 highs. In fact, 81.5% of New York Stock Exchange (NYSE) stocks and 72.4% of NASDAQ stocks were trading below their 1997 highs (*Barron's,* May 22, 2000). If the data were based on 232 NYSE stocks and 210 NASDAQ stocks, test the hypothesis $H_0: p_1 - p_2 = 0$ with $\alpha = .05$. What is the *p*-value? What is your conclusion?

**42.** *Yahoo! Internet Life* sponsored surveys in several metropolitan areas to estimate the proportion of adults using the Internet at work (*USA Today,* May 7, 2000). Results showed 40% of Washington, D.C., adults use the Internet at work, while 32% of San Francisco adults use the Internet at work. If the sample sizes are 240 and 250 respectively, do the sample results indicate that the population proportion of adults using the Internet at work in Washington, D.C., is greater than the population proportion in San Francisco? What is the *p*-value? Using $\alpha = .05$, what is your conclusion?

## SUMMARY

In this chapter we discussed procedures for developing interval estimates and conducting hypothesis tests involving two or more population means. First, we showed how to make inferences about the difference between the means of two populations when independent simple random samples are selected. We considered both the large- and small-sample cases. The *z* values from the standard normal probability distribution are used for inferences about the difference between two population means when the sample sizes are large. In the small-sample case, if the populations are normally distributed with assumed equal variances, the *t* distribution is used for inferences.

    Inferences about the difference between the means of two populations were then discussed for the matched sample design. In the matched sample design each element provides a pair of data values, one from each population. The difference between the paired data values is then used in the statistical analysis. The matched sample design is generally preferred to the independent sample design because the matched sample procedure often reduces the sampling error and improves the precision of the estimate.

Finally, interval estimation and hypothesis testing about the difference between two population proportions were discussed. Statistical procedures for analyzing the difference between proportions for two populations are similar to the procedures for analyzing the difference between two population means.

We showed how Excel can be used to develop the interval estimates and conduct the hypothesis tests discussed in the chapter. Many of the worksheets can be used as templates to solve problems encountered in practice as well as the exercises and case problems found in the text.

## GLOSSARY

**Independent samples**   Samples selected from two populations in such a way that the elements making up one sample are chosen independently of the elements making up the other sample.

**Pooled variance**   An estimate of the variance based on the combination of two sample variances. The pooled variance estimate is appropriate whenever the variances of two populations are assumed equal.

**Matched samples**   Samples in which each data value of one sample is matched with a corresponding data value of the other sample.

## KEY FORMULAS

**Point Estimator of the Difference Between the Means of Two Populations**

$$\bar{x}_1 - \bar{x}_2 \tag{10.1}$$

**Expected Value of $\bar{x}_1 - \bar{x}_2$**

$$E(\bar{x}_1 - \bar{x}_2) = \mu_1 - \mu_2 \tag{10.2}$$

**Standard Deviation of $\bar{x}_1 - \bar{x}_2$ (Independent Samples)**

$$\sigma_{\bar{x}_1 - \bar{x}_2} = \sqrt{\frac{\sigma_1^2}{n_1} + \frac{\sigma_2^2}{n_2}} \tag{10.3}$$

**Interval Estimate of the Difference Between the Means of Two Populations: Large-Sample Case ($n_1 \geq 30$ and $n_2 \geq 30$) with $\sigma_1$ and $\sigma_2$ Assumed Known**

$$\bar{x}_1 - \bar{x}_2 \pm z_{\alpha/2}\sigma_{\bar{x}_1 - \bar{x}_2} \tag{10.4}$$

**Point Estimator of $\sigma_{\bar{x}_1 - \bar{x}_2}$**

$$s_{\bar{x}_1 - \bar{x}_2} = \sqrt{\frac{s_1^2}{n_1} + \frac{s_2^2}{n_2}} \tag{10.5}$$

**Interval Estimate of the Difference Between the Means of Two Populations: Large-Sample Case ($n_1 \geq 30$ and $n_2 \geq 30$) with $\sigma_1$ and $\sigma_2$ Estimated by $s_1$ and $s_2$**

$$\bar{x}_1 - \bar{x}_2 \pm z_{\alpha/2}s_{\bar{x}_1 - \bar{x}_2} \tag{10.6}$$

**Standard Deviation of $\bar{x}_1 - \bar{x}_2$ When $\sigma_1^2 = \sigma_2^2 = \sigma^2$**

$$\sigma_{\bar{x}_1-\bar{x}_2} = \sqrt{\frac{\sigma^2}{n_1} + \frac{\sigma^2}{n_2}} = \sqrt{\sigma^2\left(\frac{1}{n_1} + \frac{1}{n_2}\right)} \tag{10.7}$$

**Pooled Variance Estimator of $\sigma^2$**

$$s^2 = \frac{(n_1 - 1)s_1^2 + (n_2 - 1)s_2^2}{n_1 + n_2 - 2} \tag{10.8}$$

**Point Estimator of $\sigma_{\bar{x}_1-\bar{x}_2}$ when $\sigma_1^2 = \sigma_2^2 = \sigma^2$**

$$s_{\bar{x}_1-\bar{x}_2} = \sqrt{s^2\left(\frac{1}{n_1} + \frac{1}{n_2}\right)} \tag{10.9}$$

**Interval Estimate of the Difference Between the Means of Two Populations: Small-Sample Case ($n_1 < 30$ and/or $n_2 < 30$) with $\sigma_1$ and $\sigma_2$ Estimated by $s_1$ and $s_2$**

$$\bar{x}_1 - \bar{x}_2 \pm t_{\alpha/2}s_{\bar{x}_1-\bar{x}_2} \tag{10.10}$$

**Test Statistic for Hypothesis Tests About the Difference Between the Means of Two Populations: Large-Sample Case**

$$z = \frac{(\bar{x}_1 - \bar{x}_2) - (\mu_1 - \mu_2)}{\sqrt{\sigma_1^2/n_1 + \sigma_2^2/n_2}} \tag{10.11}$$

**Test Statistic for Hypothesis Tests About the Difference Between the Means of Two Populations: Small-Sample Case**

$$t = \frac{(\bar{x}_1 - \bar{x}_2) - (\mu_1 - \mu_2)}{\sqrt{s^2\left(\frac{1}{n_1} + \frac{1}{n_2}\right)}} \tag{10.12}$$

**Sample Mean for Matched Samples**

$$\bar{d} = \frac{\Sigma d_i}{n}$$

**Sample Standard Deviation for Matched Samples**

$$s_d = \sqrt{\frac{\Sigma(d_i - \bar{d})^2}{n - 1}}$$

**Test Statistic for Matched Samples**

$$t = \frac{\bar{d} - \mu_d}{s_d/\sqrt{n}} \tag{10.13}$$

**Point Estimator of the Difference Between the Proportions of Two Populations**

$$\bar{p}_1 - \bar{p}_2 \tag{10.14}$$

**Expected Value of $\bar{p}_1 - \bar{p}_2$**

$$E(\bar{p}_1 - \bar{p}_2) = p_1 - p_2 \tag{10.15}$$

**Standard Deviation of $\bar{p}_1 - \bar{p}_2$**

$$\sigma_{\bar{p}_1-\bar{p}_2} = \sqrt{\frac{p_1(1 - p_1)}{n_1} + \frac{p_2(1 - p_2)}{n_2}} \tag{10.16}$$

**Point Estimator of $\sigma_{\bar{p}_1 - \bar{p}_2}$**

$$s_{\bar{p}_1 - \bar{p}_2} = \sqrt{\frac{\bar{p}_1(1 - \bar{p}_1)}{n_1} + \frac{\bar{p}_2(1 - \bar{p}_2)}{n_2}} \qquad \text{(10.17)}$$

**Interval Estimate of the Difference Between the Proportion of Two Populations: Large-Sample Case With $n_1 p_1$, $n_1(1 - p_1)$, $n_2 p_2$, and $n_2(1 - p_2) \geq 5$**

$$\bar{p}_1 - \bar{p}_2 \pm z_{\alpha/2} s_{\bar{p}_1 - \bar{p}_2} \qquad \text{(10.18)}$$

**Test Statistic for the Difference Between Two Population Proportions**

$$z = \frac{(\bar{p}_1 - \bar{p}_2) - (p_1 - p_2)}{\sigma_{\bar{p}_1 - \bar{p}_2}} \qquad \text{(10.19)}$$

**Pooled Estimator of the Population Proportion**

$$\bar{p} = \frac{n_1 \bar{p}_1 + n_2 \bar{p}_2}{n_1 + n_2} \qquad \text{(10.20)}$$

**Point Estimator of $\sigma_{\bar{p}_1 - \bar{p}_2}$ When $p_1 = p_2 = p$**

$$s_{\bar{p}_1 - \bar{p}_2} = \sqrt{\bar{p}(1 - \bar{p})\left(\frac{1}{n_1} + \frac{1}{n_2}\right)} \qquad \text{(10.21)}$$

## SUPPLEMENTARY EXERCISES

**43.** Starting annual salaries for individuals with master's and bachelor's degrees were collected in two independent random samples. Use the following data to develop a 90% confidence interval estimate of the increase in starting salary that can be expected upon completion of a master's program.

| Master's Degree | Bachelor's Degree |
|---|---|
| $n_1 = 60$ | $n_2 = 80$ |
| $\bar{x}_1 = \$45{,}000$ | $\bar{x}_2 = \$35{,}000$ |
| $s_1 = \$4000$ | $s_2 = \$3500$ |

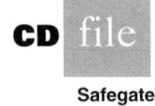

**44.** Safegate Foods, Inc., is redesigning the checkout lanes in its supermarkets throughout the country. Two designs have been suggested. Tests on customer checkout times have been conducted at two stores where the two new systems have been installed. The data collected are in the data set Safegate. Test at the .05 level of significance to determine whether there is a difference between the mean checkout times of the two systems. Which system is preferred?

**45.** Mutual funds are classified as *load* or *no-load* funds. Load funds require an investor to pay an initial fee based on a percentage of the amount invested in the fund. The no-load funds do not require this initial fee. Some financial advisors argue that the load mutual funds may be worth the extra fee because these funds provide a higher mean rate of return than the no-load mutual funds. A sample of 30 load mutual funds and a sample of 30 no-load mutual funds were selected from *Barron's Lipper Mutual Funds Quarterly*, January 12, 1998. Data were collected on the annual return for the funds over a 5-year period. The data are contained in the data set Mutual. The data for the first five load and first five no-load mutual funds are as follows.

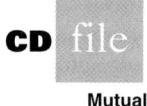

**Mutual**

| Mutual Funds—Load | Return | Mutual Funds—No Load | Return |
|---|---|---|---|
| American National Growth | 15.51 | Amana Income Fund | 13.24 |
| Arch Small Cap Equity | 14.57 | Berger One Hundred | 12.13 |
| Bartlett Cap Basic | 17.73 | Columbia International Stock | 12.17 |
| Calvert World International | 10.31 | Dodge & Cox Balanced | 16.06 |
| Colonial Fund A | 16.23 | Evergreen Fund | 17.61 |

**a.** Formulate $H_0$ and $H_a$ such that rejection of $H_0$ leads to the conclusion that the load mutual funds have a higher mean annual return over the 5-year period.
**b.** Use the 60 mutual funds in the data set Mutual to conduct the hypothesis test. Using $\alpha = .05$, what is your conclusion?
**c.** What is the $p$-value?

**46.** Figure Perfect, Inc., is a women's figure salon that specializes in weight reduction programs. Weights for a sample of clients before and after a 6-week introductory program are shown here.

| | Weight | |
|---|---|---|
| Client | Before | After |
| 1 | 140 | 132 |
| 2 | 160 | 158 |
| 3 | 210 | 195 |
| 4 | 148 | 152 |
| 5 | 190 | 180 |
| 6 | 170 | 164 |

Using $\alpha = .05$, test to determine whether the introductory program provides a statistically significant weight loss. What is your conclusion?

**47.** The Asian economy faltered during the last few months of 1997. Investors anticipated that the downturn in the Asian economy would have a negative effect on the earnings of companies in the United States during the fourth quarter of 1997. The following sample data show the earnings per share for the fourth quarter of 1996 and the fourth quarter of 1997 (*The Wall Street Journal*, January 28, 1998).

**Asia**

| Company | Earnings 1996 | Earnings 1997 |
|---|---|---|
| Atlantic Richfield | 1.16 | 1.17 |
| Balchem Corp. | 0.16 | 0.13 |
| Black & Decker Corp. | 0.97 | 1.02 |
| Dial Corp. | 0.18 | 0.23 |
| DSC Communications | 0.15 | −0.32 |
| Eastman Chemical | 0.77 | 0.36 |
| Excel Communications | 0.28 | −0.14 |
| Federal Signal | 0.40 | 0.29 |
| Ford Motor Company | 0.97 | 1.45 |
| GTE Corp | 0.81 | 0.73 |
| ITT Industries | 0.59 | 0.60 |
| Kimberly-Clark | 0.61 | −0.27 |
| Minnesota Mining & Mfr. | 0.91 | 0.89 |
| Procter & Gamble | 0.63 | 0.71 |

**a.** Formulate $H_0$ and $H_a$ such that rejection of $H_0$ leads to the conclusion that the mean earnings per share for the fourth quarter of 1997 are less than for the fourth quarter of 1996.
**b.** Use the data in the file Asia to conduct the hypothesis test. Using $\alpha = .05$, what is your conclusion?

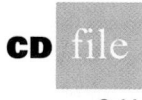

**Cable**

**48.** A cable television firm is considering submitting bids for rights to operate in two regions of the state of Florida. Surveys were conducted of the two regions to obtain data on customer acceptance of the cable television service. The data obtained are shown in the data set Cable. A response of Yes indicates that the customer surveyed indicated an intent to purchase the cable television service. Develop a 99% confidence interval for the difference between the population proportions of customer acceptance in the two regions.

**49.** A *Business Week*/Harris poll asked 1035 adults how well U.S. companies competed in the global economy; 704 respondents answered good/excellent (*Business Week,* September 11, 2000). In a smiliar poll of 1004 adults in 1996, 582 respondents answered good/excellent. Can the sample results be used to conclude that the proportion of adults responding good/excellent has *increased* over the 4 years from 1996 to 2000?

   **a.** State the null and alternative hypotheses.

   **b.** Compute the *p*-value.

   **c.** Using $\alpha = .01$, what is your conclusion?

**50.** A large automobile company selected samples of single and married male policyholders and recorded the number who had made an insurance claim over the preceding 3-year period.

| **Single Policyholders** | **Married Policyholders** |
|:---:|:---:|
| $n_1 = 400$ | $n_2 = 900$ |
| Number making claims = 76 | Number making claims = 90 |

   **a.** Using $\alpha = .05$, test to determine whether the claim rates differ between single and married male policyholders.

   **b.** Provide a 95% confidence interval for the difference between the proportions for the two populations.

**51.** Medical tests were conducted to learn about drug-resistant tuberculosis. Of 142 cases tested in New Jersey, nine were found to be drug-resistant. Of 268 cases tested in Texas, five were found to be drug-resistant. Do these data suggest a statistically significant difference between the proportions of drug-resistant cases in the two states? Test $H_0: p_1 - p_2 = 0$ at the .02 level of significance. What is the *p*-value, and what is your conclusion?

## Case Problem   **PAR, INC.**

Par, Inc., is a major manufacturer of golf equipment. Management believes that Par's market share could be increased with the introduction of a cut-resistant, longer-lasting golf ball. Therefore, the research group at Par has been investigating a new golf ball coating designed to resist cuts and provide a more durable ball. The tests with the coating have been promising.

One of the researchers voiced concern about the effect of the new coating on driving distances. Par would like the new cut-resistant ball to offer driving distances comparable to those of the current-model golf ball. To compare the driving distances for the two balls, 40 balls of each type were subjected to distance tests. The testing was performed with a mechanical hitting machine so that any difference between the mean distances for the two models could be attributed to a difference in the design. The results of the tests, with distances measured to the nearest yard, follow. These data are available on the data disk in the data set Golf.

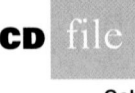

Golf

| Model | | Model | | Model | | Model | |
|:---:|:---:|:---:|:---:|:---:|:---:|:---:|:---:|
| **Current** | **New** | **Current** | **New** | **Current** | **New** | **Current** | **New** |
| 264 | 277 | 270 | 272 | 263 | 274 | 281 | 283 |
| 261 | 269 | 287 | 259 | 264 | 266 | 274 | 250 |
| 267 | 263 | 289 | 264 | 284 | 262 | 273 | 253 |
| 272 | 266 | 280 | 280 | 263 | 271 | 263 | 260 |
| 258 | 262 | 272 | 274 | 260 | 260 | 275 | 270 |
| 283 | 251 | 275 | 281 | 283 | 281 | 267 | 263 |
| 258 | 262 | 265 | 276 | 255 | 250 | 279 | 261 |
| 266 | 289 | 260 | 269 | 272 | 263 | 274 | 255 |
| 259 | 286 | 278 | 268 | 266 | 278 | 276 | 263 |
| 270 | 264 | 275 | 262 | 268 | 264 | 262 | 279 |

## Managerial Report

1. Provide descriptive statistical summaries of the data for each model.
2. Formulate and present the rationale for a hypothesis test that Par could use to compare the driving distances of the current and new golf balls.
3. Analyze the data to provide the hypothesis testing conclusion. What is the $p$-value for your test? What is your recommendation for Par, Inc.?
4. Do you see a need for larger sample sizes and more testing with the golf balls? Discuss.

# Chapter 11

# INFERENCES ABOUT POPULATION VARIANCES

**CONTENTS**

## STATISTICS IN PRACTICE

### U.S. GENERAL ACCOUNTING OFFICE*
*Washington, D.C.*

The U.S. General Accounting Office (GAO) is an independent, nonpolitical audit organization in the legislative branch of the federal government. The GAO evaluators determine the effectiveness of current and proposed federal programs. To carry out their duties, evaluators must be proficient in records review, legislative research, and statistical analysis techniques.

In one case, the GAO evaluators studied a Department of Interior program established to help clean up the nation's rivers and lakes. As part of this program, federal grants were made to small cities throughout the United States. Congress asked the GAO to determine how effectively the program was operating. To do so, the GAO examined records and visited the sites of several waste treatment plants.

One objective of the GAO audit was to ensure that the effluent (treated sewage) at the plants met certain standards. Among other things the audits reviewed sample data on the oxygen content, the pH level, and the amount of suspended solids in the effluent. A requirement of the program was that a variety of tests be taken daily at each plant and that the collected data be sent periodically to the state engineering department. The GAO's investigation of the data showed whether various characteristics of the effluent were within acceptable limits.

For example, the mean or average pH level of the effluent was examined carefully. In addition, the variance in the reported pH levels was reviewed. The following hypothesis test was conducted about the variance in pH level for the population of effluent.

$$H_0: \sigma^2 = \sigma_0^2$$
$$H_a: \sigma^2 \neq \sigma_0^2$$

In this test, $\sigma_0^2$ is the population variance in pH level expected at a properly functioning plant. In one par-

Effluent at this water treatment plant must fall within a statistically determined pH range. © PhotoDisc, Inc.

ticular plant, the null hypothesis was rejected. Further analysis showed that this plant had a variance in pH level that was significantly less than normal.

The auditors visited the plant to examine the measuring equipment and to discuss their statistical findings with the plant manager. The auditors found that the measuring equipment was not being used because the operator did not know how to work it. Instead, the operator had been told by an engineer what level of pH was acceptable and had simply recorded similar values without actually conducting the test. The unusually low variance in this plant's data had resulted in rejection of $H_0$. The GAO suspected that other plants might have similar problems and recommended an operator training program to improve the data collection aspect of the pollution control program.

In this chapter you will learn how to conduct statistical inferences about the variances of one and two populations. Two new distributions, the chi-square distribution and the $F$ distribution, will be introduced and used to make interval estimates and hypothesis tests about population variances.

*The authors thank Mr. Art Foreman and Mr. Dale Ledman of the U.S. General Accounting Office for providing this Statistics in Practice.

In the preceding four chapters we examined methods of statistical inference involving population means and population proportions. In this chapter we expand the discussion to situations involving inferences about population variances. As an example of a case in which a variance can provide important decision-making information, consider the production process of filling containers with a liquid detergent product. The filling mechanism for the process is adjusted so that the mean filling quantity is 16 ounces per container. Although a mean of 16 ounces is desired, the variance of the fillings is also critical. That is, even with the filling mechanism properly adjusted for the mean of 16 ounces, we cannot expect every container to have exactly 16 ounces. By selecting a sample of containers, we can compute a sample variance for the number of ounces placed in a container. This value will serve as an estimate of the variance for the population of containers being filled by the production process. If the sample variance is small, the production process will be continued. However, if the sample variance is excessive, overfilling and underfilling may be occurring even though the mean is correct at 16 ounces. In this case, the filling mechanism will be readjusted in an attempt to reduce the filling variance for the containers.

> *In many manufacturing applications, controlling the process variance is extremely important in maintaining quality.*

In the first section we consider inferences about the variance of a single population. Subsequently, we will discuss procedures that can be used to make inferences about the variances of two populations.

## 11.1  INFERENCES ABOUT A POPULATION VARIANCE

In preceding chapters we used the sample variance

$$s^2 = \frac{\Sigma(x_i - \bar{x})^2}{n - 1} \tag{11.1}$$

as the point estimator of the population variance $\sigma^2$. In using the sample variance as a basis for making inferences about a population variance, the sampling distribution of the quantity $(n - 1)s^2/\sigma^2$ is helpful. This sampling distribution is described as follows.

> ### Sampling Distribution of $(n - 1)s^2/\sigma^2$
>
> Whenever a simple random sample of size $n$ is selected from a normal population, the sampling distribution of
>
> $$\frac{(n - 1)s^2}{\sigma^2} \tag{11.2}$$
>
> has a chi-square distribution with $n - 1$ degrees of freedom.

> *The chi-square distribution is based on sampling from a normal population.*

Figure 11.1 shows some possible forms of the sampling distribution of $(n - 1)s^2/\sigma^2$.

Tables of areas or probabilities are readily available for the chi-square distribution. Because the sampling distribution of $(n - 1)s^2/\sigma^2$ is known to have a chi-square distribution whenever a simple random sample of size $n$ is selected from a normal population, we can use the chi-square distribution to develop interval estimates and conduct hypothesis tests about a population variance.

### Interval Estimation of $\sigma^2$

To show how the chi-square distribution can be used to develop a confidence interval estimate of a population variance $\sigma^2$, suppose that we are interested in estimating the population variance for the production filling process mentioned at the beginning of this chapter. A sample of 20 containers was selected. The data on the number of ounces in the 20 containers are listed in Table 11.1. The sample variance for these data is $s^2 = .0025$. However, we know we cannot expect the variance of a sample of 20 containers to provide the exact value of the variance for the population of containers filled by the production process. Hence, our interest will be in developing an interval estimate of the population variance.

**FIGURE 11.1**    EXAMPLES OF THE SAMPLING DISTRIBUTION OF $(n - 1)s^2/\sigma^2$
(A CHI-SQUARE DISTRIBUTION)

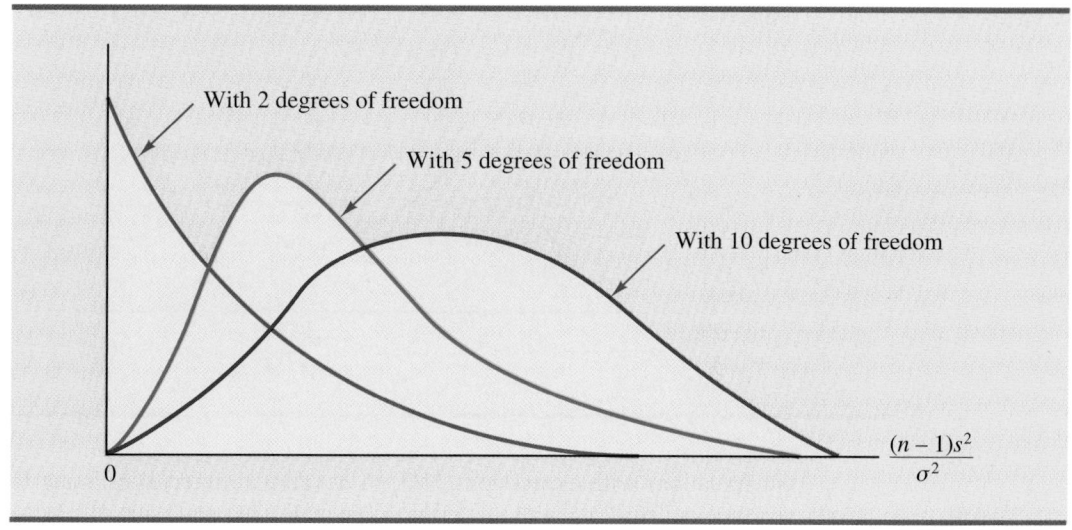

We will use the notation $\chi_\alpha^2$ to denote the value for the chi-square distribution that provides an area or probability of $\alpha$ to the *right* of the stated $\chi_\alpha^2$ value. For example, in Figure 11.2 the chi-square distribution with 19 degrees of freedom is shown with $\chi_{.025}^2 = 32.8523$ indicating that 2.5% of the chi-square values are to the right of 32.8523, and $\chi_{.975}^2 = 8.90655$ indicating that 97.5% of the chi-square values are to the right of 8.90655. Refer to Table 11.2 and verify that these chi-square values with 19 degrees of freedom are correct. Table 3 of Appendix B provides a more extensive table of chi-square distribution values.

From the graph in Figure 11.2 we see that .95, or 95%, of the chi-square values are between $\chi_{.975}^2$ and $\chi_{.025}^2$. That is, there is a .95 probability of obtaining a $\chi^2$ value such that

$$\chi_{.975}^2 \leq \chi^2 \leq \chi_{.025}^2$$

However, we stated in expression (11.2) that $(n - 1)s^2/\sigma^2$ follows a chi-square distribution, therefore we can substitute $(n - 1)s^2/\sigma^2$ for $\chi^2$ and write

$$\chi_{.975}^2 \leq \frac{(n - 1)s^2}{\sigma^2} \leq \chi_{.025}^2 \tag{11.3}$$

In effect, (11.3) provides an interval estimate in that .95, or 95%, of all possible values for $(n - 1)s^2/\sigma^2$ will be in the interval $\chi_{.975}^2$ to $\chi_{.025}^2$. We now need to do some algebraic

**TABLE 11.1**    NUMBER OF OUNCES OF LIQUID DETERGENT FOR A SAMPLE
OF 20 CONTAINERS

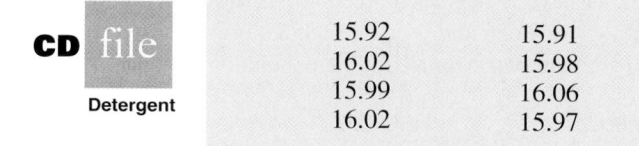

| | | Ounces | | |
|---|---|---|---|---|
| 15.92 | 15.91 | 15.97 | 16.04 | 15.90 |
| 16.02 | 15.98 | 16.07 | 16.01 | 15.96 |
| 15.99 | 16.06 | 15.94 | 16.07 | 16.00 |
| 16.02 | 15.97 | 15.96 | 16.01 | 15.99 |

**FIGURE 11.2**   A CHI-SQUARE DISTRIBUTION WITH 19 DEGREES OF FREEDOM

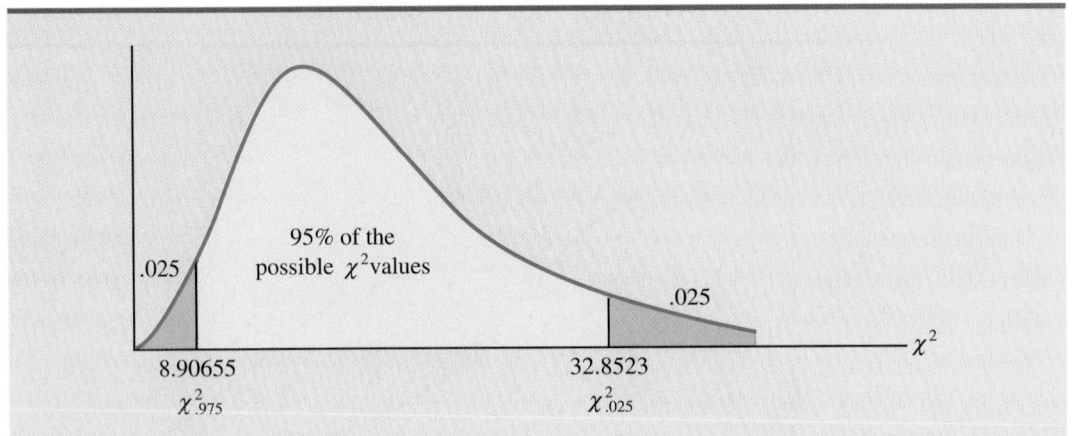

manipulations with expression (11.3) to develop an interval estimate for the population variance $\sigma^2$. Working with the leftmost inequality in expression (11.3), we have

$$\chi^2_{.975} \leq \frac{(n-1)s^2}{\sigma^2}$$

Thus

$$\sigma^2 \chi^2_{.975} \leq (n-1)s^2$$

or

$$\sigma^2 \leq \frac{(n-1)s^2}{\chi^2_{.975}} \tag{11.4}$$

Performing similar algebraic manipulations with the right-most inequality in expression (11.3) gives

$$\frac{(n-1)s^2}{\chi^2_{.025}} \leq \sigma^2 \tag{11.5}$$

The results of expressions (11.4) and (11.5) can be combined to provide

$$\frac{(n-1)s^2}{\chi^2_{.025}} \leq \sigma^2 \leq \frac{(n-1)s^2}{\chi^2_{.975}} \tag{11.6}$$

Because expression (11.3) is true for 95% of the $(n-1)s^2/\sigma^2$ values, expression (11.6) provides a 95% confidence interval estimate of the population variance $\sigma^2$.

Let us return to the problem of providing an interval estimate of the population variance of filling quantities. Recall that the sample of 20 containers provided a sample variance of $s^2 = .0025$. With a sample size of 20, we have 19 degrees of freedom. As shown in Figure 11.2, we have already determined that $\chi^2_{.975} = 8.90655$ and $\chi^2_{.025} = 32.8523$. Using these values in expression (11.6) provides the following interval estimate for the population variance.

$$\frac{(19)(.0025)}{32.8523} \leq \sigma^2 \leq \frac{(19)(.0025)}{8.90655}$$

**TABLE 11.2**    SELECTED VALUES FROM THE CHI-SQUARE DISTRIBUTION TABLE*

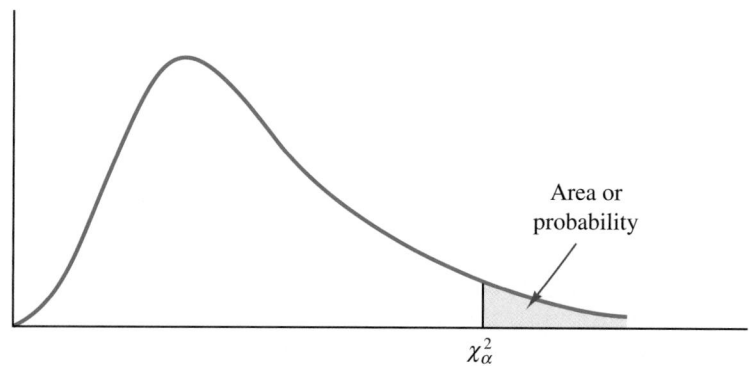

| Degrees of Freedom | Area in Upper Tail | | | | | |
|---|---|---|---|---|---|---|
| | .99 | .975 | .95 | .05 | .025 | .01 |
| 1 | $157{,}088 \times 10^{-9}$ | $982{,}069 \times 10^{-9}$ | $393{,}214 \times 10^{-8}$ | 3.84146 | 5.02389 | 6.63490 |
| 2 | .0201007 | .0506356 | .102587 | 5.99147 | 7.37776 | 9.21034 |
| 3 | .114832 | .215795 | .351846 | 7.81473 | 9.34840 | 11.3449 |
| 4 | .297110 | .484419 | .710721 | 9.48773 | 11.1433 | 13.2767 |
| 5 | .554300 | .831211 | 1.145476 | 11.0705 | 12.8325 | 15.0863 |
| 6 | .872085 | 1.237347 | 1.63539 | 12.5916 | 14.4494 | 16.8119 |
| 7 | 1.239043 | 1.68987 | 2.16735 | 14.0671 | 16.0128 | 18.4753 |
| 8 | 1.646482 | 2.17973 | 2.73264 | 15.5073 | 17.5346 | 20.0902 |
| 9 | 2.087912 | 2.70039 | 3.32511 | 16.9190 | 19.0228 | 21.6660 |
| 10 | 2.55821 | 3.24697 | 3.94030 | 18.3070 | 20.4831 | 23.2093 |
| 11 | 3.05347 | 3.81575 | 4.57481 | 19.6751 | 21.9200 | 24.7250 |
| 12 | 3.57056 | 4.40379 | 5.22603 | 21.0261 | 23.3367 | 26.2170 |
| 13 | 4.10691 | 5.00874 | 5.89186 | 22.3621 | 24.7356 | 27.6883 |
| 14 | 4.66043 | 5.62872 | 6.57063 | 23.6848 | 26.1190 | 29.1413 |
| 15 | 5.22935 | 6.26214 | 7.26094 | 24.9958 | 27.4884 | 30.5779 |
| 16 | 5.81221 | 6.90766 | 7.96164 | 26.2962 | 28.8454 | 31.9999 |
| 17 | 6.40776 | 7.56418 | 8.67176 | 27.5871 | 30.1910 | 33.4087 |
| 18 | 7.01491 | 8.23075 | 9.39046 | 28.8693 | 31.5264 | 34.8053 |
| 19 | 7.63273 | 8.90655 | 10.1170 | 30.1435 | 32.8523 | 36.1908 |
| 20 | 8.26040 | 9.59083 | 10.8508 | 31.4104 | 34.1696 | 37.5662 |
| 21 | 8.89720 | 10.28293 | 11.5913 | 32.6705 | 35.4789 | 38.9321 |
| 22 | 9.54249 | 10.9823 | 12.3380 | 33.9244 | 36.7807 | 40.2894 |
| 23 | 10.19567 | 11.6885 | 13.0905 | 35.1725 | 38.0757 | 41.6384 |
| 24 | 10.8564 | 12.4011 | 13.8484 | 36.4151 | 39.3641 | 42.9798 |
| 25 | 11.5240 | 13.1197 | 14.6114 | 37.6525 | 40.6465 | 44.3141 |
| 26 | 12.1981 | 13.8439 | 15.3791 | 38.8852 | 41.9232 | 45.6417 |
| 27 | 12.8786 | 14.5733 | 16.1513 | 40.1133 | 43.1944 | 46.9630 |
| 28 | 13.5648 | 15.3079 | 16.9279 | 41.3372 | 44.4607 | 48.2782 |
| 29 | 14.2565 | 16.0471 | 17.7083 | 42.5569 | 45.7222 | 49.5879 |
| 30 | 14.9535 | 16.7908 | 18.4926 | 43.7729 | 46.9792 | 50.8922 |
| 40 | 22.1643 | 24.4331 | 26.5093 | 55.7585 | 59.3417 | 63.6907 |
| 50 | 29.7067 | 32.3574 | 34.7642 | 67.5048 | 71.4202 | 76.1539 |
| 60 | 37.4848 | 40.4817 | 43.1879 | 79.0819 | 83.2976 | 88.3794 |

*For additional $\chi^2$ distribution values, see Table 3 of Appendix B.

or

$$.0014 \leq \sigma^2 \leq .0053$$

A confidence interval for a population standard deviation can be found by computing the square roots of the lower limit and upper limit of the confidence interval for the population variance.

Taking the square root of those values provides the following 95% confidence interval for the population standard deviation.

$$.0374 \leq \sigma \leq .0728$$

Thus, we have illustrated the process of using the chi-square distribution to establish interval estimates of a population variance and a population standard deviation. Note specifically that because $\chi^2_{.975}$ and $\chi^2_{.025}$ were used, the interval estimate has a .95 confidence coefficient. Extending expression (11.6) to the general case of any confidence coefficient, we have the following interval estimate of a population variance.

---

**Interval Estimate of a Population Variance**

$$\frac{(n-1)s^2}{\chi^2_{\alpha/2}} \leq \sigma^2 \leq \frac{(n-1)s^2}{\chi^2_{(1-\alpha/2)}} \qquad (11.7)$$

where the $\chi^2$ values are based on a chi-square distribution with $n - 1$ degrees of freedom and where $1 - \alpha$ is the confidence coefficient.

---

## Using Excel to Construct a Confidence Interval

Excel can be used to construct a 95% confidence interval of the population variance for the example involving filling containers with a liquid detergent product. Refer to Figure 11.3 as we describe the tasks involved. The formula worksheet is in the background; the value worksheet is in the foreground.

**Enter Data:** Column A shows the number of ounces of detergent for each of the 20 containers.

**Enter Functions and Formulas:** The descriptive statistics needed are provided in cells D3:D4. Excel's COUNT and VAR functions are used to compute the sample size and the sample variance, respectively.

Cells D6:D9 are used to compute the appropriate chi-square values. The confidence coefficient was entered into cell D6 and the level of significance ($\alpha$) was computed in cell D7 by entering the formula =1-D6. Excel's CHIINV function was used to compute the lower- and upper-tail chi-square values. The form of the CHIINV function is CHIINV(upper-tail probability, degrees of freedom). The formula =CHIINV(1-D7/2,D3-1) was entered into cell D8 to compute the chi-square value in the lower tail. The value worksheet shows that the chi-square value for 19 degrees of freedom is $\chi^2_{.975} = 8.9065$. Then, to compute the chi-square value corresponding to an upper-tail probability of .025, the function =CHIINV(D7/2,D3-1) was entered into cell D9. The value worksheet shows that the chi-square value obtained is $\chi^2_{.025} = 32.8523$.

Cells D11:D13 provide the point estimate and the lower and upper limits for the confidence interval. Because the point estimate is just the sample variance, we entered the formula =D4 into cell D11. Inequality (11.7) shows that the lower limit of the 95% confidence interval is

$$\frac{(n-1)s^2}{\chi^2_{\alpha/2}} = \frac{(n-1)s^2}{\chi^2_{.025}}$$

**FIGURE 11.3**   EXCEL WORKSHEET FOR THE LIQUID DETERGENT FILLING PROCESS

| | A | B | C | D | E |
|---|---|---|---|---|---|
| 1 | Ounces | | Interval Estimate of a Population Variance | | |
| 2 | 15.92 | | | | |
| 3 | 16.02 | | Sample Size | =COUNT(A2:A21) | |
| 4 | 15.99 | | Variance | =VAR(A2:A21) | |
| 5 | 16.02 | | | | |
| 6 | 15.91 | | Confidence Coefficient | 0.95 | |
| 7 | 15.98 | | Level of Significance (alpha) | =1-D6 | |
| 8 | 16.06 | | Chi-Square Value (lower tail) | =CHIINV(1-D7/2,D3-1) | |
| 9 | 15.97 | | Chi-Square Value (upper tail) | =CHIINV(D7/2,D3-1) | |
| 10 | 15.97 | | | | |
| 11 | 16.07 | | Point Estimate | =D4 | |
| 12 | 15.94 | | Lower Limit | =((D3-1)*D4)/D9 | |
| 13 | 15.96 | | Upper Limit | =((D3-1)*D4)/D8 | |
| 14 | 16.04 | | | | |
| 15 | 16.01 | | | | |
| 16 | 16.07 | | | | |
| 17 | 16.01 | | | | |
| 18 | 15.9 | | | | |
| 19 | 15.96 | | | | |
| 20 | 16 | | | | |
| 21 | 15.99 | | | | |
| 22 | | | | | |

| | A | B | C | D | E | F |
|---|---|---|---|---|---|---|
| 1 | Ounces | | Interval Estimate of a Population Variance | | | |
| 2 | 15.92 | | | | | |
| 3 | 16.02 | | Sample Size | 20 | | |
| 4 | 15.99 | | Variance | 0.0025 | | |
| 5 | 16.02 | | | | | |
| 6 | 15.91 | | Confidence Coefficient | 0.95 | | |
| 7 | 15.98 | | Level of Significance (alpha) | 0.05 | | |
| 8 | 16.06 | | Chi-Square Value (lower tail) | 8.9065 | | |
| 9 | 15.97 | | Chi-Square Value (upper tail) | 32.8523 | | |
| 10 | 15.97 | | | | | |
| 11 | 16.07 | | Point Estimate | 0.0025 | | |
| 12 | 15.94 | | Lower Limit | 0.0014 | | |
| 13 | 15.96 | | Upper Limit | 0.0053 | | |
| 14 | 16.04 | | | | | |
| 15 | 16.01 | | | | | |
| 16 | 16.07 | | | | | |
| 17 | 16.01 | | | | | |
| 18 | 15.90 | | | | | |
| 19 | 15.96 | | | | | |
| 20 | 16.00 | | | | | |
| 21 | 15.99 | | | | | |
| 22 | | | | | | |

Thus, to compute the lower limit of the 95% confidence interval, the formula $=((D3-1)*D4)/D9$ was entered into cell D12. Inequality (11.7) also shows that the upper limit of the confidence interval is

$$\frac{(n-1)s^2}{\chi^2_{(1-\alpha/2)}} = \frac{(n-1)s^2}{\chi^2_{.975}}$$

Thus, to compute the upper limit of the 95% confidence interval, the formula $=((D3-1)*D4)/D8$ was entered into cell D13. The value worksheet shows a lower limit of .0014 and an upper limit of .0053. In other words, the 95% confidence interval estimate of the population variance is from .0014 to .0053.

## Hypothesis Testing

Let us now consider an example and the statistical methodology necessary to test hypotheses about the value of a population variance. The St. Louis Metro Bus Company has recently made a concerted effort to promote an image of reliability by encouraging its drivers to maintain consistent schedules. As a standard policy the company expects arrival times at its bus stops to have low variability. In terms of the variance of arrival times, the company standard specifies an arrival time variance of 4 or less with arrival times measured in minutes. Periodically, the company collects arrival time data at various bus stops to determine whether the variability guideline is being maintained. The sample results are used to test the following hypotheses.

$$H_0: \sigma^2 \leq 4$$
$$H_a: \sigma^2 > 4$$

In tentatively assuming $H_0$ to be true, we are assuming that the variance of arrival times is within the company guidelines. We will reject $H_0$ only if the sample evidence indicates that the guidelines are not being maintained. In this sense, rejection of $H_0$ suggests that follow-up steps are necessary to reduce the arrival time variance.

Assume that a random sample of 10 bus arrivals will be taken at a particular downtown intersection. If the population of arrival times has a normal probability distribution, we know from expression (11.2) that the quantity $(n - 1)s^2/\sigma^2$ has a chi-square distribution with $n - 1$ degrees of freedom. Thus, the test statistic

$$\chi^2 = \frac{9s^2}{\sigma^2}$$

has a chi-square distribution with $n - 1 = 9$ degrees of freedom. With the null hypothesis $\sigma^2 = 4$, the sample of .10 bus arrival times provides the following observed $\chi^2$ value.

$$\chi^2 = \frac{9s^2}{4}$$

Figure 11.4 is the chi-square distribution showing the rejection region for this one-tailed test. Note that we will reject $H_0$ only if the sample variance $s^2$ leads to a large $\chi^2$ value. With $\alpha = .05$, Table 11.2 shows that with 9 degrees of freedom $\chi^2_{.05} = 16.919$. With this critical value for the test, the rejection rule is:

$$\text{Reject } H_0 \text{ if } \chi^2 > 16.919$$

The arrival times in number of minutes past 12:00 noon for the sample of 10 bus arrivals are listed in Table 11.3. The sample variance is $s^2 = 4.8$. Is this sample evidence sufficient to reject $H_0$ and conclude that the buses are not meeting the company's arrival time variance guideline? With $s^2 = 4.8$ we obtain the following $\chi^2$ value.

$$\chi^2 = \frac{9(4.8)}{4} = 10.8$$

Because $\chi^2 = 10.8$ is less than 16.919, we cannot reject $H_0$. Hence, the sample variance of $s^2 = 4.8$ is insufficient evidence to conclude that the arrival time variance is not meeting the company standard.

**FIGURE 11.4**   REJECTION REGION FOR THE ST. LOUIS METRO BUS TEST WITH $\alpha = .05$

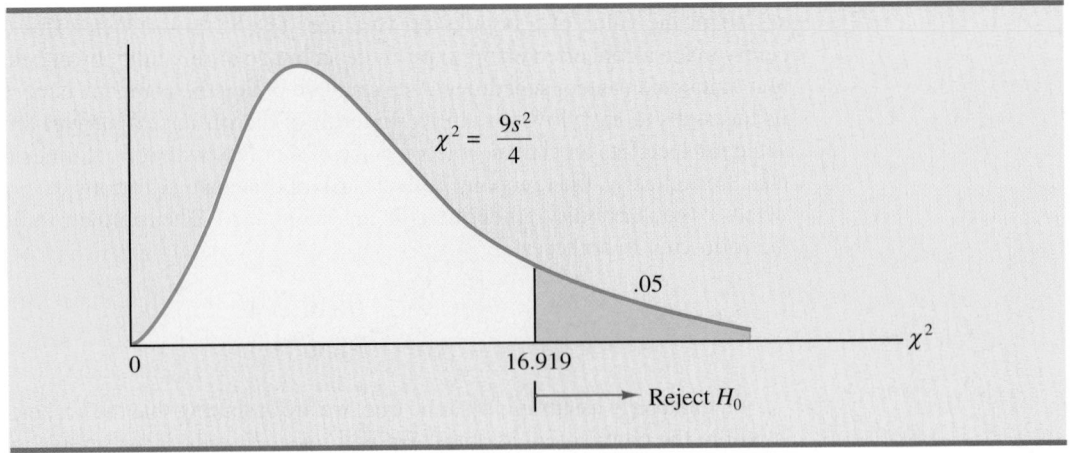

**TABLE 11.3**

ARRIVAL TIMES
IN NUMBER OF
MINUTES PAST
12:00 NOON FOR
THE ST. LOUIS
METRO BUS
EXAMPLE

| Time | |
|------|------|
| 15.2 | 17.1 |
| 17.5 | 15.0 |
| 19.6 | 15.5 |
| 16.6 | 20.0 |
| 21.3 | 16.2 |

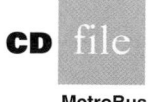

**MetroBus**

The $p$-value criterion can also be used for this hypothesis test. The usual rejection rule applies: Reject $H_0$ if $p$-value $< \alpha$. However, because it is difficult to determine the $p$-value directly from the tables of a chi-square distribution, a computer software package such as Excel is required. For the St. Louis Metro Bus example, the $p$-value associated with the test statistic $\chi^2 = 10.8$ is .2897. With a $p$-value $= .2897 > \alpha = .05$, the null hypothesis cannot be rejected. At the end of this section we will show how Excel was used to compute this $p$-value.

In practice, one-tailed tests are the most frequently encountered tests about population variances. That is, in situations involving arrival times, production times, filling weights, part dimensions, and so on, low variances are generally desired, whereas large variances tend to be unacceptable. With a statement about the maximum allowable population variance, we can test the null hypothesis that the population variance is less than or equal to the maximum allowable value against the alternative hypothesis that the population variance is greater than the maximum allowable value. We now outline the decision rule for making this one-tailed test about a population variance.

**One-Tailed Test About a Population Variance with Rejection Region in the Upper Tail**

$$H_0: \sigma^2 \leq \sigma_0^2$$
$$H_a: \sigma^2 > \sigma_0^2$$

**Test Statistic**

$$\chi^2 = \frac{(n-1)s^2}{\sigma_0^2} \tag{11.8}$$

**Rejection Rule**

Using test statistic:   Reject $H_0$ if $\chi^2 > \chi_\alpha^2$
Using $p$-value:        Reject $H_0$ if $p$-value $< \alpha$

where $\sigma_0^2$ is the hypothesized value for the population variance and $\chi_\alpha^2$ is based on a chi-square distribution with $n-1$ degrees of freedom.

Just as we saw with population means and proportions, other forms of the hypotheses can be developed. The one-tailed test for $H_0: \sigma^2 \geq \sigma_0^2$ is similar to the preceding test except that the rejection region is in the lower tail of the chi-square distribution at the critical value of $\chi_{(1-\alpha)}^2$.

**One-Tailed Test About a Population Variance with Rejection Region in the Lower Tail**

$$H_0: \sigma^2 \geq \sigma_0^2$$
$$H_a: \sigma^2 < \sigma_0^2$$

**Test Statistic**

$$\chi^2 = \frac{(n-1)s^2}{\sigma_0^2}$$

### Rejection Rule

Using test statistic:   Reject $H_0$ if $\chi^2 < \chi^2_{(1-\alpha)}$

Using $p$-value:        Reject $H_0$ if $p$-value $< \alpha$

where $\sigma_0^2$ is the hypothesized value for the population variance and $\chi^2_{(1-\alpha)}$ is based on a chi-square distribution with $n - 1$ degrees of freedom.

The two-tailed hypothesis test with $H_0$: $\sigma^2 = \sigma_0^2$, like other two-tailed tests, places an area of $\alpha/2$ in each tail of the distribution to establish the two critical values for the test. The procedure for conducting a two-tailed test about a population variance follows.

### Two-Tailed Test About a Population Variance

$$H_0: \sigma^2 = \sigma_0^2$$
$$H_a: \sigma^2 \neq \sigma_0^2$$

### Test Statistic

$$\chi^2 = \frac{(n - 1)s^2}{\sigma_0^2}$$

### Rejection Rule

Using test statistic:   Reject $H_0$ if $\chi^2 < \chi^2_{(1-\alpha/2)}$ or if $\chi^2 > \chi^2_{\alpha/2}$

Using $p$-value:        Reject $H_0$ if $p$-value $< \alpha$

where $\sigma_0^2$ is the hypothesized value for the population variance and $\chi^2_{(1-\alpha/2)}$ and $\chi^2_{\alpha/2}$ are based on a chi-square distribution with $n - 1$ degrees of freedom.

Let us demonstrate the use of the chi-square distribution in conducting a two-tailed test about a population variance by considering a situation faced by a bureau of motor vehicles. Historically, the variance in test scores for individuals applying for driver's licenses has been $\sigma^2 = 100$. A new examination with new test questions has been developed. Administrators at the bureau of motor vehicles would like the variance in the test scores for the new examination to remain at the historical level. To evaluate the variance in the new examination test scores, the following two-tailed hypothesis test has been proposed.

$$H_0: \sigma^2 = 100$$
$$H_a: \sigma^2 \neq 100$$

Rejection of $H_0$ will indicate that a change in the variance has occurred and suggest that some questions in the new examination may need revision to make the variance of the new test scores similar to the variance of the old test scores. A sample of 30 applicants for driver's licenses will be given the new version of the examination.

The chi-square distribution can be used to conduct this two-tailed test. With a .05 level of significance, the critical values will be $\chi^2_{.975}$ and $\chi^2_{.025}$. With $n - 1 = 29$ degrees of freedom, Table 11.2 shows that $\chi^2_{.975} = 16.0471$ and $\chi^2_{.025} = 45.7222$. The rejection rule for the two-tailed test becomes

$$\text{Reject } H_0 \text{ if } \chi^2 < 16.0471 \text{ or if } \chi^2 > 45.7222$$

What is the appropriate conclusion if the sample of 30 new examination scores provides a sample variance of $s^2 = 64$? With $H_0: \sigma^2 = 100$, the value of the $\chi^2$ statistic is computed to be

$$\chi^2 = \frac{(n-1)s^2}{\sigma_0^2} = \frac{29(64)}{100} = 18.56$$

Because 18.56 is not in the rejection region, we are not able to reject $H_0$. The statistical evidence does not indicate that the variance in the new examination scores differs from the historical variance in examination scores. The Excel procedure described next can be used to show that the $p$-value for this hypothesis test is .1359.

## Using Excel to Conduct a Hypothesis Test

In Chapters 9 and 10 we used Excel to conduct a variety of hypothesis tests. The procedure was general in that, once the test statistic was computed, three $p$-values were obtained: a $p$-value (Lower Tail), a $p$-value (Upper Tail), and a $p$-value (Two Tail). Then, depending on the form of the hypothesis test, the appropriate $p$-value was used to make the rejection decision. We will now adapt that approach and use Excel to conduct a hypothesis test about a population variance. The Metro Bus example will serve as an illustration. Refer to Figure 11.5 as we describe the tasks involved. The formula worksheet is in the background; the value worksheet is in the foreground.

**Enter Data:**    The arrival times in number of minutes past 12:00 noon for the 10 buses have been entered into Column A.

**Enter Functions and Formulas:**    The descriptive statistics we need are provided in cells D3:D4. Excel's COUNT function has been used to compute the sample size and Excel's VAR function has been used to compute the sample variance. The value worksheet shows $n = 10$ and $s^2 = 4.8$.

The hypothesized value of the population variance, $\sigma_0^2 = 4$, was entered into cell D6. The formula =((D3-1)*D4)/D6 was entered into cell D8 to compute the $\chi^2$ test statistic (10.8), and the formula =D3-1 was entered into cell D9 to compute the degrees of freedom associated with the test statistic. Finally, the CHIDIST function was used to compute the $p$-values in cells D11:D13. The form of the CHIDIST function is CHIDIST(test statistic, degrees of freedom); the value returned by the CHIDIST function is the upper-tail probability associated with the test statistic. To compute the $p$-value for a one-tailed test in which the rejection region is in the lower tail, we entered the function =1-CHIDIST(D8,D9) into cell D11. Similarly, to compute the $p$-value for a one-tailed test in which the rejection region is in the upper tail, we entered the function =CHIDIST(D8,D9) into cell D12. Finally, to compute the $p$-value for a two-tailed test, we entered the function =2*MIN(D11,D12) into cell D13. The value worksheet shows that $p$-value (Lower Tail) = .7103, $p$-value (Upper Tail) = .2897, and $p$-value (Two Tail) = .5793. The rejection region for the Metro Bus example is in the upper tail; thus, the appropriate $p$-value is .2897. At a .05 level of significance, we cannot reject $H_0$ because .2897 > .05. Hence, the sample variance of $s^2 = 4.8$ is insufficient evidence to conclude that the arrival time variance is not meeting the company standard.

This worksheet can be used as a template for other hypothesis tests about a population variance. Enter the data in column A, revise the ranges for the functions in cells D3 and D4 as appropriate for the data, and type the hypothesized value $\sigma_0^2$ in cell D6. The $p$-value appropriate for the test can then be selected from cells D11:D13. The worksheet can also be used for exercises in which the sample size, sample variance, and hypothesized value are

**FIGURE 11.5** EXCEL WORKSHEET FOR THE ST. LOUIS METRO BUS HYPOTHESIS TEST

| | A | B | C | D | E |
|---|---|---|---|---|---|
| 1 | Time | | Hypothesis Test About a Population Variance | | |
| 2 | 15.2 | | | | |
| 3 | 17.5 | | Sample Size | =COUNT(A2:A11) | |
| 4 | 19.6 | | Variance | =VAR(A2:A11) | |
| 5 | 16.6 | | | | |
| 6 | 21.3 | | Hypothesized value | 4 | |
| 7 | 17.1 | | | | |
| 8 | 15 | | Test Statistic | =((D3-1)*D4)/D6 | |
| 9 | 15.5 | | Degrees of Freedom | =D3-1 | |
| 10 | 20 | | | | |
| 11 | 16.2 | | *p*-value (Lower Tail) | =1-CHIDIST(D8,D9) | |
| 12 | | | *p*-value (Upper Tail) | =CHIDIST(D8,D9) | |
| 13 | | | *p*-value (Two Tail) | =2*MIN(D11,D12) | |
| 14 | | | | | |

| | A | B | C | D | E |
|---|---|---|---|---|---|
| 1 | Time | | Hypothesis Test About a Population Variance | | |
| 2 | 15.2 | | | | |
| 3 | 17.5 | | Sample Size | 10 | |
| 4 | 19.6 | | Variance | 4.8 | |
| 5 | 16.6 | | | | |
| 6 | 21.3 | | Hypothesized value | 4 | |
| 7 | 17.1 | | | | |
| 8 | 15.0 | | Test Statistic | 10.8000 | |
| 9 | 15.5 | | Degrees of Freedom | 9 | |
| 10 | 20.0 | | | | |
| 11 | 16.2 | | *p*-value (Lower Tail) | 0.7103 | |
| 12 | | | *p*-value (Upper Tail) | 0.2897 | |
| 13 | | | *p*-value (Two Tail) | 0.5793 | |
| 14 | | | | | |

given. For instance, in the previous subsection we conducted a two-tailed hypothesis test about the variance in scores on a new examination given by the bureau of motor vehicles. The sample size was 30, the sample variance was $s^2 = 64$, and the hypothesized value for the population variance was $\sigma_0^2 = 100$. Using the worksheet in Figure 11.5, we can type 30 into cell D3, 64 into cell D4, and 100 into cell D6. The correct two-tailed *p*-value will then be given in cell D13. Try it. You should get a *p*-value of .1359.

## EXERCISES

### Methods

1. Find the following chi-square distribution values from Table 11.1 or Table 3 of Appendix B.
   a. $\chi_{.05}^2$ with 5 degrees of freedom
   b. $\chi_{.025}^2$ with 15 degrees of freedom
   c. $\chi_{.975}^2$ with 20 degrees of freedom
   d. $\chi_{.01}^2$ with 10 degrees of freedom
   e. $\chi_{.95}^2$ with 18 degrees of freedom

2. A sample of 20 items provides a sample standard deviation of 5.
   a. Compute the 90% confidence interval estimate of the population variance.
   b. Compute the 95% confidence interval estimate of the population variance.
   c. Compute the 95% confidence interval estimate of the population standard deviation.

3. A sample of 16 items provides a sample standard deviation of 8. Test the following hypotheses using $\alpha = .05$. What is your conclusion?

$$H_0: \sigma^2 \leq 50$$
$$H_a: \sigma^2 > 50$$

### Applications

4. The variance in drug weights is critical in the pharmaceutical industry. For a specific drug, with weights measured in grams, a sample of 18 units provided a sample variance of $s^2 = .36$.
   a. Construct a 90% confidence interval estimate of the population variance for the weights of this drug.
   b. Construct a 90% confidence interval estimate of the population standard deviation.

**5.** The daily car rental rates for a sample of eight cities follow (*The Wall Street Journal*, December 12, 1997).

| City | Daily Car Rental Rate ($) |
|---|---|
| Atlanta | 47 |
| Chicago | 50 |
| Dallas | 53 |
| New Orleans | 45 |
| Phoenix | 40 |
| Pittsburgh | 43 |
| San Francisco | 39 |
| Seattle | 37 |

   **a.** Compute the variance and the standard deviation for these data.
   **b.** What is the 95% confidence interval estimate of the variance of car rental rates for the population?
   **c.** What is the 95% confidence interval estimate of the standard deviation for the population?

**6.** The Oppenheimer Capital Appreciation mutual fund provided a 17.6% average annual return over a 5-year period (*Fortune*, August 18, 1997). Assume that the following data show the annual returns for each of the 5 years: 10.8, 34.2, 4.2, 9.4, and 29.4. The standard deviation of the annual returns can be used as a measure of risk, with a larger standard deviation indicating more variation and therefore more uncertainty in the annual returns. A standard deviation of 18.2% was reported for the 10 aggressive growth mutual funds similar to the Oppenheimer Capital Appreciation mutual fund.
   **a.** Using the data as a sample of five annual returns, compute the sample standard deviation measure of risk for the Oppenheimer Capital Appreciation mutual fund?
   **b.** What is the 95% confidence interval for the population standard deviation of annual returns for the Oppenheimer Capital Appreciation mutual fund?

**7.** A sample of eight earnings per share estimates for 1998 is shown here (*Barron's*, December 8, 1997).

| Company | Estimated Earnings per Share |
|---|---|
| AT&T | 2.92 |
| Caterpillar | 4.65 |
| Eastman Kodak | 4.27 |
| Exxon | 3.09 |
| Hewlett-Packard | 3.57 |
| IBM | 7.04 |
| McDonald's | 2.64 |
| Wal-Mart | 1.74 |

   **a.** Compute the sample variance and sample standard deviation for these data.
   **b.** What is the 95% confidence interval for the population variance?
   **c.** What is the 95% confidence interval for the population standard deviation?

**8.** A group of 12 security analysts provided the following estimates of the year 2001 earnings per share for Qualcomm, Inc. (*Zacks.com*, June 13, 2000).

   1.40    1.40    1.45    1.49    1.37    1.27    1.40    1.55    1.40    1.42    1.48    1.63

   **a.** Compute the sample variance for the earnings per share estimates.
   **b.** Compute the sample standard deviation for the earnings per share estimates.
   **c.** Provide 95% confidence interval estimates of the population variance and the population standard deviation.

**9.** An automotive part must be machined to close tolerances to be acceptable to customers. Production specifications call for a maximum variance in the lengths of the parts of .0004. Suppose the sample variance for 30 parts turns out to be $s^2 = .0005$. Using $\alpha = .05$, test to see whether the population variance specification is being violated.

**10.** The average useful life of a VCR is 6 years with a standard deviation of .75 years (*Consumer Reports 1995 Buying Guide*). A sample of the useful life of 30 television sets provided a sample standard deviation of 2 years. Construct a hypothesis test that can be used to determine whether the standard deviation of the useful life of television sets is significantly greater than the standard deviation of the useful life of VCRs. With a .05 level of significance, what is your conclusion?

**11.** Home mortgage interest rates for 30-year fixed-rate loans vary throughout the country. During the summer of 2000, data available from various parts of the country suggested that the standard deviation of the interest rates was .096 (*The Wall Street Journal,* September 8, 2000). The corresponding variance in interest rates would be $(.096)^2 = .009216$. Consider a follow-up study in the summer of 2001. The interest rates for 30-year fixed rate loans at a sample of 20 lending institutions had a sample standard deviation of .114. Conduct a hypothesis test with $H_0$: $\sigma^2 = .009216$ to see whether the sample data indicate that the variability in interest rates changed. Use $\alpha = .05$. What is your conclusion?

**12.** A *Fortune* subscriber study found that the variance in the number of vehicles owned or leased by subscribers to *Fortune* magazine is .94. Assume a sample of 12 subscribers to another magazine provided the following data on the number of vehicles owned or leased: 2, 1, 2, 0, 3, 2, 2, 1, 2, 1, 0, and 1.
  **a.** Compute the sample variance in the number of vehicles owned or leased by the 12 subscribers of the other magazine.
  **b.** Conduct a hypothesis test to determine if the variance in the number of vehicles owned or leased by subscribers of the other magazine differs from $\sigma^2 = .94$. Using a .05 level of significance, what is your conclusion?

## 11.2    INFERENCES ABOUT THE VARIANCES OF TWO POPULATIONS

In some statistical applications we might want to compare the variances in product quality resulting from two different production processes; e.g. the variances in assembly times for two assembly methods, or the variances in temperatures for two heating devices. In making comparisons about the variances of two populations, we will be using data collected from two independent random samples, one from population 1 and another from population 2. The two sample variances $s_1^2$ and $s_2^2$ will be the basis for making inferences about the two population variances $\sigma_1^2$ and $\sigma_2^2$. Whenever the variances of two normal populations are equal ($\sigma_1^2 = \sigma_2^2$), the sampling distribution of the ratio of the two sample variances $s_1^2/s_2^2$ is as follows.

*The F distribution is based on sampling from two normal populations.*

**Sampling Distribution of $s_1^2/s_2^2$ When $\sigma_1^2 = \sigma_2^2$**

Whenever independent simple random samples of sizes $n_1$ and $n_2$ are selected from two normal populations with equal variances, the sampling distribution of

$$\frac{s_1^2}{s_2^2} \qquad\qquad \textbf{(11.9)}$$

has an $F$ distribution with $n_1 - 1$ degrees of freedom for the numerator and $n_2 - 1$ degrees of freedom for the denominator; $s_1^2$ is the sample variance for the simple random sample of $n_1$ items from population 1, and $s_2^2$ is the sample variance for the simple random sample of $n_2$ items from population 2.

Figure 11.6 is a graph of the $F$ distribution with 20 degrees of freedom for both the numerator and denominator. As can be seen from this graph, the $F$ distribution is not symmetric, and the $F$ values can never be negative. The shape of any particular $F$ distribution depends on its numerator and denominator degrees of freedom.

We will use $F_\alpha$ to denote the value for the $F$ distribution that provides an area or probability of $\alpha$ to the *right* of the stated $F_\alpha$ value. For example, as noted in Figure 11.6, $F_{.05}$ denotes the upper 5% of the $F$ values for an $F$ distribution with 20 degrees of freedom for the numerator and 20 degrees of freedom for the denominator. Table 11.4 shows that for this particular $F$ distribution, $F_{.05} = 2.12$. Table 4 of Appendix B is a more extensive table of $F$ distribution values. Let us show how the $F$ distribution can be used for a hypothesis test about the variances of two populations.

Dullus County Schools is renewing its school bus service contract for the coming year and must select one of two bus companies, the Milbank Company or the Gulf Park Company. We will use the variance of the arrival times as a primary measure of the quality of the bus service. Low variance values indicate more consistent and higher-quality service. If the variances of arrival times associated with the two services are equal, Dullus School administrators will select the company offering the better financial terms. However, if the sample data on bus arrival times for the two companies indicate a significant difference between the variances, the administrators may want to give special consideration to the company with the better or lower variance service. The appropriate hypotheses follow.

$$H_0: \sigma_1^2 = \sigma_2^2$$
$$H_a: \sigma_1^2 \neq \sigma_2^2$$

If $H_0$ can be rejected, the conclusion of unequal service quality is appropriate. In that case, the company with the lower sample variance would be preferred.

Assume that the hypothesis test will be conducted with $\alpha = .10$. Furthermore, assume that we obtain samples of arrival times from school systems currently using the two school bus services. A sample of 25 arrival times is available for the Milbank service (population 1) and a sample of 16 arrival times is available for the Gulf Park service (population 2). Figure 11.7 is the graph of the $F$ distribution with $n_1 - 1 = 24$ degrees of freedom for the numerator and $n_2 - 1 = 15$ degrees of freedom for the denominator. Note that the two-tailed rejection region is indicated by the critical values at $F_{.95}$ and $F_{.05}$.

**FIGURE 11.6**    *F* DISTRIBUTION WITH 20 DEGREES OF FREEDOM FOR THE
NUMERATOR AND 20 DEGREES OF FREEDOM FOR THE DENOMINATOR

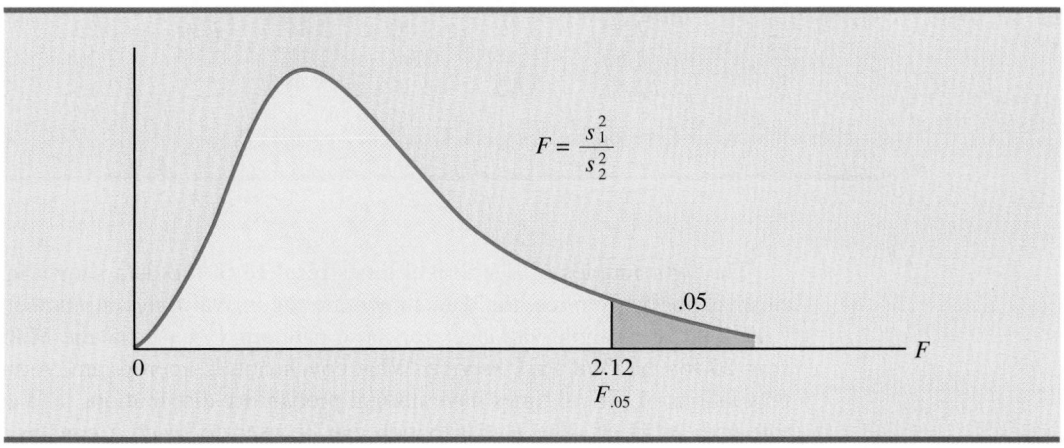

**TABLE 11.4**   SELECTED VALUES FROM THE $F$ DISTRIBUTION TABLE*

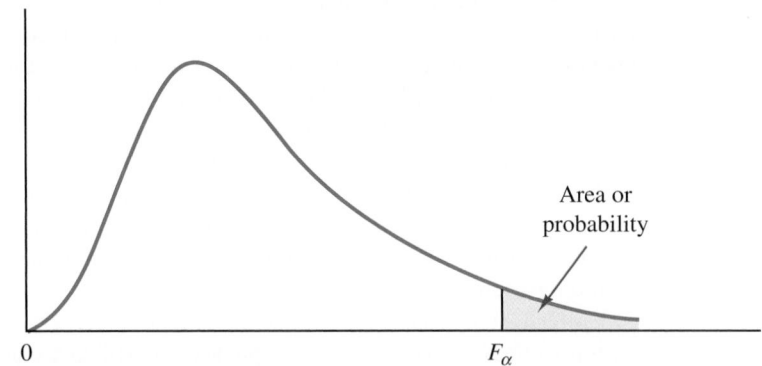

| Denominator Degrees of Freedom | \multicolumn{8}{c}{Table of $F_{.05}$ Values Numerator Degrees of Freedom} | | | | | | | |
|---|---|---|---|---|---|---|---|---|
| | **6** | **7** | **8** | **9** | **10** | **12** | **15** | **20** |
| 1 | 234.0 | 236.8 | 238.9 | 240.5 | 241.9 | 243.9 | 245.9 | 248.0 |
| 2 | 19.33 | 19.35 | 19.37 | 19.38 | 19.40 | 19.41 | 19.43 | 19.45 |
| 3 | 8.94 | 8.89 | 8.85 | 8.81 | 8.79 | 8.74 | 8.70 | 8.66 |
| 4 | 6.16 | 6.09 | 6.04 | 6.00 | 5.96 | 5.91 | 5.86 | 5.80 |
| 5 | 4.95 | 4.88 | 4.82 | 4.77 | 4.74 | 4.68 | 4.62 | 4.56 |
| 6 | 4.28 | 4.21 | 4.15 | 4.10 | 4.06 | 4.00 | 3.94 | 3.87 |
| 7 | 3.87 | 3.79 | 3.73 | 3.68 | 3.64 | 3.57 | 3.51 | 3.44 |
| 8 | 3.58 | 3.50 | 3.44 | 3.39 | 3.35 | 3.28 | 3.22 | 3.15 |
| 9 | 3.37 | 3.29 | 3.23 | 3.18 | 3.14 | 3.07 | 3.01 | 2.94 |
| 10 | 3.22 | 3.14 | 3.07 | 3.02 | 2.98 | 2.91 | 2.85 | 2.77 |
| 11 | 3.09 | 3.01 | 2.95 | 2.90 | 2.85 | 2.79 | 2.72 | 2.65 |
| 12 | 3.00 | 2.91 | 2.85 | 2.80 | 2.75 | 2.69 | 2.62 | 2.54 |
| 13 | 2.92 | 2.83 | 2.77 | 2.71 | 2.67 | 2.60 | 2.53 | 2.46 |
| 14 | 2.85 | 2.76 | 2.70 | 2.65 | 2.60 | 2.53 | 2.46 | 2.39 |
| 15 | 2.79 | 2.71 | 2.64 | 2.59 | 2.54 | 2.48 | 2.40 | 2.33 |
| 16 | 2.74 | 2.66 | 2.59 | 2.54 | 2.49 | 2.42 | 2.35 | 2.28 |
| 17 | 2.70 | 2.61 | 2.55 | 2.49 | 2.45 | 2.38 | 2.31 | 2.23 |
| 18 | 2.66 | 2.58 | 2.51 | 2.46 | 2.41 | 2.34 | 2.27 | 2.19 |
| 19 | 2.63 | 2.54 | 2.48 | 2.42 | 2.38 | 2.31 | 2.23 | 2.16 |
| 20 | 2.60 | 2.51 | 2.45 | 2.39 | 2.35 | 2.28 | 2.20 | 2.12 |
| 21 | 2.57 | 2.49 | 2.42 | 2.37 | 2.32 | 2.25 | 2.18 | 2.10 |
| 22 | 2.55 | 2.46 | 2.40 | 2.34 | 2.30 | 2.23 | 2.15 | 2.07 |
| 23 | 2.53 | 2.44 | 2.37 | 2.32 | 2.27 | 2.20 | 2.13 | 2.05 |
| 24 | 2.51 | 2.42 | 2.36 | 2.30 | 2.25 | 2.18 | 2.11 | 2.03 |

*For additional $F$ distribution values, see Table 4 of Appendix B.

The two samples of bus arrival times resulted in the data shown in Table 11.5. For each school bus service, the data shown are the arrival times in number of minutes past 7:00 A.M. The sample variances for these data are $s_1^2 = 48$ for the Milbank service and $s_2^2 = 20$ for the Gulf Park service. What conclusion is appropriate? Assume that the two populations of arrival times have normal probability distributions, and assume that $H_0$ is true with $\sigma_1^2 = \sigma_2^2$. The $F$ distribution can be used to reach a conclusion. We compute

**FIGURE 11.7**    REJECTION REGION FOR THE DULLUS COUNTY SCHOOL BUS
EXAMPLE WITH $\alpha = .10$

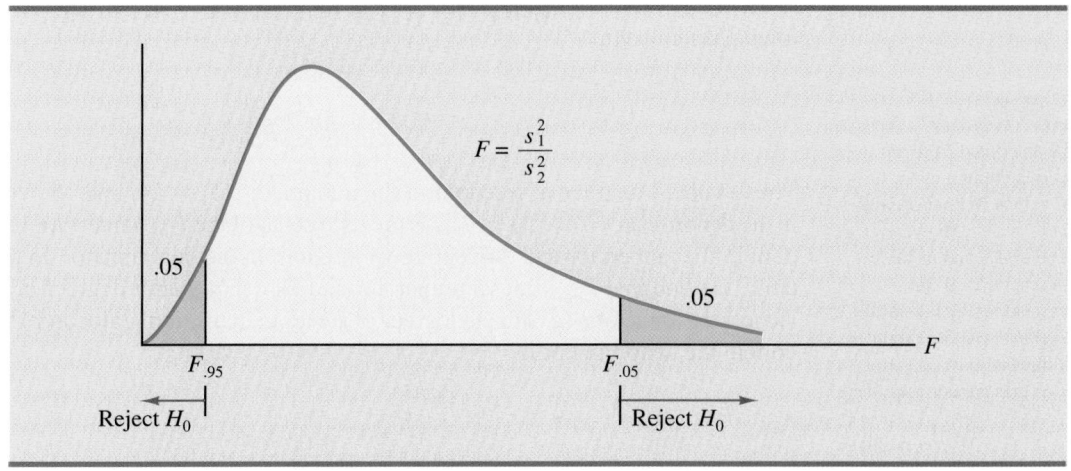

$F = s_1^2/s_2^2$ and use the rejection region shown in Figure 11.7. With the sample variances of
48 and 28, we find

$$F = \frac{s_1^2}{s_2^2} = \frac{48}{20} = 2.40$$

Using Table 4 of Appendix B, we find that the upper-tail critical value with 24 numerator
degrees of freedom and 15 denominator degrees of freedom is $F_{.05} = 2.29$. Although Table 4
does not provide $F_{.95}$ values, the determination of this lower-tail critical value is not necessary. We can already observe that $F = 2.40$ exceeds $F_{.05} = 2.29$. Thus, at the .10 level of
significance, $H_0$ is rejected. This finding leads us to the conclusion that the two bus services
differ in terms of arrival time variances. The recommendation is that the Dullus School administrators give special consideration to the better or lower variance service offered by the
Gulf Park Company.

The $p$-value criterion can also be used for a hypothesis test about two population variances. The usual rejection rule applies: Reject $H_0$ if $p$-value $< \alpha$. However, like the chi-
square distribution, it is difficult to determine the $p$-value directly from the tables of $F$
distribution. Again, a computer software package such as Excel is required. In the Dullus
County Schools example, $F = 2.40$ provided a $p$-value $= .0824$. With a $p$-value $= .0824 <$
$\alpha = .10$, the null hypothesis of equal variances is rejected. In the Excel illustration at the
end of this section, we will show how to compute this $p$-value.

In the Dullus County School bus example, you might feel that we were lucky in carrying out the two-tailed test because the lower-tail critical value $F_{.95}$, which is not provided

**TABLE 11.5**    ARRIVAL TIMES IN NUMBER OF MINUTES PAST 7:00 A.M. FOR THE
DULLUS COUNTY SCHOOL BUS EXAMPLE

| Milbank | | | | | Gulf Park | | | |
|---|---|---|---|---|---|---|---|---|
| 35.9 | 15.9 | 5.0 | 28.1 | 10.1 | 21.6 | 17.2 | 20.4 | 26.0 |
| 29.9 | 18.8 | 25.4 | 12.1 | 23.0 | 20.5 | 7.7 | 22.4 | 17.1 |
| 31.2 | 22.2 | 14.7 | 21.4 | 19.4 | 23.3 | 18.6 | 23.1 | 27.9 |
| 16.2 | 19.9 | 22.7 | 22.9 | 15.2 | 18.8 | 18.7 | 19.8 | 20.8 |
| 19.0 | 16.4 | 18.0 | 21.0 | 28.2 | | | | |

**CD** file

**Dullus**

in the $F$ distribution table, was not necessary. We were able to draw the appropriate hypothesis testing conclusion without knowing the value of $F_{.95}$. If you ever need to know a lower-tail $F$ value, $F_{(1-\alpha)}$, it can be determined by using an upper-tail $F_\alpha$ value and the following relationship.

| | |
|---|---|
| Expression (11.10) shows how lower-tail $F$ values can be computed from the corresponding upper-tail $F$ values. With the upper-tail $F$ values shown in Table 11.4 and in Table 4 of Appendix B, the corresponding lower-tail $F$ values can be computed. Tables with lower-tail $F$ values are not necessary. | |

$$F_{(1-\alpha),df_1,df_2} = \frac{1}{F_{\alpha,df_2,df_1}} \qquad \textbf{(11.10)}$$

Thus, with 24 degrees of freedom in the numerator ($df_1 = 24$) and 15 degrees of freedom in the denominator ($df_2 = 15$), $F_{.95}$ is the reciprocal of the $F_{.05}$ value with 15 degrees of freedom in the numerator and 24 degrees of freedom in the denominator. In the $F$ distribution table, we find that $F_{.05}$ with 15 numerator and 24 denominator degrees of freedom is 2.11. Hence, the value of $F_{.95}$ with 24 degrees of freedom in the numerator and 15 degrees of freedom in the denominator is

$$F_{.95} = \frac{1}{2.11} = .47$$

Although expression (11.10) can be used to compute a lower-tail $F$ value, common practice is to conduct the hypothesis test computations so that only upper-tail $F$ values are needed. In hypothesis tests with $H_0: \sigma_1^2 = \sigma_2^2$, we simply denote the population with the *larger sample variance* as population 1. That is, deciding which population to denote as either population 1 or 2 is arbitrary. By labeling the population with the larger sample variance as population 1, we guarantee that a rejection of $H_0$ can occur only in the *upper tail*. Although the lower-tail critical value still exists, we do not need to know its value because the convention of using the population with the largest sample variance as population 1 always places the ratio $s_1^2/s_2^2$ in the upper-tail direction. In the Dullus School example, population 1, the Milbank bus service, had the largest sample variance. Hence, we proceeded directly with the test. If the Gulf Park bus service had provided the largest sample variance, we would have denoted Gulf Park as population 1 and followed the same statistical testing procedure. A summary of the two-tailed test for the equality of two population variances with this procedure follows.

A hypothesis test about two population variances can be formulated so that the rejection region is always in the upper tail of the sampling distribution. This approach eliminates the need for computing lower-tail $F$ distribution values.

---

**Two-Tailed Test About the Variances of Two Populations**

$$H_0: \sigma_1^2 = \sigma_2^2$$
$$H_a: \sigma_1^2 \neq \sigma_2^2$$

Denote the population providing the *largest sample variance* as population 1.

**Test Statistic**

$$F = \frac{s_1^2}{s_2^2}$$

**Rejection Rule**

Using test statistic:   Reject $H_0$ if $F > F_{\alpha/2}$
Using $p$-value:   Reject $H_0$ if $p$-value $< \alpha$

where the value of $F_{\alpha/2}$ is based on an $F$ distribution with $n_1 - 1$ degrees of freedom for the numerator and $n_2 - 1$ degrees of freedom for the denominator.

One-tailed tests involving two population variances are also possible. Again the $F$ distribution is used, with the one-tailed rejection region enabling us to conclude whether one population variance is significantly greater or significantly less than the other. Only upper-tail $F$ values are needed. For any one-tailed test we set up the null hypothesis so that the rejection region is in the upper tail, which can be accomplished by labeling the population with the larger variance in $H_a$ as population 1. The general procedure follows.

**One-Tailed Test About the Variances of Two Populations**

$$H_0: \sigma_1^2 \leq \sigma_2^2$$
$$H_a: \sigma_1^2 > \sigma_2^2$$

**Test Statistic**

$$F = \frac{s_1^2}{s_2^2}$$

**Rejection Rule**

Using test statistic:   Reject $H_0$ if $F > F_\alpha$

Using $p$-value:        Reject $H_0$ if $p$-value $< \alpha$

where the value of $F_\alpha$ is based on an $F$ distribution with $n_1 - 1$ degrees of freedom for the numerator and $n_2 - 1$ degrees of freedom for the denominator.

Let us demonstrate the use of the $F$ distribution to conduct a one-tailed test about the variances of two populations by considering a public opinion survey. Samples of 31 men and 41 women will be used to study attitudes about current political issues. The researcher conducting the study wants to test to see whether the sample data indicate that women have a greater variation in attitude on political issues than men. In the form of the one-tailed hypothesis test given previously, women will be denoted as population 1 and men will be denoted as population 2. The hypothesis test will be stated as follows.

$$H_0: \sigma_{\text{women}}^2 \leq \sigma_{\text{men}}^2$$
$$H_a: \sigma_{\text{women}}^2 > \sigma_{\text{men}}^2$$

If $H_0$ is rejected, the researcher will have the statistical support necessary to conclude that women have a greater variation in attitude on political issues.

With the sample variance for women in the numerator and the sample variance for men in the denominator, the $F$ distribution with $41 - 1 = 40$ degrees of freedom in the numerator and $31 - 1 = 30$ degrees of freedom in the denominator will be used to conduct the one-tailed test. With a .05 level of significance, the rejection region is based on $F_{.05}$. Using Table 4 of Appendix B, we find that $F_{.05} = 1.79$. Thus, the rejection rule becomes

Reject $H_0$ if $F > 1.79$

where $F$ is computed from the ratio of the two sample variances $s_1^2/s_2^2$.

Assume that the survey shows a sample variance of $s_1^2 = 120$ for the 41 women and a sample variance of $s_2^2 = 80$ for the 31 men. What is the appropriate statistical conclusion? The $F$ statistic becomes

$$F = \frac{s_1^2}{s_2^2} = \frac{120}{80} = 1.50$$

With 1.50 less than 1.79, $H_0$ cannot be rejected. Hence, the sample results do not support the conclusion that women have a greater variation than men in their attitudes on political issues.

## Using Excel to Conduct a Hypothesis Test

In this section we show how Excel's F-Test Two-Sample for Variances tool can be used to conduct a hypothesis test about the variances of the two populations in the Dullus County school bus example. Refer to Figure 11.8 as we describe the tasks involved.

**Enter Data:** Column A contains the arrival times for the Milbank service and column B contains the arrival times for the Gulf Park service.

**Apply Tools:** The following steps describe how to use Excel's F-Test Two-Sample for Variances tool.

**Step 1.** Select the **Tools** pull-down menu
**Step 2.** Choose the **Data Analysis** option
**Step 3.** When the Data Analysis dialog box appears:
Choose **F-Test Two-Sample for Variances**
Click **OK**
**Step 4.** When the F-Test Two-Sample for Variances dialog box appears:
Enter A1:A26 in the **Variable 1 Range** box
Enter B1:B17 in the **Variable 2 Range** box
Select **Labels**
Enter .05 in the **Alpha** box*
Select **Output Range**
Enter D1 in the **Output Range** box (to identify the upper left corner of the section of the worksheet where the output will appear)
Click **OK**

**FIGURE 11.8**  EXCEL WORKSHEET FOR THE DULLUS COUNTY SCHOOL BUS EXAMPLE

| | A | B | C | D | E | F | G |
|---|---|---|---|---|---|---|---|
| 1 | **Milbank** | **Gulf Park** | | F-Test Two-Sample for Variances | | | |
| 2 | 35.9 | 21.6 | | | | | |
| 3 | 29.9 | 20.5 | | | *Milbank* | *Gulf Park* | |
| 4 | 31.2 | 23.3 | | Mean | 20.5040 | 20.2438 | |
| 5 | 16.2 | 18.8 | | Variance | 47.9996 | 20.0000 | |
| 6 | 19.0 | 17.2 | | Observations | 25 | 16 | |
| 7 | 15.9 | 7.7 | | df | 24 | 15 | |
| 8 | 18.8 | 18.6 | | F | 2.4000 | | |
| 9 | 22.2 | 18.7 | | P(F<=f) one-tail | 0.0412 | | |
| 10 | 19.9 | 20.4 | | F Critical one-tail | 2.2878 | | |
| 11 | 16.4 | 22.4 | | | | | |
| 16 | 18.0 | 27.9 | | | | | |
| 17 | 28.1 | 20.8 | | | | | |
| 18 | 12.1 | | | | | | |
| 25 | 15.2 | | | | | | |
| 26 | 28.2 | | | | | | |
| 27 | | | | | | | |

Note: Rows 12–15 and 19–24 are hidden.

*This Excel procedure uses alpha as the area in one tail. The Dullus County school bus hypothesis test is a two-tailed test using $\alpha = .10$, with an area of .05 in the lower tail and an area of .05 in the upper tail.

The output labeled P(F $\leq$ f) one-tail, .0412, can be used to determine the $p$-value for the hypothesis test. If the Dullus County school bus example had been a one-tailed hypothesis test, .0412 would have been the $p$-value for the test. But, because it is a two-tailed test, we must multiply this value by 2 to obtain the correct $p$-value. Thus, the two-tailed $p$-value we are looking for is 2(.0412) = .0824. Because .0824 < $\alpha$ = .10, we can reject the null hypothesis that the two population variances are equal.

## NOTES AND COMMENTS

1. Researchers have noted that the $F$ distribution is sensitive to the assumption of normal populations. The $F$ distribution should not be used unless it is reasonable to assume that both populations are at least approximately normally distributed.
2. The $t$ test for the equality of two population means discussed in Chapter 10 requires the assumption that $\sigma_1^2 = \sigma_2^2$. It is sometimes suggested that a hypothesis test $H_0$: $\sigma_1^2 = \sigma_2^2$ based on the $F$ distribution be used prior to the $t$ test to indicate whether the $t$ test assumption of $\sigma_1^2 = \sigma_2^2$ appears valid. Unfortunately, researchers have reported that the $F$ test has a small probability of detecting cases in which the $t$ test performs poorly, and therefore have concluded that the $F$ test is not an effective preliminary test for the $t$ test (*The American Statistician*, November 1990).

## EXERCISES

### Methods

13. Find the following $F$ distribution values from Table 4 of Appendix B. Note: numerator degrees of freedom are the first value shown.
    a. $F_{.05}$ with degrees of freedom 12 and 10
    b. $F_{.025}$ with degrees of freedom 20 and 15
    c. $F_{.01}$ with degrees of freedom 8 and 12
    d. $F_{.975}$ with degrees of freedom 10 and 20

14. A sample of 16 items from population 1 has a sample variance of $s_1^2 = 5.8$ and a sample of 20 items from population 2 has a sample variance of $s_2^2 = 2.4$. Conduct the following hypothesis test at the .05 level of significance.

$$H_0: \sigma_1^2 \leq \sigma_2^2$$
$$H_a: \sigma_1^2 > \sigma_2^2$$

What is your conclusion?

15. Consider the following hypothesis test.

$$H_0: \sigma_1^2 = \sigma_2^2$$
$$H_a: \sigma_1^2 \neq \sigma_2^2$$

What is your conclusion if $n_1 = 25$, $s_1^2 = 4.0$, $n_2 = 21$, and $s_2^2 = 8.2$? Use $\alpha = .05$.

### Applications

16. Media Metrix and Jupiter Communications gathered data on the time adults and the time teens spend online during a month (*USA Today*, September 14, 2000). The study concluded that on average, adults spend more time online than teens. Assume that a follow-up study sampled 25 adults and 30 teens. The standard deviations of the time online during a month were 94 minutes for adults and 58 minutes for teens. Do the sample results support the conclusion that adults have a greater variance in online time than teens? Use $\alpha = .01$.

**17.** Most individuals are aware of the fact that the average annual repair cost for an automobile depends on the age of the automobile. A researcher is interested in finding out whether the variance of the annual repair costs also increases with the age of the automobile. A sample of 25 automobiles 4 years old showed a sample standard deviation for annual repair costs of $170 and a sample of 25 automobiles 2 years old showed a sample standard deviation for annual repair costs of $100.

   **a.** State the null and alternative versions of the research hypothesis that the variance in annual repair costs is larger for the older automobiles.

   **b.** For a .01 level of significance, what is your conclusion? Discuss the reasonableness of your findings.

**18.** The standard deviation in the 12-month earnings per share for 10 companies in the airline industry was 4.27, and the standard deviation in the 12-month earning per share for 7 companies in the automotive industry was 2.27 (*Business Week*, August 14, 2000). Conduct a test for equal variances at $\alpha = .05$. What is your conclusion about the variability in earnings per share for the airline industry and the automotive industry?

**19.** The variance in a production process is an important measure of the quality of the process. A large variance often signals an opportunity for improvement in the process by finding ways to reduce the process variance. Data showing the weight of tea bags in grams for two machines were presented in *Quality Progress* (February 1995). Conduct a statistical test to determine whether the variances in the bag weights for the two machines differ significantly. Use a .05 level of significance. What is your conclusion? Which machine, if either, provides the greater opportunity for quality improvements?

| Machine 1 | 2.95 | 3.45 | 3.50 | 3.75 | 3.48 | 3.26 | 3.33 | 3.20 |
|---|---|---|---|---|---|---|---|---|
|  | 3.16 | 3.20 | 3.22 | 3.38 | 3.90 | 3.36 | 3.25 | 3.28 |
|  | 3.20 | 3.22 | 2.98 | 3.45 | 3.70 | 3.34 | 3.18 | 3.35 |
|  | 3.12 |  |  |  |  |  |  |  |
| Machine 2 | 3.22 | 3.30 | 3.34 | 3.28 | 3.29 | 3.25 | 3.30 | 3.27 |
|  | 3.38 | 3.34 | 3.35 | 3.19 | 3.35 | 3.05 | 3.36 | 3.28 |
|  | 3.30 | 3.28 | 3.30 | 3.20 | 3.16 | 3.33 |  |  |

**20.** On the basis of data provided by a Romac salary survey, the variance in annual salaries for seniors in public accounting firms is approximately 2.1 and the variance in annual salaries for managers in public accounting firms is approximately 11.1. The salary data were provided in thousands of dollars. Assuming that the salary data were based on samples of 25 seniors and 25 managers, test the hypothesis that the population variances in the salaries are equal. With a .05 level of significance, what is your conclusion?

**21.** The Dow Jones Industrial Average varies as investors buy and sell shares of the 30 stocks that make up the average. Samples of the Dow Jones Industrial Average taken at different times during the first 5 days of November 1997 and the first 5 days of December 1997 are as follow (*Barron's,* December 8, 1997).

**CD** file

DowJones

| November | December |
|---|---|
| 7493 | 8066 |
| 7525 | 8209 |
| 7760 | 7842 |
| 7499 | 7943 |
| 7555 | 7846 |
| 7690 | 8071 |
| 7668 | 8055 |
| 7600 | 8159 |
| 7516 | 7828 |
| 7711 | 8109 |

    **a.** Compute the variances of the Dow Jones Industrial Average values for the two time periods.

    **b.** Using a .05 level of significance, test to determine whether the population variances for the two time periods are equal. What is your conclusion?

**22.** A research hypothesis is that the variance of stopping distances of automobiles on wet pavement is substantially greater than the variance of stopping distances of automobiles on dry pavement. In the research study, 16 automobiles traveling at the same speeds are tested for stopping distances on wet pavement and then tested for stopping distances on dry pavement. On wet pavement, the standard deviation of stopping distances is 32 feet. On dry pavement, the standard deviation is 16 feet.

    **a.** At a .05 level of significance, do the sample data justify the conclusion that the variance in stopping distances on wet pavement is greater than the variance in stopping distances on dry pavement?

    **b.** What are the implications of your statistical conclusions in terms of driving safety recommendations?

## SUMMARY

In this chapter we have presented statistical procedures that can be used to make inferences about population variances. In the process we have introduced two new probability distributions: the chi-square distribution and the $F$ distribution. The chi-square distribution can be used as the basis for interval estimation and hypothesis tests about the variance of a normal population.

    We illustrated the use of the $F$ distribution in hypothesis tests about the variances of two normal populations. In particular, we showed that with independent simple random samples of sizes $n_1$ and $n_2$ selected from two normal populations with equal variances ($\sigma_1^2 = \sigma_2^2$), the sampling distribution of the ratio of the two sample variances ($s_1^2/s_2^2$) has an $F$ distribution with $n_1 - 1$ degrees of freedom for the numerator and $n_2 - 1$ degrees of freedom for the denominator.

    We developed Excel worksheets for interval estimation and hypothesis testing concerning a single population variance. For the case of hypothesis tests involving two population variances, we showed how to use Excel's F-Test Two-Sample for Variances tool.

## KEY FORMULAS

**Interval Estimate of a Population Variance**

$$\frac{(n-1)s^2}{\chi_{\alpha/2}^2} \leq \sigma^2 \leq \frac{(n-1)s^2}{\chi_{(1-\alpha/2)}^2} \tag{11.7}$$

**Test Statistic for Hypothesis Tests About One Population Variance**

$$\chi^2 = \frac{(n-1)s^2}{\sigma_0^2} \tag{11.8}$$

**Test Statistic for Hypothesis Tests About Two Population Variances**

$$F = \frac{s_1^2}{s_2^2} \tag{11.9}$$

## SUPPLEMENTARY EXERCISES

**23.** Because of staffing decisions, managers of the Gibson-Marimont Hotel are interested in the variability in the number of rooms occupied per day during a particular season of the year. A sample of 20 days of operation shows a sample mean of 290 rooms occupied per day and a sample standard deviation of 30 rooms.
   **a.** What is the point estimate of the population variance?
   **b.** Provide a 90% confidence interval estimate of the population variance.
   **c.** Provide a 90% confidence interval estimate of the population standard deviation.

**24.** Initial public offerings (IPOs) of stocks are on average underpriced. The standard deviation measures the dispersion, or variation, in the underpricing-overpricing indicator. A sample of 13 Canadian IPOs that were subsequently traded on the Toronto Stock Exchange had a standard deviation of 14.95. Develop a 95% confidence interval estimate of the population standard deviation for the underpricing-overpricing indicator.

**25.** The estimated daily living costs for an executive traveling to various major cities follow (*Business Traveler,* June 1995). The estimates include a single room at a four-star hotel, beverages, breakfast, taxi fares, and incidental costs.

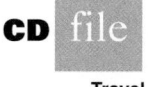

**Travel**

| City | Daily Living Cost ($) | City | Daily Living Cost ($) |
|------|------|------|------|
| Bangkok | 242.87 | Madrid | 283.56 |
| Bogota | 260.93 | Mexico City | 212.00 |
| Bombay | 139.16 | Milan | 284.08 |
| Cairo | 194.19 | Paris | 436.72 |
| Dublin | 260.76 | Rio de Janeiro | 240.87 |
| Frankfurt | 355.36 | Seoul | 310.41 |
| Hong Kong | 346.32 | Tel Aviv | 223.73 |
| Johannesburg | 165.37 | Toronto | 181.25 |
| Lima | 250.08 | Warsaw | 238.20 |
| London | 326.76 | Washington, D.C. | 250.61 |

   **a.** Compute the sample mean.
   **b.** Compute the sample standard deviation.
   **c.** Compute a 95% confidence interval for the population standard deviation.

**26.** Part variability is critical in the manufacturing of ball bearings. Large variances in the size of the ball bearings cause bearing failure and rapid wearout. Production standards call for a maximum variance of .0001 when the bearing sizes are measured in inches. A sample of 15 bearings shows a sample standard deviation of .014 inches.
   **a.** Using $\alpha = .10$, determine whether the sample indicates that the maximum acceptable variance is being exceeded.
   **b.** Compute the 90% confidence interval estimate of the variance of the ball bearings in the population.

**27.** The filling variance for boxes of cereal is designed to be .02 or less. A sample of 41 boxes of cereal shows a sample standard deviation of .16 ounces. Using $\alpha = .05$, determine whether the variance in the cereal box fillings is exceeding the design specification.

**28.** City Trucking, Inc., claims consistent delivery times for its routine customer deliveries. A sample of 22 truck deliveries shows a sample variance of 1.5. Test to determine whether $H_0: \sigma^2 \leq 1$ can be rejected. Use $\alpha = .10$.

**29.** Using a sample of 9 days over the past 6 months, a dentist has seen the following numbers of patients: 22, 25, 20, 18, 15, 22, 24, 19, and 26. If the number of patients seen per day is normally distributed, would an analysis of these sample data reject the hypothesis that the variance in the number of patients seen per day is equal to 10? Use a .10 level of significance. What is your conclusion?

30.  A sample standard deviation for the number of passengers taking a particular airline flight is 8. A 95% confidence interval estimate of the population standard deviation is 5.86 passengers to 12.62 passengers.

   a.  Was a sample size of 10 or 15 used in the statistical analysis?

   b.  If the sample standard deviation of $s = 8$ had been based on a sample of 25 flights, what change would you expect in the 95% confidence interval for the population standard deviation? Compute a 95% confidence interval estimate of $\sigma$ assuming $s = 8$ and $n = 25$.

31.  Each day the major stock markets have a group of leading gainers in price (stocks that go up the most). On one day the standard deviation in the percent change for a sample of 10 NASDAQ leading gainers was 15.8. On the same day, the standard deviation in the percent change for a sample of 10 NYSE leading gainers was 7.9 (*USA Today*, September 14, 2000). Conduct a test for equal population variances to see whether it can be concluded that there is a difference in the volatility of the leading gainers on the two exchanges. Use $\alpha = .10$. What is your conclusion?

32.  The grade point averages of 352 students who completed a college course in financial accounting have a standard deviation of .940. The grade point averages of 73 students who dropped out of the same course have a standard deviation of .797. Do the data indicate a difference between the variances of grade point averages for students who completed a financial accounting course and students who dropped out? Use a .05 level of significance.

33.  The accounting department analyzes the variance of the weekly unit costs reported by two production departments. A sample of 16 cost reports for each of the two departments shows cost variances of 2.3 and 5.4, respectively. Is this sample sufficient to conclude that the two production departments differ in terms of unit cost variance? Use $\alpha = .10$.

34.  Two new assembly methods are tested and the variances in assembly times are reported. Using $\alpha = .10$, test for equality of the two population variances.

| Method | Sample Size | Sample Variance |
|--------|-------------|-----------------|
| A      | 31          | 25              |
| B      | 25          | 12              |

## Case Problem   AIR FORCE TRAINING PROGRAM

An Air Force introductory course in electronics uses a personalized system of instruction whereby each student views a videotaped lecture and then is given a programmed instruction text. The students work independently with the text until they have completed the training and passed a test. Of concern is the varying pace at which the students complete this portion of their training program. Some students are able to cover the programmed instruction text relatively quickly, whereas other students work much longer with the text and require additional time to complete the course. The fast students wait until the slow students complete the introductory course before the entire group proceeds together with other aspects of their training.

   A proposed alternative system involves use of computer-assisted instruction. In this method, all students view the same videotaped lecture and then each is assigned to a computer terminal for further instruction. The computer guides the student, working independently, through the self-training portion of the course.

   To compare the proposed and current methods of instruction, an entering class of 122 students was assigned randomly to one of the two methods. One group of 61 students used the current programmed-text method and the other group of 61 students used the proposed computer-assisted method. The time in hours was recorded for each student in the study. The following data are provided on the data disk in the data set Training.

| | | | Course Completion Times (hours) for Current Training Method | | | | | | | |
|---|---|---|---|---|---|---|---|---|---|---|
| 76 | 76 | 77 | 74 | 76 | 74 | 74 | 77 | 72 | 78 | 73 |
| 78 | 75 | 80 | 79 | 72 | 69 | 79 | 72 | 70 | 70 | 81 |
| 76 | 78 | 72 | 82 | 72 | 73 | 71 | 70 | 77 | 78 | 73 |
| 79 | 82 | 65 | 77 | 79 | 73 | 76 | 81 | 69 | 75 | 75 |
| 77 | 79 | 76 | 78 | 76 | 76 | 73 | 77 | 84 | 74 | 74 |
| 69 | 79 | 66 | 70 | 74 | 72 | | | | | |

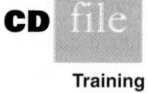

Training

| | | | Course Completion Times (hours) for Proposed Computer-Assisted Method | | | | | | | |
|---|---|---|---|---|---|---|---|---|---|---|
| 74 | 75 | 77 | 78 | 74 | 80 | 73 | 73 | 78 | 76 | 76 |
| 74 | 77 | 69 | 76 | 75 | 72 | 75 | 72 | 76 | 72 | 77 |
| 73 | 77 | 69 | 77 | 75 | 76 | 74 | 77 | 75 | 78 | 72 |
| 77 | 78 | 78 | 76 | 75 | 76 | 76 | 75 | 76 | 80 | 77 |
| 76 | 75 | 73 | 77 | 77 | 77 | 79 | 75 | 75 | 72 | 82 |
| 76 | 76 | 74 | 72 | 78 | 71 | | | | | |

## Managerial Report

1. Use appropriate descriptive statistics to summarize the training time data for each method. What similarities and/or differences do you observe from the sample data?
2. Use the methods of Chapter 10 to comment on any difference between the population means for the two methods. Discuss your findings.
3. Compute the standard deviation and variance for each training method. Conduct a hypothesis test about the equality of population variances for the two training methods. Discuss your findings.
4. What conclusion can you reach about any differences between the two methods? What is your recommendation? Explain.
5. Can you suggest other data or testing that might be desirable before making a final decision on the training program to be used in the future?

# TESTS OF GOODNESS OF FIT AND INDEPENDENCE

**Chapter 12**

**CONTENTS**

## STATISTICS IN PRACTICE

### UNITED WAY*
*Rochester, New York*

United Way of Greater Rochester is a nonprofit organization dedicated to improving the quality of life for all people in the seven counties it serves by meeting the community's most important human care needs.

The annual United Way/Red Cross fund-raising campaign, conducted each spring, funds hundreds of programs offered by more than 200 service providers. These providers meet a wide variety of human needs—physical, mental, and social—and serve people of all ages, backgrounds, and economic means. Because of enormous volunteer involvement, United Way of Greater Rochester is able to hold its operating costs at just eight cents of every dollar raised.

The United Way of Greater Rochester decided to conduct a survey to learn more about community perceptions of charities. Focus-group interviews were held with professional, service, and general worker groups to get preliminary information on perceptions. The information obtained was then used to help develop the questionnaire for the survey. The questionnaire was pretested, modified, and distributed to 440 individuals; 323 completed questionnaires were obtained.

A variety of descriptive statistics, including frequency distributions and crosstabulations, were provided from the data collected. An important part of the analysis involved the use of contingency tables and chi-square tests of independence. One use of such statistical tests was to determine whether perceptions of administrative expenses were independent of occupation.

The hypotheses for the test of independence were:

$H_0$: Perception of United Way administrative expenses is independent of the occupation of the respondent.

$H_a$: Perception of United Way administrative expenses is not independent of the occupation of the respondent.

*The authors are indebted to Dr. Philip R. Tyler, Marketing Consultant to the United Way, for providing this Statistics in Practice.

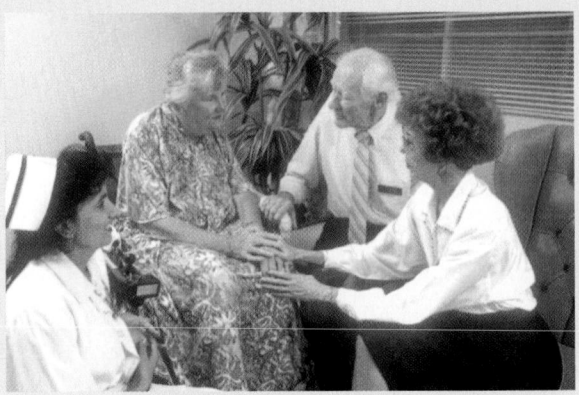

Statistical surveys help United Way adjust its programs to better meet the needs of the people it serves. © Tony Freeman/PhotoEdit, Inc.

Two questions in the survey provided the data for the statistical test. One question obtained data on perceptions of the percentage of funds going to administrative expenses (up to 10%, 11–20%, and 21% or more). The other question asked for the occupation of the respondent.

The chi-square test at a 5% level of significance led to rejection of the null hypothesis of independence and to the conclusion that perceptions of United Way's administrative expenses did vary by occupation. Actual administrative expenses were less than 9%, but 35% of the respondents perceived that administrative expenses were 21% or more. Hence, many had inaccurate perceptions of administrative expenses. In this group, production-line, clerical, sales, and professional-technical employees had more inaccurate perceptions than other groups.

The community perceptions study helped United Way of Rochester to develop adjustments to its program and fund-raising activities.

In this chapter, you will learn how a statistical test of independence, such as that described here, is conducted.

In Chapter 11 we showed how the chi-square distribution could be used in interval estimation and in hypothesis tests about a population variance. Here, we introduce two additional hypothesis testing procedures, both based on the use of the chi-square distribution. Like other hypothesis testing procedures, these tests compare sample results with those that are expected when the null hypothesis is true. The conclusion of the hypothesis test is based on how "close" the sample results are to the expected results.

In the following section we introduce a goodness of fit test for a multinomial population. Later we discuss the test for independence using contingency tables and then show goodness of fit tests for Poisson and normal probability distributions.

## 12.1    GOODNESS OF FIT TEST: A MULTINOMIAL POPULATION

In this section we consider the case in which each element of a population is assigned to one and only one of several classes or categories. Such a population is a **multinomial population.** The multinomial probability distribution can be thought of as an extension of the binomial distribution to the case of three or more categories of outcomes. On each trial of a multinomial experiment, one and only one of the outcomes occurs. Each trial of the experiment is assumed to be independent, and the probabilities of the outcomes stay the same for each trial.

*The assumptions for the multinomial experiment parallel those for the binomial experiment with the exception that the multinomial experiment has three or more outcomes per trial.*

As an example, consider the market share study being conducted by Scott Marketing Research. Over the past year market shares have stabilized at 30% for company A, 50% for company B, and 20% for company C. Recently company C has developed a "new and improved" product that has replaced its current entry in the market. Scott Marketing Research has been retained by company C to determine whether the new product will alter market shares.

In this example, the population of interest is a multinomial population; each customer is classified as buying from company A, company B, or company C. Thus, we have a multinomial population with three classifications or categories. Let us use the following notation for the proportions.

$$p_A = \text{market share for company A}$$
$$p_B = \text{market share for company B}$$
$$p_C = \text{market share for company C}$$

Scott Marketing Research will conduct a sample survey and compute the proportion preferring each company's product. A hypothesis test will then be conducted to see whether the new product has caused a change in market shares. Assuming that company C's new product will not alter the market shares, the null and alternative hypotheses are stated as follows.

$$H_0\text{: } p_A = .30, p_B = .50, \text{ and } p_C = .20$$

$$H_a\text{: The population proportions are not}$$
$$p_A = .30, p_B = .50, \text{ and } p_C = .20$$

If the sample results lead to the rejection of $H_0$, Scott Marketing Research will have evidence that the introduction of the new product has had an impact on the market shares.

Let us assume that the market research firm has used a consumer panel of 200 customers for the study. Each individual has been asked to specify a purchase preference among the three alternatives: company A's product, company B's product, and company C's new product. The 200 responses are summarized here.

*The consumer panel of 200 customers in which each individual is asked to select one of three alternatives is equivalent to a multinomial experiment consisting of 200 trials.*

| Observed Frequency | | |
|---|---|---|
| **Company A's Product** | **Company B's Product** | **Company C's New Product** |
| 48 | 98 | 54 |

We now can perform a **goodness of fit test** that will determine whether the sample of 200 customer purchase preferences is consistent with the null hypothesis. The goodness of fit test is based on a comparison of the sample of *observed* results with the *expected* results under the assumption that the null hypothesis is true. Hence, the next step is to compute expected purchase preferences for the 200 customers under the assumption that $p_A = .30$, $p_B = .50$, and $p_C = .20$. Doing so provides the expected results.

| | Expected Frequency | |
|---|---|---|
| **Company A's Product** | **Company B's Product** | **Company C's New Product** |
| $200(.30) = 60$ | $200(.50) = 100$ | $200(.20) = 40$ |

Thus, we see that the expected frequency for each category is found by multiplying the sample size of 200 by the hypothesized proportion for the category.

The goodness of fit test now focuses on the differences between the observed frequencies and the expected frequencies. Large differences between observed and expected frequencies cast doubt on the assumption that the hypothesized proportions or market shares are correct. Whether the differences between the observed and expected frequencies are "large" or "small" is a question answered with the aid of the following test statistic.

**Test Statistic for Goodness of Fit**

$$\chi^2 = \sum_{i=1}^{k} \frac{(f_i - e_i)^2}{e_i} \qquad (12.1)$$

where

$f_i$ = observed frequency for category $i$
$e_i$ = expected frequency for category $i$
$k$ = the number of categories

*Note:* The test statistic has a chi-square distribution with $k - 1$ degrees of freedom provided that the expected frequencies are 5 *or more* for all categories.

Let us return to the market share data for the three companies. Because the expected frequencies are all 5 or more, we can proceed with the computation of the chi-square test statistic. The calculations necessary to compute the chi-square test statistic for the Scott Marketing Research market share study are shown in Table 12.1. We see that the value of the test statistic is $\chi^2 = 7.34$.

Suppose we test the null hypothesis that the multinomial population has the proportions of $p_A = .30$, $p_B = .50$, and $p_C = .20$ at the $\alpha = .05$ level of significance. Because we will reject the null hypothesis if the differences between the observed and expected frequencies are *large*, we will place a rejection area of .05 in the upper tail of the chi-square distribution. Checking the chi-square distribution table (Table 3 of Appendix B), we find that with $k - 1 = 3 - 1 = 2$ degrees of freedom, $\chi^2_{.05} = 5.99$. With $7.34 > 5.99$, we reject $H_0$. In rejecting $H_0$ we are concluding that the introduction of the new product by company C will alter the current market share structure.

The test for goodness of fit is always a one-tailed test with the rejection region in the upper tail of the chi-square distribution.

**TABLE 12.1**    COMPUTATION OF THE CHI-SQUARE TEST STATISTIC FOR THE SCOTT MARKETING RESEARCH MARKET SHARE STUDY

| Category | Hypothesized Proportion | Observed Frequency $(f_i)$ | Expected Frequency $(e_i)$ | Difference $(f_i - e_i)$ | Squared Difference $(f_i - e_i)^2$ | Squared Difference Divided by Expected Frequency $(f_i - e_i)^2/e_i$ |
|---|---|---|---|---|---|---|
| Company A | .30 | 48 | 60 | −12 | 144 | 2.40 |
| Company B | .50 | 98 | 100 | −2 | 4 | 0.04 |
| Company C | .20 | 54 | 40 | 14 | 196 | 4.90 |
| Total | | 200 | | | | 7.34 |

*The p-value criterion can also be used for the goodness of fit test.*

Computer software packages such as Excel can greatly simplify the computations needed to perform a goodness of fit test for a multinomial popoulation. In the next subsection we will show how Excel was used to compute a p-value of .0255 for the Scott Marketing Research hypothesis test. Using the p-value, the decision of whether to reject $H_0$ at a given level of significance $\alpha$ is

$$\text{Reject } H_0 \text{ if the } p\text{-value} < \alpha$$

Because the p-value = .0255 < $\alpha$ = .05, we reject $H_0$ and conclude that the introduction of the new product will alter the current market share structure.

Although no further conclusions can be made as a result of the hypothesis test, we can compare the observed and expected frequencies informally to obtain an idea of how the market share structure may change. Considering company C, we find that the observed frequency of 54 is larger than the expected frequency of 40. Because the expected frequency was based on current market shares, the larger observed frequency suggests that the new product will have a positive effect on company C's market share. Comparisons of the observed and expected frequencies for the other two companies indicate that company C's gain in market share will hurt company A more than company B.

Let us summarize the general steps that can be used to conduct a goodness of fit test for any hypothesized multinomial population distribution.

**Multinomial Distribution Goodness of Fit Test: A Summary**

1. State the null and alternative hypotheses.

   $H_0$: The population follows a multinomial probability distribution with specified probabilities for each of the $k$ categories

   $H_a$: The population does not follow a multinomial probability distribution with the specified probabilities for each of the $k$ categories

2. Select a random sample and record the observed frequencies $f_i$ for each category.
3. Assuming the null hypothesis is true, determine the expected frequency $e_i$ in each category by multiplying the category probability by the sample size.
4. Compute the value of the test statistic.

$$\chi^2 = \sum_{i=1}^{k} \frac{(f_i - e_i)^2}{e_i}$$

**5.** Rejection rule

Using test statistic:   Reject $H_0$ if $\chi^2 > \chi_\alpha^2$

Using $p$-value:          Reject $H_0$ if $p$-value $< \alpha$

where $\alpha$ is the level of significance for the test and there are $k - 1$ degrees of freedom.

## Using Excel to Conduct a Goodness of Fit Test

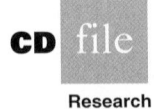

**Research**

Excel can be used to conduct a goodness of fit test for the Scott Marketing Research Study. Refer to Figure 12.1 as we describe the tasks involved. The formula worksheet is in the background; the value worksheet is in the foreground.

**Enter Data:**   Column A is used to identify each of the 200 customers who made up the consumer panel in the study. Column B shows the purchase preference (A, B, or C) for each customer. The hypothesized proportions, 0.3, 0.5, and 0.2, were entered into cells E4:E6.

**Enter Functions and Formulas:**   Excel's COUNTIF function was used to count the number of customers who preferred company A's product by entering the following formula into cell F4:

$$=COUNTIF(B2:B201,\text{``A''})$$

The COUNTIF function was also used in cells F5 and F6 to count the number of customers who preferred company B's product and company C's product, respectively. The SUM function was used in cell F7 to compute the total frequency. To compute the expected frequency for company A, the formula =E4*F7 was entered into cell G4; similar formulas were entered into cells G5 and G6 to compute the expected frequencies for company B and company C, respectively.

**FIGURE 12.1**   EXCEL WORKSHEET FOR THE SCOTT MARKETING RESEARCH MARKET SHARE

| | A | B | C | D | E | F | G | H | I | J | K |
|---|---|---|---|---|---|---|---|---|---|---|---|
| 1 | Customer | Product | | | | | | | | Squared Diff. | |
| 2 | 1 | B | | | Hyp. | Obs. | Exp. | | Squared | Divided by | |
| 3 | 2 | A | | Category | Proportion | Freq. | Freq. | Diff. | Diff. | Exp. Freq. | |
| 4 | 3 | C | | Company A | 0.3 | =COUNTIF(B2:B201,"A") | =E4*F7 | =F4-G4 | =H4^2 | =I4/G4 | |
| 5 | 4 | C | | Company B | 0.5 | =COUNTIF(B2:B201,"B") | =E5*F7 | =F5-G5 | =H5^2 | =I5/G5 | |
| 6 | 5 | C | | Company C | 0.2 | =COUNTIF(B2:B201,"C") | =E6*F7 | =F6-G6 | =H6^2 | =I6/G6 | |
| 7 | 6 | A | | | Total | =SUM(F4:F6) | | | | =SUM(J4:J6) | |
| 8 | 7 | A | | | | | | | | | |
| 9 | 8 | A | | Number of Categories | 3 | | | | | | |
| 10 | 9 | C | | | | | | | | | |
| 11 | 10 | A | | Test Statistic | =J7 | | | | | | |
| 12 | 11 | C | | Degrees of Freedom | =F9-1 | | | | | | |
| 13 | 12 | B | | | | | | | | | |
| 14 | 13 | C | | $p$-value | =CHIDIST(F11,F12) | | | | | | |
| 15 | 14 | A | | | | | | | | | |
| 200 | 199 | C | | | | | | | | | |
| 201 | 200 | C | | | | | | | | | |
| 202 | | | | | | | | | | | |

| | A | B | C | D | E | F | G | H | I | J |
|---|---|---|---|---|---|---|---|---|---|---|
| 1 | Customer | Product | | | | | | | | Squared Diff. |
| 2 | 1 | B | | | Hyp. | Obs. | Exp. | | Squared | Divided by |
| 3 | 2 | A | | Category | Proportion | Freq. | Freq. | Diff. | Diff. | Exp. Freq. |
| 4 | 3 | C | | Company A | 0.3 | 48 | 60 | -12 | 144 | 2.4 |
| 5 | 4 | C | | Company B | 0.5 | 98 | 100 | -2 | 4 | 0.04 |
| 6 | 5 | C | | Company C | 0.2 | 54 | 40 | 14 | 196 | 4.9 |
| 7 | 6 | A | | | Total | 200 | | | | 7.34 |
| 8 | 7 | A | | | | | | | | |
| 9 | 8 | A | | Number of Categories | 3 | | | | | |
| 10 | 9 | C | | | | | | | | |
| 11 | 10 | A | | Test Statistic | 7.34 | | | | | |
| 12 | 11 | C | | Degrees of Freedom | 2 | | | | | |
| 13 | 12 | B | | | | | | | | |
| 14 | 13 | C | | $p$-value | 0.0255 | | | | | |
| 15 | 14 | A | | | | | | | | |
| 200 | 199 | C | | | | | | | | |
| 201 | 200 | C | | | | | | | | |
| 202 | | | | | | | | | | |

Note: Rows 16–199 are hidden.

The difference between the observed frequency and the expected frequency for company A was computed by entering the formula =F4-G4 into cell H4. The squared difference for company A was computed by entering the formula =H4^2 into cell I4, and the squared difference divided by the expected frequency was computed by entering the formula =I4/G4 into cell J4. The formulas in cells H4:J4 were then copied into cells H5:J6 to make the same computation for company B and company C. Finally, the formula =SUM(J4:J6) was entered into cell J7 to compute the value of the test statistic (7.34). Note that the worksheet computations in Figure 12.1 parallel the computations shown in Table 12.1.

The number of categories, 3, was entered into cell F9. The test statistic computed in cell J7 was displayed in cell F11 by entering the formula =J7, and the degrees of freedom for the test was computed in cell F12 by entering the formula =F9-1. Finally, Excel's CHIDIST function was used to compute the $p$-value in cell F14. The form of the CHIDIST function is CHIDIST(test statistic, degrees of freedom); the value returned by the function is the upper-tail probability associated with the test statistic. Because the rejection region for a goodness of fit test is always in the upper tail, the value provided by the CHIDIST function is the $p$-value. Thus, to compute the $p$-value for the Scott Marketing Research goodness of fit test we entered the following formula into cell F14:

$$=CHIDIST(F11,F12)$$

The value worksheet shows that the resulting $p$-value is 0.0255. The decision of whether to reject $H_0$ at a given level of significance $\alpha$, is:

$$\text{Reject } H_0 \text{ if the } p\text{-value} < \alpha$$

Thus, with $\alpha = .05$ and the $p$-value $= 0.0255$, we reject $H_0$ and conclude that the introduction of the new product by company C will alter the current market share structure.

## NOTES AND COMMENTS

1. For $\chi^2$ goodness of fit tests the rejection region is always in the upper tail. The differences between observed and expected frequencies are squared, and larger differences lead to larger values for $\chi^2$.
2. Many applications of the goodness of fit test involve choosing a sample and observing the category to which each sampled item belongs. In such cases one must take care to choose a random sample. Otherwise, the independence assumption will not be satisfied.

## EXERCISES

### Methods

1. Test the following hypotheses using the $\chi^2$ goodness of fit test.

$$H_0: p_A = .40, p_B = .40, \text{ and } p_C = .20$$

$$H_a: \text{The population proportions are not}$$
$$p_A = .40, p_B = .40, \text{ and } p_C = .20$$

A sample of size 200 yielded 60 in category A, 120 in category B, and 20 in category C. Use $\alpha = .01$ and test to see whether the proportions are as stated in $H_0$.

2.  Suppose we have a multinomial population with four categories: A, B, C, and D. The null hypothesis is that the proportion of items is the same in every category. The null hypothesis is

$$H_0: p_A = p_B = p_C = p_D = .25$$

A sample of size 300 yielded the following results.

A: 85    B: 95    C: 50    D: 70

Use $\alpha = .05$ to determine whether $H_0$ should be rejected.

## Applications

3.  During the first 13 weeks of the television season, the Saturday evening 8:00 P.M. to 9:00 P.M. audience proportions were recorded as ABC 29%, CBS 28%, NBC 25%, and others 18%. A sample of 300 homes two weeks after a Saturday night schedule revision yielded the following viewing audience data: ABC 95 homes, CBS 70 homes, NBC 89 homes, and others 46 homes. Test with $\alpha = .05$ to determine whether the viewing audience proportions have changed.

**M&MCandy**

4.  M&M/MARS, makers of M&M® Chocolate Candies, conducted a national poll in which more than 10 million people indicated their preference for a new color. The tally of this poll resulted in the replacement of tan-colored M&Ms with a new blue color. In the brochure "Colors," made available by M&M/MARS Consumer Affairs, the distribution of colors for the plain candies is as follows:

| Brown | Yellow | Red | Orange | Green | Blue |
|:-----:|:------:|:---:|:------:|:-----:|:----:|
| 30% | 20% | 20% | 10% | 10% | 10% |

In a study reported in *Chance* (no. 4, 1996), samples of 1-pound bags were used to determine whether the reported percentages were indeed valid. The results obtained for a sample of 506 plain candies are shown in the data set M&MCandy. Use $\alpha = .05$ to determine whether these data support the percentages reported by the company.

5.  One of the questions on the *Business Week* 1996 Subscriber Study was, "When making investment purchases, do you use full service or discount brokerage firms?" Survey results showed that 264 respondents use full service brokerage firms only, 255 use discount brokerage firms only, and 229 use both full service and discount firms. Use $\alpha = .10$ to determine whether there are any differences in preference among the three service choices.

6.  Negative appeals have been recognized as an effective method of persuasion in advertising. A study in *The Journal of Advertising* (Summer 1997) reported the results of a content analysis of guilt advertisements in 24 magazines. The number of ads with guilt appeals that appeared in selected magazine types follow.

| Magazine Type | Number of Ads With Guilt Appeals |
|:--------------|:-----:|
| News and opinion | 20 |
| General editorial | 15 |
| Family-oriented | 30 |
| Business/financial | 22 |
| Female-oriented | 16 |
| African-American | 12 |

Using $\alpha = .10$ test to see whether there is a difference in the proportion of ads with guilt appeals among the six types of magazines.

7. Consumer panel preferences for three proposed store displays follow.

| Display A | Display B | Display C |
|-----------|-----------|-----------|
| 43 | 53 | 39 |

Use $\alpha = .05$ and test to see whether there is a difference in preference among the three display designs.

8. How well do airline companies serve their customers? A study showed the following customer ratings: 3% excellent, 28% good, 45% fair, and 24% poor (*Business Week,* September 11, 2000). In a similar study of service by telephone companies, assume that a sample of 400 adults found the following customer ratings: 24 excellent, 124 good, 172 fair, and 80 poor. Is the distribution of the customer ratings for telephone companies different from the distribution of customer ratings for airline companies? Test with $\alpha = .01$. What is your conclusion?

## 12.2  TEST OF INDEPENDENCE

Another important application of the chi-square distribution involves using sample data to test for the independence of two variables. Let us illustrate the test of independence by considering the study conducted by the Alber's Brewery of Tucson, Arizona. Alber's manufactures and distributes three types of beer: light, regular, and dark. In an analysis of the market segments for the three beers, the firm's market research group has raised the question of whether preferences for the three beers differ among male and female beer drinkers. If beer preference is independent of the gender of the beer drinker, one advertising campaign will be initiated for all of Alber's beers. However, if beer preference depends on the gender of the beer drinker, the firm will tailor its promotions to different target markets.

A test of independence addresses the question of whether the beer preference (light, regular, or dark) is independent of the gender of the beer drinker (male, female). The hypotheses for this test of independence are:

$H_0$: Beer preference is independent of the gender of the beer drinker
$H_a$: Beer preference is not independent of the gender of the beer drinker

*To test whether two variables are independent, one sample is selected and crosstabulation is used to summarize the data for the two variables simultaneously.*

Table 12.2 can be used to describe the situation being studied. After identification of the population as all male and female beer drinkers, a sample can be selected and each individual asked to state his or her preference for the three Alber's beers. Every individual in the sample will be classified in one of the six cells in the table. For example, an individual may be a male preferring regular beer (cell (1,2)), a female preferring light beer (cell (2,1)), a female preferring dark beer (cell (2,3)), and so on. Because we have listed all possible combinations of beer preference and gender or, in other words, listed all possible contingencies,

**TABLE 12.2**  CONTINGENCY TABLE FOR BEER PREFERENCE AND GENDER OF BEER DRINKER

| Gender | Beer Preference | | |
|--------|------------------|----------------|----------------|
| | **Light** | **Regular** | **Dark** |
| **Male** | cell(1,1) | cell(1,2) | cell(1,3) |
| **Female** | cell(2,1) | cell(2,2) | cell(2,3) |

**TABLE 12.3**    SAMPLE RESULTS FOR BEER PREFERENCES OF MALE AND FEMALE BEER DRINKERS (OBSERVED FREQUENCIES)

| Gender | Beer Preference | | | Total |
|---|---|---|---|---|
| | Light | Regular | Dark | |
| Male | 20 | 40 | 20 | 80 |
| Female | 30 | 30 | 10 | 70 |
| Total | 50 | 70 | 30 | 150 |

Table 12.2 is called a **contingency table.** The test of independence uses the contingency table format and for that reason is sometimes referred to as a **contingency table test.**

Suppose a simple random sample of 150 beer drinkers has been selected. After tasting each beer, the individuals in the sample are asked to state their preference or first choice. The crosstabulation in Table 12.3 summarizes the responses for the study. As we see, the data for the test of independence are collected in terms of counts or frequencies for each cell or category. Of the 150 individuals in the sample, 20 were men who favored light beer, 40 were men who favored regular beer, 20 were men who favored dark beer, and so on.

The data in Table 12.3 are the observed frequencies for the six classes or categories. If we can determine the expected frequencies under the assumption of independence between beer preference and gender of the beer drinker, we can use the chi-square distribution to determine whether there is a significant difference between observed and expected frequencies.

Expected frequencies for the cells of the contingency table are based on the following rationale. First we assume that the null hypothesis of independence between beer preference and gender of the beer drinker is true. Then we note that in the entire sample of 150 beer drinkers, a total of 50 prefer light beer, 70 prefer regular beer, and 30 prefer dark beer. In terms of fractions we conclude that $50/150 = 1/3$ of the beer drinkers prefer light beer, $70/150 = 7/15$ prefer regular beer, and $30/150 = 1/5$ prefer dark beer. If the *independence* assumption is valid, we argue that these fractions must be applicable to both male and female beer drinkers. Thus, under the assumption of independence, we would expect the sample of 80 male beer drinkers to show that $(1/3)80 = 26.67$ prefer light beer, $(7/15)80 = 37.33$ prefer regular beer, and $(1/5)80 = 16$ prefer dark beer. Application of the same fractions to the 70 female beer drinkers provides the expected frequencies shown in Table 12.4.

Let $e_{ij}$ denote the expected frequency for the contingency table category in row $i$ and column $j$. With this notation, let us reconsider the expected frequency calculation for males (row $i = 1$) who prefer regular beer (column $j = 2$); that is, expected frequency $e_{12}$. Following the preceding argument for the computation of expected frequencies, we can show that

$$e_{12} = (7/15)80 = 37.33$$

**TABLE 12.4**    EXPECTED FREQUENCIES IF BEER PREFERENCE IS INDEPENDENT OF THE GENDER OF THE BEER DRINKER

| Gender | Beer Preference | | | Total |
|---|---|---|---|---|
| | Light | Regular | Dark | |
| Male | 26.67 | 37.33 | 16.00 | 80 |
| Female | 23.33 | 32.67 | 14.00 | 70 |
| Total | 50.00 | 70.00 | 30.00 | 150 |

This expression can be written slightly differently as

$$e_{12} = (7/15)80 = (70/150)80 = \frac{(80)(70)}{150} = 37.33$$

Note that 80 in the expression is the total number of males (row 1 total), 70 is the total number of individuals preferring regular beer (column 2 total), and 150 is the total sample size. Hence, we see that

$$e_{12} = \frac{(\text{Row 1 Total})(\text{Column 2 Total})}{\text{Sample Size}}$$

Generalization of the expression shows that the following formula provides the expected frequencies for a contingency table in the test of independence.

**Expected Frequencies for Contingency Tables Under the Assumption of Independence**

$$e_{ij} = \frac{(\text{Row } i \text{ Total})(\text{Column } j \text{ Total})}{\text{Sample Size}} \tag{12.2}$$

Using the formula for male beer drinkers who prefer dark beer, we find an expected frequency of $e_{13} = (80)(30)/150 = 16.00$, as shown in Table 12.4. Use equation (12.2) to verify the other expected frequencies shown in Table 12.4.

The test procedure for comparing the observed frequencies of Table 12.3 with the expected frequencies of Table 12.4 is similar to the goodness of fit calculations made in Section 12.1. Specifically, the $\chi^2$ value based on the observed and expected frequencies is computed as follows.

**Test Statistic for Independence**

$$\chi^2 = \sum_i \sum_j \frac{(f_{ij} - e_{ij})^2}{e_{ij}} \tag{12.3}$$

where

$f_{ij}$ = observed frequency for contingency table category in row $i$ and column $j$

$e_{ij}$ = expected frequency for contingency table category in row $i$ and column $j$ based on the assumption of independence

*Note:* With $n$ rows and $m$ columns in the contingency table, the test statistic has a chi-square distribution with $(n - 1)(m - 1)$ degrees of freedom provided that the expected frequencies are five or more for all categories.

The double summation in equation (12.3) is used to indicate that the calculation must be made for all the cells in the contingency table.

By reviewing the expected frequencies in Table 12.4, we see that the expected frequencies are five or more for each category. We therefore proceed with the computation of

**TABLE 12.5**    COMPUTATION OF THE CHI-SQUARE TEST STATISTIC FOR DETERMINING WHETHER BEER PREFERENCE IS INDEPENDENT OF THE GENDER OF THE BEER DRINKER

| Gender | Beer Preference | Observed Frequency $(f_{ij})$ | Expected Frequency $(e_{ij})$ | Difference $(f_{ij} - e_{ij})$ | Squared Difference $(f_{ij} - e_{ij})^2$ | Squared Difference Divided by Expected Frequency $(f_{ij} - e_{ij})^2/e_{ij}$ |
|---|---|---|---|---|---|---|
| Male | Light | 20 | 26.67 | −6.67 | 44.49 | 1.67 |
| Male | Regular | 40 | 37.33 | 2.67 | 7.13 | 0.19 |
| Male | Dark | 20 | 16.00 | 4.00 | 16.00 | 1.00 |
| Female | Light | 30 | 23.33 | 6.67 | 44.49 | 1.91 |
| Female | Regular | 30 | 32.67 | −2.67 | 7.13 | 0.22 |
| Female | Dark | 10 | 14.00 | −4.00 | 16.00 | 1.14 |
| | Total | 150 | | | | 6.13 |

the chi-square test statistic. The calculations necessary to compute the chi-square test statistic for determining whether beer preference is independent of the gender of the beer drinker are shown in Table 12.5. We see that the value of the test statistic is $\chi^2 = 6.13$.

The number of degrees of freedom for the appropriate chi-square distribution is computed by multiplying the number of rows minus 1 by the number of columns minus 1. With two rows and three columns, we have $(2 - 1)(3 - 1) = (1)(2) = 2$ degrees of freedom for the test of independence of beer preference and gender of the beer drinker. With $\alpha = .05$ for the level of significance of the test, Table 3 of Appendix B shows an upper-tail $\chi^2$ value of $\chi^2_{.05} = 5.99$. Note that we are again using the upper-tail value because we will reject the null hypothesis only if the differences between observed and expected frequencies provide a large $\chi^2$ value. In our example, $\chi^2 = 6.13$ is greater than the critical value of $\chi^2_{.05} = 5.99$. Thus, we reject the null hypothesis of independence and conclude that beer preference is not independent of the gender of the beer drinker.

Computer software packages such as Excel can greatly simplify the computations needed to perform a test of independence and to provide the $p$-value for the test. In the next subsection we will show how Excel was used to compute a $p$-value of .0468 for the Alber's Brewery test of independence. Because the $p$-value = .0468 < $\alpha = .05$, we reject $H_0$ and conclude that beer preference is not independent of the gender of the beer drinker.

Although no further statistical conclusions can be made as a result of the test, we can compare the observed and expected frequencies informally to obtain an idea about the dependence between beer preference and gender. Refer to Tables 12.3 and 12.4. We see that male beer drinkers have higher observed than expected frequencies for both regular and dark beers, whereas female beer drinkers have a higher observed than expected frequency only for light beer. These observations give us insight about the beer preference differences between male and female beer drinkers.

Let us summarize the steps in a contingency table test of independence.

> *The test for independence is always a one-tailed test with the rejection region in the upper tail of the chi-square distribution.*

**Test of Independence: A Summary**

1. State the null and alternative hypotheses.

     $H_0$: The column variable is independent of the row variable

     $H_a$: The column variable is not independent of the row variable

2. Select a random sample and record the observed frequencies for each cell of the contingency table.

**3.** Use equation (12.2) to compute the expected frequency for each cell.

**4.** Use equation (12.3) to compute the value of the $\chi^2$ test statistic.

**5.** Rejection rule

$$\text{Using test statistic:}\quad \text{Reject } H_0 \text{ if } \chi^2 > \chi_\alpha^2$$

$$\text{Using } p\text{-value:}\qquad \text{Reject } H_0 \text{ if } p\text{-value} < \alpha$$

where $\alpha$ is the level of significance; with $n$ rows and $m$ columns providing $(n - 1)(m - 1)$ degrees of freedom.

## Using Excel to Conduct a Test of Independence

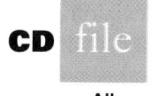

**Albers**

Excel can be used to conduct a test of independence for the Alber's Brewery example. Refer to Figure 12.2 as we describe the tasks involved. The formula worksheet is in the background; the value worksheet is in the foreground.

**Enter Data:**   Column A is used to identify each of the 150 individuals in the study. Column B shows the gender and column C shows the beer preference (Light, Regular, or Dark for each individual).

**Apply Tools:**   Using Excel's PivotTable tool (see Section 2.4 for details regarding how to use this tool), we developed the crosstabulation shown in cells E3:I7. The values in cells F5:H6 are the observed frequencies for the Alber's Brewery study.

**Enter Functions and Formulas:**   To compute the expected frequencies for the Alber's Brewery contingency table under the assumption of independence, we use equation (12.2).

**FIGURE 12.2**   EXCEL WORKSHEET FOR THE ALBER'S BREWERY TEST OF INDEPENDENCE

Note: Rows 17–148 are hidden.

| | A | B | C | D | E | F | G | H | I | J |
|---|---|---|---|---|---|---|---|---|---|---|
| 1 | Individual | Gender | Preference | | | | | | | |
| 2 | 1 | Female | Light | | | | | | | |
| 3 | 2 | Female | Regular | | Count of Individual | Preference ▾ | | | | |
| 4 | 3 | Male | Regular | | Gender ▾ | Light | Regular | Dark | Grand Total | |
| 5 | 4 | Female | Light | | Male | 20 | 40 | 20 | 80 | |
| 6 | 5 | Female | Light | | Female | 30 | 30 | 10 | 70 | |
| 7 | 6 | Female | Regular | | Grand Total | 50 | 70 | 30 | 150 | |
| 8 | 7 | Male | Regular | | | | | | | |
| 9 | 8 | Female | Dark | | Expected Frequencies | | | | | |
| 10 | 9 | Female | Regular | | | Light | Regular | Dark | | |
| 11 | 10 | Male | Dark | | Male | =F7*I5/I7 | =G7*I5/I7 | =H7*I5/I7 | | |
| 12 | 11 | Male | Regular | | Female | =F7*I6/I7 | =G7*I6/I7 | =H7*I6/I7 | | |
| 13 | 12 | Male | Regular | | | | | | | |
| 14 | 13 | Female | Regular | | | | chi-square | =CHIINV(H15,2) | | |
| 15 | 14 | Female | Regular | | | | p-value | =CHITEST(F5:H6,F11:H12) | | |
| 16 | 15 | Male | Light | | | | | | | |
| 149 | 148 | Male | Regular | | | | | | | |
| 150 | 149 | Female | Light | | | | | | | |
| 151 | 150 | Female | Regular | | | | | | | |
| 152 | | | | | | | | | | |

| | A | B | C | D | E | F | G | H | I | J |
|---|---|---|---|---|---|---|---|---|---|---|
| 1 | Individual | Gender | Preference | | | | | | | |
| 2 | 1 | Female | Light | | | | | | | |
| 3 | 2 | Female | Regular | | Count of Individual | Preference ▾ | | | | |
| 4 | 3 | Male | Regular | | Gender ▾ | Light | Regular | Dark | Grand Total | |
| 5 | 4 | Female | Light | | Male | 20 | 40 | 20 | 80 | |
| 6 | 5 | Female | Light | | Female | 30 | 30 | 10 | 70 | |
| 7 | 6 | Female | Regular | | Grand Total | 50 | 70 | 30 | 150 | |
| 8 | 7 | Male | Regular | | | | | | | |
| 9 | 8 | Female | Dark | | Expected Frequencies | | | | | |
| 10 | 9 | Female | Regular | | | Light | Regular | Dark | | |
| 11 | 10 | Male | Dark | | Male | 26.6667 | 37.3333 | 16 | | |
| 12 | 11 | Male | Regular | | Female | 23.3333 | 32.6667 | 14 | | |
| 13 | 12 | Male | Regular | | | | | | | |
| 14 | 13 | Female | Regular | | | | chi-square | 6.1225 | | |
| 15 | 14 | Female | Regular | | | | p-value | 0.0468 | | |
| 16 | 15 | Male | Light | | | | | | | |
| 149 | 148 | Male | Regular | | | | | | | |
| 150 | 149 | Female | Light | | | | | | | |
| 151 | 150 | Female | Regular | | | | | | | |
| 152 | | | | | | | | | | |

Thus, to compute the expected number of male drinkers who prefer light beer we entered the formula =F7*I5/I7 into cell F11. To compute the expected number of male drinkers who prefer regular beer we entered the formula =G7*I5/I7 into cell G11, and to compute the expected number of male drinkers who prefer dark beer we entered the formula =H7*I5/I7 into cell H11. Similar formulas were entered into cells F12:H12 to compute the expected frequencies for the females in the study.

Cells F5:H6 contain the observed frequencies, and cells F11:H12 contain the expected frequencies for the Alber's Brewery study. Although a cell formula could be written to compute equation (12.3), the $\chi^2$ test statistic for independence, it is simpler to use Excel's CHITEST function to compute the p-value for the test. To compute the p-value associated with this goodness of fit test, we entered the following function into cell H15:

$$=\text{CHITEST(F5:H6,F11:H12)}$$

The value worksheet shows that the resulting p-value is 0.0468. The decision of whether to reject $H_0$ at a given level of significance $\alpha$ is

$$\text{Reject } H_0 \text{ if the p-value} < \alpha$$

Thus, with $\alpha = .05$ and the p-value $= 0.0468$, we reject $H_0$ and conclude that beer preference is not independent of the gender of the beer drinker.

In using the Excel approach it was not necessary for us to compute the value of the test statistic; Excel did this calculation automatically as part of its procedure for computing the p-value. But, because the sampling distribution of the test statistic for the test of independence is a chi-square distribution, we can use Excel's CHIINV function to look up the value of the test statistic for independence corresponding to the p-value of 0.0468. In the previous section we indicated that the CHIINV function has two arguments: the upper-tail area and the degrees of freedom. The upper-tail area corresponds to the p-value of 0.0468 and the degrees of freedom are $(n-1)(m-1) = (2-1)(3-1) = 2$. Thus, in cell H14 we entered the following function in order to compute the test statistic:

$$=\text{CHIINV(H15,2)}$$

The value spreadsheet shows that the test statistic is 6.1225. The slight difference between 6.1225 and the value that we computed in Table 12.5 (6.13) using equation (12.3) is simply due to the additional accuracy Excel used in making the computation.

## NOTES AND COMMENTS

The test statistic for the chi-square tests in this chapter requires an expected frequency of five for each category. When a category has fewer than five, it is often appropriate to combine two adjacent categories to obtain an expected frequency of five or more in each category.

## EXERCISES

## Methods

9. The following $2 \times 3$ contingency table contains observed frequencies for a sample of 200. Test for independence of the row and column variables using the $\chi^2$ test with $\alpha = .025$.

| Row Variable | Column Variable | | |
|---|---|---|---|
| | **A** | **B** | **C** |
| **P** | 20 | 44 | 50 |
| **Q** | 30 | 26 | 30 |

10.  The following $3 \times 3$ contingency table contains observed frequencies for a sample of 240. Test for independence of the row and column variables using the $\chi^2$ test with $\alpha = .05$.

| | Column Variable | | |
|---|---|---|---|
| Row Variable | A | B | C |
| P | 20 | 30 | 20 |
| Q | 30 | 60 | 25 |
| R | 10 | 15 | 30 |

# Applications

11.  One of the questions on the *Business Week* 1996 Subscriber Study was, "In the past 12 months, when traveling for business, what type of airline ticket did you purchase most often?" The data obtained are shown in the following contingency table.

| | Type of Flight | |
|---|---|---|
| Type of Ticket | Domestic Flights | International Flights |
| First class | 29 | 22 |
| Business/executive class | 95 | 121 |
| Full fare economy/coach class | 518 | 135 |

Using $\alpha = .05$, test for the independence of type of flight and type of ticket. What is your conclusion?

12.  In a study of brand loyalty in the automotive industry, new-car customers were asked whether the make of their new car was the same as the make of their previous car (*Business Week,* May 8, 2000). The breakdown of 600 responses shows the brand loyalty for domestic, European, and Asian cars.

| | Manufacturer | | |
|---|---|---|---|
| Purchased | Domestic | European | Asian |
| Same Make | 125 | 55 | 68 |
| Different Make | 140 | 105 | 107 |

a.  Test a hypothesis to determine whether brand loyalty is independent of the manufacturer. Use $\alpha = .05$. What is your conclusion?

b.  If a significant difference is found, which manufacturer appears to have the greatest brand loyalty?

13.  Starting positions for business and engineering graduates are classified by industry as shown in the following table.

| | Industry | | | |
|---|---|---|---|---|
| Major | Oil | Chemical | Electrical | Computer |
| Business | 30 | 15 | 15 | 40 |
| Engineering | 30 | 30 | 20 | 20 |

Use $\alpha = .01$ and test for independence of major and industry type.

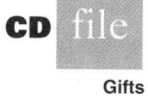

14.  The results of a study conducted by Marist Institute for Public Opinion showed who men and women say is the most difficult person for them to buy holiday gifts for (*USA Today,* December 15, 1997). Suppose that a follow-up study consisting of 100 men and 100 women was conducted. The data collected are shown in the data set Gifts. Use $\alpha = .05$ and test for independence of gender and the most difficult person to buy for. What is your conclusion?

15. Negative appeals have been recognized as an effective method of persuasion in advertising. A study in *The Journal of Advertising* (Summer 1997) reported the results of a content analysis of guilt and fear advertisements in 24 magazines. The number of ads with guilt and fear appeals that appeared in selected magazine types follows.

| | Type of Appeal | |
| --- | --- | --- |
| Magazine Type | Number of Ads with Guilt Appeals | Number of Ads with Fear Appeals |
| News and opinion | 20 | 10 |
| General editorial | 15 | 11 |
| Family-oriented | 30 | 19 |
| Business/financial | 22 | 17 |
| Female-oriented | 16 | 14 |
| African-American | 12 | 15 |

Use the chi-square test of independence with a .01 level of significance to analyze the data. What is your conclusion?

16. Businesses are increasingly placing orders online. The Performance Measurement Group collected data on the rates of correctly filled electronic orders by industry (*Investor's Business Daily*, May 8, 2000). Assume a sample of 700 electronic orders provided the following results.

| | Industry | | | |
| --- | --- | --- | --- | --- |
| Order | Pharmaceutical | Consumer | Computers | Telecommunications |
| Correct | 207 | 136 | 151 | 178 |
| Incorrect | 3 | 4 | 9 | 12 |

a. Test a hypothesis to determine whether correctness of order fulfillment is independent of industry. Use $\alpha = .05$. What is your conclusion?
b. Which industry has the highest percentage of correctly filled orders?

17. Three suppliers provide the following data on defective parts.

| | Part Quality | | |
| --- | --- | --- | --- |
| Supplier | Good | Minor Defect | Major Defect |
| A | 90 | 3 | 7 |
| B | 170 | 18 | 7 |
| C | 135 | 6 | 9 |

Use $\alpha = .05$ and test for independence between supplier and part quality. What does the result of your analysis tell the purchasing department?

18. A study of educational levels of voters and their political party affiliations yielded the following results.

| | Party Affiliation | | |
| --- | --- | --- | --- |
| Educational Level | Democratic | Republican | Independent |
| Did not complete high school | 40 | 20 | 10 |
| High school degree | 30 | 35 | 15 |
| College degree | 30 | 45 | 25 |

Use $\alpha = .01$ and determine whether party affiliation is independent of the educational level of the voters.

**19.** On the syndicated Siskel and Ebert television show the hosts often created the impression that they strongly disagreed about which movies were best. An article in *Chance* (no. 2, 1997) reported the results of ratings of 160 movies by Siskel and Ebert. Each review is categorized as Pro ("thumbs up"), Con ("thumbs down"), or Mixed.

|               | Ebert Rating |       |     |
|---------------|:------------:|:-----:|:---:|
| Siskel Rating | Con          | Mixed | Pro |
| **Con**       | 24           | 8     | 13  |
| **Mixed**     | 8            | 13    | 11  |
| **Pro**       | 10           | 9     | 64  |

Use the chi-square test of independence with a .01 level of significance to analyze the data. What is your conclusion?

## 12.3 GOODNESS OF FIT TEST: POISSON AND NORMAL DISTRIBUTIONS

In Section 12.1 we introduced the goodness of fit test for a multinomial population. In general, the goodness of fit test can be used with any hypothesized probability distribution. In this section we illustrate the goodness of fit test procedure for cases in which the population is hypothesized to have a Poisson or a normal probability distribution. As we shall see, the goodness of fit test and the use of the chi-square distribution for the test follow the same general procedure used for the goodness of fit test in Section 12.1.

### Poisson Distribution

Let us illustrate the goodness of fit test for the case in which the hypothesized population distribution is a Poisson distribution. As an example, consider the arrival of customers at Dubek's Food Market in Tallahassee, Florida. Because of some recent staffing problems, Dubek's managers have asked a local consulting firm to assist with the scheduling of clerks for the checkout lanes. After reviewing the checkout lane operation, the consulting firm makes a recommendation for a clerk-scheduling procedure. The procedure, based on a mathematical analysis of waiting lines, is applicable only if the number of customers arriving during a specified time period follows the Poisson probability distribution. Therefore, before the scheduling process is implemented, data on customer arrivals must be collected and a statistical test conducted to see whether an assumption of a Poisson distribution for arrivals is reasonable.

We define the arrivals at the store in terms of the *number of customers* entering the store during 5-minute intervals. Hence, the following null and alternative hypotheses are appropriate for the Dubek's Food Market study.

$H_0$: The number of customers entering the store during 5-minute intervals has a Poisson probability distribution

$H_a$: The number of customers entering the store during 5-minute intervals does not have a Poisson distribution

If a sample of customer arrivals indicates $H_0$ cannot be rejected, Dubek's will proceed with the implementation of the consulting firm's scheduling procedure. However, if the sample leads to the rejection of $H_0$, the assumption of the Poisson distribution for the arrivals cannot be made, and other scheduling procedures will have to be considered.

To test the assumption of a Poisson distribution for the number of arrivals during weekday morning hours, a store employee randomly selects a sample of 128 5-minute intervals

**TABLE 12.6**

OBSERVED
FREQUENCY
OF DUBEK'S
CUSTOMER
ARRIVALS FOR
A SAMPLE OF
128 5-MINUTE
TIME PERIODS

| Number of Customers Arriving | Observed Frequency |
|:---:|:---:|
| 0 | 2 |
| 1 | 8 |
| 2 | 10 |
| 3 | 12 |
| 4 | 18 |
| 5 | 22 |
| 6 | 22 |
| 7 | 16 |
| 8 | 12 |
| 9 | 6 |
| Total | 128 |

When the expected number in some category is less than five, the assumptions for the $\chi^2$ test are not satisfied. When this happens, adjacent categories can be combined to increase the expected number to five.

during weekday mornings over a 3-week period. For each 5-minute interval in the sample, the store employee records the number of customer arrivals. In summarizing the data, the employee determines the number of 5-minute intervals having no arrivals, the number of 5-minute intervals having one arrival, the number of 5-minute intervals having two arrivals, and so on. These data are summarized in Table 12.6.

Table 12.6 gives the observed frequencies for the 10 categories. We now want to use a goodness of fit test to determine whether the sample of 128 time periods supports the hypothesized Poisson probability distribution. To conduct the goodness of fit test, we need to consider the expected frequency for each of the 10 categories under the assumption that the Poisson distribution of arrivals is true. That is, we need to compute the expected number of time periods in which no customers, one customer, two customers, and so on would arrive if, in fact, the customer arrivals have a Poisson distribution.

The Poisson probability function, which was first introduced in Chapter 5, is

$$f(x) = \frac{\mu^x e^{-\mu}}{x!} \qquad (12.4)$$

In this function, $\mu$ represents the mean or expected number of customers arriving per 5-minute period, $x$ is the random variable indicating the number of customers arriving during a 5-minute period, and $f(x)$ is the probability that $x$ customers will arrive in a 5-minute interval.

Before we use equation (12.4) to compute Poisson probabilities, we must obtain an estimate of $\mu$, the mean number of customer arrivals during a 5-minute time period. The sample mean for the data in Table 12.6 provides this estimate. With no customers arriving in two 5-minute time periods, one customer arriving in eight 5-minute time periods, and so on, the total number of customers who arrived during the sample of 128 5-minute time periods is given by $0(2) + 1(8) + 2(10) + \cdots + 9(6) = 640$. The 640 customer arrivals over the sample of 128 periods provide a mean arrival rate of $\mu = 640/128 = 5$ customers per 5-minute period. With this value for the mean of the Poisson probability distribution, an estimate of the Poisson probability function for Dubek's Food Market is

$$f(x) = \frac{5^x e^{-5}}{x!} \qquad (12.5)$$

This probability function can be evaluated for different values of $x$ to determine the probability associated with each category of arrivals. These probabilities are given in Table 12.7. For example, the probability of zero customers arriving during a 5-minute interval is $f(0) = .0067$, the probability of one customer arriving during a 5-minute interval is $f(1) = .0337$, and so on. As we saw in Section 12.1, the expected frequencies for the categories are found by multiplying the probabilities by the sample size. For example, the expected number of periods with zero arrivals is given by $(.0067)(128) = .8576$, the expected number of periods with one arrival is given by $(.0337)(128) = 4.3136$, and so on.

Before we make the usual chi-square calculations to compare the observed and expected frequencies, note that in Table 12.7, four of the categories have an expected frequency less than five. This condition violates the requirements for use of the chi-square distribution. However, expected category frequencies less than five cause no difficulty here, because adjacent categories can be combined to satisfy the "at least five" expected frequency requirement. In particular, we will combine 0 and 1 into a single category and then combine 9 with "10 or more" into another single category. Thus, the rule of a minimum expected frequency of five in each category is satisfied. Table 12.8 shows the observed and expected frequencies after combining categories.

**TABLE 12.7**    EXPECTED FREQUENCY OF DUBEK'S CUSTOMER ARRIVALS, ASSUMING A POISSON PROBABILITY DISTRIBUTION WITH $\mu = 5$

| Number of Customers Arriving (x) | Poisson Probability $f(x)$ | Expected Number of 5-Minute Time Periods with x Arrivals, 128 $f(x)$ |
|---|---|---|
| 0 | .0067 | 0.8576 |
| 1 | .0337 | 4.3136 |
| 2 | .0842 | 10.7776 |
| 3 | .1404 | 17.9712 |
| 4 | .1755 | 22.4640 |
| 5 | .1755 | 22.4640 |
| 6 | .1462 | 18.7136 |
| 7 | .1044 | 13.3632 |
| 8 | .0653 | 8.3584 |
| 9 | .0363 | 4.6464 |
| 10 or more | .0318 | 4.0704 |
| | Total | 128.0000 |

As in Section 12.1, the goodness of fit test focuses on the differences between observed and expected frequencies, $f_i - e_i$. Thus, we will use the observed and expected frequencies shown in Table 12.8, to compute the chi-square test statistic.

$$\chi^2 = \sum_{i=1}^{k} \frac{(f_i - e_i)^2}{e_i}$$

The calculations necessary to compute the chi-square test statistic are shown in Table 12.9. The value of the test statistic is $\chi^2 = 10.9766$.

> The Poisson distribution has a single parameter $\mu$ that is estimated from the sample data. This causes a loss of one degree of freedom.

In general, the chi-square distribution for a goodness of fit test has $k - p - 1$ degrees of freedom, where $k$ is the number of categories and $p$ is the number of population parameters estimated from the sample data. For the Poisson distribution goodness of fit test we are considering, Table 12.9 shows $k = 9$ categories. Because the sample data were used to estimate

**TABLE 12.8**    OBSERVED AND EXPECTED FREQUENCIES FOR DUBEK'S CUSTOMER ARRIVALS AFTER COMBINING CATEGORIES

| Number of Customers Arriving | Observed Frequency $(f_i)$ | Expected Frequency $(e_i)$ |
|---|---|---|
| 0 or 1 | 10 | 5.1712 |
| 2 | 10 | 10.7776 |
| 3 | 12 | 17.9712 |
| 4 | 18 | 22.4640 |
| 5 | 22 | 22.4640 |
| 6 | 22 | 18.7136 |
| 7 | 16 | 13.3632 |
| 8 | 12 | 8.3584 |
| 9 or more | 6 | 8.7168 |
| Total | 128 | 128.0000 |

**TABLE 12.9**  COMPUTATION OF THE CHI-SQUARE TEST STATISTIC FOR THE DUBEK'S FOOD MARKET STUDY

| Number of Customers Arriving ($x$) | Observed Frequency ($f_i$) | Expected Frequency ($e_i$) | Difference ($f_i - e_i$) | Squared Difference ($f_i - e_i)^2$ | Squared Difference Divided by Expected Frequency ($f_i - e_i)^2/e_i$ |
|---|---|---|---|---|---|
| 0 or 1 | 10 | 5.1712 | 4.8288 | 23.3173 | 4.5091 |
| 2 | 10 | 10.7776 | −0.7776 | 0.6047 | 0.0561 |
| 3 | 12 | 17.9712 | −5.9712 | 35.6552 | 1.9840 |
| 4 | 18 | 22.4640 | −4.4640 | 19.9273 | 0.8871 |
| 5 | 22 | 22.4640 | −0.4640 | 0.2153 | 0.0096 |
| 6 | 22 | 18.7136 | 3.2864 | 10.8004 | 0.5771 |
| 7 | 16 | 13.3632 | 2.6368 | 6.9527 | 0.5203 |
| 8 | 12 | 8.3584 | 3.6416 | 13.2613 | 1.5866 |
| 9 or more | 6 | 8.7168 | −2.7168 | 7.3810 | 0.8468 |
| Total | 128 | 128.0000 | | | 10.9767 |

the mean of the Poisson distribution, $p = 1$. Thus, there are $k - p - 1 = k - 2 = 9 - 2 = 7$ degrees of freedom for the chi-square distribution in the Dubek's Food Market study.

Suppose we test the null hypothesis that the probability distribution for the customer arrivals is a Poisson distribution with a .05 level of significance. Table 3 of Appendix B shows that with seven degrees of freedom, $\chi^2_{.05} = 14.07$. As in similar one-tailed tests, we will reject $H_0$ if $\chi^2 > \chi^2_\alpha$.

Checking the preceding calculations, we find a computed $\chi^2 = 10.9767$. This value is less than the critical value of 14.07, therefore we cannot reject the null hypothesis. Hence, for this analysis, the assumption of a Poisson probability distribution for weekday morning customer arrivals cannot be rejected. With this statistical finding, Dubek's managers will proceed with the consulting firm's scheduling procedure for weekday mornings.

*The p-value is shown to equal .1403 in the following Excel subsection.*

## Using Excel to Conduct a Poisson Distribution Goodness of Fit Test

In Section 12.1 we showed how Excel could be used to conduct a multinomial goodness of fit test. A similar approach can be used to conduct a Poisson distribution goodness of fit test. Refer to Figure 12.1 as we discuss the approach. The nine categories corresponding to the number of arrivals in Table 12.9 would replace the three companies listed in column D of the worksheet, and the probability associated with each category of arrivals would be computed in column E using Excel's Poisson function. The only data are the observed frequencies, which would be typed directly into column F. The expected frequencies would be computed in column G by multiplying the probabilities in column E by the sample size. The formulas in columns H, I, and J used to compute the $\chi^2$ test statistic using equation (12.1) are the same as in the worksheet in Figure 12.1. The chi-square value obtained is 10.9628; it is slightly different than that found in Table 12.9 (10.9767) due to rounding of intermediate calculations. The only other change necessary is that the cell formula for the degrees of freedom must be changed from $k - 1$ for the multinomial goodness of fit test to $k - 2$ for the Poisson distribution goodness of fit test. With these changes, the p-value for the test is computed using Excel's CHIDIST function as we described in Section 12.1. For the Dubek's Food Market goodness of fit test, CHIDIST(10.9628,7) provides a p-value of

.1403. With .1403 > $\alpha$ = .05, we cannot reject the null hypothesis that the number of customers entering the store during 5-minute intervals has a Poisson distribution.

A summary of the steps involved in conducting a Poisson distribution goodness of fit test follows.

---

**Poisson Distribution Goodness of Fit Test: A Summary**

1. State the null and alternative hypotheses.

$H_0$: The population has a Poisson probability distribution
$H_a$: The population does not have a Poisson probability distribution

2. Select a random sample and
   a. Record the observed frequency $f_i$ for each value of the Poisson random variable.
   b. Compute the mean number of occurrences $\mu$.
3. Compute the expected frequency of occurrences $e_i$ for each value of the Poisson random variable. Multiply the sample size by the Poisson probability of occurrence for each value of the Poisson random variable. If there are fewer than five expected occurrences for some values, combine adjacent values and reduce the number of categories as necessary.
4. Compute the value of the test statistic.

$$\chi^2 = \sum_{i=1}^{k} \frac{(f_i - e_i)^2}{e_i}$$

5. Rejection rule

Using test statistic:   Reject $H_0$ if $\chi^2 > \chi_\alpha^2$
Using $p$-value:        Reject if $p$-value $< \alpha$

where $\alpha$ is the level of significance and there are $k - 2$ degrees of freedom.

---

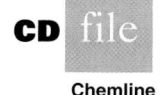

**Chemline**

**TABLE 12.10**

CHEMLINE
EMPLOYEE
APTITUTDE TEST
SCORES FOR
50 RANDOMLY
CHOSEN JOB
APPLICANTS

| | | | | | |
|---|---|---|---|---|---|
| 71 | 66 | 61 | 65 | 54 | 93 |
| 60 | 86 | 70 | 70 | 73 | 73 |
| 55 | 63 | 56 | 62 | 76 | 54 |
| 82 | 79 | 76 | 68 | 53 | 58 |
| 85 | 80 | 56 | 61 | 61 | 64 |
| 65 | 62 | 90 | 69 | 76 | 79 |
| 77 | 54 | 64 | 74 | 65 | 65 |
| 61 | 56 | 63 | 80 | 56 | 71 |
| 79 | 84 | | | | |

## Normal Distribution

The goodness of fit test for a normal probability distribution is also based on the use of the chi-square distribution. It is similar to the procedure we discussed for the Poisson distribution. In particular, observed frequencies for several categories of sample data are compared to expected frequencies under the assumption that the population has a normal distribution. Because the normal probability distribution is continuous, we must modify the way the categories are defined and how the expected frequencies are computed. Let us demonstrate the goodness of fit test for a normal probability distribution by considering the job applicant test data for Chemline, Inc., listed in Table 12.10.

Chemline hires approximately 400 new employees annually for its four plants located throughout the United States. The personnel director has asked whether a normal distribution could be applied to the population of potential employees' test scores. If such a distribution can be used, the distribution would be helpful in evaluating specific test scores. That is, scores in the upper 20%, lower 40%, and so on, could be identified quickly. Hence, we want to test the null hypothesis that the population of test scores follows a normal probability distribution.

Let us first use the data in Table 12.10 to develop estimates of the mean and standard deviation of the normal distribution that will be considered in the null hypothesis. We use the sample mean $\bar{x}$ and the sample standard deviation $s$ as point estimators of the mean and standard deviation of the normal distribution. The calculations follow.

$$\bar{x} = \frac{\Sigma x_i}{n} = \frac{3421}{50} = 68.42$$

$$s = \sqrt{\frac{\Sigma(x_i - \bar{x})^2}{n-1}} = \sqrt{\frac{5310.0369}{49}} = 10.41$$

Using these values, we state the following hypotheses about the distribution of the job applicant test scores.

$H_0$: The population of test scores has a normal distribution with mean 68.42 and standard deviation 10.41

$H_a$: The population of test scores does not have a normal distribution with mean 68.42 and standard deviation 10.41

The hypothesized normal distribution is shown in Figure 12.3.

Now let us consider a way of defining the categories for a goodness of fit test involving a normal distribution. For the discrete probability distribution in the Poisson distribution test, the categories were readily defined in terms of the number of customers arriving, such as 0, 1, 2, and so on. However, with the continuous, normal probability distribution, we must use a different procedure for defining the categories. We need to define the categories in terms of *intervals* of test scores.

With a continuous probability distribution, establish intervals such that each interval has an expected frequency of five or more.

Recall the rule of thumb for an expected frequency of at least five in each interval or category. We have to define the categories of test scores such that the expected frequencies will be at least five for each category. With a sample size of 50, one way of doing this is to divide the normal distribution into 10 equal-probability intervals (see Figure 12.4). With a sample size of 50, we would expect five outcomes in each interval or category, and the rule of thumb for expected frequencies would be satisfied.

**FIGURE 12.3**    HYPOTHESIZED NORMAL DISTRIBUTION OF TEST SCORES FOR THE CHEMLINE EXAMPLE

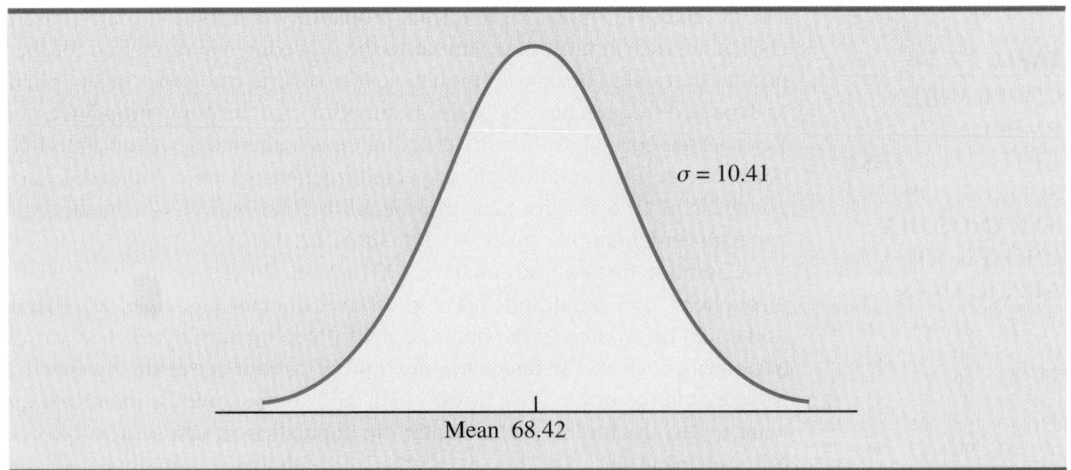

**FIGURE 12.4**    NORMAL PROBABILITY DISTRIBUTION FOR THE CHEMLINE EXAMPLE WITH 10 EQUAL-PROBABILITY INTERVALS

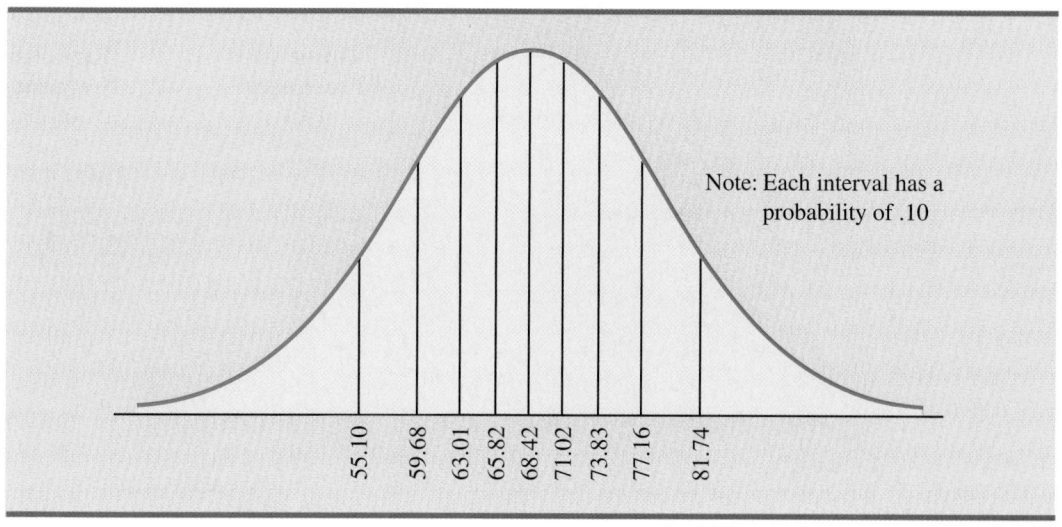

Note: Each interval has a probability of .10

55.10  59.68  63.01  65.82  68.42  71.02  73.83  77.16  81.74

Let us look more closely at the procedure for calculating the category boundaries. With a hypothesized normal probability distribution, the standard normal probability tables can be used to determine these boundaries. First consider the test score cutting off the lowest 10% of the test scores. From Table 1 of Appendix B we find that the $z$ value for this test score is $-1.28$. Therefore, the test score of $x = 68.42 - 1.28(10.41) = 55.10$ provides the cutoff value for the lowest 10% of the scores. For the lowest 20%, we find $z = -.84$, and thus $x = 68.42 - .84(10.41) = 59.68$. Working through the normal distribution in a similar manner provides the following test score values.

| | |
|---|---|
| Lower 10%: | $68.42 - 1.28(10.41) = 55.10$ |
| Lower 20%: | $68.42 - .84(10.41) = 59.68$ |
| Lower 30%: | $68.42 - .52(10.41) = 63.01$ |
| Lower 40%: | $68.42 - .25(10.41) = 65.82$ |
| Mid-score: | $68.42 + 0(10.41) = 68.42$ |
| Upper 40%: | $68.42 + .25(10.41) = 71.02$ |
| Upper 30%: | $68.42 + .52(10.41) = 73.83$ |
| Upper 20%: | $68.42 + .84(10.41) = 77.16$ |
| Upper 10%: | $68.42 + 1.28(10.41) = 81.74$ |

These cutoff or interval boundary points are identified on the graph in Figure 12.4.

With the categories or intervals of test scores now defined and with the known expected frequency of five per category, we can return to the sample data of Table 12.10 and determine the observed frequencies for the categories. Doing so provides the results in Table 12.11.

With the results in Table 12.11, the goodness of fit calculations proceed exactly as before. Namely, we compare the observed and expected results by computing a $\chi^2$ value. The computations necessary to compute the chi-square test statistic are shown in Table 12.12. We see that the value of the test statistic is $\chi^2 = 7.2$.

**TABLE 12.11** OBSERVED AND EXPECTED FREQUENCIES FOR THE CHEMLINE EXAMPLE

| Test Score Interval | Observed Frequency $(f_i)$ | Expected Frequency $(e_i)$ |
|---|---|---|
| Less than 55.10 | 5 | 5 |
| 55.10 to 59.68 | 5 | 5 |
| 59.68 to 63.01 | 9 | 5 |
| 63.01 to 65.82 | 6 | 5 |
| 65.82 to 68.42 | 2 | 5 |
| 68.42 to 71.02 | 5 | 5 |
| 71.02 to 73.83 | 2 | 5 |
| 73.83 to 77.16 | 5 | 5 |
| 77.16 to 81.74 | 5 | 5 |
| 81.74 and Over | 6 | 5 |
| Total | 50 | 50 |

To determine whether the computed $\chi^2$ value of 7.2 is large enough to reject $H_0$, we need to refer to the appropriate chi-square probability distribution tables. Using the rule for computing the number of degrees of freedom for the goodness of fit test, we have $k - p - 1 = 10 - 2 - 1 = 7$ degrees of freedom, where there are $k = 10$ categories and $p = 2$ parameters (mean and standard deviation) estimated from the sample data. Using a .10 level of significance for this hypothesis test, we have $\chi^2_{.10} = 12.017$ for the upper-tail rejection region. With $7.2 < 12.017$, we conclude that the null hypothesis cannot be rejected. Hence, the hypothesis that the probability distribution for the Chemline job applicant test scores is a normal probability distribution cannot be rejected.

As usual, the $p$-value approach can also be used for this hypothesis is test. We note in the Using Excel subsection that follows that the $p$-value is .4084.

**TABLE 12.12** COMPUTATION OF THE CHI-SQUARE TEST STATISTIC FOR THE CHEMLINE EXAMPLE

| Test Score Interval | Observed Frequency $(f_i)$ | Expected Frequency $(e_i)$ | Difference $(f_i - e_i)$ | Squared Difference $(f_i - e_i)^2$ | Squared Difference Divided by Expected Frequency $(f_i - e_i)^2/e_i$ |
|---|---|---|---|---|---|
| Less than 55.10 | 5 | 5 | 0 | 0 | 0.0 |
| 55.10 to 59.68 | 5 | 5 | 0 | 0 | 0.0 |
| 59.68 to 63.01 | 9 | 5 | 4 | 16 | 3.2 |
| 63.01 to 65.82 | 6 | 5 | 1 | 1 | 0.2 |
| 65.82 to 68.42 | 2 | 5 | $-3$ | 9 | 1.8 |
| 68.42 to 71.02 | 5 | 5 | 0 | 0 | 0.0 |
| 71.02 to 73.83 | 2 | 5 | $-3$ | 9 | 1.8 |
| 73.83 to 77.16 | 5 | 5 | 0 | 0 | 0.0 |
| 77.16 to 81.74 | 5 | 5 | 0 | 0 | 0.0 |
| 81.74 and Over | 6 | 5 | 1 | 1 | 0.2 |
| Total | 50 | 50 | | | 7.2 |

A summary of the normal distribution goodness of fit test follows:

**Normal Distribution Goodness of Fit Test: A Summary**

1. State the null and alternative hypotheses.

   $H_0$: The population has a normal probability distribution
   $H_a$: The population does not have a normal probability distribution

2. Select a random sample and
   a. Compute the sample mean and sample standard deviation.
   b. Define intervals of values so that the expected frequency is at least five for each interval. Using equal probability intervals is a good approach.
   c. Record the observed frequency of data values $f_i$ in each interval defined.
3. Compute the expected number of occurrences $e_i$ for each interval of values defined in step 2(b). Multiply the sample size by the probability of a normal random variable being in the interval.
4. Compute the value of the test statistic.

$$\chi^2 = \sum_{i=1}^{k} \frac{(f_i - e_i)^2}{e_i}$$

5. Rejection rule

   Using test statistic:    Reject $H_0$ if $\chi^2 > \chi_\alpha^2$
   Using $p$-value:          Reject $H_0$ if $p$-value $< \alpha$

   where $\alpha$ is the level of significance and there are $k - 3$ degrees of freedom.

## Using Excel to Conduct a Normal Distribution Goodness of Fit Test

In Section 12.1 we showed how Excel could be used to conduct a multinomial goodness of fit test. A similar approach can be used to conduct a normal distribution goodness of fit test. Refer to Figure 12.1 as we discuss the approach. The 10 categories corresponding the test score intervals would replace the three companies listed in column D of the worksheet. The only data would be the observed and expected frequencies; they would be typed directly into columns F and G. The formulas in columns H, I, and J used to compute the $\chi^2$ test statistic using equation (12.1) are the same as in the worksheet in Figure 12.1. The only other change necessary is that the cell formula for the degrees of freedom must be changed from $k - 1$ for the multinomial goodness of fit test to $k - 3$ for the normal distribution goodness of fit test. With these changes, the $p$-value for the test is computed using Excel's CHIDIST function as we described in Section 12.1. For the Chemline goodness of fit test CHIDIST(7.2,7) provides a $p$-value of .4084. With .4084 $> \alpha = .10$, we cannot reject the null hypothesis that the Chemline applicant test scores follow a normal distribution.

## EXERCISES

## Methods

**20.** Data on the number of occurrences per time period and observed frequencies follow. Use $\alpha = .05$ and the goodness of fit test to see whether the data fit a Poisson distribution.

| Number of Occurrences | Observed Frequency |
|:---:|:---:|
| 0 | 39 |
| 1 | 30 |
| 2 | 30 |
| 3 | 18 |
| 4 | 3 |

**21.** The following data are believed to have come from a normal probability distribution. Use the goodness of fit test and $\alpha = .025$ to test this claim.

| 17 | 23 | 22 | 24 | 19 | 23 | 18 | 22 | 20 | 13 | 11 | 21 | 18 | 20 | 21 |
|----|----|----|----|----|----|----|----|----|----|----|----|----|----|----|
| 21 | 18 | 15 | 24 | 23 | 23 | 43 | 29 | 27 | 26 | 30 | 28 | 33 | 23 | 29 |

## Applications

**22.** The number of automobile accidents per day in a particular city is believed to have a Poisson distribution. A sample of 80 days during the past year gives the following data. Do these data support the belief that the number of accidents per day has a Poisson distribution? Use $\alpha = .05$.

| Number of Accidents | Observed Frequency (days) |
|:---:|:---:|
| 0 | 34 |
| 1 | 25 |
| 2 | 11 |
| 3 | 7 |
| 4 | 3 |

**23.** The number of incoming phone calls at a company switchboard during 1-minute intervals is believed to have a Poisson distribution. Use $\alpha = .10$ and the following data to test the assumption that the incoming phone calls have a Poisson distribution.

| Number of Incoming Phone Calls During a 1-Minute Interval | Observed Frequency |
|:---:|:---:|
| 0 | 15 |
| 1 | 31 |
| 2 | 20 |
| 3 | 15 |
| 4 | 13 |
| 5 | 4 |
| 6 | 2 |

**24.** The weekly demand for a product is believed to be normally distributed. Use a goodness of fit test and the following data to test this assumption. Use $\alpha = .10$. The sample mean is 24.5 and the sample standard deviation is 3.

| | | | | |
|---|---|---|---|---|
| 18 | 20 | 22 | 27 | 22 |
| 25 | 22 | 27 | 25 | 24 |
| 26 | 23 | 20 | 24 | 26 |
| 27 | 25 | 19 | 21 | 25 |
| 26 | 25 | 31 | 29 | 25 |
| 25 | 28 | 26 | 28 | 24 |

**25.** Use $\alpha = .01$ and conduct a goodness of fit test to see whether the following sample appears to have been selected from a normal probability distribution.

| | | | | | | | | | | | | | | |
|---|---|---|---|---|---|---|---|---|---|---|---|---|---|---|
| 55 | 86 | 94 | 58 | 55 | 95 | 55 | 52 | 69 | 95 | 90 | 65 | 87 | 50 | 56 |
| 55 | 57 | 98 | 58 | 79 | 92 | 62 | 59 | 88 | 65 | | | | | |

After you complete the goodness of fit calculations, construct a histogram of the data. Does the histogram representation support the conclusion reached with the goodness of fit test? (*Note:* $\bar{x} = 71$ and $s = 17$.)

## SUMMARY

In this chapter we introduced the goodness of fit test and the test of independence, both of which are based on the use of the chi-square distribution. The purpose of the goodness of fit test is to determine whether a hypothesized probability distribution can be used as a model for a particular population of interest. The computations for conducting the goodness of fit test involve comparing observed frequencies from a sample with expected frequencies when the hypothesized probability distribution is assumed true. A chi-square distribution is used to determine whether the differences between observed and expected frequencies are large enough to reject the hypothesized probability distribution. We illustrated the goodness of fit test for multinomial, Poisson, and normal probability distributions.

A test of independence for two variables is an extension of the methodology employed in the goodness of fit test for a multinomial population. A contingency table is used to determine the observed and expected frequencies. Then a chi-square value is computed. Large chi-square values, caused by large differences between observed and expected frequencies, lead to the rejection of the null hypothesis of independence.

## GLOSSARY

**Multinomial population**   A population in which each element is assigned to one and only one of several categories. The multinomial probability distribution can be thought of as an extension of the binomial probability distribution to the case of three or more categories of outcomes.

**Goodness of fit test**   A statistical test conducted to determine whether to reject a hypothesized probability distribution for a population.

**Contingency table**   A crosstabulation table used to summarize observed and expected frequencies for a test of independence.

## KEY FORMULAS

**Test Statistic for Goodness of Fit**

$$\chi^2 = \sum_{i=1}^{k} \frac{(f_i - e_i)^2}{e_i} \tag{12.1}$$

**Expected Frequencies for Contingency Tables Under the Assumption of Independence**

$$e_{ij} = \frac{(\text{Row } i \text{ Total})(\text{Column } j \text{ Total})}{\text{Sample Size}} \tag{12.2}$$

**Test Statistic for Independence**

$$\chi^2 = \sum_{i} \sum_{j} \frac{(f_{ij} - e_{ij})^2}{e_{ij}} \tag{12.3}$$

## SUPPLEMENTARY EXERCISES

**26.** In setting sales quotas, the marketing manager makes the assumption that order potentials are the same for each of four sales territories. A sample of 200 sales follows. Should the manager's assumption be rejected? Use $\alpha = .05$.

| | Sales Territories | | |
|:-:|:-:|:-:|:-:|
| **I** | **II** | **III** | **IV** |
| 60 | 45 | 59 | 36 |

**27.** Seven percent of mutual fund investors rate corporate stocks "very safe," 58% rate them "somewhat safe," 24% rate them "not very safe," 4% rate them "not at all safe," and 7% are "not sure." A *Business Week*/Harris poll asked 529 mutual fund investors how they would rate corporate bonds on safety. The responses are as follows.

| Safety Rating | Frequency |
|:--|:-:|
| Very safe | 48 |
| Somewhat safe | 323 |
| Not very safe | 79 |
| Not at all safe | 16 |
| Not sure | 63 |

Do mutual fund investors' attitudes toward corporate bonds differ from their attitudes toward corporate stocks? Support your conclusion with a statistical test using $\alpha = .01$.

**Park**

**28.** A community park is to be opened soon. A sample of 140 individuals has been asked to state their preference for when they would most like to visit the park. The sample results are shown in the data set Park. In developing a staffing plan, should the park manager plan on the same number of individuals visiting the park each day? Support your conclusion with a statistical test using $\alpha = .05$.

**29.** A regional transit authority is concerned about the number of riders on one of its bus routes. In setting up the route, the assumption is that the number of riders is the same on every day from Monday through Friday. Using the following data, test with $\alpha = .05$ to determine whether the transit authority's assumption is correct.

| Day | Number of Riders |
|---|---|
| Monday | 13 |
| Tuesday | 16 |
| Wednesday | 28 |
| Thursday | 17 |
| Friday | 16 |

**30.** The results of *Computerworld's* Annual Job Satisfaction Survey showed that 28% of Information Systems (IS) managers are very satisfied with their job, 46% are somewhat satisfied, 12% are neither satisfied or dissatisfied, 10% are somewhat dissatisfied, and 4% are very dissatisfied (*Computerworld*, May 26, 1997). Suppose that a sample of 500 computer programmers yielded the following results.

| Category | Number of Respondents |
|---|---|
| Very satisfied | 105 |
| Somewhat satisfied | 235 |
| Neither | 55 |
| Somewhat dissatisfied | 90 |
| Very dissatisfied | 15 |

Test using $\alpha = .05$ to determine whether the job satisfaction for computer programmers is different from the job satisfaction for IS managers.

**31.** A sample of parts provided the following contingency table data on part quality by production shift.

| | Part Quality | |
|---|---|---|
| Shift | Number Good | Number Defective |
| First | 368 | 32 |
| Second | 285 | 15 |
| Third | 176 | 24 |

Use $\alpha = .05$ and test the hypothesis that part quality is independent of the production shift. What is your conclusion?

**32.** *The Wall Street Journal* 1996 Subscriber Study showed data on the employment status of subscribers. Sample results corresponding to subscribers of the eastern and western editions are shown here.

| | Region | |
|---|---|---|
| Employment Status | Eastern Edition | Western Edition |
| Full-time | 1105 | 574 |
| Part-time | 31 | 15 |
| Self-employed/consultant | 229 | 186 |
| Not employed | 485 | 344 |

Using $\alpha = .05$, test the hypothesis that employment status is independent of the region. What is your conclusion?

**33.** A lending institution supplied the following data on loan approvals by four loan officers. Use $\alpha = .05$ and test to determine whether the loan approval decision is independent of the loan officer reviewing the loan application.

|  | Loan Approval Decision | |
| --- | --- | --- |
| **Loan Officer** | **Approved** | **Rejected** |
| **Miller** | 24 | 16 |
| **McMahon** | 17 | 13 |
| **Games** | 35 | 15 |
| **Runk** | 11 | 9 |

**34.** Data on the marital status of men and women ages 20 to 29 were obtained as part of a national survey. The results from a sample of 350 men and 400 women follow. These data are representative of results published in the *U.S. Current Population Report* (*The Statistical Abstract of the United States,* 1999).

|  | Marital Status | | |
| --- | --- | --- | --- |
| **Gender** | **Never Married** | **Married** | **Divorced** |
| **Men** | 234 | 106 | 10 |
| **Women** | 216 | 168 | 16 |

   **a.** Using $\alpha = .01$, test for independence between marital status and gender. What is your conclusion?
   **b.** Summarize the percent in each marital status category for men and for women.

**35.** The following crosstabulation shows industry type and P/E ratio for 100 companies in the consumer products and banking industries.

|  | P/E Ratio | | | | | |
| --- | --- | --- | --- | --- | --- | --- |
| **Industry** | **5–9** | **10–14** | **15–19** | **20–24** | **25–29** | **Total** |
| **Consumer** | 4 | 10 | 18 | 10 | 8 | 50 |
| **Banking** | 14 | 14 | 12 | 6 | 4 | 50 |
| Total | 18 | 24 | 30 | 16 | 12 | 100 |

Does there appear to be a relationship between industry type and P/E ratio? Support your conclusion with a statistical test using $\alpha = .05$.

**36.** The following data were collected on the number of emergency ambulance calls for an urban county and a rural county in Virginia.

|  | Day of Week | | | | | | | |
| --- | --- | --- | --- | --- | --- | --- | --- | --- |
| **County** | **Sun** | **Mon** | **Tue** | **Wed** | **Thur** | **Fri** | **Sat** | **Total** |
| **Urban** | 61 | 48 | 50 | 55 | 63 | 73 | 43 | 393 |
| **Rural** | 7 | 9 | 16 | 13 | 9 | 14 | 10 | 78 |
| Total | 68 | 57 | 66 | 68 | 72 | 87 | 53 | 471 |

Conduct a test for independence using $\alpha = .05$. What is your conclusion?

**37.** A random sample of final examination grades for a college course follows.

| | | | | | | | | | | | | | | |
| --- | --- | --- | --- | --- | --- | --- | --- | --- | --- | --- | --- | --- | --- | --- |
| 55 | 85 | 72 | 99 | 48 | 71 | 88 | 70 | 59 | 98 | 80 | 74 | 93 | 85 | 74 |
| 82 | 90 | 71 | 83 | 60 | 95 | 77 | 84 | 73 | 63 | 72 | 95 | 79 | 51 | 85 |
| 76 | 81 | 78 | 65 | 75 | 87 | 86 | 70 | 80 | 64 | | | | | |

Use $\alpha = .05$ and test to determine whether a normal probability distribution should be rejected as being representative of the population's distribution of grades.

38. The office occupancy rates were reported for four California metropolitan areas. Do the following data suggest that the office vacancies were independent of metropolitan area? Use a .05 level of significance. What is your conclusion?

| Occupancy Status | Los Angeles | San Diego | San Francisco | San Jose |
|---|---|---|---|---|
| Occupied | 160 | 116 | 192 | 174 |
| Vacant | 40 | 34 | 33 | 26 |

39. A salesperson makes four calls per day. A sample of 100 days gives the following frequencies of sales volumes.

| Number of Sales | Observed Frequency (days) |
|---|---|
| 0 | 30 |
| 1 | 32 |
| 2 | 25 |
| 3 | 10 |
| 4 | 3 |

Records show sales are made to 30% of all sales calls. Assuming independent sales calls, the number of sales per day should follow a binomial probability distribution. The binomial probability function presented in Chapter 5 is

$$f(x) = \frac{n!}{x!(n-x)!} p^x (1-p)^{n-x}$$

For this exercise, assume that the population has a binomial distribution with $n = 4$, $p = .30$, and $x = 0, 1, 2, 3,$ and 4.

a. Compute the expected frequencies for $x = 0, 1, 2, 3,$ and 4 by using the binomial probability function. Combine categories if necessary to satisfy the requirement that the expected frequency is five or more for all categories.

b. Use the goodness of fit test to determine whether the assumption of a binomial distribution should be rejected. Use $\alpha = .05$. (Because no parameters of the binomial distribution were estimated from the sample data, the degrees of freedom are $k - 1$ where $k$ is the number of categories.)

## Case Problem    A BIPARTISAN AGENDA FOR CHANGE

In a study conducted by Zogby International for the *Democrat and Chronicle*, more than 700 New Yorkers were polled to determine whether the New York state government works. Respondents surveyed were asked questions involving pay cuts for state legislators, restrictions on lobbyists, terms limits for legislators, and whether state citizens should be able to put matters directly on the state ballot for a vote (*Democrat and Chronicle*, December 7, 1997). The results regarding several proposed reforms had broad support, crossing all demographic and political lines.

Suppose that a follow-up survey of 100 individuals who live in the western region of New York was conducted. The party affiliation (Democrat, Independent, Republican) of each individual surveyed was recorded, as well as their responses to the following three questions.

1. Should legislative pay be cut for every day the state budget is late?
   Yes _____     No _____
2. Should there be more restrictions on lobbyists?
   Yes _____     No _____
3. Should there be term limits requiring that legislators serve a fixed number of years?
   Yes _____     No _____

The responses were coded using 1 for a *yes* response and 2 for a *no* response. The complete data set is available on the data disk in the data set named NYReform.

**CD file**

**NYReform**

## Managerial Report

1. Use descriptive statistics to summarize the data from this study. What are your preliminary conclusions about the independence of the response (yes or no) and party affiliation for each of the three questions in the survey?
2. With regard to question 1, test for the independence of the response (yes and no) and party affiliation. Use $\alpha = .05$.
3. With regard to question 2, test for the independence of the response (yes and no) and party affiliation. Use $\alpha = .05$.
4. With regard to question 3, test for the independence of the response (yes and no) and party affiliation. Use $\alpha = .05$.
5. Does it appear that there is broad support for change across all political lines? Explain.

# ANALYSIS OF VARIANCE AND EXPERIMENTAL DESIGN

**CONTENTS**

## STATISTICS IN PRACTICE

### BURKE MARKETING SERVICES, INC.*
*Cincinnati, Ohio*

Burke Marketing Services, Inc., is one of the most experienced market research firms in the industry. Burke writes more proposals, on more projects, every day than any other market research company in the world. Supported by state-of-the-art technology, Burke offers a wide variety of research capabilities, providing answers to nearly any marketing question.

In one study, Burke was retained by a firm to evaluate potential new versions of a children's dry cereal. To maintain confidentiality, we refer to the cereal manufacturer as the Anon Company. The four key factors that Anon's product developers thought would enhance the taste of the cereal were:

1. Ratio of wheat to corn in the cereal flake.
2. Type of sweetener: sugar, honey, or artificial.
3. Presence or absence of flavor bits with a fruit taste.
4. Short or long cooking time.

An experiment was designed to determine what effects these four factors had on cereal taste. For example, one test cereal was made with a specified ratio of wheat to corn, sugar as the sweetener, flavor bits, and a short cooking time; another test cereal was made with a different ratio of wheat to corn and the other three factors the same, and so on. Groups of children then taste-tested the cereals and stated what they thought about the taste of each.

*The authors are indebted to Dr. Ronald Tatham of Burke Marketing Services for providing this Statistics in Practice.

Burke's research provides valuable statistical information on what customers want from a product. © Laura Dwight/CORBIS.

Analysis of variance was the statistical method used to study the data obtained from the taste tests. The results of the analysis showed that:

- The flake composition and sweetener type were very influential in taste evaluation.
- The flavor bits actually detracted from the taste of the cereal.
- The cooking time had no effect on the taste.

This information helped Anon identify the factors that would lead to the best-tasting cereal.

The experimental design employed by Burke and the subsequent analysis of variance were helpful in making a product design recommendation. In this chapter, we will see how such procedures are carried out.

Sir Ronald Alymer Fisher (1890–1962) invented the branch of statistics known as experimental design. In addition to being accomplished in statistics, he was a noted scientist in the field of genetics.

In this chapter we introduce a statistical procedure called *analysis of variance* (ANOVA). First, we show how ANOVA can be used to test for the equality of three or more population means using data obtained from an observational study. Then, we discuss the use of ANOVA for analyzing data obtained from three types of experimental studies: a completely randomized design, a randomized block design, and a factorial experiment. In the following chapters we will see that ANOVA plays a key role in analyzing the results of regression analysis involving both experimental and observational data.

## 13.1   AN INTRODUCTION TO ANALYSIS OF VARIANCE

National Computer Products, Inc. (NCP), manufactures printers and fax machines at plants located in Atlanta, Dallas, and Seattle. To measure how much employees at these plants know about total quality management, a random sample of six employees was selected from each plant and given a quality awareness examination. The examination scores obtained for these 18 employees are listed in Table 13.1. The sample means, sample variances, and sample standard deviations for each group are also provided. Managers want to use these data to test the hypothesis that the population mean examination score is the same for all three plants.

We will define population 1 as all employees at the Atlanta plant, population 2 as all employees at the Dallas plant, and population 3 as all employees at the Seattle plant. Let

$$\mu_1 = \text{mean examination score for population 1}$$
$$\mu_2 = \text{mean examination score for population 2}$$
$$\mu_3 = \text{mean examination score for population 3}$$

Although we will never know the actual values of $\mu_1, \mu_2,$ and $\mu_3$, we want to use the sample results to test the following hypotheses.

$$H_0: \mu_1 = \mu_2 = \mu_3$$
$$H_a: \text{Not all population means are equal}$$

If $H_0$ is rejected, we cannot conclude that all population means are different. Rejecting $H_0$ means that at least two population means have different values.

As we will demonstrate shortly, analysis of variance is a statistical procedure that can be used to determine whether the observed differences in the three sample means are large enough to reject $H_0$.

In the introduction to this chapter we stated that analysis of variance can be used to analyze data obtained from both an observational study and an experimental study. In order to provide a common set of terminology for discussing the use of analysis of variance in both types of studies, we need to introduce the concepts of a **response variable**, a **factor**, and a **treatment**.

The two variables in the NCP example are plant location and score on the quality awareness examination. Because the objective is to determine whether the mean examination score is the same for plants located in Atlanta, Dallas, and Seattle, examination score is referred to as the dependent or response variable and plant location as the independent variable or factor. In general, the values of a factor selected for investigation are referred to as levels of the factor or treatments. Thus, in the NCP example the three treatments are Atlanta, Dallas, and Seattle. These three treatments define the populations of interest in the NCP example. For each treatment or population, the response variable is the examination score.

**TABLE 13.1    EXAMINATION SCORES FOR 18 EMPLOYEES**

| Observation | Plant 1 Atlanta | Plant 2 Dallas | Plant 3 Seattle |
|---|---|---|---|
| 1 | 85 | 71 | 59 |
| 2 | 75 | 75 | 64 |
| 3 | 82 | 73 | 62 |
| 4 | 76 | 74 | 69 |
| 5 | 71 | 69 | 75 |
| 6 | 85 | 82 | 67 |
| Sample mean | 79 | 74 | 66 |
| Sample variance | 34 | 20 | 32 |
| Sample standard deviation | 5.83 | 4.47 | 5.66 |

CD file

NCP

## Assumptions for Analysis of Variance

Three assumptions are required to use analysis of variance.

If the sample sizes are equal, analysis of variance is not sensitive to departures from the assumption of normally distributed populations.

1. *For each population, the response variable is normally distributed.* Implication: In the NCP example, the examination scores (response variable) must be normally distributed at each plant.
2. *The variance of the response variable, denoted $\sigma^2$, is the same for all of the populations.* Implication: In the NCP example, the variance of examination scores must be the same for all three plants.
3. *The observations must be independent.* Implication: In the NCP example, the examination score for each employee must be independent of the examination score for any other employee.

## A Conceptual Overview

If the means for the three populations are equal, we would expect the three sample means to be close together. In fact, the closer the three sample means are to one another, the more evidence we have for the conclusion that the population means are equal. Alternatively, the more the sample means differ, the more evidence we have for the conclusion that the population means are not equal. In other words, if the variability among the sample means is "small," it supports $H_0$; if the variability among the sample means is "large," it supports $H_a$.

If the null hypothesis, $H_0: \mu_1 = \mu_2 = \mu_3$, is true, we can use the variability among the sample means to develop an estimate of $\sigma^2$. First, note that if the assumptions for analysis of variance are satisfied, each sample will have come from the same normal probability distribution with mean $\mu$ and variance $\sigma^2$. Recall from Chapter 7 that the sampling distribution of the sample mean $\bar{x}$ for a simple random sample of size $n$ from a normal population will be normally distributed with mean $\mu$ and variance $\sigma^2/n$. Figure 13.1 illustrates such a sampling distribution.

Thus, if the null hypothesis is true, we can think of each of the three sample means, $\bar{x}_1 = 79$, $\bar{x}_2 = 74$, and $\bar{x}_3 = 66$, from Table 13.1 as values drawn at random from the sampling distribution shown in Figure 13.1. In this case, the mean and variance of the three $\bar{x}$ values can be used to estimate the mean and variance of the sampling distribution. When the sample sizes are equal, as in the NCP example, the best estimate of the mean of the sam-

**FIGURE 13.1**    SAMPLING DISTRIBUTION OF $\bar{x}$ GIVEN $H_0$ IS TRUE

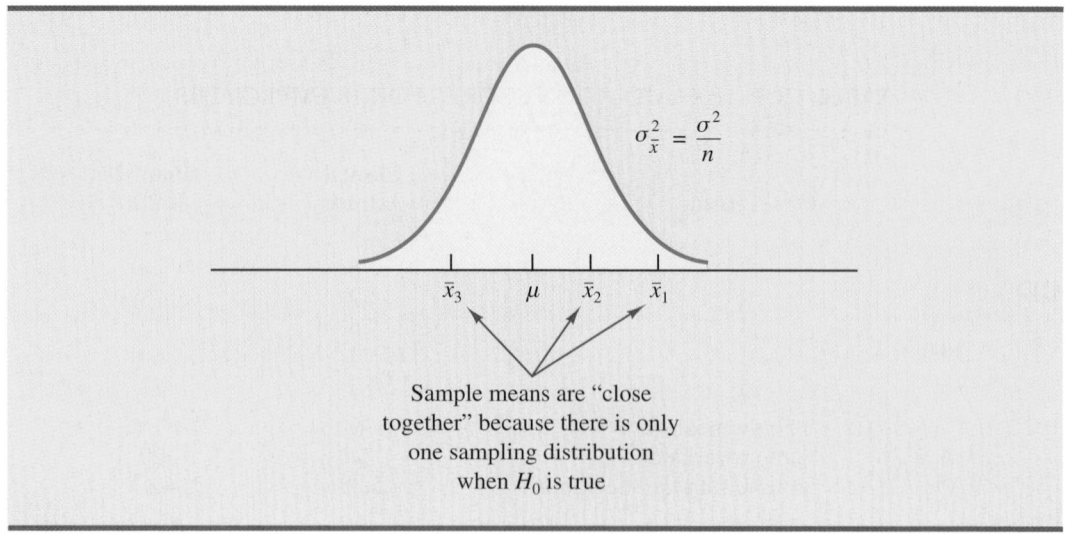

pling distribution of $\bar{x}$ is the mean or average of the sample means. Thus, in the NCP example, an estimate of the mean of the sampling distribution of $\bar{x}$ is $(79 + 74 + 66)/3 = 73$. We refer to this estimate as the *overall sample mean*. An estimate of the variance of the sampling distribution of $\bar{x}$ is provided by the variance of the three sample means.

$$s_{\bar{x}}^2 = \frac{(79 - 73)^2 + (74 - 73)^2 + (66 - 73)^2}{3 - 1} = \frac{86}{2} = 43$$

Because $\sigma_{\bar{x}}^2 = \sigma^2/n$, solving for $\sigma^2$ gives

$$\sigma^2 = n\sigma_{\bar{x}}^2$$

Hence,

$$\text{Estimate of } \sigma^2 = n \,(\text{Estimate of } \sigma_{\bar{x}}^2) = ns_{\bar{x}}^2 = 6(43) = 258$$

The result, $ns_{\bar{x}}^2 = 258$, is referred to as the *between-treatments* estimate of $\sigma^2$.

The between-treatments estimate of $\sigma^2$ is based on the assumption that the null hypothesis is true. In this case, each sample comes from the same population, and there is only one sampling distribution of $\bar{x}$. To illustrate what happens when $H_0$ is false, suppose the population means all differ. Note that because the three samples are from normal populations with different means, they will result in three different sampling distributions. Figure 13.2 shows that in this case, the sample means are not as close together as they were when $H_0$ was true. Thus, $s_{\bar{x}}^2$ will be larger, causing the between-treatments estimate of $\sigma^2$ to be larger. In general, when the population means are not equal, the between-treatments estimate will overestimate the population variance $\sigma^2$.

The variation within each of the samples also has an effect on the conclusion we reach in analysis of variance. When a simple random sample is selected from each population, each of the sample variances provides an unbiased estimate of $\sigma^2$. Hence, we can combine or pool the individual estimates of $\sigma^2$ into one overall estimate. The estimate of $\sigma^2$ obtained in this way is called the *pooled* or *within-treatments* estimate of $\sigma^2$. Because each sample variance provides an estimate of $\sigma^2$ based only on the variation within each sample, the

**FIGURE 13.2**   SAMPLING DISTRIBUTION FOR $\bar{x}$ GIVEN $H_0$ IS FALSE

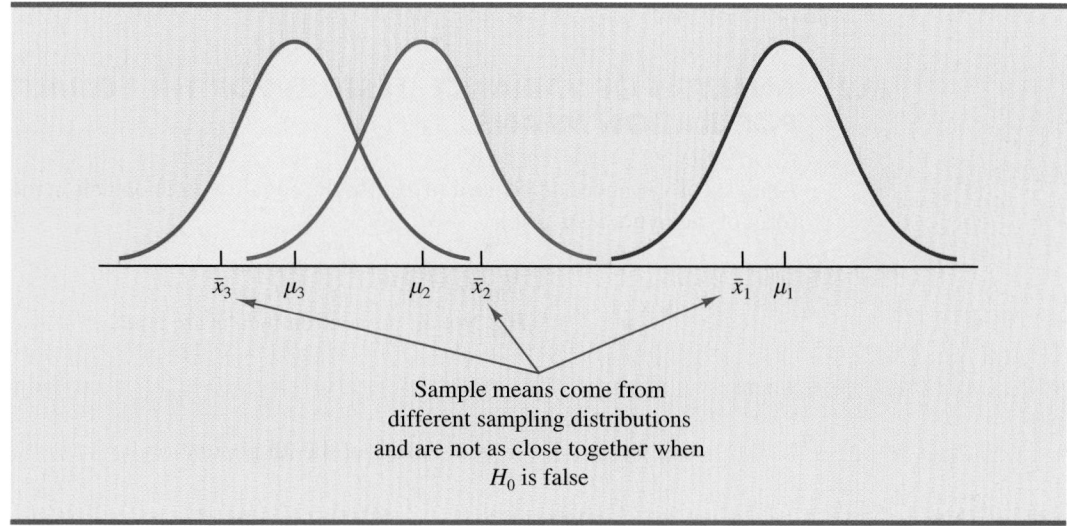

Sample means come from
different sampling distributions
and are not as close together when
$H_0$ is false

within-treatments estimate of $\sigma^2$ is not affected by whether the population means are equal. When the sample sizes are equal, the within-treatments estimate of $\sigma^2$ can be obtained by computing the average of the individual sample variances. For the NCP example we obtain

$$\text{Within-Treatments Estimate of } \sigma^2 = \frac{34 + 20 + 32}{3} = \frac{86}{3} = 28.67$$

In the NCP example, the between-treatments estimate of $\sigma^2$ (258) is much larger than the within-treatments estimate of $\sigma^2$ (28.67). In fact, the ratio of these two estimates is $258/28.67 = 9.00$. Recall, however, that the between-treatments approach provides a good estimate of $\sigma^2$ only if the null hypothesis is true; if the null hypothesis is false, the between-treatments approach overestimates $\sigma^2$. The within-treatments approach provides a good estimate of $\sigma^2$ in either case. Thus, if the null hypothesis is true, the two estimates will be similar and their ratio will be close to 1. If the null hypothesis is false, the between-treatments estimate will be larger than the within-treatments estimate, and their ratio will be large. In the next section we will show how large this ratio must be to reject $H_0$.

In summary, the logic behind ANOVA is based on the development of two independent estimates of the common population variance $\sigma^2$. One estimate of $\sigma^2$ is based on the variability among the sample means themselves, and the other estimate of $\sigma^2$ is based on the variability of the data within each sample. By comparing these two estimates of $\sigma^2$, we will be able to determine whether the population means are equal.

## NOTES AND COMMENTS

1. In Sections 10.1 and 10.2 we presented statistical methods for testing the hypothesis that the means of two populations are equal. ANOVA can also be used to test the hypothesis that the means of two populations are equal. In practice, however, analysis of variance is only used when dealing with three or more population means.

2. In Section 10.2 we discussed how to test for the equality of two population means whenever one or both sample sizes are less than 30. As part of that discussion we illustrated the process of combining the results of two independent random samples to provide one estimate of $\sigma^2$; that process was referred to as pooling, and the resulting sample variance was referred to as the pooled estimator of $\sigma^2$. In analysis of variance, the within-treatments estimate of $\sigma^2$ is simply the generalization of that concept to the case of more than two samples; that is why we also referred to the within-treatments estimator as the pooled estimator of $\sigma^2$.

## 13.2 ANALYSIS OF VARIANCE: TESTING FOR THE EQUALITY OF $k$ POPULATION MEANS

Analysis of variance can be used to test for the equality of $k$ population means. The general form of the hypothesis test is

$$H_0: \mu_1 = \mu_2 = \cdots = \mu_k$$
$$H_a: \text{Not all population means are equal}$$

where

$$\mu_j = \text{mean of the } j\text{th population}$$

We assume that a simple random sample of size $n_j$ has been selected from each of the $k$ populations or treatments. For the resulting sample data, let

$$x_{ij} = \text{value of observation } i \text{ for treatment } j$$
$$n_j = \text{number of observations for treatment } j$$
$$\bar{x}_j = \text{sample mean for treatment } j$$
$$s_j^2 = \text{sample variance for treatment } j$$
$$s_j = \text{sample standard deviation for treatment } j$$

The formulas for the sample mean and sample variance for treatment $j$ are as follow.

$$\bar{x}_j = \frac{\sum\limits_{i=1}^{n_j} x_{ij}}{n_j} \tag{13.1}$$

$$s_j^2 = \frac{\sum\limits_{i=1}^{n_j} (x_{ij} - \bar{x}_j)^2}{n_j - 1} \tag{13.2}$$

The overall sample mean, denoted $\bar{\bar{x}}$, is the sum of all the observations divided by the total number of observations. That is,

$$\bar{\bar{x}} = \frac{\sum\limits_{j=1}^{k} \sum\limits_{i=1}^{n_j} x_{ij}}{n_T} \tag{13.3}$$

where

$$n_T = n_1 + n_2 + \cdots + n_k \tag{13.4}$$

If the size of each sample is $n$, $n_T = kn$; in this case equation (13.3) reduces to

$$\bar{\bar{x}} = \frac{\sum\limits_{j=1}^{k} \sum\limits_{i=1}^{n_j} x_{ij}}{nk} = \frac{\sum\limits_{j=1}^{k} \sum\limits_{i=1}^{n_j} x_{ij}/n}{k} = \frac{\sum\limits_{j=1}^{k} \bar{x}_j}{k} \tag{13.5}$$

In other words, whenever the sample sizes are the same, the overall sample mean is just the average of the $k$ sample means.

Because each sample in the NCP example consists of $n = 6$ observations, the overall sample mean can be computed by using equation (13.5). For the data in Table 13.1 we obtained the following result.

$$\bar{\bar{x}} = \frac{79 + 74 + 66}{3} = 73$$

If the null hypothesis is true ($\mu_1 = \mu_2 = \mu_3 = \mu$), the overall sample mean of 73 is the best estimate of the population mean $\mu$.

## Between-Treatments Estimate of Population Variance

In the preceding section, we introduced the concept of a between-treatments estimate of $\sigma^2$ and showed how to compute it when the sample sizes were equal. This estimate of $\sigma^2$ is called the *mean square due to treatments* and is denoted MSTR. The general formula for computing MSTR is

$$\text{MSTR} = \frac{\sum_{j=1}^{k} n_j(\bar{x}_j - \bar{\bar{x}})^2}{k - 1} \tag{13.6}$$

The numerator in equation (13.6) is called the *sum of squares due to treatments* and is denoted SSTR. The denominator, $k - 1$, represents the degrees of freedom associated with SSTR. Hence, the mean square due to treatments can be computed by the following formula.

**Mean Square Due to Treatments**

$$\text{MSTR} = \frac{\text{SSTR}}{k - 1} \tag{13.7}$$

where

$$\text{SSTR} = \sum_{j=1}^{k} n_j(\bar{x}_j - \bar{\bar{x}})^2 \tag{13.8}$$

If $H_0$ is true, MSTR provides an unbiased estimate of $\sigma^2$. However, if the means of the $k$ populations are not equal, MSTR is not an unbiased estimate of $\sigma^2$; in fact, in that case, MSTR should overestimate $\sigma^2$.

For the NCP data in Table 13.1, we obtain the following results.

$$\text{SSTR} = \sum_{j=1}^{k} n_j(\bar{x}_j - \bar{\bar{x}})^2 = 6(79 - 73)^2 + 6(74 - 73)^2 + 6(66 - 73)^2 = 516$$

$$\text{MSTR} = \frac{\text{SSTR}}{k - 1} = \frac{516}{2} = 258$$

## Within-Treatments Estimate of Population Variance

In the preceding section we introduced the concept of a within-treatments estimate of $\sigma^2$ and showed how to compute it when the sample sizes were equal. This estimate of $\sigma^2$ is called the *mean square due to error* and is denoted MSE. The general formula for computing MSE is

$$\text{MSE} = \frac{\sum_{j=1}^{k}(n_j - 1)s_j^2}{n_T - k} \tag{13.9}$$

The numerator in equation (13.9) is called the *sum of squares due to error* and is denoted SSE. The denominator of MSE is referred to as the degrees of freedom associated with SSE. Hence, the formula for MSE can also be stated as follows.

**Mean Square Due to Error**

$$MSE = \frac{SSE}{n_T - k} \qquad \textbf{(13.10)}$$

where

$$SSE = \sum_{j=1}^{k}(n_j - 1)s_j^2 \qquad \textbf{(13.11)}$$

Note that MSE is based on the variation within each of the treatments; it is not influenced by whether the null hypothesis is true. Thus, MSE always provides an unbiased estimate of $\sigma^2$.

For the NCP data in Table 13.1 we obtain the following results.

$$SSE = \sum_{j=1}^{k}(n_j - 1)s_j^2 = (6-1)34 + (6-1)20 + (6-1)32 = 430$$

$$MSE = \frac{SSE}{n_T - k} = \frac{430}{18-3} = \frac{430}{15} = 28.67$$

## Comparing the Variance Estimates: The $F$ Test

Let us assume that the null hypothesis is true. In that case, MSTR and MSE provide two independent, unbiased estimates of $\sigma^2$. Recall from Chapter 11 that for normal populations, the sampling distribution of the ratio of two independent estimates of $\sigma^2$ follows an $F$ distribution. Hence, if the null hypothesis is true and the ANOVA assumptions are valid, the sampling distribution of MSTR/MSE is an $F$ distribution with numerator degrees of freedom equal to $k - 1$ and denominator degrees of freedom equal to $n_T - k$.

If the means of the $k$ populations are not equal, the value of MSTR/MSE will be inflated because MSTR overestimates $\sigma^2$. Hence, we will reject $H_0$ if the resulting value of MSTR/MSE appears to be too large to have been selected at random from an $F$ distribution with degrees of freedom $k - 1$ in the numerator and $n_T - k$ in the denominator. The value of $F = $ MSTR/MSE that will cause us to reject $H_0$ depends on $\alpha$, the level of significance. Once $\alpha$ is selected, a critical value can be determined. Figure 13.3 shows the sampling

**FIGURE 13.3**    SAMPLING DISTRIBUTION OF $F = $ MSTR/MSE; THE CRITICAL VALUE FOR REJECTING THE NULL HYPOTHESIS OF EQUALITY OF MEANS IS $F_\alpha$

Sampling distribution of $F = $ MSTR/MSE

$\alpha$

$F$

$F_\alpha$
Critical value

distribution of $F = $ MSTR/MSE and the rejection region associated with a level of significance equal to $\alpha$, where $F_\alpha$ denotes the critical value.

Suppose the manager responsible for making the decision in the National Computer Products example was willing to accept a probability of making a Type I error of $\alpha = .05$. From Table 4 of Appendix B we can determine the critical $F$ value by locating the value corresponding to numerator degrees of freedom equal to $k - 1 = 3 - 1 = 2$ and denominator degrees of freedom equal to $n_T - k = 18 - 3 = 15$. Thus, we obtain the critical value $F_{.05} = 3.68$. Note that this means that if the null hypothesis is true, we will observe a value greater than 3.68 only 5% of the time. Moreover, the theory behind the analysis of variance tells us that if the null hypothesis is true, the ratio of MSTR/MSE is a value from this $F$ distribution. Hence, the appropriate rejection rule for the NCP example is written

$$\text{Reject } H_0 \text{ if } F = \text{MSTR/MSE} > 3.68$$

Recall that MSTR $= 258$ and MSE $= 28.67$. Because $F = $ MSTR/MSE $= 258/28.67 = 9.00$ is greater than the critical value, $F_{.05} = 3.68$, we have sufficient evidence to reject the null hypothesis that the means of the three populations are equal. In other words, analysis of variance supports the conclusion that the population mean examination scores at the three NCP plants are not equal.

The $p$-value criterion can also be used for this hypothesis test. The usual rejection rule applies: Reject $H_0$ if $p$-value $< \alpha$. Excel makes computing the $p$-value easy. For example, for the NCP example, simply enter $=$FDIST(9,2,15) in any cell of a worksheet; the result, .0027, is the $p$-value associated with the test statistic $F = 9.00$. With a $p$-value $= .0027 < \alpha = .05$, the null hypothesis that the means of the three populations are equal can be rejected. A summary of the overall procedure for testing for the equality of $k$ population means follows.

**Test for the Equality of $k$ Population Means**

$$H_0: \mu_1 = \mu_2 = \cdots = \mu_k$$
$$H_a: \text{Not all population means are equal}$$

**Test Statistic**

$$F = \frac{\text{MSTR}}{\text{MSE}} \qquad\qquad \textbf{(13.12)}$$

**Rejection Rule**

Using test statistic:    Reject $H_0$ if $F > F_\alpha$
Using $p$-value:         Reject $H_0$ if $p$-value $< \alpha$

where the value of $F_\alpha$ is based on an $F$ distribution with $k - 1$ numerator degrees of freedom and $n_T - k$ denominator degrees of freedom.

## ANOVA Table

The results of the preceding calculations can be displayed conveniently in a table referred to as the analysis of variance or **ANOVA table**. Table 13.2 is the analysis of variance table for the National Computer Products example. The sum of squares associated with the source

**TABLE 13.2**    ANALYSIS OF VARIANCE TABLE FOR THE NCP EXAMPLE

| Source of Variation | Sum of Squares | Degrees of Freedom | Mean Square | $F$ |
|---|---|---|---|---|
| Treatments | 516 | 2 | 258.00 | 9.00 |
| Error | 430 | 15 | 28.67 | |
| Total | 946 | 17 | | |

of variation referred to as "Total" is called the total sum of squares (SST). Note that the results for the NCP example suggest that SST = SSTR + SSE, and that the degrees of freedom associated with this total sum of squares is the sum of the degrees of freedom associated with the between-treatments estimate of $\sigma^2$ and the within-treatments estimate of $\sigma^2$.

We point out that SST divided by its degrees of freedom $n_T - 1$ is nothing more than the overall sample variance that would be obtained if we treated the entire set of 18 observations as one data set. With the entire data set as one sample, the formula for computing the total sum of squares, SST, is

$$\text{SST} = \sum_{j=1}^{k} \sum_{i=1}^{n_j} (x_{ij} - \bar{\bar{x}})^2 \qquad \textbf{(13.13)}$$

It can be shown that the results we observed for the analysis of variance table for the NCP example also apply to other problems. That is,

$$\text{SST} = \text{SSTR} + \text{SSE} \qquad \textbf{(13.14)}$$

Analysis of variance can be thought of as a statistical procedure for partitioning the total sum of squares into separate components.

In other words, SST can be partitioned into two sums of squares: the sum of squares due to treatments and the sum of squares due to error. Note also that the degrees of freedom corresponding to SST, $n_T - 1$, can be partitioned into the degrees of freedom corresponding to SSTR, $k - 1$, and the degrees of freedom corresponding to SSE, $n_T - k$. The analysis of variance can be viewed as the process of **partitioning** the total sum of squares and the degrees of freedom into their corresponding sources: treatments and error. Dividing the sum of squares by the appropriate degrees of freedom provides the variance estimates and the $F$ value used to test the hypothesis of equal population means.

## Using Excel's Anova: Single Factor Tool

Excel's Anova: Single Factor tool can be used to conduct a hypothesis test about the difference between the population means for the National Computer Products example. Refer to the Excel worksheet shown in Figure 13.4 as we describe the tasks involved.

**Enter Data:**    Column A is used to identify the observations at each of the plants. Columns B, C, and D contain the examination scores for the three plants.

**Apply Tools:**    The following steps describe how to use Excel's Anova: Single Factor tool to test the hypothesis that the mean examination score is the same for all three plants.

   **Step 1.** Select the **Tools** pull-down menu
   **Step 2.** Choose the **Data Analysis** option
   **Step 3.** Choose **Anova: Single Factor** from the list of Analysis Tools

**FIGURE 13.4**    EXCEL ANOVA OUTPUT FOR THE NCP EXAMPLE

| | A | B | C | D | E | F | G | H |
|---|---|---|---|---|---|---|---|---|
| 1 | **Observation** | **Atlanta** | **Dallas** | **Seattle** | | | | |
| 2 | 1 | 85 | 71 | 59 | | | | |
| 3 | 2 | 75 | 75 | 64 | | | | |
| 4 | 3 | 82 | 73 | 62 | | | | |
| 5 | 4 | 76 | 74 | 69 | | | | |
| 6 | 5 | 71 | 69 | 75 | | | | |
| 7 | 6 | 85 | 82 | 67 | | | | |
| 8 | | | | | | | | |
| 9 | Anova: Single Factor | | | | | | | |
| 10 | | | | | | | | |
| 11 | SUMMARY | | | | | | | |
| 12 | *Groups* | *Count* | *Sum* | *Average* | *Variance* | | | |
| 13 | Atlanta | 6 | 474 | 79 | 34 | | | |
| 14 | Dallas | 6 | 444 | 74 | 20 | | | |
| 15 | Seattle | 6 | 396 | 66 | 32 | | | |
| 16 | | | | | | | | |
| 17 | | | | | | | | |
| 18 | ANOVA | | | | | | | |
| 19 | *Source of Variation* | *SS* | *df* | *MS* | *F* | *P-value* | *F crit* | |
| 20 | Between Groups | 516 | 2 | 258 | 9 | 0.0027 | 3.68 | |
| 21 | Within Groups | 430 | 15 | 28.6667 | | | | |
| 22 | | | | | | | | |
| 23 | Total | 946 | 17 | | | | | |
| 24 | | | | | | | | |

**Step 4.** When the Anova: Single Factor dialog box appears (see Figure 13.5):
Enter B1:D7 in the **Input Range** box
Select Grouped By **Columns**
Select **Labels**
Enter .05 in the **Alpha** box
Select **Output Range**
Enter A9 in the **Output Range** box (to identify the upper left corner of the section of the worksheet where the output will appear)
Click **OK**

The output, titled *Anova: Single Factor,* appears in cells A9:G23 of the worksheet. Cells A11:E15 provide a summary of the data. Note that the sample mean and sample variance for each plant is the same as shown in Table 13.1. The ANOVA table, shown in cells A18:G23, is basically the same as the ANOVA table shown in Table 13.2. Excel identifies the Treatments source of variation using the label *Between Groups* and the Error source of variation using the label *Within Groups*. In addition, the Excel output provides the *p*-value associated with the test as well as the critical *F* value.

We can make the hypothesis testing decision by comparing the computed *F* value shown in cell E20, $F = 9$, to the critical *F* value shown in cell G20, $F_{.05} = 3.68$. Because $F = 9$ is greater than $F_{.05} = 3.68$, we can reject the null hypothesis and conclude that the population mean examination scores at the three NCP plants are not equal.

Alternatively, we can use the *p*-value shown in cell F20, 0.0027, to make the hypothesis testing decision. The *p*-value approach to hypothesis testing for analysis of variance is

**FIGURE 13.5**   DIALOG BOX FOR ANOVA: SINGLE FACTOR

basically the same as the $p$-value approach for other hypothesis tests. That is, given the level of significance $\alpha$, the decision whether to reject $H_0$ can be made as follows:

$$\text{Reject } H_0 \text{ if the } p\text{-value} < \alpha$$

Thus, at the $\alpha = .05$ level of significance, we reject $H_0$ because the $p$-value $= 0.0027 < \alpha = .05$. Hence, using the $p$-value approach we still conclude that the mean examination scores differ among the three plants.

## NOTES AND COMMENTS

1. The overall sample mean can also be computed as a weighted average of the $k$ sample means.

$$\bar{\bar{x}} = \frac{n_1 \bar{x}_1 + n_2 \bar{x}_2 + \cdots + n_k \bar{x}_k}{n_T}$$

   In problems where the sample means are provided, this formula is simpler than equation (13.3) for computing the overall mean.

2. If each sample consists of $n$ observations, equation (13.6) can be written as

$$\text{MSTR} = \frac{n \sum_{j=1}^{k} (\bar{x}_j - \bar{\bar{x}})^2}{k - 1} = n \left[ \frac{\sum_{j=1}^{k} (\bar{x}_j - \bar{\bar{x}})^2}{k - 1} \right]$$
$$= n s_{\bar{x}}^2$$

   Note that this result is the same as presented in Section 13.1 when we introduced the concept of the between-treatments estimate of $\sigma^2$. Equation (13.6) is simply a generalization of this result to the unequal sample-size case.

3. If each sample has $n$ observations, $n_T = kn$; thus, $n_T - k = k(n - 1)$, and equation (13.9) can be rewritten as

$$\text{MSE} = \frac{\sum_{j=1}^{k} (n - 1)s_j^2}{k(n - 1)} = \frac{(n - 1) \sum_{j=1}^{k} s_j^2}{k(n - 1)} = \frac{\sum_{j=1}^{k} s_j^2}{k}$$

   In other words, if the sample sizes are the same, MSE is just the average of the $k$ sample variances. Note that it is the same result we used in Section 13.1 when we introduced the concept of the within-treatments estimate of $\sigma^2$.

4. Confidence interval estimates for each of the $k$ population means can be developed using

$$\bar{x} \pm t_{\alpha/2} \frac{\sqrt{\text{MSE}}}{\sqrt{n}} \qquad \textbf{(13.15)}$$

   The degrees of freedom for the $t$ value are the degrees of freedom associated with the within-treatments estimate of $\sigma^2$.

## EXERCISES

## Methods

1.  Samples of five observations were selected from each of three populations. The data obtained follow.

    | | Sample 1 | Sample 2 | Sample 3 |
    |---|---|---|---|
    | | 32 | 44 | 33 |
    | | 30 | 43 | 36 |
    | | 30 | 44 | 35 |
    | | 26 | 46 | 36 |
    | | 32 | 48 | 40 |
    | Sample mean | 30 | 45 | 36 |
    | Sample variance | 6.00 | 4.00 | 6.50 |

    a.  Compute the between-treatments estimate of $\sigma^2$.
    b.  Compute the within-treatments estimate of $\sigma^2$.
    c.  At the $\alpha = .05$ level of significance, can we reject the null hypothesis that the means of the three populations are equal?
    d.  Set up the ANOVA table for this problem.

2.  Four observations were selected from each of three populations. The data obtained follow.

    | | Sample 1 | Sample 2 | Sample 3 |
    |---|---|---|---|
    | | 165 | 174 | 169 |
    | | 149 | 164 | 154 |
    | | 156 | 180 | 161 |
    | | 142 | 158 | 148 |
    | Sample mean | 153 | 169 | 158 |
    | Sample variance | 96.67 | 97.33 | 82.00 |

    a.  Compute the between-treatments estimate of $\sigma^2$.
    b.  Compute the within-treatments estimate of $\sigma^2$.
    c.  At the $\alpha = .05$ level of significance, can we reject the null hypothesis that the three population means are equal? Explain.
    d.  Set up the ANOVA table for this problem.

3.  Samples were selected from three populations. The data obtained follow.

    | | Sample 1 | Sample 2 | Sample 3 |
    |---|---|---|---|
    | | 93 | 77 | 88 |
    | | 98 | 87 | 75 |
    | | 107 | 84 | 73 |
    | | 102 | 95 | 84 |
    | | | 85 | 75 |
    | | | 82 | |
    | $\bar{x}_j$ | 100 | 85 | 79 |
    | $s_j^2$ | 35.33 | 35.60 | 43.50 |

    a.  Compute the between-treatments estimate of $\sigma^2$.
    b.  Compute the within-treatments estimate of $\sigma^2$.
    c.  At the $\alpha = .05$ level of significance, can we reject the null hypothesis that the three population means are equal? Explain.
    d.  Set up the ANOVA table for this problem.

**4.** A random sample of 16 observations was selected from each of four populations. A portion of the ANOVA table follows.

| Source of Variation | Sum of Squares | Degrees of Freedom | Mean Square | F |
|---|---|---|---|---|
| Treatments | | | 400 | |
| Error | | | | |
| Total | 1500 | | | |

**a.** Provide the missing entries for the ANOVA table.
**b.** At the $\alpha = .05$ level of significance, can we reject the null hypothesis that the means of the four populations are equal?

**5.** Random samples of 25 observations were selected from each of three populations. For these data, SSTR = 120 and SSE = 216.
**a.** Set up the ANOVA table for this problem.
**b.** At the $\alpha = .05$ level of significance, what is the critical $F$ value?
**c.** At the $\alpha = .05$ level of significance, can we reject the null hypothesis that the three population means are equal?

## Applications

**6.** To test whether the mean time needed to mix a batch of material is the same for machines produced by three manufacturers, the Jacobs Chemical Company obtained the following data on the time (in minutes) needed to mix the material. Use these data to test whether the population mean times for mixing a batch of material differ for the three manufacturers. Use $\alpha = .05$.

| | Manufacturer | |
|---|---|---|
| **1** | **2** | **3** |
| 20 | 28 | 20 |
| 26 | 26 | 19 |
| 24 | 31 | 23 |
| 22 | 27 | 22 |

**7.** Managers at all levels of an organization need adequate information to perform their respective tasks. One study investigated the effect the source has on the dissemination of information. In this particular study the sources of information were a superior, a peer, and a subordinate. In each case, a measure of dissemination was obtained, with higher values indicating greater dissemination of information. Using $\alpha = .05$ and the following data, test whether the source of information significantly affects dissemination. What is your conclusion, and what does it suggest about the use and dissemination of information?

| Superior | Peer | Subordinate |
|---|---|---|
| 8 | 6 | 6 |
| 5 | 6 | 5 |
| 4 | 7 | 7 |
| 6 | 5 | 4 |
| 6 | 3 | 3 |
| 7 | 4 | 5 |
| 5 | 7 | 7 |
| 5 | 6 | 5 |

**8.** A study investigated the perception of corporate ethical values among individuals specializing in marketing. Using $\alpha = .05$ and the following data (higher scores indicate higher ethical values), test for significant differences in perception among the three groups of specialists.

| Marketing Managers | Marketing Research | Advertising |
| --- | --- | --- |
| 6 | 5 | 6 |
| 5 | 5 | 7 |
| 4 | 4 | 6 |
| 5 | 4 | 5 |
| 6 | 5 | 6 |
| 4 | 4 | 6 |

**9.** A study reported in the *Journal of Small Business Management* concluded that self-employed individuals experience higher job stress than individuals who are not self-employed. In this study job stress was assessed with a 15-item scale designed to measure various aspects of ambiguity and role conflict. Ratings for each of the 15 items were made using a scale with 1–5 response options ranging from strong agreement to strong disagreement. The sum of the ratings for the 15 items for each individual surveyed is between 15 and 75, with higher values indicating a higher degree of job stress (*Journal of Small Business Management,* October 1997). Suppose that a similar approach, using a 20-item scale with 1–5 response options, was used to measure the job stress of individuals for 15 randomly selected real estate agents, 15 architects, and 15 stockbrokers. The results obtained follow.

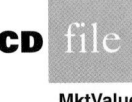

**Stress**

| Real Estate Agent | Architect | Stockbroker |
| --- | --- | --- |
| 81 | 43 | 65 |
| 48 | 63 | 48 |
| 68 | 60 | 57 |
| 69 | 52 | 91 |
| 54 | 54 | 70 |
| 62 | 77 | 67 |
| 76 | 68 | 83 |
| 56 | 57 | 75 |
| 61 | 61 | 53 |
| 65 | 80 | 71 |
| 64 | 50 | 54 |
| 69 | 37 | 72 |
| 83 | 73 | 65 |
| 85 | 84 | 58 |
| 75 | 58 | 58 |

Using $\alpha = .05$, test for any significant difference in job stress among the three professions.

**10.** The *Business Week* Global 1000 ranks companies on the basis of their market value (*Business Week,* July 7, 1997). The following table shows the price/earnings ratios for 29 companies classified as being in the finance economic sector. An industry code of 1 indicates a banking firm, a code of 2 a financial services firm, and a code of 3 an insurance firm. At the .05 level of significance, test whether the mean price/earnings ratio is the same for these three groups of financial firms.

**CD file**

**MktValue**

| Company | Industry Code | P/E | Company | Industry Code | P/E |
| --- | --- | --- | --- | --- | --- |
| Citicorp | 1 | 15 | Fifth Third Bancorp | 1 | 23 |
| NationsBank | 1 | 14 | Bank of New York | 1 | 17 |
| Wells Fargo | 1 | 25 | First Chicago NBD | 1 | 13 |
| First Union | 1 | 13 | Mellon Bank | 1 | 16 |
| KeyCorp | 1 | 14 | Fleet Financial Group | 1 | 15 |
| Chase Manhattan | 1 | 12 | First Bank System | 1 | 16 |

| Company | Industry Code | P/E | Company | Industry Code | P/E |
|---|---|---|---|---|---|
| American Express | 2 | 19 | Allstate | 3 | 14 |
| Travelers | 2 | 15 | Marsh & McLennan | 3 | 20 |
| Merrill Lynch | 2 | 12 | American General | 3 | 16 |
| MBNA | 2 | 24 | Cigna | 3 | 12 |
| Cincinnati Financial | 2 | 19 | Lincoln National | 3 | 13 |
| Franklin Resources | 2 | 22 | AFLAC | 3 | 21 |
| Fannie Mae | 2 | 17 | Equitable | 3 | 11 |
| American International Group | 3 | 21 | Chubb | 3 | 20 |
| | | | General Re | 3 | 15 |

## 13.3   MULTIPLE COMPARISON PROCEDURES

When we use analysis of variance to test whether the means of $k$ populations are equal, rejection of the null hypothesis allows us to conclude only that the population means are *not all equal.* In some cases we will want to go a step further and determine where the differences among means occur. The purpose of this section is to introduce two **multiple comparison procedures** that can be used to conduct statistical comparisons between pairs of population means.

### Fisher's LSD

Suppose that analysis of variance has provided statistical evidence to reject the null hypothesis of equal population means. In this case, Fisher's least significant difference (LSD) procedure can be used to determine where the differences occur. To illustrate the use of Fisher's LSD procedure in making pairwise comparisons of population means, recall the NCP example introduced in Section 13.1. Using analysis of variance, we concluded that the population mean examination scores are not the same at the three plants. In this case, the follow-up question is: We believe the plants differ, but where do the differences occur? That is, do the means of populations 1 and 2 differ? Or those of populations 1 and 3? Or those of populations 2 and 3?

In Chapter 10 we presented a statistical procedure for testing the hypothesis that the means of two populations are equal. With a slight modification in how we estimate the population variance, Fisher's LSD procedure is based on the $t$ test statistic presented for the two-population case. A summary of Fisher's LSD procedure is presented below.

---

**Fisher's LSD Procedure**

$$H_0: \mu_i = \mu_j$$
$$H_a: \mu_i \neq \mu_j$$

**Test Statistic**

$$t = \frac{\bar{x}_i - \bar{x}_j}{\sqrt{\text{MSE}\left(\dfrac{1}{n_i} + \dfrac{1}{n_j}\right)}} \qquad \textbf{(13.16)}$$

**Rejection Rule**

Using test statistic:   Reject $H_0$ if $t < -t_{\alpha/2}$ or $t > t_{\alpha/2}$
Using $p$-value:   Reject $H_0$ if $p$-value $< \alpha$

where the value of $t_{\alpha/2}$ is based on a $t$ distribution with $n_T - k$ degrees of freedom.

---

Let us now apply this procedure to determine whether there is a significant difference between the means of population 1 (Atlanta) and population 2 (Dallas). Table 13.1 shows that the sample mean is 79 for the Atlanta plant and 74 for the Dallas plant. Table 13.2 shows that the value of MSE is 28.67; it is the estimate of $\sigma^2$ and is based on 15 degrees of freedom. At the .05 level of significance, the $t$ distribution table shows that with $n_T - k = 18 - 3 = 15$ degrees of freedom, $t_{.025} = 2.131$. Thus, if $t < -2.131$ or $t > 2.131$, we reject $H_0: \mu_1 = \mu_2$. For the NCP data we obtain the following $t$ value.

$$t = \frac{79 - 74}{\sqrt{28.67\left(\frac{1}{6} + \frac{1}{6}\right)}} = 1.62$$

Because $t = 1.62$, we do not have sufficient statistical evidence to reject the null hypothesis; hence, we cannot conclude that the population mean examination score at the Atlanta plant is different from the population mean examination score at the Dallas plant.

The $p$-value criterion can also be used for this hypothesis test. Excel makes computing the $p$-value corresponding to $t = 1.62$ easy. For example, for the NCP example problem, simply enter =TDIST(1.62,15,2) in any cell of a worksheet; the result of .1261 is the $p$-value associated with the test statistic $t = 1.62$. With a $p$-value $= .1261 > \alpha = .05$, we cannot conclude that the population mean score at the Atlanta plant is different from the population mean score at the Dallas plant.

Many practitioners find it easier to determine how large the difference between the sample means must be to reject $H_0$. In this case the test statistic is $\bar{x}_i - \bar{x}_j$, and the test is conducted by the following procedure.

**Fisher's LSD Procedure Based on the Test Statistic $\bar{x}_i - \bar{x}_j$**

$$H_0: \mu_i = \mu_j$$
$$H_a: \mu_i \neq \mu_j$$

**Test Statistic**

$$\bar{x}_i - \bar{x}_j$$

**Rejection Rule at a Level of Significance $\alpha$**

$$\text{Reject } H_0 \text{ if } |\bar{x}_i - \bar{x}_j| > \text{LSD}$$

where

$$\text{LSD} = t_{\alpha/2}\sqrt{\text{MSE}\left(\frac{1}{n_i} + \frac{1}{n_j}\right)} \qquad \textbf{(13.17)}$$

For the NCP example the value of LSD at the .05 level of significance is

Excel's Single Factor tool (see Figure 13.4) provides the sample sizes and MSE. To compute LSD enter the appropriate formula for equation (13.17) into an empty cell in the worksheet

$$\text{LSD} = 2.131\sqrt{28.67\left(\frac{1}{6} + \frac{1}{6}\right)} = 6.59$$

When the sample sizes are equal, the same value for LSD is computed for each pairwise test. In such cases we can simply compare the magnitude of the difference between any two sample means with the value of LSD. For example, the difference between the sample means for population 1 (Atlanta) and population 3 (Seattle) is $79 - 66 = 13$. This difference is greater than 6.59, which means we can reject the null hypothesis that the population mean examination score for the Atlanta plant is equal to the population mean score for the Seattle plant. Similarly, with the difference between the sample means for populations 2 and 3 of $74 - 66 = 8 > 6.59$, we can also reject the hypothesis that the population mean examination score for the Dallas plant is equal to the population mean examination score for the Seattle plant. In effect, our conclusion is that the Atlanta and Dallas plants both differ from the Seattle plant.

Fisher's LSD can also be used to develop a confidence interval estimate of the difference between the means of two populations. The general procedure follows.

**Confidence Interval Estimate of the Difference Between Two Population Means Using Fisher's LSD Procedure**

$$\bar{x}_i - \bar{x}_j \pm \text{LSD} \tag{13.18}$$

where

$$\text{LSD} = t_{\alpha/2} \sqrt{\text{MSE}\left(\frac{1}{n_i} + \frac{1}{n_j}\right)} \tag{13.19}$$

and $t_{\alpha/2}$ is based on a $t$ distribution with $n_T - k$ degrees of freedom.

If the confidence interval in equation (13.18) includes the value zero, we cannot reject the null hypothesis that the two population means are equal. However, if the confidence interval does not include the value zero, we conclude that there is a difference between the population means. For the NCP example, recall that $\text{LSD} = 6.59$ (corresponding to $t_{.025} = 2.131$). Thus, a 95% confidence interval estimate of the difference between the means of populations 1 and 2 is $79 - 74 \pm 6.59 = 5 \pm 6.59 = -1.59$ to 11.59; because this interval includes zero, we cannot reject the null hypothesis that the two population means are equal.

## Type I Error Rates

We began the discussion of Fisher's LSD procedure with the premise that analysis of variance had given us statistical evidence to reject the null hypothesis of equal population means. We showed how Fisher's LSD procedure can be used in such cases to determine where the differences occur. Technically, it is referred to as a *protected* or *restricted* LSD test because it is employed only if we first find a significant $F$ value by using analysis of variance. To see why this distinction is important in multiple comparison tests, we need to explain the difference between a *comparisonwise* Type I error rate and an *experimentwise* Type I error rate.

In the NCP example we used Fisher's LSD procedure to make three pairwise comparisons.

| Test 1 | Test 2 | Test 3 |
|---|---|---|
| $H_0: \mu_1 = \mu_2$ | $H_0: \mu_1 = \mu_3$ | $H_0: \mu_2 = \mu_3$ |
| $H_a: \mu_1 \neq \mu_2$ | $H_a: \mu_1 \neq \mu_3$ | $H_a: \mu_2 \neq \mu_3$ |

In each case, we used a level of significance of $\alpha = .05$. Therefore, for each test, if the null hypothesis is true, the probability that we will make a Type I error is $\alpha = .05$; hence, the probability that we will not make a Type I error on each test is $1 - .05 = .95$. In discussing multiple comparison procedures we refer to this probability of a Type I error ($\alpha = .05$) as the **comparisonwise Type I error rate**; comparisonwise Type I error rates indicate the level of significance associated with a single pairwise comparison.

Let us now consider a slightly different question. What is the probability that in making three pairwise comparisons, we will commit a Type I error on at least one of the three tests? To answer this question, note that the probability that we will not make a Type I error on any of the three tests is $(.95)(.95)(.95) = .8574$.* Therefore, the probability of making at least one Type I error is $1 - .8574 = .1426$. Thus, when we use Fisher's LSD procedure to make all three pairwise comparisons, the Type I error rate associated with this approach is not .05, but actually .1426; we refer to this error rate as the *overall* or **experimentwise Type I error rate**. To avoid confusion, we denote the experimentwise Type I error rate as $\alpha_{EW}$.

The experimentwise Type I error rate gets larger for problems with more populations. For example, a problem with five populations has 10 possible pairwise comparisons. If we tested all possible pairwise comparisons by using Fisher's LSD with a comparisonwise error rate of $\alpha = .05$, the experimentwise Type I error rate would be $1 - (1 - .05)^{10} = .40$. In such cases, practitioners look to alternatives that provide better control over the experimentwise error rate.

One alternative for controlling the overall experimentwise error rate, referred to as the Bonferroni adjustment, involves using a smaller comparisonwise error rate for each test. For example, if we want to test $C$ pairwise comparisons and want the maximum probability of making a Type I error for the overall experiment to be $\alpha_{EW}$, we simply use a comparisonwise error rate equal to $\alpha_{EW}/C$. In the NCP example, if we want to use Fisher's LSD procedure to test all three pairwise comparisons with a maximum experimentwise error rate of $\alpha_{EW} = .05$, we set the comparisonwise error rate to be $\alpha = .05/3 = .017$. For a problem with five populations and 10 possible pairwise comparisons, the Bonferroni adjustment would suggest a comparisonwise error rate of $.05/10 = .005$. Recall from our discussion of hypothesis testing in Chapter 9 that for a fixed sample size, any decrease in the probability of making a Type I error will result in an increase in the probability of making a Type II error, which corresponds to accepting the hypothesis that the two population means are equal when in fact they are not equal. As a result, many practitioners are reluctant to perform individual tests with a low comparisonwise Type I error rate because of the increased risk of making a Type II error.

Several other procedures, such as Tukey's procedure and Duncan's multiple range test, have been developed to help in such situations. However, there is considerable controversy in the statistical community as to which procedure is "best." The truth is that no one procedure is best for all types of problems.

## EXERCISES

### Methods

11. In Exercise 1, five observations were selected from each of three populations. For these data, $\bar{x}_1 = 30$, $\bar{x}_2 = 45$, $\bar{x}_3 = 36$, and MSE $= 5.5$. At the $\alpha = .05$ level of significance, the null hypothesis of equal population means was rejected. In the following calculations, use $\alpha = .05$.
    a. Using Fisher's LSD procedure, test to see whether there is a significant difference between the means of populations 1 and 2, populations 1 and 3, and populations 2 and 3.
    b. Use Fisher's LSD procedure to develop a 95% confidence interval estimate of the difference between the means of populations 1 and 2.

*The assumption is that the three tests are independent, and hence the joint probability of the three events can be obtained by simply multiplying the individual probabilities. In fact, the three tests are not independent because MSE is used in each test; therefore, the error involved is even greater than that shown.

**12.** Four observations were selected from each of three populations. The data obtained are shown. In the following calculations, use $\alpha = .05$.

|  | Sample 1 | Sample 2 | Sample 3 |
|---|---|---|---|
|  | 63 | 82 | 69 |
|  | 47 | 72 | 54 |
|  | 54 | 88 | 61 |
|  | 40 | 66 | 48 |
| $\bar{x}_j$ | 51 | 77 | 58 |
| $s_j^2$ | 96.67 | 97.34 | 81.99 |

**a.** Using analysis of variance, test for a significant difference among the means of the three populations.

**b.** Use Fisher's LSD procedure to see which means are different.

## Applications

 **13.** Refer to Exercise 6. At the $\alpha = .05$ level of significance, use Fisher's LSD procedure to test for the equality of the means for manufacturers 1 and 3. What conclusion can you draw after carrying out this test?

 **14.** Refer to Exercise 13. Use Fisher's LSD procedure to develop a 95% confidence interval estimate of the difference between the means for manufacturer 1 and manufacturer 2.

**15.** Refer to Exercise 8. At the $\alpha = .05$ level of significance, we can conclude that the perceptions for marketing managers, marketing research specialists, and advertising specialists differ. Use the procedures in this section to determine where the differences occur. Use $\alpha = .05$.

**16.** To test for any significant difference in the number of hours between breakdowns for four machines, the following data were obtained.

| Machine 1 | Machine 2 | Machine 3 | Machine 4 |
|---|---|---|---|
| 6.4 | 8.7 | 11.1 | 9.9 |
| 7.8 | 7.4 | 10.3 | 12.8 |
| 5.3 | 9.4 | 9.7 | 12.1 |
| 7.4 | 10.1 | 10.3 | 10.8 |
| 8.4 | 9.2 | 9.2 | 11.3 |
| 7.3 | 9.8 | 8.8 | 11.5 |

**a.** At the $\alpha = .05$ level of significance, what is the difference, if any, in the population mean times among the four machines?

**b.** Use Fisher's LSD procedure to test for the equality of the means for machines 2 and 4. Use a .05 level of significance.

**17.** Refer to Exercise 16. Use the Bonferroni adjustment to test for a significant difference between all pairs of means. Assume that a maximum overall experimentwise error rate of .05 is desired.

**18.** Refer to Exercise 10. At the .05 level of significance, we can conclude that the mean price/earnings ratios of banking firms, financial services firms, and insurance firms differ. Use the procedures in this section to determine where the differences occur. Use $\alpha = .05$.

## 13.4   INTRODUCTION TO EXPERIMENTAL DESIGN

Statistical studies can be classified as being either experimental or observational. In an *experimental study*, variables of interest are identified. Then, one or more factors in the study are controlled so that data can be obtained about how the factors influence the variables. In

Cause-and-effect relationships can be difficult to establish in observational studies; such relationships are easier to establish in experimental studies.

*observational* or *nonexperimental* studies, no attempt is made to control the factors. A survey (see Chapter 18) is perhaps the most common type of observational study.

The NCP example that we used to introduce analysis of variance is an illustration of an observational statistical study. To measure how much NCP employees knew about total quality management, a random sample of six employees was selected from each of NCP's three plants and given a quality awareness examination. The examination scores for these employees were then analyzed by analysis of variance to test the hypothesis that the population mean examination score is the same for all three plants.

As an example of an experimental statistical study, let us consider the problem facing Chemitech, Inc. Chemitech has developed a new filtration system for municipal water supplies. The components for the new filtration system will be purchased from several suppliers, and Chemitech will assemble the components at its plant in Columbia, South Carolina. The industrial engineering group has been given the responsibility of determining the best assembly method for the new filtration system. After considering a variety of possible approaches, the group has narrowed the alternatives to three: method A, method B, and method C. These methods differ in the sequence of steps used to assemble the product. Managers at Chemitech want to determine which assembly method can produce the greatest number of filtration systems per week.

In the Chemitech experiment, assembly method is the independent variable or **factor.** Because the three assembly methods correspond to this factor, we say that this experiment has three associated treatments; each **treatment** corresponds to one of the three assembly methods. The Chemitech problem is an example of a **single-factor experiment** involving a qualitative factor (method of assembly). Other experiments may consist of multiple factors; some factors may be qualitative and some may be quantitative.

The three assembly methods or treatments define the three populations of interest for the Chemitech experiment. One population is all Chemitech employees who use assembly method A, another is those who use method B, and the third is those who use method C. Note that for each population the dependent or response variable is the number of filtration systems assembled per week, and the primary statistical objective of the experiment is to determine whether the mean number of units produced per week is the same for all three populations.

Randomization is the process of assigning the treatments to the experimental units at random. Prior to the work of Sir R. A. Fisher, treatments were assigned on a systematic or subjective basis.

Suppose a random sample of three employees is selected from all assembly workers at the Chemitech production facility. In experimental design terminology, the three randomly selected workers are the **experimental units.** The experimental design that we will use for the Chemitech problem is called a **completely randomized design.** This type of design requires that each of the three assembly methods or treatments be assigned randomly to one of the experimental units or workers. For example, method A might be randomly assigned to the second worker, method B to the first worker, and method C to the third worker. The concept of *randomization,* as illustrated in this example, is an important principle of all experimental designs.

Note that the experiment would result in only one measurement or number of units assembled for each treatment. In other words, we have a sample size of one corresponding to each treatment. To obtain additional data for each assembly method, we must repeat or replicate the basic experimental process. Suppose, for example, that instead of selecting just three workers at random we had selected 15 workers and then randomly assigned each of the three treatments to five of the workers. Because each method of assembly is assigned to five workers, we say that five replicates have been obtained. The process of *replication* is another important principle of experimental design. Figure 13.6 shows the completely randomized design for the Chemitech experiment.

## Data Collection

Once we are satisfied with the experimental design, we proceed by collecting and analyzing the data. In the Chemitech case, the employees would be instructed in how to perform the assembly method they have been assigned and then would begin assembling the new filtra-

**FIGURE 13.6**    COMPLETELY RANDOMIZED DESIGN FOR THE CHEMITECH
ASSEMBLY METHOD EXPERIMENT

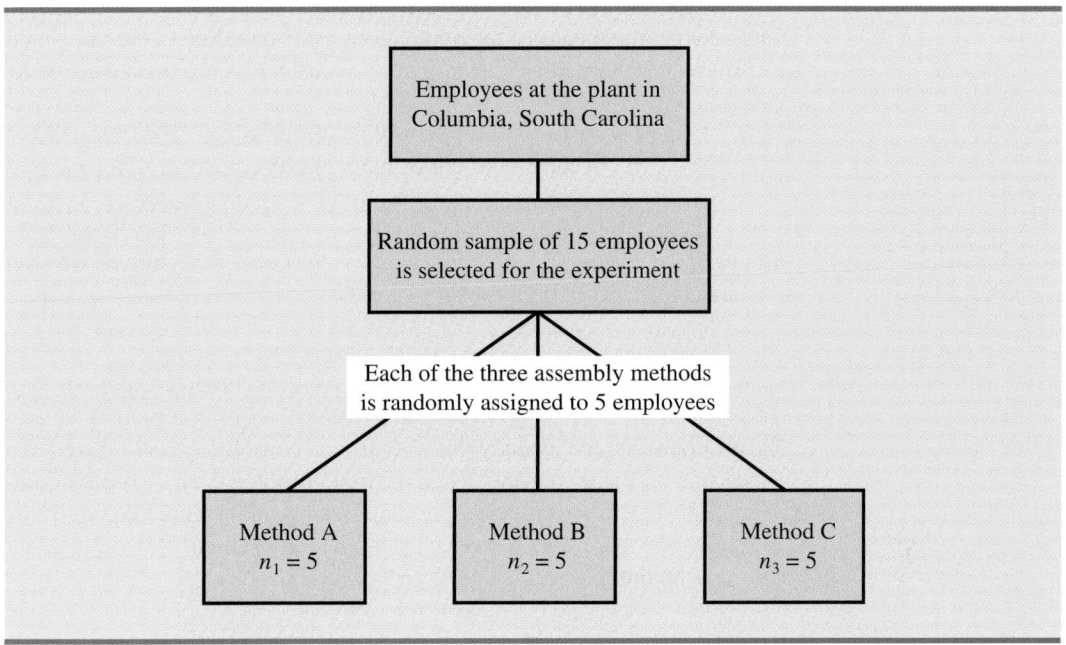

tion systems using that method. Suppose assignment and training has been done, and the
number of units assembled by each employee during one week is as shown in Table 13.3.
The sample mean number of units produced with each of the three assembly methods is reported in the following table.

| Assembly Method | Mean Number Produced |
|-----------------|----------------------|
| A | 62 |
| B | 66 |
| C | 52 |

**TABLE 13.3**    NUMBER OF UNITS PRODUCED BY 15 WORKERS

|  | | Method | |
|--------------------------|------|------|------|
| **Observation** | **A** | **B** | **C** |
| 1 | 58 | 58 | 48 |
| 2 | 64 | 69 | 57 |
| 3 | 55 | 71 | 59 |
| 4 | 66 | 64 | 47 |
| 5 | 67 | 68 | 49 |
| Sample mean | 62 | 66 | 52 |
| Sample variance | 27.5 | 26.5 | 31.0 |
| Sample standard deviation | 5.24 | 5.15 | 5.57 |

From these data, method B appears to result in higher production rates than either of the other methods.

The real issue is whether the three sample means observed are different enough for us to conclude that the means of the populations corresponding to the three methods of assembly are different. To write this question in statistical terms, we introduce the following notation.

$\mu_1$ = mean number of units produced per week for method A
$\mu_2$ = mean number of units produced per week for method B
$\mu_3$ = mean number of units produced per week for method C

Although we will never know the actual values of $\mu_1$, $\mu_2$, and $\mu_3$, we want to use the sample means to test the following hypotheses.

$$H_0: \mu_1 = \mu_2 = \mu_3$$
$$H_a: \text{Not all population means are equal}$$

The problem we face in analyzing data from a completely randomized experimental design is the same problem we faced when we first introduced analysis of variance as a method for testing whether the means of more than two populations are equal. In the next section we will show how analysis of variance is applied in problem situations such as the Chemitech assembly method.

## NOTES AND COMMENTS

1. Randomization in experimental design is the analog of random sampling in an observational study.
2. In many medical experiments, potential bias is eliminated by using a double-blind study. In such studies neither the physician applying the treatment nor the subject knows which treatment is being applied. Many other types of experiments could benefit from this type of study.

## 13.5 COMPLETELY RANDOMIZED DESIGNS

The hypotheses we want to test when analyzing the data from a completely randomized design are exactly the same as the general form of the hypotheses we presented in Section 13.2.

$$H_0: \mu_1 = \mu_2 = \cdots = \mu_k$$
$$H_a: \text{Not all population means are equal}$$

Hence, to test for the equality of means in situations where the data have been collected in a completely randomized experimental design, we can use analysis of variance as introduced in Sections 13.1 and 13.2. Recall that analysis of variance requires the calculation of two independent estimates of the population variance $\sigma^2$.

### Between-Treatments Estimate of Population Variance

The between-treatments estimate of $\sigma^2$ is referred to as the *mean square due to treatments* and is denoted MSTR. The formula for computing MSTR follows:

$$\text{MSTR} = \frac{\sum_{j=1}^{k} n_j (\bar{x}_j - \bar{\bar{x}})^2}{k-1} \tag{13.20}$$

The numerator in equation (13.20) is called the *sum of squares between* or *sum of squares due to treatments* and is denoted SSTR. The denominator $k - 1$ represents the degrees of freedom associated with SSTR.

For the Chemitech data in Table 13.3, we obtain the following results (note: $\bar{\bar{x}} = 60$).

$$\text{SSTR} = \sum_{j=1}^{k} n_j(\bar{x}_j - \bar{\bar{x}})^2 = 5(62 - 60)^2 + 5(66 - 60)^2 + 5(52 - 60)^2 = 520$$

$$\text{MSTR} = \frac{\text{SSTR}}{k - 1} = \frac{520}{3 - 1} = 260$$

## Within-Treatments Estimate of Population Variance

The within-treatments estimate of $\sigma^2$ is referred to as the *mean square due to error* and is denoted MSE. The formula for computing MSE follows.

$$\text{MSE} = \frac{\sum_{j=1}^{k}(n_j - 1)s_j^2}{n_T - k} \tag{13.21}$$

The numerator in equation (13.21) is called the *sum of squares within* or *sum of squares due to error* and is denoted SSE. The denominator of MSE is referred to as the degrees of freedom associated with the within-treatment variance estimate.

For the Chemitech data in Table 13.3, we obtain the following results.

$$\text{SSE} = \sum_{j=1}^{k}(n_j - 1)s_j^2 = 4(27.5) + 4(26.5) + 4(31) = 340$$

$$\text{MSE} = \frac{\text{SSE}}{n_T - k} = \frac{340}{15 - 3} = 28.33$$

## Comparing the Variance Estimates: The $F$ Test

If the null hypothesis is true and the ANOVA assumptions are valid, the sampling distribution of MSTR/MSE is an $F$ distribution with numerator degrees of freedom equal to $k - 1$ and denominator degrees of freedom equal to $n_T - k$. Recall also that if the means of the $k$ populations are not equal, the value of MSTR/MSE will be inflated because MSTR overestimates $\sigma^2$. Hence we will reject $H_0$ if the resulting value of MSTR/MSE appears to be too large to have been selected at random from an $F$ distribution with degrees of freedom $k - 1$ in the numerator and $n_T - k$ in the denominator.

For the Chemitech problem the value of $F = \text{MSTR/MSE} = 260/28.33 = 9.18$. The critical $F$ value is based on two numerator degrees of freedom and 12 denominator degrees of freedom. For a .05 level of significance, Table 4 of Appendix B shows a value of $F_{.05} = 3.89$. Because the observed value of $F$ is greater than the critical value, we reject the null hypothesis and conclude that not all of the population means are equal.

The $p$-value criterion can also be used for this hypothesis test. The usual rejection rule applies: Reject $H_0$ if $p$-value $< \alpha$. Excel makes computing the $p$-value easy. For example, for the Chemitech problem, simply enter =FDIST(9.18,2,12) in any cell of a worksheet; the result of .0038 is the $p$-value associated with the test statistic $F = 9.18$. With a $p$-value $= .0038 < \alpha = .05$, the null hypothesis that the means of the three populations are equal can be rejected.

**TABLE 13.4** ANOVA TABLE FOR A COMPLETELY RANDOMIZED DESIGN

| Source of Variation | Sum of Squares | Degrees of Freedom | Mean Square | $F$ |
|---|---|---|---|---|
| Treatments | SSTR | $k - 1$ | $MSTR = \dfrac{SSTR}{k - 1}$ | $\dfrac{MSTR}{MSE}$ |
| Error | SSE | $n_T - k$ | $MSE = \dfrac{SSE}{n_T - k}$ | |
| Total | SST | $n_T - 1$ | | |

## ANOVA Table

We can now write the result that shows how the total sum of squares, SST, is partitioned.

$$SST = SSTR + SSE \tag{13.22}$$

This result also holds true for the degrees of freedom associated with each of these sums of squares; that is, the total degrees of freedom is the sum of the degrees of freedom associated with SSTR and SSE. The general form of the ANOVA table for a completely randomized design is shown in Table 13.4; Table 13.5 is the corresponding ANOVA table for the Chemitech problem.

## Using Excel's Anova: Single Factor Tool

In Section 13.2 we showed how Excel's Anova: Single Factor tool could be used to test for the equality of $k$ population means. Because the hypotheses we want to test when analyzing the data from a completely randomized design are exactly the same as the general form of the hypotheses we presented in Section 13.2, Excel's Anova: Single Factor tool can also be used to test for the equality of means in situations where the data have been collected in a completely randomized design.

The data for the Chemitech problem and the corresponding Anova: Singe Factor output are shown in Figure 13.7. We can use the $p$-value shown in cell F19, 0.0038, to make the hypothesis testing decision. Thus, at the $\alpha = .05$ level of significance, we reject $H_0$ because the $p$-value $= 0.0038 < \alpha = .05$.

## Pairwise Comparisons

We can use Fisher's LSD procedure to test all possible pairwise comparisons for the Chemitech problem. At the .05 level of significance, the $t$ distribution table shows that with

**TABLE 13.5** ANOVA TABLE FOR THE CHEMITECH PROBLEM

| Source of Variation | Sum of Squares | Degrees of Freedom | Mean Square | $F$ |
|---|---|---|---|---|
| Treatments | 520 | 2 | 260.00 | 9.18 |
| Error | 340 | 12 | 28.33 | |
| Total | 860 | 14 | | |

**FIGURE 13.7**   EXCEL'S ANOVA OUTPUT FOR THE CHEMITECH PROBLEM

| | A | B | C | D | E | F | G | H |
|---|---|---|---|---|---|---|---|---|
| 1 | Observation | Method A | Method B | Method C | | | | |
| 2 | 1 | 58 | 58 | 48 | | | | |
| 3 | 2 | 64 | 69 | 57 | | | | |
| 4 | 3 | 55 | 71 | 59 | | | | |
| 5 | 4 | 66 | 64 | 47 | | | | |
| 6 | 5 | 67 | 68 | 49 | | | | |
| 7 | | | | | | | | |
| 8 | Anova: Single Factor | | | | | | | |
| 9 | | | | | | | | |
| 10 | SUMMARY | | | | | | | |
| 11 | Groups | Count | Sum | Average | Variance | | | |
| 12 | Method A | 5 | 310 | 62 | 27.5 | | | |
| 13 | Method B | 5 | 330 | 66 | 26.5 | | | |
| 14 | Method C | 5 | 260 | 52 | 31 | | | |
| 15 | | | | | | | | |
| 16 | | | | | | | | |
| 17 | ANOVA | | | | | | | |
| 18 | Source of Variation | SS | df | MS | F | P-value | F crit | |
| 19 | Between Groups | 520 | 2 | 260 | 9.18 | 0.0038 | 3.89 | |
| 20 | Within Groups | 340 | 12 | 28.3333 | | | | |
| 21 | | | | | | | | |
| 22 | Total | 860 | 14 | | | | | |
| 23 | | | | | | | | |

$n_T - k = 15 - 3 = 12$ degrees of freedom, $t_{.025} = 2.179$. Using MSE = 28.33 in equation (13.17), we obtain Fisher's least significant difference.

$$LSD = t_{\alpha/2}\sqrt{MSE\left(\frac{1}{n_i} + \frac{1}{n_j}\right)} = 2.179\sqrt{28.33\left(\frac{1}{5} + \frac{1}{5}\right)} = 7.34$$

If the magnitude of the difference between any two sample means exceeds 7.34, we can reject the hypothesis that the corresponding population means are equal. For the Chemitech data in Table 13.3, we obtain the following results.

| Sample Differences | Significant? |
|---|---|
| Method A − Method B = 62 − 66 = −4 | No |
| Method A − Method C = 62 − 52 = 10 | Yes |
| Method B − Method C = 66 − 52 = 14 | Yes |

Thus, the difference in the population means is attributable to the difference between the means for method A and method C and the difference between the means for method B and method C. Methods A and B therefore are preferred to method C. However, more testing should be done to compare method A with method B. The current study does not provide sufficient statistical evidence to conclude that these two methods differ.

## EXERCISES

## Methods

**19.** The following data are from a completely randomized design.

| | Treatment | | |
|---|---|---|---|
| | **A** | **B** | **C** |
| | 162 | 142 | 126 |
| | 142 | 156 | 122 |
| | 165 | 124 | 138 |
| | 145 | 142 | 140 |
| | 148 | 136 | 150 |
| | 174 | 152 | 128 |
| $\bar{x}_j$ | 156 | 142 | 134 |
| $s_j^2$ | 164.4 | 131.2 | 110.4 |

a. Compute the sum of squares between treatments.
b. Compute the mean square between treatments.
c. Compute the sum of squares due to error.
d. Compute the mean square due to error.
e. At the $\alpha = .05$ level of significance, test whether the means for the three treatments are equal.

**20.** Refer to Exercise 19.
a. Set up the ANOVA table.
b. At the $\alpha = .05$ level of significance, use Fisher's least significant difference procedure to test all possible pairwise comparisons. What conclusion can you draw after carrying out this procedure?

**21.** In a completely randomized experimental design, seven experimental units were used for each of the five levels of the factor. Complete the following ANOVA table.

| Source of Variation | Sum of Squares | Degrees of Freedom | Mean Square | F |
|---|---|---|---|---|
| Treatments | 300 | | | |
| Error | | | | |
| Total | 460 | | | |

**22.** Refer to Exercise 21.
a. What hypothesis test is implied in this problem?
b. At the $\alpha = .05$ level of significance, can we reject the null hypothesis in part (a)? Explain.

**23.** In an experiment designed to test the output levels of three different treatments, the following results were obtained: SST = 400, SSTR = 150, $n_T = 19$. Set up the ANOVA table and test for any significant difference between the mean output levels of the three treatments. Use $\alpha = .05$.

**24.** In a completely randomized experimental design, 12 experimental units were used for the first treatment, 15 for the second treatment, and 20 for the third treatment. Complete the following ANOVA table. At a .05 level of significance, is there a significant difference between the treatments?

| Source of Variation | Sum of Squares | Degrees of Freedom | Mean Square | F |
|---|---|---|---|---|
| Treatments | 1200 | | | |
| Error | | | | |
| Total | 1800 | | | |

25. Develop the analysis of variance computations for the following experimental design. Using $\alpha = .05$, is there a significant difference between the treatment means?

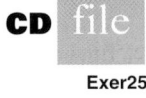

**Exer25**

Treatment

| | A | B | C |
|---|---|---|---|
| | 136 | 107 | 92 |
| | 120 | 114 | 82 |
| | 113 | 125 | 85 |
| | 107 | 104 | 101 |
| | 131 | 107 | 89 |
| | 114 | 109 | 117 |
| | 129 | 97 | 110 |
| | 102 | 114 | 120 |
| | | 104 | 98 |
| | | 89 | 106 |
| $\bar{x}_j$ | 119 | 107 | 100 |
| $s_j^2$ | 146.86 | 96.44 | 173.78 |

## Applications

26. Three different methods for assembling a product were proposed by an industrial engineer. To investigate the number of units assembled correctly with each method, 30 employees were randomly selected and randomly assigned to the three proposed methods in such a way that each method was used by 10 workers. The number of units assembled correctly was recorded, and the analysis of variance procedure was applied to the resulting data set. The following results were obtained: SST = 10,800; SSTR = 4560.
    a. Set up the ANOVA table for this problem.
    b. Using $\alpha = .05$, test for any significant difference in the means for the three assembly methods.

27. In an experiment designed to test the breaking strength of four types of cables, the following results were obtained: SST = 85.05, SSTR = 61.64, $n_T = 24$. Set up the ANOVA table and test for any significant difference in the mean breaking strength of the four cables. Use $\alpha = .05$.

28. To study the effect of temperature on yield in a chemical process, five batches were produced at each of three temperature levels. The results follow. Construct an analysis of variance table. Using a .05 level of significance, test to see whether the temperature level appears to have an effect on the mean yield of the process.

Temperature

| 50°C | 60°C | 70°C |
|---|---|---|
| 34 | 30 | 23 |
| 24 | 31 | 28 |
| 36 | 34 | 28 |
| 39 | 23 | 30 |
| 32 | 27 | 31 |

29. Auditors must make judgments about various aspects of an audit on the basis of their own direct experience, indirect experience, or a combination of the two. In a study, auditors were asked to make judgments about the frequency of errors to be found in an audit. The judgments by the auditors were then compared to the actual results. Suppose the following data were obtained from a similar study; lower scores indicate better judgments.

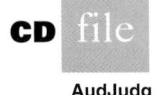

**AudJudg**

| Direct | Indirect | Combination |
|---|---|---|
| 17.0 | 16.6 | 25.2 |
| 18.5 | 22.2 | 24.0 |
| 15.8 | 20.5 | 21.5 |

(*continued*)

| Direct | Indirect | Combination |
|--------|----------|-------------|
| 18.2 | 18.3 | 26.8 |
| 20.2 | 24.2 | 27.5 |
| 16.0 | 19.8 | 25.8 |
| 13.3 | 21.2 | 24.2 |

Using $\alpha = .05$, test to see whether the basis for the judgment affects the quality of the judgment. What is your conclusion?

**30.** Four different paints are advertised as having the same drying time. To check the manufacturer's claims, five samples were tested for each of the paints. The time in minutes until the paint was dry enough for a second coat to be applied was recorded. The following data were obtained.

| Paint 1 | Paint 2 | Paint 3 | Paint 4 |
|---------|---------|---------|---------|
| 128 | 144 | 133 | 150 |
| 137 | 133 | 143 | 142 |
| 135 | 142 | 137 | 135 |
| 124 | 146 | 136 | 140 |
| 141 | 130 | 131 | 153 |

**CD** file

Paint

At the $\alpha = .05$ level of significance, test to see whether the mean drying time is the same for each type of paint.

**31.** Three top-of-the-line mid-sized automobiles manufactured in the United States have been test-driven and compared on a variety of criteria by a well-known automotive magazine. In the area of gasoline mileage performance, five automobiles of each brand were each test-driven 500 miles; the miles per gallon data obtained follow. Use the analysis of variance procedure with $\alpha = .05$ to determine whether there is a significant difference in the mean number of miles per gallon for the three types of automobiles.

| | Automobile | |
|---|---|---|
| A | B | C |
| 19 | 19 | 24 |
| 21 | 20 | 26 |
| 20 | 22 | 23 |
| 19 | 21 | 25 |
| 21 | 23 | 27 |

**32.** Refer to Exercise 29. Use Fisher's least significant difference procedure to test all possible pairwise comparisons. What conclusion can you draw after carrying out this procedure? Use $\alpha = .05$.

**33.** Refer to Exercise 31. Use Fisher's least significant difference procedure to test all possible pairwise comparisons. What conclusion can you draw after carrying out this procedure? Use $\alpha = .05$.

## 13.6 RANDOMIZED BLOCK DESIGN

Thus far we have considered the completely randomized experimental design. Recall that to test for a difference among treatment means, we computed an $F$ value by using the ratio

$$F = \frac{\text{MSTR}}{\text{MSE}}$$

(13.23)

A completely randomized design is useful when the experimental units are homogeneous. If the experimental units are heterogeneous, blocking is often used to form homogeneous groups.

A problem can arise whenever differences due to extraneous factors (ones not considered in the experiment) cause the MSE term in this ratio to become large. In such cases, the F value in equation (13.23) can become small, signaling no difference among treatment means when in fact such a difference exists.

In this section we present an experimental design known as a randomized block design. Its purpose is to control some of the extraneous sources of variation by removing such variation from the MSE term. This design tends to provide a better estimate of the true error variance and leads to a more powerful hypothesis test in terms of the ability to detect differences among treatment means. To illustrate, let us consider a stress study for air traffic controllers.

## Air Traffic Controller Stress Test

A study measuring the fatigue and stress of air traffic controllers has resulted in proposals for modification and redesign of the controller's work station. After consideration of several designs for the work station, three specific alternatives have been selected as having the best potential for reducing controller stress. The key question is: To what extent do the three alternatives differ in terms of their effect on controller stress? To answer this question, we need to design an experiment that will provide measurements of air traffic controller stress under each alternative.

Experimental studies in business often involve experimental units that are highly heterogeneous; as a result, randomized block designs are often employed.

In a completely randomized design, a random sample of controllers would be assigned to each work station alternative. However, controllers are believed to differ substantially in their ability to handle stressful situations. What is high stress to one controller might be only moderate or even low stress to another. Hence, when considering the within-group source of variation (MSE), we must realize that this variation includes both random error and error due to individual controller differences. In fact, managers expected controller variability to be a major contributor to the MSE term.

Blocking in experimental design is similar to stratification in sampling.

One way to separate the effect of the individual differences is to use a randomized block design. Such a design will identify the variability stemming from individual controller differences and remove it from the MSE term. The randomized block design calls for a single sample of controllers. Each controller in the sample is tested with each of the three work station alternatives. In experimental design terminology, the work station is the *factor of interest* and the controllers are the *blocks*. The three treatments or populations associated with the work station factor correspond to the three work station alternatives. For simplicity, we refer to the work station alternatives as system A, system B, and system C.

The *randomized* aspect of the randomized block design is the random order in which the treatments (systems) are assigned to the controllers. If every controller were to test the three systems in the same order, any observed difference in systems might be due to the order of the test rather than to true differences in the systems.

To provide the necessary data, the three work station alternatives were installed at the Cleveland Control Center in Oberlin, Ohio. Six controllers were selected at random and assigned to operate each of the systems. A follow-up interview and a medical examination of each controller participating in the study provided a measure of the stress for each controller on each system. The data are reported in Table 13.6.

Table 13.7 is a summary of the stress data collected. In this table we have included column totals (treatments) and row totals (blocks) as well as some sample means that will be helpful in making the sum of squares computations for the ANOVA procedure. Because lower stress values are viewed as better, the sample data seem to favor system B with its mean stress rating of 13. However, the usual question remains: Do the sample results justify the conclusion that the population mean stress levels for the three systems differ? That is, are the differences statistically significant? An analysis of variance computation similar to the one performed for the completely randomized design can be used to answer this statistical question.

**TABLE 13.6** A RANDOMIZED BLOCK DESIGN FOR THE AIR TRAFFIC CONTROLLER STRESS TEST

**AirTraf**

|  |  | Treatments | | |
| --- | --- | --- | --- | --- |
|  |  | System A | System B | System C |
| Blocks | Controller 1 | 15 | 15 | 18 |
|  | Controller 2 | 14 | 14 | 14 |
|  | Controller 3 | 10 | 11 | 15 |
|  | Controller 4 | 13 | 12 | 17 |
|  | Controller 5 | 16 | 13 | 16 |
|  | Controller 6 | 13 | 13 | 13 |

**TABLE 13.7** SUMMARY OF STRESS DATA FOR THE AIR TRAFFIC CONTROLLER STRESS TEST

|  |  | Treatments | | | Row or Block Totals | Block Means |
| --- | --- | --- | --- | --- | --- | --- |
|  |  | System A | System B | System C |  |  |
| Blocks | Controller 1 | 15 | 15 | 18 | 48 | $\bar{x}_{1.} = 48/3 = 16.0$ |
|  | Controller 2 | 14 | 14 | 14 | 42 | $\bar{x}_{2.} = 42/3 = 14.0$ |
|  | Controller 3 | 10 | 11 | 15 | 36 | $\bar{x}_{3.} = 36/3 = 12.0$ |
|  | Controller 4 | 13 | 12 | 17 | 42 | $\bar{x}_{4.} = 42/3 = 14.0$ |
|  | Controller 5 | 16 | 13 | 16 | 45 | $\bar{x}_{5.} = 45/3 = 15.0$ |
|  | Controller 6 | 13 | 13 | 13 | 39 | $\bar{x}_{6.} = 39/3 = 13.0$ |
| Column or Treatment Totals |  | 81 | 78 | 93 | 252 | $\bar{\bar{x}} = \dfrac{252}{18} = 14.0$ |
| Treatment Means |  | $\bar{x}_{.1} = \dfrac{81}{6}$ $= 13.5$ | $\bar{x}_{.2} = \dfrac{78}{6}$ $= 13.0$ | $\bar{x}_{.3} = \dfrac{93}{6}$ $= 15.5$ |  |  |

## ANOVA Procedure

The ANOVA procedure for the randomized block design requires us to partition the sum of squares total (SST) into three groups: sum of squares due to treatments, sum of squares due to blocks, and sum of squares due to error. The formula for this partitioning follows.

$$\text{SST} = \text{SSTR} + \text{SSBL} + \text{SSE} \tag{13.24}$$

This sum of squares partition is summarized in the ANOVA table for the randomized block design as shown in Table 13.8. The notation used in the table is

$$k = \text{the number of treatments}$$
$$b = \text{the number of blocks}$$
$$n_T = \text{the total sample size } (n_T = kb)$$

Note that the ANOVA table also shows how the $n_T - 1$ total degrees of freedom are partitioned such that $k - 1$ degrees of freedom go to treatments, $b - 1$ go to blocks, and $(k - 1)(b - 1)$ go to the error term. The mean square column shows the sum of squares divided by the degrees of freedom, and $F = \text{MSTR/MSE}$ is the $F$ ratio used to test for a sig-

**TABLE 13.8**    ANOVA TABLE FOR THE RANDOMIZED BLOCK DESIGN
WITH $k$ TREATMENTS AND $b$ BLOCKS

| Source of Variation | Sum of Squares | Degrees of Freedom | Mean Square | F |
|---|---|---|---|---|
| Treatments | SSTR | $k-1$ | $\text{MSTR} = \dfrac{\text{SSTR}}{k-1}$ | $\dfrac{\text{MSTR}}{\text{MSE}}$ |
| Blocks | SSBL | $b-1$ | $\text{MSBL} = \dfrac{\text{SSBL}}{b-1}$ | |
| Error | SSE | $(k-1)(b-1)$ | $\text{MSE} = \dfrac{\text{SSE}}{(k-1)(b-1)}$ | |
| Total | SST | $n_T - 1$ | | |

nificant difference among the treatment means. The primary contribution of the randomized block design is that, by including blocks, we have removed the individual controller differences from the MSE term and obtained a more powerful test for the stress differences attributable to the three work station alternatives.

## Computations and Conclusions

To compute the $F$ statistic needed to test for a difference among treatment means with a randomized block design, we need to compute MSTR and MSE. To calculate these two mean squares, we must first compute SSTR and SSE; in doing so, we will also compute SSBL and SST. To simplify the presentation, we perform the calculations in four steps. In addition to $k$, $b$, and $n_T$ as previously defined, the following notation is used.

$x_{ij}$ = value of the observation corresponding to treatment $j$ in block $i$

$\bar{x}_{\cdot j}$ = sample mean of the $j$th treatment

$\bar{x}_{i\cdot}$ = sample mean for the $i$th block

$\bar{\bar{x}}$ = overall sample mean

**Step 1.** Compute the total sum of squares (SST)

$$\text{SST} = \sum_{i=1}^{b}\sum_{j=1}^{k}(x_{ij} - \bar{\bar{x}})^2 \tag{13.25}$$

**Step 2.** Compute the sum of squares due to treatments (SSTR)

$$\text{SSTR} = b\sum_{j=1}^{k}(\bar{x}_{\cdot j} - \bar{\bar{x}})^2 \tag{13.26}$$

**Step 3.** Compute the sum of squares due to blocks (SSBL)

$$\text{SSBL} = k\sum_{i=1}^{b}(\bar{x}_{i\cdot} - \bar{\bar{x}})^2 \tag{13.27}$$

**Step 4.** Compute the sum of squares due to error (SSE)

$$\text{SSE} = \text{SST} - \text{SSTR} - \text{SSBL} \tag{13.28}$$

For the air traffic controller data in Table 13.7, these steps lead to the following sums of squares.

**Step 1.** $SST = (15 - 14)^2 + (15 - 14)^2 + (18 - 14)^2 + \cdots + (13 - 14)^2 = 70$

**Step 2.** $SSTR = 6[(13.5 - 14)^2 + (13.0 - 14)^2 + (15.5 - 14)^2] = 21$

**Step 3.** $SSBL = 3[(16 - 14)^2 + (14 - 14)^2 + (12 - 14)^2 + (14 - 14)^2 + (15 - 14)^2 + (13 - 14)^2] = 30$

**Step 4.** $SSE = 70 - 21 - 30 = 19$

These sums of squares divided by their degrees of freedom provide the corresponding mean square values shown in Table 13.9. The $F$ ratio used to test for differences between treatment means is $MSTR/MSE = 10.5/1.9 = 5.53$. Checking the $F$ values in Table 4 of Appendix B, we find that the critical $F$ value at $\alpha = .05$ (two numerator degrees of freedom and 10 denominator degrees of freedom) is 4.10. With $F = 5.53$, we reject the null hypothesis $H_0: \mu_1 = \mu_2 = \mu_3$ and conclude that the population mean stress levels differ for the three work station alternatives.

The $p$-value criterion can also be used for this hypothesis test. The usual rejection rule applies: Reject $H_0$ if $p$-value $< \alpha$. Excel makes computing the $p$-value easy. For example, for the air traffic controller stress test, simply enter =FDIST(5.53,2,10) in any cell of a worksheet; the result of .0241 is the $p$-value associated with the test statistic $F = 5.53$. With a $p$-value $= .0241 < \alpha = 05$, we reject the null hypothesis and conclude that the work station designs differ in terms of the mean stress effects on air traffic controllers.

Some general comments can be made about the randomized block design. The experimental design described in this section is a *complete* block design; the word "complete" indicates that each block is subjected to all $k$ treatments. That is, all controllers (blocks) were tested with all three systems (treatments). Experimental designs in which some but not all treatments are applied to each block are referred to as *incomplete* block designs. A discussion of incomplete block designs is beyond the scope of this text.

Because each controller in the air traffic controller stress test was required to use all three systems, this approach guarantees a complete block design. In some cases, however, blocking is carried out with "similar" experimental units in each block. For example, assume that in a pretest of air traffic controllers, the population of controllers was divided into groups ranging from extremely high-stress individuals to extremely low-stress individuals. The blocking could still be accomplished by having three controllers from each of the stress classifications participate in the study. Each block would then consist of three controllers in the same stress group. The randomized aspect of the block design would be the random assignment of the three controllers in each block to the three systems.

Finally, note that the ANOVA table shown in Table 13.8 provides an $F$ value to test for treatment effects but *not* for blocks. The reason is that the experiment was designed to test a single factor—work station design. The blocking based on individual stress differences was conducted to remove such variation from the MSE term. However, the study was not designed to test specifically for individual differences in stress.

**TABLE 13.9** ANOVA TABLE FOR THE AIR TRAFFIC CONTROLLER STRESS TEST

| Source of Variation | Sum of Squares | Degrees of Freedom | Mean Square | F |
|---|---|---|---|---|
| Treatments | 21 | 2 | 10.5 | 10.5/1.9 = 5.53 |
| Blocks | 30 | 5 | 6.0 | |
| Error | 19 | 10 | 1.9 | |
| Total | 70 | 17 | | |

Some analysts compute $F = $ MSB/MSE and use that statistic to test for significance of the blocks. Then they use the result as a guide to whether the same type of blocking would be desired in future experiments. However, if individual stress difference is to be a factor in the study, a different experimental design should be used. A test of significance on blocks should not be performed as a basis for a conclusion about a second factor.

## Using Excel's Anova: Two-Factor Without Replication Tool

In this subsection we show how Excel's Anova: Two-Factor Without Replication tool can be used to test whether the mean stress levels for air traffic controllers are the same for the three work stations. Refer to the Excel worksheet shown in Figure 13.8 as we describe the tasks involved.

**Enter Data:**    Column A is used to identify each of the air traffic controllers in the study. Columns B, C, and D contain the stress level scores for the three systems.

**Apply Tools:**    The following steps describe how to use Excel's Anova: Two-Factor Without Replication tool to test the hypothesis that the mean stress level score is the same for all three systems.

> **Step 1.**  Select the **Tools** pull-down menu
> **Step 2.**  Choose the **Data Analysis** option
> **Step 3.**  Choose **Anova: Two Factor Without Replication** from the list of Analysis Tools

**FIGURE 13.8**    EXCEL'S ANOVA OUTPUT FOR AIR TRAFFIC CONTROLLER STRESS TEST

| | A | B | C | D | E | F | G | H |
|---|---|---|---|---|---|---|---|---|
| 1 | **Controller** | **System A** | **System B** | **System C** | | | | |
| 2 | 1 | 15 | 15 | 18 | | | | |
| 3 | 2 | 14 | 14 | 14 | | | | |
| 4 | 3 | 10 | 11 | 15 | | | | |
| 5 | 4 | 13 | 12 | 17 | | | | |
| 6 | 5 | 16 | 13 | 16 | | | | |
| 7 | 6 | 13 | 13 | 13 | | | | |
| 8 | | | | | | | | |
| 9 | Anova: Two-Factor Without Replication | | | | | | | |
| 10 | | | | | | | | |
| 11 | *SUMMARY* | *Count* | *Sum* | *Average* | *Variance* | | | |
| 12 | 1 | 3 | 48 | 16 | 3 | | | |
| 13 | 2 | 3 | 42 | 14 | 0 | | | |
| 14 | 3 | 3 | 36 | 12 | 7 | | | |
| 15 | 4 | 3 | 42 | 14 | 7 | | | |
| 16 | 5 | 3 | 45 | 15 | 3 | | | |
| 17 | 6 | 3 | 39 | 13 | 0 | | | |
| 18 | | | | | | | | |
| 19 | System A | 6 | 81 | 13.5 | 4.3 | | | |
| 20 | System B | 6 | 78 | 13 | 2 | | | |
| 21 | System C | 6 | 93 | 15.5 | 3.5 | | | |
| 22 | | | | | | | | |
| 23 | | | | | | | | |
| 24 | ANOVA | | | | | | | |
| 25 | *Source of Variation* | *SS* | *df* | *MS* | *F* | *P-value* | *F crit* | |
| 26 | Rows | 30 | 5 | 6 | 3.16 | 0.0574 | 3.33 | |
| 27 | Columns | 21 | 2 | 10.5 | 5.53 | 0.0242 | 4.10 | |
| 28 | Error | 19 | 10 | 1.9 | | | | |
| 29 | | | | | | | | |
| 30 | Total | 70 | 17 | | | | | |
| 31 | | | | | | | | |

**Step 4.** When the Anova: Two Factor Without Replication dialog box appears:

Enter A1:D7 in the **Input Range** box

Select **Labels**

Enter .05 in the **Alpha** box

Select **Output Range**

Enter A9 in the **Output Range** box (to identify the upper left corner of the section of the worksheet where the output will appear)

Click **OK**

The output, titled Anova: Two-Factor Without Replication, appears in cells A9:G30 of the worksheet. Cells A11:E21 provide a summary of the data. The ANOVA table shown in cells A24:G30 is basically the same as the ANOVA table shown in Table 13.9. The label Rows corresponds to the blocks in the problem and the label Columns corresponds to the treatments. The Excel output provides the $p$-value associated with the test as well as the critical $F$ value.

We can make the hypothesis testing decision by comparing the computed $F$ value shown in cell E27 of $F = 5.53$ to the critical $F$ value shown in cell G27, $F_{.05} = 4.10$. Because $F = 5.53$ is greater than $F_{.05} = 4.10$, we can reject the null hypothesis and conclude that the population mean stress scores for the three systems are not equal. Alternatively, we can use the $p$-value shown in cell F27, 0.0242, to make the hypothesis testing decision. Thus, at the $\alpha = .05$ level of significance, we reject $H_0$ because the $p$-value $= .0242 < \alpha = .05$. Hence, using the $p$-value approach we also conclude that the mean stress scores differ among the three systems.

## NOTES AND COMMENTS

**1.** The matched-samples $t$ test introduced in Chapter 10 is an example of a randomized block design with two blocks.

**2.** The error degrees of freedom are less for a randomized block design than for a completely randomized design because $b - 1$ degrees of freedom are lost for the $b$ blocks. If $n$ is small, the potential effects due to blocks can be masked because of the loss of error degrees of freedom; for large $n$, the effects are minimized.

## EXERCISES

### Methods

**34.** Consider the experimental results for the following randomized block design. Make the calculations necessary to set up the analysis of variance table.

|  |  | Treatments | | |
|---|---|---|---|---|
|  |  | **A** | **B** | **C** |
|  | **1** | 10 | 9 | 8 |
|  | **2** | 12 | 6 | 5 |
| **Blocks** | **3** | 18 | 15 | 14 |
|  | **4** | 20 | 18 | 18 |
|  | **5** | 8 | 7 | 8 |

Using $\alpha = .05$, test for any significant differences.

**35.** The following data were obtained for a randomized block design involving five treatments and three blocks: SST = 430, SSTR = 310, SSBL = 85. Set up the ANOVA table and test for any significant differences. Use $\alpha = .05$.

**36.** An experiment has been conducted for four treatments with eight blocks. Complete the following analysis of variance table.

| Source of Variation | Sum of Squares | Degrees of Freedom | Mean Square | F |
|---|---|---|---|---|
| Treatments | 900 | | | |
| Blocks | 400 | | | |
| Error | | | | |
| Total | 1800 | | | |

Using $\alpha = .05$, test for any significant differences.

## Applications

**37.** An automobile dealer conducted a test to determine if the time in minutes needed to complete a minor engine tune-up depends on whether a computerized engine analyzer or an electronic analyzer is used. Because tune-up time varies among compact, intermediate, and full-size cars, the three types of cars were used as blocks in the experiment. The data obtained follow.

| | | Analyzer | |
|---|---|---|---|
| | | Computerized | Electronic |
| | **Compact** | 50 | 42 |
| Car | **Intermediate** | 55 | 44 |
| | **Full-size** | 63 | 46 |

Using $\alpha = .05$, test for any significant differences.

**38.** Five different auditing procedures were compared in terms of total audit time. To control for possible variation due to the person conducting the audit, four accountants were selected randomly and treated as blocks in the experiment. The following values were obtained by the ANOVA procedure: SST = 100, SSTR = 45, SSBL = 36. Using $\alpha = .05$, test for any significant difference in the mean total audit time for the five auditing procedures.

**39.** An important factor in selecting software for word-processing and database management systems is the time required to learn how to use the system. To evaluate three file management systems, a firm designed a test involving five word-processing operators. Because operator variability was believed to be a significant factor, each of the five operators was trained on each of the three file management systems. The data obtained follow.

| | | System | | |
|---|---|---|---|---|
| | | A | B | C |
| | 1 | 16 | 16 | 24 |
| | 2 | 19 | 17 | 22 |
| Operator | 3 | 14 | 13 | 19 |
| | 4 | 13 | 12 | 18 |
| | 5 | 18 | 17 | 22 |

Using $\alpha = .05$, test for any difference in the mean training time (in hours) for the three systems.

**40.** A study reported in the *Journal of the American Medical Association* investigated the cardiac demands of heavy snow shoveling. Ten healthy men underwent exercise testing with a treadmill and a cycle ergometer modified for arm cranking. The men then cleared two tracts of heavy, wet snow by using a lightweight plastic snow shovel and an electric snow thrower. Each subject's heart rate, blood pressure, oxygen uptake, and perceived exertion during snow removal were compared with the values obtained during treadmill and arm-crank ergometer testing. The following table gives the heart rates in beats per minute that are consistent with the study results for each of the 10 subjects.

**CD** file

**Snow**

| Subject | Treadmill | Arm-Crank Ergometer | Snow Shovel | Snow Thrower |
|---------|-----------|---------------------|-------------|--------------|
| 1 | 177 | 205 | 180 | 98 |
| 2 | 151 | 177 | 164 | 120 |
| 3 | 184 | 166 | 167 | 111 |
| 4 | 161 | 152 | 173 | 122 |
| 5 | 192 | 142 | 179 | 151 |
| 6 | 193 | 172 | 205 | 158 |
| 7 | 164 | 191 | 156 | 117 |
| 8 | 207 | 170 | 160 | 123 |
| 9 | 177 | 181 | 175 | 127 |
| 10 | 174 | 154 | 191 | 109 |

At the .05 level of significance, test for any significant differences.

## 13.7 FACTORIAL EXPERIMENTS

The experimental designs we have considered thus far enable us to draw statistical conclusions about one factor. However, in some experiments we want to draw conclusions about more than one variable or factor. **Factorial experiments** and their corresponding ANOVA computations are valuable designs when simultaneous conclusions about two or more factors are required. The term *factorial* is used because the experimental conditions include all possible combinations of the factors. For example, for *a* levels of factor A and *b* levels of factor B, the experiment will involve collecting data on *ab* treatment combinations. In this section we will show the analysis for a two-factor factorial experiment. The basic approach can be extended to experiments involving more than two factors.

As an illustration of a two-factor factorial experiment, we will consider a study involving the Graduate Management Admissions Test (GMAT), a standardized test used by graduate schools of business to evaluate an applicant's ability to pursue a graduate program in that field. Scores on the GMAT range from 200 to 800, with higher scores implying higher aptitude.

In an attempt to improve students' performance on the GMAT exam, a major Texas university is considering offering the following three GMAT preparation programs.

**1.** A 3-hour review session covering the types of questions generally asked on the GMAT.
**2.** A 1-day program covering relevant exam material, along with the taking and grading of a sample exam.
**3.** An intensive 10-week course involving the identification of each student's weaknesses and the setting up of individualized programs for improvement.

Hence, one factor in this study is the GMAT preparation program, which has three treatments: 3-hour review, 1-day program, and 10-week course. Before selecting the prepara-

**TABLE 13.10**    NINE TREATMENT COMBINATIONS FOR THE TWO-FACTOR GMAT
EXPERIMENT

| | | Factor B: College | | |
| --- | --- | --- | --- | --- |
| | | **Business** | **Engineering** | **Arts and Sciences** |
| **Factor A:** | **3-hour review** | 1 | 2 | 3 |
| **Preparation** | **1-day program** | 4 | 5 | 6 |
| **Program** | **10-week course** | 7 | 8 | 9 |

tion program to adopt, further study will be conducted to determine how the proposed programs affect GMAT scores.

The GMAT is usually taken by students from three colleges: the College of Business, the College of Engineering, and the College of Arts and Sciences. Therefore, a second factor of interest in the experiment is whether a student's undergraduate college affects the GMAT score. This second factor, undergraduate college, also has three treatments: business, engineering, and arts and sciences. The factorial design for this experiment with three treatments corresponding to factor A, the preparation program, and three treatments corresponding to factor B, the undergraduate college, will have a total of $3 \times 3 = 9$ treatment combinations. These treatment combinations or experimental conditions are summarized in Table 13.10.

Assume that a sample of two students will be selected corresponding to each of the nine treatment combinations shown in Table 13.10: two business students will take the 3-hour review, two will take the 1-day program, and two will take the 10-week course. In addition, two engineering students and two arts and sciences students will take each of the three preparation programs. In experimental design terminology, the sample size of two for each treatment combination indicates that we have two **replications.** Additional replications and a larger sample size could easily have been used, but we elected to minimize the computational aspects for this illustration.

This experimental design requires that six students who plan to attend graduate school be randomly selected from *each* of the three undergraduate colleges. Then two students from each college should be assigned randomly to each preparation program, resulting in a total of 18 students being used in the study.

Let us assume that the students have been randomly selected, have participated in the preparation program, and have taken the GMAT. The scores obtained are reported in Table 13.11.

**TABLE 13.11**    GMAT SCORES FOR THE TWO-FACTOR EXPERIMENT

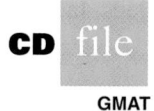

GMAT

| | | Factor B: College | | |
| --- | --- | --- | --- | --- |
| | | **Business** | **Engineering** | **Arts and Sciences** |
| | **3-hour review** | 500 | 540 | 480 |
| | | 580 | 460 | 400 |
| **Factor A:** | **1-day program** | 460 | 560 | 420 |
| **Preparation** | | 540 | 620 | 480 |
| **Program** | **10-week course** | 560 | 600 | 480 |
| | | 600 | 580 | 410 |

The analysis of variance computations with the data in Table 13.11 will provide answers to the following questions.

- **Main effect (factor A):** Do the preparation programs differ in terms of effect on GMAT scores?
- **Main effect (factor B):** Do the undergraduate colleges differ in terms of effect on GMAT scores?
- **Interaction effect (factors A and B):** Do students in some colleges do better on one type of preparation program whereas others do better on a different type of preparation program?

The term interaction refers to a new effect that we can now study because we have used a factorial experiment. If the interaction effect has a significant impact on the GMAT scores, we can conclude that the effect of the type of preparation program depends on the undergraduate college.

## ANOVA Procedure

The ANOVA procedure for the two-factor factorial experiment is similar to the completely randomized experiment and the randomized block experiment in that we again partition the sum of squares and the degrees of freedom into their respective sources. The formula for partitioning the sum of squares for the two-factor factorial experiments follows.

$$\text{SST} = \text{SSA} + \text{SSB} + \text{SSAB} + \text{SSE} \qquad \textbf{(13.29)}$$

The partitioning of the sum of squares and degrees of freedom is summarized in Table 13.12. The following notation is used.

$a$ = number of levels of factor A

$b$ = number of levels of factor B

$r$ = number of replications

$n_T$ = total number of observations taken in the experiment; $n_T = abr$

## Computations and Conclusions

To compute the $F$ statistics needed to test for the significance of factor A, factor B, and the interaction, we need to compute MSA, MSB, MSAB, and MSE. To calculate these four mean squares, we must first compute SSA, SSB, SSAB, and SSE; in doing so we will also compute SST. To simplify the presentation, we perform the calculations in five steps. In addition to $a$, $b$, $r$, and $n_T$ as previously defined, the following notation is used.

$x_{ijk}$ = observation corresponding to the $k$th replicate taken from treatment $i$ of factor A and treatment $j$ of factor B

$\bar{x}_{i\cdot}$ = sample mean for the observations in treatment $i$ (factor A)

$\bar{x}_{\cdot j}$ = sample mean for the observations in treatment $j$ (factor B)

$\bar{x}_{ij}$ = sample mean for the observations corresponding to the combination of treatment $i$ (factor A) and treatment $j$ (factor B)

$\bar{\bar{x}}$ = overall sample mean of all $n_T$ observations

**TABLE 13.12**   ANOVA TABLE FOR THE TWO-FACTOR FACTORIAL EXPERIMENT WITH $r$ REPLICATIONS

| Source of Variation | Sum of Squares | Degrees of Freedom | Mean Square | F |
|---|---|---|---|---|
| Factor A | SSA | $a - 1$ | $\text{MSA} = \dfrac{\text{SSA}}{a - 1}$ | $\dfrac{\text{MSA}}{\text{MSE}}$ |
| Factor B | SSB | $b - 1$ | $\text{MSB} = \dfrac{\text{SSB}}{b - 1}$ | $\dfrac{\text{MSB}}{\text{MSE}}$ |
| Interaction | SSAB | $(a - 1)(b - 1)$ | $\text{MSAB} = \dfrac{\text{SSAB}}{(a - 1)(b - 1)}$ | $\dfrac{\text{MSAB}}{\text{MSE}}$ |
| Error | SSE | $ab(r - 1)$ | $\text{MSE} = \dfrac{\text{SSE}}{ab(r - 1)}$ | |
| Total | SST | $n_T - 1$ | | |

**Step 1.** Compute the total sum of squares

$$\text{SST} = \sum_{i=1}^{a}\sum_{j=1}^{b}\sum_{k=1}^{r}(x_{ijk} - \bar{\bar{x}})^2 \tag{13.30}$$

**Step 2.** Compute the sum of squares for factor A

$$\text{SSA} = br\sum_{i=1}^{a}(\bar{x}_{i\cdot} - \bar{\bar{x}})^2 \tag{13.31}$$

**Step 3.** Compute the sum of squares for factor B

$$\text{SSB} = ar\sum_{j=1}^{b}(\bar{x}_{\cdot j} - \bar{\bar{x}})^2 \tag{13.32}$$

**Step 4.** Compute the sum of squares for interaction

$$\text{SSAB} = r\sum_{i=1}^{a}\sum_{j=1}^{b}(\bar{x}_{ij} - \bar{x}_{i\cdot} - \bar{x}_{\cdot j} + \bar{\bar{x}})^2 \tag{13.33}$$

**Step 5.** Compute the sum of squares due to error

$$\text{SSE} = \text{SST} - \text{SSA} - \text{SSB} - \text{SSAB} \tag{13.34}$$

Table 13.13 reports the data collected in the experiment and the various sums that will help us with the sum of squares computations. Using equations (13.30) to (13.34), we have the following sums of squares for the GMAT two-factor factorial experiment.

**Step 1.**   $\text{SST} = (500 - 515)^2 + (580 - 515)^2 + (540 - 515)^2 + \cdots +$
    $(410 - 515)^2 = 82{,}450$

**Step 2.**   $\text{SSA} = (3)(2)[(493.33 - 515)^2 + (513.33 - 515)^2 +$
    $(538.33 - 515)^2] = 6100$

**Step 3.**   $\text{SSB} = (3)(2)[(540 - 515)^2 + (560 - 515)^2 + (445 - 515)^2] = 45{,}300$

**Step 4.**  $\text{SSAB} = 2[(540 - 493.33 - 540 + 515)^2 + (500 - 493.33 -$
    $560 + 515)^2 + \cdots + (445 - 538.33 - 445 + 515)^2] = 11{,}200$

**Step 5.**   $\text{SSE} = 82{,}450 - 6100 - 45{,}300 - 11{,}200 = 19{,}850$

**TABLE 13.13** GMAT SUMMARY DATA FOR THE TWO-FACTOR EXPERIMENT

| | | Factor B: College | | | Row Totals | Factor A Means |
|---|---|---|---|---|---|---|
| | Treatment combination totals | Business | Engineering | Arts and Sciences | | |
| **Factor A: Preparation Program** | **3-hour review** | 500 580 $\overline{1080}$ $\bar{x}_{11} = \frac{1080}{2} = 540$ | 540 460 $\overline{1000}$ $\bar{x}_{12} = \frac{1000}{2} = 500$ | 480 400 $\overline{880}$ $\bar{x}_{13} = \frac{880}{2} = 440$ | 2960 | $\bar{x}_{1\cdot} = \frac{2960}{6} = 493.33$ |
| | **1-day program** | 460 540 $\overline{1000}$ $\bar{x}_{21} = \frac{1000}{2} = 500$ | 560 620 $\overline{1180}$ $\bar{x}_{22} = \frac{1180}{2} = 590$ | 420 480 $\overline{900}$ $\bar{x}_{23} = \frac{900}{2} = 450$ | 3080 | $\bar{x}_{2\cdot} = \frac{3080}{6} = 513.33$ |
| | **10-week course** | 560 600 $\overline{1160}$ $\bar{x}_{31} = \frac{1160}{2} = 580$ | 600 580 $\overline{1180}$ $\bar{x}_{32} = \frac{1180}{2} = 590$ | 480 410 $\overline{890}$ $\bar{x}_{33} = \frac{890}{2} = 445$ | 3230 | $\bar{x}_{3\cdot} = \frac{3230}{6} = 538.33$ |
| | **Column Totals** | 3240 | 3360 | 2670 | 9270 ⟵ Overall total | |
| | **Factor B Means** | $\bar{x}_{\cdot1} = \frac{3240}{6} = 540$ | $\bar{x}_{\cdot2} = \frac{3360}{6} = 560$ | $\bar{x}_{\cdot3} = \frac{2670}{6} = 445$ | | $\bar{\bar{x}} = \frac{9270}{18} = 515$ |

These sums of squares divided by their corresponding degrees of freedom, as shown in Table 13.14, provide the appropriate mean square values for testing the two main effects (preparation program and undergraduate college) and the interaction effect. The $F$ ratio used to test for differences among preparation programs is 1.38. The critical $F$ value at $\alpha = .05$ (with two numerator degrees of freedom and nine denominator degrees of freedom) is 4.26. With $F = 1.38$, we cannot reject the null hypothesis and must conclude that there is no significant difference among the three preparation programs. However, for the undergraduate college effect, $F = 10.27$ exceeds the critical $F$ value of 4.26. Hence, the analysis of variance results enables us to conclude that there is a difference in GMAT test scores among the three undergraduate colleges; that is, the three undergraduate colleges do not provide the same preparation for performance on the GMAT. Finally, the interaction $F$ value of $F = 1.27$ (critical $F$ value $= 3.63$ at $\alpha = .05$) means that we cannot identify a significant interaction effect. Therefore, we have no reason to believe that the three preparation programs differ in their ability to prepare students from the different colleges for the GMAT.

Undergraduate college was found to be a significant factor. Checking the calculations in Table 13.13, we see that the sample means are: business students $\bar{x}_{.1} = 540$, engineering students $\bar{x}_{.2} = 560$, and arts and sciences students $\bar{x}_{.3} = 445$. Tests on individual treatment means can be conducted; yet after reviewing the three sample means, we would anticipate no difference in preparation for business and engineering graduates. However, the arts and sciences students appear to be significantly less prepared for the GMAT than students in the other colleges. Perhaps this observation will lead the university to consider other options for assisting these students in preparing for graduate management admission tests.

*Excel's FDIST function makes it easy to compute the $p$-value for each $F$ value.*

## Using Excel's Anova: Two-Factor With Replication Tool

Excel's Anova: Two-Factor With Replication tool can be used to analyze the data for the two-factor GMAT experiment. Refer to the Excel worksheet shown in Figure 13.9 as we describe the tasks involved.

**Enter Data:**   Column A is used to identify each of the preparation programs (Factor A) in the study. Column B contains the GMAT scores for the Business students, Column C contains the GMAT scores for the Engineering students, and Column D contains the GMAT scores for the Arts and Sciences students.

**Apply Tools:** The following steps describe how to use Excel's Anova: Two-Factor With Replication tool to test the null hypothesis that the mean stress level score is the same for all three systems.

> **Step 1.**  Select the **Tools** pull-down menu
> **Step 2.**  Choose the **Data Analysis** option
> **Step 3.**  Choose **Anova: Two-Factor With Replication** from the list of Analysis Tools

**TABLE 13.14**   ANOVA TABLE FOR THE TWO-FACTOR GMAT EXPERIMENT

| Source of Variation | Sum of Squares | Degrees of Freedom | Mean Square | F |
|---|---|---|---|---|
| Factor A | 6,100 | 2 | 3,050 | 3,050/2206 = 1.38 |
| Factor B | 45,300 | 2 | 22,650 | 22,650/2206 = 10.27 |
| Interaction | 11,200 | 4 | 2,800 | 2,800/2206 = 1.27 |
| Error | 19,850 | 9 | 2,206 | |
| Total | 82,450 | 17 | | |

**FIGURE 13.9**   EXCEL'S ANOVA OUTPUT FOR THE GMAT EXPERIMENT

| | A | B | C | D | E | F | G | H |
|---|---|---|---|---|---|---|---|---|
| 1 | | **Business** | **Engineering** | **Arts and Sciences** | | | | |
| 2 | **3-hour review** | 500 | 540 | 480 | | | | |
| 3 | | 580 | 460 | 400 | | | | |
| 4 | **1-day program** | 460 | 560 | 420 | | | | |
| 5 | | 540 | 620 | 480 | | | | |
| 6 | **10-week course** | 560 | 600 | 480 | | | | |
| 7 | | 600 | 580 | 410 | | | | |
| 8 | | | | | | | | |
| 9 | Anova: Two-Factor With Replication | | | | | | | |
| 10 | | | | | | | | |
| 11 | SUMMARY | Business | Engineering | Arts and Sciences | Total | | | |
| 12 | *3-hour review* | | | | | | | |
| 13 | Count | 2 | 2 | 2 | 6 | | | |
| 14 | Sum | 1080 | 1000 | 880 | 2960 | | | |
| 15 | Average | 540 | 500 | 440 | 493.3333 | | | |
| 16 | Variance | 3200 | 3200 | 3200 | 3946.667 | | | |
| 17 | | | | | | | | |
| 18 | *1-day program* | | | | | | | |
| 19 | Count | 2 | 2 | 2 | 6 | | | |
| 20 | Sum | 1000 | 1180 | 900 | 3080 | | | |
| 21 | Average | 500 | 590 | 450 | 513.3333 | | | |
| 22 | Variance | 3200 | 1800 | 1800 | 5386.667 | | | |
| 23 | | | | | | | | |
| 24 | *10-week course* | | | | | | | |
| 25 | Count | 2 | 2 | 2 | 6 | | | |
| 26 | Sum | 1160 | 1180 | 890 | 3230 | | | |
| 27 | Average | 580 | 590 | 445 | 538.3333 | | | |
| 28 | Variance | 800 | 200 | 2450 | 5936.667 | | | |
| 29 | | | | | | | | |
| 30 | *Total* | | | | | | | |
| 31 | Count | 6 | 6 | 6 | | | | |
| 32 | Sum | 3240 | 3360 | 2670 | | | | |
| 33 | Average | 540 | 560 | 445 | | | | |
| 34 | Variance | 2720 | 3200 | 1510 | | | | |
| 35 | | | | | | | | |
| 36 | | | | | | | | |
| 37 | ANOVA | | | | | | | |
| 38 | *Source of Variation* | *SS* | *df* | *MS* | *F* | *P-value* | *F crit* | |
| 39 | Sample | 6100 | 2 | 3050 | 1.38 | 0.2994 | 4.26 | |
| 40 | Columns | 45300 | 2 | 22650 | 10.27 | 0.0048 | 4.26 | |
| 41 | Interaction | 11200 | 4 | 2800 | 1.27 | 0.3503 | 3.63 | |
| 42 | Within | 19850 | 9 | 2205.5556 | | | | |
| 43 | | | | | | | | |
| 44 | Total | 82450 | 17 | | | | | |
| 45 | | | | | | | | |

**Step 4.** When the Anova: Two-Factor With Replication dialog box appears (see Figure 13.10):

> Enter A1:D7 in the **Input Range** box
> Enter 2 in the **Rows per sample** box
> Enter .05 in the **Alpha** box
> Select **Output Range**
> Enter A9 in the **Output Range** box (to identify the upper left corner of the section of the worksheet where the output will appear)
> Click **OK**

The output, titled Anova: Two-Factor With Replication, appears in cells A9:G44 of the worksheet. Cells A11:E34 provide a summary of the data. The ANOVA table, shown in cells A37:G44, is basically the same as the ANOVA table shown in Table 13.14. The label Sample corresponds

**FIGURE 13.10**   EXCEL'S ANOVA: TWO-FACTOR WITH REPLICATION DIALOG BOX

to Factor A, the label Columns corresponds to Factor B, and the label Within corresponds to Error. The Excel output provides the $p$-value associated with the test as well as the critical $F$ values.

We can make the hypothesis testing decision for Factor A (Preparation Program) by comparing the computed $F$ value shown in cell E39, $F = 1.38$, to the critical $F$ value shown in cell G39, $F_{.05} = 4.26$. Because $F = 1.38$ is less than $F_{.05} = 4.26$, we cannot reject the null hypothesis and must conclude no significant difference among the three preparation programs. Alternatively, we can use the $p$-value of 0.2994 shown in cell F39 to make the hypothesis testing decision. Thus, at the $\alpha = .05$ level of significance, we cannot reject $H_0$ because the $p$-value $= 0.2994 > \alpha = .05$.

We can make the hypothesis testing decision for Factor B (College) by comparing the computed $F$ value shown in cell E40, $F = 10.27$, to the critical $F$ value shown in cell G40, $F_{.05} = 4.26$. Because $F = 10.27$ is greater than $F_{.05} = 4.26$, we reject the null hypothesis and conclude that there is a difference in GMAT test scores among the three undergraduate colleges. Alternatively, we can use the $p$-value of 0.0048 shown in cell F40 to make the hypothesis testing decision. Thus, at the $\alpha = .05$ level of significance, we reject $H_0$ because the $p$-value $= 0.0048 < \alpha = .05$. Finally, the interaction $F$ value of 1.27 in cell E41 and the interaction $p$-value of 0.3503 in cell F41 means that we cannot identify a significant interaction effect.

## EXERCISES

## Methods

**41.**   A factorial experiment involving two levels of factor A and three levels of factor B resulted in the following data.

|  |  | Factor B | | |
|---|---|---|---|---|
|  |  | **Level 1** | **Level 2** | **Level 3** |
|  | **Level 1** | 135<br>165 | 90<br>66 | 75<br>93 |
| **Factor A** |  |  |  |  |
|  | **Level 2** | 125<br>95 | 127<br>105 | 120<br>136 |

Test for any significant main effect and any interaction. Use $\alpha = .05$.

42. The calculations for a factorial experiment involving four levels of factor A, three levels of factor B, and three replications resulted in the following data: SST = 280, SSA = 26, SSB = 23, SSAB = 175. Set up the ANOVA table and test for any significant main effects and any interaction effect. Use $\alpha = .05$.

## Applications

43. A mail-order catalog firm designed a factorial experiment to test the effect of the size of a magazine advertisement and the advertisement design on the number of catalog requests received (in the thousands). Three advertising designs and two different-sized advertisements were considered. The data obtained follow. Use the ANOVA procedure for factorial designs to test for any significant effects due to type of design, size of advertisement, or interaction. Use $\alpha = .05$.

|  |  | Size of Advertisement | |
|---|---|---|---|
|  |  | **Small** | **Large** |
| Design | **A** | 8<br>12 | 12<br>8 |
|  | **B** | 22<br>14 | 26<br>30 |
|  | **C** | 10<br>18 | 18<br>14 |

44. An amusement park has been studying methods for decreasing the waiting time (minutes) for rides by loading and unloading riders more efficiently. Two alternative loading/unloading methods have been proposed. To account for potential differences due to the type of ride and the possible interaction between the method of loading and unloading and the type of ride, a factorial experiment was designed. Using the following data, test for any significant effect due to the loading and unloading method, the type of ride, and interaction. Use $\alpha = .05$.

|  |  | Type of Ride | | |
|---|---|---|---|---|
|  |  | **Roller Coaster** | **Screaming Demon** | **Log Flume** |
| Loading Method | **Method 1** | 41<br>43 | 52<br>44 | 50<br>46 |
|  | **Method 2** | 49<br>51 | 50<br>46 | 48<br>44 |

45. The U.S. Bureau of Labor Statistics collects information on the earnings of men and women for different occupations. Suppose that a reporter for *The Tampa Tribune* wanted to investigate whether there were any differences between the weekly salaries of men and women employed as financial managers, computer programmers, and pharmacists. A sample of five men and women was selected from each of the three occupations, and the weekly salary for each individual in the sample was recorded. The data obtained follow.

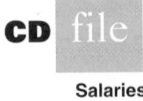

**Salaries**

| Weekly Salary ($) | Occupation | Gender |
|---|---|---|
| 872 | Financial Manager | Male |
| 859 | Financial Manager | Male |
| 1028 | Financial Manager | Male |
| 1117 | Financial Manager | Male |
| 1019 | Financial Manager | Male |
| 519 | Financial Manager | Female |
| 702 | Financial Manager | Female |
| 805 | Financial Manager | Female |
| 558 | Financial Manager | Female |
| 591 | Financial Manager | Female |

| Weekly Salary ($) | Occupation | Gender |
|---|---|---|
| 747 | Computer Programmer | Male |
| 766 | Computer Programmer | Male |
| 901 | Computer Programmer | Male |
| 690 | Computer Programmer | Male |
| 881 | Computer Programmer | Male |
| 884 | Computer Programmer | Female |
| 765 | Computer Programmer | Female |
| 685 | Computer Programmer | Female |
| 700 | Computer Programmer | Female |
| 671 | Computer Programmer | Female |
| 1105 | Pharmacist | Male |
| 1144 | Pharmacist | Male |
| 1085 | Pharmacist | Male |
| 903 | Pharmacist | Male |
| 998 | Pharmacist | Male |
| 813 | Pharmacist | Female |
| 985 | Pharmacist | Female |
| 1006 | Pharmacist | Female |
| 1034 | Pharmacist | Female |
| 817 | Pharmacist | Female |

At the $\alpha = .05$ level of significance, test for any significant effect due to occupation, gender, and interaction.

**46.** A study reported in *The Accounting Review* examined the separate and joint effects of two levels of time pressure (low and moderate) and three levels of knowledge (naive, declarative, and procedural) on key word selection behavior in tax research. Subjects were given a tax case containing a set of facts, a tax issue, and a key word index consisting of 1336 key words. They were asked to select the key words they believed would refer them to a tax authority relevant to resolving the tax case. Prior to the experiment, a group of tax experts had determined that there were 19 relevant key words in the index. Subjects in the naive group had little or no declarative or procedural knowledge, subjects in the declarative group had significant declarative knowledge but little or no procedural knowledge, and subjects in the procedural group had significant declarative knowledge and procedural knowledge. Declarative knowledge consists of knowledge of both the applicable tax rules and the technical terms used to describe such rules. Procedural knowledge is knowledge of the rules that guide the tax researcher's search for relevant key words. Subjects in the low time pressure situation were told they had 25 minutes to complete the problem, an amount of time which should be "more than adequate" to complete the case; subjects in the moderate time pressure situation were told they would have "only" 11 minutes to complete the case (*The Accounting Review*, January 1995). Suppose 25 subjects were selected for each of the six treatment combinations and the sample means for each treatment combination are as follows (standard deviations are in parentheses).

| | | Knowledge | | |
|---|---|---|---|---|
| | | **Naive** | **Declarative** | **Procedural** |
| **Time Pressure** | **Low** | 1.13 (1.12) | 1.56 (1.33) | 2.00 (1.54) |
| | **Moderate** | 0.48 (0.80) | 1.68 (1.36) | 2.86 (1.80) |

Use the ANOVA procedure to test for any significant differences due to time pressure, knowledge, and interaction. Use a .05 level of significance. Assume that the total sum of squares for this experiment is 327.50.

## SUMMARY

In this chapter we have shown how analysis of variance can be used to test for differences among means of several populations or treatments. We introduced the completely randomized design, the randomized block design, and the two-factor factorial design. The completely randomized design and the randomized block design are used to draw conclusions about differences in the means of a single factor. The primary purpose of blocking in the randomized block design is to remove extraneous sources of variation from the error term. Such blocking provides a better estimate of the true error variance and a better test to determine whether the population or treatment means of the factor differ significantly.

We showed that the basis for the statistical tests used in analysis of variance and experimental design is the development of two independent estimates of the population variance $\sigma^2$. In the single-factor case, one estimator is based on the variation between the treatments; this estimator provides an unbiased estimate of $\sigma^2$ only if the means $\mu_1, \mu_2, \ldots,$ $\mu_k$ are all equal. A second estimator of $\sigma^2$ is based on the variation of the observations within each sample; this estimator will always provide an unbiased estimate of $\sigma^2$. By computing the ratio of these two estimators (the $F$ statistic) we developed a rejection rule for determining whether to reject the null hypothesis that the population or treatment means are equal. In all the experimental designs considered, the partitioning of the sum of squares and degrees of freedom into their various sources enabled us to compute the appropriate values for the analysis of variance calculations and tests. We also showed how Fisher's LSD procedure and the Bonferroni adjustment can be used to perform pairwise comparisons to determine which means are different.

## GLOSSARY

**Response variable** Another word for the dependent variable of interest.

**Factor** Another word for the independent variable of interest.

**Treatment** Different levels of a factor.

**ANOVA table** A table used to summarize the analysis of variance computations and results. It contains columns showing the source of variation, the sum of squares, the degrees of freedom, the mean square, and the $F$ value(s).

**Partitioning** The process of allocating the total sum of squares and degrees of freedom to the various components.

**Multiple comparison procedures** Statistical procedures that can be used to conduct statistical comparisons between pairs of population means.

**Comparisonwise Type I error rate** The probability of a Type I error associated with a single pairwise comparison.

**Experimentwise Type I error rate** The probability of making a Type I error on at least one of several pairwise comparisons.

**Single-factor experiment** An experiment involving only one factor with $k$ populations or treatments.

**Experimental units** The objects of interest in the experiment.

**Completely randomized design** An experimental design in which the treatments are randomly assigned to the experimental units.

**Blocking** The process of using the same or similar experimental units for all treatments. The purpose of blocking is to remove a source of variation from the error term and hence provide a more powerful test for a difference in population or treatment means.

**Randomized block design**    An experimental design employing blocking.

**Factorial experiment**    An experimental design that allows statistical conclusions about two or more factors.

**Replications**    The number of times each experimental condition is repeated in an experiment.

**Interaction**    The effect produced when the levels of one factor interact with the levels of another factor in influencing the response variable.

## KEY FORMULAS

# Testing for the Equality of $k$ Population Means

**Sample Mean for Treatment $j$**

$$\bar{x}_j = \frac{\sum_{i=1}^{n_j} x_{ij}}{n_j} \tag{13.1}$$

**Sample Variance for Treatment $j$**

$$s_j^2 = \frac{\sum_{i=1}^{n_j} (x_{ij} - \bar{x}_j)^2}{n_j - 1} \tag{13.2}$$

**Overall Sample Mean**

$$\bar{\bar{x}} = \frac{\sum_{j=1}^{k} \sum_{i=1}^{n_j} x_{ij}}{n_T} \tag{13.3}$$

$$n_T = n_1 + n_2 + \cdots + n_k \tag{13.4}$$

**Mean Square Due to Treatments**

$$\text{MSTR} = \frac{\text{SSTR}}{k - 1} \tag{13.7}$$

**Sum of Squares Due to Treatments**

$$\text{SSTR} = \sum_{j=1}^{k} n_j (\bar{x}_j - \bar{\bar{x}})^2 \tag{13.8}$$

**Mean Square Due to Error**

$$\text{MSE} = \frac{\text{SSE}}{n_T - k} \tag{13.10}$$

**Sum of Squares Due to Error**

$$\text{SSE} = \sum_{j=1}^{k} (n_j - 1) s_j^2 \tag{13.11}$$

**Test for the Equality of $k$ Population Means**

$$F = \frac{\text{MSTR}}{\text{MSE}} \tag{13.12}$$

**Total Sum of Squares**

$$SST = \sum_{j=1}^{k} \sum_{i=1}^{n_j} (x_{ij} - \bar{\bar{x}})^2 \tag{13.13}$$

**Partition of Sum of Squares**

$$SST = SSTR + SSE \tag{13.14}$$

## Multiple Comparison Procedures

**Test Statistic for LSD Procedure**

$$t = \frac{\bar{x}_i - \bar{x}_j}{\sqrt{MSE\left(\dfrac{1}{n_i} + \dfrac{1}{n_j}\right)}} \tag{13.16}$$

**Fisher's LSD**

$$LSD = t_{\alpha/2} \sqrt{MSE\left(\frac{1}{n_i} + \frac{1}{n_j}\right)} \tag{13.17}$$

## Completely Randomized Designs

**Mean Square Due to Treatments**

$$MSTR = \frac{\displaystyle\sum_{j=1}^{k} n_j (\bar{x}_j - \bar{\bar{x}})^2}{k - 1} \tag{13.20}$$

**Mean Square Due to Error**

$$MSE = \frac{\displaystyle\sum_{j=1}^{k} (n_j - 1) s_j^2}{n_T - k} \tag{13.21}$$

## Randomized Block Designs

**Total Sum of Squares**

$$SST = \sum_{i=1}^{b} \sum_{j=1}^{k} (x_{ij} - \bar{\bar{x}})^2 \tag{13.25}$$

**Sum of Squares Due to Treatments**

$$SSTR = b \sum_{j=1}^{k} (\bar{x}_{\cdot j} - \bar{\bar{x}})^2 \tag{13.26}$$

**Sum of Squares Due to Blocks**

$$SSBL = k \sum_{i=1}^{b} (\bar{x}_{i\cdot} - \bar{\bar{x}})^2$$  (13.27)

**Sum of Squares Due to Error**

$$SSE = SST - SSTR - SSBL$$  (13.28)

# Factorial Experiments

**Total Sum of Squares**

$$SST = \sum_{i=1}^{a} \sum_{j=1}^{b} \sum_{k=1}^{r} (x_{ijk} - \bar{\bar{x}})^2$$  (13.30)

**Sum of Squares for Factor A**

$$SSA = br \sum_{i=1}^{a} (\bar{x}_{i\cdot} - \bar{\bar{x}})^2$$  (13.31)

**Sum of Squares for Factor B**

$$SSB = ar \sum_{j=1}^{b} (\bar{x}_{\cdot j} - \bar{\bar{x}})^2$$  (13.32)

**Sum of Squares for Interaction**

$$SSAB = r \sum_{i=1}^{a} \sum_{j=1}^{b} (\bar{x}_{ij} - \bar{x}_{i\cdot} - \bar{x}_{\cdot j} + \bar{\bar{x}})^2$$  (13.33)

**Sum of Squares for Error**

$$SSE = SST - SSA - SSB - SSAB$$  (13.34)

## SUPPLEMENTARY EXERCISES

**47.** A simple random sample of the asking prices ($1000s) of four houses currently for sale in each of two residential areas resulted in the following data.

| Area 1 | Area 2 |
|--------|--------|
| 92 | 90 |
| 89 | 102 |
| 98 | 96 |
| 105 | 88 |

**a.** Use the procedure developed in Chapter 10 to test whether the mean asking price is the same in both areas. Use $\alpha = .05$.

**b.** Use the ANOVA procedure to test whether the mean asking price is the same. Compare your analysis with part (a). Use $\alpha = .05$.

**c.** Suppose that data were collected for another residential area. The asking prices for the simple random sample from the third area were $81,000, $86,000, $75,000, and $90,000. Is the mean asking price the same for all three areas? Use $\alpha = .05$.

**48.** Buyers of sport utility vehicles (SUVs) and pickup trucks find a wide choice in today's market-place. One of the factors that is important to many buyers is the resale value of the vehicle. The following table shows the resale value (%) after 2 years for 10 SUVs, 10 small pickup trucks, and 10 full-size pickup trucks (*Kiplinger's New Cars & Trucks 2000 Buyer's Guide*).

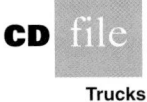

**CD** file

**Trucks**

| Sport Utility | Resale Value | Small Pickup | Resale Value |
|---|---|---|---|
| Chevrolet Blazer LS | 55 | Chevrolet S-10 Extended Cab | 46 |
| Ford Explorer Sport | 57 | Dodge Dakota Club Cab Sport | 53 |
| GMC Yukon XL 1500 | 67 | Ford Ranger XLT Regular Cab | 48 |
| Honda CR-V | 65 | Ford Ranger XLT Supercab | 55 |
| Isuzu VehiCross | 62 | GMC Sonoma Regular Cab | 44 |
| Jeep Cherokee Limited | 57 | Isuzu Hombre Spacecab | 41 |
| Mercury Mountaineer | 59 | Mazda B4000 SE Cab Plus | 51 |
| Nissan Pathfinder XE | 54 | Nissan Frontier XE Regular Cab | 51 |
| Toyota 4Runner | 55 | Toyota Tacoma Xtracab | 49 |
| Toyota RAV4 | 55 | Toyota Tacoma Xtracab V6 | 50 |

| Full-Size Pickup | Resale Value |
|---|---|
| Chevrolet K2500 | 60 |
| Chevrolet Silverado 2500 Ext | 64 |
| Dodge Ram 1500 | 54 |
| Dodge Ram Quad Cab 2500 | 63 |
| Dodge Ram Regular Cab 2500 | 59 |
| Ford F150 XL | 58 |
| Ford F-350 Super Duty Crew Cab XL | 64 |
| GMC New Sierra 1500 Ext Cab | 68 |
| Toyota Tundra Access Cab Limited | 53 |
| Toyota Tundra Regular Cab | 58 |

At the $\alpha = .05$ level of significance, test for any significant difference in the mean resale value for the three types of vehicles.

**49.** The following data show the age of 12 top executives for major marketers of food, retail, and personal care products (*Advertising Age,* December 1, 1997).

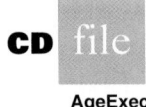

**CD** file

**AgeExec**

| Company | Category | Executive | Age |
|---|---|---|---|
| Campbell Soup Co. | Food | Dale F. Morrison | 48 |
| General Mills | Food | Stephen W. Sanger | 51 |
| Kellogg Co. | Food | Arnold G. Langbo | 59 |
| RJR Nabisco | Food | Stephen F. Goldstone | 51 |
| Estee Lauder Cos. | Personal Care | Leonard A. Lauder | 64 |
| Gillette Co. | Personal Care | Alfred M. Zeien | 67 |
| Procter & Gamble Co. | Personal Care | John E. Pepper | 59 |
| Unilever | Personal Care | Morris Tabaksblat | 59 |
| Federated Department Stores | Retail | James W. Zimmerman | 53 |
| J.C. Penny Co. | Retail | James E. Oesterreicher | 55 |
| Sears Roebuck & Co. | Retail | Arthur C. Martinez | 57 |
| Kmart Corp. | Retail | Floyd Hall | 58 |

At the $\alpha = .05$ level of significance, is there a significant difference in the mean age of executives for the three categories of companies?

**50.** A study reported in the *Journal of Small Business Management* concluded that self-employed individuals do not experience higher job satisfaction than individuals who are not self-employed. In this study, job satisfaction is measured using 18 items, each of which is rated using a Likert-type scale with 1–5 response options ranging from strong agreement to strong disagreement. A higher score on this scale indicates a higher degree of job satisfaction. The sum of the ratings for the 18 items, ranging from 18–90, is used as the measure of job satisfaction (*Journal of Small Business Management,* October 1997). Suppose that this approach was used to measure the job satisfaction for lawyers, physical therapists, cabinetmakers, and systems analysts. The results obtained for a sample of 10 individuals from each profession follow.

**Satisjob**

| Lawyer | Physical Therapist | Cabinetmaker | Systems Analyst |
|--------|--------------------|--------------|-----------------|
| 44 | 55 | 54 | 44 |
| 42 | 78 | 65 | 73 |
| 74 | 80 | 79 | 71 |
| 42 | 86 | 69 | 60 |
| 53 | 60 | 79 | 64 |
| 50 | 59 | 64 | 66 |
| 45 | 62 | 59 | 41 |
| 48 | 52 | 78 | 55 |
| 64 | 55 | 84 | 76 |
| 38 | 50 | 60 | 62 |

At the $\alpha = .05$ level of significance, test for any difference in the job satisfaction among the four professions.

51. Crown Plaza Hotels and Resorts offered special weekend rates at hotels and resorts nationwide. A sample of 30 properties from three regions of the country provided the following room rates (*USA Today,* April 14, 2000).

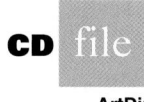

**Resorts**

| West | Rate ($) | South | Rate ($) | Northeast | Rate ($) |
|------|----------|-------|----------|-----------|----------|
| Albuquerque | 89 | Atlanta | 105 | Albany | 89 |
| Irvine | 79 | Dallas | 80 | Boston | 139 |
| Las Vegas | 119 | Greenville | 79 | Hartford | 85 |
| Los Angeles | 99 | Houston | 79 | New York | 159 |
| Palo Alto | 109 | Jackson | 69 | Philadelphia | 99 |
| Phoenix | 149 | Macon | 69 | Pittsfield | 99 |
| Portland | 79 | Miami | 89 | Providence | 149 |
| San Francisco | 139 | Orlando | 119 | Washington | 159 |
| San Jose | 99 | Richmond | 109 | White Plains | 109 |
| Seattle | 119 | Tampa | 119 | Worcester | 124 |

At the $\alpha = .05$ level of significance, test whether the mean rates are the same for the three regions.

52. According to the sixth annual survey of ad agency employees conducted by the accounting firm Altschuler, Melvoin & Glasser, ad agency employees can expect another banner year in compensation (*Advertising Age,* December 1, 1997). To investigate whether there is any difference in the annual compensation for art directors, suppose that a sample of 10 art directors was selected from each of four regions: West, South, North Central, and Northeast. The base salary ($1000s) for each of the individuals sampled follows.

**ArtDir**

| West | South | North Central | Northeast |
|------|-------|---------------|-----------|
| 60.9 | 50.8 | 49.5 | 65.9 |
| 45.9 | 39.6 | 42.3 | 58.6 |
| 62.1 | 44.2 | 35.5 | 49.3 |
| 66.6 | 40.0 | 49.1 | 52.9 |
| 68.0 | 53.9 | 56.7 | 48.5 |
| 65.0 | 45.4 | 41.4 | 52.9 |
| 49.4 | 61.1 | 51.3 | 52.4 |
| 62.3 | 42.3 | 49.4 | 48.1 |
| 62.6 | 38.4 | 42.1 | 46.5 |
| 57.2 | 38.3 | 55.7 | 45.9 |

At the $\alpha = .05$ level of significance, test whether the mean base salary for art directors is the same for each of the four regions.

**53.** The National Football League rates prospects position by position on a scale that ranges from 5 to 9. The ratings are interpreted as follows: 8–9 should start the first year; 7.0–7.9 should start; 6.0–6.9 will make the team as backup; and 5.0–5.9, can make the club and contribute. The following table shows the ratings for three positions for 40 NFL prospects (*USA Today,* April 14, 2000). Does there appear to be any significant effect on the rating due to the player's position?

**NFL**

| Wide Receiver | | Guard | | Offensive Tackle | |
|---|---|---|---|---|---|
| **Name** | **Rating** | **Name** | **Rating** | **Name** | **Rating** |
| Peter Warrick | 9.0 | Cosey Coleman | 7.4 | Chris Samuels | 8.5 |
| Plaxico Burress | 8.8 | Travis Claridge | 7.0 | Stockar McDougle | 8.0 |
| Sylvester Morris | 8.3 | Kaulana Noa | 6.8 | Chris McIngosh | 7.8 |
| Travis Taylor | 8.1 | Leander Jordan | 6.7 | Adrian Klemm | 7.6 |
| Laveranues Coles | 8.0 | Chad Clifton | 6.3 | Todd Wade | 7.3 |
| Dez White | 7.9 | Manula Savea | 6.1 | Marvel Smith | 7.1 |
| Jerry Porter | 7.4 | Ryan Johanningmeir | 6.0 | Michael Thompson | 6.8 |
| Ron Dugans | 7.1 | Mark Tauscher | 6.0 | Bobby Williams | 6.8 |
| Todd Pinkston | 7.0 | Blaine Saipaia | 6.0 | Darnell Alford | 6.4 |
| Dennis Northcutt | 7.0 | Richard Mercier | 5.8 | Terrance Beadles | 6.3 |
| Anthony Lucas | 6.9 | Damion McIntosh | 5.3 | Tutan Reyes | 6.1 |
| Darrell Jackson | 6.6 | Jeno James | 5.0 | Greg Robinson-Ran | 6.0 |
| Danny Farmer | 6.5 | Al Jackson | 5.0 | | |
| Sherrod Gideon | 6.4 | | | | |
| Trevor Gaylor | 6.2 | | | | |

**54.** In a completely randomized experimental design, three brands of paper towels were tested for their ability to absorb water. Equal-size towels were used, with four sections of towels tested per brand. The absorbency rating data follow. At a .05 level of significance, does there appear to be a difference in the ability of the brands to absorb water?

| | Brand | |
|---|---|---|
| *x* | *y* | *z* |
| 91 | 99 | 83 |
| 100 | 96 | 88 |
| 88 | 94 | 89 |
| 89 | 99 | 76 |

**55.** Following are the percentage changes in the Dow Jones Industrial Average in each of the four years of six presidential terms. Does there appear to be any significant effect due to the year of the presidential term on stock market performance? Use $\alpha = .05$.

**MktPerf**

| First Year | Second Year | Third Year | Fourth Year |
|---|---|---|---|
| 10.9 | −18.9 | 15.2 | 4.3 |
| −15.2 | 4.8 | 6.1 | 14.6 |
| −16.7 | −27.6 | 38.3 | 17.9 |
| −17.3 | −3.1 | 4.2 | 14.9 |
| −9.2 | 19.6 | 20.3 | −3.7 |
| 27.7 | 22.6 | 2.3 | 11.8 |
| 27.0 | −4.3 | 20.3 | 4.2 |
| 13.7 | 2.1 | 33.5 | 26.0 |

**56.** Three different assembly methods have been proposed for a new product. A completely randomized experimental design was chosen to determine which assembly method results in the greatest number of parts produced per hour, and 30 workers were randomly selected and assigned to use one of the proposed methods. The number of units produced by each worker follows.

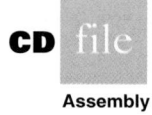

**Assembly**

**Method**

| A | B | C |
|---|---|---|
| 97 | 93 | 99 |
| 73 | 100 | 94 |
| 93 | 93 | 87 |
| 100 | 55 | 66 |
| 73 | 77 | 59 |
| 91 | 91 | 75 |
| 100 | 85 | 84 |
| 86 | 73 | 72 |
| 92 | 90 | 88 |
| 95 | 83 | 86 |

Use these data and test to see whether the mean number of parts produced is the same with each method. Use $\alpha = .05$.

57. Hargreaves Automotive Parts, Inc., wanted to compare the mileage for four different types of brake linings. Thirty linings of each type were produced and placed on a fleet of rental cars. The number of miles that each brake lining lasted until it no longer met the required federal safety standard was recorded, and an average value was computed for each type of lining. The following data were obtained.

| Type | Sample Size | Sample Mean | Standard Deviation |
|---|---|---|---|
| A | 30 | 32,000 | 1450 |
| B | 30 | 27,500 | 1525 |
| C | 30 | 34,200 | 1650 |
| D | 30 | 30,300 | 1400 |

Test to see whether the corresponding population means are equal. Use $\alpha = .05$.

58. A manufacturer of batteries for electronic toys and calculators is considering three new battery designs. An attempt was made to determine whether the mean lifetime in hours is the same for each of the three designs.

| Design A | Design B | Design C |
|---|---|---|
| 78 | 112 | 115 |
| 98 | 99 | 101 |
| 88 | 101 | 100 |
| 96 | 116 | 120 |

Test to see whether the population means are equal. Use $\alpha = .05$.

59. A study was conducted to investigate browsing activity by shoppers. Each shopper was initially classified as a nonbrowser, light browser, or heavy browser. For each shopper in the study a measure was obtained to determine how comfortable the shopper was in a store. Higher scores indicated greater comfort. The following data are consistent with that study.

**Browsing**

| Nonbrowser | Light Browser | Heavy Browser |
|---|---|---|
| 4 | 5 | 5 |
| 5 | 6 | 7 |
| 6 | 5 | 5 |
| 3 | 4 | 7 |
| 3 | 7 | 4 |
| 4 | 4 | 6 |
| 5 | 6 | 5 |
| 4 | 5 | 7 |

a. Using $\alpha = .05$, test for differences among comfort levels for the three types of browsers.
b. Use Fisher's LSD procedure to compare the comfort levels of nonbrowsers and light browsers. Use $\alpha = .05$. What is your conclusion?

**60.** A research firm tests the miles-per-gallon characteristics of three brands of gasoline. Because of different gasoline performance characteristics in different brands of automobiles, five brands of automobiles are selected and treated as blocks in the experiment. That is, each brand of automobile is tested with each type of gasoline. The results of the experiment (in miles per gallon) follow.

| | | Gasoline Brands | | |
| --- | --- | --- | --- | --- |
| | | **I** | **II** | **III** |
| | **A** | 18 | 21 | 20 |
| | **B** | 24 | 26 | 27 |
| **Automobiles** | **C** | 30 | 29 | 34 |
| | **D** | 22 | 25 | 24 |
| | **E** | 20 | 23 | 24 |

At $\alpha = .05$, is there a significant difference in the mean miles-per-gallon characteristics of the three brands of gasoline?

**61.** Analyze the experimental data provided in Exercise 60 using the ANOVA procedure for completely randomized designs. Compare your findings with those obtained in Exercise 60. What is the advantage of attempting to remove the block effect?

**62.** Each month *Internet Magazine* accesses over 100 Internet Service Providers (ISPs) in order to check the availability of the ISP and test the speed of the connection by measuring the time (seconds) it takes to download a number of popular Web pages. The following data show the download time for 22 free ISPs for Web sites located in the United Kingdom, United States, and Europe (*Internet Magazine*, January 2000).

**ISP**

| ISP Name | UK | US | Europe |
| --- | --- | --- | --- |
| Abel Gratis | 10.62 | 14.64 | 17.08 |
| Breathe | 11.67 | 14.14 | 19.86 |
| btclick.com | 12.12 | 16.43 | 21.30 |
| Bun | 11.13 | 14.09 | 15.83 |
| Cable & Wireless Life | 9.99 | 13.07 | 18.43 |
| conX | 12.63 | 15.97 | 22.12 |
| Freebeeb | 11.71 | 15.52 | 19.57 |
| Free-Online | 13.77 | 13.98 | 23.35 |
| Freeserve | 10.65 | 13.62 | 25.56 |
| FreeUK | 12.20 | 14.96 | 18.95 |
| Icom-Web | 9.62 | 11.66 | 15.91 |
| IPNet | 13.82 | 16.70 | 22.86 |
| I-way Soho | 14.86 | 12.86 | 19.32 |
| LineOne | 12.01 | 17.82 | 21.88 |
| Madasafish | 13.38 | 15.59 | 19.61 |
| NetDirect Online | 11.71 | 15.52 | 19.57 |
| Netscape Online | 10.84 | 12.66 | 16.52 |
| Screaming.net (BT Line) | 13.23 | 15.91 | 23.08 |
| Telinco Internet Services | 12.83 | 15.34 | 18.76 |
| UK Online | 10.39 | 13.28 | 21.04 |
| UKPeople | 13.79 | 19.82 | 19.76 |
| Virgin Net | 12.17 | 15.47 | 21.94 |

At $\alpha = .05$, is there a significant difference in the mean download time for Web sites located in the three countries?

**63.** A factorial experiment was designed to test for any significant differences in the time needed to perform English-to-foreign-language translations with two computerized language translators. Because the type of language translated was also considered a significant factor, translations were made with both systems for three different languages: Spanish, French, and German. Use the following data for translation time in hours.

| | Language | | |
|---|---|---|---|
| | **Spanish** | **French** | **German** |
| System 1 | 8 12 | 10 14 | 12 16 |
| System 2 | 6 10 | 14 16 | 16 22 |

Test for any significant differences due to language translator, type of language, and interaction. Use $\alpha = .05$.

**64.** A manufacturing company designed a factorial experiment to determine whether the number of defective parts produced by two machines differed and if the number of defective parts produced also depended on whether raw material needed by each machine was loaded manually or by an automatic feed system. The following data give the numbers of defective parts produced. Using $\alpha = .05$, test for any significant effect due to machine, loading system, and interaction.

| | Loading System | |
|---|---|---|
| | **Manual** | **Automatic** |
| Machine 1 | 30 34 | 30 26 |
| Machine 2 | 20 22 | 24 28 |

## Case Problem 1    WENTWORTH MEDICAL CENTER

As part of a long-term study of individuals 65 years of age or older, sociologists and physicians at the Wentworth Medical Center in upstate New York investigated the relationship between geographic location and depression. A sample of 60 individuals, all in reasonably good health, was selected; 20 individuals were residents of Florida, 20 were residents of New York, and 20 were residents of North Carolina. Each of the individuals sampled was given a standardized test to measure depression. The data collected follow; higher test scores indicate higher levels of depression. These data are available on the data disk in the file Medical1.

A second part of the study considered the relationship between geographic location and depression for individuals 65 years of age or older who had a chronic health condition such as arthritis, hypertension, and/or heart ailment. A sample of 60 individuals with such conditions was identified. Again, 20 were residents of Florida, 20 were residents of New York, and 20 were residents of North Carolina. The levels of depression recorded for this study follow. These data are available on the data disk in the file Medical2.

Medical1

Medical2

| | Data from Medical1 | | | Data from Medical2 | | |
|---|---|---|---|---|---|---|
| | **Florida** | **New York** | **North Carolina** | **Florida** | **New York** | **North Carolina** |
| | 3 | 8 | 10 | 13 | 14 | 10 |
| | 7 | 11 | 7 | 12 | 9 | 12 |
| | 7 | 9 | 3 | 17 | 15 | 15 |
| | 3 | 7 | 5 | 17 | 12 | 18 |
| | 8 | 8 | 11 | 20 | 16 | 12 |

*(continued)*

| Data from Medical1 | | | Data from Medical2 | | |
|---|---|---|---|---|---|
| **Florida** | **New York** | **North Carolina** | **Florida** | **New York** | **North Carolina** |
| 8 | 7 | 8 | 21 | 24 | 14 |
| 8 | 8 | 4 | 16 | 18 | 17 |
| 5 | 4 | 3 | 14 | 14 | 8 |
| 5 | 13 | 7 | 13 | 15 | 14 |
| 2 | 10 | 8 | 17 | 17 | 16 |
| 6 | 6 | 8 | 12 | 20 | 18 |
| 2 | 8 | 7 | 9 | 11 | 17 |
| 6 | 12 | 3 | 12 | 23 | 19 |
| 6 | 8 | 9 | 15 | 19 | 15 |
| 9 | 6 | 8 | 16 | 17 | 13 |
| 7 | 8 | 12 | 15 | 14 | 14 |
| 5 | 5 | 6 | 13 | 9 | 11 |
| 4 | 7 | 3 | 10 | 14 | 12 |
| 7 | 7 | 8 | 11 | 13 | 13 |
| 3 | 8 | 11 | 17 | 11 | 11 |

## Managerial Report

1. Use descriptive statistics to summarize the data from the two studies. What are your preliminary observations about the depression scores?
2. Use analysis of variance on both data sets. State the hypotheses being tested in each case. What are your conclusions?
3. Use inferences about individual treatment means where appropriate. What are your conclusions?
4. Discuss extensions of this study or other analyses that you feel might be helpful.

## Case Problem 2   COMPENSATION FOR ID PROFESSIONALS

For the last 10 years *Industrial Distribution* has been tracking compensation of industrial distribution (ID) professionals. Results for the 358 respondents in the 1997 Annual Salary Survey showed that 27% of the respondents work for companies with sales over $40 million, with the typical ID professional working for a $12 million firm. Those who work for small to mid-sized companies (between $6 million and $20 million) report higher earnings than those in larger firms. The lowest paid employees work for firms with sales of less than $1 million. The typical outside salesperson made $50,000 in 1996, and the typical inside salesperson earned just $30,000 (*Industrial Distribution,* November 1997). Suppose that a local chapter of ID professionals in the greater San Francisco area conducted a survey of its membership to study the relationship, if any, between the years of experience and salary for individuals employed in outside and inside sales positions. On the survey, respondents were asked to specify one of three levels of years of experience: low (1–10 years); medium (11–20 years); and high (21 or more years). A portion of the data obtained follow. The complete data set, consisting of 120 observations, is available on the data disk in the file IDSalary.

| Observation | Salary $ | Position | Experience |
|---|---|---|---|
| 1 | 28938 | Inside | Medium |
| 2 | 27694 | Inside | Medium |
| 3 | 45515 | Outside | Low |
| 4 | 27031 | Inside | Medium |
| 5 | 37283 | Outside | Low |
| 6 | 32718 | Inside | Low |
| 7 | 54081 | Outside | High |
| 8 | 23621 | Inside | Low |
| 9 | 47835 | Outside | High |
| 10 | 29768 | Inside | Medium |
| . | . | . | . |
| . | . | . | . |
| . | . | . | . |
| 115 | 33080 | Inside | High |
| 116 | 53702 | Outside | Medium |
| 117 | 58131 | Outside | Medium |
| 118 | 32788 | Inside | High |
| 119 | 28070 | Inside | Medium |
| 120 | 35259 | Outside | Low |

**IDSalary**

## Managerial Report

1. Use descriptive statistics to summarize the data.
2. Develop a 95% confidence interval estimate of the mean annual salary for all sales-persons, regardless of years of experience and type of position.
3. Develop a 95% confidence interval estimate of the mean salary for outside salepersons. Compare your results with the national value reported by *Industrial Distribution*.
4. Develop a 95% confidence interval estimate of the mean salary for inside salespersons. Compare your results with the national value reported by *Industrial Distribution*.
5. Ignoring the years of experience, develop a 95% confidence interval estimate of the mean difference between the annual salary for outside salespersons and the mean annual salary for inside salespersons. What is your conclusion?
6. Use analysis of variance to test for any significant differences due to position. Use a .05 level of significance, and for now, ignore the effect of years of experience.
7. Use analysis of variance to test for any significant differences due to years of experience. Use a .05 level of significance, and for now, ignore the effect of position.
8. At the .05 level of significance test for any significant differences due to position, years of experience, and interaction.

# SIMPLE LINEAR REGRESSION

**CONTENTS**

## STATISTICS IN PRACTICE

### POLAROID CORPORATION*
*Cambridge, Massachusetts*

Polaroid's consumer photography business began in 1947 when the company's founder, Dr. Edwin Land, announced a one-step dry process for producing a finished photograph within one minute after taking the picture. The first Polaroid Land camera and Polaroid Land film went on sale in 1949. Since then, Polaroid's continuous experimentation and development in chemistry, optics, and electronics have produced photographic systems of ever higher quality, reliability, and convenience.

Polaroid's other major business segment, technical and industrial photography, focuses on making Polaroid's instant photography a key component of the growing number of imaging systems used in today's visual communications environment. To this end, Polaroid markets a wide variety of instant photographic systems, cameras, components, and films for professional, industrial, scientific, and medical uses. Other businesses include magnetics, sunglasses, industrial polarizers, chemicals, custom coating, and holography.

Sensitometry, the measurement of the sensitivity of photographic materials, provides the information on many characteristics of film, such as its useful exposure range. Within Polaroid's central sensitometry laboratory, scientists systematically sample and analyze instant films that have been stored at temperature and humidity levels approximating those to which the films will be subjected after they have been purchased by consumers. To investigate the relationship between film speed and the age of a Polaroid extended range color professional print film, Polaroid's central sensitometry lab selected film samples ranging in age (time since manufacture) from one to 13 months. The data showed that film speed decreases with age, and that a straight-line or linear relationship could be used to approximate the relationship between change in film speed and age of the film.

_____

*The authors are indebted to Lawrence Friedman, Manager of Photographic Quality, for providing this Statistics in Practice.

Regression analysis enables Polaroid to produce films with the performance levels its customers require.
© Joe Higgins/South-Western.

Using regression analysis, Polaroid was able to develop the following equation relating the change in the film speed to the film's age.

$$\hat{y} = -19.8 - 7.6x$$

where

$$\hat{y} = \text{change in film speed}$$
$$x = \text{film age in months}$$

This equation shows that the average decrease in film speed is 7.6 units per month. The information provided by this analysis, when coupled with consumer purchase and use patterns, enables Polaroid to make manufacturing adjustments that help the company produce films with the performance levels its customers require.

In this chapter you will learn how regression analysis can be used to develop an equation relating two variables, such as the change in film speed to the age of the film in the Polaroid example.

Managerial decisions often are based on the relationship between two or more variables. For example, after considering the relationship between advertising expenditures and sales, a marketing manager might attempt to predict sales for a given level of advertising expenditures. In another case, a public utility might use the relationship between the daily high temperature and the demand for electricity to predict electricity usage on the basis of next month's anticipated daily high temperatures. Sometimes a manager will rely on intuition to

The statistical methods used in studying the relationship between two variables were first employed by Sir Francis Galton (1822–1911). Galton was interested in studying the relationship between a father's height and the son's height. Galton's disciple, Karl Pearson (1857–1936), analyzed the relationship between the father's height and the son's height for 1078 pairs of subjects.

judge how two variables are related. However, if data can be obtained, a statistical procedure called *regression analysis* can be used to develop an equation showing how the variables are related.

In regression terminology, the variable being predicted is called the **dependent variable.** The variable or variables being used to predict the value of the dependent variable are called the **independent variables.** For example, in analyzing the effect of advertising expenditures on sales, a marketing manager's desire to predict sales would suggest making sales the dependent variable. Advertising expenditure would be the independent variable used to help predict sales. In statistical notation, $y$ denotes the dependent variable and $x$ denotes the independent variable.

The simplest type of regression analysis involving one independent variable and one dependent variable, in which the relationship between the variables is approximated by a straight line, is called **simple linear regression.** Regression analysis involving two or more independent variables is called *multiple regression analysis;* multiple regression and cases involving curvilinear relationships are covered in Chapters 15 and 16.

## 14.1 SIMPLE LINEAR REGRESSION MODEL

Armand's Pizza Parlors is a chain of Italian food restaurants located in a five-state area. The most successful locations for Armand's have been near college campuses. The managers believe that quarterly sales for these restaurants (denoted by $y$) are related positively to the size of the student population (denoted by $x$); that is, restaurants near campuses with a large student population tend to generate more sales than those located near campuses with a small population. Using regression analysis, we can develop an equation showing how the dependent variable $y$ is related to the independent variable $x$.

### Regression Model and Regression Equation

In the Armand's Pizza Parlors example, every restaurant has associated with it a value of $x$ (student population) and a corresponding value of $y$ (quarterly sales). The equation that describes how $y$ is related to $x$ and an error term is called the *regression model.* The regression model used in simple linear regression follows.

> **Simple Linear Regression Model**
>
> $$y = \beta_0 + \beta_1 x + \epsilon \qquad (14.1)$$

In the **simple linear regression model,** $y$ is a linear function of $x$ (the $\beta_0 + \beta_1 x$ part) plus $\epsilon$. $\beta_0$ and $\beta_1$ are referred to as the parameters of the model, and $\epsilon$ (the Greek letter epsilon) is a random variable referred to as the error term. The error term accounts for the variability in $y$ that cannot be explained by the linear relationship between $x$ and $y$.

In Section 14.4 we will discuss the assumptions for the simple linear regression model and $\epsilon$. One of the assumptions is that the mean or expected value of $\epsilon$ is zero. A consequence of this assumption is that the mean or expected value of $y$, denoted $E(y)$, is equal to $\beta_0 + \beta_1 x$; in other words, the mean value of $y$ is a linear function of $x$. The equation that describes how the mean value of $y$ is related to $x$ is called the regression equation. The regression equation for simple linear regression follows.

**Simple Linear Regression Equation**

$$E(y) = \beta_0 + \beta_1 x \qquad\qquad (14.2)$$

The graph of the **simple linear regression equation** is a straight line; $\beta_0$ is the $y$ intercept of the regression line, $\beta_1$ is the slope, and $E(y)$ is the mean or expected value of $y$ for a given value of $x$. Examples of possible regression lines for simple linear regression are shown in Figure 14.1. The regression line in panel A of the figure shows that the mean value of $y$ is related positively to $x$, with larger values of $E(y)$ associated with larger values of $x$. The regression line in panel B shows that the mean value of $y$ is related negatively to $x$, with smaller values of $E(y)$ associated with larger values of $x$. The regression line in panel C shows that the mean value of $y$ is not related to $x$; that is, the mean value of $y$ is the same for every value of $x$.

## Estimated Regression Equation

If the values of the parameters $\beta_0$ and $\beta_1$ were known, we could use equation (14.2) to compute the mean value of $y$ for a known value of $x$. Unfortunately, the parameter values are not known in practice and must be estimated by using sample data. Sample statistics (denoted $b_0$ and $b_1$) are computed as estimates of the parameters $\beta_0$ and $\beta_1$. Substituting the values of the sample statistics $b_0$ and $b_1$ for $\beta_0$ and $\beta_1$ in the regression equation, we obtain the **estimated simple linear regression equation.**

**Estimated Simple Linear Regression Equation**

$$\hat{y} = b_0 + b_1 x \qquad\qquad (14.3)$$

The graph of the estimated simple linear regression equation is called the *estimated regression line;* $b_0$ is the $y$ intercept, $b_1$ is the slope, and $\hat{y}$ (pronounced y hat) is the estimated value of $y$ for a given value of $x$. In the next section, we show how data from a sample can be used to compute the values of $b_0$ and $b_1$ in the estimated regression equation. Figure 14.2 is a summary of the estimation process for simple linear regression.

**FIGURE 14.1**    POSSIBLE REGRESSION LINES IN SIMPLE LINEAR REGRESSION

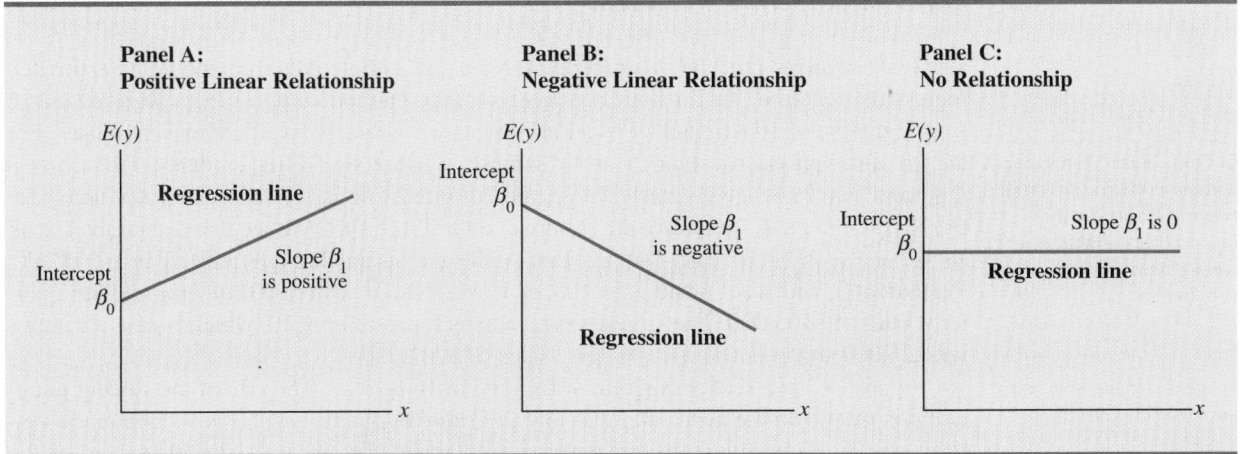

**FIGURE 14.2     THE ESTIMATION PROCESS IN SIMPLE LINEAR REGRESSION**

The estimation of $\beta_0$ and $\beta_1$ is a statistical process much like the estimation of $\mu$ discussed in Chapter 7. $\beta_0$ and $\beta_1$ are the unknown parameters of interest, and $b_0$ and $b_1$ are the sample statistics used to estimate the parameters.

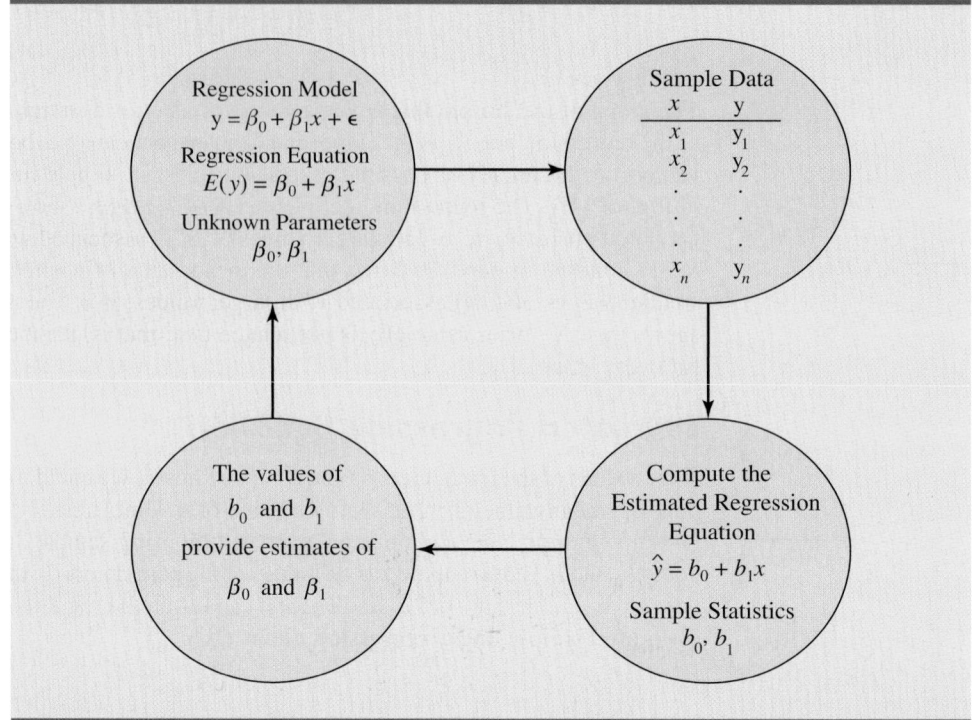

## NOTES AND COMMENTS

Regression analysis *cannot* be interpreted as a procedure for establishing a *cause-and-effect* relationship between variables. It can only indicate how or to what extent variables are *associated* with each other. Any conclusions about cause and effect must be based on the *judgment* of the individual or individuals most knowledgeable about the application.

## 14.2 / LEAST SQUARES METHOD

The **least squares method** is a procedure for using sample data to compute an estimated regression equation. To illustrate the least squares method, suppose data were collected from a sample of 10 Armand's Pizza Parlor restaurants located near college campuses. For the *i*th observation or restaurant in the sample, $x_i$ is the size of the student population (in thousands) and $y_i$ is the quarterly sales (in thousands of dollars). The values of $x_i$ and $y_i$ for the 10 restaurants in the sample are summarized in Table 14.1. We see that restaurant 1, with $x_1 = 2$ and $y_1 = 58$, is near a campus with 2000 students and has quarterly sales of $58,000. Restaurant 2, with $x_2 = 6$ and $y_2 = 105$, is near a campus with 6000 students and has quarterly sales of $105,000. The largest sales value is for restaurant 10, which is near a campus with 26,000 students and has quarterly sales of $202,000.

In simple linear regression, each observation consists of two values: one for the independent variable and one for the dependent variable.

Figure 14.3 is a scatter diagram of the data in Table 14.1. The size of the student population is shown on the horizontal axis and the value of quarterly sales is shown on the vertical axis. **Scatter diagrams** for regression analysis are constructed with values of the independent variable *x* on the horizontal axis and values of the dependent variable *y* on the

Scatter diagrams were first introduced in Chapter 2.

**TABLE 14.1**   STUDENT POPULATION AND QUARTERLY SALES DATA
FOR 10 ARMAND'S PIZZA PARLORS

| Restaurant $i$ | Student Population (1000s) $x_i$ | Quarterly Sales ($1000s) $y_i$ |
|:---:|:---:|:---:|
| 1 | 2 | 58 |
| 2 | 6 | 105 |
| 3 | 8 | 88 |
| 4 | 8 | 118 |
| 5 | 12 | 117 |
| 6 | 16 | 137 |
| 7 | 20 | 157 |
| 8 | 20 | 169 |
| 9 | 22 | 149 |
| 10 | 26 | 202 |

vertical axis. The scatter diagram enables us to observe the data graphically and to draw
preliminary conclusions about the possible relationship between the variables.

What preliminary conclusions can be drawn from Figure 14.3? Quarterly sales appear
to be higher at campuses with larger student populations. In addition, for these data the relationship between the size of the student population and quarterly sales appears to be approximated by a straight line; indeed, there seems to be a positive linear relationship

**FIGURE 14.3**   SCATTER DIAGRAM OF STUDENT POPULATION AND QUARTERLY
SALES FOR ARMAND'S PIZZA PARLORS

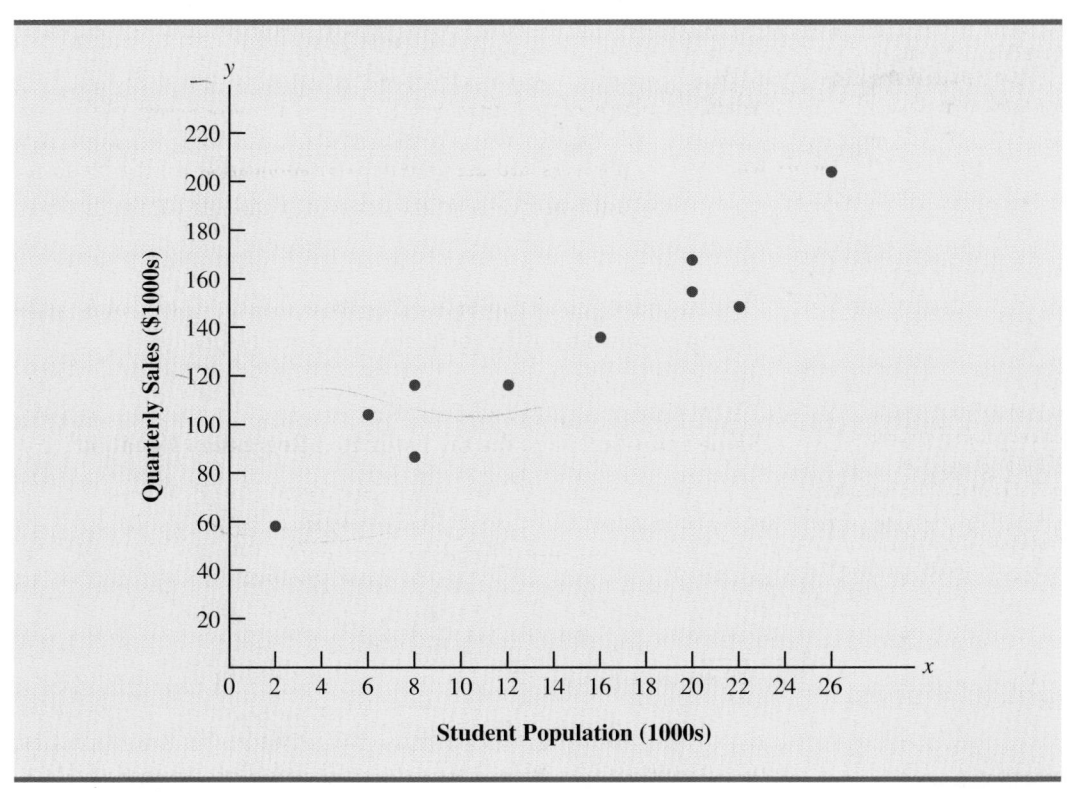

between $x$ and $y$. We therefore choose the simple linear regression model to represent the relationship between quarterly sales and student population. Given that choice, our next task is to use the sample data in Table 14.1 to determine the values of $b_0$ and $b_1$ in the estimated simple linear regression equation. For the $i$th restaurant, the estimated regression equation is

$$\hat{y}_i = b_0 + b_1 x_i \tag{14.4}$$

where

$\hat{y}_i$ = estimated value of quarterly sales ($1000s) for the $i$th restaurant
$b_0$ = the $y$ intercept of the estimated regression line
$b_1$ = the slope of the estimated regression line
$x_i$ = size of the student population (1000s) for the $i$th restaurant

With $y_i$ denoting the observed (actual) quarterly sales for restaurant $i$ and $\hat{y}_i$ in equation (14.4) representing the estimated value of quarterly sales for restaurant $i$, every restaurant in the sample will have an observed value of quarterly sales $y_i$ and an estimated value of quarterly sales $\hat{y}_i$. For the estimated regression line to provide a good fit to the data, we want the differences between the observed values and the estimated values to be small.

The least squares method uses the sample data to provide the values of $b_0$ and $b_1$ that minimize the *sum of the squares of the deviations* between the observed values of the dependent variable $y_i$ and the estimated values of the dependent variable $\hat{y}_i$. The criterion for the least squares method is given by equation (14.5).

**Least Squares Criterion**

Carl Friedrich Gauss (1777–1855) proposed the least squares method.

$$\min \Sigma(y_i - \hat{y}_i)^2 \tag{14.5}$$

where

$y_i$ = observed value of the dependent variable for the $i$th observation
$\hat{y}_i$ = estimated value of the dependent variable for the $i$th observation

Differential calculus can be used to show that the values of $b_0$ and $b_1$ that minimize (14.5) can be found by using equations (14.6) and (14.7).

In computing $b_1$ with a calculator, carry as many significant digits as possible in the intermediate calculations. We recommend carrying at least four significant digits.

**Slope and $y$-Intercept for the Estimated Regression Equation[1]**

$$b_1 = \frac{\Sigma(x_i - \bar{x})(y_i - \bar{y})}{\Sigma(x_i - \bar{x})^2} \tag{14.6}$$

$$b_0 = \bar{y} - b_1\bar{x} \tag{14.7}$$

---

[1] An alternate formula for $b_1$ is

$$b_1 = \frac{\Sigma x_i y_i - (\Sigma x_i \Sigma y_i)/n}{\Sigma x_i^2 - (\Sigma x_i)^2/n}$$

This form of equation (14.6) is often recommended when using a calculator to compute $b_1$.

where

$$x_i = \text{value of the independent variable for the } i\text{th observation}$$
$$y_i = \text{value of the dependent variable for the } i\text{th observation}$$
$$\bar{x} = \text{mean value for the independent variable}$$
$$\bar{y} = \text{mean value for the dependent variable}$$
$$n = \text{total number of observations}$$

Some of the calculations necessary to develop the least squares estimated regression equation for Armand's Pizza Parlors are shown in Table 14.2. With the sample of 10 restaurants, we have $n = 10$ observations. Because equations (14.6) and (14.7) require $\bar{x}$ and $\bar{y}$, we begin the calculations by computing $\bar{x}$ and $\bar{y}$.

$$\bar{x} = \frac{\Sigma x_i}{n} = \frac{140}{10} = 14$$

$$\bar{y} = \frac{\Sigma y_i}{n} = \frac{1300}{10} = 130$$

Using equations (14.6) and (14.7), and the information in Table 14.2, we can compute the slope and intercept of the estimated regression equation for Armand's Pizza Parlors. The calculation of the slope ($b_1$) proceeds as follows.

$$b_1 = \frac{\Sigma(x_i - \bar{x})(y_i - \bar{y})}{\Sigma(x_i - \bar{x})^2}$$

$$= \frac{2840}{568}$$

$$= 5$$

**TABLE 14.2**    CALCULATIONS FOR THE LEAST SQUARES ESTIMATED REGRESSION EQUATION FOR ARMAND PIZZA PARLORS

The calculations in this table can be easily made in an Excel worksheet.

| Restaurant $i$ | $x_i$ | $y_i$ | $x_i - \bar{x}$ | $y_i - \bar{y}$ | $(x_i - \bar{x})(y_i - \bar{y})$ | $(x_i - \bar{x})^2$ |
|---|---|---|---|---|---|---|
| 1 | 2 | 58 | $-12$ | $-72$ | 864 | 144 |
| 2 | 6 | 105 | $-8$ | $-25$ | 200 | 64 |
| 3 | 8 | 88 | $-6$ | $-42$ | 252 | 36 |
| 4 | 8 | 118 | $-6$ | $-12$ | 72 | 36 |
| 5 | 12 | 117 | $-2$ | $-13$ | 26 | 4 |
| 6 | 16 | 137 | 2 | 7 | 14 | 4 |
| 7 | 20 | 157 | 6 | 27 | 162 | 36 |
| 8 | 20 | 169 | 6 | 39 | 234 | 36 |
| 9 | 22 | 149 | 8 | 19 | 152 | 64 |
| 10 | 26 | 202 | 12 | 72 | 864 | 144 |
| Totals | 140 | 1300 | | | 2840 | 568 |
| | $\Sigma x_i$ | $\Sigma y_i$ | | | $\Sigma(x_i - \bar{x})(y_i - \bar{y})$ | $\Sigma(x_i - \bar{x})^2$ |

The calculation of the $y$ intercept ($b_0$) follows.

$$b_0 = \bar{y} - b_1\bar{x}$$
$$= 130 - 5(14)$$
$$= 60$$

Thus, the estimated regression equation is

$$\hat{y} = 60 + 5x$$

Figure 14.4 shows the graph of this equation on the scatter diagram.

The slope of the estimated regression equation ($b_1 = 5$) is positive, implying that as student population increases, quarterly sales increase. In fact, we can conclude (because quarterly sales are measured in $1000s and student population in 1000s) that an increase in the student population of 1000 is associated with an increase of $5000 in expected quarterly sales; that is, quarterly sales are expected to increase by $5 per student.

If we believe the least squares estimated regression equation adequately describes the relationship between $x$ and $y$, it would seem reasonable to use the estimated regression equation to predict the value of $y$ for a given value of $x$. For example, if we wanted to predict sales for a restaurant to be located near a campus with 16,000 students, we would compute

$$\hat{y} = 60 + 5(16) = 140$$

*Using the estimated regression equation to make predictions outside the range of the values of the independent variable should be done with caution, because outside that range we cannot be sure that the same relationship is valid.*

**FIGURE 14.4**    GRAPH OF THE ESTIMATED REGRESSION EQUATION FOR ARMAND'S PIZZA PARLORS: $\hat{y} = 60 + 5x$

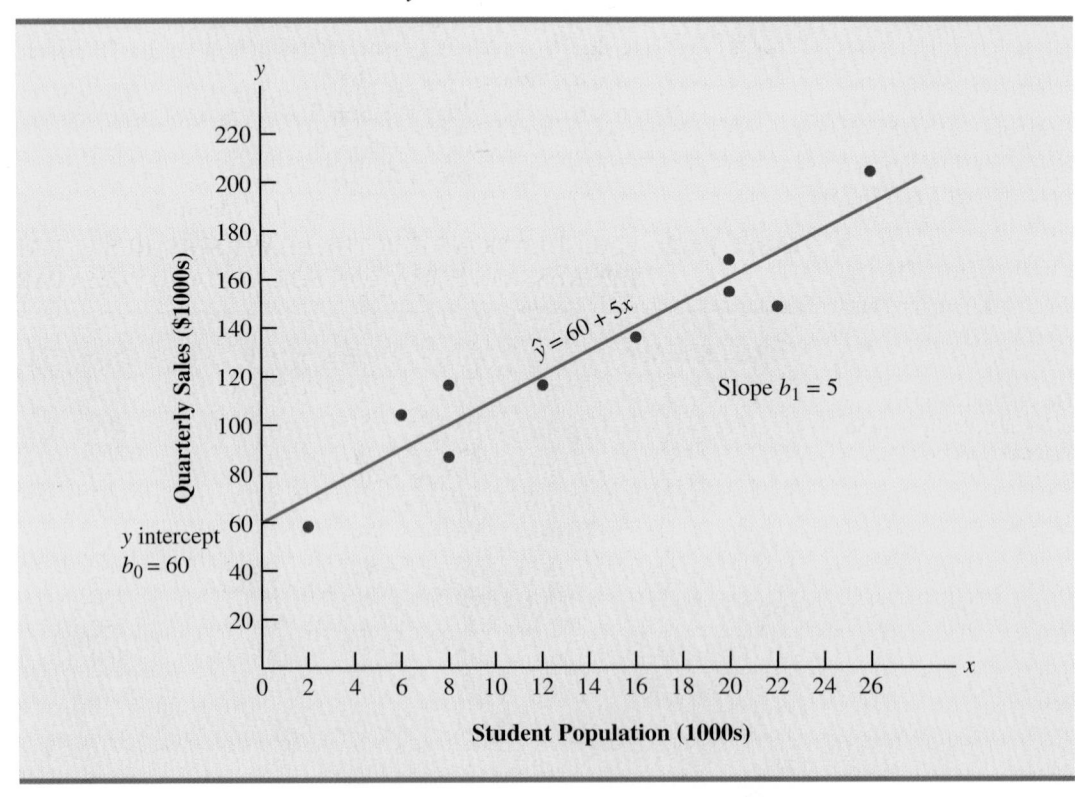

Hence, we would predict quarterly sales of $140,000 for this restaurant. In the following sections we will discuss methods for assessing the appropriateness of using the estimated regression equation for prediction.

## Using Excel to Develop a Scatter Diagram and Compute the Estimated Regression Equation

In Section 2.4 we showed how Excel's Chart Wizard could be used to construct a scatter diagram. Once a scatter diagram has been developed, Excel's Chart menu provides options for computing the estimated regression equation and displaying the graph of the estimated regression equation. We will demonstrate these capabilities using the Armand's Pizza Parlor data appearing in Table 14.1. Refer to Figure 14.5 as we describe the tasks involved.

**Enter Data:**   The labels Restaurant, Population, and Sales have been entered into cells A1:C1 of the worksheet. To identify each of the 10 observations, we entered the numbers 1 through 10 into cells A2:A11. The sample data have been entered into cells B2:C11.

**Apply Tools:**   We will first use Excel's Chart Wizard to produce a scatter diagram. We will then show how options available on the Chart menu can be used to compute the estimated regression equation and to display the estimated regression line.

**Step 1.** Select cells B1:C11
**Step 2.** Select the **Chart Wizard** (or select the **Insert** pull-down menu and choose the **Chart** option)
**Step 3.** When the **Chart Wizard—Step 1 of 4—Chart Type** dialog box appears:
Choose **XY (Scatter)** in the **Chart type** list
Choose **Scatter** from the **Chart sub-type** display
Select **Next >**
**Step 4.** When the **Chart Wizard—Step 2 of 4—Chart Source Data** dialog box appears:
Select **Next >**
**Step 5.** When the **Chart Wizard—Step 3 of 4—Chart Options** dialog box appears:
Select the **Titles** tab and then
Delete **Sales** in the Chart title box
Enter **Student Population (1000s)** in the **Value (X)** axis box
Enter **Quarterly Sales ($1000s)** in the **Value (Y)** axis box
Select the **Legend** tab and then
Remove the check in the **Show Legend** box
Select **Next >**
**Step 6.** When the **Chart Wizard—Step 4 of 4—Chart Location** dialog box appears:
Specify a location for the new chart (we used the default setting of the current worksheet)
Select **Finish** to display the scatter diagram
**Step 7.** Position the mouse pointer over any data point and right click to display the **Chart** menu
**Step 8.** Select the **Add Trendline** option
**Step 9.** When the Add Trendline dialog box appears:
On the **Type** tab select **Linear**
On the **Options** tab select the **Display equation on chart** box
Click **OK**

Figure 14.5 shows the scatter diagram, the estimated regression equation, and the graph of the estimated regression equation obtained.

**FIGURE 14.5**    SCATTER DIAGRAM, ESTIMATED REGRESSION EQUATION, AND THE ESTIMATED REGRESSION LINE FOR ARMAND'S PIZZA PARLORS

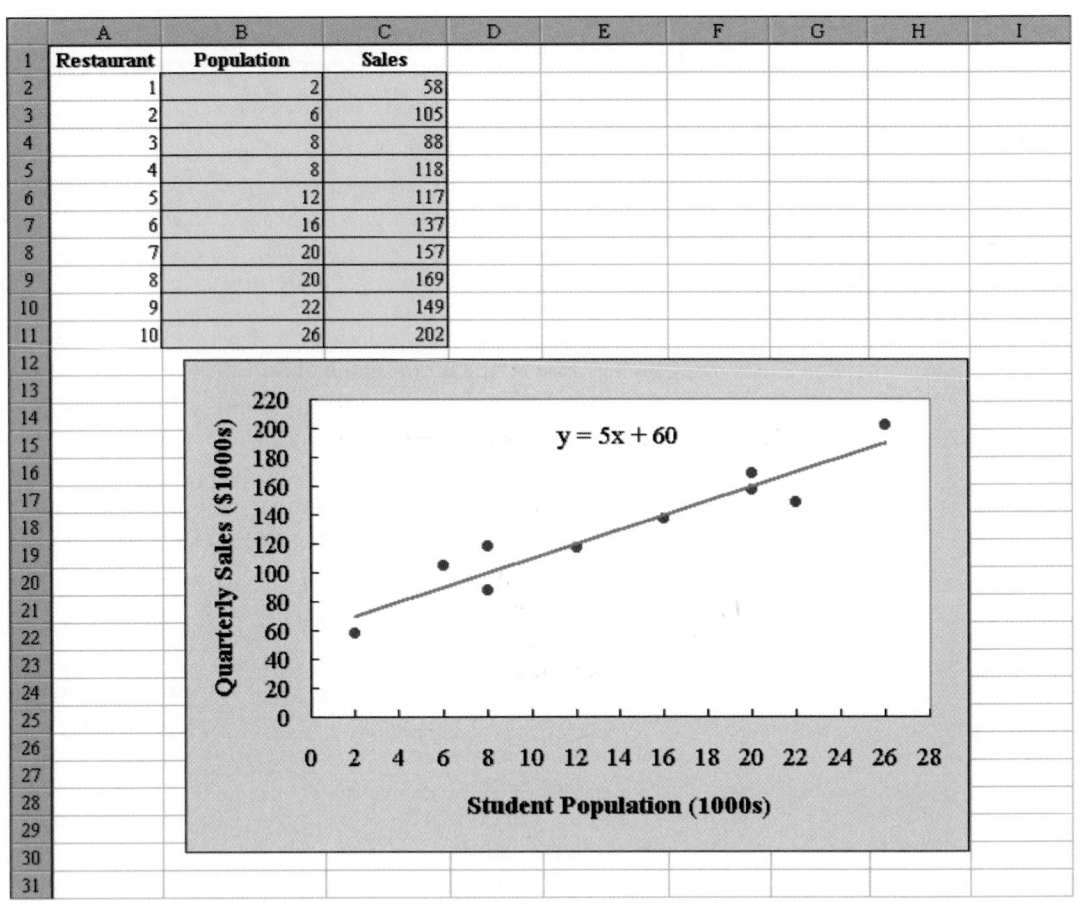

## NOTES AND COMMENTS

**1.** The least squares method provides an estimated regression equation that minimizes the sum of squared deviations between the observed values of the dependent variable $y_i$ and the estimated values of the dependent variable $\hat{y}_i$. The least squares criterion chooses the equation that provides the best fit. If some other criterion were used, such as minimizing the sum of the absolute deviations between $y_i$ and $\hat{y}_i$, a different equation would be obtained. In practice, the least squares method is the most widely used.

**2.** Excel's INTERCEPT and SLOPE functions can also be used to compute the $y$ intercept and slope of the estimated regression equation. For instance, for the Armand's data shown in columns B and C of Figure 14.5, the formula =INTERCEPT (C2:C11,B2:B11) can be entered into any empty cell of the worksheet to compute the $y$ intercept of the estimated regression line, and the formula =SLOPE(C2:C11,B2:B11) can be entered into any empty cell to compute the slope of the estimated regression equation.

## EXERCISES

## Methods

1. Given are five observations for two variables, $x$ and $y$.

| $x_i$ | 1 | 2 | 3 | 4 | 5 |
|-------|---|---|---|----|----|
| $y_i$ | 3 | 7 | 5 | 11 | 14 |

   a. Develop a scatter diagram for these data.
   b. What does the scatter diagram developed in part (a) indicate about the relationship between the two variables?
   c. Try to approximate the relationship between $x$ and $y$ by drawing a straight line through the data.
   d. Develop the estimated regression equation by computing the values of $b_0$ and $b_1$ using equations (14.6) and (14.7).
   e. Use the estimated regression equation to predict the value of $y$ when $x = 4$.

2. Given are five observations for two variables, $x$ and $y$.

| $x_i$ | 2 | 3 | 5 | 1 | 8 |
|-------|----|----|----|----|----|
| $y_i$ | 25 | 25 | 20 | 30 | 16 |

   a. Develop a scatter diagram for these data.
   b. What does the scatter diagram developed in part (a) indicate about the relationship between the two variables?
   c. Try to approximate the relationship between $x$ and $y$ by drawing a straight line through the data.
   d. Develop the estimated regression equation by computing the values of $b_0$ and $b_1$ using equations (14.6) and (14.7).
   e. Use the estimated regression equation to predict the value of $y$ when $x = 6$.

3. Given are five observations collected in a regression study with two variables.

| $x_i$ | 2 | 4 | 5 | 7 | 8 |
|-------|---|---|---|---|---|
| $y_i$ | 2 | 3 | 2 | 6 | 4 |

   a. Develop a scatter diagram for these data.
   b. Develop the estimated regression equation for these data.
   c. Use the estimated regression equation to predict the value of $y$ when $x = 4$.

## Applications

4. The following data were collected on the height (inches) and weight (pounds) of women swimmers.

| **Height** | 68 | 64 | 62 | 65 | 66 |
|------------|-----|-----|-----|-----|-----|
| **Weight** | 132 | 108 | 102 | 115 | 128 |

   a. Develop a scatter diagram for these data with height as the independent variable.
   b. What does the scatter diagram developed in part (a) indicate about the relationship between the two variables?
   c. Try to approximate the relationship between height and weight by drawing a straight line through the data.
   d. Develop the estimated regression equation by computing the values of $b_0$ and $b_1$ using equations (14.6) and (14.7).
   e. If a swimmer's height is 63 inches, what would you estimate her weight to be?

**5.** The following data show the media expenditures (millions of dollars) and the case sales (millions) for seven major brands of soft drinks (*Superbrands '98,* October 20, 1997).

| Brand | Media Expenditures ($) | Case Sales |
|---|---|---|
| Coca-Cola Classic | 131.3 | 1929.2 |
| Pepsi-Cola | 92.4 | 1384.6 |
| Diet Coke | 60.4 | 811.4 |
| Sprite | 55.7 | 541.5 |
| Dr. Pepper | 40.2 | 536.9 |
| Mountain Dew | 29.0 | 535.6 |
| 7-Up | 11.6 | 219.5 |

  **a.** Develop a scatter diagram for these data with media expenditures as the independent variable.

  **b.** What does the scatter diagram developed in part (a) indicate about the relationship between the two variables?

  **c.** Draw a straight line through the data to approximate a linear relationship between media expenditures and case sales.

  **d.** Use the least squares method to develop the estimated regression equation.

  **e.** Provide an interpretation for the slope of the estimated regression equation.

  **f.** Predict the case sales for a brand with a media expenditure of $70 million.

**6.** Airline performance data for U.S. airlines were reported in *The Wall Street Journal Almanac 1998.* Data on the percentage of flights arriving on time and the number of complaints per 100,000 passengers follow.

| Airline | Percentage on Time | Complaints |
|---|---|---|
| Southwest | 81.8 | 0.21 |
| Continental | 76.6 | 0.58 |
| Northwest | 76.6 | 0.85 |
| US Airways | 75.7 | 0.68 |
| United | 73.8 | 0.74 |
| American | 72.2 | 0.93 |
| Delta | 71.2 | 0.72 |
| America West | 70.8 | 1.22 |
| TWA | 68.5 | 1.25 |

  **a.** Develop a scatter diagram for these data with percentage on time as the independent variable.

  **b.** What does the scatter diagram developed in part (a) indicate about the relationship between the two variables?

  **c.** Develop the estimated regression equation showing how the number of complaints per 100,000 passengers is related to the percentage of flights arriving on time.

  **d.** Provide an interpretation for the slope of the estimated regression equation.

  **e.** What is the estimated number of complaints per 100,000 passengers if the percentage of flights arriving on time is 80%?

**7.** The Dow Jones Industrial Average (DJIA) and the Standard & Poor's 500 (S&P) indexes are both used as measures of overall movement in the stock market. The DJIA is based on the price movements of 30 large companies; the S&P 500 is an index composed of 500 stocks. Some say the S&P 500 is a better measure of stock market performance because it is broader based. The closing prices for the DJIA and the S&P 500 for 10 weeks, beginning February 11, 2000, follow (*Barron's,* April 17, 2000).

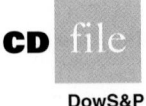

**CD file**

**DowS&P**

| Date | DJIA | S&P |
|---|---|---|
| February 11 | 10425 | 1387 |
| February 18 | 10220 | 1346 |
| February 25 | 9862 | 1333 |

| Date | DJIA | S&P |
|------|------|-----|
| March 3 | 10367 | 1409 |
| March 10 | 9929 | 1395 |
| March 17 | 10595 | 1464 |
| March 24 | 11113 | 1527 |
| March 31 | 10922 | 1499 |
| April 7 | 11111 | 1516 |
| April 14 | 10306 | 1357 |

a.  Develop a scatter diagram for these data with DJIA as the independent variable.
b.  Develop the least squares estimated regression equation.
c.  Suppose the closing price for the DJIA is 11,000. Estimate the closing price for the S&P 500.

8.  Nielsen Media Research collects data showing which advertisers get the most exposure during prime-time TV on ABC, CBS, NBC, Fox, UPN, and WB networks. Data showing the number of times the ad was aired and the number of household exposures in millions for the week of April 28–May 4, 1997, follow (*USA Today,* May 5, 1997).

| Advertised Brand | Times Ad Aired | Household Exposures |
|------------------|----------------|---------------------|
| Wendy's | 28 | 191.7 |
| Ford Escort | 20 | 174.6 |
| *Austin Powers* movie | 14 | 161.3 |
| Nissan | 16 | 161.1 |
| Pizza Hut | 16 | 147.7 |
| Saturn | 16 | 146.3 |
| *Father's Day* movie | 11 | 138.2 |

a.  Develop the estimated regression equation showing how the number of times an ad is aired is related to the number of household exposures.
b.  Provide an interpretation for the slope of the estimated regression equation.
c.  What is the estimated number of household exposures if an ad is aired 15 times?

9.  A sales manager has collected the following data on years of experience and annual sales.

| Salesperson | Years of Experience | Annual Sales ($1000s) |
|-------------|---------------------|------------------------|
| 1 | 1 | 80 |
| 2 | 3 | 97 |
| 3 | 4 | 92 |
| 4 | 4 | 102 |
| 5 | 6 | 103 |
| 6 | 8 | 111 |
| 7 | 10 | 119 |
| 8 | 10 | 123 |
| 9 | 11 | 117 |
| 10 | 13 | 136 |

a.  Develop a scatter diagram for these data with years of experience as the independent variable.
b.  Develop an estimated regression equation that can be used to predict annual sales given the years of experience.
c.  Use the estimated regression equation to predict annual sales for a salesperson with nine years of experience.

**10.** *PC World* provided ratings for the top 15 notebook PCs (*PC World,* February 2000). The performance score is a measure of how fast a PC can run a mix of common business applications as compared to how fast a baseline machine can run them. For example, a PC with a performance score of 200 is twice as fast as the baseline machine. A 100-point scale was used to provide an overall rating for each notebook tested in the study. A score in the 90s is exceptional, while one in the 70s is above average. The performance scores and the overall ratings for the 15 notebooks follow.

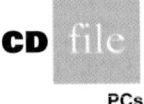

**PCs**

| Notebook | Performance Score | Overall Rating |
|---|---|---|
| AMS Tech Roadster 15CTA380 | 115 | 67 |
| Compaq Armada M700 | 191 | 78 |
| Compaq Prosignia Notebook 150 | 153 | 79 |
| Dell Inspiron 3700 C466GT | 194 | 80 |
| Dell Inspiron 7500 R500VT | 236 | 84 |
| Dell Latitude Cpi A366XT | 184 | 76 |
| Enpower ENP-313 Pro | 184 | 77 |
| Gateway Solo 9300LS | 216 | 92 |
| HP Pavilion Notebook PC | 185 | 83 |
| IBM ThinkPad I Series 1480 | 183 | 78 |
| Micro Express NP7400 | 189 | 77 |
| Micron TransPort NX PII-400 | 202 | 78 |
| NEC Versa SX | 192 | 78 |
| Sceptre Soundx 5200 | 141 | 73 |
| Sony VAIO PCG-F340 | 187 | 77 |

**a.** Develop a scatter diagram for these data with performance score as the independent variable.
**b.** Develop the least squares estimated regression equation.
**c.** Estimate the overall rating for a new PC that has a performance score of 225.

**11.** The following data show the hotel revenue and the gaming revenue, in millions of dollars, for 10 Las Vegas casino hotels (*Cornell Hotel And Restaurant Administration Quarterly,* October 1997).

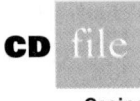

**Casino**

| Company | Hotel Revenue ($) | Gaming Revenue ($) |
|---|---|---|
| Boyd Gaming | 303.5 | 548.2 |
| Circus Circus Enterprises | 664.8 | 664.8 |
| Grand Casinos | 121.0 | 270.7 |
| Hilton Corp. Gaming Div. | 429.6 | 511.0 |
| MGM Grand, Inc. | 373.1 | 404.7 |
| Mirage Resorts | 670.9 | 782.8 |
| Primadonna Resorts | 66.4 | 130.7 |
| Rio Hotel & Casino | 105.8 | 105.5 |
| Sahara Gaming | 102.4 | 148.7 |
| Station Casinos | 135.8 | 358.5 |

**a.** Develop a scatter diagram for these data with hotel revenue as the independent variable.
**b.** Is there a linear relationship between the two variables?
**c.** Develop the estimated regression equation relating the gaming revenue to the hotel revenue.
**d.** Suppose that the hotel revenue was $500 million. What is an estimate of the gaming revenue?

12. The following table gives the number of employees and the revenue (millions of dollars) for 20 companies (*Fortune,* April 17, 2000).

**CD** file

EmpRev

| Company | Employees | Revenue ($millions) |
|---|---|---|
| Sprint | 77600 | 19930 |
| Chase Manhattan | 74801 | 33710 |
| Computer Sciences | 50000 | 7660 |
| Wells Fargo | 89355 | 21795 |
| Sunbeam | 12200 | 2398 |
| CBS | 29000 | 7510 |
| Time Warner | 69722 | 27333 |
| Steelcase | 16200 | 2743 |
| Georgia-Pacific | 57000 | 17796 |
| Toro | 1275 | 4673 |
| American Financial | 9400 | 3334 |
| Fluor | 53561 | 12417 |
| Phillips Petroleum | 15900 | 13852 |
| Cardinal Health | 36000 | 25034 |
| Borders Group | 23500 | 2999 |
| MCI Worldcom | 77000 | 37120 |
| Consolidated Edison | 14269 | 7491 |
| IBP | 45000 | 14075 |
| Super Value | 50000 | 17421 |
| H&R Block | 4200 | 1669 |

a. Develop a scatter diagram for these data with number of employees as the independent variable.
b. What does the scatter diagram developed in (a) indicate about the relationship between the number of employees and revenue?
c. Develop the estimated regression equation for these data.
d. Use the estimated regression equation to predict the revenue for a firm that has 75,000 employees.

13. To the Internal Revenue Service, the reasonableness of total itemized deductions depends on the taxpayer's adjusted gross income. Large deductions, which include charity and medical deductions, are more reasonable for taxpayers with large adjusted gross incomes. If a taxpayer claims larger than average itemized deductions for a given level of income, the chances of an IRS audit are increased. Data on adjusted gross income and the average amount of itemized deductions follow (*Money,* October 1994). The data are in thousands of dollars.

| Adjusted Gross Income ($1000s) | Total Itemized Deductions ($1000s) |
|---|---|
| 22 | 9.6 |
| 27 | 9.6 |
| 32 | 10.1 |
| 48 | 11.1 |
| 65 | 13.5 |
| 85 | 17.7 |
| 120 | 25.5 |

a. Develop a scatter diagram for these data with adjusted gross income as the independent variable.
b. Develop the estimated regression equation.
c. Predict a reasonable level of total itemized deductions for a taxpayer with an adjusted gross income of $52,500. If this taxpayer has claimed total itemized deductions of $20,400, would the IRS agent's request for an audit appear justified? Explain.

**14.** The following data report the occupancy rates (%) and room rates ($) for the largest U.S. hotel markets (*The Wall Street Journal Almanac 1998*).

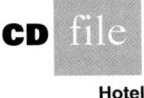

**Hotel**

| Market | Average Room Rate ($) | Occupancy Rate (%) |
|---|---|---|
| Los Angeles–Long Beach | 75.91 | 67.9 |
| Chicago | 92.04 | 72.0 |
| Washington | 94.42 | 68.4 |
| Atlanta | 81.69 | 67.7 |
| Dallas | 74.76 | 69.5 |
| San Diego | 80.86 | 68.7 |
| Anaheim–Santa Ana | 70.04 | 69.5 |
| San Francisco | 106.47 | 78.7 |
| Houston | 66.11 | 62.0 |
| Miami–Hialeah | 85.83 | 71.2 |
| Oahu Island | 107.11 | 80.7 |
| Phoenix | 95.34 | 71.4 |
| Boston | 105.51 | 73.5 |
| Tampa–St. Petersburg | 67.45 | 63.4 |
| Detroit | 64.79 | 68.7 |
| Philadelphia | 83.56 | 70.1 |
| Nashville | 70.12 | 67.1 |
| Seattle | 82.60 | 73.4 |
| Minneapolis–St. Paul | 73.64 | 69.8 |
| New Orleans | 99.00 | 70.6 |

**a.** Develop a scatter diagram for these data with average room rate as the independent variable.
**b.** Develop the estimated regression equation relating the occupancy rate to the average room rate.
**c.** Predict the occupancy rate for a hotel with an average room rate of $80.

## 14.3 COEFFICIENT OF DETERMINATION

For the Armand's Pizza Parlors example, we developed the estimated regression equation $\hat{y} = 60 + 5x$ to approximate the linear relationship between the size of the student population $x$ and quarterly sales $y$. A question now is: How well does the estimated regression equation fit the data? In this section, we show that the **coefficient of determination** provides a measure of the goodness of fit for the estimated regression equation.

For the $i$th observation, the difference between the observed value of the dependent variable, $y_i$, and the estimated value of the dependent variable, $\hat{y}_i$, is called the *$i$th residual.* The $i$th residual represents the error in using $\hat{y}_i$ to estimate $y_i$. Thus, for the $i$th observation, the residual is $y_i - \hat{y}_i$. The sum of squares of these residuals or errors is the quantity that is minimized by the least squares method. This quantity, also known as the *sum of squares due to error,* is denoted by SSE.

**Sum of Squares Due to Error**

$$SSE = \Sigma(y_i - \hat{y}_i)^2 \tag{14.8}$$

The value of SSE is a measure of the error in using the estimated regression equation to estimate the values of the dependent variable in the sample.

**TABLE 14.3**    CALCULATION OF SSE FOR ARMAND'S PIZZA PARLORS

| Restaurant $i$ | $x_i$ = Student Population (1000s) | $y_i$ = Quarterly Sales ($1000s) | $\hat{y}_i = 60 + 5x_i$ | $y_i - \hat{y}_i$ | $(y_i - \hat{y}_i)^2$ |
|---|---|---|---|---|---|
| 1 | 2 | 58 | 70 | −12 | 144 |
| 2 | 6 | 105 | 90 | 15 | 225 |
| 3 | 8 | 88 | 100 | −12 | 144 |
| 4 | 8 | 118 | 100 | 18 | 324 |
| 5 | 12 | 117 | 120 | −3 | 9 |
| 6 | 16 | 137 | 140 | −3 | 9 |
| 7 | 20 | 157 | 160 | −3 | 9 |
| 8 | 20 | 169 | 160 | 9 | 81 |
| 9 | 22 | 149 | 170 | −21 | 441 |
| 10 | 26 | 202 | 190 | 12 | 144 |
| | | | | | SSE = 1530 |

In Table 14.3 we show the calculations required to compute the sum of squares due to error for the Armand's Pizza Parlors example. For instance, for restaurant 1 the values of the independent and dependent variables are $x_1 = 2$ and $y_1 = 58$. Using the estimated regression equation, we find that the estimated value of quarterly sales for restaurant 1 is $\hat{y}_1 = 60 + 5(2) = 70$. Thus, the error (residual) in using $\hat{y}_1$ to estimate $y_1$ for restaurant 1 is $y_1 - \hat{y}_1 = 58 - 70 = -12$. The squared error, $(-12)^2 = 144$, is shown in the last column of Table 14.3. After computing and squaring the residuals (errors) for each restaurant in the sample, we sum them to obtain SSE = 1530. Thus, SSE = 1530 measures the error in using the estimated regression equation $\hat{y} = 60 + 5x$ to predict quarterly sales.

Now suppose we are asked to develop an estimate of quarterly sales without knowledge of the size of the student population. Without knowledge of any related variables, we would use the sample mean as an estimate of quarterly sales at any given restaurant. We earlier computed the mean value of quarterly sales for the sample of 10 Armand's restaurants as $\bar{y} = \Sigma y_i/n = 1300/10 = 130$. In Table 14.4 we show the sum of squared deviations obtained

**TABLE 14.4**    COMPUTATION OF THE TOTAL SUM OF SQUARES FOR ARMAND'S
PIZZA PARLORS

| Restaurant $i$ | $x_i$ = Student Population (1000s) | $y_i$ = Quarterly Sales ($1000s) | $y_i - \bar{y}$ | $(y_i - \bar{y})^2$ |
|---|---|---|---|---|
| 1 | 2 | 58 | −72 | 5,184 |
| 2 | 6 | 105 | −25 | 625 |
| 3 | 8 | 88 | −42 | 1,764 |
| 4 | 8 | 118 | −12 | 144 |
| 5 | 12 | 117 | −13 | 169 |
| 6 | 16 | 137 | 7 | 49 |
| 7 | 20 | 157 | 27 | 729 |
| 8 | 20 | 169 | 39 | 1,521 |
| 9 | 22 | 149 | 19 | 361 |
| 10 | 26 | 202 | 72 | 5,184 |
| | | | | SST = 15,730 |

by using the sample mean $\bar{y} = 130$ to estimate quarterly sales for each restaurant in the sample. For the $i$th restaurant in the sample, the difference $y_i - \bar{y}$ provides a measure of the error involved if we had used $\bar{y}$ to estimate sales. The corresponding sum of squares, called the *total sum of squares,* is denoted SST.

SST is the numerator of the formula for sample variance shown in Chapter 3.

**Total Sum of Squares**

$$SST = \Sigma(y_i - \bar{y})^2 \tag{14.9}$$

The sum at the bottom of the last column in Table 14.4 is the total sum of squares for Armand's Pizza Parlors; it is SST = 15,730.

In Figure 14.6 we show the estimated regression line $\hat{y} = 60 + 5x$ and the line corresponding to $\bar{y} = 130$. Note that the points cluster more closely around the estimated regression line than they do about the line $\bar{y} = 130$. For example, for the 10th restaurant in the sample we see that the error is much larger when $\bar{y} = 130$ is used as an estimate of $y_{10}$ than when $\hat{y}_{10} = 60 + 5(26) = 190$ is used. We can think of SST as a measure of how well the observations cluster about the $\bar{y}$ line and SSE as a measure of how well the observations cluster about the $\hat{y}$ line.

To measure how much the $\hat{y}$ values on the estimated regression line deviate from $\bar{y}$, another sum of squares is computed. This sum of squares, called the *sum of squares due to regression,* is denoted SSR.

**Sum of Squares Due to Regression**

$$SSR = \Sigma(\hat{y}_i - \bar{y})^2 \tag{14.10}$$

From the preceding discussion, we should expect that SST, SSR, and SSE are related. Indeed, the relationship among these three sums of squares provides one of the most important results in statistics.

SSR can be thought of as the explained portion of SST, and SSE can be thought of as the unexplained portion of SST.

**Relationship Among SST, SSR, and SSE**

$$SST = SSR + SSE \tag{14.11}$$

where

$$SST = \text{total sum of squares}$$
$$SSR = \text{sum of squares due to regression}$$
$$SSE = \text{sum of squares due to error}$$

Equation (14.11) shows that the total sum of squares can be partitioned into two components, the regression sum of squares and the sum of squares due to error. Hence, if the values of any two of these sum of squares are known, the third sum of squares can be computed easily. For instance, in the Armand's Pizza Parlors example, we already know that SSE = 1530 and SST = 15,730; therefore, solving for SSR in equation (14.11), we find that the sum of squares due to regression is

$$SSR = SST - SSE = 15,730 - 1530 = 14,200$$

**FIGURE 14.6**    DEVIATIONS ABOUT THE ESTIMATED REGRESSION LINE AND THE LINE $y = \bar{y}$ FOR ARMAND'S PIZZA PARLORS

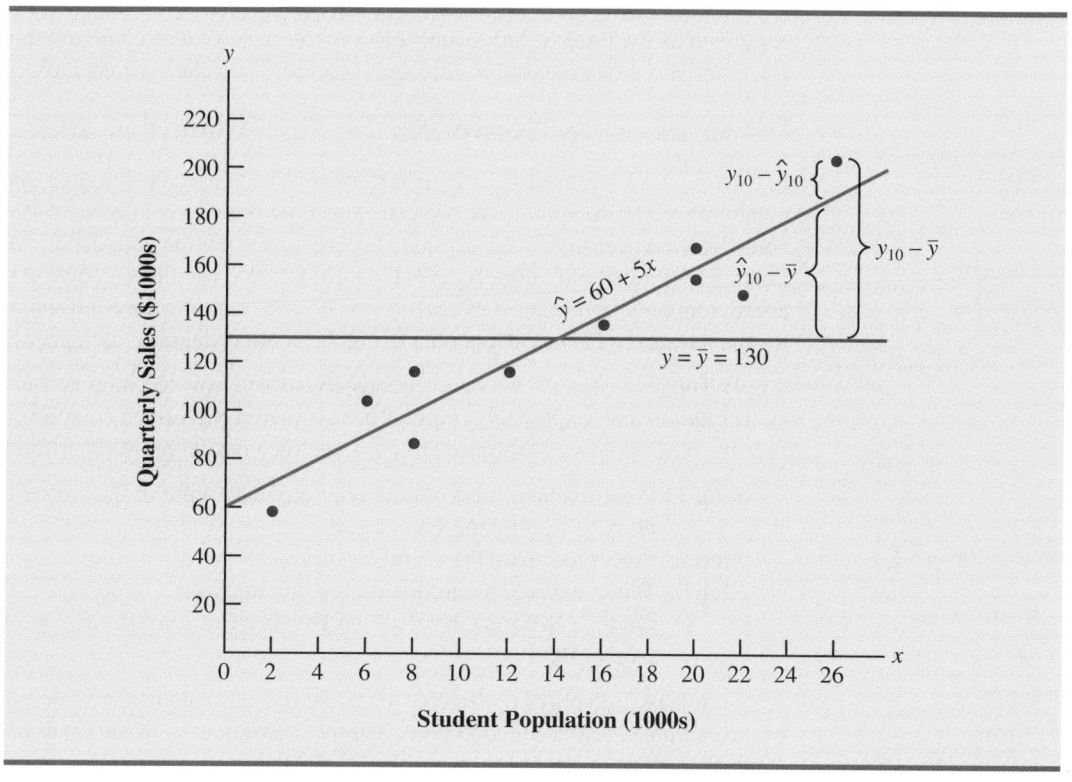

Now let us see how the three sums of squares, SST, SSR, and SSE, can be used to provide a measure of the goodness of fit for the estimated regression equation. The estimated regression equation would provide a perfect fit if every value of the dependent variable $y_i$ happened to lie on the estimated regression line. In this case, $y_i - \hat{y}_i$ would be zero for each observation, resulting in SSE = 0. Because SST = SSR + SSE, we see that for a perfect fit SSR must equal SST, and the ratio (SSR/SST) must equal one. Poorer fits will result in larger values for SSE. Solving for SSE in equation (14.11), we see that SSE = SST − SSR. Hence, the largest value for SSE (and hence the poorest fit) occurs when SSR = 0 and SSE = SST.

The ratio SSR/SST, which will be between zero and one, is used to evaluate the goodness of fit for the estimated regression equation. This ratio is called the *coefficient of determination* and is denoted by $r^2$.

**Coefficient of Determination**

$$r^2 = \frac{SSR}{SST} \qquad (14.12)$$

For the Armand's Pizza Parlors example, the value of the coefficient of determination is

$$r^2 = \frac{SSR}{SST} = \frac{14{,}200}{15{,}730} = .9027$$

When we express the coefficient of determination as a percentage, $r^2$ can be interpreted as the percentage of the total sum of squares that can be explained by using the estimated regression equation. For Armand's Pizza Parlors, we can conclude that 90.27% of the total sum of squares can be explained by using the estimated regression equation $\hat{y} = 60 + 5x$ to predict quarterly sales. In other words, 90.27% of the variability in quarterly sales can be explained by the linear relationship between the size of the student population and quarterly sales. We should be pleased to find such a good fit for the estimated regression equation.

## Using Excel to Compute the Coefficient of Determination

In Section 14.2 we used Excel's Chart Wizard to construct a scatter diagram for the Armand's Pizza Parlors data. We then showed how options available on Excel's Chart menu could be used to compute the estimated regression equation and display the graph of the estimated regression equation. Excel's Chart menu also provides an option for computing the coefficient of determination. We will show how to compute the coefficient of determination for the Armand's Pizza Parlors data using the scatter diagram that appears in Figure 14.5.

**Apply Tools:**   Because we have already illustrated how to compute the estimated regression equation and display the graph of the estimated regression equation, we will only provide the additional steps required to compute the coefficient of determination.

**Step 1.** Position the mouse pointer over any data point in the scatter diagram and right click to display the **Chart** menu
**Step 2.** Select the **Add Trendline** option
**Step 3.** When the Add Trendline dialog box appears:
On the **Options** tab select the **Display R-squared value on chart** box
Click **OK**

Figure 14.7 displays the scatter diagram, the estimated regression equation, the graph of the estimated regression equation, and the coefficient of determination for the Armand's Pizza Parlors data. We see that $r^2 = .9027$.

## Correlation Coefficient

In Chapter 3 we introduced the **correlation coefficient** as a descriptive measure of the strength of linear association between two variables, $x$ and $y$. Values of the correlation coefficient are always between $-1$ and $+1$. A value of $+1$ indicates that the two variables $x$ and $y$ are perfectly related in a positive linear sense. That is, all data points are on a straight line that has a positive slope. A value of $-1$ indicates that $x$ and $y$ are perfectly related in a negative linear sense, with all data points on a straight line that has a negative slope. Values of the correlation coefficient close to zero indicate that $x$ and $y$ are not linearly related.

In Section 3.5 we presented the equation for computing the sample correlation coefficient. If a regression analysis has already been performed and the coefficient of determination $r^2$ has been computed, the sample correlation coefficient can be computed as follows.

**Sample Correlation Coefficient**

$$r_{xy} = (\text{sign of } b_1)\sqrt{\text{Coefficient of Determination}}$$

$$= (\text{sign of } b_1)\sqrt{r^2} \tag{14.13}$$

where

$b_1 = $ the slope of the estimated regression equation $\hat{y} = b_0 + b_1 x$

**FIGURE 14.7** USING EXCEL TO COMPUTE THE COEFFICIENT OF DETERMINATION

| | A | B | C | D | E | F | G | H | I | J |
|---|---|---|---|---|---|---|---|---|---|---|
| 1 | Restaurant | Population | Sales | | | | | | | |
| 2 | 1 | 2 | 58 | | | | | | | |
| 3 | 2 | 6 | 105 | | | | | | | |
| 4 | 3 | 8 | 88 | | | | | | | |
| 5 | 4 | 8 | 118 | | | | | | | |
| 6 | 5 | 12 | 117 | | | | | | | |
| 7 | 6 | 16 | 137 | | | | | | | |
| 8 | 7 | 20 | 157 | | | | | | | |
| 9 | 8 | 20 | 169 | | | | | | | |
| 10 | 9 | 22 | 149 | | | | | | | |
| 11 | 10 | 26 | 202 | | | | | | | |

$y = 5x + 60$

$R^2 = 0.9027$

The sign for the sample correlation coefficient is positive if the estimated regression equation has a positive slope ($b_1 > 0$) and negative if the estimated regression equation has a negative slope ($b_1 < 0$).

For the Armand's Pizza Parlor example, the value of the coefficient of determination corresponding to the estimated regression equation $\hat{y} = 60 + 5x$ is .9027. Because the slope of the estimated regression equation is positive, equation (14.13) shows that the sample correlation coefficient is $+\sqrt{.9027} = +.9501$. A sample correlation coefficient of $r_{xy} = +.9501$ indicates a strong positive linear association between $x$ and $y$.

In the case of a linear relationship between two variables, both the coefficient of determination and the sample correlation coefficient provide measures of the strength of the relationship. The coefficient of determination provides a measure between zero and one whereas the sample correlation coefficient provides a measure between $-1$ and $+1$. Although the sample correlation coefficient is restricted to a linear relationship between two variables, the coefficient of determination can be used for nonlinear relationships and for relationships that have two or more independent variables. In that sense, the coefficient of determination has a wider range of applicability.

## NOTES AND COMMENTS

1. In developing the least squares estimated regression equation and computing the coefficient of determination, we made no probabilistic assumptions and no statistical tests for significance of the relationship between $x$ and $y$. Larger values of $r^2$ simply imply that the least squares line provides a better fit to the data; that is, the observations are more closely grouped about the least squares line. But, using only $r^2$, we can draw no conclusion about whether the relationship between $x$ and $y$ is statistically significant. Such a conclusion must be based on considerations that involve the sample size and the properties of the appropriate sampling distributions of the least squares estimators.

2. As a practical matter, for typical data found in the social sciences, values of $r^2$ as low as .25 are often considered useful. For data in the physical and life sciences, $r^2$ values of .60 or greater are often found; in fact, in some cases, $r^2$ values greater than .90 can be found. In business applications, $r^2$ values vary greatly, depending on the unique characteristics of each application.

## EXERCISES

### Methods

**15.** The data from Exercise 1 follow.

| $x_i$ | 1 | 2 | 3 | 4 | 5 |
|---|---|---|---|---|---|
| $y_i$ | 3 | 7 | 5 | 11 | 14 |

The estimated regression equation for these data is $\hat{y} = .20 + 2.60x$.
   a. Compute SSE, SST, and SSR using equations (14.8), (14.9), and (14.10).
   b. Compute the coefficient of determination $r^2$. Comment on the goodness of fit.
   c. Compute the sample correlation coefficient.

**16.** The data from Exercise 2 follow.

| $x_i$ | 2 | 3 | 5 | 1 | 8 |
|---|---|---|---|---|---|
| $y_i$ | 25 | 25 | 20 | 30 | 16 |

The estimated regression equation for these data is $\hat{y} = 30.33 + 1.88x$.
   a. Compute SSE, SST, and SSR.
   b. Compute the coefficient of determination $r^2$. Comment on the goodness of fit.
   c. Compute the sample correlation coefficient.

**17.** The data from Exercise 3 follow.

| $x_i$ | 2 | 4 | 5 | 7 | 8 |
|---|---|---|---|---|---|
| $y_i$ | 2 | 3 | 2 | 6 | 4 |

The estimated regression equation for these data is $\hat{y} = .75 + .51x$. What percentage of the total sum of squares can be accounted for by the estimated regression equation? What is the value of the sample correlation coefficient?

### Applications

**18.** The following data are the grade point averages $x$ and the monthly salaries $y$ for students who had obtained a bachelor's degree in business administration with a major in information systems. The estimated regression equation for these data is $\hat{y} = 1790.5 + 581.1x$.

| GPA | Monthly Salary ($) |
|---|---|
| 2.6 | 3300 |
| 3.4 | 3600 |

| GPA | Monthly Salary ($) |
|-----|--------------------|
| 3.6 | 4000 |
| 3.2 | 3500 |
| 3.5 | 3900 |
| 2.9 | 3600 |

a. Compute SST, SSR, and SSE.
b. Compute the coefficient of determination $r^2$. Comment on the goodness of fit.
c. What is the value of the sample correlation coefficient?

19. The data from Exercise 7 follow.

| Date | $x$ = DJIA | $y$ = S&P |
|------|-----------|-----------|
| February 11 | 10425 | 1387 |
| February 18 | 10220 | 1346 |
| February 25 | 9862 | 1333 |
| March 3 | 10367 | 1409 |
| March 10 | 9929 | 1395 |
| March 17 | 10595 | 1464 |
| March 24 | 11113 | 1527 |
| March 31 | 10922 | 1499 |
| April 7 | 11111 | 1516 |
| April 14 | 10306 | 1357 |

**CD** file

DowS&P

The estimated regression equation for these data is $\hat{y} = -137.63 + .1489x$. What percentage of the total sum of squares can be accounted for by the estimated regression equation? Comment on the goodness of fit. What is the sample correlation coefficient?

20. The typical household income and typical home price for a sample of 18 cities follow (*Places Rated Almanac*, 2000). Data are in thousands of dollars.

| City | Income | Home Price |
|------|--------|-----------|
| Akron, OH | 74.1 | 114.9 |
| Atlanta, GA | 82.4 | 126.9 |
| Birmingham, AL | 71.2 | 130.9 |
| Bismarck, ND | 62.8 | 92.8 |
| Cleveland, OH | 79.2 | 135.8 |
| Columbia, SC | 66.8 | 116.7 |
| Denver, CO | 82.6 | 161.9 |
| Detroit, MI | 85.3 | 145.0 |
| Fort Lauderdale, FL | 75.8 | 145.3 |
| Hartford, CT | 89.1 | 162.1 |
| Lancaster, PA | 75.2 | 125.9 |
| Madison, WI | 78.8 | 145.2 |
| Naples, FL | 100.0 | 173.6 |
| Nashville, TN | 77.3 | 125.9 |
| Philadelphia, PA | 87.0 | 151.5 |
| Savannah, GA | 67.8 | 108.1 |
| Toledo, OH | 71.2 | 101.1 |
| Washington, DC | 97.4 | 191.9 |

**CD** file

Cities

a. Use these data to develop an estimated regression equation that could be used to estimate the typical home price for a city given the typical household income.
b. Compute $r^2$. Would you feel comfortable using this estimated regression equation to estimate the typical home price for a city?
c. Estimate the typical home price for a city that has a typical household income of $95,000.

**21.** An important application of regression analysis in accounting is in the estimation of cost. By collecting data on volume and cost and using the least squares method to develop an estimated regression equation relating volume and cost, an accountant can estimate the cost associated with a particular manufacturing operation. Consider the following sample of production volumes and total cost data for a manufacturing operation.

| Production Volume (units) | Total Cost ($) |
|---|---|
| 400 | 4000 |
| 450 | 5000 |
| 550 | 5400 |
| 600 | 5900 |
| 700 | 6400 |
| 750 | 7000 |

**a.** Use these data to develop an estimated regression equation that could be used to predict the total cost for a given production volume.
**b.** What is the variable, or additional, cost per unit produced?
**c.** Compute the coefficient of determination. What percentage of the variation in total cost can be explained by production volume?
**d.** The company's production schedule shows 500 units must be produced next month. What is the estimated total cost for this operation?

**22.** Are company presidents and chief executive officers paid according to the profit performance of the company? The following table lists corporate data on percentage change in return on equity over a 2-year period and percentage change in the pay of presidents and chief executive officers immediately after the 2-year period (*Business Week,* April 21, 1997).

| Company | 2-Year Change in Return on Equity (%) | Change in Executive Compensation (%) |
|---|---|---|
| Dow Chemical | 201.3 | 18 |
| Rohm & Haas | 146.5 | 28 |
| Morton International | 76.7 | 10 |
| Union Carbide | 158.2 | 28 |
| Praxair | −34.9 | 15 |
| Air Products & Chemicals | 73.2 | −9 |
| Eastman Chemical | −7.9 | −20 |

**a.** Develop the estimated regression equation with the 2-year percentage change in return on equity as the independent variable.
**b.** Compute $r^2$. Would you feel comfortable using the percentage change in return on equity over a 2-year period to predict the percentage change in the pay of presidents and chief executive officers? Discuss.
**c.** What is the sample correlation coefficient? Does it reflect a strong or weak relationship between return on equity and executive compensation?

## 14.4 MODEL ASSUMPTIONS

In regression analysis, we begin by making an assumption about the appropriate model for the relationship between the dependent variable and the independent variable. In the case of simple linear regression, the assumed regression model is

$$y = \beta_0 + \beta_1 x + \epsilon$$

Then, the least squares method is used to develop values for $b_0$ and $b_1$, the estimates of the model parameters $\beta_0$ and $\beta_1$, respectively. The resulting estimated regression equation is

$$\hat{y} = b_0 + b_1 x$$

We saw that the value of the coefficient of determination ($r^2$) is a measure of the goodness of fit of the estimated regression equation. However, even with a large value of $r^2$, the estimated regression equation should not be used until further analysis of the appropriateness of the assumed model has been conducted. An important step in determining whether the assumed model is appropriate involves testing for the significance of the relationship. The tests of significance in regression analysis are based on the following assumptions about the error term $\epsilon$.

---

**Assumptions About the Error Term $\epsilon$ in the Regression Model**

$$y = \beta_0 + \beta_1 x + \epsilon$$

1. The error term $\epsilon$ is a random variable with a mean or expected value of zero; that is, $E(\epsilon) = 0$.
   *Implication:* Because $\beta_0$ and $\beta_1$ are constants, $E(\beta_0) = \beta_0$ and $E(\beta_1) = \beta_1$; thus, for a given value of $x$, the expected value of $y$ is

   $$E(y) = \beta_0 + \beta_1 x \qquad\qquad \textbf{(14.14)}$$

   As we indicated previously, (14.14) is referred to as the regression equation.

2. The variance of $\epsilon$, denoted by $\sigma^2$, is the same for all values of $x$.
   *Implication:* The variance of $y$ at a given value of $x$ equals $\sigma^2$ and is the same for all values of $x$.

3. The values of $\epsilon$ are independent.
   *Implication:* The value of $\epsilon$ for a particular value of $x$ is not related to the value of $\epsilon$ for any other value of $x$; thus, the value of $y$ for a particular value of $x$ is not related to the value of $y$ for any other value of $x$.

4. The error term $\epsilon$ is a normally distributed random variable.
   *Implication:* Because $y$ is a linear function of $\epsilon$, $y$ is also a normally distributed random variable.

---

Figure 14.8 is an illustration of the model assumptions and their implications; note that in this graphical interpretation, the value of $E(y)$ changes according to the specific value of $x$ considered. However, regardless of the $x$ value, the probability distribution of $\epsilon$ and hence the probability distributions of $y$ are normally distributed, each with the same variance. The specific value of the error $\epsilon$ at any particular point depends on whether the actual value of $y$ is greater than or less than $E(y)$.

At this point, we must keep in mind that we are also making an assumption or hypothesis about the form of the relationship between $x$ and $y$. That is, we have assumed that a straight line represented by $\beta_0 + \beta_1 x$ is the basis for the relationship between the variables. We must not lose sight of the fact that some other model, for instance $y = \beta_0 + \beta_1 x^2 + \epsilon$, may turn out to be a better model for the underlying relationship.

**FIGURE 14.8**     ASSUMPTIONS FOR THE REGRESSION MODEL

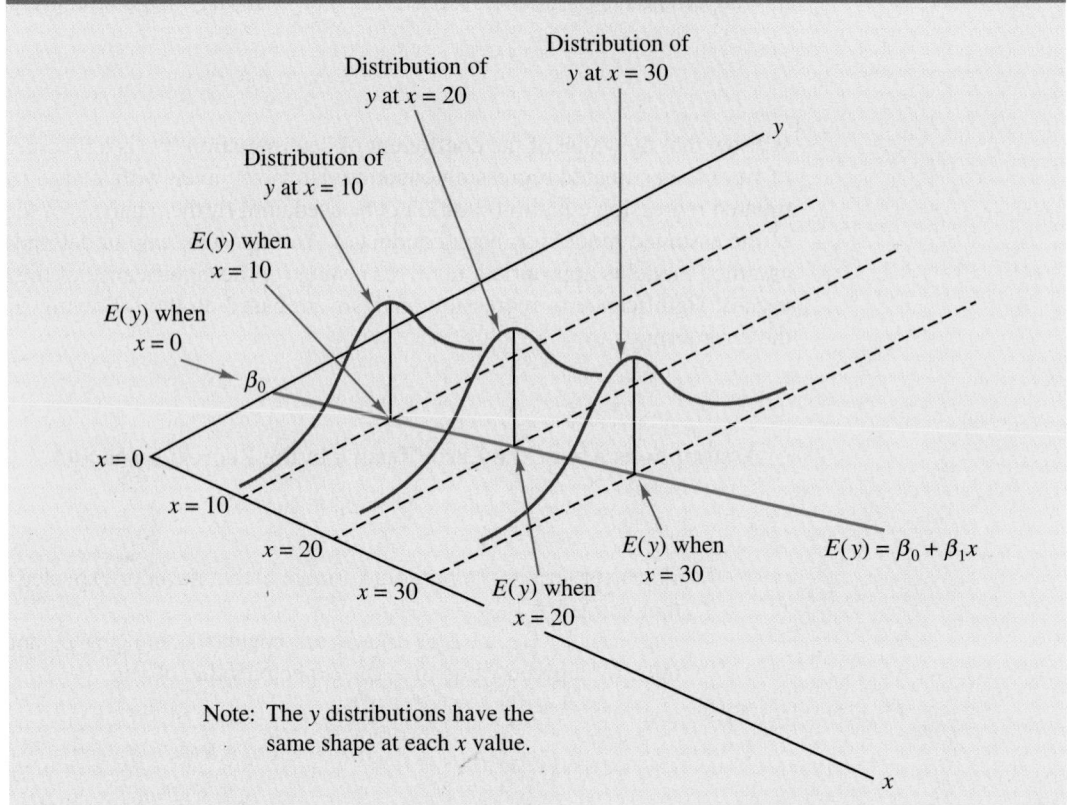

Note: The $y$ distributions have the
same shape at each $x$ value.

## 14.5    TESTING FOR SIGNIFICANCE

In a simple linear regression equation the mean or expected value of $y$ is a linear function of $x$: $E(y) = \beta_0 + \beta_1 x$. If the value of $\beta_1$ is zero, $E(y) = \beta_0 + (0)x = \beta_0$. In this case, the mean value of $y$ does not depend on the value of $x$ and hence we would conclude that $x$ and $y$ are not linearly related. Alternatively, if the value of $\beta_1$ is not equal to zero, we would conclude that the two variables are related. Thus, to test for a significant regression relationship, we must conduct a hypothesis test to determine whether the value of $\beta_1$ is zero. The tests used require an estimate of $\sigma^2$, the variance of $\epsilon$.

### Estimate of $\sigma^2$

From the regression model and its assumptions we can conclude that $\sigma^2$, the variance of $\epsilon$, also represents the variance of the $y$ values about the regression line. Recall that the deviations of the $y$ values about the estimated regression line are called *residuals*. Thus, SSE, the sum of squared residuals, is a measure of the variability of the $y$ values about the estimated regression line. The **mean square error** (MSE) provides the estimate of $\sigma^2$; it is SSE divided by its degrees of freedom.

With $\hat{y}_i = b_0 + b_1 x_i$, SSE can be written as

$$SSE = \Sigma(y_i - \hat{y}_i)^2 = \Sigma(y_i - b_0 - b_1 x_i)^2$$

Every sum of squares has associated with it a number called its degrees of freedom. Statisticians have shown that SSE has $n - 2$ degrees of freedom because two parameters ($\beta_0$ and

$\beta_1$) must be estimated to compute SSE. Thus, the mean square error is computed by dividing SSE by $n - 2$. Because the value of MSE provides an estimate of $\sigma^2$, the notation $s^2$ is also used.

**Estimate of $\sigma^2$**

$$s^2 = \text{MSE} = \frac{\text{SSE}}{n - 2} \qquad (14.15)$$

In Section 14.3 we showed that for the Armand's Pizza Parlors example, SSE = 1530; hence,

$$s^2 = \text{MSE} = \frac{1530}{8} = 191.25$$

provides an estimate of $\sigma^2$.

To estimate $\sigma$ we take the square root of $s^2$.

**Estimate of $\sigma$**

$$s = \sqrt{\text{MSE}} = \sqrt{\frac{\text{SSE}}{n - 2}} \qquad (14.16)$$

For the Armand's Pizza Parlors example, $s = \sqrt{\text{MSE}} = \sqrt{191.25} = 13.829$. In the following discussion, we will use $s$ to conduct tests for a significant relationship between $x$ and $y$.

## $t$ Test

The simple linear regression model is $y = \beta_0 + \beta_1 x + \epsilon$. If $x$ and $y$ are linearly related, we must have $\beta_1 \neq 0$. The purpose of the $t$ test is to see whether we can use the sample data to conclude that $\beta_1 \neq 0$. We will conduct the following hypothesis test about $\beta_1$.

$$H_0: \beta_1 = 0$$
$$H_a: \beta_1 \neq 0$$

If $H_0$ is rejected, we will conclude that $\beta_1 \neq 0$ and that the two variables have a statistically significant relationship. However, if $H_0$ cannot be rejected, we will have insufficient evidence to conclude that a significant relationship exists. The properties of the sampling distribution of $b_1$, the least squares estimator of $\beta_1$, provide the basis for the hypothesis test.

First, let us consider what would have happened if we had used a different random sample for the same regression study. For example, suppose that Armand's Pizza Parlors had used the quarterly sales data for a different sample of 10 restaurants. A regression analysis of this new sample might result in an estimated regression equation similar to our previous estimated regression equation $\hat{y} = 60 + 5x$. However, it is doubtful that we would obtain exactly the same equation (with an intercept of exactly 60 and a slope of exactly 5). Indeed,

$b_0$ and $b_1$, the least squares estimators, are sample statistics that have their own sampling distributions. The properties of the sampling distribution of $b_1$ follow.

---

**Sampling Distribution of $b_1$**

The standard deviation of $b_1$ is also referred to as the standard error of $b_1$.

*Expected Value*

$$E(b_1) = \beta_1$$

*Standard Deviation*

$$\sigma_{b_1} = \frac{\sigma}{\sqrt{\Sigma(x_i - \bar{x})^2}} \qquad (14.17)$$

*Distribution Form*

Normal

---

Note that the expected value of $b_1$ is equal to $\beta_1$, so $b_1$ is an unbiased estimator of $\beta_1$.

Because we do not know the value of $\sigma$, we develop an estimate of $\sigma_{b_1}$, denoted $s_{b_1}$, by estimating $\sigma$ with $s$ in equation (14.17). Thus, we obtain the following estimate of $\sigma_{b_1}$.

---

**Estimated Standard Deviation of $b_1$**

$s_{b_1}$ provides an estimate of the standard error of $b_1$.

$$s_{b_1} = \frac{s}{\sqrt{\Sigma(x_i - \bar{x})^2}} \qquad (14.18)$$

---

For Armand's Pizza Parlors, $s = 13.829$ and $\Sigma(x_i - \bar{x})^2 = 568$ (see Table 14.2). Thus, we have

$$s_{b_1} = \frac{13.829}{\sqrt{568}} = .5803$$

as the estimated standard deviation of $b_1$.

The $t$ test for a significant relationship is based on the fact that the test statistic

$$\frac{b_1 - \beta_1}{s_{b_1}}$$

follows a $t$ distribution with $n - 2$ degrees of freedom. If the null hypothesis is true, then $\beta_1 = 0$ and $t = b_1/s_{b_1}$. With $b_1/s_{b_1}$ as the test statistic, the steps of the $t$ test for a significant relationship are as follows.

---

**$t$ Test for Significance in Simple Linear Regression**

$$H_0: \beta_1 = 0$$
$$H_a: \beta_1 \neq 0$$

**Test Statistic**

$$t = \frac{b_1}{s_{b_1}} \qquad (14.19)$$

**Rejection Rule**

Using test statistic:   Reject $H_0$ if $t < -t_{\alpha/2}$ or if $t > t_{\alpha/2}$

Using $p$-value:            Reject $H_0$ if $p$-value $< \alpha$

where $t_{\alpha/2}$ is based on a $t$ distribution with $n - 2$ degrees of freedom.

Let us conduct this test of significance for Armand's Pizza Parlors at the $\alpha = .01$ level of significance. The test statistic (14.19) is

$$t = \frac{b_1}{s_{b_1}} = \frac{5}{.5803} = 8.62$$

From Table 2 of Appendix B we find that the two-tailed $t$ value corresponding to $\alpha = .01$ and $n - 2 = 10 - 2 = 8$ degrees of freedom is $t_{.005} = 3.355$. With $8.62 > 3.355$, we reject $H_0$ and conclude at the .01 level of significance that $\beta_1$ is not equal to zero. The statistical evidence is sufficient to conclude that we have a significant relationship between student population and sales.

The $p$-value criterion can also be used for this hypothesis test. The two-tailed $p$-value associated with the test statistic $t = 8.62$ is $.0000255$. With $.0000255 < \alpha = .01$ we would reject $H_0$ and conclude that we have a significant relationship between student population and sales. In the next section, we will see that the $p$-value for this hypothesis test is computed automatically as part of the output when we use Excel's regression tool.

*Excel's TDIST function can also be used to compute the $p$-value (see Chapter 9).*

## Confidence Interval for $\beta_1$

The form of a confidence interval for $\beta_1$ is as follows:

$$b_1 \pm t_{\alpha/2} s_{b_1}$$

The point estimator is $b_1$ and the margin of error is $t_{\alpha/2} s_{b_1}$. The confidence coefficient associated with this interval is $1 - \alpha$, and $t_{\alpha/2}$ is the $t$ value providing an area of $\alpha/2$ in the upper tail of a $t$ distribution with $n - 2$ degrees of freedom. For example, suppose that we wanted to develop a 99% confidence interval estimate of $\beta_1$ for Armand's Pizza Parlors. From Table 2 of Appendix B we find that the $t$ value corresponding to $\alpha = .01$ and $n - 2 = 10 - 2 = 8$ degrees of freedom is $t_{.005} = 3.355$. Thus, the 99% confidence interval estimate of $\beta_1$ is

$$b_1 \pm t_{\alpha/2} s_{b_1} = 5 \pm 3.355(.5803) = 5 \pm 1.95$$

or 3.05 to 6.95.

In using the $t$ test for significance, the hypotheses tested were

$$H_0: \beta_1 = 0$$
$$H_a: \beta_1 \neq 0$$

At the $\alpha = .01$ level of significance, we can use the 99% confidence interval as an alternative for drawing the hypothesis testing conclusion for the Armand's data. Because 0, the hypothesized value of $\beta_1$, is not included in the confidence interval (3.05 to 6.95), we can reject $H_0$ and conclude that a significant statistical relationship exists between student population and sales. In general, a confidence interval can be used to test any two-sided hypothesis about $\beta_1$. If the hypothesized value of $\beta_1$ is contained in the confidence interval, do not reject $H_0$. Otherwise, reject $H_0$.

## *F* **Test**

An *F* test, based on the *F* probability distribution, can also be used to test for significance in regression. With only one independent variable, the *F* test will provide the same conclusion as the *t* test; that is, if the *t* test indicates $\beta_1 \neq 0$ and hence a significant relationship, the *F* test will also indicate a significant relationship. But with more than one independent variable, only the *F* test can be used to test for an overall significant relationship.

The logic behind the use of the *F* test for determining whether the regression relationship is statistically significant is based on the development of two independent estimates of $\sigma^2$. We have just seen that MSE provides an estimate of $\sigma^2$. If the null hypothesis $H_0: \beta_1 = 0$ is true, the sum of squares due to regression, SSR, divided by its degrees of freedom provides another independent estimate of $\sigma^2$. This estimate is called the *mean square due to regression,* or simply the *mean square regression,* and is denoted MSR. In general,

$$\text{MSR} = \frac{\text{SSR}}{\text{Regression Degrees of Freedom}}$$

For the models we consider in this text, the regression degrees of freedom is always equal to the number of independent variables; thus,

$$\text{MSR} = \frac{\text{SSR}}{\text{Number of Independent Variables}} \qquad \textbf{(14.20)}$$

Because only one independent variable is used in the Armand's Pizza Parlors example, we have MSR = SSR/1 = SSR. Hence, for Armand's Pizza Parlors, MSR = SSR = 14,200.

If the null hypothesis ($H_0: \beta_1 = 0$) is true, MSR and MSE are two independent estimates of $\sigma^2$ and the sampling distribution of MSR/MSE follows an *F* distribution with numerator degrees of freedom equal to one and denominator degrees of freedom equal to $n - 2$. Therefore, when $\beta_1 = 0$, the value of MSR/MSE should be close to one. However, if the null hypothesis is false ($\beta_1 \neq 0$), MSR will overestimate $\sigma^2$ and the value of MSR/MSE will be inflated; thus, large values of MSR/MSE lead to the rejection of $H_0$ and the conclusion that the relationship between *x* and *y* is statistically significant. A summary of how the *F* test is used to test for a significant relationship follows.

*F* **Test for Significance**

$$H_0: \beta_1 = 0$$
$$H_a: \beta_1 \neq 0$$

**Test Statistic**

$$F = \frac{\text{MSR}}{\text{MSE}} \qquad \textbf{(14.21)}$$

**Rejection Rule**

Using test statistic:   Reject $H_0$ if $F > F_\alpha$

Using $p$-value:       Reject $H_0$ if $p$-value $< \alpha$

where $F_\alpha$ is based on an $F$ distribution with 1 degree of freedom in the numerator and $n - 2$ degrees of freedom in the denominator

Let us conduct the $F$ test for the Armand's Pizza Parlors example at the $\alpha = .01$ level of significance. The test statistic is

$$F = \frac{\text{MSR}}{\text{MSE}} = \frac{14{,}200}{191.25} = 74.25$$

*The F test and the t test provide identical results for simple linear regression.*

From Table 4 of Appendix B we find that the $F$ value corresponding to $\alpha = .01$ with one degree of freedom in the numerator and $n - 2 = 10 - 2 = 8$ degrees of freedom in the denominator is $F_{.01} = 11.26$. With $74.25 > 11.26$, we reject $H_0$ and conclude at the .01 level of significance that $\beta_1$ is not equal to zero. The $F$ test has provided the statistical evidence necessary to conclude that we have a significant relationship between student population and sales.

*Excel's FDIST function can also be used to compute the p-value.*

We stated at the beginning of this subsection that, for simple linear regression, the $F$ test would provide the same hypothesis testing conclusion as the $t$ test. The $p$-value associated with $F = 74.25$ is .0000255. This $p$-value is the same as found for the $t$ test in the previous subsection and confirms our earlier comment that the $F$ test and the $t$ test lead to the same conclusion. In the next section, we will see that the $p$-value for the $F$ test is computed automatically as part of the output when we use Excel's regression tool.

In Chapter 13 we covered analysis of variance (ANOVA) and showed how an **ANOVA table** could be used to provide a convenient summary of the computational aspects of analysis of variance. A similar ANOVA table can be used to summarize the results of the $F$ test for significance in regression. Table 14.5 is the general form of the ANOVA table for regression studies involving one independent variable. Table 14.6 is the ANOVA table with the $F$ test computations we have just performed for Armand's Pizza Parlors. Regression, Error, and Total are listed as the three sources of variation, with SSR, SSE, and SST appearing as the corresponding sum of squares in column two. The degrees of freedom, 1 for Regression, $n - 2$ for Error, and $n - 1$ for Total, are shown in column three. Column 4 contains

**TABLE 14.5**    GENERAL FORM OF THE ANOVA TABLE FOR SIMPLE LINEAR REGRESSION

*In every analysis of variance table the total sum of squares is the sum of the regression sum of squares and the error sum of squares; in addition, the total degrees of freedom is the sum of the regression degrees of freedom and the error degrees of freedom.*

| Source of Variation | Sum of Squares | Degrees of Freedom | Mean Square | $F$ |
|---|---|---|---|---|
| Regression | SSR | 1 | $\text{MSR} = \dfrac{\text{SSR}}{1}$ | $F = \dfrac{\text{MSR}}{\text{MSE}}$ |
| Error | SSE | $n - 2$ | $\text{MSE} = \dfrac{\text{SSE}}{n - 2}$ | |
| Total | SST | $n - 1$ | | |

**TABLE 14.6**   ANOVA TABLE FOR THE ARMAND'S PIZZA PARLORS PROBLEM

| Source of Variation | Sum of Squares | Degrees of Freedom | Mean Square | F |
|---|---|---|---|---|
| Regression | 14,200 | 1 | $\dfrac{14,200}{1} = 14,200$ | $\dfrac{14,200}{191.25} = 74.25$ |
| Error | 1,530 | 8 | $\dfrac{1530}{8} = 191.25$ | |
| Total | 15,730 | 9 | | |

the values of MSR and MSE, and column 5 contains the value of $F = $ MSR/MSE. Almost all computer printouts of regression analysis include an ANOVA table summary.

## Some Cautions About the Interpretation of Significance Tests

Regression analysis, which can be used to identify how variables are associated with one another, cannot be used as evidence of a cause-and-effect relationship.

Rejecting the null hypothesis $H_0: \beta_1 = 0$ and concluding that the relationship between $x$ and $y$ is significant does not enable us to conclude that a cause-and-effect relationship is present between $x$ and $y$. Concluding a cause-and-effect relationship exists is warranted only if the analyst has theoretical justification that the relationship is in fact causal. In the Armand's Pizza Parlors example, we can conclude that a significant relationship exists between the size of the student population $x$ and quarterly sales $y$; moreover, the estimated regression equation $\hat{y} = 60 + 5x$ provides the least squares estimate of the relationship. We cannot, however, conclude that changes in student population $x$ cause changes in quarterly sales $y$ just because we have identified a statistically significant relationship. The appropriateness of such a cause-and-effect conclusion depends on the amount of supporting theoretical justification and on good judgment on the part of the analyst. In this case, Armand's managers had good reason to believe that increases in the student population were a likely cause of increased quarterly sales. Thus, the result of the significance test enabled them to conclude that a cause-and-effect relationship was present.

In addition, just because we are able to reject $H_0: \beta_1 = 0$ and demonstrate statistical significance does not enable us to conclude that the relationship between $x$ and $y$ is linear. We can state only that $x$ and $y$ are related and that a linear relationship explains a significant portion of the variability in $y$ over the range of values for $x$ observed in the sample. Figure 14.9 illustrates this situation. The test for significance has rejected the null hypothesis $H_0: \beta_1 = 0$ and has led to the conclusion that $x$ and $y$ are significantly related, but the figure shows that the actual relationship between $x$ and $y$ is not linear. Although the linear approximation provided by $\hat{y} = b_0 + b_1 x$ is good over the range of $x$ values observed in the sample, it becomes poor for $x$ values outside that range.

Given a significant relationship, we should feel confident in using the estimated regression equation for predictions corresponding to $x$ values within the range of the $x$ values observed in the sample. For Armand's Pizza Parlors, this range corresponds to values of $x$ between 2 and 26. But unless reasons indicate that the model is valid beyond this range, predictions outside the range of the independent variable should be made with caution. For Armand's Pizza Parlors, because the regression relationship has been found significant at the .01 level, we should feel confident using it to predict quarterly sales for restaurants where the associated student population is between 2000 and 26,000.

**FIGURE 14.9**   EXAMPLE OF A LINEAR APPROXIMATION OF A NONLINEAR
RELATIONSHIP

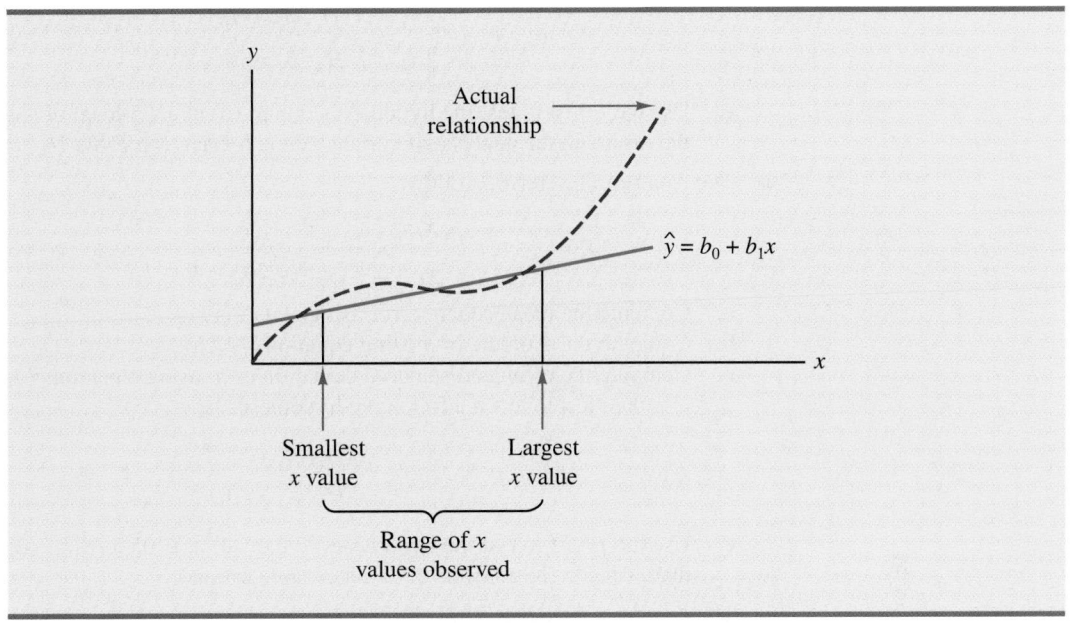

## NOTES AND COMMENTS

1. The assumptions made about the error term (Section 14.4) are what allow the tests of statistical significance in this section. The properties of the sampling distribution of $b_1$ and the subsequent $t$ and $F$ tests follow directly from these assumptions.

2. Do not confuse statistical significance with practical significance. With very large sample sizes, statistically significant results can be obtained for small values of $b_1$; in such cases, one must exercise care in concluding that the relationship has practical significance.

3. A test of significance for a linear relationship between $x$ and $y$ can also be performed by using the sample correlation coefficient $r_{xy}$. With $\rho_{xy}$ denoting the population correlation coefficient, the hypotheses are as follows.

$$H_0: \rho_{xy} = 0$$
$$H_a: \rho_{xy} \neq 0$$

A significant relationship can be concluded if $H_0$ is rejected. However, the $t$ and $F$ tests presented previously in this section give the same result as the test for significance using the correlation coefficient. Conducting a test for significance using the correlation coefficient therefore is not necessary if a $t$ or $F$ test has already been conducted.

## EXERCISES

### Methods

**23.** The data from Exercise 1 follow.

| $x_i$ | 1 | 2 | 3 | 4 | 5 |
|---|---|---|---|---|---|
| $y_i$ | 3 | 7 | 5 | 11 | 14 |

**a.** Compute the mean square error using equation (14.15).
**b.** Compute the estimate of $\sigma$ using equation (14.16).

   **c.** Compute the estimated standard deviation of $b_1$ using equation (14.18).

   **d.** Use the $t$ test to test the following hypotheses ($\alpha = .05$):

$$H_0: \beta_1 = 0$$
$$H_a: \beta_1 \neq 0$$

   **e.** Use the $F$ test to test the hypotheses in part (d) at a .05 level of significance. Present the results in the analysis of variance table format (see Table 14.5).

**24.** The data from Exercise 2 follow.

| $x_i$ | 2 | 3 | 5 | 1 | 8 |
|-------|-----|-----|-----|-----|-----|
| $y_i$ | 25 | 25 | 20 | 30 | 16 |

   **a.** Compute the mean square error using equation (14.15).

   **b.** Compute the estimate of $\sigma$ using equation (14.16).

   **c.** Compute the estimated standard deviation of $b_1$ using equation (14.18).

   **d.** Use the $t$ test to test the following hypotheses ($\alpha = .05$):

$$H_0: \beta_1 = 0$$
$$H_a: \beta_1 \neq 0$$

   **e.** Use the $F$ test to test the hypotheses in part (d) at a .05 level of significance. Present the results in the analysis of variance table format.

**25.** The data from Exercise 3 follow.

| $x_i$ | 2 | 4 | 5 | 7 | 8 |
|-------|-----|-----|-----|-----|-----|
| $y_i$ | 2 | 3 | 2 | 6 | 4 |

   **a.** Compute the estimate of $\sigma$.

   **b.** Test for a significant relationship by using the $t$ test. Use $\alpha = .05$.

   **c.** Use the $F$ test to test for a significant relationship. Use $\alpha = .05$. What is your conclusion?

## Applications

**26.** In Exercise 18 the data on grade point average and monthly salary were as follows.

| GPA | Monthly Salary ($) | GPA | Monthly Salary ($) |
|-----|-----|-----|-----|
| 2.6 | 3300 | 3.2 | 3500 |
| 3.4 | 3600 | 3.5 | 3900 |
| 3.6 | 4000 | 2.9 | 3600 |

   **a.** Does the $t$ test indicate a significant relationship between grade point average and monthly salary? What is your conclusion? Use $\alpha = .05$.

   **b.** Test for a significant relationship using the $F$ test. What is your conclusion? Use $\alpha = .05$.

   **c.** Show the ANOVA table.

**27.** Refer to Exercise 9, where an estimated regression equation relating years of experience and annual sales was developed. At a .05 level of significance, determine whether years of experience and annual sales are related.

**28.** Refer to Exercise 10, where an estimated regression equation relating the performance score and the overall rating for notebook PCs was developed. At the .05 level of significance, test whether these two variables are related. Show the ANOVA table. What is your conclusion?

**29.** Refer to Exercise 21, where data on production volume and cost were used to develop an estimated regression equation relating production volume and cost for a particular manufacturing operation. Using $\alpha = .05$, test whether the production volume is significantly related to the total cost. Show the ANOVA table. What is your conclusion?

**30.** Refer to Exercise 22, where the following data were used to determine whether company presidents and chief executive officers are paid on the basis of company profit performance (*Business Week,* April 21, 1997).

| Company | 2-Year Change in Return on Equity (%) | Change in Executive Compensation (%) |
|---|---|---|
| Dow Chemical | 201.3 | 18 |
| Rohm & Haas | 146.5 | 28 |
| Morton International | 76.7 | 10 |
| Union Carbide | 158.2 | 28 |
| Praxair | −34.9 | 15 |
| Air Products & Chemicals | 73.2 | −9 |
| Eastman Chemical | −7.9 | −20 |

Do these data indicate a significant relationship between the two variables? Conduct the appropriate statistical test and state your conclusion. Use $\alpha = .05$.

**31.** Refer to Exercise 20, where an estimated regression equation was developed relating typical household income and typical home price. Test whether the typical household income for a city and the typical home price are related at the .01 level of significance.

## 14.6  EXCEL'S REGRESSION TOOL

In previous sections of this chapter we have shown how Excel can be used for various tasks in a regression analysis. Excel also has a more comprehensive Regression tool. The Regression tool provides an analysis of all the concepts we have introduced. In this section we will illustrate how Excel's Regression tool can be used to perform a complete regression analysis, including statistical tests of significance for the Armand's data in Table 14.1.

### Using Excel's Regression Tool for the Armand's Pizza Parlors Problem

Refer to Figures 14.10 and 14.11 as we describe the tasks involved to use Excel's Regression tool to perform the regression analysis computations for the Armand's data.

**Enter Data:**   The labels Restaurant, Population, and Sales have been entered into cells A1:C1 of the worksheet. To identify each of the 10 observations, we entered the numbers 1 through 10 into cells A2:A11. The sample data have been entered into cells B2:C11.

**Apply Tools:**   The following steps describe how to use Excel to perform the regression analysis computations performed in Sections 14.2–14.5.

**Step 1.** Select the **Tools** pull-down menu
**Step 2.** Choose the **Data Analysis** option
**Step 3.** Choose **Regression** from the list of Analysis Tools
**Step 4.** When the Regression dialog box appears (see Figure 14.11):
  Enter C1:C11 in the **Input Y Range** box
  Enter B1:B11 in the **Input X Range** box
  Select **Labels**
  Select **Confidence Level**
  Enter 99 in the **Confidence Level** box
  Select **Output Range**
  Enter A13 in the **Output Range** box (to identify the upper left corner of the section of the worksheet where the output will appear)
  Click **OK**

**FIGURE 14.10    REGRESSION TOOL OUTPUT FOR ARMAND'S PIZZA PARLORS**

|    | A | B | C | D | E | F | G | H | I | J |
|----|---|---|---|---|---|---|---|---|---|---|
| 1 | Restaurant | Population | Sales | | | | | | | |
| 2 | 1 | 2 | 58 | | | | | | | |
| 3 | 2 | 6 | 105 | | | | | | | |
| 4 | 3 | 8 | 88 | | | | | | | |
| 5 | 4 | 8 | 118 | | | | | | | |
| 6 | 5 | 12 | 117 | | | | | | | |
| 7 | 6 | 16 | 137 | | | | | | | |
| 8 | 7 | 20 | 157 | | | | | | | |
| 9 | 8 | 20 | 169 | | | | | | | |
| 10 | 9 | 22 | 149 | | | | | | | |
| 11 | 10 | 26 | 202 | | | | | | | |
| 12 | | | | | | | | | | |
| 13 | SUMMARY OUTPUT | | | | | | | | | |
| 14 | | | | | | | | | | |
| 15 | *Regression Statistics* | | | | | | | | | |
| 16 | Multiple R | 0.9501 | | | | | | | | |
| 17 | R Square | 0.9027 | | | | | | | | |
| 18 | Adjusted R Square | 0.8906 | | | | | | | | |
| 19 | Standard Error | 13.8293 | | | | | | | | |
| 20 | Observations | 10 | | | | | | | | |
| 21 | | | | | | | | | | |
| 22 | ANOVA | | | | | | | | | |
| 23 | | *df* | *SS* | *MS* | *F* | *Significance F* | | | | |
| 24 | Regression | 1 | 14200 | 14200 | 74.2484 | 2.55E-05 | | | | |
| 25 | Residual | 8 | 1530 | 191.25 | | | | | | |
| 26 | Total | 9 | 15730 | | | | | | | |
| 27 | | | | | | | | | | |
| 28 | | *Coefficients* | *Standard Error* | *t Stat* | *P-value* | *Lower 95%* | *Upper 95%* | *Lower 99.0%* | *Upper 99.0%* | |
| 29 | Intercept | 60 | 9.2260 | 6.5033 | 0.0002 | 38.7247 | 81.2753 | 29.0431 | 90.9569 | |
| 30 | Population | 5 | 0.5803 | 8.6167 | 2.55E-05 | 3.6619 | 6.3381 | 3.0530 | 6.9470 | |
| 31 | | | | | | | | | | |

The regression output, titled SUMMARY OUTPUT, begins with row 13 in Figure 14.10. Because Excel initially displays the output using standard column widths, many of the row and column labels are unreadable. In several places we have reformatted to improve readability. We have also reformatted cells displaying numerical values to a maximum of four decimal places. Numbers displayed using scientific notation have not been modified. Regression output in future figures will be similarly reformatted to improve readability.

*The Excel output can be reformatted to improve readability.*

The first section of the output, titled *Regression Statistics,* contains summary statistics such as the coefficient of determination (R Square). The second section of the output, titled ANOVA, contains the analysis of variance table. The last section of the output, which is not titled, contains the estimated regression coefficients and related information. Let us begin our interpretation of the regression output with the information contained in cells A28:I30.

## Interpretation of Estimated Regression Equation Output

The information in row 29 provides information about the $y$ intercept of the estimated regression line and the information in row 30 provides information about the slope of the estimated regression line. The $y$ intercept of the estimated regression line, $b_0 = 60$, is shown in cell B29, and the slope of the estimated regression line, $b_1 = 5$, is shown in cell B30. The label Intercept in cell A29 and the label Population in cell A30 are used to identify these two values.

In Section 14.5 we showed that the estimated standard deviation of $b_1$ is $s_{b_1} = .5803$. Note that the value in cell C30 is 0.5803. Thus, cell C30 contains the estimated standard deviation of $b_1$. As we indicated previously, the standard deviation of $b_1$ is also referred to as the stan-

**FIGURE 14.11**   REGRESSION DIALOG BOX FOR THE ARMAND'S PIZZA
PARLORS PROBLEM

dard error of $b_1$. Thus, $s_{b_1}$ provides an estimate of the standard error of $b_1$. The label Standard Error in cell C28 is Excel's way of indicating that the value in cell C30 is the estimate of the standard error, or standard deviation, of $b_1$.

In Section 14.5 we stated that the form of the null and alternative hypotheses needed to test for a significant relationship between population and sales are as follows:

$$H_0: \beta_1 = 0$$
$$H_a: \beta_1 \neq 0$$

Recall that the $t$ test for a significant relationship required the computation of the $t$ statistic, $t = b_1/s_{b_1}$. For the Armand's data, the value of $t$ that we computed was $t = 5/.5803 = 8.62$. Note that after rounding, the value in cell D30 is 8.62. The label in cell D28, $t$ Stat, reminds us that cell D30 contains the value of the $t$ test statistic.

$t$ **Test**   The information in cell E30 provides a means for conducting a test of significance. The value in cell E30 is the $p$-value associated with the $t$ test for significance. Excel has displayed the $p$-value using scientific notation. To obtain the decimal equivalent, we move the decimal point 5 places to the left; after rounding we obtain a value of .0000255. Thus, the $p$-value associated with the $t$ test for significance is .0000255. Given the level of significance $\alpha$, the decision of whether to reject $H_0$ can be made as follows:

Reject $H_0$ if $p$-value $< \alpha$

Because the $p$-value $= .0000255 < \alpha = .01$, we can reject $H_0$ and conclude that we have a significant relationship between student population and sales. Because $p$-values are provided as part of the computer output for regression analysis, the *p*-value approach is most often used for hypothesis tests in regression analysis.

The information in cells F28:I30 can be used to develop confidence interval estimates of the *y* intercept and slope of the estimated regression equation. Excel always provides the lower and upper limits for a 95% confidence interval. Recall that in the Regression dialog box (see Figure 14.11) we selected Confidence Level and entered 99 in the Confidence Level box. As a result, Excel's Regression tool also provides the lower and upper limits for a 99% confidence interval. For instance, the value in cell H30 is the lower limit for the 99% confidence interval estimate of $\beta_1$ and the value in cell I30 is the upper limit. Thus, after rounding, the 99% confidence interval estimate of $\beta_1$ is 3.05 to 6.95. The values in cells F30 and G30 provide the lower and upper limits for the 95% confidence interval. Thus, the 95% confidence interval is 3.66 to 6.34.

## Interpretation of ANOVA Output

The information in cells A22:F26 summarizes the analysis of variance computations for the Armand's data. The three sources of variation are labeled Regression, Residual, and Total. The label *df* in cell B23 stands for degrees of freedom, the label *SS* in cell C23 stands for sum of squares, and the label *MS* in cell D23 stands for mean square. Looking at cells C24:C26, we see that the regression sum of squares is 14200, the residual or error sum of squares is 1530, and the total sum of squares is 15730. The values in cells B24:B26 are the degrees of freedom corresponding to each sum of squares. Thus, the regression sum of squares has 1 degree of freedom, the residual or error sum of squares has 8 degrees of freedom, and the total sum of squares has 9 degrees of freedom. As we discussed previously, the regression degrees of freedom plus the residual degrees of freedom is equal to the total degrees of freedom, and the regression sum of squares plus the residual sum of squares is equal to the total sum of squares.

*Excel refers to the error sum of squares as the residual sum of squares.*

In Section 14.5 we stated that the mean square error, obtained by dividing the error or residual sum of squares by its degrees of freedom, provides an estimate of $\sigma^2$. The value in cell D25, 191.25, is the mean square error for the Armand's regression output. We also stated that the mean square regression is the sum of squares due to regression divided by the regression degrees of freedom. Because the regression degrees of freedom is always equal to 1 for simple linear regression, the mean square regression is the same as the value of the regression sum of squares. The value in cell D24, 14200, is the mean square regression.

*F* **Test** In Section 14.5 we showed that an *F* test, based upon the *F* probability distribution, could be used to test for significance in regression. The value in cell F24, .0000255, is the *p*-value associated with the *F* test for significance. Given the level of significance $\alpha$, the decision of whether to reject $H_0$ can be made as follows:

$$\text{Reject } H_0 \text{ if } p\text{-value} < \alpha$$

Because the *p*-value = .0000255 < $\alpha$ = .01, we can reject $H_0$ and conclude that we have a significant relationship between student population and sales. Note that it is the same conclusion that we obtained using the *p*-value approach for the *t* test for significance. In fact, because the *t* test for significance is equivalent to the *F* test for significance in simple linear regression, the *p*-values provided by both approaches are identical. The label Excel uses to identify the *p*-value for the *F* test for significance, shown in cell F23, is *Significance F*. In Chapter 9 we also stated that the *p*-value is often referred to as the observed level of significance. Thus, the label *Significance F* may be more meaningful if you think of the value in cell F24 as the observed level of significance for the *F* test.

## Interpretation of Regression Statistics Output

The output in cells A15:B20 summarizes the regression statistics. The number of observations in the data set, 10, is shown in cell B20. The coefficient of determination, .9027, appears in cell B17; the corresponding label, R Square, is shown in cell A17. The square root of the coefficient of determination provides the sample correlation coefficient of 0.9501 shown in cell B16. Note that Excel uses the label Multiple R (cell A16) to identify this value. In cell A19, the label Standard Error is used to identify the value of $s$, the estimate of $\sigma$. Cell B19 shows that the value of $s$ is 13.8293. We caution the reader to keep in mind that in the Excel output, the label Standard Error appears in two different places. In the Regression Statistics section of the output the label Standard Error refers to $s$, the estimate of $\sigma$. In the Estimated Regression Equation section of the output, the label Standard Error refers to $s_{b_1}$, the estimated standard deviation of the sampling distribution of $b_1$.

## EXERCISES

## Applications

**32.** Following is a portion of the Excel output for a regression analysis relating maintenance expense (dollars per month) to usage (hours per week) for a particular brand of computer terminal.

**ANOVA**

|  | df | SS |
|---|---|---|
| Regression | 1 | 1575.76 |
| Residual | 8 | 349.14 |
| Total | 9 | 1924.90 |

|  | Coefficients | Standard Error | t Stat |
|---|---|---|---|
| Intercept | 6.1092 | .9361 | |
| Usage | 0.8951 | .149 | |

**a.** Write the estimated regression equation.
**b.** Use a $t$ test to determine whether monthly maintenance expense is related to usage at the .05 level of significance.
**c.** Did the estimated regression equation provide a good fit? Explain.

**33.** The commercial division of a real estate firm conducted a study to determine the extent of the relationship between annual gross rents ($1000s) and the selling price ($1000s) for apartment buildings. Data were collected on several properties sold, and Excel's Regression tool was used to develop an estimated regression equation. A portion of the Excel output follows.

**ANOVA**

|  | df | SS | MS | F |
|---|---|---|---|---|
| Regression | 1 | 41587.3 | | |
| Residual | 7 | | | |
| Total | 8 | 51984.1 | | |

|  | Coefficients | Standard Error | t Stat |
|---|---|---|---|
| Intercept | 20.000 | 3.2213 | 6.21 |
| Annual Gross Rents | 7.210 | 1.3626 | 5.29 |

   **a.** How many apartment buildings were in the sample?
   **b.** Write the estimated regression equation.
   **c.** Use the $t$ test to determine whether the selling price is related to annual gross rents.
   **d.** Use the $F$ test to determine whether the selling price is related to annual gross rents.
   **e.** Estimate the selling price of an apartment building with gross annual rents of $50,000.

**34.** To determine whether the annual sales at a branch office are related to the number of salespersons at the branch office, a firm used the data from a sample of 30 branch offices to develop an estimated regression equation relating these two variables. A portion of the Excel output that was obtained follows.

**ANOVA**

|  | df | SS | MS | F |
|---|---|---|---|---|
| Regression |  | 6828.6 |  |  |
| Residual |  |  |  |  |
| Total |  | 9127.4 |  |  |

|  | Coefficients | Standard Error | t Stat | P-value |
|---|---|---|---|---|
| Intercept | 80.0 | 11.333 |  |  |
| Number of Salespersons | 50.0 | 5.482 |  |  |

   **a.** Write the estimated regression equation.
   **b.** Compute the $F$ statistic and test the significance of the relationship at the .05 level of significance.
   **c.** Compute the $t$ statistic and test the significance of the relationship at the .05 level of significance.
   **d.** Compute the $p$-value associated with the $t$ test for significance.

**35.** A sample of 15 companies taken from the *Stock Investor Pro* database was used to obtain the following data on the price/earnings (P/E) ratio and the gross profit margin for each company (*Stock Investor Pro,* American Association of Individual Investors, August 21, 1997).

**StockPro**

| Firm | Gross Profit Margin (%) | P/E Ratio |
|---|---|---|
| Abbott Laboratories | 23.7 | 22.3 |
| American Home Products | 21.1 | 22.6 |
| Amoco | 11.0 | 16.7 |
| Bristol Meyers Squibb Co. | 26.6 | 25.9 |
| Chevron | 11.6 | 18.3 |
| Exxon | 9.8 | 18.7 |
| General Electric Company | 13.4 | 13.1 |
| Hewlett-Packard | 9.7 | 23.3 |
| IBM | 11.5 | 17.3 |
| Merck & Co. Inc. | 25.6 | 26.2 |
| Mobil | 8.2 | 18.7 |
| Pfizer | 25.1 | 34.6 |
| Pharmacia & Upjohn, Inc. | 15.0 | 22.3 |
| Texaco | 7.3 | 12.3 |
| Travelers Group Inc. | 17.8 | 28.7 |

   **a.** Determine the estimated regression equation that can be used to predict the price/earnings ratio given the gross profit margin.
   **b.** Use the $F$ test to determine whether the gross profit margin and the P/E ratio are related. What is your conclusion at the .05 level of significance?
   **c.** Use the $t$ test to determine whether the gross profit margin and the P/E ratio are related. What is your conclusion at the .05 level of significance? Is the conclusion that you reached here the same as in part (b)? Explain.
   **d.** Did the estimated regression equation provide a good fit to the data? Explain.

**36.** A 10-year study conducted by the American Heart Association provided data on how age related to the risk of strokes. Suppose that the following data were obtained in a follow-up study. Risk is interpreted as the probability (times 100) that the patient will have a stroke over the next 10-year period.

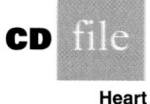

**Heart**

| Patient | Risk | Age |
|---|---|---|
| 1 | 12 | 57 |
| 2 | 24 | 67 |
| 3 | 13 | 58 |
| 4 | 56 | 86 |
| 5 | 28 | 59 |
| 6 | 51 | 76 |
| 7 | 18 | 56 |
| 8 | 31 | 78 |
| 9 | 37 | 80 |
| 10 | 15 | 78 |
| 11 | 22 | 71 |
| 12 | 36 | 70 |
| 13 | 15 | 67 |
| 14 | 48 | 77 |
| 15 | 15 | 60 |
| 16 | 36 | 82 |
| 17 | 8 | 66 |
| 18 | 34 | 80 |
| 19 | 3 | 62 |
| 20 | 37 | 59 |

**a.** Develop an estimated regression equation that can be used to relate the risk of a stroke to the person's age.
**b.** Is the relationship between risk and age significant at the .05 level of significance?
**c.** Did the estimated regression equation provide a good fit to the data? Explain.

**37.** The National Association of Home Builders ranks the most and least affordable housing markets, based on the proportion of homes that a family earning the median income in that market could afford to buy. Data showing the median income ($1000s) and the median sale price ($1000s) for a sample of 12 housing markets that appeared on the list of most affordable markets follow (*The Wall Street Journal Almanac 1998*).

**HomeBldg**

| Market | Income ($1000s) | Price ($1000s) |
|---|---|---|
| Syracuse, NY | 41.8 | 76 |
| Springfield, IL | 47.7 | 91 |
| Lima, OH | 40.0 | 65 |
| Dayton, OH | 44.3 | 88 |
| Beaumont, TX | 37.3 | 70 |
| Lakeland, FL | 35.9 | 73 |
| Baton Rouge, LA | 39.3 | 85 |
| Nashua, NH | 56.9 | 118 |
| Racine, WI | 46.7 | 81 |
| Des Moines, IA | 48.3 | 89 |
| Minneapolis–St. Paul, MN | 54.6 | 110 |
| Wilmington, DE–MD | 55.5 | 110 |

**a.** Use these data to develop an estimated regression equation that could be used to predict the median price for a market given the median income for the market.
**b.** Use the *t* test to determine whether the median sale price is related to the median income. What is your conclusion at the .05 level of significance?
**c.** Did the estimated regression equation provide a good fit? Explain.

**38.** Cushman & Wakefield, Inc., collects data showing the office building vacancy rates and rental rates for markets in the United States. The following data show the overall vacancy rates (%) and the average rental rates (per square foot) for the central business district for 18 selected markets (*The Wall Street Journal Almanac 1998*).

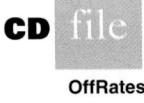

OffRates

| Market | Vacancy Rate (%) | Average Rental Rate ($) |
|---|---|---|
| Atlanta | 21.9 | 18.54 |
| Boston | 6.0 | 33.70 |
| Hartford | 22.8 | 19.67 |
| Baltimore | 18.1 | 21.01 |
| Washington | 12.7 | 35.09 |
| Philadelphia | 14.5 | 19.41 |
| Miami | 20.0 | 25.28 |
| Tampa | 19.2 | 17.02 |
| Chicago | 16.0 | 24.04 |
| San Francisco | 6.6 | 31.42 |
| Phoenix | 15.9 | 18.74 |
| San Jose | 9.2 | 26.76 |
| West Palm Beach | 19.7 | 27.72 |
| Detroit | 20.0 | 18.20 |
| Brooklyn | 8.3 | 25.00 |
| Downtown, NY | 17.1 | 29.78 |
| Midtown, NY | 10.8 | 37.03 |
| Midtown South, NY | 11.1 | 28.64 |

a. Develop a scatter diagram for these data; plot the vacancy rate on the horizontal axis.
b. Does there appear to be any relationship between these two variables?
c. Develop the estimated regression equation that could be used to predict the average rental rate given the overall vacancy rate.
d. Test the significance of the relationship at the .05 level of significance.
e. Did the estimated regression equation provide a good fit? Explain.
f. Develop a point estimate of the expected rental rate for markets with a 25% vacancy rate in the central business district.
g. The overall vacancy rate in the central business district in Ft. Lauderdale is 11.3%. What is the expected rental rate for Ft. Lauderdale?

## 14.7 USING THE ESTIMATED REGRESSION EQUATION FOR ESTIMATION AND PREDICTION

The simple linear regression model is an assumption about the relationship between $x$ and $y$. Using the least squares method, we obtained the estimated simple linear regression equation. If the results show a statistically significant relationship between $x$ and $y$, and the fit provided by the estimated regression equation appears to be good, the estimated regression equation should be useful for estimation and prediction.

### Point Estimation

In the Armand's Pizza Parlors example, the estimated regression equation $\hat{y} = 60 + 5x$ provides an estimate of the relationship between the size of the student population $x$ and quarterly sales $y$. We can use the estimated regression equation to develop a point estimate of the mean value of $y$ for a particular value of $x$ or to predict an individual value of $y$ corresponding to a given value of $x$. For instance, suppose Armand's managers want a point estimate of the mean quarterly sales for all restaurants located near college campuses with 10,000 students. Using the estimated regression equation $\hat{y} = 60 + 5x$, we see that for

$x = 10$ (or 10,000 students), $\hat{y} = 60 + 5(10) = 110$. Thus, a point estimate of the mean quarterly sales for all restaurants located near campuses with 10,000 students is $110,000.

Now suppose Armand's managers want to predict sales for an individual restaurant located near Talbot College, a school with 10,000 students. In this case we are not interested in the mean value for all restaurants located near campuses with 10,000 students; we are just interested in predicting quarterly sales for one individual restaurant. As it turns out, the point estimate is the same as the point estimate for the mean value of $y$. Hence, we would predict quarterly sales of $\hat{y} = 60 + 5(10) = 110$ or $110,000 for this one restaurant.

## Interval Estimation

Point estimates do not provide any information about the precision associated with the estimates. For that we must develop interval estimates much like those in Chapters 8, 10, and 11. The first type of interval estimate, a **confidence interval estimate,** is an interval estimate of the *mean value of y* for a given value of $x$. The second type of interval estimate, a **prediction interval estimate,** is used whenever we want an interval estimate of an *individual value of y* corresponding to a given value of $x$. The point estimate of the mean value of $y$ is the same as the point estimate of an individual value of $y$. But, the interval estimates we obtain for the two cases are different.

*Confidence intervals and prediction intervals indicate the precision of the regression results. Narrower intervals indicate a higher degree of precision.*

## Confidence Interval Estimate of the Mean Value of $y$

The estimated regression equation provides a point estimate of the mean value of $y$ for a given value of $x$. In describing the confidence interval estimation procedure, we will use the following notation.

$$x_p = \text{the particular or given value of the independent variable } x$$
$$E(y_p) = \text{the mean or expected value of the dependent variable } y$$
$$\text{when } x = x_p$$
$$\hat{y}_p = b_0 + b_1 x_p = \text{the point estimate of } E(y_p) \text{ when } x = x_p$$

Using this notation to estimate the mean quarterly sales for all Armand's restaurants located near a campus with 10,000 students, we have $x_p = 10$; thus, $E(y_p)$ denotes the unknown mean value of sales for all restaurants where $x_p = 10$. The point estimate of $E(y_p)$ is provided by $\hat{y}_p = 60 + 5(10) = 110$.

In general, we cannot expect $\hat{y}_p$ to equal $E(y_p)$ exactly. If we want to make an inference about how close $\hat{y}_p$ is to the true mean value $E(y_p)$, we will have to estimate the variance of $\hat{y}_p$. The formula for estimating the variance of $\hat{y}_p$ given $x_p$, denoted by $s_{\hat{y}_p}^2$, is

$$s_{\hat{y}_p}^2 = s^2\left[\frac{1}{n} + \frac{(x_p - \bar{x})^2}{\Sigma(x_i - \bar{x})^2}\right]$$

**(14.22)**

The estimate of the standard deviation of $\hat{y}_p$ is given by the square root of (14.22).

$$s_{\hat{y}_p} = s\sqrt{\frac{1}{n} + \frac{(x_p - \bar{x})^2}{\Sigma(x_i - \bar{x})^2}}$$

**(14.23)**

The computational results for Armand's Pizza Parlors in Section 14.5 provided $s = 13.829$. With $x_p = 10$, $\bar{x} = 14$, and $\Sigma(x_i - \bar{x})^2 = 568$, we can use (14.23) to obtain

$$s_{\hat{y}_p} = 13.829\sqrt{\frac{1}{10} + \frac{(10 - 14)^2}{568}}$$
$$= 13.829\sqrt{.1282} = 4.95$$

The general expression for a confidence interval estimate of $E(y_p)$ follows.

> **Confidence Interval Estimate of $E(y_p)$**
>
> $$\hat{y}_p \pm t_{\alpha/2}s_{\hat{y}_p} \qquad\qquad (14.24)$$
>
> where the confidence coefficient is $1 - \alpha$ and $t_{\alpha/2}$ is based on a $t$ distribution with $n - 2$ degrees of freedom.

Using expression (14.24) to develop a 95% confidence interval estimate of the mean quarterly sales for all Armand's restaurants located near campuses with 10,000 students, we need the value of $t$ for $\alpha/2 = .025$ and $n - 2 = 10 - 2 = 8$ degrees of freedom. Using Table 2 of Appendix B, we have $t_{.025} = 2.306$. Thus, with $\hat{y}_p = 110$ and a margin of error of $t_{\alpha/2}s_{\hat{y}_p} = 2.306(4.95) = 11.415$, the 95% confidence interval estimate is

$$110 \pm 11.415$$

In dollars, the 95% confidence interval for the mean quarterly sales of all restaurants near campuses with 10,000 students is $\$110,000 \pm \$11,415$. Therefore, the confidence interval estimate for the mean quarterly sales when the student population is 10,000 is $\$98,585$ to $\$121,415$.

Note that the estimated standard deviation of $\hat{y}_p$ given by equation (14.23) is smallest when $x_p = \bar{x}$ and the quantity $x_p - \bar{x} = 0$. In this case, the estimated standard deviation of $\hat{y}_p$ becomes

$$s_{\hat{y}_p} = s\sqrt{\frac{1}{n} + \frac{(\bar{x} - \bar{x})^2}{\Sigma(x_i - \bar{x})^2}} = s\sqrt{\frac{1}{n}}$$

This result implies that we can make the best or most precise estimate of the mean value of $y$ whenever $x_p = \bar{x}$. In fact, the further $x_p$ is from $\bar{x}$, the larger $x_p - \bar{x}$ becomes. As a result, confidence intervals for the mean value of $y$ will become wider as $x_p$ deviates more from $\bar{x}$. This pattern is shown graphically in Figure 14.12.

## Prediction Interval Estimate of an Individual Value of $y$

Suppose that instead of estimating the mean value of quarterly sales for all Armand's restaurants located near campuses with 10,000 students, we want to estimate the quarterly sales for an individual restaurant located near Talbot College, a school with 10,000 students. As noted previously, the point estimate of an individual value of $y$ given $x = x_p$ is provided by the estimated regression equation with $\hat{y}_p = b_0 + b_1x_p$. For the restaurant at Talbot College, we have $x_p = 10$ and a corresponding estimated quarterly sales of $\hat{y}_p = 60 + 5(10) = 110$, or $\$110,000$. Note that this value is the same as the point estimate of the mean quarterly sales for all restaurants located near campuses with 10,000 students.

To develop a prediction interval estimate, we must first estimate the variance associated with using $\hat{y}_p$ as an estimate of an individual value of $y$ when $x = x_p$. This variance is made up of the sum of the following two components.

1. The variance of individual $y$ values about the mean $E(y_p)$, an estimate of which is given by $s^2$.
2. The variance associated with using $\hat{y}_p$ to estimate $E(y_p)$, an estimate of which is given by $s_{\hat{y}_p}^2$.

**FIGURE 14.12**    CONFIDENCE INTERVALS FOR THE MEAN QUARTERLY SALES $y$ AT GIVEN VALUES OF STUDENT POPULATION $x$

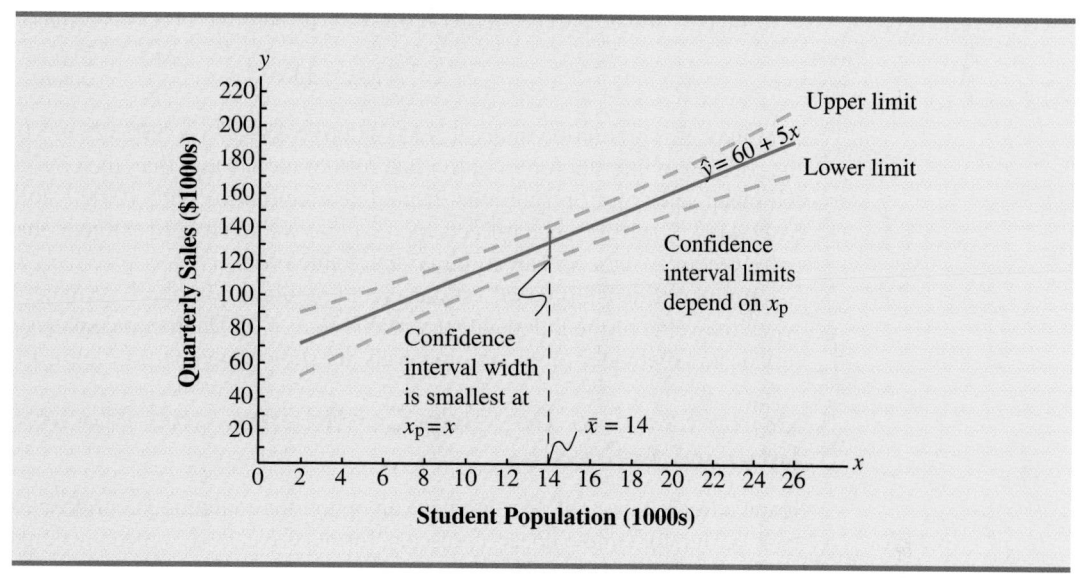

The formula for estimating the variance of an individual value of $y_p$, denoted by $s_{ind}^2$, is

$$s_{ind}^2 = s^2 + s_{\hat{y}_p}^2$$

$$= s^2 + s^2\left[\frac{1}{n} + \frac{(x_p - \bar{x})^2}{\Sigma(x_i - \bar{x})^2}\right]$$

$$= s^2\left[1 + \frac{1}{n} + \frac{(x_p - \bar{x})^2}{\Sigma(x_i - \bar{x})^2}\right] \tag{14.25}$$

Hence, an estimate of the standard deviation of an individual value of $y_p$ is given by

$$s_{ind} = s\sqrt{1 + \frac{1}{n} + \frac{(x_p - \bar{x})^2}{\Sigma(x_i - \bar{x})^2}} \tag{14.26}$$

For Armand's Pizza Parlors, the estimated standard deviation corresponding to the prediction of quarterly sales for one specific restaurant located near a campus with 10,000 students is computed as follows.

$$s_{ind} = 13.829\sqrt{1 + \frac{1}{10} + \frac{(10 - 14)^2}{568}}$$

$$= 13.829\sqrt{1.1282}$$

$$= 14.69$$

The general expression for a prediction interval estimate of an individual value of $y$ follows.

**Prediction Interval Estimate of $y_p$**

The margin of error associated with this interval estimate is $t_{\alpha/2}s_{ind}$.

$$\hat{y}_p \pm t_{\alpha/2}s_{ind} \tag{14.27}$$

where the confidence coefficient is $1 - \alpha$ and $t_{\alpha/2}$ is based on a $t$ distribution with $n - 2$ degrees of freedom.

The 95% prediction interval for quarterly sales at Armand's Talbot College restaurant can be found by using $t_{.025} = 2.306$ and $s_{ind} = 14.69$. Thus, with $\hat{y}_p = 110$ and a margin of error of $t_{\alpha/2}s_{ind} = 2.306(14.69) = 33.875$, the 95% prediction interval estimate is

$$110 \pm 33.875$$

In dollars, this prediction interval is $\$110,000 \pm \$33,875$ or $\$76,125$ to $\$143,875$. Note that the prediction interval for an individual restaurant is wider than the confidence interval for the mean sales of all restaurants located near campuses with 10,000 students ($\$98,585$ to $\$121,415$). The difference reflects the fact that we are able to estimate the mean value of $y$ more precisely than we can an individual value of $y$.

Both confidence interval estimates and prediction interval estimates are most precise when the value of the independent variable is $x_p = \bar{x}$. The general shapes of confidence intervals and the wider prediction intervals are shown together in Figure 14.13.

## Using Excel to Develop Confidence and Prediction Interval Estimates

Excel's Regression tool does not have an option for computing confidence and prediction intervals. But, for simple linear regression, formulas can be designed to compute these intervals using equations (14.24) and (14.27) along with the output provided by the Regression tool. The general expression for a confidence or prediction interval is: point estimate $\pm$ margin of error. Thus, we must develop formulas for computing a point estimate and the margin of error.

We begin by showing how to develop a 95% confidence interval estimate of the mean quarterly sales for all Armand's restaurants located near a campus with 10,000 students. In Section 14.6, we showed how Excel's Regression tool could be applied to the Armand's problem. The output provided by the Regression tool is shown again in cells A13:I30 of Figure 14.14. Now refer to cells E1:F13 of that figure as we describe the tasks involved in developing a confidence interval. The formula worksheet is in the background; the value worksheet is in the foreground.

**FIGURE 14.13**   CONFIDENCE AND PREDICTION INTERVALS FOR QUARTERLY SALES $y$ AT GIVEN VALUES OF STUDENT POPULATION $x$

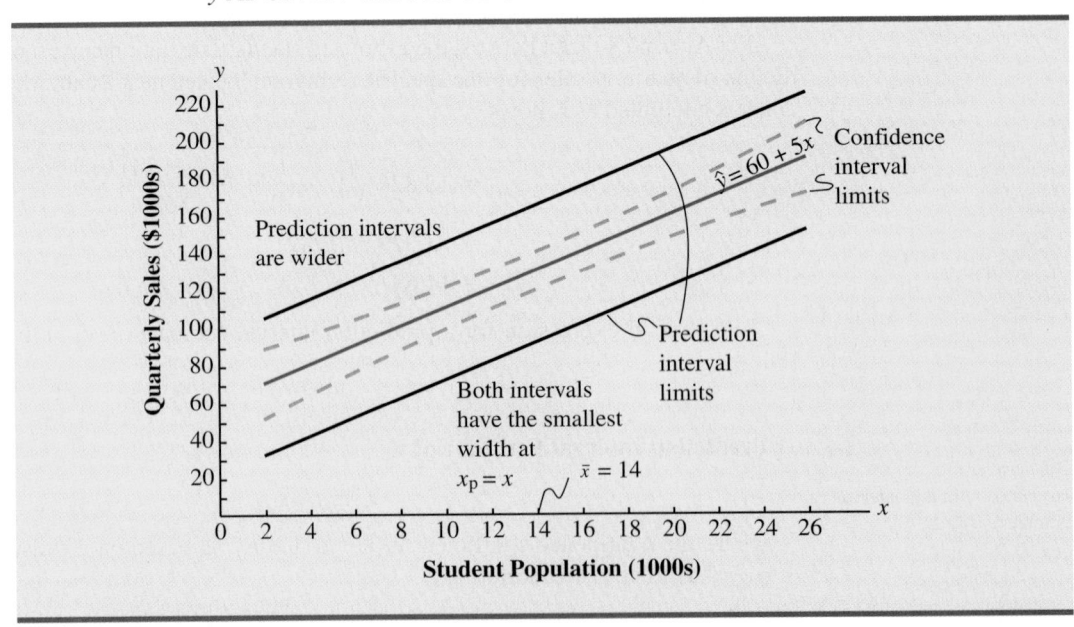

Chapter 14 Simple Linear Regression **611**

**FIGURE 14.14** USING EXCEL TO COMPUTE CONFIDENCE AND PREDICTION INTERVALS

| | A | B | C | D | E | F | G | H | I |
|---|---|---|---|---|---|---|---|---|---|
| 1 | Restaurant | Population | Sales | | Confidence Interval | | | | |
| 2 | 1 | 2 | 58 | | Given value of x | 10 | | | |
| 3 | 2 | 6 | 105 | | xbar | =AVERAGE(B2:B11) | | | |
| 4 | 3 | 8 | 88 | | x-xbar | =F2-F3 | | | |
| 5 | 4 | 8 | 118 | | (x-xbar)sq | =F4^2 | | | |
| 6 | 5 | 12 | 117 | | Sum of (x-xbar)sq | =DEVSQ(B2:B11) | | | |
| 7 | 6 | 16 | 137 | | Var of yhat | =D25*(1/B20+F5/F6) | | | |
| 8 | 7 | 20 | 157 | | Stdev of yhat | =SQRT(F7) | | | |
| 9 | 8 | 20 | 169 | | t value | =TINV(0.05,8) | | | |
| 10 | 9 | 22 | 149 | | Margin of Error | =F9*F8 | | | |
| 11 | 10 | 26 | 202 | | Point Estimate | =B29+B30*F2 | | | |
| 12 | | | | | Lower Limit | =F11-F10 | | | |
| 13 | SUMMARY OUTPUT | | | | Upper Limit | =F11+F10 | | | |
| 14 | | | | | | | | | |
| 15 | Regression Statistics | | | | Prediction Interval | | | | |
| 16 | Multiple R | 0.95012295520 | | | Var of yind | =D25+F7 | | | |
| 17 | R Square | 0.90273363000 | | | Stdev of yind | =SQRT(F16) | | | |
| 18 | Adjusted R Square | 0.89057533375 | | | Margin of Error | =F9*F17 | | | |
| 19 | Standard Error | 13.8293166859 | | | Lower Limit | =F11-F18 | | | |
| 20 | Observations | 10 | | | Upper Limit | =F11+F18 | | | |
| 21 | | | | | | | | | |
| 22 | ANOVA | | | | | | | | |
| 23 | | df | | | | | | | |
| 24 | Regression | 1 | | | | | | | |
| 25 | Residual | 8 | | | | | | | |
| 26 | Total | 9 | | | | | | | |
| 27 | | | | | | | | | |
| 28 | | Coefficients | | | | | | | |
| 29 | Intercept | 60 | | | | | | | |
| 30 | Population | 5 | | | | | | | |
| 31 | | | | | | | | | |

| | A | B | C | D | E | F | G | H | I | J |
|---|---|---|---|---|---|---|---|---|---|---|
| 1 | Restaurant | Population | Sales | | Confidence Interval | | | | | |
| 2 | 1 | 2 | 58 | | Given value of x | 10 | | | | |
| 3 | 2 | 6 | 105 | | xbar | 14 | | | | |
| 4 | 3 | 8 | 88 | | x-xbar | -4 | | | | |
| 5 | 4 | 8 | 118 | | (x-xbar)sq | 16 | | | | |
| 6 | 5 | 12 | 117 | | Sum of (x-xbar)sq | 568 | | | | |
| 7 | 6 | 16 | 137 | | Var of yhat | 24.5123 | | | | |
| 8 | 7 | 20 | 157 | | Stdev of yhat | 4.9510 | | | | |
| 9 | 8 | 20 | 169 | | t value | 2.3060 | | | | |
| 10 | 9 | 22 | 149 | | Margin of Error | 11.4170 | | | | |
| 11 | 10 | 26 | 202 | | Point Estimate | 110 | | | | |
| 12 | | | | | Lower Limit | 98.5830 | | | | |
| 13 | SUMMARY OUTPUT | | | | Upper Limit | 121.4170 | | | | |
| 14 | | | | | | | | | | |
| 15 | Regression Statistics | | | | Prediction Interval | | | | | |
| 16 | Multiple R | 0.9501 | | | Var of yind | 215.7623 | | | | |
| 17 | R Square | 0.9027 | | | Stdev of yind | 14.6889 | | | | |
| 18 | Adjusted R Square | 0.8906 | | | Margin of Error | 33.8726 | | | | |
| 19 | Standard Error | 13.8293 | | | Lower Limit | 76.1274 | | | | |
| 20 | Observations | 10 | | | Upper Limit | 143.8726 | | | | |
| 21 | | | | | | | | | | |
| 22 | ANOVA | | | | | | | | | |
| 23 | | df | SS | MS | F | Significance F | | | | |
| 24 | Regression | 1 | 14200 | 14200 | 74.2484 | 2.55E-05 | | | | |
| 25 | Residual | 8 | 1530 | 191.25 | | | | | | |
| 26 | Total | 9 | 15730 | | | | | | | |
| 27 | | | | | | | | | | |
| 28 | | Coefficients | Standard Error | t Stat | P-value | Lower 95% | Upper 95% | Lower 99.0% | Upper 99.0% | |
| 29 | Intercept | 60 | 9.2260 | 6.5033 | 0.0002 | 38.7247 | 81.2753 | 29.0431 | 90.9569 | |
| 30 | Population | 5 | 0.5803 | 8.6167 | 2.55E-05 | 3.6619 | 6.3381 | 3.0530 | 6.9470 | |
| 31 | | | | | | | | | | |

**Enter Data:** The data (cells B2:C11) and regression output (cells A13:I30) that were initially developed in Figure 14.10 are used as a starting point here.

**Enter Functions and Formulas:** Because we want to develop a 95% confidence interval estimate of the mean quarterly sales for restaurants near campuses with 10,000 students, $x_p = 10$ and we enter a value of 10 into cell F2. Excel's AVERAGE function is used to compute $\bar{x}$ in cell F3, the formula =F2 − F3 is entered into cell F4 to compute the value of $x_p - \bar{x}$, and the formula =F4^2 is entered into cell F5 to compute the value of $(x_p - \bar{x})^2$. Excel's DEVSQ function can be used to compute $\Sigma(x_i - \bar{x})^2$ by entering the following formula into cell F6:

$$=\text{DEVSQ(B2:B11)}$$

To identify this sum of squares we entered the label "Sum of (x − xbar)sq" into cell E6.

We can now compute $s_{\hat{y}_p}^2$ using equation (14.22) by entering the formula =D25* (1/B20+F5/F6) into cell F7. We then enter the formula =SQRT(F7) into cell F8 to compute $s_{\hat{y}_p}$, the estimate of the standard deviation of $\hat{y}_p$. To compute the $t$ value required by equation (14.24), we entered the formula =TINV(0.05,8) into cell F9. Finally, the margin of error $t_{\alpha/2}s_{\hat{y}_p}$ is computed by entering the formula =F9*F8 into cell F10. To compute $\hat{y}_p$, the point estimate of $E(y_p)$, we entered the formula =B29+B30*F2 into cell F11. The lower and upper limits of the 95% confidence interval are then computed by entering the formulas =F11−F10 and =F11+F10 into cells F12 and F13 respectively.

The value worksheet shows that the 95% confidence interval estimate is 98.583 to 121.417. In dollars, the 95% confidence interval for the mean quarterly sales of restaurants located near campuses with 10,000 students is $98,583 to $121,417. To develop confidence intervals for other values of $x_p$ we simply use this worksheet as a template and enter another value for student population in cell F2. The new confidence interval will appear in cells F12 and F13. If a confidence interval for another value of $\alpha$ is desired, we can just insert the new value of $\alpha$ for the first argument of the TINV function in cell F9.

The confidence interval formulas developed here cannot be applied directly as a template for other regression problems because the number of observations will likely be different and the location of the regression output will not be in the same worksheet cells. The same cells (E1:F13) can be used to develop the confidence interval but the cell references used in cells F3, F6, F7, and F11 will need to be modified to reflect the location of the data and the regression output. The level of significance and the degrees of freedom used for TINV in cell F9 may also need to be changed.

The design of formulas to compute a prediction interval utilizes some of the same information used to develop a confidence interval. However, equation (14.27) shows that $s_{ind}$, instead of $s_{\hat{y}_p}$, is used in computing the margin of error. Refer to cells E15:F20 of the worksheet in Figure 14.14 as we describe the tasks involved in computing a 95% prediction interval for Armand's Pizza.

**Enter Functions and Formulas:** To compute $s_{ind}^2 = s^2 + s_{\hat{y}_p}^2$ we entered the formula =D25+F7 into cell F16. Then, in cell F17 we entered the formula =SQRT(F16) to compute $s_{ind}$. The labels "Var of yind" and "Stdev of yind" were entered into cells E16 and E17 to identify these values. To compute the margin of error the formula =F9*F17 was entered into cell F18. The formulas =F11−F18 and =F11+F18 were into cells F19 and F20 respectively to compute the lower and upper limits.

The 95% prediction interval is 76.127 to 143.873. In dollars, the 95% prediction interval is $76,127 to $143,873. To develop prediction intervals for other values of $x_p$ we simply enter another value for student population in cell F2 and the new prediction interval will appear in cells F19 and F20. If a prediction interval for another value of $\alpha$ is desired, we can just insert the new value of $\alpha$ for the first argument of the TINV function in cell F9.

## EXERCISES

### Methods

**39.** The data from Exercise 1 follow.

| $x_i$ | 1 | 2 | 3 | 4 | 5 |
|-------|---|---|---|----|----|
| $y_i$ | 3 | 7 | 5 | 11 | 14 |

a. Use equation (14.23) to estimate the standard deviation of $\hat{y}_p$ when $x = 4$.
b. Use equation (14.24) to develop a 95% confidence interval estimate of the expected value of $y$ when $x = 4$.

In other words, the $i$th residual is the error resulting from using the estimated regression equation to predict the value of $y_i$. The residuals for the Armand's Pizza Parlors example are computed in Table 14.7. The observed values of the dependent variable are in the second column and the estimated values of the dependent variable, obtained using the estimated regression equation $\hat{y}_i = 60 + 5x_i$, are in the third column. The corresponding residuals are in the fourth column. An analysis of these residuals will help determine whether the assumptions that have been made about the regression model are appropriate.

Let us now review the regression assumptions for the Armand's Pizza Parlors example. A simple linear regression model was assumed.

$$y = \beta_0 + \beta_1 x + \epsilon \qquad (14.29)$$

This model indicates that we assumed sales ($y$) to be a linear function of the size of the student population ($x$) plus an error term $\epsilon$. In Section 14.4 we made the following assumptions about the error term $\epsilon$.

1. $E(\epsilon) = 0$.
2. The variance of $\epsilon$, denoted by $\sigma^2$, is the same for all values of $x$.
3. The values of $\epsilon$ are independent.
4. The error term $\epsilon$ has a normal probability distribution.

These assumptions provide the theoretical basis for the $t$ test and the $F$ test used to determine whether the relationship between $x$ and $y$ is significant, and for the confidence and prediction interval estimates presented in Section 14.7. If the assumptions about the error term $\epsilon$ appear questionable, the hypothesis tests about the significance of the regression relationship and the interval estimation results may not be valid.

The residuals provide the best information about $\epsilon$; hence residual analysis is an important step in determining whether the assumptions for $\epsilon$ are appropriate. Much of residual analysis is based on an examination of graphical plots. In this section, we discuss a plot of the residuals against values of the independent variable $x$.

## Residual Plot Against $x$

A residual plot against the independent variable $x$ is a graph in which the values of the independent variable are represented by the horizontal axis and the corresponding residual values are represented by the vertical axis. A point is plotted for each residual. The first coordinate for each point is given by the value of $x_i$ and the second coordinate is given by the corresponding value of the residual $y_i - \hat{y}_i$. To develop a residual plot against $x$ with the Armand's

**TABLE 14.7    RESIDUALS FOR ARMAND'S PIZZA PARLORS**

| Student Population $x_i$ | Sales $y_i$ | Estimated Sales $\hat{y}_i = 60 + 5x_i$ | Residuals $y_i - \hat{y}_i$ |
|---|---|---|---|
| 2 | 58 | 70 | $-12$ |
| 6 | 105 | 90 | 15 |
| 8 | 88 | 100 | $-12$ |
| 8 | 118 | 100 | 18 |
| 12 | 117 | 120 | $-3$ |
| 16 | 137 | 140 | $-3$ |
| 20 | 157 | 160 | $-3$ |
| 20 | 169 | 160 | 9 |
| 22 | 149 | 170 | $-21$ |
| 26 | 202 | 190 | 12 |

Pizza Parlors data from Table 14.7, the coordinates of the first point are $(2, -12)$, corresponding to $x_1 = 2$ and $y_1 - \hat{y}_1 = -12$; the coordinates of the second point are $(6, 15)$, corresponding to $x_2 = 6$ and $y_2 - \hat{y}_2 = 15$, and so on. Figure 14.15 is the resulting residual plot.

Before interpreting the results for this residual plot, let us consider some general patterns that might be observed in any residual plot. Three examples are shown in Figure 14.16. If the assumption that the variance of $\epsilon$ is the same for all values of $x$ and the assumed regression model is an adequate representation of the relationship between the variables, the residual plot should give an overall impression of a horizontal band of points such as the one in panel A of Figure 14.16. However, if the variance of $\epsilon$ is not the same for all values of $x$—for example, if variability about the regression line is greater for larger values of $x$—a pattern such as the one in panel B of Figure 14.16 could be observed. In this case, the assumption of a constant variance of $\epsilon$ is violated. Another possible residual plot is shown in panel C. In this case, we would conclude that the assumed regression model is not an adequate representation of the relationship between the variables. A curvilinear regression model or multiple regression model should be considered.

Now let us return to the residual plot for Armand's Pizza Parlors shown in Figure 14.15. The residuals appear to approximate the horizontal pattern in panel A of Figure 14.16. Hence, we conclude that the residual plot does not provide evidence that the assumptions made for Armand's regression model should be challenged. At this point, we are confident in the conclusion that Armand's simple linear regression model is valid.

Experience and good judgment are always factors in the effective interpretation of residual plots. Seldom does a residual plot conform precisely to one of the patterns shown in Figure 14.16. Yet analysts who frequently conduct regression studies and frequently review residual plots become adept at understanding the differences between patterns that are reasonable and patterns that indicate the assumptions of the model should be questioned. A residual plot as shown here is one of the techniques that is used to assess the validity of the assumptions for a regression model.

**FIGURE 14.15**     PLOT OF THE RESIDUALS AGAINST THE INDEPENDENT VARIABLE $x$ FOR ARMAND'S PIZZA PARLORS

**FIGURE 14.16**    RESIDUAL PLOTS FROM THREE REGRESSION STUDIES

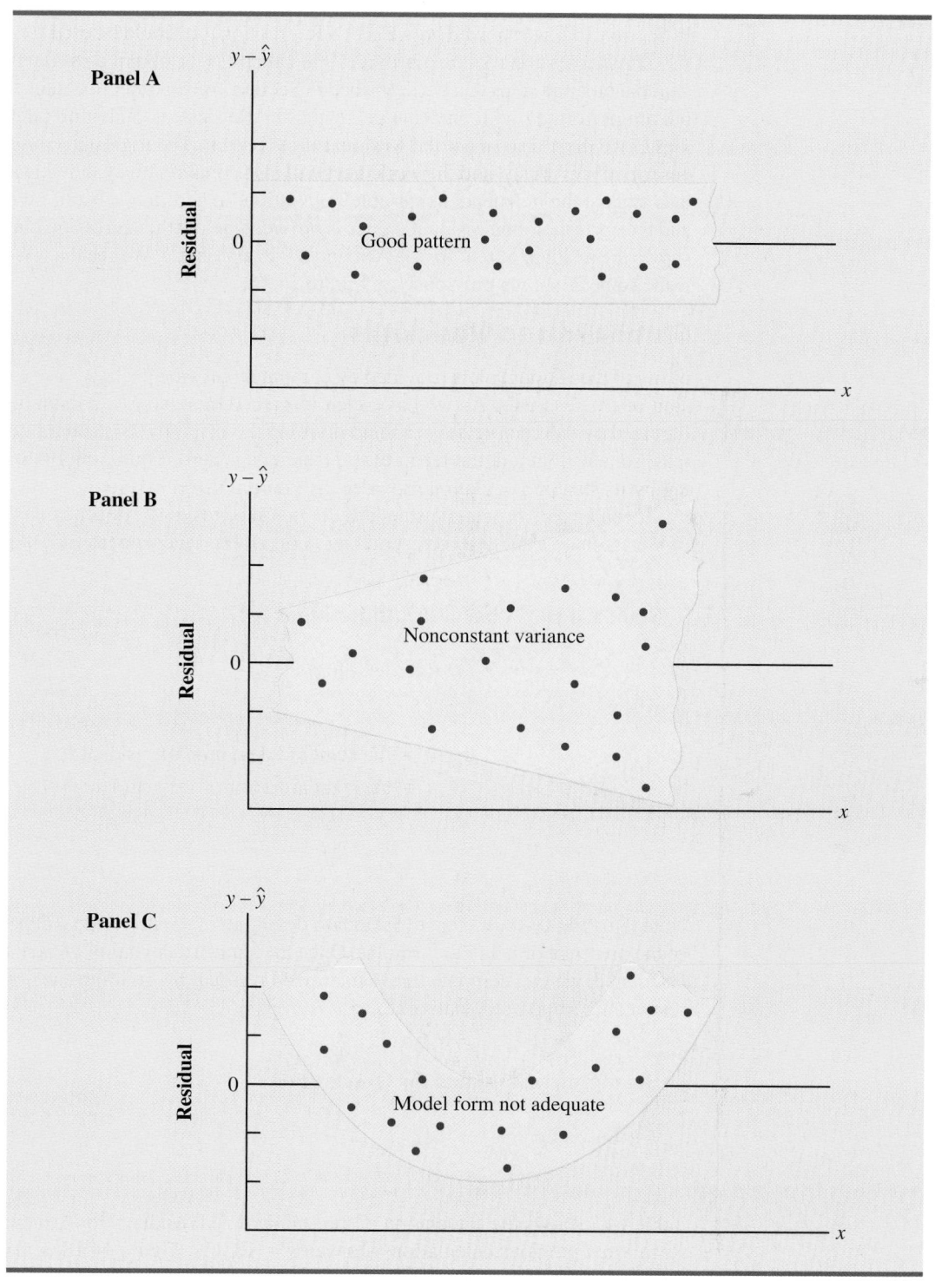

## Using Excel's Regression Tool to Construct a Residual Plot

In Section 14.6 we showed how Excel's Regression tool could be used for regression analysis. The Regression tool also provides the capability to obtain a residual plot. To obtain a residual plot, the steps that we described in Section 14.6 in order to obtain the regression output are performed with one change. When the Regression dialog box appears (see Figure 14.11) we must also select the Residual Plots option. The regression output will appear as described previously, and the worksheet will also contain a chart showing a plot of the residuals against the independent variable Population. In addition, a list of predicted values of $y$ and the corresponding residual values is provided below the regression output. Figure 14.17 shows the residual output for the Armand's Pizza problem. We see that the shape of this plot is the same as shown previously in Figure 14.15.

## Standardized Residuals

Many of the residual plots provided by computer software packages use a standardized version of the residuals. As we have seen in preceding chapters, a random variable is standardized by subtracting its mean and dividing the result by its standard deviation. With the least squares method, the mean of the residuals is zero. Thus, simply dividing each residual by its standard deviation provides the **standardized residual.**

It can be shown that the standard deviation of residual $i$ depends on the standard error of the estimate $s$ and the corresponding value of the independent variable $x_i$.

---

**Standard Deviation of the $i$th Residual[2]**

$$s_{y_i - \hat{y}_i} = s\sqrt{1 - h_i}$$

(14.30)

where

$$s_{y_i - \hat{y}_i} = \text{the standard deviation of residual } i$$
$$s = \text{the standard error of the estimate}$$
$$h_i = \frac{1}{n} + \frac{(x_i - \bar{x})^2}{\Sigma(x_i - \bar{x})^2}$$

(14.31)

---

Note that (14.30) shows that the standard deviation of the $i$th residual depends on $x_i$ because of the presence of $h_i$ in the formula.[3] Once the standard deviation of each residual has been calculated, we can compute the standardized residual by dividing each residual by its corresponding standard deviation.

---

**Standardized Residual for Observation $i$**

$$\frac{y_i - \hat{y}_i}{s_{y_i - \hat{y}_i}}$$

(14.32)

---

Table 14.8 shows the calculation of the standardized residuals for Armand's Pizza Parlors. Recall that previous calculations showed $s = 13.829$. Figure 14.18 is the plot of the standardized residuals against the independent variable $x$.

---

[2] This equation actually provides an estimate of the standard deviation of the $i$th residual, because $s$ is used instead of $\sigma$. The value of $\sigma$ is never known when working with real data and is always estimated by $s$.

[3] $h_i$ is referred to as the leverage of observation $i$. Leverage will be discussed further when we consider influential observations in Section 14.9.

**FIGURE 14.17**    EXCEL RESIDUAL OUTPUT FOR THE ARMAND'S PIZZA PARLORS PROBLEM

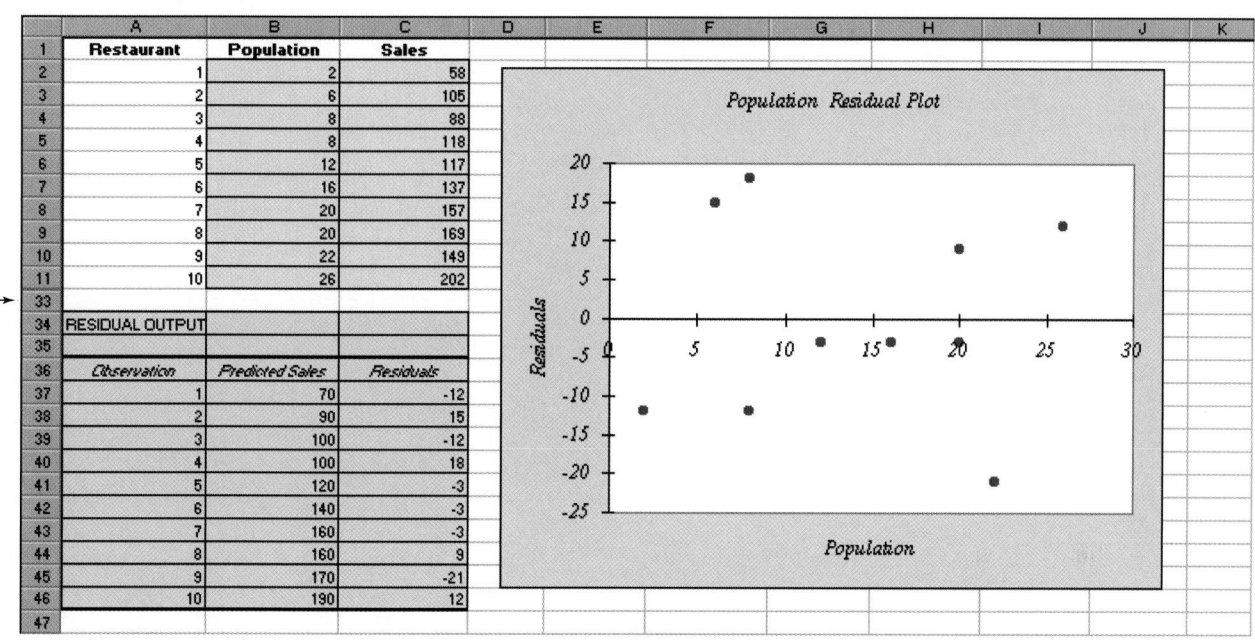

—Note: Rows 12–32 are hidden.

Small departures from normality do not have a great effect on the statistical tests used in regression analysis.

The standardized residual plot can provide insight about the assumption that the error term $\epsilon$ has a normal distribution. If this assumption is satisfied, the distribution of the standardized residuals should appear to come from a standard normal probability distribution.[4] Thus, when looking at a standardized residual plot, we should expect to see approximately 95% of the standardized residuals between $-2$ and $+2$. We see in Figure 14.18 that for the

**TABLE 14.8**    COMPUTATION OF STANDARDIZED RESIDUALS FOR ARMAND'S PIZZA PARLORS

| Restaurant $i$ | $x_i$ | $x_i - \bar{x}$ | $(x_i - \bar{x})^2$ | $\dfrac{(x_i - \bar{x})^2}{\Sigma(x_i - \bar{x})^2}$ | $h_i$ | $s_{y_i - \hat{y}_i}$ | $y_i - \hat{y}_i$ | Standardized Residual |
|---|---|---|---|---|---|---|---|---|
| 1 | 2 | $-12$ | 144 | .2535 | .3535 | 11.1193 | $-12$ | $-1.0792$ |
| 2 | 6 | $-8$ | 64 | .1127 | .2127 | 12.2709 | 15 | 1.2224 |
| 3 | 8 | $-6$ | 36 | .0634 | .1634 | 12.6493 | $-12$ | $-.9487$ |
| 4 | 8 | $-6$ | 36 | .0634 | .1634 | 12.6493 | 18 | 1.4230 |
| 5 | 12 | $-2$ | 4 | .0070 | .1070 | 13.0682 | $-3$ | $-.2296$ |
| 6 | 16 | 2 | 4 | .0070 | .1070 | 13.0682 | $-3$ | $-.2296$ |
| 7 | 20 | 6 | 36 | .0634 | .1634 | 12.6493 | $-3$ | $-.2372$ |
| 8 | 20 | 6 | 36 | .0634 | .1634 | 12.6493 | 9 | .7115 |
| 9 | 22 | 8 | 64 | .1127 | .2127 | 12.2709 | $-21$ | $-1.7114$ |
| 10 | 26 | 12 | 144 | .2535 | .3535 | 11.1193 | 12 | 1.0792 |
| | | Total | 568 | | | | | |

*Note:* The values of the residuals were computed in Table 14.7.

[4]Because $s$ is used instead of $\sigma$ in (14.30), the probability distribution of the standardized residuals is not technically normal. However, in most regression studies, the sample size is large enough that a normal approximation is very good.

**FIGURE 14.18**    PLOT OF THE STANDARDIZED RESIDUALS AGAINST THE
INDEPENDENT VARIABLE $x$ FOR ARMAND'S PIZZA PARLORS

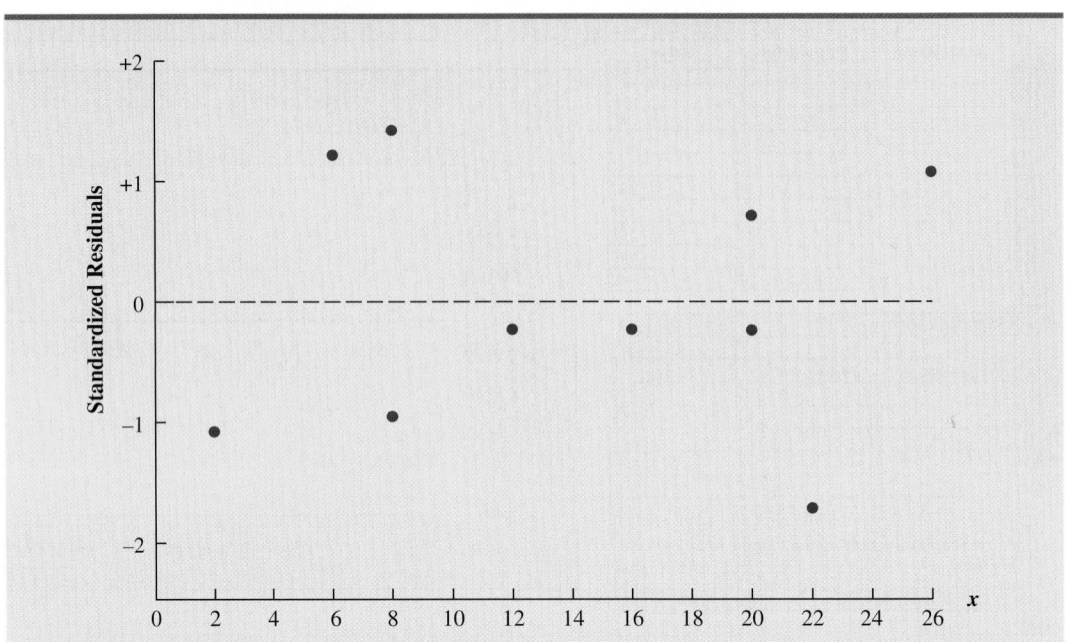

Armand's example all standardized residuals are between $-2$ and $+2$. Therefore, on the basis of the standardized residuals, we have no reason to question the assumption that $\epsilon$ has a normal distribution.

In the following subsection we will show how Excel can be used to construct what it calls a standardized residual plot. Excel's standardized residual plot is really an approximation of the true standardized residual plot. In Excel, the standard deviation of the $i$th residual is not computed using equation (14.30). Instead, Excel estimates $s_{y_i - \hat{y}_i}$ using the standard deviation of the $n$ residual values. Then, dividing each residual by this estimate, Excel obtains what it refers to as a standard residual. The plot of these standard residuals is what you get when you request a plot of the standardized residuals using Excel's Regression tool.

We will illustrate how to construct a standardized residual plot using Excel for the Armand's Pizza Parlors problem. The residuals for the Armand's Pizza Parlors problem are $-12$, $15$, $-12$, $18$, $-3$, $-3$, $-3$, $9$, $-21$, and $12$. Using Excel's STDEV function, we computed a standard deviation of 13.0384 for these 10 data values. To compute the standard residuals, Excel divides each residual by 13.0384; the results are shown in Table 14.9. Both the standardized residuals, computed in Table 14.8, and Excel's standard residuals are shown. There is not a great deal of difference between Excel's standard residuals and the true standardized residuals. In general, the differences get smaller as the sample size increases. Often we are only interested in identifying the general pattern of the points in a standardized residual plot; in such cases, the small differences between the standardized residuals and Excel's standard residuals will have little effect on the pattern observed. Thus these differences will not influence the conclusions reached when we use the residual plot to validate model assumptions.

## Using Excel to Construct a Standardized Residual Plot

The Regression tool and the Chart Wizard can be used to obtain Excel's standardized residual plot. First, the steps that we described in Section 14.6 in order to conduct a regression analysis are performed with one change. When the Regression dialog box appears (see Fig-

**TABLE 14.9**   COMPUTATION OF EXCEL'S STANDARD RESIDUALS

| Restaurant $i$ | Values from Table 14.8 | | | Values Using Excel | |
|---|---|---|---|---|---|
| | $y_i - \hat{y}_i$ | $s_{y_i - \hat{y}_i}$ | Standardized Residuals | Estimate of $s_{y_i - \hat{y}_i}$ | Standard Residuals |
| 1 | −12 | 11.1193 | −1.0792 | 13.0384 | −0.9204 |
| 2 | 15 | 12.2709 | 1.2224 | 13.0384 | 1.1504 |
| 3 | −12 | 12.6493 | −.9487 | 13.0384 | −0.9204 |
| 4 | 18 | 12.6493 | 1.4230 | 13.0384 | 1.3805 |
| 5 | −3 | 13.0682 | −.2296 | 13.0384 | −0.2301 |
| 6 | −3 | 13.0682 | −.2296 | 13.0384 | −0.2301 |
| 7 | −3 | 12.6493 | −.2372 | 13.0384 | −0.2301 |
| 8 | 9 | 12.6493 | .7115 | 13.0384 | 0.6903 |
| 9 | −21 | 12.2709 | −1.7114 | 13.0384 | −1.6106 |
| 10 | 12 | 11.1193 | 1.0792 | 13.0384 | 0.9204 |

ure 14.11), we must select the Standardized Residuals option. In addition to the regression output described previously, the output will contain a list of predicted values of $y$, residuals, and standard residuals, as shown in cells A34:D46 in Figure 14.19.

The Standardized Residuals option does not automatically produce a standardized residual plot. But we can use Excel's Chart Wizard to develop a scatter diagram in which the values of the independent variable are placed on the horizontal axis and the values of the standard residuals are placed on the vertical axis. The procedure that describes how to use Excel's Chart Wizard to develop a scatter diagram in regression analysis was described in Section 14.2. Because the Chart Wizard requires that the two variables being plotted be located in adjacent columns of the worksheet, we copied the data and heading for the independent variable Population into cells F36:F46 and the data and heading for the standard residuals into cells G36:G46.

Using the data in cells F36:G46 and the Chart Wizard we obtained the scatter diagram shown in Figure 14.19; this scatter diagram is Excel's version of the standardized residual plot for the Armand's Pizza problem. Comparing Excel's version of the standardized residual plot to the standardized residual plot in Figure 14.18, we see the same pattern evident. All of the standardized residuals in both figures are between −2 and +2, indicating no reason to question the assumption that $\epsilon$ has a normal distribution.

## Normal Probability Plot

**TABLE 14.10**

NORMAL SCORES FOR $n = 10$

| Order Statistic | Normal Score |
|---|---|
| 1 | −1.55 |
| 2 | −1.00 |
| 3 | −.65 |
| 4 | −.37 |
| 5 | −.12 |
| 6 | .12 |
| 7 | .37 |
| 8 | .65 |
| 9 | 1.00 |
| 10 | 1.55 |

Another approach for determining the validity of the assumption that the error term has a normal distribution is the **normal probability plot.** To show how a normal probability plot is developed, we introduce the concept of *normal scores.*

Suppose 10 values are selected randomly from a normal probability distribution with a mean of zero and a standard deviation of one, and that the sampling process is repeated over and over with the values in each sample of 10 ordered from smallest to largest. For now, let us consider only the smallest value in each sample. The random variable representing the smallest value obtained in repeated sampling is called the first-order statistic.

Statisticians have shown that for samples of size 10 from a standard normal probability distribution, the expected value of the first-order statistic is −1.55. This expected value is called a normal score. For the case with a sample of size $n = 10$, there are 10 order statistics and 10 normal scores (see Table 14.10). In general, if we have a data set consisting of $n$ observations, there are $n$ order statistics and hence $n$ normal scores.

**FIGURE 14.19    EXCEL'S STANDARDIZED RESIDUAL PLOT AGAINST THE INDEPENDENT VARIABLE POPULATION FOR ARMAND'S PIZZA PROBLEM**

| | A | B | C | D | E | F | G | H |
|---|---|---|---|---|---|---|---|---|
| 34 | RESIDUAL OUTPUT | | | | | | | |
| 35 | | | | | | | | |
| 36 | Observation | Predicted Sales | Residuals | Standard Residuals | | Population | Standard Residuals | |
| 37 | 1 | 70 | -12 | -0.9204 | | 2 | -0.9204 | |
| 38 | 2 | 90 | 15 | 1.1504 | | 6 | 1.1504 | |
| 39 | 3 | 100 | -12 | -0.9204 | | 8 | -0.9204 | |
| 40 | 4 | 100 | 18 | 1.3805 | | 8 | 1.3805 | |
| 41 | 5 | 120 | -3 | -0.2301 | | 12 | -0.2301 | |
| 42 | 6 | 140 | -3 | -0.2301 | | 16 | -0.2301 | |
| 43 | 7 | 160 | -3 | -0.2301 | | 20 | -0.2301 | |
| 44 | 8 | 160 | 9 | 0.6903 | | 20 | 0.6903 | |
| 45 | 9 | 170 | -21 | -1.6106 | | 22 | -1.6106 | |
| 46 | 10 | 190 | 12 | 0.9204 | | 26 | 0.9204 | |
| 47 | | | | | | | | |
| 48 | | | | | | | | |
| 49 | | | | | | | | |
| 50 | | | | | | | | |
| 51 | | | | | | | | |
| 52 | | | | | | | | |
| 53 | | | | | | | | |
| 54 | | | | | | | | |
| 55 | | | | | | | | |
| 56 | | | | | | | | |
| 57 | | | | | | | | |
| 58 | | | | | | | | |
| 59 | | | | | | | | |
| 60 | | | | | | | | |
| 61 | | | | | | | | |

Note: Rows 1–33 are hidden.

**TABLE 14.11**

**NORMAL SCORES AND ORDERED STANDARDIZED RESIDUALS FOR ARMAND'S PIZZA PARLORS**

| Normal Scores | Ordered Standardized Residuals |
|---|---|
| -1.55 | -1.7114 |
| -1.00 | -1.0792 |
| -.65 | -.9487 |
| -.37 | -.2372 |
| -.12 | -.2296 |
| .12 | -.2296 |
| .37 | .7115 |
| .65 | 1.0792 |
| 1.00 | 1.2224 |
| 1.55 | 1.4230 |

Let us now show how the 10 normal scores can be used to determine whether the standardized residuals for Armand's Pizza Parlors appear to come from a standard normal probability distribution. We begin by ordering the 10 standardized residuals from Table 14.8. The 10 normal scores and the ordered standardized residuals are shown together in Table 14.11. If the normality assumption is satisfied, the smallest standardized residual should be close to the smallest normal score, the next smallest standardized residual should be close to the next smallest normal score, and so on. If we were to develop a plot with the normal scores on the horizontal axis and the corresponding standardized residuals on the vertical axis, the plotted points should cluster closely around a 45-degree line passing through the origin if the standardized residuals are approximately normally distributed. Such a plot is referred to as a *normal probability plot*.

Figure 14.20 is the normal probability plot for the Armand's Pizza Parlors example. Judgment is used to determine whether the pattern observed deviates from the line enough to conclude that the standardized residuals are not from a standard normal probability distribution. In Figure 14.20, we see that the points are grouped closely about the line. We therefore conclude that the assumption of the error term having a normal probability distribution is reasonable. In general, the more closely the points are clustered about the 45-degree line, the stronger the evidence supporting the normality assumption. Any substantial curvature in the normal probability plot is evidence that the residuals have not come from a normal distribution.

**FIGURE 14.20**    NORMAL PROBABILITY PLOT FOR ARMAND'S PIZZA PARLORS

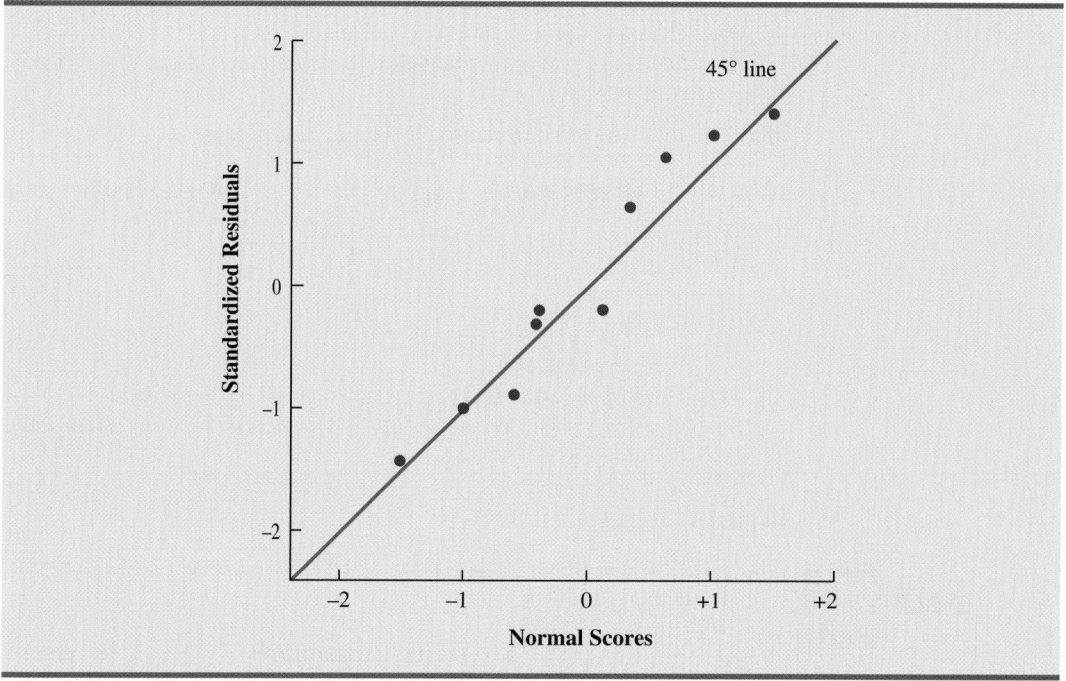

## NOTES AND COMMENTS

1. The analysis of residuals is the primary method statisticians use to verify that the assumptions associated with a regression model are valid. Even if no violations are found, it does not necessarily follow that the model will yield good predictions. However, if in addition the statistical tests support the conclusion of significance and the coefficient of determination is large, we should be able to develop good estimates using the estimated regression equation.

2. When model assumptions are found to be violated, the appropriate corrective action must be based on good judgment; recommendations from an experienced statistician can be valuable. If one or more assumptions are questionable, but not

necessarily invalid, the user should be cautious in using and interpreting the regression results.

3. Another variation of the residual plot places the predicted value of the dependent variable $\hat{y}$ on the horizontal axis and the residual values on the vertical axis. A point is plotted for each residual; the first coordinate for each point is given by $\hat{y}_i$ and the second coordinate is given by the corresponding value of the $i$th residual $y_i - \hat{y}_i$. For simple linear regression, both the residual plot against $x$ and the residual plot against $\hat{y}$ provide the same information. In multiple regression analysis, the residual plot against $\hat{y}$ is more widely used. We will discuss the use of residual plots against $\hat{y}$ in Chapter 15.

## EXERCISES

### Methods

47. Given are data for two variables, $x$ and $y$.

| $x_i$ | 6 | 11 | 15 | 18 | 20 |
|-------|---|----|----|----|----|
| $y_i$ | 6 | 8  | 12 | 20 | 30 |

a. Develop an estimated regression equation for these data.
b. Compute the residuals.

c. Develop a plot of the residuals against the independent variable $x$. Do the assumptions about the error terms seem to be satisfied?
d. Compute the standardized residuals.
e. Develop a plot of the standardized residuals against $x$. What conclusions can you draw from this plot?

48. The following data were used in a regression study.

| Observation | $x_i$ | $y_i$ | Observation | $x_i$ | $y_i$ |
|---|---|---|---|---|---|
| 1 | 2 | 4 | 6 | 7 | 6 |
| 2 | 3 | 5 | 7 | 7 | 9 |
| 3 | 4 | 4 | 8 | 8 | 5 |
| 4 | 5 | 6 | 9 | 9 | 11 |
| 5 | 7 | 4 | | | |

a. Develop an estimated regression equation for these data.
b. Construct a plot of the residuals. Do the assumptions about the error term seem to be satisfied?

## Applications

49. Data on advertising expenditures ($1000s) and revenue ($1000s) for the Four Seasons Restaurant follow.

| Advertising Expenditures | Revenue |
|---|---|
| 1 | 19 |
| 2 | 32 |
| 4 | 44 |
| 6 | 40 |
| 10 | 52 |
| 14 | 53 |
| 20 | 54 |

a. Let $x$ equal advertising expenditures ($1000s) and $y$ equal revenue ($1000s). Use the method of least squares to develop a straight-line approximation of the relationship between the two variables.
b. Test whether revenue and advertising expenditures are related at a .05 level of significance.
c. Develop a plot of the residuals against the independent variable.
d. What conclusions can you draw from residual analysis? Should this model be used, or should we look for a better one?

50. Refer to Exercise 9, where an estimated regression equation relating years of experience and annual sales was developed.
a. Compute the residuals and construct a residual plot for this problem.
b. Do the assumptions about the error terms seem reasonable in light of the residual plot?

51. American Depository Receipts (ADRs) are certificates traded on the NYSE representing shares of a foreign company held on deposit in a bank in its home country. The following table shows the price/earnings (P/E) ratio and the percentage return on investment (ROE) for 10 Indian companies that are likely new ADRs (*Bloomberg Personal Finance*, April 2000).

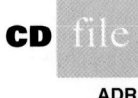

| Company | ROE | P/E |
|---|---|---|
| Bharti Televentures | 6.43 | 36.88 |
| Gujarat Ambuja Cements | 13.49 | 27.03 |
| Hindalco Industries | 14.04 | 10.83 |
| ICICI | 20.67 | 5.15 |
| Mahanagar Telephone Nigam | 22.74 | 13.35 |

|  | **ROE** | **P/E** |
|---|---|---|
| NIIT | 46.23 | 95.59 |
| Pentamedia Graphics | 28.90 | 54.85 |
| Satyam Computer Services | 54.01 | 189.21 |
| Silverline Technologies | 28.02 | 75.86 |
| Videsh Sanchar Nigam | 27.04 | 13.17 |

**a.** Use Excel to develop an estimated regression equation relating $y$ = P/E and $x$ = ROE.

**b.** Construct a residual plot of the standardized residuals against the independent variable.

**c.** Do the assumptions about the error terms and model form seem reasonable in light of the residual plot?

## 14.9   OUTLIERS AND INFLUENTIAL OBSERVATIONS

In this section we discuss how to identify observations that can be classified as outliers or as being especially influential in determining the estimated regression equation. Some steps that should be taken when such observations are identified are provided.

### Detecting Outliers

An **outlier** is a data point (observation) that does not fit the trend shown by the remaining data. Outliers represent observations that are suspect and warrant careful examination. They may represent erroneous data; if so, they should be corrected. They may signal a violation of model assumptions; if so, another model should be considered. Finally, they may simply be unusual values that have occurred by chance. In this case, they should be retained.

**TABLE 14.12**

DATA SET ILLUSTRATING THE EFFECT OF AN OUTLIER

| $x_i$ | $y_i$ |
|---|---|
| 1 | 45 |
| 1 | 55 |
| 2 | 50 |
| 3 | 75 |
| 3 | 40 |
| 3 | 45 |
| 4 | 30 |
| 4 | 35 |
| 5 | 25 |
| 6 | 15 |

**CD file**

**Outlier**

To illustrate the process of detecting outliers, consider the data set in Table 14.12; Figure 14.21 shows the scatter diagram for these data and a portion of the Regression tool output, including the residual output obtained using the Standardized Residuals option. The estimated regression equation is $\hat{y} = 64.958 - 7.3305x$ and R Square is .4968; thus, only 49.68% of the variability in the values of $y$ is explained by the estimated regression equation. However, except for observation 4 ($x_4 = 3$, $y_4 = 75$), a pattern suggesting a strong negative linear relationship is apparent. Indeed, given the pattern of the rest of the data, we would have expected $y_4$ to be much smaller and hence would consider observation 4 to be an outlier. For the case of simple linear regression, one can often detect outliers by simply examining the scatter diagram.

The standardized residuals can also be used to identify outliers. If an observation deviates greatly from the pattern of the rest of the data, the corresponding standardized residual will be large in absolute value. We recommend considering any observation with a standardized residual of less than $-2$ or greater than $+2$ as an outlier. With normally distributed errors, standardized residuals should be outside these limits approximately 5% of the time. In the residual output section of Figure 14.21 we see that the standard residual value for observation 4 is 2.68; this value suggests we treat observation 4 as an outlier.

In deciding how to handle an outlier, we should first check to see whether it is a valid observation. Perhaps an error has been made in initially recording the data or in entering the data into the worksheet. For example, suppose that in checking the data in Table 14.12, we find that an error has been made and that the correct value for observation 4 is $x_4 = 3$, $y_4 = 30$. Figure 14.22 shows a portion of the Regression tool output after correction of the value of $y_4$. The estimated regression equation is $\hat{y} = 59.237 - 6.9492x$ and R Square is .8380. Note also that no standard residuals are less than $-2$ or greater than $+2$; hence, the revised data contain no outliers. We see that using the incorrect data value had a substantial effect on the goodness of fit. With the correct data, the value of R Square has increased

**FIGURE 14.21**     EXCEL OUTPUT FOR THE OUTLIER DATA SET

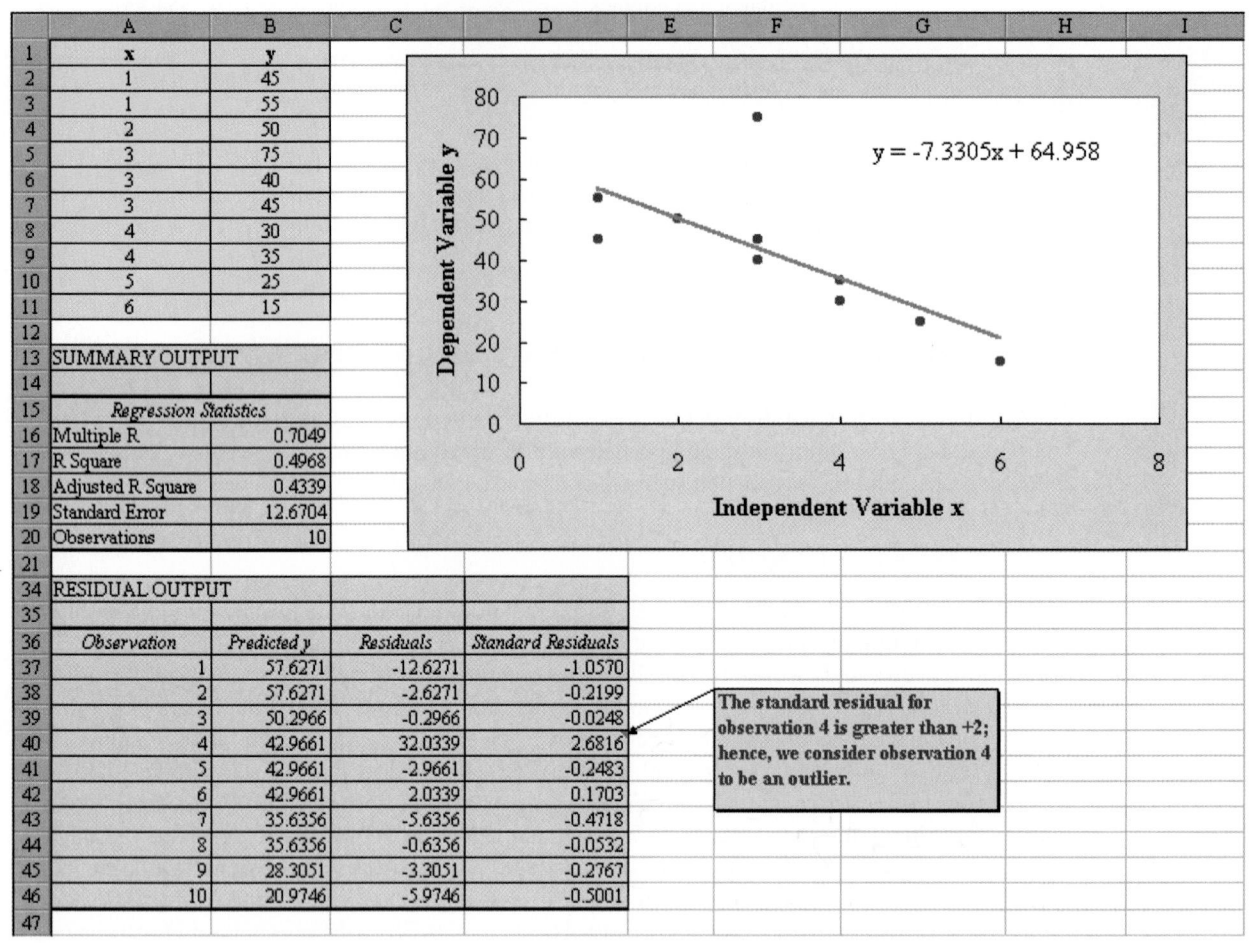

Note: Rows 22–33 are hidden.

from .4968 to .8380 and the value of $b_0$ has decreased from 64.958 to 59.237. The slope of the line has changed from $-7.3305$ to $-6.9492$. The identification of the outlier enables us to correct the data error and improve the regression results.

## Detecting Influential Observations

An **influential observation** is an observation that has a strong influence on the regression results. An influential observation may be an outlier (an observation with a $y$ value that deviates substantially from the trend of the remaining data), it may correspond to an $x$ value far from its mean (extreme $x$ value), or it may be caused by a combination of a somewhat off-trend $y$ value and a somewhat extreme $x$ value. Because influential observations may have such a dramatic effect on the estimated regression equation, they must be examined carefully. First, we should check to make sure no error has been made in collecting or recording the data. If such an error has occurred, it can be corrected and a new estimated regression equation developed. If the observation is valid, we might consider ourselves for-

**FIGURE 14.22**    EXCEL OUTPUT FOR THE REVISED OUTLIER DATA SET

| | A | B | C | D | E | F | G | H | I |
|---|---|---|---|---|---|---|---|---|---|
| 1 | **x** | **y** | | | | | | | |
| 2 | 1 | 45 | | | | | | | |
| 3 | 1 | 55 | | | 60 | | | | |
| 4 | 2 | 50 | | | | | | | |
| 5 | 3 | 30 | | 50 | | | y = -6.9492x + 59.237 | | |
| 6 | 3 | 40 | | | | | | | |
| 7 | 3 | 45 | | 40 | | | | | |
| 8 | 4 | 30 | | | | | | | |
| 9 | 4 | 35 | | 30 | | | | | |
| 10 | 5 | 25 | | | | | | | |
| 11 | 6 | 15 | | 20 | | | | | |
| 12 | | | | | | | | | |
| 13 | SUMMARY OUTPUT | | | 10 | | | | | |
| 14 | | | | | | | | | |
| 15 | *Regression Statistics* | | | 0 | | | | | |
| 16 | Multiple R | 0.9154 | | | | | | | |
| 17 | R Square | 0.8380 | | 0 | 2 | 4 | 6 | 8 | |
| 18 | Adjusted R Square | 0.8177 | | | | | | | |
| 19 | Standard Error | 5.2481 | | | **Independent Variable x** | | | | |
| 20 | Observations | 10 | | | | | | | |
| 21 | | | | | | | | | |
| 34 | RESIDUAL OUTPUT | | | | | | | | |
| 35 | | | | | | | | | |
| 36 | *Observation* | *Predicted y* | *Residuals* | *Standard Residuals* | | | | | |
| 37 | 1 | 52.2881 | -7.2881 | -1.4730 | | | | | |
| 38 | 2 | 52.2881 | 2.7119 | 0.5481 | | | | | |
| 39 | 3 | 45.3390 | 4.6610 | 0.9420 | | | | | |
| 40 | 4 | 38.3898 | -8.3898 | -1.6956 | | | | | |
| 41 | 5 | 38.3898 | 1.6102 | 0.3254 | | | | | |
| 42 | 6 | 38.3898 | 6.6102 | 1.3359 | | | | | |
| 43 | 7 | 31.4407 | -1.4407 | -0.2912 | | | | | |
| 44 | 8 | 31.4407 | 3.5593 | 0.7194 | | | | | |
| 45 | 9 | 24.4915 | 0.5085 | 0.1028 | | | | | |
| 46 | 10 | 17.5424 | -2.5424 | -0.5138 | | | | | |
| 47 | | | | | | | | | |

Note: Rows 22–33 are hidden.

The y-axis is labeled "Dependent Variable y".

tunate to have it. Such a point, if valid, can contribute to a better understanding of the appropriate model and can lead to a better estimated regression equation.

To illustrate the process of detecting influential observations, consider the data set in Table 14.13. The top part of Figure 14.23 shows the scatter diagram for these data and the graph of the corresponding estimated regression equation $\hat{y} = 127.47 - .04251x$. The bottom part of Figure 14.23 shows the scatter diagram for the data in Table 14.13 with observation 7 ($x_7 = 70$, $y_7 = 100$) deleted; for these data the estimated regression equation is $\hat{y} = 138.18 - 1.0909x$. With observation 7 deleted, the value of $b_0$ has increased from 127.47 to 138.18. The slope of the line has changed from $-0.4251$ to $-1.0909$. The effect of observation 7 on the regression results is dramatic and is confirmed by looking at the graphs of the two estimated regression equations. Clearly observation 7 is influential.

Observations with extreme values for the independent variables are called **high leverage points.** Observation 7 in the data set shown in Table 14.13 (which we have identified as being influential) is a point with high leverage. The leverage of an observation is determined by how far the value of the independent variable is from its mean value. For the

**TABLE 14.13**

DATA SET
ILLUSTRATING
THE EFFECT OF
AN INFLUENTIAL
OBSERVATION

| $x_i$ | $y_i$ |
|-------|-------|
| 10 | 125 |
| 10 | 130 |
| 15 | 120 |
| 20 | 115 |
| 20 | 120 |
| 25 | 110 |
| 70 | 100 |

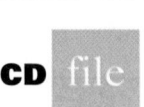

**Influential**

single-independent-variable case, the leverage of the $i$th observation, denoted $h_i$, can be computed using equation (14.33).

**Leverage of Observation $i$**

$$h_i = \frac{1}{n} + \frac{(x_i - \bar{x})^2}{\Sigma(x_i - \bar{x})^2} \qquad \textbf{(14.33)}$$

From the formula, it is clear that the farther $x_i$ is from its mean $\bar{x}$, the higher the leverage of observation $i$. For the data in Table 14.13, the leverage of observation 7 is computed using equation (14.33) as follows:

$$h_i = \frac{1}{n} + \frac{(x_i - \bar{x})^2}{\Sigma(x_i - \bar{x})^2} = \frac{1}{7} + \frac{(70 - 24.286)^2}{2621.43} = .94$$

For simple linear regression, one major statistical software package (Minitab) identifies observations as having high leverage if $h_i > 6/n$; for the data in Table 14.13, $6/n = 6/7 = .86$. Thus, because $h_i = .94 > .86$, observation 7 would be identified as having high leverage. Data points having high leverage are often influential. Influential observations that are caused by an interaction of somewhat large residuals and somewhat high leverage can be

**FIGURE 14.23**   SCATTER DIAGRAMS FOR THE DATA SET WITH AN INFLUENTIAL OBSERVATION

|   | A | B | C | D | E | F | G | H | I | J | K |
|---|---|---|---|---|---|---|---|---|---|---|---|
| 1 | Data Set Including Observation 7 | | | | | | | | | | |
| 2 | Observation | x | y | | | | | | | | |
| 3 | 1 | 10 | 125 | | | | | | | | |
| 4 | 2 | 10 | 130 | | | | | | | | |
| 5 | 3 | 15 | 120 | | | | | | | | |
| 6 | 4 | 20 | 115 | | | | | | | | |
| 7 | 5 | 20 | 120 | | | | | | | | |
| 8 | 6 | 25 | 110 | | | | | | | | |
| 9 | 7 | 70 | 100 | | | | | | | | |
| 10 | | | | | | | | | | | |
| 11 | | | | | | | | | | | |
| 12 | | | | | | | | | | | |
| 13 | | | | | | | | | | | |
| 14 | | | | | | | | | | | |
| 15 | Data Set With Observation 7 Deleted | | | | | | | | | | |
| 16 | Observation | x | y | | | | | | | | |
| 17 | 1 | 10 | 125 | | | | | | | | |
| 18 | 2 | 10 | 130 | | | | | | | | |
| 19 | 3 | 15 | 120 | | | | | | | | |
| 20 | 4 | 20 | 115 | | | | | | | | |
| 21 | 5 | 20 | 120 | | | | | | | | |
| 22 | 6 | 25 | 110 | | | | | | | | |
| 23 | | | | | | | | | | | |
| 24 | | | | | | | | | | | |
| 25 | | | | | | | | | | | |
| 26 | | | | | | | | | | | |
| 27 | | | | | | | | | | | |

Scatter Diagram Including Observation 7 — $y = -0.4251x + 127.47$

Scatter Diagram With Observation 7 Deleted — $y = -1.0909x + 138.18$

difficult to detect. Diagnostic procedures are available that take both into account in determining when an observation is influential. More advanced books on regression analysis discuss the use of such procedures. Excel does not have built-in capabilities for identifying outliers and high leverage points. Thus, we recommend reviewing the scatter diagram after fitting the regression line. For any points significantly off the line, rerun the regression analysis after deleting the observation. If the results change dramatically, the point in question is an influential observation.

## EXERCISES

### Methods

**52.** Consider the following data for two variables, $x$ and $y$.

| $x_i$ | 135 | 110 | 130 | 145 | 175 | 160 | 120 |
|-------|-----|-----|-----|-----|-----|-----|-----|
| $y_i$ | 145 | 100 | 120 | 120 | 130 | 130 | 110 |

a. Develop a scatter diagram for these data. Does the scatter diagram indicate any outliers in the data? In general, what implications does this finding have for simple linear regression?
b. Compute the standardized residuals for these data. Do there appear to be any outliers in the data? Explain.

**53.** Consider the following data for two variables, $x$ and $y$.

| $x_i$ | 4 | 5 | 7 | 8 | 10 | 12 | 12 | 22 |
|-------|---|---|---|---|----|----|----|----|
| $y_i$ | 12 | 14 | 16 | 15 | 18 | 20 | 24 | 19 |

a. Develop a scatter diagram for these data. Does the scatter diagram indicate any influential observations? Explain.
b. Compute the standardized residuals for these data. Do there appear to be any outliers in the data? Explain.
c. Compute the leverage values for these data. Do there appear to be any influential observations in these data? Explain.

### Applications

**54.** The following data show the media expenditures ($ millions) and the shipments in bbls. (millions) for 10 major brands of beer (*Superbrands '98,* October 20, 1997).

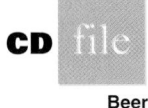

**Beer**

| Brand | Media Expenditures ($millions) | Shipments |
|-------|--------------------------------|-----------|
| Budweiser | 120.0 | 36.3 |
| Bud Light | 68.7 | 20.7 |
| Miller Lite | 100.1 | 15.9 |
| Coors Light | 76.6 | 13.2 |
| Busch | 8.7 | 8.1 |
| Natural Light | 0.1 | 7.1 |
| Miller Genuine Draft | 21.5 | 5.6 |
| Miller High Life | 1.4 | 4.4 |
| Busch Light | 5.3 | 4.3 |
| Milwaukee's Best | 1.7 | 4.3 |

a. Develop the estimated regression equation for these data.
b. Use residual analysis to determine whether any outliers and/or influential observations are present. Briefly summarize your findings and conclusions.

**55.** Nielsen Media Research collects data showing the number of households tuned in to shows that carry a particular advertisement. This information is useful to advertisers because it tells them how many consumers they are reaching. The following data show the number of household exposures in millions and the number of times the ad was aired for the week of November 24–30, 1997 (*USA Today,* December 15, 1997).

**CD** file

**Nielsen2**

| Advertised Brand | Times Ad Aired | Household Exposures |
|---|---|---|
| Sears | 95 | 758.8 |
| J.C. Penney | 46 | 323.0 |
| Burger King | 41 | 275.3 |
| Polaroid One Step Express | 38 | 241.8 |
| Wendy's | 29 | 219.9 |
| McDonald's | 32 | 198.5 |
| Target | 25 | 193.8 |
| Kmart | 21 | 189.7 |
| Visa | 21 | 161.9 |
| Nissan Frontier | 16 | 160.0 |

**a.** Develop the estimated regression equation that can be used to predict the number of household exposures given the number of times the ad was aired.
**b.** Use residual analysis to determine whether any outliers and/or influential observations are present. Briefly summarize your findings and conclusions.

**56.** The market capitalization and the salary of the chief executive officer (CEO) for 20 companies are shown in the following table (*The Wall Street Journal,* February 24, 2000, and April 6, 2000).

**CD** file

**CEO**

| | Market Cap. ($millions) | CEO Salary ($1000s) |
|---|---|---|
| Anheuser-Busch | 32,977.4 | 1,130 |
| AT&T | 162,365.1 | 1,400 |
| Charles Schwab | 31,363.8 | 800 |
| Chevron | 56,849.0 | 1,350 |
| DuPont | 68,848.0 | 1,000 |
| General Elec. | 507,216.8 | 3,325 |
| Gillette | 44,180.1 | 978 |
| IBM | 194,455.9 | 2,000 |
| Johnson & Johnson | 143,131.0 | 1,365 |
| Kimberly-Clark | 35,377.5 | 950 |
| Merrill Lynch | 31,062.1 | 700 |
| Motorola | 92,923.7 | 1,275 |
| Philip Morris | 54,421.2 | 1,625 |
| Procter & Gamble | 144,152.9 | 1,318.3 |
| Qualcomm | 116,840.8 | 773 |
| Schering-Plough | 62,259.4 | 1,200 |
| Sun Microsystems | 120,966.5 | 116 |
| Texaco | 30,040.7 | 950 |
| USWest | 36,450.8 | 897 |
| Walt Disney | 61,288.1 | 750 |

**a.** Develop the estimated regression equation that can be used to predict the CEO salary given the market capitalization.
**b.** Use residual analysis to determine whether any outliers and/or influential observations are present. Briefly summarize your findings and conclusions.

## SUMMARY

In this chapter we first showed how regression analysis can be used to determine how a dependent variable $y$ is related to an independent variable $x$. In simple linear regression, the regression model is $y = \beta_0 + \beta_1 x + \epsilon$. The simple linear regression equation $E(y) = \beta_0 + \beta_1 x$ describes how the mean or expected value of $y$ is related to $x$. We used sample data and the least squares method to develop the estimated regression equation $\hat{y} = b_0 + b_1 x$. In effect, $b_0$ and $b_1$ are the sample statistics used to estimate the unknown model parameters $\beta_0$ and $\beta_1$.

The coefficient of determination was presented as a measure of the goodness of fit for the estimated regression equation; it can be interpreted as the proportion of the variation in the dependent variable $y$ that can be explained by the estimated regression equation. We reviewed correlation as a descriptive measure of the strength of a linear relationship between two variables.

The assumptions about the regression model and its associated error term $\epsilon$ were discussed, and $t$ and $F$ tests, based on those assumptions, were presented as a means for determining whether the relationship between two variables is statistically significant. We showed how to use the estimated regression equation to develop confidence interval estimates of the mean value of $y$ and prediction interval estimates of individual values of $y$.

We used Excel extensively in simple linear regression. We showed how the Chart Wizard could be used to develop a scatter diagram and to fit a trend line to data, and in Section 14.6, we introduced the use of Excel's Regression tool for performing a comprehensive analysis of a regression problem. In Section 14.8 we showed how the Regression tool could also be used to develop a residual plot and how we could use the residuals to validate the regression model assumptions. The chapter concluded with a section on how to identify outliers and influential observations.

## GLOSSARY

**Dependent variable**   The variable that is being predicted or explained. It is denoted by $y$.

**Independent variable**   The variable that is doing the predicting or explaining. It is denoted by $x$.

**Simple linear regression**   Regression analysis involving one independent variable and one dependent variable in which the relationship between the variables is approximated by a straight line.

**Simple linear regression model**   The equation that describes how $y$ is related to $x$ and an error term $\epsilon$: $y = \beta_0 + \beta_1 x + \epsilon$.

**Simple linear regression equation**   The equation that describes how the mean or expected value of the dependent variable is related to the independent variable: $E(y) = \beta_0 + \beta_1 x$.

**Estimated simple linear regression equation**   The estimate of the regression equation developed from sample data by using the least squares method: $\hat{y} = b_0 + b_1 x$.

**Least squares method**   The procedure used to develop the estimated regression equation. The objective is to minimize $\Sigma(y_i - \hat{y}_i)^2$.

**Scatter diagram**   A graph of bivariate data in which the independent variable is on the horizontal axis and the dependent variable is on the vertical axis.

**Coefficient of determination**   A measure of the goodness of fit of the estimated regression equation. It can be interpreted as the proportion of the variability in the dependent variable $y$ that is explained by the estimated regression equation.

*i*th Residual   The difference between the observed value of the dependent variable and the value predicted using the estimated regression equation; that is, for the *i*th observation the *i*th residual is $y_i - \hat{y}_i$.

**Correlation coefficient**   A measure of the strength of the linear relationship between two variables.

**Mean square error**   The estimate of $\sigma^2$, the variance of the error term $\epsilon$. It is denoted by MSE or $s^2$.

**Standard error of the estimate**   The square root of the mean square error, denoted by $s$. It is the estimate of $\sigma$, the standard deviation of the error term $\epsilon$.

**ANOVA table**   The analysis of variance table used to summarize the computations associated with the $F$ test for significance.

**Confidence interval estimate**   The interval estimate of the mean value of $y$ for a given value of $x$.

**Prediction interval estimate**   The interval estimate of an individual value of $y$ for a given value of $x$.

**Residual analysis**   The analysis of the residuals used to determine whether the assumptions made about the regression model appear to be valid.

**Standardized residual**   The value obtained by dividing a residual by its standard deviation.

**Normal probability plot**   A graph of the standardized residuals plotted against values of the normal scores. This plot helps determine whether the assumption that the error term has a normal probability distribution appears to be valid.

**Outlier**   A data point or observation that does not fit the trend shown by the remaining data.

**Influential observation**   An observation that has a strong influence on the regression results.

**High leverage points**   Observations with extreme values for the independent variables.

## KEY FORMULAS

**Simple Linear Regression Model**

$$y = \beta_0 + \beta_1 x + \epsilon \tag{14.1}$$

**Simple Linear Regression Equation**

$$E(y) = \beta_0 + \beta_1 x \tag{14.2}$$

**Estimated Simple Linear Regression Equation**

$$\hat{y} = b_0 + b_1 x \tag{14.3}$$

**Least Squares Criterion**

$$\min \Sigma(y_i - \hat{y}_i)^2 \tag{14.5}$$

**Slope and *y*-Intercept for the Estimated Regression Equation**

$$b_1 = \frac{\Sigma(x_i - \bar{x})(y_i - \bar{y})}{\Sigma(x_i - \bar{x})^2} \tag{14.6}$$

$$b_0 = \bar{y} - b_1\bar{x} \tag{14.7}$$

**Sum of Squares Due to Error**

$$SSE = \Sigma(y_i - \hat{y}_i)^2 \tag{14.8}$$

**Total Sum of Squares**

$$SST = \Sigma(y_i - \bar{y})^2 \tag{14.9}$$

**Sum of Squares Due to Regression**

$$SSR = \Sigma(\hat{y}_i - \bar{y})^2 \tag{14.10}$$

**Relationship Among SST, SSR, and SSE**

$$SST = SSR + SSE \tag{14.11}$$

**Coefficient of Determination**

$$r^2 = \frac{SSR}{SST} \tag{14.12}$$

**Sample Correlation Coefficient**

$$r_{xy} = (\text{sign of } b_1)\sqrt{\text{Coefficient of Determination}}$$
$$= (\text{sign of } b_1)\sqrt{r^2} \tag{14.13}$$

**Mean Square Error (Estimate of $\sigma^2$)**

$$s^2 = MSE = \frac{SSE}{n - 2} \tag{14.15}$$

**Standard Error of the Estimate**

$$s = \sqrt{MSE} = \sqrt{\frac{SSE}{n - 2}} \tag{14.16}$$

**Standard Deviation of $b_1$**

$$\sigma_{b_1} = \frac{\sigma}{\sqrt{\Sigma(x_i - \bar{x})^2}} \tag{14.17}$$

**Estimated Standard Deviation of $b_1$**

$$s_{b_1} = \frac{s}{\sqrt{\Sigma(x_i - \bar{x})^2}} \tag{14.18}$$

**$t$ Test Statistic**

$$t = \frac{b_1}{s_{b_1}} \tag{14.19}$$

**Mean Square Due to Regression**

$$MSR = \frac{SSR}{\text{number of independent variables}} \tag{14.20}$$

**$F$ Test Statistic**

$$F = \frac{MSR}{MSE} \tag{14.21}$$

**Estimated Standard Deviation of $\hat{y}_p$**

$$s_{\hat{y}_p} = s\sqrt{\frac{1}{n} + \frac{(x_p - \bar{x})^2}{\Sigma(x_i - \bar{x})^2}} \qquad \textbf{(14.23)}$$

**Confidence Interval Estimate of $E(y_p)$**

$$\hat{y}_p \pm t_{\alpha/2}s_{\hat{y}_p} \qquad \textbf{(14.24)}$$

**Estimated Standard Deviation When Predicting an Individual Value**

$$s_{ind} = s\sqrt{1 + \frac{1}{n} + \frac{(x_p - \bar{x})^2}{\Sigma(x_i - \bar{x})^2}} \qquad \textbf{(14.26)}$$

**Prediction Interval Estimate of $y_p$**

$$\hat{y}_p \pm t_{\alpha/2}s_{ind} \qquad \textbf{(14.27)}$$

**Residual for Observation $i$**

$$y_i - \hat{y}_i \qquad \textbf{(14.28)}$$

**Standard Deviation of the $i$th Residual**

$$s_{y_i - \hat{y}_i} = s\sqrt{1 - h_i} \qquad \textbf{(14.30)}$$

$$h_i = \frac{1}{n} + \frac{(x_i - \bar{x})^2}{\Sigma(x_i - \bar{x})^2} \qquad \textbf{(14.31)}$$

**Standardized Residual for Observation $i$**

$$\frac{y_i - \hat{y}_i}{s_{y_i - \hat{y}_i}} \qquad \textbf{(14.32)}$$

## SUPPLEMENTARY EXERCISES

**57.** Does a high value of $r^2$ imply that two variables are causally related? Explain.

**58.** In your own words, explain the difference between an interval estimate of the mean value of $y$ for a given $x$ and an interval estimate for an individual value of $y$ for a given $x$.

**59.** What is the purpose of testing whether $\beta_1 = 0$? If we reject $\beta_1 = 0$, does it imply a good fit?

**60.** The data in the following table show the number of shares selling (millions) and the expected price (average of projected low price and projected high price) for 10 selected initial public stock offerings (*USA Today,* November 17, 1997).

**IPO**

| Company | Shares Selling | Expected Price ($) |
|---|---|---|
| American Physician | 5.0 | 15 |
| Apex Silver Mines | 9.0 | 14 |
| Dan River | 6.7 | 15 |
| Franchise Mortgage | 8.75 | 17 |
| Gene Logic | 3.0 | 11 |
| International Home Foods | 13.6 | 19 |
| PRT Group | 4.6 | 13 |
| Rayovac | 6.7 | 14 |
| RealNetworks | 3.0 | 10 |
| Software AG Systems | 7.7 | 13 |

a. Develop an estimated regression equation with the number of shares selling as the independent variable and the expected price as the dependent variable.
b. At the .05 level of significance, is there a significant relationship between the two variables?
c. Did the estimated regression equation provide a good fit? Explain.
d. Use the estimated regression equation to estimate the expected price for a firm considering an initial public offering of 6 million shares.

61. Corporate share repurchase programs are often touted as a benefit for shareholders. But Robert Gabele, director of insider research for First Call/Thomson Financial, has noted that many of these have been undertaken solely to acquire stock for a company's incentive options for top managers. Across all companies, existing stock options in 1998 represented 6.2 percent of all common shares outstanding. The following data show the number of shares covered by option grants and the number of shares outstanding for 13 companies (*Bloomberg Personal Finance,* January/February 2000).

| Company | Shares of Option Grants Outstanding (millions) | Common Shares Outstanding (millions) |
|---|---|---|
| Adobe Systems | 20.3 | 61.8 |
| Apple Computer | 52.7 | 160.9 |
| Applied Materials | 109.1 | 375.4 |
| Autodesk | 15.7 | 58.9 |
| Best Buy | 44.2 | 203.8 |
| Fruit of the Loom | 14.2 | 66.9 |
| ITT Industries | 18.0 | 87.9 |
| Merrill Lynch | 89.9 | 365.5 |
| Novell | 120.2 | 335.0 |
| Parametric Technology | 78.3 | 269.3 |
| Reebok International | 12.8 | 56.1 |
| Silicon Graphics | 52.6 | 188.8 |
| Toys R Us | 54.8 | 247.6 |

a. Develop the estimated regression equation that could be used to estimate the number of shares of option grants outstanding given the number of common shares outstanding.
b. Use the estimated regression equation to estimate the number of shares of option grants outstanding for a company that has 150 million shares of common stock outstanding.
c. Do you believe the estimated regression equation would provide a good prediction of the number of shares of option grants outstanding? Use $r^2$ to support your answer.

62. *Value Line* (February 24, 1995) reported the market beta for Woolworth Corporation at 1.25. Market betas for individual stocks are determined by simple linear regression. For each stock, the dependent variable is its quarterly percentage return (capital appreciation plus dividends) minus the percentage return that could be obtained from a risk-free investment (the Treasury Bill rate is used as the risk-free rate). The independent variable is the quarterly percentage return (capital appreciation plus dividends) for the stock market (S&P 500) minus the percentage return from a risk-free investment. An estimated regression equation is developed with quarterly data; the market beta for the stock is the slope of the estimated regression equation ($b_1$). The value of the market beta is often interpreted as a measure of the risk associated with the stock. Market betas greater than 1 indicate that the stock is more volatile than the market average; market betas less than 1 indicate that the stock is less volatile than the market average. The following figures are the differences between the percentage return and the risk-free return for 10 quarters for the S&P 500 and IBM.

| S&P 500 | IBM |
|---|---|
| 1.2 | −0.7 |
| −2.5 | −2.0 |
| −3.0 | −5.5 |

(*continued*)

| S&P 500 | IBM |
|---------|-----|
| 2.0 | 4.7 |
| 5.0 | 1.8 |
| 1.2 | 4.1 |
| 3.0 | 2.6 |
| −1.0 | 2.0 |
| .5 | −1.3 |
| 2.5 | 5.5 |

a. Develop an estimated regression equation that can be used to determine the market beta for IBM. What is IBM's market beta?
b. Test for a significant relationship at the .05 level of significance.
c. Did the estimated regression equation provide a good fit? Explain.
d. Use the market betas of Woolworth and IBM to compare the risk associated with the two stocks.

63. The daily high and low temperatures for 20 cities follow (*USA Today*, May 9, 2000).

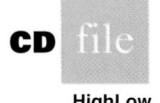

**HighLow**

| City | Low | High |
|------|-----|------|
| Athens | 54 | 75 |
| Bangkok | 74 | 92 |
| Cairo | 57 | 84 |
| Copenhagen | 39 | 64 |
| Dublin | 46 | 64 |
| Havana | 68 | 86 |
| Hong Kong | 72 | 81 |
| Johannesburg | 50 | 61 |
| London | 48 | 73 |
| Manila | 75 | 93 |
| Melbourne | 50 | 66 |
| Montreal | 52 | 64 |
| Paris | 55 | 77 |
| Rio de Janeiro | 61 | 80 |
| Rome | 54 | 81 |
| Seoul | 50 | 64 |
| Singapore | 75 | 90 |
| Sydney | 55 | 68 |
| Tokyo | 59 | 79 |
| Vancouver | 43 | 57 |

a. Develop a scatter diagram with low temperature on the horizontal axis and high temperature on the vertical axis.
b. What does the scatter diagram developed in part (a) indicate about the relationship between the two variables?
c. Develop the estimated regression equation that could be used to predict the high temperature given the low temperature.
d. Test for a significant relationship at the .05 level of significance.
e. Did the estimated regression equation provide a good fit? Explain.
f. What is the value of the sample correlation coefficient?

64. Jensen Tire & Auto is in the process of deciding whether to purchase a maintenance contract for its new computer wheel alignment and balancing machine. Managers feel that maintenance expense should be related to usage and have collected the following information on weekly usage (hours) and annual maintenance expense ($100s).

| Weekly Usage (hours) | Annual Maintenance Expense |
|----------------------|----------------------------|
| 13 | 17.0 |
| 10 | 22.0 |
| 20 | 30.0 |
| 28 | 37.0 |

| Weekly Usage (hours) | Annual Maintenance Expense |
|---|---|
| 32 | 47.0 |
| 17 | 30.5 |
| 24 | 32.5 |
| 31 | 39.0 |
| 40 | 51.5 |
| 38 | 40.0 |

**a.** Develop the estimated regression equation that relates annual maintenance expense to weekly usage.
**b.** Test the significance of the relationship in part (a) at a .05 level of significance.
**c.** Jensen expects to use the new machine 30 hours per week. Develop a 95% prediction interval for the company's annual maintenance expense.
**d.** If the maintenance contract costs $3000 per year, would you recommend purchasing it? Why or why not?

**65.** In a manufacturing process the assembly line speed (feet per minute) was thought to affect the number of defective parts found during the inspection process. To test this theory, managers devised a situation in which the same batch of parts was inspected visually at a variety of line speeds. The following table lists the collected data.

| Line Speed | Number of Defective Parts Found |
|---|---|
| 20 | 21 |
| 20 | 19 |
| 40 | 15 |
| 30 | 16 |
| 60 | 14 |
| 40 | 17 |

**a.** Develop the estimated regression equation that relates line speed to the number of defective parts found.
**b.** At a .05 level of significance, determine whether line speed and number of defective parts found are related.
**c.** Did the estimated regression equation provide a good fit to the data?
**d.** Develop a 95% confidence interval to predict the mean number of defective parts for a line speed of 50 feet per minute.

**66.** A sociologist was hired by a large city hospital to investigate the relationship between the number of unauthorized days that employees are absent per year and the distance (miles) between home and work for the employees. A sample of 10 employees was chosen, and the following data were collected.

| Distance to Work | Number of Days Absent |
|---|---|
| 1 | 8 |
| 3 | 5 |
| 4 | 8 |
| 6 | 7 |
| 8 | 6 |
| 10 | 3 |
| 12 | 5 |
| 14 | 2 |
| 14 | 4 |
| 18 | 2 |

**a.** Develop a scatter diagram for these data. Does a linear relationship appear reasonable? Explain.
**b.** Develop the least squares estimated regression equation.

**c.** Is there a significant relationship between the two variables? Use $\alpha = .05$.

**d.** Did the estimated regression equation provide a good fit? Explain.

**e.** Use the estimated regression equation in part (b) to develop a 95% confidence interval estimate of the expected number of days absent for employees living 5 miles from the company.

**67.** The regional transit authority for a major metropolitan area wants to determine whether there is any relationship between the age of a bus and the annual maintenance cost. A sample of 10 buses resulted in the following data.

| Age of Bus (years) | Maintenance Cost ($) |
|:---:|:---:|
| 1 | 350 |
| 2 | 370 |
| 2 | 480 |
| 2 | 520 |
| 2 | 590 |
| 3 | 550 |
| 4 | 750 |
| 4 | 800 |
| 5 | 790 |
| 5 | 950 |

**a.** Develop the least squares estimated regression equation.

**b.** Test to see whether the two variables are significantly related with $\alpha = .05$.

**c.** Did the least squares line provide a good fit to the observed data? Explain.

**d.** Develop a 95% prediction interval for the maintenance cost for a specific bus that is 4 years old.

**68.** A marketing professor at Givens College is interested in the relationship between hours spent studying and total points earned in a course. Data collected on 10 students who took the course last quarter follow.

| Hours Spent Studying | Total Points Earned |
|:---:|:---:|
| 45 | 40 |
| 30 | 35 |
| 90 | 75 |
| 60 | 65 |
| 105 | 90 |
| 65 | 50 |
| 90 | 90 |
| 80 | 80 |
| 55 | 45 |
| 75 | 65 |

**a.** Develop an estimated regression equation showing how total points earned is related to hours spent studying.

**b.** Test the significance of the model with $\alpha = .05$.

**c.** Predict the total points earned by Mark Sweeney. He spent 95 hours studying.

**d.** Develop a 95% prediction interval for the total points earned by Mark Sweeney.

**69.** The Transactional Records Access Clearinghouse at Syracuse University reported data showing the odds of an Internal Revenue Service audit. The following table shows the average adjusted gross income reported and the percent of the returns that were audited for 20 selected IRS districts (*The Wall Street Journal Almanac 1998*).

**CD** file

**IRSAudit**

| District | Adjusted Gross Income ($) | Percent Audited |
|:---|:---:|:---:|
| Los Angeles | 36,664 | 1.3 |
| Sacramento | 38,845 | 1.1 |
| Atlanta | 34,886 | 1.1 |

| District | Adjusted Gross Income ($) | Percent Audited |
|----------|---------------------------|-----------------|
| Boise | 32,512 | 1.1 |
| Dallas | 34,531 | 1.0 |
| Providence | 35,995 | 1.0 |
| San Jose | 37,799 | 0.9 |
| Cheyenne | 33,876 | 0.9 |
| Fargo | 30,513 | 0.9 |
| New Orleans | 30,174 | 0.9 |
| Oklahoma City | 30,060 | 0.8 |
| Houston | 37,153 | 0.8 |
| Portland | 34,918 | 0.7 |
| Phoenix | 33,291 | 0.7 |
| Augusta | 31,504 | 0.7 |
| Albuquerque | 29,199 | 0.6 |
| Greensboro | 33,072 | 0.6 |
| Columbia | 30,859 | 0.5 |
| Nashville | 32,566 | 0.5 |
| Buffalo | 34,296 | 0.5 |

**a.** Develop the estimated regression equation that could be used to predict the percent audited given the average adjusted gross income reported.

**b.** At the .05 level of significance, determine whether the adjusted gross income and the percent audited are related.

**c.** Did the estimated regression equation provide a good fit? Explain.

**d.** Use the estimated regression equation developed in part (a) to calculate a 95% confidence interval estimate of the expected percent audited for districts with an average adjusted gross income of $35,000.

## Case Problem 1    SPENDING AND STUDENT ACHIEVEMENT

Is the educational achievement level of students related to how much the state in which they reside spends on education? In many communities this important question is being asked by taxpayers who are being asked by their school districts to increase the amount of tax revenue spent on education. In this case, you will be asked to analyze data on spending and achievement scores in order to determine whether there is any relationship between spending and student achievement in the public schools.

The federal government's National Assessment of Educational Progress (NAEP) program is frequently used to measure the educational achievement of students. Table 14.14 shows the total current spending per pupil per year, and the composite NAEP test score for 35 states that participated in the NAEP program. These data are available on the data disk in the file named NAEP. The composite score is the sum of the math, science, and reading scores on the 1996 (1994 for reading) NAEP test. Pupils tested are in grade 8, except for reading, which is given to fourth-graders only. The maximum possible score is 1300. Table 14.15 shows the spending per pupil for 14 states that did not participate in relevant NAEP surveys. These data were reported in an article on spending and achievement level appearing in *Forbes* (November 3, 1997).

### Managerial Report

1. Develop numerical and graphical summaries of the data.
2. Use regression analysis to investigate the relationship between the amount spent per pupil and the composite score on the NAEP test. Discuss your findings.

**TABLE 14.14**  SPENDING PER PUPIL AND COMPOSITE SCORES FOR STATES
THAT PARTICIPATED IN THE NAEP PROGRAM

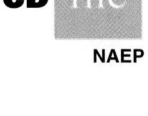

**NAEP**

| State | Spending per Pupil ($) | Composite Score |
|---|---|---|
| Louisiana | 4049 | 581 |
| Mississippi | 3423 | 582 |
| California | 4917 | 580 |
| Hawaii | 5532 | 580 |
| South Carolina | 4304 | 603 |
| Alabama | 3777 | 604 |
| Georgia | 4663 | 611 |
| Florida | 4934 | 611 |
| New Mexico | 4097 | 614 |
| Arkansas | 4060 | 615 |
| Delaware | 6208 | 615 |
| Tennessee | 3800 | 618 |
| Arizona | 4041 | 618 |
| West Virginia | 5247 | 625 |
| Maryland | 6100 | 625 |
| Kentucky | 5020 | 626 |
| Texas | 4520 | 627 |
| New York | 8162 | 628 |
| North Carolina | 4521 | 629 |
| Rhode Island | 6554 | 638 |
| Washington | 5338 | 639 |
| Missouri | 4483 | 641 |
| Colorado | 4772 | 644 |
| Indiana | 5128 | 649 |
| Utah | 3280 | 650 |
| Wyoming | 5515 | 657 |
| Connecticut | 7629 | 657 |
| Massachusetts | 6413 | 658 |
| Nebraska | 5410 | 660 |
| Minnesota | 5477 | 661 |
| Iowa | 5060 | 665 |
| Montana | 4985 | 667 |
| Wisconsin | 6055 | 667 |
| North Dakota | 4374 | 671 |
| Maine | 5561 | 675 |

3. Do you think that the estimated regression equation developed for these data could be used to estimate the composite scores for the states that did not participate in the NAEP program?

4. Suppose that you only considered states that spend at least $4000 per pupil but not more than $6000 per pupil. For these states, does the relationship between the two variables appear to be any different from the complete data set? Discuss the results of your findings and whether you think deleting states with spending less than $4000 per year and more than $6000 per pupil is appropriate.

5. Develop estimates of the composite scores for the states that did not participate in the NAEP program.

6. Based upon your analyses, do you think that the educational achievement level of students is related to how much the state spends on education?

**TABLE 14.15**    SPENDING PER PUPIL AND FOR STATES THAT DID NOT PARTICIPATE
IN THE NAEP PROGRAM

| State | Spending per Pupil ($) |
|---|---|
| Idaho | 3602 |
| South Dakota | 4067 |
| Oklahoma | 4265 |
| Nevada | 4658 |
| Kansas | 5164 |
| Illinois | 5297 |
| New Hampshire | 5387 |
| Ohio | 5438 |
| Oregon | 5588 |
| Vermont | 6269 |
| Michigan | 6391 |
| Pennsylvania | 6579 |
| Alaska | 7890 |

## Case Problem 2    **U.S. DEPARTMENT OF TRANSPORTATION**

As part of a study on transportation safety, the U.S. Department of Transportation collected data on the number of fatal accidents per 1000 licenses and the percentage of licensed drivers under the age of 21 in a sample of 42 cities. Data collected over a 1-year period follow. These data are available on the data disk in the file named Safety.

**Safety**

| Percent Under 21 | Fatal Accidents per 1000 Licenses | Percent Under 21 | Fatal Accidents per 1000 Licenses |
|---|---|---|---|
| 13 | 2.962 | 17 | 4.100 |
| 12 | 0.708 | 8 | 2.190 |
| 8 | 0.885 | 16 | 3.623 |
| 12 | 1.652 | 15 | 2.623 |
| 11 | 2.091 | 9 | 0.835 |
| 17 | 2.627 | 8 | 0.820 |
| 18 | 3.830 | 14 | 2.890 |
| 8 | 0.368 | 8 | 1.267 |
| 13 | 1.142 | 15 | 3.224 |
| 8 | 0.645 | 10 | 1.014 |
| 9 | 1.028 | 10 | 0.493 |
| 16 | 2.801 | 14 | 1.443 |
| 12 | 1.405 | 18 | 3.614 |
| 9 | 1.433 | 10 | 1.926 |
| 10 | 0.039 | 14 | 1.643 |
| 9 | 0.338 | 16 | 2.943 |
| 11 | 1.849 | 12 | 1.913 |
| 12 | 2.246 | 15 | 2.814 |
| 14 | 2.855 | 13 | 2.634 |
| 14 | 2.352 | 9 | 0.926 |
| 11 | 1.294 | 17 | 3.256 |

## Managerial Report

1. Develop numerical and graphical summaries of the data.
2. Use regression analysis to investigate the relationship between the number of fatal accidents and the percentage of drivers under the age of 21. Discuss your findings.
3. What conclusion and/or recommendations can you derive from your analysis?

### Case Problem 3   ALUMNI GIVING

Alumni donations are an important source of revenue for colleges and universities. If administrators could determine the factors that influence increases in the percentage of alumni who make a donation, they might be able to implement policies that could lead to increased revenues. Research shows that students who are more satisfied with their contact with teachers are more likely to graduate. As a result, one might suspect that smaller class sizes and lower student-faculty ratios might lead to a higher percentage of satisfied graduates, which in turn might lead to increases in the percentage of alumni who make a donation. Table 14.16 shows data for 48 universities (*America's Best Colleges,* Year 2000 Edition). The column labeled % of Classes Under 20 shows the percentage of classes offered with fewer than 20 students. The column labeled Student/Faculty Ratio is the number of students enrolled divided by the total number of faculty. Finally, the column labeled Alumni Giving Rate is the percentage of alumni who made a donation to the university.

## Managerial Report

1. Develop numerical and graphical summaries of the data.
2. Use regression analysis to develop an estimated regression equation that could be used to predict the alumni giving rate given the percentage of classes with fewer than 20 students.
3. Use regression analysis to develop an estimated regression equation that could be used to predict the alumni giving rate given the student-faculty ratio.
4. Which of the two estimated regression equations provides the best fit? For this estimated regression equation, perform an analysis of the residuals and discuss your findings and conclusions.
5. What conclusions and/or recommendations can you derive from your analysis?

**TABLE 14.16**  DATA FOR 48 NATIONAL UNIVERSITIES

**CD** file

Alumni

| School | % of Classes Under 20 | Student/Faculty Ratio | Alumni Giving Rate |
|---|---|---|---|
| Boston College | 39 | 13 | 25 |
| Brandeis University | 68 | 8 | 33 |
| Brown University | 60 | 8 | 40 |
| California Institute of Technology | 65 | 3 | 46 |
| Carnegie Mellon University | 67 | 10 | 28 |
| Case Western Reserve Univ. | 52 | 8 | 31 |
| College of William and Mary | 45 | 12 | 27 |
| Columbia University | 69 | 7 | 31 |
| Cornell University | 72 | 13 | 35 |
| Dartmouth College | 61 | 10 | 53 |
| Duke University | 68 | 8 | 45 |
| Emory University | 65 | 7 | 37 |
| Georgetown University | 54 | 10 | 29 |
| Harvard University | 73 | 8 | 46 |
| Johns Hopkins University | 64 | 9 | 27 |
| Lehigh University | 55 | 11 | 40 |
| Massachusetts Inst. of Technology | 65 | 6 | 44 |
| New York University | 63 | 13 | 13 |
| Northwestern University | 66 | 8 | 30 |
| Pennsylvania State Univ. | 32 | 19 | 21 |
| Princeton University | 68 | 5 | 67 |
| Rice University | 62 | 8 | 40 |
| Stanford University | 69 | 7 | 34 |
| Tufts University | 67 | 9 | 29 |
| Tulane University | 56 | 12 | 17 |
| U. of California–Berkeley | 58 | 17 | 18 |
| U. of California–Davis | 32 | 19 | 7 |
| U. of California–Irvine | 42 | 20 | 9 |
| U. of California–Los Angeles | 41 | 18 | 13 |
| U. of California–San Diego | 48 | 19 | 8 |
| U. of California–Santa Barbara | 45 | 20 | 12 |
| U. of Chicago | 65 | 4 | 36 |
| U. of Florida | 31 | 23 | 19 |
| U. of Illinois–Urbana Champaign | 29 | 15 | 23 |
| U. of Michigan–Ann Arbor | 51 | 15 | 13 |
| U. of North Carolina–Chapel Hill | 40 | 16 | 26 |
| U. of Notre Dame | 53 | 13 | 49 |
| U. of Pennsylvania | 65 | 7 | 41 |
| U. of Rochester | 63 | 10 | 23 |
| U. of Southern California | 53 | 13 | 22 |
| U. of Texas–Austin | 39 | 21 | 13 |
| U. of Virginia | 44 | 13 | 28 |
| U. of Washington | 37 | 12 | 12 |
| U. of Wisconsin–Madison | 37 | 13 | 13 |
| Vanderbilt University | 68 | 9 | 31 |
| Wake Forest University | 59 | 11 | 38 |
| Washington University–St. Louis | 73 | 7 | 33 |
| Yale University | 77 | 7 | 50 |

# Chapter 15

# MULTIPLE REGRESSION

**CONTENTS**

## STATISTICS IN PRACTICE

### CHAMPION INTERNATIONAL CORPORATION*
*Stamford, Connecticut*

Champion International Corporation is one of the largest forest product companies in the world, with more than 3 million acres of timberlands in the United States. It produces building materials such as lumber and plywood, white paper products such as printing and writing grades of white paper, and brown paper products such as linerboard and corrugated containers. To make these paper products, Champion's pulp mills process wood chips and chemicals to produce wood pulp. The wood pulp is then used at a paper mill to produce paper products.

In the production of white paper products, the pulp must be bleached to remove any discoloration. A key bleaching agent used in the process is chlorine dioxide, which, because of its combustible nature, is usually produced at Champion pulp mill facilities and then piped in solution form into the bleaching tower of the pulp mill. To improve one of the processes Champion uses to produce chlorine dioxide, a study was undertaken to look at process control and efficiency. One of the aspects studied was the chemical-feed rate for chlorine dioxide production.

To produce the chlorine dioxide, four chemicals flow at metered rates into the chlorine dioxide generator. The chlorine dioxide produced in the generator flows to an absorber where chilled water absorbs the chlorine dioxide gas to form a chlorine dioxide solution. The solution is then piped into the paper mill. A key part of controlling the process involves the chemical-feed rates. Historically, the chemical-feed rates were simply set by experienced operators; this approach, however, led to overcontrol by the operators. Consequently, chemical engineers at the mill requested that a set of control equations, one for each chemical feed, be developed to aid the operators in setting the rates.

_____
*The authors are indebted to Marian Williams and Bill Griggs of Champion International Corporation for providing this Statistics in Practice.

Using multiple regression analysis, Champion International developed a better bleaching process for its paper products. © Lester Lefkowitz/The Stock Market.

Using multiple regression analysis, statistical analysts at Champion were able to develop an estimated multiple regression equation for each of the four chemicals used in the process. Each equation related the production of chlorine dioxide to the amount of chemical used and the concentration level of the chlorine dioxide solution. The resulting set of four equations was programmed into a microcomputer at each mill. In the new system, operators enter the concentration of the chlorine dioxide solution and the desired production rate; the computer software then calculates the chemical feed needed to achieve the desired production rate. Since the operators have begun using the control equations, the chlorine dioxide generator efficiency has increased, and the number of times the concentrations have been within acceptable ranges has increased significantly.

Champion used multiple regression analysis to develop its control equations. In this chapter we will discuss how Excel can be used for such purposes. Most of the concepts introduced in Chapter 14 for simple linear regression can be directly extended to the multiple regression case.

In Chapter 14 we presented simple linear regression and demonstrated its use in developing an equation that describes the relationship between two variables. Recall that the variable being predicted or explained by the equation is called the dependent variable and the variable being used to predict or explain the dependent variable is called the independent variable. In this chapter we continue our study of regression analysis by considering situations involving two or more independent variables. This subject area is called **multiple regression analysis.** It enables us to consider more factors and thus obtain better estimates than are possible with simple linear regression.

## 15.1    MULTIPLE REGRESSION MODEL

Multiple regression analysis is the study of how a dependent variable $y$ is related to two or more independent variables. In the general case, we will use $p$ to denote the number of independent variables.

### Regression Model and Regression Equation

The concepts of a regression model and a regression equation introduced in the preceding chapter are applicable in the multiple regression case. The equation that describes how the dependent variable $y$ is related to the independent variables $x_1, x_2, \ldots x_p$ and an error term is called the **multiple regression model**. We begin with the assumption that the multiple regression model has the following form.

**Multiple Regression Model**

$$y = \beta_0 + \beta_1 x_1 + \beta_2 x_2 + \cdots + \beta_p x_p + \epsilon \qquad \text{(15.1)}$$

In the multiple regression model, $\beta_0, \beta_1, \beta_2, \ldots, \beta_p$ are the parameters and $\epsilon$ (the Greek letter epsilon) is a random variable. A close examination of this model reveals that $y$ is a linear function of $x_1, x_2, \ldots, x_p$ (the $\beta_0 + \beta_1 x_1 + \beta_2 x_2 + \cdots + \beta_p x_p$ part) plus an error term $\epsilon$. The error term accounts for the variability in $y$ that cannot be explained by the linear effect of the $p$ independent variables.

In Section 15.4 we will discuss the assumptions for the multiple regression model and $\epsilon$. One of the assumptions is that the mean or expected value of $\epsilon$ is zero. A consequence of this assumption is that the mean or expected value of $y$, denoted $E(y)$, is equal to $\beta_0 + \beta_1 x_1 + \beta_2 x_2 + \cdots + \beta_p x_p$. The equation that describes how the mean value of $y$ is related to $x_1, x_2, \ldots, x_p$ is called the **multiple regression equation.**

**Multiple Regression Equation**

$$E(y) = \beta_0 + \beta_1 x_1 + \beta_2 x_2 + \cdots + \beta_p x_p \qquad \text{(15.2)}$$

### Estimated Multiple Regression Equation

If the values of $\beta_0, \beta_1, \beta_2, \ldots, \beta_p$ were known, equation (15.2) could be used to compute the mean value of $y$ at given values of $x_1, x_2, \ldots, x_p$. Unfortunately, these parameter values will not, in general, be known and must be estimated from sample data. A simple random sample is used to compute sample statistics $b_0, b_1, b_2, \ldots, b_p$ that are used as the point estimators of the parameters $\beta_0, \beta_1, \beta_2, \ldots, \beta_p$. These sample statistics provide the following **estimated multiple regression equation.**

**Estimated Multiple Regression Equation**

$$\hat{y} = b_0 + b_1 x_1 + b_2 x_2 + \cdots + b_p x_p \qquad \text{(15.3)}$$

where

$$b_0, b_1, b_2, \ldots, b_p \text{ are the estimates of } \beta_0, \beta_1, \beta_2, \ldots, \beta_p$$
$$\hat{y} = \text{estimated value of the dependent variable}$$

**FIGURE 15.1**   THE ESTIMATION PROCESS FOR MULTIPLE REGRESSION

In simple linear regression, $b_0$ and $b_1$ were the sample statistics used to estimate the parameters $\beta_0$ and $\beta_1$. Multiple regression parallels this statistical inference process, with $b_0$, $b_1, b_2, \ldots, b_p$ denoting the sample statistics used to estimate $\beta_0, \beta_1, \beta_2, \ldots, \beta_p$.

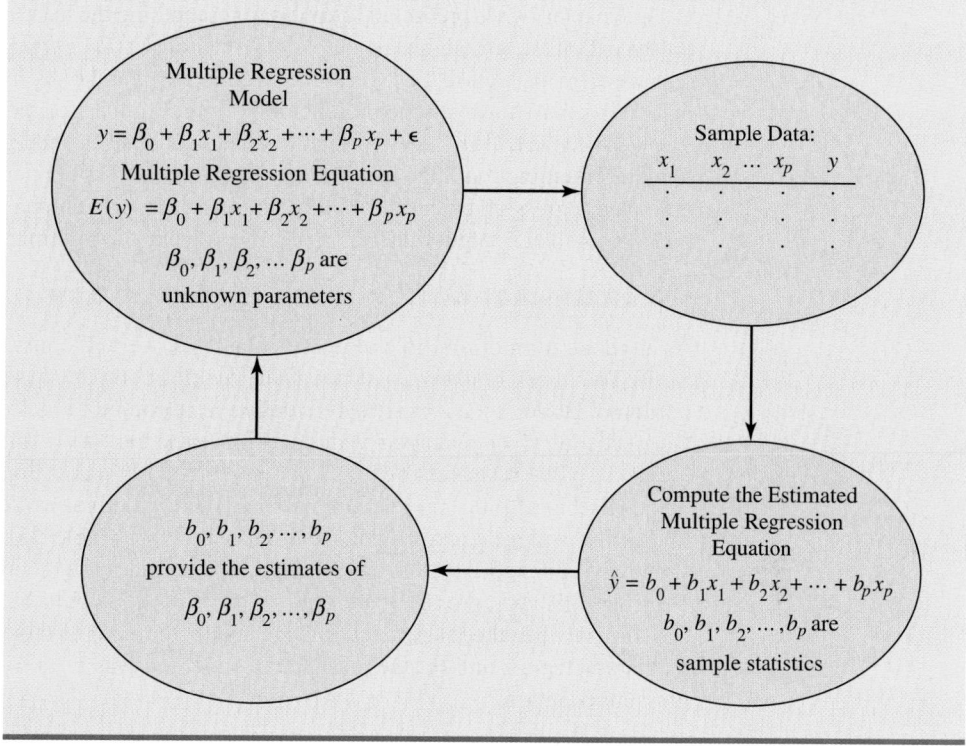

The estimation process for multiple regression is shown in Figure 15.1.

## 15.2   LEAST SQUARES METHOD

In Chapter 14, we used the **least squares method** to develop the estimated regression equation that best approximated the straight-line relationship between the dependent and independent variables. This same approach is used to develop the estimated multiple regression equation. The least squares criterion is restated as follows.

---

**Least Squares Criterion**

$$\min \Sigma(y_i - \hat{y}_i)^2 \tag{15.4}$$

where

$y_i$ = observed value of the dependent variable for the $i$th observation
$\hat{y}_i$ = estimated value of the dependent variable for the $i$th observation

---

The estimated values of the dependent variable are computed by using the estimated multiple regression equation,

$$\hat{y} = b_0 + b_1x_1 + b_2x_2 + \cdots + b_px_p$$

As expression (15.4) shows, the least squares method uses sample data to provide the values of $b_0, b_1, b_2, \ldots, b_p$ that make the sum of squared residuals [the deviations between the observed values of the dependent variable ($y_i$) and the estimated values of the dependent variable ($\hat{y}_i$)] a minimum.

In Chapter 14 we presented formulas for computing the least squares estimators $b_0$ and $b_1$ for the estimated simple linear regression equation $\hat{y} = b_0 + b_1 x$. With relatively small data sets, we were able to use those formulas to compute $b_0$ and $b_1$ by manual calculations. In multiple regression, however, the presentation of the formulas for the regression coefficients $b_0$, $b_1, b_2, \ldots, b_p$ involves the use of matrix algebra and is beyond the scope of this text. Therefore, in presenting multiple regression, we will focus on how Excel can be used to obtain the estimated regression equation and other information. The emphasis will be on how to interpret the computer output rather than on how to make the multiple regression computations.

## An Example: Butler Trucking Company

As an illustration of multiple regression analysis, we will consider a problem faced by the Butler Trucking Company, an independent trucking company in southern California. A major portion of Butler's business involves deliveries throughout its local area. To develop better work schedules, the managers want to estimate the total daily travel time for their drivers.

Initially the managers believed that the total daily travel time would be closely related to the number of miles traveled in making the daily deliveries. A simple random sample of 10 driving assignments provided the data shown in Table 15.1 and the scatter diagram shown in Figure 15.2. After reviewing this scatter diagram, the managers hypothesized that the simple linear regression model $y = \beta_0 + \beta_1 x_1 + \epsilon$ could be used to describe the relationship between the total travel time ($y$) and the number of miles traveled ($x_1$). To estimate the parameters $\beta_0$ and $\beta_1$, the least squares method was used to develop the estimated regression equation.

$$\hat{y} = b_0 + b_1 x_1 \qquad (15.5)$$

In Figure 15.3, we show the Excel output* from applying simple linear regression to the data in Table 15.1. The estimated regression equation is

$$\hat{y} = 1.2739 + .0678x_1$$

At the .05 level of significance, the $F$ value of 15.8146 and its corresponding $p$-value of .0041 indicate that the relationship is significant; that is, we can reject $H_0: \beta_1 = 0$ because

**TABLE 15.1**    PRELIMINARY DATA FOR BUTLER TRUCKING

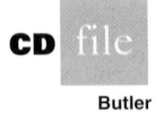

Butler

| Driving Assignment | $x_1$ = Miles Traveled | $y$ = Travel Time (hours) |
|:---:|:---:|:---:|
| 1 | 100 | 9.3 |
| 2 | 50 | 4.8 |
| 3 | 100 | 8.9 |
| 4 | 100 | 6.5 |
| 5 | 50 | 4.2 |
| 6 | 80 | 6.2 |
| 7 | 75 | 7.4 |
| 8 | 65 | 6.0 |
| 9 | 90 | 7.6 |
| 10 | 90 | 6.1 |

*Excel's Regression tool was used to obtain the output. Section 14.6 describes the tasks used for simple linear regression.

**FIGURE 15.2**   SCATTER DIAGRAM OF PRELIMINARY DATA FOR BUTLER TRUCKING

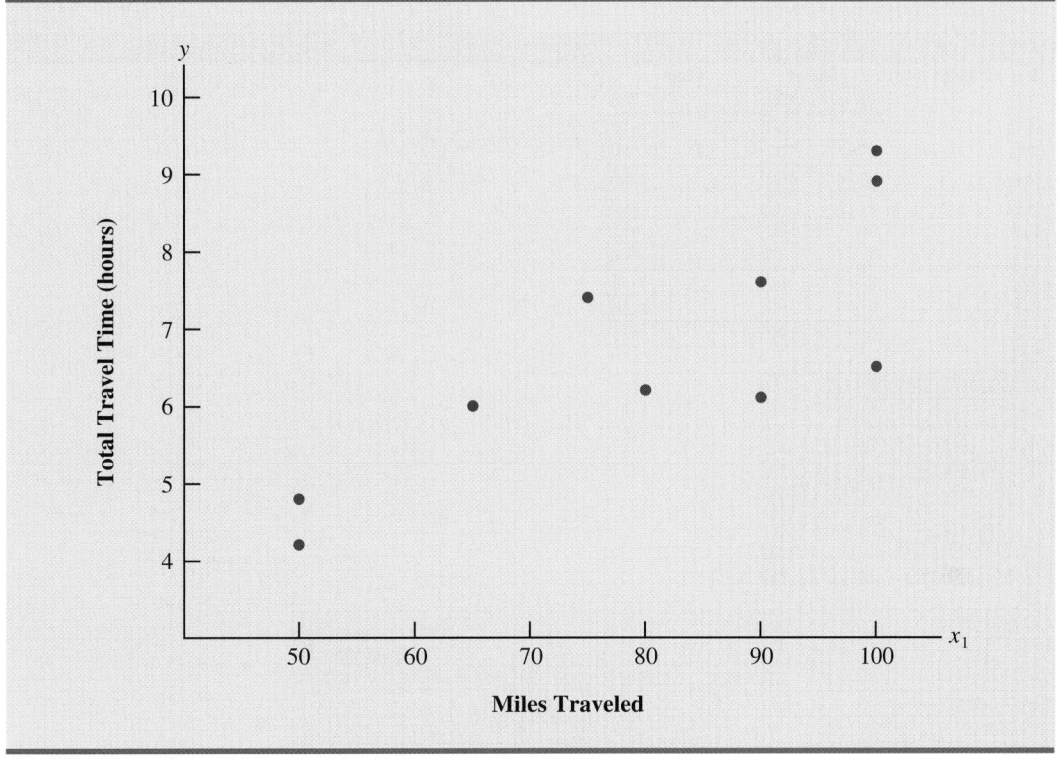

the $p$-value is less than $\alpha = .05$. Note that the same conclusion is obtained from the $t$ value of 3.9768 and its associated $p$-value of .0041. Thus, we can conclude that the relationship between the total travel time and the number of miles traveled is significant; longer travel times are associated with more miles traveled. With a coefficient of determination of R Square = .6641, we see that 66.41% of the variability in travel time can be explained by the linear effect of the number of miles traveled. This finding is fairly good, but the managers might want to consider adding a second independent variable to explain some of the remaining variability in the dependent variable.

In attempting to identify another independent variable, the managers felt that the number of deliveries could also contribute to the total travel time. The Butler Trucking data, with the number of deliveries added, are shown in Table 15.2. To develop the estimated multiple regression equation with both miles traveled ($x_1$) and number of deliveries ($x_2$) as independent variables, we will use Excel's Regression tool.

## Using Excel's Regression Tool to Develop the Estimated Multiple Regression Equation

In Section 14.6 we showed how Excel's Regression tool could be used to determine the estimated regression equation for the Armand's Pizza Parlors problem. We can use the same procedure with minor modifications to develop the estimated multiple regression equation for the Butler Trucking problem. Refer to Figure 15.4 as we describe the tasks involved.

**Enter Data:**   The labels Assignment, Miles, Deliveries, and Time have been entered into cells A1:D1 of the worksheet, and the sample data have been entered into cells B2:D11. The numbers 1–10 have been entered into cells A2:A11 to identify each observation.

**FIGURE 15.3**   EXCEL OUTPUT FOR BUTLER TRUCKING WITH ONE INDEPENDENT VARIABLE

|     | A | B | C | D | E | F | G | H | I | J |
|-----|---|---|---|---|---|---|---|---|---|---|
| 1 | Assignment | Miles | Time | | | | | | | |
| 2 | 1 | 100 | 9.3 | | | | | | | |
| 3 | 2 | 50 | 4.8 | | | | | | | |
| 4 | 3 | 100 | 8.9 | | | | | | | |
| 5 | 4 | 100 | 6.5 | | | | | | | |
| 6 | 5 | 50 | 4.2 | | | | | | | |
| 7 | 6 | 80 | 6.2 | | | | | | | |
| 8 | 7 | 75 | 7.4 | | | | | | | |
| 9 | 8 | 65 | 6 | | | | | | | |
| 10 | 9 | 90 | 7.6 | | | | | | | |
| 11 | 10 | 90 | 6.1 | | | | | | | |
| 12 | | | | | | | | | | |
| 13 | SUMMARY OUTPUT | | | | | | | | | |
| 14 | | | | | | | | | | |
| 15 | *Regression Statistics* | | | | | | | | | |
| 16 | Multiple R | 0.8149 | | | | | | | | |
| 17 | R Square | 0.6641 | | | | | | | | |
| 18 | Adjusted R Square | 0.6221 | | | | | | | | |
| 19 | Standard Error | 1.0018 | | | | | | | | |
| 20 | Observations | 10 | | | | | | | | |
| 21 | | | | | | | | | | |
| 22 | ANOVA | | | | | | | | | |
| 23 | | *df* | *SS* | *MS* | *F* | *Significance F* | | | | |
| 24 | Regression | 1 | 15.8713 | 15.8713 | 15.8146 | 0.0041 | | | | |
| 25 | Residual | 8 | 8.0287 | 1.0036 | | | | | | |
| 26 | Total | 9 | 23.9 | | | | | | | |
| 27 | | | | | | | | | | |
| 28 | | *Coefficients* | *Standard Error* | *t Stat* | *P-value* | *Lower 95%* | *Upper 95%* | *Lower 99.0%* | *Upper 99.0%* | |
| 29 | Intercept | 1.2739 | 1.4007 | 0.9095 | 0.3897 | -1.9562 | 4.5040 | -3.4261 | 5.9739 | |
| 30 | Miles | 0.0678 | 0.0171 | 3.9768 | 0.0041 | 0.0285 | 0.1072 | 0.0106 | 0.1251 | |
| 31 | | | | | | | | | | |

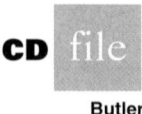

**TABLE 15.2**   DATA FOR BUTLER TRUCKING WITH MILES TRAVELED ($x_1$) AND NUMBER OF DELIVERIES ($x_2$) AS THE INDEPENDENT VARIABLES

| Driving Assignment | $x_1$ = Miles Traveled | $x_2$ = Number of Deliveries | $y$ = Travel Time (hours) |
|---|---|---|---|
| 1 | 100 | 4 | 9.3 |
| 2 | 50 | 3 | 4.8 |
| 3 | 100 | 4 | 8.9 |
| 4 | 100 | 2 | 6.5 |
| 5 | 50 | 2 | 4.2 |
| 6 | 80 | 2 | 6.2 |
| 7 | 75 | 3 | 7.4 |
| 8 | 65 | 4 | 6.0 |
| 9 | 90 | 3 | 7.6 |
| 10 | 90 | 2 | 6.1 |

**FIGURE 15.4**   EXCEL OUTPUT FOR BUTLER TRUCKING WITH TWO INDEPENDENT VARIABLES

| | A | B | C | D | E | F | G | H | I | J |
|---|---|---|---|---|---|---|---|---|---|---|
| 1 | Assignment | Miles | Deliveries | Time | | | | | | |
| 2 | 1 | 100 | 4 | 9.3 | | | | | | |
| 3 | 2 | 50 | 3 | 4.8 | | | | | | |
| 4 | 3 | 100 | 4 | 8.9 | | | | | | |
| 5 | 4 | 100 | 2 | 6.5 | | | | | | |
| 6 | 5 | 50 | 2 | 4.2 | | | | | | |
| 7 | 6 | 80 | 2 | 6.2 | | | | | | |
| 8 | 7 | 75 | 3 | 7.4 | | | | | | |
| 9 | 8 | 65 | 4 | 6 | | | | | | |
| 10 | 9 | 90 | 3 | 7.6 | | | | | | |
| 11 | 10 | 90 | 2 | 6.1 | | | | | | |
| 12 | | | | | | | | | | |
| 13 | SUMMARY OUTPUT | | | | | | | | | |
| 14 | | | | | | | | | | |
| 15 | *Regression Statistics* | | | | | | | | | |
| 16 | Multiple R | 0.9507 | | | | | | | | |
| 17 | R Square | 0.9038 | | | | | | | | |
| 18 | Adjusted R Square | 0.8763 | | | | | | | | |
| 19 | Standard Error | 0.5731 | | | | | | | | |
| 20 | Observations | 10 | | | | | | | | |
| 21 | | | | | | | | | | |
| 22 | ANOVA | | | | | | | | | |
| 23 | | *df* | *SS* | *MS* | *F* | *Significance F* | | | | |
| 24 | Regression | 2 | 21.6006 | 10.8003 | 32.8784 | 0.0003 | | | | |
| 25 | Residual | 7 | 2.2994 | 0.3285 | | | | | | |
| 26 | Total | 9 | 23.9 | | | | | | | |
| 27 | | | | | | | | | | |
| 28 | | *Coefficients* | *Standard Error* | *t Stat* | *P-value* | *Lower 95%* | *Upper 95%* | *Lower 99.0%* | *Upper 99.0%* | |
| 29 | Intercept | -0.8687 | 0.9515 | -0.9129 | 0.3916 | -3.1188 | 1.3813 | -4.1986 | 2.4612 | |
| 30 | Miles | 0.0611 | 0.0099 | 6.1824 | 0.0005 | 0.0378 | 0.0845 | 0.0265 | 0.0957 | |
| 31 | Deliveries | 0.9234 | 0.2211 | 4.1763 | 0.0042 | 0.4006 | 1.4463 | 0.1496 | 1.6972 | |
| 32 | | | | | | | | | | |

**Apply Tools:**   The following steps describe how to use the Regression tool for the multiple regression analysis.

**Step 1.**   Select the **Tools** pull-down menu
**Step 2.**   Choose the **Data Analysis** option
**Step 3.**   Choose **Regression** from the list of Analysis Tools
**Step 4.**   When the Regression dialog box appears (see Figure 15.5):
Enter D1:D11 in the **Input Y Range** box
Enter B1:C11 in the **Input X Range** box
Select **Labels**
Select **Confidence Level**
Enter 99 in the **Confidence Level** box
Select **Output Range**
Enter A13 in the **Output Range** box (to identify the upper left corner of the section of the worksheet where the output will appear)
Click **OK**

In the Excel output shown in Figure 15.4 the label for the independent variable $x_1$ is Miles (see cell A30), and the label for the independent variable $x_2$ is Deliveries (see cell A31). The estimated regression equation is

$$\hat{y} = -.8687 + .0611x_1 + .9234x_2 \qquad \textbf{(15.6)}$$

Note that using Excel's Regression tool for multiple regression is almost the same as using it for simple linear regression. The major difference is that in the multiple regression case a larger range of cells has to be provided in order to identify the independent variables.

## Note on Interpretation of Coefficients

Compare the relationship between the estimated regression equation with only the miles traveled as an independent variable and the estimated regression equation that includes the number of deliveries as a second independent variable. Note that the value of $b_1$ is not the same in both cases. In simple linear regression, we interpret $b_1$ as an estimate of the change in $y$ for a 1-unit change in the independent variable. For example, in the Butler Trucking Company problem involving only one independent variable, number of miles traveled, $b_1 = .0678$. Thus, .0678 is an estimate of the expected increase in travel time corresponding to an increase of 1 mile in the distance traveled. In multiple regression analysis, this interpretation must be modified somewhat. That is, in multiple regression analysis, we interpret each regression coefficient as follows: $b_i$ represents an estimate of the change in y corresponding to a 1-unit change in $x_i$ when all other independent variables are held constant. In the Butler Trucking example involving two independent variables, $b_1 = .0611$. Thus, .0611 hours is an estimate of the expected increase in travel time corresponding to an increase of 1 mile in the distance traveled when the number of deliveries is held constant. Similarly, because $b_2 = .9234$, an estimate of the expected increase in travel time corresponding to an increase of one delivery when the number of miles traveled is held constant is .9234 hours.

**FIGURE 15.5**   REGRESSION DIALOG BOX FOR THE BUTLER TRUCKING PROBLEM

## EXERCISES

## Methods

1.  The estimated regression equation for a problem involving two independent variables and 10 observations follows.

$$\hat{y} = 29.1270 + .5906x_1 + .4980x_2$$

   a.  Interpret $b_1$ and $b_2$ in this estimated regression equation.
   b.  Estimate $y$ when $x_1 = 180$ and $x_2 = 310$.

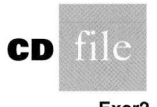

Exer2

2.  Consider the following data for a dependent variable $y$ and two independent variables, $x_1$ and $x_2$.

| $x_1$ | $x_2$ | $y$ |
|------|------|-----|
| 30 | 12 | 94 |
| 47 | 10 | 108 |
| 25 | 17 | 112 |
| 51 | 16 | 178 |
| 40 | 5 | 94 |
| 51 | 19 | 175 |
| 74 | 7 | 170 |
| 36 | 12 | 117 |
| 59 | 13 | 142 |
| 76 | 16 | 211 |

   a.  Using these data, develop an estimated regression equation relating $y$ to $x_1$. Estimate $y$ if $x_1 = 45$.
   b.  Using these data, develop an estimated regression equation relating $y$ to $x_2$. Estimate $y$ if $x_2 = 15$.
   c.  Using these data, develop an estimated regression equation relating $y$ to $x_1$ and $x_2$. Estimate $y$ if $x_1 = 45$ and $x_2 = 15$.

3.  In a regression analysis involving 30 observations, the following estimated regression equation was obtained.

$$\hat{y} = 17.6 + 3.8x_1 - 2.3x_2 + 7.6x_3 + 2.7x_4$$

   a.  Interpret $b_1$, $b_2$, $b_3$, and $b_4$ in this estimated regression equation.
   b.  Estimate $y$ when $x_1 = 10$, $x_2 = 5$, $x_3 = 1$, and $x_4 = 2$.

## Applications

4.  A shoe store has developed the following estimated regression equation relating sales to inventory investment and advertising expenditures.

$$\hat{y} = 25 + 10x_1 + 8x_2$$

where

$$x_1 = \text{inventory investment (\$1000s)}$$
$$x_2 = \text{advertising expenditures (\$1000s)}$$
$$y = \text{sales (\$1000s)}$$

   a.  Estimate sales resulting from a $15,000 investment in inventory and an advertising budget of $10,000.
   b.  Interpret $b_1$ and $b_2$ in this estimated regression equation.

**5.** The owner of Showtime Movie Theaters, Inc., would like to estimate weekly gross revenue as a function of advertising expenditures. Historical data for a sample of 8 weeks follow.

Showtime

| Weekly Gross Revenue ($1000s) | Television Advertising ($1000s) | Newspaper Advertising ($1000s) |
|---|---|---|
| 96 | 5.0 | 1.5 |
| 90 | 2.0 | 2.0 |
| 95 | 4.0 | 1.5 |
| 92 | 2.5 | 2.5 |
| 95 | 3.0 | 3.3 |
| 94 | 3.5 | 2.3 |
| 94 | 2.5 | 4.2 |
| 94 | 3.0 | 2.5 |

  **a.** Develop an estimated regression equation with television advertising expenditures as the independent variable.
  **b.** Develop an estimated regression equation with both television advertising expenditures and newspaper advertising expenditures as the independent variables.
  **c.** Is the estimated regression equation coefficient for television advertising expenditures the same in parts (a) and (b)? Interpret the coefficient in each case.
  **d.** What is the estimate of the weekly gross revenue for a week when $3500 is spent on television advertising and $1800 is spent on newspaper advertising?

**6.** The following table reports the horsepower, curb weight, and the speed at ¼ mile for 16 sports and GT cars (*1998 Road & Track Sports & GT Cars*).

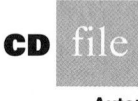

Auto1

| Sports & GT Car | Curb Weight (lb.) | Horsepower | Speed at ¼ mile (mph) |
|---|---|---|---|
| Acura Integra Type R | 2577 | 195 | 90.7 |
| Acura NSX-T | 3066 | 290 | 108.0 |
| BMW Z3 2.8 | 2844 | 189 | 93.2 |
| Chevrolet Camaro Z28 | 3439 | 305 | 103.2 |
| Chevrolet Corvette Convertible | 3246 | 345 | 102.1 |
| Dodge Viper RT/10 | 3319 | 450 | 116.2 |
| Ford Mustang GT | 3227 | 225 | 91.7 |
| Honda Prelude Type SH | 3042 | 195 | 89.7 |
| Mercedes-Benz CLK320 | 3240 | 215 | 93.0 |
| Mercedes-Benz SLK230 | 3025 | 185 | 92.3 |
| Mitsubishi 3000GT VR-4 | 3737 | 320 | 99.0 |
| Nissan 240SX SE | 2862 | 155 | 84.6 |
| Pontiac Firebird Trans Am | 3455 | 305 | 103.2 |
| Porsche Boxster | 2822 | 201 | 93.2 |
| Toyota Supra Turbo | 3505 | 320 | 105.0 |
| Volvo C70 | 3285 | 236 | 97.0 |

  **a.** Use curb weight as the independent variable and the speed at ¼ mile as the dependent variable. What is the estimated regression equation?
  **b.** Use curb weight and horsepower as two independent variables and the speed at ¼ mile as the dependent variable. What is the estimated regression equation?
  **c.** The 1999 Porsche 911 Carrera has been advertised as having a curb weight of 2910 pounds and an engine with 296 horsepower. Use the results of part (b) to predict the speed at ¼ mile for the Porsche 911.

7. Heller Company manufactures lawn mowers and related lawn equipment. The managers believe the quantity of lawn mowers sold depends on the price of the mower and the price of a competitor's mower. Let

$$y = \text{quantity sold (1000s)}$$
$$x_1 = \text{price of competitor's mower (\$)}$$
$$x_2 = \text{price of Heller's mower (\$)}$$

The managers want to develop an estimated regression equation that relates quantity sold to the prices of the Heller mower and the competitor's mower. The following table lists prices in 10 cities.

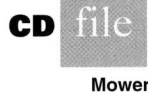

**Mower**

| Competitor's Price ($x_1$) | Heller's Price ($x_2$) | Quantity Sold ($y$) |
|---|---|---|
| 120 | 100 | 102 |
| 140 | 110 | 100 |
| 190 | 90 | 120 |
| 130 | 150 | 77 |
| 155 | 210 | 46 |
| 175 | 150 | 93 |
| 125 | 250 | 26 |
| 145 | 270 | 69 |
| 180 | 300 | 65 |
| 150 | 250 | 85 |

a. Determine the estimated regression equation that can be used to predict the quantity sold given the competitor's price and Heller's price.
b. Interpret $b_1$ and $b_2$.
c. Predict the quantity sold in a city where Heller prices its mower at \$160 and the competitor prices its mower at \$170.

8. The following table gives the annual return, the safety rating (0 = riskiest, 10 = safest), and the annual expense ratio for 20 foreign funds (*Mutual Funds,* March 2000).

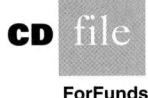

**ForFunds**

| | Safety Rating | Annual Expense Ratio (%) | Annual Return (%) |
|---|---|---|---|
| Accessor Int'l Equity "Adv" | 7.1 | 1.59 | 49 |
| Aetna "I" International | 7.2 | 1.35 | 52 |
| Amer Century Int'l Discovery "Inv" | 6.8 | 1.68 | 89 |
| Columbia International Stock | 7.1 | 1.56 | 58 |
| Concert Inv "A" Int'l Equity | 6.2 | 2.16 | 131 |
| Dreyfus Founders Int'l Equity "F" | 7.4 | 1.80 | 59 |
| Driehaus International Growth | 6.5 | 1.88 | 99 |
| Excelsior "Inst" Int'l Equity | 7.0 | 0.90 | 53 |
| Julius Baer International Equity | 6.9 | 1.79 | 77 |
| Marshall International Stock "Y" | 7.2 | 1.49 | 54 |
| MassMutual Int'l Equity "S" | 7.1 | 1.05 | 57 |
| Morgan Grenfell Int'l Sm Cap "Inst" | 7.7 | 1.25 | 61 |
| New England "A" Int'l Equity | 7.0 | 1.83 | 88 |
| Pilgrim Int'l Small Cap "A" | 7.0 | 1.94 | 122 |
| Republic International Equity | 7.2 | 1.09 | 71 |
| Sit International Growth | 6.9 | 1.50 | 51 |
| Smith Barney "A" Int'l Equity | 7.0 | 1.28 | 60 |
| State St Research "S" Int'l Equity | 7.1 | 1.65 | 50 |
| Strong International Stock | 6.5 | 1.61 | 93 |
| Vontobel International Equity | 7.0 | 1.50 | 47 |

a. Using these data, develop an estimated regression equation relating the annual return to the safety rating and the annual expense ratio.

b. Estimate the annual return for a firm that has a safety rating of 7.5 and annual expense ratio of 2%.

9. Two experts provided subjective lists of school districts that they think are among the best in the country. For each school district the average class size, the combined SAT score, and the percentage of students who attended a 4-year college were provided.

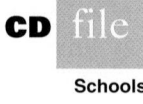

**Schools**

| District | Average Class Size | Combined SAT Score | % Attend 4-Year College |
|----------|--------------------|--------------------|-------------------------|
| Blue Springs, MO | 25 | 1083 | 74 |
| Garden City, NY | 18 | 997 | 77 |
| Indianapolis, IN | 30 | 716 | 40 |
| Newport Beach, CA | 26 | 977 | 51 |
| Novi, MI | 20 | 980 | 53 |
| Piedmont, CA | 28 | 1042 | 75 |
| Pittsburg, PA | 21 | 983 | 66 |
| Scarsdale, NY | 20 | 1110 | 87 |
| Wayne, PA | 22 | 1040 | 85 |
| Weston, MA | 21 | 1031 | 89 |
| Farmingdale, NY | 22 | 947 | 81 |
| Mamaroneck, NY | 20 | 1000 | 69 |
| Mayfield, OH | 24 | 1003 | 48 |
| Morristown, NJ | 22 | 972 | 64 |
| New Rochelle, NY | 23 | 1039 | 55 |
| Newtown Square, PA | 17 | 963 | 79 |
| Omaha, NE | 23 | 1059 | 81 |
| Shaker Heights, OH | 23 | 940 | 82 |

a. Using these data, develop an estimated regression equation relating the percentage of students who attend a 4-year college to the average class size and the combined SAT score.

b. Estimate the percentage of students who attend a 4-year college if the average class size is 20 and the combined SAT score is 1000.

10. *Auto Rental News* provided the following data, which show the number of cars in service (1000s), the number of locations, and the rental revenue ($ millions) for 15 car rental companies. (*The Wall Street Journal Almanac 1998*).

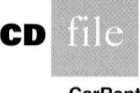

**CarRent**

| Company | Cars | Locations | Revenue |
|---------|------|-----------|---------|
| Alamo | 130 | 171 | 1180 |
| Avis | 190 | 1130 | 1500 |
| Budget | 126 | 1052 | 1500 |
| Dollar | 63.5 | 450 | 560 |
| Enterprise | 315.1 | 2636 | 2060 |
| FRCS (Ford) | 55.25 | 1784 | 312.5 |
| Hertz | 250 | 1200 | 2400 |
| National | 135 | 935 | 1200 |
| Payless | 15 | 100 | 47 |
| PROP (Chrysler) | 27 | 1500 | 160 |
| Rent-A-Wreck | 10.9 | 460 | 78 |
| Snappy | 15.5 | 259 | 85 |
| Thrifty | 34 | 480 | 340 |
| U-Save | 13.5 | 500 | 95 |
| Value | 18 | 45 | 150.1 |

    **a.**  Determine the estimated regression equation that can be used to predict the rental revenue given the number of cars in service.

    **b.**  Provide an interpretation for the slope of the estimated regression equation developed in part (a).

    **c.**  Determine the estimated regression equation that can be used to predict the rental revenue given the number of cars in service and the number of locations.

## 15.3   MULTIPLE COEFFICIENT OF DETERMINATION

In simple linear regression we showed that the total sum of squares can be partitioned into two components: the sum of squares due to regression and the sum of squares due to error. The same partition applies to the sum of squares in multiple regression.

**Relationship Among SST, SSR, and SSE**

$$\text{SST} = \text{SSR} + \text{SSE} \tag{15.7}$$

where

$$\text{SST} = \text{total sum of squares} = \Sigma(y_i - \bar{y})^2$$
$$\text{SSR} = \text{sum of squares due to regression} = \Sigma(\hat{y}_i - \bar{y})^2$$
$$\text{SSE} = \text{sum of squares due to error} = \Sigma(y_i - \hat{y}_i)^2$$

Because computing the three sums of squares is very tedious, we rely on computer packages to determine these values. The analysis of variance part of the Excel output in Figure 15.4 shows the three sums of squares for the Butler Trucking problem with two independent variables: SST = 23.9, SSR = 21.6006, and SSE = 2.2994. With only one independent variable (number of miles traveled), the Excel output in Figure 15.3 shows that SST = 23.9, SSR = 15.8713, and SSE = 8.0287. The value of SST is the same in both cases because it does not depend on $\hat{y}$, but SSR increases and SSE decreases when a second independent variable (number of deliveries) is added. The implication is that the estimated multiple regression equation provides a better fit for the observed sample data.

    In Chapter 14, we used the coefficient of determination, $r^2 = \text{SSR/SST}$, to measure the goodness of fit for the estimated regression equation. The same concept applies to multiple regression. The term **multiple coefficient of determination** indicates that we are measuring the goodness of fit for the estimated multiple regression equation. The multiple coefficient of determination, denoted $R^2$, is computed as follows.

**Multiple Coefficient of Determination**

$$R^2 = \frac{\text{SSR}}{\text{SST}} \tag{15.8}$$

The multiple coefficient of determination can be interpreted as the proportion of the variability in the dependent variable that can be explained by the estimated multiple regression equation. Hence, when multiplied by 100, it can be interpreted as the percentage of the variability in $y$ that can be explained by the estimated regression equation.

In the two-independent-variable Butler Trucking example, with SSR = 21.6006 and SST = 23.9, we have

$$R^2 = \frac{21.6006}{23.9} = .9038$$

Therefore, 90.38% of the variability in travel time $y$ is explained by the estimated multiple regression equation with miles traveled and number of deliveries as the independent variables. In Figure 15.4, we see that the multiple coefficient of determination is also provided by the Excel output; it is denoted by R Square = .9038.

Figure 15.3 shows that the R Square value for the estimated regression equation with only one independent variable, number of miles traveled $(x_1)$, is .6641. Thus, the percentage of the variability in travel times that is explained by the estimated regression equation increases from 66.41% to 90.38% when number of deliveries is added as a second independent variable. In general, $R^2$ always increases as independent variables are added to the model.

Many analysts prefer adjusting $R^2$ for the number of independent variables to avoid overestimating the impact of adding an independent variable on the amount of variability explained by the estimated regression equation. With $n$ denoting the number of observations and $p$ denoting the number of independent variables, the **adjusted multiple coefficient of determination** is computed as follows.

> If a variable is added to the model, $R^2$ becomes larger even if the variable added is not statistically significant.

> The adjusted multiple coefficient of determination compensates for the number of independent variables in the model.

### Adjusted Multiple Coefficient of Determination

$$R_a^2 = 1 - (1 - R^2)\frac{n - 1}{n - p - 1} \tag{15.9}$$

For the Butler Trucking example with $n = 10$ and $p = 2$, we have

$$R_a^2 = 1 - (1 - .9038)\frac{10 - 1}{10 - 2 - 1} = .8763$$

Thus, after adjusting for the two independent variables, we have an adjusted multiple coefficient of determination of .8763. This value is provided by the Excel output in Figure 15.4 as Adjusted R Square = .8763.

## EXERCISES

### Methods

**11.** In Exercise 1, the following estimated regression equation based on 10 observations was presented.

$$\hat{y} = 29.1270 + .5906x_1 + .4980x_2$$

The values of SST and SSR are 6724.125 and 6216.375, respectively.
  **a.** Find SSE.
  **b.** Compute $R^2$.
  **c.** Compute $R_a^2$.
  **d.** Comment on the goodness of fit.

**12.** In Exercise 2, 10 observations were provided for a dependent variable $y$ and two independent variables $x_1$ and $x_2$; for these data SST $= 15{,}182.9$, and SSR $= 14{,}052.2$.
   **a.** Compute $R^2$.
   **b.** Compute $R_a^2$.
   **c.** Does the estimated regression equation explain a large amount of the variability in the data? Explain.

**13.** In Exercise 3, the following estimated regression equation based on 30 observations was presented.

$$\hat{y} = 17.6 + 3.8x_1 - 2.3x_2 + 7.6x_3 + 2.7x_4$$

The values of SST and SSR are 1805 and 1760, respectively.
   **a.** Compute $R^2$.
   **b.** Compute $R_a^2$.
   **c.** Comment on the goodness of fit.

## Applications

**14.** In Exercise 4, the following estimated regression equation relating sales to inventory investment and advertising expenditures was given.

$$\hat{y} = 25 + 10x_1 + 8x_2$$

The data used to develop the model came from a survey of 10 stores; for those data, SST $= 16{,}000$ and SSR $= 12{,}000$.
   **a.** For the estimated regression equation given, compute $R^2$.
   **b.** Compute $R_a^2$.
   **c.** Does the model appear to explain a large amount of variability in the data? Explain.

**15.** In Exercise 5, the owner of Showtime Movie Theaters, Inc., used multiple regression analysis to predict gross revenue ($y$) as a function of television advertising expenditures ($x_1$) and newspaper advertising expenditures ($x_2$). The estimated regression equation was

$$\hat{y} = 83.2 + 2.29x_1 + 1.30x_2$$

The computer solution provided SST $= 25.5$ and SSR $= 23.435$.
   **a.** Compute and interpret $R^2$ and $R_a^2$.
   **b.** When television advertising expenditures was the only independent variable, $R^2 = .653$ and $R_a^2 = .595$. Do you prefer the multiple regression results? Explain.

**16.** In Exercise 6, data were given on curb weight, horsepower, and speed of a sports and GT car at $\frac{1}{4}$ mile for 16 cars (*1998 Road & Track Sports & GT Cars*).
   **a.** Did the estimated regression equation that uses only curb weight to predict the speed at $\frac{1}{4}$ mile provide a good fit? Explain.
   **b.** Discuss the benefits of using both the curb weight and the horsepower to predict the speed at $\frac{1}{4}$ mile.

**17.** In Exercise 9, an estimated regression equation was developed relating the percentage of students who attend a 4-year college to the average class size and the combined SAT score.
   **a.** Compute and interpret $R^2$ and $R_a^2$.
   **b.** Does the estimated regression equation provide a good fit to the data? Explain.

**18.** Refer to Exercise 10, where data were reported on the number of cars in service (1000s), the number of locations, and the rental revenue ($ millions) for 15 car rental companies (*The Wall Street Journal Almanac 1998*).
   **a.** In part (c) of Exercise 10, an estimated regression equation was developed relating the rental revenue to the number of cars in service and the number of locations. What are the values of $R^2$ and $R_a^2$?
   **b.** Does the estimated regression equation provide a good fit to the data? Explain.

## 15.4 MODEL ASSUMPTIONS

In Section 15.1 we introduced the following multiple regression model.

**Multiple Regression Model**

$$y = \beta_0 + \beta_1 x_1 + \beta_2 x_2 + \cdots + \beta_p x_p + \epsilon \qquad \textbf{(15.10)}$$

The assumptions about the error term $\epsilon$ in the multiple regression model parallel those for the simple linear regression model.

**Assumptions About the Error Term $\epsilon$ in the Multiple Regression Model**
$$y = \beta_0 + \beta_1 x_1 + \cdots + \beta_p x_p + \epsilon$$

1. The error $\epsilon$ is a random variable with mean or expected value of zero; that is, $E(\epsilon) = 0$.
   *Implication:* For given values of $x_1, x_2, \ldots, x_p$, the expected, or average, value of $y$ is given by

   $$E(y) = \beta_0 + \beta_1 x_1 + \beta_2 x_2 + \cdots + \beta_p x_p. \qquad \textbf{(15.11)}$$

   Equation (15.11) is the multiple regression equation we introduced in Section 15.1. In this equation, $E(y)$ represents the average of all possible values of $y$ that might occur for the given values of $x_1, x_2, \ldots, x_p$.
2. The variance of $\epsilon$ is denoted by $\sigma^2$ and is the same for all values of the independent variables $x_1, x_2, \ldots, x_p$.
   *Implication:* The variance of $y$ equals $\sigma^2$ and is the same for all values of $x_1, x_2, \ldots, x_p$.
3. The values of $\epsilon$ are independent.
   *Implication:* The size of the error for a particular set of values for the independent variables is not related to the size of the error for any other set of values.
4. The error $\epsilon$ is a normally distributed random variable reflecting the deviation between the $y$ value and the expected value of $y$ given by $\beta_0 + \beta_1 x_1 + \beta_2 x_2 + \cdots + \beta_p x_p$.
   *Implication:* Because $\beta_0, \beta_1, \ldots, \beta_p$ are constants for the given values of $x_1, x_2, \ldots, x_p$, the dependent variable $y$ is also a normally distributed random variable.

To obtain more insight about the form of the relationship given by equation (15.11), consider the following two-independent-variable multiple regression equation.

$$E(y) = \beta_0 + \beta_1 x_1 + \beta_2 x_2$$

The graph of this equation is a plane in three-dimensional space. Figure 15.6 is such a graph. Note that $\epsilon$ is shown as the difference between the actual $y$ value and the expected value of $y$, $E(y)$, when $x_1 = x_1^*$ and $x_2 = x_2^*$.

**FIGURE 15.6**    GRAPH OF THE REGRESSION EQUATION FOR MULTIPLE REGRESSION
ANALYSIS WITH TWO INDEPENDENT VARIABLES

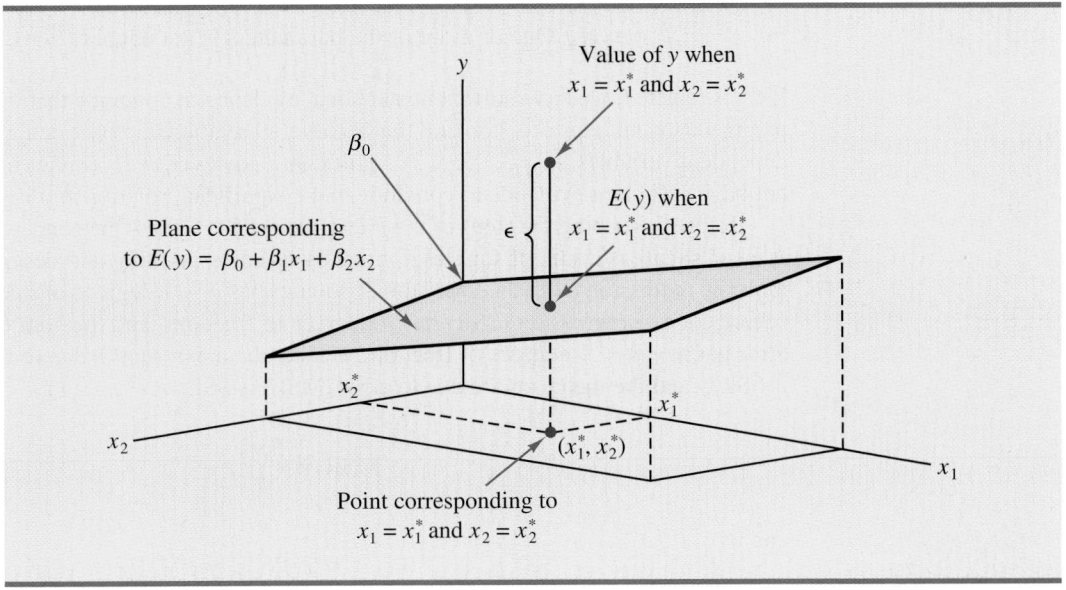

In regression analysis, the term *response variable* is often used in place of the term *dependent variable*. Furthermore, because the multiple regression equation generates a plane or surface, its graph is called a *response surface*.

## 15.5    TESTING FOR SIGNIFICANCE

In this section we show how to conduct significance tests for a multiple regression relationship. The significance tests we used in simple linear regression were a $t$ test and an $F$ test. In simple linear regression, both tests provide the same conclusion; that is, if the null hypothesis is rejected, we conclude that $\beta_1 \neq 0$. In multiple regression, the $t$ test and the $F$ test have different purposes.

1.  The $F$ test is used to determine whether a significant relationship exists between the dependent variable and the set of all the independent variables; we will refer to the $F$ test as the test for *overall significance*.
2.  If the $F$ test shows an overall significance, the $t$ test is used to determine whether each of the individual independent variables is significant. A separate $t$ test is conducted for each of the independent variables in the model; we refer to each of these $t$ tests as a test for *individual significance*.

In the material that follows, we will explain the $F$ test and the $t$ test and apply each to the Butler Trucking Company example.

### $F$ Test

The multiple regression model as defined in Section 15.4 is

$$y = \beta_0 + \beta_1 x_1 + \beta_2 x_2 + \cdots + \beta_p x_p + \epsilon$$

The hypotheses for the $F$ test involve the parameters of the multiple regression model.

$$H_0: \beta_1 = \beta_2 = \cdots = \beta_p = 0$$
$$H_a: \text{One or more of the parameters is not equal to zero}$$

If $H_0$ is rejected, we have sufficient statistical evidence to conclude that one or more of the parameters is not equal to zero and that the overall relationship between $y$ and the set of independent variables $x_1, x_2, \ldots, x_p$ is significant. However, if $H_0$ cannot be rejected, we do not have sufficient evidence to conclude that a significant relationship is present.

Before describing the steps of the $F$ test, we need to review the concept of *mean square*. A mean square is a sum of squares divided by its corresponding degrees of freedom. In the multiple regression case, the total sum of squares has $n - 1$ degrees of freedom, the sum of squares due to regression (SSR) has $p$ degrees of freedom, and the sum of squares due to error has $n - p - 1$ degrees of freedom. Hence, the mean square due to regression (MSR) is SSR/$p$ and the mean square due to error (MSE) is SSE/$(n - p - 1)$.

$$\text{MSR} = \frac{\text{SSR}}{p} \tag{15.12}$$

and

$$\text{MSE} = \frac{\text{SSE}}{n - p - 1} \tag{15.13}$$

As discussed in Chapter 14, MSE provides an unbiased estimate of $\sigma^2$, the variance of the error term $\epsilon$. If $H_0: \beta_1 = \beta_2 = \cdots = \beta_p = 0$ is true, MSR also provides an unbiased estimate of $\sigma^2$, and the value of MSR/MSE should be close to 1. However, if $H_0$ is false, MSR overestimates $\sigma^2$ and the value of MSR/MSE becomes larger. To determine how large the value of MSR/MSE must be to reject $H_0$, we make use of the fact that if $H_0$ is true and the assumptions about the multiple regression model are valid, the sampling distribution of MSR/MSE is an $F$ distribution with $p$ degrees of freedom in the numerator and $n - p - 1$ degrees of freedom in the denominator. A summary of the $F$ test for significance in multiple regression follows.

**$F$ Test for Overall Significance**

$$H_0: \beta_1 = \beta_2 = \cdots = \beta_p = 0$$
$$H_a: \text{One or more of the parameters is not equal to zero}$$

**Test Statistic**

$$F = \frac{\text{MSR}}{\text{MSE}} \tag{15.14}$$

**Rejection Rule**

Using test statistic:   Reject $H_0$ if $F > F_\alpha$
Using $p$-value:        Reject $H_0$ if $p$-value $< \alpha$

where $F_\alpha$ is based on an $F$ distribution with $p$ degrees of freedom in the numerator and $n - p - 1$ degrees of freedom in the denominator.

Let us apply the $F$ test to the Butler Trucking Company multiple regression problem. With two independent variables, the hypotheses are written as follows.

$$H_0: \beta_1 = \beta_2 = 0$$
$$H_a: \beta_1 \text{ and/or } \beta_2 \text{ is not equal to zero}$$

Figure 15.7 shows a portion of the Excel output shown previously in Figure 15.4, with miles traveled ($x_1$) and number of deliveries ($x_2$) as the two independent variables. In the analysis of variance part of the output, we see that MSR $=$ 10.8003 and MSE $=$ .3285. Using (15.14), we obtain the test statistic.

$$F = \frac{10.8003}{.3285} = 32.9$$

With a level of significance $\alpha = .01$, Table 4 of Appendix B shows that with two degrees of freedom in the numerator and seven degrees of freedom in the denominator, $F_{.01} = 9.55$. With $32.9 > 9.55$, we reject $H_0: \beta_1 = \beta_2 = 0$ and conclude that a significant relationship is present between travel time $y$ and the two independent variables, miles traveled and number of deliveries. The Significance $F$ or $p$-value $=$ .0003 in the last column of the analysis of variance table (Figure 15.7) also indicates that we can reject $H_0: \beta_1 = \beta_2 = 0$ because the $p$-value is less than $\alpha$.

As noted previously, the mean square error provides an unbiased estimate of $\sigma^2$, the variance of the error term $\epsilon$. Referring to Figure 15.7, we see that the estimate of $\sigma^2$ is MSE $=$ .3285. The square root of MSE is the estimate of the standard deviation of the error

**FIGURE 15.7**    PARTIAL EXCEL OUTPUT FOR THE BUTLER TRUCKING PROBLEM WITH TWO
INDEPENDENT VARIABLES

|  | A | B | C | D | E | F | G | H | I |
|---|---|---|---|---|---|---|---|---|---|
| 13 | SUMMARY OUTPUT | | | | | | | | |
| 14 | | | | | | | | | |
| 15 | *Regression Statistics* | | | | | | | | |
| 16 | Multiple R | 0.9507 | | | | | | | |
| 17 | R Square | 0.9038 | | | | | | | |
| 18 | Adjusted R Square | 0.8763 | | | | | | | |
| 19 | Standard Error | 0.5731 | | | | | | | |
| 20 | Observations | 10 | | | | | | | |
| 21 | | | | | | | | | |
| 22 | ANOVA | | | | | | | | |
| 23 | | *df* | *SS* | *MS* | *F* | *Significance F* | | | |
| 24 | Regression | 2 | 21.6006 | 10.8003 | 32.8784 | 0.0003 | | | |
| 25 | Residual | 7 | 2.2994 | 0.3285 | | | | | |
| 26 | Total | 9 | 23.9 | | | | | | |
| 27 | | | | | | | | | |
| 28 | | *Coefficients* | *Standard Error* | *t Stat* | *P-value* | | | | |
| 29 | Intercept | -0.8687 | 0.9515 | -0.9129 | 0.3916 | | | | |
| 30 | Miles | 0.0611 | 0.0099 | 6.1824 | 0.0005 | | | | |
| 31 | Deliveries | 0.9234 | 0.2211 | 4.1763 | 0.0042 | | | | |
| 32 | | | | | | | | | |
| 33 | | | | | | | | | |
| 34 | | | | | | | | | |
| 35 | | | | | | | | | |

The *Significance F* value in cell F24 is the *p*-value used to test for overall significance.

The *p*-value in cell E30 is used to test for the individual significance of Miles.

The *p*-value in cell E31 is used to test for the individual significance of Deliveries.

Note: Rows 1–12 are hidden.

term. As defined in Section 14.5, this standard deviation is called the standard error of the estimate and is denoted $s$. Hence, we have $s = \sqrt{\text{MSE}} = \sqrt{.3285} = .5731$. Note that the value of the standard error of the estimate appears in cell B19 of the Excel output in Figure 15.7.

Table 15.3 is the general analysis of variance (ANOVA) table that provides the $F$ test results for a multiple regression model. The test statistic $F$ appears in the last column and can be compared to $F_{\alpha}$ with $p$ degrees of freedom in the numerator and $n - p - 1$ degrees of freedom in the denominator to make the hypothesis testing conclusion. By reviewing the Excel output for Butler Trucking Company in Figure 15.7, we see that Excel's analysis of variance table contains this information as well as the $p$-values for the $F$ test.

### $t$ Test

If the $F$ test shows that the multiple regression relationship is significant, a $t$ test can be conducted to determine the significance of each of the individual parameters. The $t$ test for individual significance follows.

---

**$t$ Test for Individual Significance**

For any parameter $\beta_i$

$$H_0: \beta_i = 0$$
$$H_a: \beta_i \neq 0$$

**Test Statistic**

$$t = \frac{b_i}{s_{b_i}} \tag{15.15}$$

**Rejection Rule**

Using test statistic:    Reject $H_0$ if $t < -t_{\alpha/2}$ or if $t > t_{\alpha/2}$

Using $p$-value:        Reject $H_0$ if $p$-value $< \alpha$

where $t_{\alpha/2}$ is based on a $t$ distribution with $n - p - 1$ degrees of freedom.

---

In the test statistic, $s_{b_i}$ is the estimate of the standard deviation of $b_i$. The value of $s_{b_i}$ will be provided by the computer software package.

**TABLE 15.3**    ANOVA TABLE FOR A MULTIPLE REGRESSION MODEL WITH $p$ INDEPENDENT VARIABLES

| Source | Sum of Squares | Degrees of Freedom | Mean Square | $F$ |
|---|---|---|---|---|
| Regression | SSR | $p$ | $\text{MSR} = \dfrac{\text{SSR}}{p}$ | $F = \dfrac{\text{MSR}}{\text{MSE}}$ |
| Error | SSE | $n - p - 1$ | $\text{MSE} = \dfrac{\text{SSE}}{n - p - 1}$ | |
| Total | SST | $n - 1$ | | |

Let us conduct the $t$ test for the Butler Trucking regression problem. Refer to cells B30:E31 in the Excel ouput shown in Figure 15.7. Values of $b_1$, $b_2$, $s_{b_1}$, and $s_{b_2}$ are as follows.

$$b_1 = .0611 \quad s_{b_1} = .0099$$
$$b_2 = .9234 \quad s_{b_2} = .2211$$

Using (15.15), we obtain the test statistic for the hypotheses involving parameters $\beta_1$ and $\beta_2$.

$$t = .0611/.0099 = 6.1717$$
$$t = .9234/.2211 = 4.1764$$

The $t$ values in the Excel output are 6.1824 and 4.1763. The difference is due to rounding.

Note that both of these $t$ test values are provided by the Excel output in Figure 15.7. Using $\alpha = .01$ and $n - p - 1 = 10 - 2 - 1 = 7$ degrees of freedom, we can use Table 2 of Appendix B to find $t_{.005} = 3.499$. With $6.1717 > 3.499$, we reject $H_0$: $\beta_1 = 0$. Similarly, with $4.1764 > 3.499$, we reject $H_0$: $\beta_2 = 0$. Note that the $p$-values of .0005 and .0042 on the Excel output also indicate rejection of these hypotheses at the $\alpha = .01$ level of significance. Hence, both parameters are statistically significant.

## Multicollinearity

We have used the term *independent variable* in regression analysis to refer to any variable being used to predict or explain the value of the dependent variable. The term does not mean, however, that the independent variables themselves are independent in any statistical sense. On the contrary, most independent variables in a multiple regression problem are correlated to some degree with one another. For example, in the Butler Trucking example involving the two independent variables $x_1$ (miles traveled) and $x_2$ (number of deliveries), we could treat the miles traveled as the dependent variable and the number of deliveries as the independent variable to determine whether those two variables are themselves related. We could then compute the sample correlation coefficient $r_{x_1 x_2}$ to determine the extent to which the variables are related. Doing so yields $r_{x_1 x_2} = .16$. Thus, we find some degree of linear association between the two independent variables. In multiple regression analysis, **multicollinearity** refers to the correlation among the independent variables.

To provide a better perspective of the potential problems of multicollinearity, let us consider a modification of the Butler Trucking example. Instead of $x_2$ being the number of deliveries, let $x_2$ denote the number of gallons of gasoline consumed. Clearly, $x_1$ (the miles traveled) and $x_2$ are related; that is, we know that the number of gallons of gasoline used depends on the number of miles traveled. Hence, we would conclude logically that $x_1$ and $x_2$ are highly correlated independent variables.

Assume that we obtain the equation $\hat{y} = b_0 + b_1 x_1 + b_2 x_2$ and find that the $F$ test shows the relationship to be significant. Then suppose we conduct a $t$ test on $\beta_1$ to determine whether $\beta_1 \neq 0$, and we cannot reject $H_0$: $\beta_1 = 0$. Does this mean that travel time is not related to miles traveled? Not necessarily. What it probably means is that with $x_2$ already in the model, $x_1$ does not make a significant contribution to determining the value of $y$. This interpretation makes sense in our example; if we know the amount of gasoline consumed, we do not gain much additional information useful in predicting $y$ by knowing the miles traveled. Similarly, a $t$ test might lead us to conclude $\beta_2 = 0$ on the grounds that, with $x_1$ in the model, knowledge of the amount of gasoline consumed does not add much.

When the independent variables are highly correlated, it is not possible to determine the separate effect of any particular independent variable on the dependent variable.

To summarize, in $t$ tests for the significance of individual parameters, the difficulty caused by multicollinearity is that it is possible to conclude that none of the individual parameters are significantly different from zero when an $F$ test on the overall multiple regression equation indicates a significant relationship. This problem is avoided when there is little correlation among the independent variables.

A sample correlation coefficient greater than $+0.7$ or less than $-0.7$ for two independent variables is a rule of thumb warning of potential problems with multicollinearity.

Statisticians have developed several tests for determining whether multicollinearity is high enough to cause problems. According to the rule of thumb test, multicollinearity is a potential problem if the absolute value of the sample correlation coefficient exceeds .7 for any two of the independent variables. The other types of tests are more advanced and beyond the scope of this text.

If possible, every attempt should be made to avoid including independent variables that are highly correlated. In practice, however, strict adherence to this policy is rarely possible. When decision makers have reason to believe substantial multicollinearity is present, they must be aware that separating the effects of the individual independent variables on the dependent variable is difficult.

## NOTES AND COMMENTS

Ordinarily, multicollinearity does not affect the way in which we perform our regression analysis or interpret the output from a study. However, when multicollinearity is severe—that is, when two or more of the independent variables are highly correlated with one another—we can have difficulty interpreting the results of $t$ tests on the individual parameters. In addition to the type of problem illustrated in this section, severe cases of multicollinearity have been shown to result in least squares estimates that have the wrong sign. That is,

in simulated studies where researchers created the underlying regression model and then applied the least squares technique to develop estimates of $\beta_0$, $\beta_1$, $\beta_2$, and so on, it has been shown that under conditions of high multicollinearity the least squares estimates can have a sign opposite that of the parameter being estimated. For example, $\beta_2$ might actually be $+10$ and $b_2$, its estimate, might turn out to be $-2$. Thus, little faith can be placed in the individual coefficients if multicollinearity is present to a high degree.

## EXERCISES

### Methods

**19.** In Exercise 1, the following estimated regression equation based on 10 observations was presented.

$$\hat{y} = 29.1270 + .5906x_1 + .4980x_2$$

Here SST = 6724.125, SSR = 6216.375, $s_{b_1}$ = .0813, and $s_{b_2}$ = .0567.
  **a.** Compute MSR and MSE.
  **b.** Compute $F$ and perform the appropriate $F$ test. Use $\alpha = .05$.
  **c.** Perform a $t$ test for the significance of $\beta_1$. Use $\alpha = .05$.
  **d.** Perform a $t$ test for the significance of $\beta_2$. Use $\alpha = .05$.

**20.** Refer to the data presented in Exercise 2. The estimated regression equation for these data is

$$\hat{y} = -18.4 + 2.01x_1 + 4.74x_2$$

Here SST = 15,182.9, SSR = 14,052.2, $s_{b_1}$ = .2471, and $s_{b_2}$ = .9484.
  **a.** Test for a significant relationship among $x_1$, $x_2$, and $y$. Use $\alpha = .05$.
  **b.** Is $\beta_1$ significant? Use $\alpha = .05$.
  **c.** Is $\beta_2$ significant? Use $\alpha = .05$.

**21.** The following estimated regression equation was developed for a model involving two independent variables.

$$\hat{y} = 40.7 + 8.63x_1 + 2.71x_2$$

After $x_2$ was dropped from the model, the least squares method was used to obtain an estimated regression equation involving only $x_1$ as an independent variable.

$$\hat{y} = 42.0 + 9.01x_1$$

**a.** Give an interpretation of the coefficient of $x_1$ in both models.
**b.** Could multicollinearity explain why the coefficient of $x_1$ differs in the two models? If so, how?

## Applications

**22.** In Exercise 4 the following estimated regression equation relating sales to inventory investment and advertising expenditures was given.

$$\hat{y} = 25 + 10x_1 + 8x_2$$

The data used to develop the model came from a survey of 10 stores; for these data SST = 16,000 and SSR = 12,000.
**a.** Compute SSE, MSE, and MSR.
**b.** Use an $F$ test and a .05 level of significance to determine whether there is a relationship among the variables.

**23.** Refer to Exercise 5.

**a.** Use $\alpha = .01$ to test the hypotheses

$$H_0: \beta_1 = \beta_2 = 0$$
$$H_a: \beta_1 \text{ and/or } \beta_2 \text{ is not equal to zero}$$

for the model $y = \beta_0 + \beta_1 x_1 + \beta_2 x_2 + \epsilon$, where

$$x_1 = \text{television advertising expenditures (\$1000s)}$$
$$x_2 = \text{newspaper advertising expenditures (\$1000s)}$$

**b.** Use $\alpha = .05$ to test the significance of $\beta_1$. Should $x_1$ be dropped from the model?
**c.** Use $\alpha = .05$ to test the significance of $\beta_2$. Should $x_2$ be dropped from the model?

**24.** Refer to the data in Exercise 6. Use curb weight and horsepower to predict the speed of a sports and GT car at ¼ mile.
**a.** Use the $F$ test to determine the overall significance of the relationship. What is your conclusion at the .05 level of significance?
**b.** Use the $t$ test to determine the significance of each independent variable. What is your conclusion at the .05 level of significance?

**25.** A sample of 16 companies taken from the *Stock Investor Pro* database was used to obtain the following data on the price/earnings (P/E) ratio, the gross profit margin, and the sales growth for each company (*Stock Investor Pro*, American Association of Individual Investors, August 21, 1997).

| Firm | P/E Ratio | Gross Profit Margin (%) | Sales Growth (%) |
|---|---|---|---|
| Abbott Laboratories | 22.3 | 23.7 | 10.0 |
| American Home Products | 22.6 | 21.1 | 5.3 |
| Amoco | 16.7 | 11.0 | 16.5 |
| Bristol Meyers Squibb Co. | 25.9 | 26.6 | 9.4 |
| Chevron | 18.3 | 11.6 | 18.4 |
| Exxon | 18.7 | 9.8 | 8.3 |

*(continued)*

| Firm | P/E Ratio | Gross Profit Margin (%) | Sales Growth (%) |
|------|-----------|-------------------------|-------------------|
| General Electric Company | 13.1 | 13.4 | 13.1 |
| Hewlett-Packard | 23.3 | 9.7 | 21.9 |
| IBM | 17.3 | 11.5 | 5.6 |
| Merck & Co., Inc. | 26.2 | 25.6 | 18.9 |
| Mobil | 18.7 | 8.2 | 8.1 |
| Pfizer | 34.6 | 25.1 | 12.8 |
| Pharmacia & Upjohn, Inc. | 22.3 | 15.0 | 2.7 |
| Procter & Gamble Co. | 5.4 | 14.9 | 5.4 |
| Texaco | 12.3 | 7.3 | 23.7 |
| Travelers Group, Inc. | 28.7 | 17.8 | 28.7 |

a. Determine the estimated regression equation that can be used to predict the price/earnings ratio given the gross profit margin and the sales growth.

b. Use the $F$ test to determine the overall significance of the relationship. What is your conclusion at the .05 level of significance?

c. Use the $t$ test to determine the significance of each independent variable. What is your conclusion at the .05 level of significance?

d. Remove any independent variable that is not significant from the estimated regression equation. What is your recommended estimated regression equation? Compare the $R^2$ with the value of $R^2$ from part (a). Discuss the differences.

26. In Exercise 10 an estimated regression equation was developed relating the rental revenue ($ millions) to the number of cars in service (1000s) and the number of locations.

a. Test for a significant relationship between the dependent variable and the two independent variables. Use $\alpha = .05$.

b. Is the number of cars in service significant? Use $\alpha = .05$.

c. Is the number of locations significant? Use $\alpha = .05$.

## 15.6  USING THE ESTIMATED REGRESSION EQUATION FOR ESTIMATION AND PREDICTION

The procedures for estimating the mean value of $y$ and predicting an individual value of $y$ in multiple regression are similar to those in regression analysis involving one independent variable. First, recall that in Chapter 14 we showed that the point estimate of the expected value of $y$ for a given value of $x$ was the same as the point estimate of an individual value of $y$. In both cases, we used $\hat{y} = b_0 + b_1x$ as the point estimate.

In multiple regression we use the same procedure. That is, we substitute the given values of $x_1, x_2, \ldots, x_p$ into the estimated regression equation and use the corresponding value of $\hat{y}$ as the point estimate. Suppose that for the Butler Trucking example we want to use the estimated regression equation involving $x_1$ (miles traveled) and $x_2$ (number of deliveries) to develop two estimates:

1. A *confidence interval estimate* of the mean travel time for all trucks that travel 100 miles and make two deliveries.
2. A *prediction interval estimate* of the travel time for *one specific* truck that travels 100 miles and makes two deliveries.

Using the estimated regression equation $\hat{y} = -.869 + .0611x_1 + .923x_2$ with $x_1 = 100$ and $x_2 = 2$, we obtain the following value of $\hat{y}$.

$$\hat{y} = -.8687 + .0611(100) + .9234(2) = 7.09$$

Hence, the point estimate of travel time in both cases is approximately 7 hours.

**TABLE 15.4**    THE 95% CONFIDENCE AND PREDICTION INTERVAL ESTIMATES
FOR BUTLER TRUCKING

| Value of $x_1$ | Value of $x_2$ | Value of $\hat{y}$ | Confidence Interval | | Prediction Interval | |
|---|---|---|---|---|---|---|
| | | | Lower Limit | Upper Limit | Lower Limit | Upper Limit |
| 50 | 2 | 4.035 | 3.146 | 4.924 | 2.414 | 5.656 |
| 50 | 3 | 4.958 | 4.127 | 5.789 | 3.369 | 6.548 |
| 50 | 4 | 5.882 | 4.815 | 6.948 | 4.157 | 7.606 |
| 100 | 2 | 7.092 | 6.258 | 7.925 | 5.500 | 8.683 |
| 100 | 3 | 8.015 | 7.385 | 8.645 | 6.520 | 9.510 |
| 100 | 4 | 8.938 | 8.135 | 9.742 | 7.363 | 10.514 |

The PredInt.xls macro included on the data disk can be used to develop confidence and prediction intervals.

To develop interval estimates for the mean value of $y$ and for an individual value of $y$, we use a procedure similar to that for regression analysis involving one independent variable. The formulas required are beyond the scope of the text, but computer packages for multiple regression analysis will often provide confidence intervals once the values of $x_1$, $x_2, \ldots, x_p$ are specified by the user. Unfortunately, Excel's Regression tool does not have this capability. However, by running the PredInt.xls macro included on the data disk, you will be able to develop confidence and prediction interval estimates. In Table 15.4 we show 95% confidence and prediction interval estimates for the Butler Trucking example for selected values of $x_1$ and $x_2$; these values were obtained by using the PredInt macro. Note that the interval estimate for an individual value of $y$ is wider than the interval estimate for the expected value of $y$. This difference simply reflects the fact that for given values of $x_1$ and $x_2$ we can estimate the mean travel time for all trucks with more precision than we can predict the travel time for one specific truck.

## EXERCISES

### Methods

**27.** In Exercise 1, the following estimated regression equation based on 10 observations was presented.

$$\hat{y} = 29.1270 + .5906x_1 + .4980x_2$$

    **a.** Develop a point estimate of the mean value of $y$ when $x_1 = 180$ and $x_2 = 310$.
    **b.** Develop a point estimate for an individual value of $y$ when $x_1 = 180$ and $x_2 = 310$.

**28.** Refer to the data in Exercise 2. The estimated regression equation for those data is

$$\hat{y} = -18.4 + 2.01x_1 + 4.74x_2$$

    **a.** Develop a 95% confidence interval estimate of the mean value of $y$ when $x_1 = 45$ and $x_2 = 15$.
    **b.** Develop a 95% prediction interval estimate of $y$ when $x_1 = 45$ and $x_2 = 15$.

### Applications

**29.** In Exercise 5, the owner of Showtime Movie Theaters, Inc., used multiple regression analysis to predict gross revenue ( $y$ ) as a function of television advertising expenditures ( $x_1$ ) and newspaper advertising expenditures ( $x_2$ ). The estimated regression equation was

$$\hat{y} = 83.2 + 2.29x_1 + 1.30x_2$$

**a.** What is the gross revenue expected for a week when \$3500 is spent on television advertising ($x_1 = 3.5$) and \$1800 is spent on newspaper advertising ($x_2 = 1.8$)?

**b.** Provide a 95% confidence interval estimate for the mean revenue of all weeks with the expenditures listed in part (a).

**c.** Provide a 95% prediction interval estimate for next week's revenue, assuming that the advertising expenditures will be allocated as in part (a).

**30.** In Exercise 6, data were given on curb weight, horsepower, and speed at ¼ mile for 16 sports and GT cars (*1998 Road and Track Sports & GT Cars*).

**a.** Estimate the ¼-mile speed of a 1999 Porsche 911 Carrera that has a curb weight of 2910 pounds and a horsepower of 296.

**b.** Provide a 95% confidence interval estimate for the ¼-mile speed of all sports and GT cars with the characteristics listed in part (a).

**c.** Provide a 95% prediction interval estimate for the 1999 Porsche 911 Carrera described in part (a).

**31.** In Exercise 9, an estimated regression equation was developed relating the percentage of students who attend a 4-year college to the average class size and the combined SAT score.

**a.** Develop a 95% confidence interval estimate of the mean percentage of students who attend a 4-year college for a school district that has an average class size of 25 and whose students have a combined SAT score of 1000.

**b.** Suppose that a school district in Conway, South Carolina, has an average class size of 25 and a combined SAT score of 950. Develop a 95% prediction interval estimate of the percentage of students who attend a 4-year college.

## 15.7 QUALITATIVE INDEPENDENT VARIABLES

*Independent variables may be qualitative or quantitative.*

Thus far, the examples we have considered have involved quantitative independent variables such as student population, distance traveled, and number of deliveries. In many situations, however, we must work with **qualitative independent variables** such as gender (male, female), method of payment (cash, credit card, check), and so on. The purpose of this section is to show how qualitative variables are handled in regression analysis. To illustrate the use and interpretation of a qualitative independent variable, we will consider a problem facing the managers of Johnson Filtration, Inc.

### An Example: Johnson Filtration, Inc.

Johnson Filtration, Inc., provides maintenance service for water-filtration systems throughout southern Florida. Customers contact Johnson with requests for maintenance service on their water-filtration systems. To estimate the service time and the service cost, Johnson's managers want to predict the repair time necessary for each maintenance request. Hence, repair time in hours is the dependent variable. Repair time is believed to be related to two factors, the number of months since the last maintenance service and the type of repair problem (mechanical or electrical). Data for a sample of 10 service calls are reported in Table 15.5.

Let $y$ denote the repair time in hours and $x_1$ denote the number of months since the last maintenance service. The regression model that uses only $x_1$ to predict $y$ is

$$y = \beta_0 + \beta_1 x_1 + \epsilon$$

Using Excel's Regression tool to develop the estimated regression equation, we obtained the partial Excel output shown in Figure 15.8. The estimated regression equation is

$$\hat{y} = 2.1473 + .3041 x_1 \qquad \textbf{(15.16)}$$

and type of repair ($p$-value = .0051) are statistically significant. In addition, R Square = .8592 and Adjusted R Square = .8190 indicate that the estimated regression equation does a good job of explaining the variability in repair times. Thus, equation (15.17) should prove helpful in estimating the repair time necessary for the various service calls.

## Interpreting the Parameters

The multiple regression equation for the Johnson Filtration example is

$$E(y) = \beta_0 + \beta_1 x_1 + \beta_2 x_2 \tag{15.18}$$

To understand how to interpret the parameters $\beta_0$, $\beta_1$, and $\beta_2$ when a qualitative variable is present, consider the case when $x_2 = 0$ (mechanical repair). Using $E(y \mid \text{mechanical})$ to denote the mean repair time *given* a mechanical repair, we have

$$E(y \mid \text{mechanical}) = \beta_0 + \beta_1 x_1 + \beta_2(0) = \beta_0 + \beta_1 x_1 \tag{15.19}$$

Similarly, for an electrical repair ($x_2 = 1$), we have

$$E(y \mid \text{electrical}) = \beta_0 + \beta_1 x_1 + \beta_2(1) = \beta_0 + \beta_1 x_1 + \beta_2 \tag{15.20}$$
$$= (\beta_0 + \beta_2) + \beta_1 x_1$$

Comparing equations (15.19) and (15.20), we see that the expected repair time is a linear function of $x_1$ for both mechanical and electrical repairs. The slope of both equations is $\beta_1$, but the $y$-intercept differs. The $y$-intercept is $\beta_0$ in equation (15.19) for mechanical repairs and ($\beta_0 + \beta_2$) in equation (15.20) for electrical repairs. The interpretation of $\beta_2$ is that it indicates the difference between the expected repair time for an electrical repair and the expected repair time for a mechanical repair.

If $\beta_2$ is positive, the expected repair time for an electrical repair will be greater than that for a mechanical repair; if $\beta_2$ is negative, the expected repair time for an electrical repair will be less than that for a mechanical repair. Finally, if $\beta_2 = 0$, there is no difference in repair time between electrical and mechanical repairs and the type of repair is not related to the repair time.

Using the estimated multiple regression equation $\hat{y} = .9305 + .3876 x_1 + 1.2627 x_2$, we see that .9305 is the estimate of $\beta_0$ and 1.2627 is the estimate of $\beta_2$. Thus, when $x_2 = 0$ (mechanical repair)

$$\hat{y} = .9305 + .3876 x_1 \tag{15.21}$$

and when $x_2 = 1$ (electrical repair)

$$\hat{y} = .9305 + .3876 x_1 + 1.2627(1) \tag{15.22}$$
$$= 2.1932 + .3876 x_1$$

In effect, the use of a dummy variable for type of repair has provided two equations that can be used to predict the repair time, one corresponding to mechanical repairs and one corresponding to electrical repairs. In addition, with $b_2 = 1.2627$, we have learned that, on average, electrical repairs require 1.2627 hours longer than mechanical repairs.

Figure 15.10 is the plot of the Johnson data from Table 15.6. Repair time in hours ($y$) is represented by the vertical axis and months since last service ($x_1$) is represented by the horizontal axis. A data point for a mechanical repair is indicated by an M and a data point for an electrical repair is indicated by an E. Equations (15.21) and (15.22) are plotted on the

**FIGURE 15.10**    SCATTER DIAGRAM FOR THE JOHNSON FILTRATION REPAIR DATA FROM TABLE 15.6

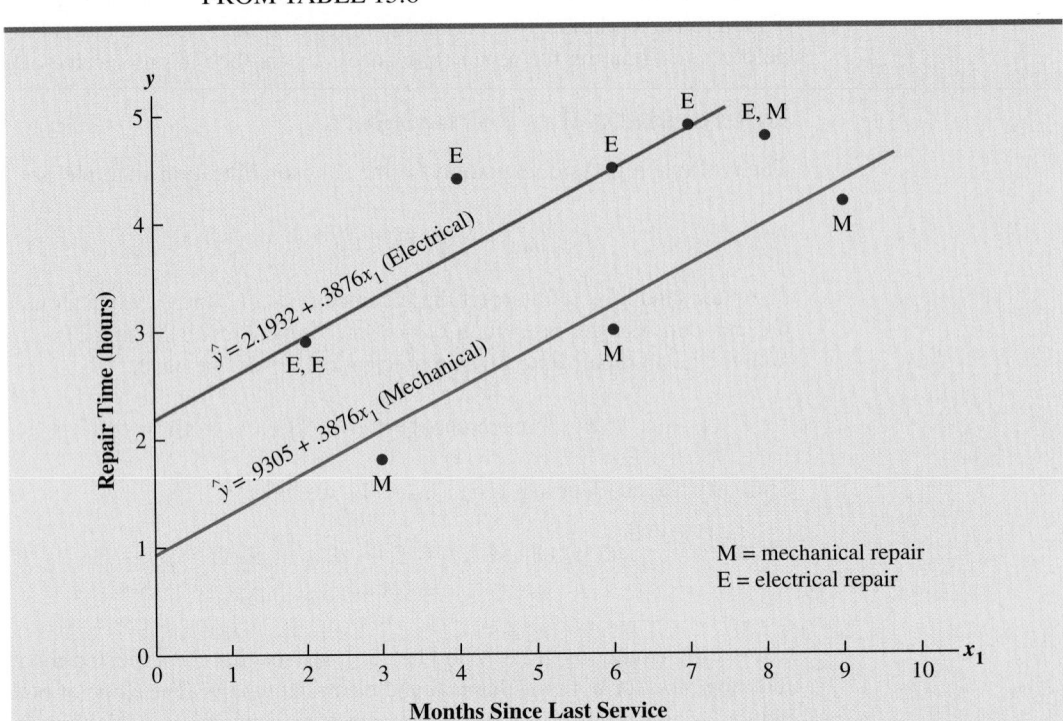

graph to show graphically the two equations that can be used to predict the repair time, one corresponding to mechanical repairs and one corresponding to electrical repairs.

## More Complex Qualitative Variables

Because the qualitative variable for the Johnson Filtration example had two levels (mechanical and electrical), defining a dummy variable with zero indicating a mechanical repair and one indicating an electrical repair was easy. However, when a qualitative variable has more than two levels, care must be taken in both defining and interpreting the dummy variables. As we will show, if a qualitative variable has $k$ levels, $k - 1$ dummy variables are required, with each dummy variable being coded as 0 or 1.

> A qualitative variable with $k$ levels must be modeled using $k - 1$ dummy variables. Care must be taken in defining and interpreting the dummy variables.

For example, suppose a manufacturer of copy machines has organized the sales territories for a particular state into three regions: A, B, and C. The managers want to use regression analysis to help predict the number of copiers sold per week. With the number of units sold as the dependent variable, they are considering several independent variables (the number of sales personnel, advertising expenditures, and so on). Suppose the managers believe sales region is also an important factor in predicting the number of copiers sold. Because sales region is a qualitative variable with three levels, A, B, and C, we will need $3 - 1 = 2$ dummy variables to represent the sales region. Each variable can be coded 0 or 1 as follows.

$$x_1 = \begin{cases} 1 & \text{if sales region B} \\ 0 & \text{otherwise} \end{cases}$$

$$x_2 = \begin{cases} 1 & \text{if sales region C} \\ 0 & \text{otherwise} \end{cases}$$

With this definition, we have the following values of $x_1$ and $x_2$.

| Region | $x_1$ | $x_2$ |
|--------|-------|-------|
| A | 0 | 0 |
| B | 1 | 0 |
| C | 0 | 1 |

Observations corresponding to region A would be coded $x_1 = 0$, $x_2 = 0$; observations corresponding to region B would be coded $x_1 = 1$, $x_2 = 0$; and observations corresponding to region C would be coded $x_1 = 0$, $x_2 = 1$.

The regression equation relating the expected value of the number of units sold, $E(y)$, to the dummy variables would be written as

$$E(y) = \beta_0 + \beta_1 x_1 + \beta_2 x_2$$

To help us interpret the parameters $\beta_0$, $\beta_1$, and $\beta_2$, consider the following three variations of the regression equation.

$$E(y \mid \text{region A}) = \beta_0 + \beta_1(0) + \beta_2(0) = \beta_0$$
$$E(y \mid \text{region B}) = \beta_0 + \beta_1(1) + \beta_2(0) = \beta_0 + \beta_1$$
$$E(y \mid \text{region C}) = \beta_0 + \beta_1(0) + \beta_2(1) = \beta_0 + \beta_2$$

Thus, $\beta_0$ is the mean or expected value of sales for region A; $\beta_1$ is the difference between the mean number of units sold in region B and the mean number of units sold in region A; and $\beta_2$ is the difference between the mean number of units sold in region C and the mean number of units sold in region A.

Two dummy variables were required because sales region is a qualitative variable with three levels. But, the assignment of $x_1 = 0$, $x_2 = 0$ to indicate region A, $x_1 = 1$, $x_2 = 0$ to indicate region B, and $x_1 = 0$, $x_2 = 1$ to indicate region C was arbitrary. For example, we could have chosen $x_1 = 1$, $x_2 = 0$ to indicate region A, $x_1 = 0$, $x_2 = 0$ to indicate region B, and $x_1 = 0$, $x_2 = 1$ to indicate region C. In that case, $\beta_1$ would have been interpreted as the mean difference between regions A and B and $\beta_2$ as the mean difference between regions C and B.

The important point to remember is that when a qualitative variable has $k$ levels, $k - 1$ dummy variables are required in the multiple regression analysis. Thus, if the sales region example had a fourth region, labeled D, three dummy variables would be necessary with $x_3$ defined as follows.

$$x_3 = \begin{cases} 1 \text{ if sales region D} \\ 0 \text{ otherwise} \end{cases}$$

# EXERCISES

## Methods

**32.** Consider a regression study involving a dependent variable $y$, a quantitative independent variable $x_1$, and a qualitative variable with two levels (level 1 and level 2).
  **a.** Write a multiple regression equation relating $x_1$ and the qualitative variable to $y$.
  **b.** What is the expected value of $y$ corresponding to level 1 of the qualitative variable?
  **c.** What is the expected value of $y$ corresponding to level 2 of the qualitative variable?
  **d.** Interpret the parameters in your regression equation.

**33.** Consider a regression study involving a dependent variable $y$, a quantitative independent variable $x_1$, and a qualitative independent variable with three possible levels (level 1, level 2, and level 3).

   **a.** How many dummy variables are required to represent the qualitative variable?
   **b.** Write a multiple regression equation relating $x_1$ and the qualitative variable to $y$.
   **c.** Interpret the parameters in your regression equation.

## Applications

**SELF** test

**34.** The following regression model has been proposed to predict sales at a fast-food outlet.

$$y = \beta_0 + \beta_1 x_1 + \beta_2 x_2 + \beta_3 x_3 + \epsilon$$

where

$$x_1 = \text{number of competitors within 1 mile}$$
$$x_2 = \text{population within 1 mile (1000s)}$$
$$x_3 = \begin{cases} 1 \text{ if drive-up window present} \\ 0 \text{ otherwise} \end{cases}$$
$$y = \text{sales (\$1000s)}$$

The following estimated regression equation was developed after 20 outlets were surveyed.

$$\hat{y} = 10.1 - 4.2x_1 + 6.8x_2 + 15.3x_3$$

   **a.** What is the expected amount of sales attributable to the drive-up window?
   **b.** Predict sales for a store with two competitors, a population of 8000 within 1 mile, and no drive-up window.
   **c.** Predict sales for a store with one competitor, a population of 3000 within 1 mile, and a drive-up window.

**35.** Refer to the Johnson Filtration problem introduced in this section. Suppose that in addition to information on the number of months since the machine was serviced and whether a mechanical or an electrical failure had occurred, the managers obtained a list showing which repairperson had performed the service. The revised data follow.

**Repair**

| Repair Time in Hours | Months Since Last Service | Type of Repair | Repairperson |
|---|---|---|---|
| 2.9 | 2 | Electrical | Dave Newton |
| 3.0 | 6 | Mechanical | Dave Newton |
| 4.8 | 8 | Electrical | Bob Jones |
| 1.8 | 3 | Mechanical | Dave Newton |
| 2.9 | 2 | Electrical | Dave Newton |
| 4.9 | 7 | Electrical | Bob Jones |
| 4.2 | 9 | Mechanical | Bob Jones |
| 4.8 | 8 | Mechanical | Bob Jones |
| 4.4 | 4 | Electrical | Bob Jones |
| 4.5 | 6 | Electrical | Dave Newton |

   **a.** Ignore for now the months since the last maintenance service ($x_1$) and the repairperson who performed the service. Develop the estimated simple linear regression equation to predict the repair time ($y$) given the type of repair ($x_2$). Recall that $x_2 = 0$ if the type of repair is mechanical and 1 if the type of repair is electrical.
   **b.** Does the equation that you developed in part (a) provide a good fit for the observed data? Explain.

**c.** Ignore for now the months since the last maintenance service and the type of repair associated with the machine. Develop the estimated simple linear regression equation to predict the repair time given the repairperson who performed the service. Let $x_3 = 0$ if Bob Jones performed the service and $x_3 = 1$ if Dave Newton performed the service.

**d.** Does the equation that you developed in part (c) provide a good fit for the observed data? Explain.

**36.** This problem is an extension of the situation described in Exercise 35.

    **a.** Develop the estimated regression equation to predict the repair time given the number of months since the last maintenance service, the type of repair, and the repairperson who performed the service.

    **b.** At the .05 level of significance, test whether the estimated regression equation developed in part (a) represents a significant relationship between the independent variables and the dependent variable.

    **c.** Is the addition of the independent variable $x_3$, the repairperson who performed the service, statistically significant? Use $\alpha = .05$. What explanation can you give for the results observed?

**37.** The National Football League rates prospects position by position on a scale that ranges from 5 to 9. The ratings are interpreted as follows: 8.0–9.0 should start the first year; 7.0–7.9 should start; 6.0–6.9 will make the team as backup; and 5.0–5.9 can make the club and contribute. The following table shows the position, weight, speed (for 40 yards), and ratings for 25 NFL prospects (*USA Today*, April 14, 2000).

**Football**

| Name | Position | Weight (pounds) | Speed (seconds) | Rating |
|---|---|---|---|---|
| Cosey Coleman | Guard | 322 | 5.38 | 7.4 |
| Travis Claridge | Guard | 303 | 5.18 | 7.0 |
| Kaulana Noa | Guard | 317 | 5.34 | 6.8 |
| Leander Jordan | Guard | 330 | 5.46 | 6.7 |
| Chad Clifton | Guard | 334 | 5.18 | 6.3 |
| Manula Savea | Guard | 308 | 5.32 | 6.1 |
| Ryan Johanningmei | Guard | 310 | 5.28 | 6.0 |
| Mark Tauscher | Guard | 318 | 5.37 | 6.0 |
| Blaine Saipaia | Guard | 321 | 5.25 | 6.0 |
| Richard Mercier | Guard | 295 | 5.34 | 5.8 |
| Damion McIntosh | Guard | 328 | 5.31 | 5.3 |
| Jeno James | Guard | 320 | 5.64 | 5.0 |
| Al Jackson | Guard | 304 | 5.20 | 5.0 |
| Chris Samuels | Offensive tackle | 325 | 4.95 | 8.5 |
| Stockar McDougle | Offensive tackle | 361 | 5.50 | 8.0 |
| Chris McIngosh | Offensive tackle | 315 | 5.39 | 7.8 |
| Adrian Klemm | Offensive tackle | 307 | 4.98 | 7.6 |
| Todd Wade | Offensive tackle | 326 | 5.20 | 7.3 |
| Marvel Smith | Offensive tackle | 320 | 5.36 | 7.1 |
| Michael Thompson | Offensive tackle | 287 | 5.05 | 6.8 |
| Bobby Williams | Offensive tackle | 332 | 5.26 | 6.8 |
| Darnell Alford | Offensive tackle | 334 | 5.55 | 6.4 |
| Terrance Beadles | Offensive tackle | 312 | 5.15 | 6.3 |
| Tutan Reyes | Offensive tackle | 299 | 5.35 | 6.1 |
| Greg Robinson-Ran | Offensive tackle | 333 | 5.59 | 6.0 |

    **a.** Develop a dummy variable that will account for the player's position.

    **b.** Develop an estimated regression equation to show how rating is related to position, weight, and speed.

    **c.** At the .05 level of significance, test whether the estimated regression equation developed in part (b) indicates a significant relationship between the independent variables and the dependent variable.

**d.** Does the estimated regression equation provide a good fit for the observed data? Explain.

**e.** Is position a significant factor in the player's rating? Use $\alpha = .05$. Explain.

**f.** Suppose a new offensive tackle prospect who weighs 300 pounds ran the 40 yards in 5.1 seconds. Use the estimated regression equation developed in part (b) to estimate the rating for this player.

**38.** A 10-year study conducted by the American Heart Association provided data on how age, blood pressure, and smoking relate to the risk of strokes. Assume that the following data are from a portion of this study. Risk is interpreted as the probability (times 100) that the patient will have a stroke over the next 10-year period. For the smoking variable, define a dummy variable with 1 indicating a smoker and 0 indicating a nonsmoker.

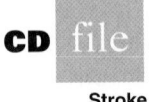

**Stroke**

| Risk | Age | Blood Pressure | Smoker |
|------|-----|----------------|--------|
| 12 | 57 | 152 | No |
| 24 | 67 | 163 | No |
| 13 | 58 | 155 | No |
| 56 | 86 | 177 | Yes |
| 28 | 59 | 196 | No |
| 51 | 76 | 189 | Yes |
| 18 | 56 | 155 | Yes |
| 31 | 78 | 120 | No |
| 37 | 80 | 135 | Yes |
| 15 | 78 | 98 | No |
| 22 | 71 | 152 | No |
| 36 | 70 | 173 | Yes |
| 15 | 67 | 135 | Yes |
| 48 | 77 | 209 | Yes |
| 15 | 60 | 199 | No |
| 36 | 82 | 119 | Yes |
| 8 | 66 | 166 | No |
| 34 | 80 | 125 | Yes |
| 3 | 62 | 117 | No |
| 37 | 59 | 207 | Yes |

**a.** Using these data, develop an estimated regression equation that relates risk of a stroke to the person's age, blood pressure, and whether the person is a smoker.

**b.** Is smoking a significant factor in the risk of a stroke? Explain. Use $\alpha = .05$.

**c.** What is the probability of a stroke over the next 10 years for Art Speen, a 68-year-old smoker who has blood pressure of 175? What action might the physician recommend for this patient?

## 15.8 RESIDUAL ANALYSIS

In Chapter 14 we showed how a residual plot against the independent variable $x$ can be used to validate the assumptions for a simple linear regression model. Because multiple regression analysis deals with two or more independent variables, we would have to examine a residual plot against each of the independent variables to use this approach. The more common approach in multiple regression analysis is to develop a residual plot against the predicted values $\hat{y}$.

### Residual Plot Against $\hat{y}$

A residual plot against the predicted values $\hat{y}$ represents the predicted value of the dependent variable $\hat{y}$ on the horizontal axis and the residual values on the vertical axis. A point is plotted for each residual. The first coordinate for each point is given by $\hat{y}_i$ and the second

**TABLE 15.7**   PREDICTED VALUES AND RESIDUALS FOR THE BUTLER
TRUCKING PROBLEM

| Miles Traveled $(x_1)$ | Deliveries $(x_2)$ | Travel Time $(y)$ | Predicted Time $(\hat{y})$ | Residual $(y - \hat{y})$ |
|---|---|---|---|---|
| 100 | 4 | 9.3 | 8.9385 | 0.3615 |
| 50 | 3 | 4.8 | 4.9583 | −0.1583 |
| 100 | 4 | 8.9 | 8.9385 | −0.0385 |
| 100 | 2 | 6.5 | 7.0916 | −0.5916 |
| 50 | 2 | 4.2 | 4.0349 | 0.1651 |
| 80 | 2 | 6.2 | 5.8689 | 0.3311 |
| 75 | 3 | 7.4 | 6.4867 | 0.9133 |
| 65 | 4 | 6.0 | 6.7987 | −0.7987 |
| 90 | 3 | 7.6 | 7.4037 | 0.1963 |
| 90 | 2 | 6.1 | 6.4803 | −0.3803 |

coordinate is given by the corresponding value of the $i$th residual $y_i - \hat{y}_i$. For the Butler Trucking multiple regression example, the estimated regression equation that we developed using Excel (see Figure 15.4) was

$$\hat{y}_i = -.8687 + .0611x_1 + .9234x_2$$

where $x_1$ = miles traveled and $x_2$ = number of deliveries. Table 15.7 shows the predicted values and residuals based on this equation. The residual plot against $\hat{y}$ for Butler Trucking is shown in Figure 15.11. The residual plot does not indicate any abnormalities.

A residual plot against $\hat{y}$ can also be used when performing residual analysis in simple linear regression. In fact, the pattern for a residual plot against $\hat{y}$ in simple linear regression is the same as the pattern of the residual plot against $x$. Thus, for simple linear regression the residual plot against $\hat{y}$ and the residual plot against $x$ provide the same information. In multiple regression analysis, however, it is preferable to use the residual plot against $\hat{y}$ to determine whether the models' assumptions are satisfied.

**FIGURE 15.11**   RESIDUAL PLOT AGAINST THE PREDICTED TIME $\hat{y}$
FOR THE BUTLER TRUCKING

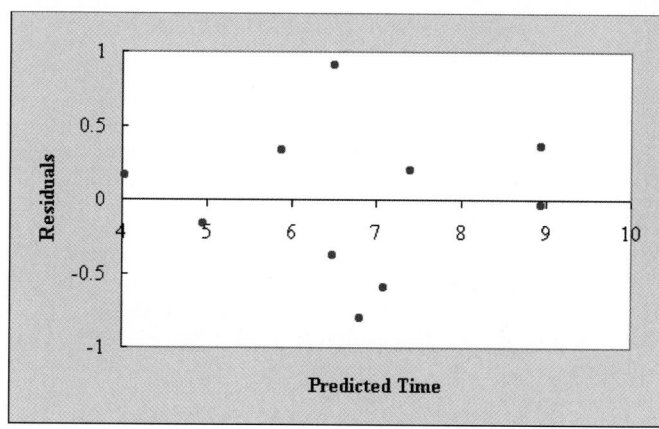

## Standardized Residual Plot Against $\hat{y}$

In Chapter 14 we pointed out that standardized residuals were frequently used in residual plots. We showed how to construct a standardized residual plot against $x$ and discussed how the standardized residual plot could be used to identify outliers and provide insight about the assumption that the error term $\epsilon$ has a normal distribution. Recall that we recommended considering any observation with a standardized residual of less than $-2$ or greater than $+2$ as an outlier. With normally distributed errors, standardized residuals should be outside these limits approximately 5% of the time.

In multiple regression analysis, the computation of the standardized residuals is too complex to be done by hand. But, as we showed in Section 14.8, Excel's Regression tool can be used to compute the standard residuals. In multiple regression analysis we use the same procedure to compute the standard residuals. Instead of developing a standardized residual plot against each of the independent variables, we will construct one standardized residual plot against the predicted values $\hat{y}$.

Figure 15.12 shows the standard residuals and the corresponding standardized residual plot against $\hat{y}$ (Predicted Time) for the Butler Trucking problem developed using Excel's Regression tool and the Chart Wizard. The standardized residual plot does not indicate any

**FIGURE 15.12** STANDARDIZED RESIDUAL PLOT AGAINST THE PREDICTED VALUES $\hat{y}$ FOR THE BUTLER TRUCKING PROBLEM

| | A | B | C | D | E | F | G | H |
|---|---|---|---|---|---|---|---|---|
| 35 | RESIDUAL OUTPUT | | | | | | | |
| 36 | | | | | | | | |
| 37 | Observation | Predicted Time | Residuals | Standard Residuals | | Predicted Time | Residuals | |
| 38 | 1 | 8.9385 | 0.3615 | 0.7153 | | 8.9385 | 0.3615 | |
| 39 | 2 | 4.9583 | -0.1583 | -0.3132 | | 4.9583 | -0.1583 | |
| 40 | 3 | 8.9385 | -0.0385 | -0.0761 | | 8.9385 | -0.0385 | |
| 41 | 4 | 7.0916 | -0.5916 | -1.1704 | | 7.0916 | -0.5916 | |
| 42 | 5 | 4.0349 | 0.1651 | 0.3267 | | 4.0349 | 0.1651 | |
| 43 | 6 | 5.8689 | 0.3311 | 0.6550 | | 5.8689 | 0.3311 | |
| 44 | 7 | 6.4867 | 0.9133 | 1.8069 | | 6.4867 | 0.9133 | |
| 45 | 8 | 6.7987 | -0.7987 | -1.5802 | | 6.7987 | -0.7987 | |
| 46 | 9 | 7.4037 | 0.1963 | 0.3884 | | 7.4037 | 0.1963 | |
| 47 | 10 | 6.4803 | -0.3803 | -0.7523 | | 6.4803 | -0.3803 | |
| 48 | | | | | | | | |
| 49 | | | | | | | | |

Note: Rows 1–34 are hidden.

abnormalities, and no standardized residual is less than $-2$ or greater than $+2$. Note that the pattern of the standardized residual plot against $\hat{y}$ is the same as the pattern of the residual plot against $\hat{y}$ shown in Figure 15.11. But the standardized residual plot is preferred because it enables us to check for outliers and determine whether the assumption of normality for the regression model is reasonable.

## EXERCISES

## Methods

**39.** Data for two variables, $x$ and $y$, follow.

| $x_i$ | 1 | 2 | 3 | 4 | 5 |
|-------|---|---|---|----|----|
| $y_i$ | 3 | 7 | 5 | 11 | 14 |

    **a.** Develop the estimated regression equation for these data.
    **b.** Plot the residuals against $\hat{y}$. Does the residual plot support the assumptions about $\epsilon$? Explain.
    **c.** Plot the standardized residuals against $\hat{y}$. Do any outliers appear in these data? Explain.

**40.** Data for two variables, $x$ and $y$, follow.

| $x_i$ | 22 | 24 | 26 | 28 | 40 |
|-------|----|----|----|----|----|
| $y_i$ | 12 | 21 | 31 | 35 | 70 |

    **a.** Develop the estimated regression equation for these data.
    **b.** Compute the standardized residuals for these data. Can any of these observations be classified as an outlier? Explain.
    **c.** Develop a standardized residual plot against $\hat{y}$. Does the residual plot support the assumptions about $\epsilon$? Explain.

## Applications

**41.** Exercise 5 gave the following data on weekly gross revenue ($1000s), television advertising expenditures ($1000s), and newspaper advertising expenditures ($1000s) for Showtime Movie Theaters.

CD file

Showtime

| Weekly Gross Revenue ($1000s) | Television Advertising ($1000s) | Newspaper Advertising ($1000s) |
|------|-----|-----|
| 96 | 5.0 | 1.5 |
| 90 | 2.0 | 2.0 |
| 95 | 4.0 | 1.5 |
| 92 | 2.5 | 2.5 |
| 95 | 3.0 | 3.3 |
| 94 | 3.5 | 2.3 |
| 94 | 2.5 | 4.2 |
| 94 | 3.0 | 2.5 |

    **a.** Find an estimated regression equation relating weekly gross revenue to television expenditures and newspaper advertising expenditures.
    **b.** Plot the standardized residuals against $\hat{y}$. Does the residual plot support the assumptions about $\epsilon$? Explain.
    **c.** Check for any outliers in these data. What are your conclusions?

**42.** Exercise 6 provided data on the curb weight, horsepower, and ¼-mile speed for 16 popular sports and GT cars. Suppose that the price of each sports and GT car is also available. The complete data set is as follows:

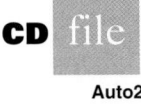

CD file

Auto2

| Sports & GT Car | Price ($1000s) | Curb Weight (lb.) | Horsepower | Speed at ¼ mile (mph) |
|---|---|---|---|---|
| Accura Integra Type R | 25.035 | 2577 | 195 | 90.7 |
| Accura NSX-T | 93.758 | 3066 | 290 | 108.0 |
| BMW Z3 2.8 | 40.900 | 2844 | 189 | 93.2 |
| Chevrolet Camaro Z28 | 24.865 | 3439 | 305 | 103.2 |
| Chevrolet Corvette Convertible | 50.144 | 3246 | 345 | 102.1 |
| Dodge Viper RT/10 | 69.742 | 3319 | 450 | 116.2 |
| Ford Mustang GT | 23.200 | 3227 | 225 | 91.7 |
| Honda Prelude Type SH | 26.382 | 3042 | 195 | 89.7 |
| Mercedes-Benz CLK320 | 44.988 | 3240 | 215 | 93.0 |
| Mercedes-Benz SLK230 | 42.762 | 3025 | 185 | 92.3 |
| Mitsubishi 3000GT VR-4 | 47.518 | 3737 | 320 | 99.0 |
| Nissan 240SX SE | 25.066 | 2862 | 155 | 84.6 |
| Pontiac Firebird Trans Am | 27.770 | 3455 | 305 | 103.2 |
| Porsche Boxster | 45.560 | 2822 | 201 | 93.2 |
| Toyota Supra Turbo | 40.989 | 3505 | 320 | 105.0 |
| Volvo C70 | 41.120 | 3285 | 236 | 97.0 |

**a.** Find the estimated regression equation, which uses price and horsepower to predict ¼-mile speed.

**b.** Plot the standardized residuals against $\hat{y}$. Does the residual plot support the assumption about $\epsilon$? Explain.

**c.** Check for any outliers. What are your conclusions?

**43.** In Exercise 9, data were provided showing the percentage of students who attend a 4-year college, the average class size, and the combined SAT score.

**a.** Develop an estimated regression equation that can be used to predict the percentage of students who attend a 4-year college given the combined SAT score.

**b.** Based on the estimated regression equation developed in (a), do these data contain any outliers? Explain.

**c.** Develop an estimated regression equation that can be used to predict the percentage of students who attend a 4-year college given the average class size and the combined SAT score.

**d.** Based upon the estimated regression equation developed in part (c), do these data contain any outliers? Explain.

## SUMMARY

In this chapter, we introduced multiple regression analysis as an extension of simple linear regression analysis presented in Chapter 14. Multiple regression analysis enables us to understand how a dependent variable is related to two or more independent variables. The regression equation $E(y) = \beta_0 + \beta_1 x_1 + \beta_2 x_2 + \cdots + \beta_p x_p$ shows that the expected value or mean value of the dependent variable $y$ is related to the values of the independent variables $x_1, x_2, \ldots, x_p$. Sample data and the least squares method are used to develop the estimated regression equation $\hat{y} = b_0 + b_1 x_1 + b_2 x_2 + \cdots + b_p x_p$. In effect $b_0, b_1, b_2, \ldots, b_p$ are sample statistics used to estimate the unknown model parameters $\beta_0, \beta_1, \beta_2, \ldots, \beta_p$. Excel output was used throughout the chapter to emphasize the fact that statistical software packages are the only realistic means of performing the numerous computations required in multiple regression analysis.

The multiple coefficient of determination was presented as a measure of the goodness of fit of the estimated regression equation. It determines the proportion of the variation of $y$ that can be explained by the estimated regression equation. The adjusted multiple coefficient of determination is a similar measure of goodness of fit that adjusts for the number of independent variables and thus avoids overestimating the impact of adding more independent variables.

An $F$ test and a $t$ test were presented as ways to determine statistically whether the relationship among the variables is significant. The $F$ test is used to determine whether there is a significant overall relationship between the dependent variable and the set of all independent variables. The $t$ test is used to determine whether there is a significant relationship between the dependent variable and an individual independent variable given the other independent variables in the regression model. Correlation among the independent variables, known as multicollinearity, was discussed.

The section on qualitative independent variables showed how dummy variables can be used to incorporate qualitative data into multiple regression analysis. The chapter concluded with a section on how residual analysis can be used to validate the model assumptions and detect outliers.

## GLOSSARY

**Multiple regression analysis**    Regression analysis involving two or more independent variables.

**Multiple regression model**    The mathematical equation that describes how the dependent variable $y$ is related to the independent variables $x_1, x_2, \ldots, x_p$ and an error term $\epsilon$.

**Multiple regression equation**    The mathematical equation relating the expected value or mean value of the dependent variable to the values of the independent variables; that is $E(y) = \beta_0 + \beta_1 x_1 + \beta_2 x_2 + \cdots + \beta_p x_p$.

**Estimated multiple regression equation**    The estimate of the multiple regression equation based on sample data and the least squares method; it is $\hat{y} = b_0 + b_1 x_1 + b_2 x_2 + \cdots + b_p x_p$.

**Least squares method**    The method used to develop the estimated regression equation. It minimizes the sum of squared residuals (the deviations between the observed values of the dependent variable, $y_i$, and the estimated values of the dependent variable, $\hat{y}_i$).

**Multiple coefficient of determination**    A measure of the goodness of fit of the estimated multiple regression equation. It can be interpreted as the proportion of the variability in the dependent variable that is explained by the estimated regression equation.

**Adjusted multiple coefficient of determination**    A measure of the goodness of fit of the estimated multiple regression equation that adjusts for the number of independent variables in the model and thus avoids overestimating the impact of adding more independent variables.

**Multicollinearity**    The term used to describe the correlation among the independent variables.

**Qualitative independent variable**    An independent variable with qualitative data.

**Dummy variable**    A variable, coded as 0 or 1, used to model the effect of qualitative independent variables. A dummy variable is also called an indicator variable.

## KEY FORMULAS

**Multiple Regression Model**

$$y = \beta_0 + \beta_1 x_1 + \beta_2 x_2 + \cdots + \beta_p x_p + \epsilon \tag{15.1}$$

**Multiple Regression Equation**

$$E(y) = \beta_0 + \beta_1 x_1 + \beta_2 x_2 + \cdots + \beta_p x_p \tag{15.2}$$

**Estimated Multiple Regression Equation**

$$\hat{y} = b_0 + b_1 x_1 + b_2 x_2 + \cdots + b_p x_p \tag{15.3}$$

**Multiple Coefficient of Determination**

$$R^2 = \frac{\text{SSR}}{\text{SST}} \tag{15.8}$$

**Adjusted Multiple Coefficient of Determination**

$$R_a^2 = 1 - (1 - R^2)\frac{n - 1}{n - p - 1} \tag{15.9}$$

**F Test for Overall Significance**

$$F = \frac{\text{MSR}}{\text{MSE}} \tag{15.14}$$

**t Test for Individual Significance**

$$t = \frac{b_i}{s_{b_i}} \tag{15.15}$$

## SUPPLEMENTARY EXERCISES

**44.** The admissions officer for Clearwater College developed the following estimated regression equation relating the final college GPA to the student's high-school GPA and SAT mathematics score.

$$\hat{y} = -1.41 + .0235x_1 + .00486x_2$$

where

$$x_1 = \text{high-school grade point average}$$
$$x_2 = \text{SAT mathematics score}$$
$$y = \text{final college grade point average}$$

**a.** Interpret the coefficients in this estimated regression equation.
**b.** Estimate the final college GPA for a student who has a high-school GPA of 84 and a score of 540 on the SAT mathematics test.

**45.** The personnel director for Electronics Associates developed the following estimated regression equation relating an employee's score on a job satisfaction test to his or her length of service and wage rate.

$$\hat{y} = 14.4 - 8.69x_1 + 13.5x_2$$

where

$$x_1 = \text{length of service (years)}$$
$$x_2 = \text{wage rate (dollars)}$$
$$y = \text{job satisfaction test score (higher scores}$$
$$\text{indicate greater job satisfaction)}$$

**a.** Interpret the coefficients in this estimated regression equation.
**b.** Develop an estimate of the job satisfaction test score for an employee who has 4 years of service and makes \$6.50 per hour.

**46.** A partial computer output from a regression analysis using Excel's Regression tool follows.

| | A | B | C | D | E | F | G |
|---|---|---|---|---|---|---|---|
| 1 | SUMMARY OUTPUT | | | | | | |
| 2 | | | | | | | |
| 3 | *Regression Statistics* | | | | | | |
| 4 | Multiple R | | | | | | |
| 5 | R Square | 0.923 | | | | | |
| 6 | Adjusted R Square | | | | | | |
| 7 | Standard Error | 3.35 | | | | | |
| 8 | Observations | | | | | | |
| 9 | | | | | | | |
| 10 | ANOVA | | | | | | |
| 11 | | *df* | *SS* | *MS* | *F* | *Significance F* | |
| 12 | Regression | | 1612 | | | | |
| 13 | Residual | 12 | | | | | |
| 14 | Total | | | | | | |
| 15 | | | | | | | |
| 16 | | *Coefficients* | *Standard Error* | *t Stat* | *P-value* | | |
| 17 | Intercept | 8.103 | 2.667 | | | | |
| 18 | X1 | 7.602 | 2.105 | | | | |
| 19 | X2 | 3.111 | 0.613 | | | | |
| 20 | | | | | | | |

**a.** Compute the missing entries in this output.
**b.** Using $\alpha = .05$, test for overall significance.
**c.** Use the $t$ test and $\alpha = .05$ to test $H_0: \beta_1 = 0$ and $H_0: \beta_2 = 0$.

**47.** Recall that in Exercise 44, the admissions officer for Clearwater College developed the following estimated regression equation relating final college GPA to the student's SAT mathematics score and high-school GPA.

$$\hat{y} = -1.41 + .0235x_1 + .00486x_2$$

where

$$x_1 = \text{high-school grade point average}$$
$$x_2 = \text{SAT mathematics score}$$
$$y = \text{final college grade point average}$$

A portion of the Excel Regression tool output follows.

| | A | B | C | D | E | F | G |
|---|---|---|---|---|---|---|---|
| 1 | SUMMARY OUTPUT | | | | | | |
| 2 | | | | | | | |
| 3 | *Regression Statistics* | | | | | | |
| 4 | Multiple R | | | | | | |
| 5 | R Square | | | | | | |
| 6 | Adjusted R Square | | | | | | |
| 7 | Standard Error | | | | | | |
| 8 | Observations | | | | | | |
| 9 | | | | | | | |
| 10 | ANOVA | | | | | | |
| 11 | | *df* | *SS* | *MS* | *F* | *Significance F* | |
| 12 | Regression | | 1.76209 | | | | |
| 13 | Residual | | | | | | |
| 14 | Total | 9 | 1.88 | | | | |
| 15 | | | | | | | |
| 16 | | *Coefficients* | *Standard Error* | *t Stat* | *P-value* | | |
| 17 | Intercept | -1.4053 | 0.4848 | | | | |
| 18 | X1 | 0.023467 | 0.0086666 | | | | |
| 19 | X2 | 0.00486 | 0.001077 | | | | |
| 20 | | | | | | | |

a. Complete the missing entries in this output.
b. Using $\alpha = .05$, test for overall significance.
c. Did the estimated regression equation provide a good fit to the data? Explain.
d. Use the $t$ test and $\alpha = .05$ to test $H_0: \beta_1 = 0$ and $H_0: \beta_2 = 0$.

48. Recall that in Exercise 45 the personnel director for Electronics Associates developed the following estimated regression equation relating an employee's score on a job satisfaction test to length of service and wage rate.

$$\hat{y} = 14.4 - 8.69x_1 + 13.5x_2$$

where

$$x_1 = \text{length of service (years)}$$
$$x_2 = \text{wage rate (dollars)}$$
$$y = \text{job satisfaction test score (higher scores indicate greater job satisfaction)}$$

A portion of Excel's Regression tool output follows.

| | A | B | C | D | E | F | G |
|---|---|---|---|---|---|---|---|
| 1 | SUMMARY OUTPUT | | | | | | |
| 2 | | | | | | | |
| 3 | *Regression Statistics* | | | | | | |
| 4 | Multiple R | | | | | | |
| 5 | R Square | | | | | | |
| 6 | Adjusted R Square | | | | | | |
| 7 | Standard Error | 3.773 | | | | | |
| 8 | Observations | | | | | | |
| 9 | | | | | | | |
| 10 | ANOVA | | | | | | |
| 11 | | *df* | *SS* | *MS* | *F* | *Significance F* | |
| 12 | Regression | | | | | | |
| 13 | Residual | | 71.17 | | | | |
| 14 | Total | | 720 | | | | |
| 15 | | | | | | | |
| 16 | | *Coefficients* | *Standard Error* | *t Stat* | *P-value* | | |
| 17 | Intercept | 14.4 | 8.191 | | | | |
| 18 | X1 | -8.69 | 1.555 | | | | |
| 19 | X2 | 13.517 | 2.085 | | | | |
| 20 | | | | | | | |

**a.** Complete the missing entries in this output.
**b.** Using $\alpha = .05$, test for overall significance.
**c.** Did the estimated regression equation provide a good fit to the data? Explain.
**d.** Use the $t$ test and $\alpha = .05$ to test $H_0: \beta_1 = 0$ and $H_0: \beta_2 = 0$.

**49.** A sample of 30 computer hardware companies taken from the *Stock Investor Pro* provided the following data on the price per share, book value per share, and the return on equity per share for each (*Stock Investor Pro,* American Association of Individual Investors, August 21, 1997).

| Company | Price per Share | Book Value per Share | Return on Equity per Share (%) |
|---|---|---|---|
| Amdahl Corporation | 12.31 | 4.94 | −49.7 |
| Apple Computer, Inc. | 21.75 | 9.46 | −71.8 |
| Auspex Systems, Inc. | 11.00 | 4.95 | 17.2 |
| Capital Associates | 3.25 | 4.33 | 5.1 |
| Compaq Computer Corp. | 65.50 | 9.58 | 20.8 |
| Data General Corporation | 35.94 | 8.46 | 13.3 |
| Dell Computer Corporation | 82.06 | 2.33 | 74.5 |
| Digi International | 15.00 | 7.35 | −11.9 |
| Digital Equipment Corp. | 43.00 | 22.40 | −12.9 |
| En Pointe Technologies | 14.25 | 4.11 | 18.8 |
| Equitrac Corporation | 16.25 | 6.83 | 10.7 |
| Franklin Electronic Pbls. | 12.88 | 9.13 | 9.0 |
| Gateway 2000, Inc. | 39.13 | 6.07 | 28.8 |
| Hewlett-Packard Company | 61.50 | 14.14 | 18.7 |
| IBM | 101.38 | 20.12 | 29.9 |

(*continued*)

| Company | Price per Share | Book Value per Share | Return on Equity per Share (%) |
|---|---|---|---|
| Ingram Micro, Inc. | 28.75 | 6.35 | 15.1 |
| Maxwell Technologies, Inc. | 30.50 | 3.78 | 11.8 |
| MicroAge, Inc. | 27.19 | 12.59 | 9.8 |
| Micron Electronics, Inc. | 16.31 | 3.64 | 28.3 |
| Network Computing Devices | 11.88 | 3.56 | 4.0 |
| Pomeroy Computer Resources | 33.00 | 10.03 | 16.5 |
| Sequent Computer Systems | 28.19 | 10.64 | 3.3 |
| Silicon Graphics, Inc. | 27.44 | 9.12 | −4.3 |
| Southern Electronics Corp. | 15.13 | 6.15 | 16.1 |
| Stratus Computer, Inc. | 55.50 | 22.38 | 11.1 |
| Sun Microsystems, Inc. | 48.00 | 6.40 | 26.2 |
| Tandem Computers, Inc. | 34.24 | 9.49 | 8.7 |
| Tech Data Corporation | 38.94 | 10.25 | 14.3 |
| Unisys Corporation | 11.31 | 0.68 | 1.6 |
| Vitech America, Inc. | 14.63 | 3.48 | 24.3 |

a. Develop an estimated regression equation that can be used to predict the price per share given the book value per share. At the .05 level of significance, test for a significant relationship.

b. Did the estimated regression equation developed in part (a) provide a good fit to the data? Explain.

c. Develop an estimated regression equation that can be used to predict the price per share given the book value per share and the return on equity per share. At the .05 level of significance, test for overall significance.

50. Following are data on price, curb weight, horsepower, time to go from 0 to 60 miles per hour, and the speed at ¼ mile for 16 sports and GT cars (*1998 Road & Track Sports & GT Cars*).

**CD** file

Auto3

| Sports & GT Car | Price ($1000s) | Curb Weight (lb.) | Horse-power | 0 to 60 (seconds) | Speed at ¼ mile (mph) |
|---|---|---|---|---|---|
| Acura Integra Type R | 25.035 | 2577 | 195 | 7.0 | 90.7 |
| Acura NSX-T | 93.758 | 3066 | 290 | 5.0 | 108.0 |
| BMW Z3 2.8 | 40.900 | 2844 | 189 | 6.6 | 93.2 |
| Chevrolet Camaro Z28 | 24.865 | 3439 | 305 | 5.4 | 103.2 |
| Chevrolet Corvette Convertible | 50.144 | 3246 | 345 | 5.2 | 102.1 |
| Dodge Viper RT/10 | 69.742 | 3319 | 450 | 4.4 | 116.2 |
| Ford Mustang GT | 23.200 | 3227 | 225 | 6.8 | 91.7 |
| Honda Prelude Type SH | 26.382 | 3042 | 195 | 7.7 | 89.7 |
| Mercedes-Benz CLK320 | 44.988 | 3240 | 215 | 7.2 | 93.0 |
| Mercedes-Benz SLK230 | 42.762 | 3025 | 185 | 6.6 | 92.3 |
| Mitsubishi 3000GT VR-4 | 47.518 | 3737 | 320 | 5.7 | 99.0 |
| Nissan 240SX SE | 25.066 | 2862 | 155 | 9.1 | 84.6 |
| Pontiac Firebird Trans Am | 27.770 | 3455 | 305 | 5.4 | 103.2 |
| Porsche Boxster | 45.560 | 2822 | 201 | 6.1 | 93.2 |
| Toyota Supra Turbo | 40.989 | 3505 | 320 | 5.3 | 105.0 |
| Volvo C70 | 41.120 | 3285 | 236 | 6.3 | 97.0 |

a. Develop an estimated regression equation with price, curb weight, horsepower, and time to go from 0 to 60 mph as four independent variables to predict the speed at ¼ mile.

b. Use the *F* test to determine the significance of the regression results. At a .05 level of significance, what is your conclusion?

c. Use the *t* test to determine the significance of each independent variable. At a .05 level of significance, what is your conclusion?

d. Delete any independent variable that is not significant and provide your recommended estimated regression equation.
e. Develop a standardized residual plot. Does the pattern of the residual plot appear to be reasonable?
f. Do the data show any outliers?

51. Nielsen Media Research collects data showing which advertisers get the most exposure during prime time TV on ABC, CBS, NBC, Fox, UPN, and WB networks. Data showing the number of household exposures in millions and the number of times the ad was aired for the week of April 28–May 4, 1997, follow (*USA Today*, May 5, 1997).

| Advertised Brand | Times Ad Aired | Household Exposures |
|---|---|---|
| Burger King | 86 | 616.7 |
| McDonald's | 54 | 439.2 |
| Sears | 33 | 338.0 |
| Wendy's | 28 | 191.7 |
| Ford Escort | 20 | 174.6 |
| *Austin Powers* movie | 14 | 161.3 |
| Nissan | 16 | 161.1 |
| Pizza Hut | 16 | 147.7 |
| Saturn | 16 | 146.3 |
| *Father's Day* movie | 11 | 138.2 |

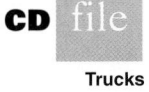

**Nielsen**

a. Develop a scatter diagram with number of times the ad is aired as the independent variable and household expenditures as the dependent variable. Is there anything unusual about the pattern of the points in this scatter diagram? Explain.
b. Develop the estimated regression equation showing how the number of times an ad is aired is related to the number of household exposures. Is the relationship between the two variables significant? Use a .05 level of significance.
c. Consider the addition of the independent variable BigAds, where the value of BigAds is 1 if the number of times an ad is aired is greater than 30, and 0 otherwise. Develop an estimated regression equation that can be used to predict household expenditures given the number of times an ad is aired and the dummy variable BigAds.
d. Using $\alpha = .05$, is the dummy variable added in part (c) significant?
e. What role does the dummy variable play in modeling the relationship between the number of times an ad is aired and household exposures?

52. Today's marketplace offers a wide choice to buyers of sport utility vehicles (SUVs) and pickup trucks. An important factor to many buyers is the resale value of the vehicle. The following table shows the resale value (%) after 2 years and the suggested retail price for 10 SUVs, 10 small pickup trucks, and 10 full-size pickup trucks (*Kiplinger's New Cars & Trucks 2000 Buyer's Guide*).

| Vehicle | Type of Vehicle | Suggested Retail Price ($) | Resale Value (%) |
|---|---|---|---|
| Chevrolet Blazer LS | sport utility | 19,495 | 55 |
| Ford Explorer Sport | sport utility | 20,495 | 57 |
| GMC Yukon XL 1500 | sport utility | 26,789 | 67 |
| Honda CR-V | sport utility | 18,965 | 65 |
| Isuzu VehiCross | sport utility | 30,186 | 62 |
| Jeep Cherokee Limited | sport utility | 25,745 | 57 |
| Mercury Mountaineer Monterrey | sport utility | 29,895 | 59 |
| Nissan Pathfinder XE | sport utility | 26,919 | 54 |
| Toyota 4Runner | sport utility | 22,418 | 55 |

**Trucks**

(*continued*)

| Vehicle | Type of Vehicle | Suggested Retail Price ($) | Resale Value (%) |
|---|---|---|---|
| Toyota RAV4 | sport utility | 17,148 | 55 |
| Chevrolet S-10 Extended Cab | small pickup | 18,847 | 46 |
| Dodge Dakota Club Cab Sport | small pickup | 16,870 | 53 |
| Ford Ranger XLT Regular Cab | small pickup | 18,510 | 48 |
| Ford Ranger XLT Supercab | small pickup | 20,225 | 55 |
| GMC Sonoma Regular Cab | small pickup | 16,938 | 44 |
| Isuzu Hombre Spacecab | small pickup | 18,820 | 41 |
| Mazda B4000 SE Cab Plus | small pickup | 23,050 | 51 |
| Nissan Frontier XE Regular Cab | small pickup | 12,110 | 51 |
| Toyota Tacoma Xtracab | small pickup | 18,228 | 49 |
| Toyota Tacoma Xtracab V6 | small pickup | 19,318 | 50 |
| Chevrolet K2500 | full-size pickup | 24,417 | 60 |
| Chevrolet Silverado 2500 Ext | full-size pickup | 24,140 | 64 |
| Dodge Ram 1500 | full-size pickup | 17,460 | 54 |
| Dodge Ram Quad Cab 2500 | full-size pickup | 32,770 | 63 |
| Dodge Ram Regular Cab 2500 | full-size pickup | 23,140 | 59 |
| Ford F150 XL | full-size pickup | 22,875 | 58 |
| Ford F-350 Super Duty Crew Cab XL | full-size pickup | 34,295 | 64 |
| GMC New Sierra 1500 Ext Cab | full-size pickup | 27,089 | 68 |
| Toyota Tundra Access Cab Limited | full-size pickup | 25,605 | 53 |
| Toyota Tundra Regular Cab | full-size pickup | 15,835 | 58 |

**a.** Develop an estimated regression equation that can be used to predict the resale value given the suggested retail price. At the .05 level of significance, test for a significant relationship.
**b.** Did the estimated regression equation developed in part (a) provide a good fit to the data? Explain.
**c.** Develop an estimated regression equation that can be used to predict the resale value given the suggested retail price and the type of vehicle.
**d.** Use the $F$ test to determine the significance of the regression results. At a .05 level of significance, what is your conclusion?

## Case Problem 1   CONSUMER RESEARCH, INC.

Consumer Research, Inc., is an independent agency that conducts research on consumer attitudes and behaviors for a variety of firms. In one study, a client asked for an investigation of consumer characteristics that can be used to predict the amount charged by credit card users. Data were collected on annual income, household size, and annual credit card charges for a sample of 50 consumers. The data follow and are on the data disk in the data set named Consumer.

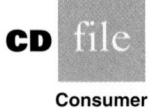

CD file

Consumer

| Income ($1000s) | Household Size | Amount Charged ($) | Income ($1000s) | Household Size | Amount Charged ($) |
|---|---|---|---|---|---|
| 54 | 3 | 4016 | 54 | 6 | 5573 |
| 30 | 2 | 3159 | 30 | 1 | 2583 |
| 32 | 4 | 5100 | 48 | 2 | 3866 |
| 50 | 5 | 4742 | 34 | 5 | 3586 |
| 31 | 2 | 1864 | 67 | 4 | 5037 |
| 55 | 2 | 4070 | 50 | 2 | 3605 |

| Income ($1000s) | Household Size | Amount Charged ($) | Income ($1000s) | Household Size | Amount Charged ($) |
|---|---|---|---|---|---|
| 37 | 1 | 2731 | 67 | 5 | 5345 |
| 40 | 2 | 3348 | 55 | 6 | 5370 |
| 66 | 4 | 4764 | 52 | 2 | 3890 |
| 51 | 3 | 4110 | 62 | 3 | 4705 |
| 25 | 3 | 4208 | 64 | 2 | 4157 |
| 48 | 4 | 4219 | 22 | 3 | 3579 |
| 27 | 1 | 2477 | 29 | 4 | 3890 |
| 33 | 2 | 2514 | 39 | 2 | 2972 |
| 65 | 3 | 4214 | 35 | 1 | 3121 |
| 63 | 4 | 4965 | 39 | 4 | 4183 |
| 42 | 6 | 4412 | 54 | 3 | 3730 |
| 21 | 2 | 2448 | 23 | 6 | 4127 |
| 44 | 1 | 2995 | 27 | 2 | 2921 |
| 37 | 5 | 4171 | 26 | 7 | 4603 |
| 62 | 6 | 5678 | 61 | 2 | 4273 |
| 21 | 3 | 3623 | 30 | 2 | 3067 |
| 55 | 7 | 5301 | 22 | 4 | 3074 |
| 42 | 2 | 3020 | 46 | 5 | 4820 |
| 41 | 7 | 4828 | 66 | 4 | 5149 |

## Managerial Report

1. Use methods of descriptive statistics to summarize the data. Comment on the findings.
2. Develop estimated regression equations, first using annual income as the independent variable and then using household size as the independent variable. Which variable is the better predictor of annual credit card charges? Discuss your findings.
3. Develop an estimated regression equation with annual income and household size as the independent variables. Discuss your findings.
4. What is the predicted annual credit card charge for a three-person household with an annual income of $40,000?
5. Discuss the need for other independent variables that could be added to the model. What additional variables might be helpful?

## Case Problem 2    NFL QUARTERBACK RATING

The National Football League (NFL) records weekly performance statistics for individuals and teams. These data can be obtained by accessing the homepage for the NFL (www.nfl.com). For many fans, one of the most interesting statistics is the rating used to evaluate the passing performance of quarterbacks. Four categories are used as a basis for compiling a passing rating:

1. Percentage of touchdown passes per attempt
2. Percentage of completions per attempt
3. Percentage of interceptions per attempt
4. Average yards gained per attempt

To illustrate how to compute the rating, consider the performance for Steve Young, the highest rated quarterback in the NFL in 1997. For the 1997 season, Steve Young attempted 356 passes, completed 241 passes for a total of 3029 yards, and had 19 touchdown passes and 6 interceptions. Five steps are needed to compute the passing rating for Steve Young.

**Step 1.** Compute the ratio of the number of touchdowns (19) to the number of passes attempted (356); the value obtained is 19/356 = 0.0534. Divide this result by 0.05 to obtain the value for the touchdown component of the rating; the value obtained is 0.0534/0.05 = 1.0680.

**Step 2.** Compute the ratio of the number of passes completed (241) to the number of passes attempted (356); the value obtained is 241/356 = 0.6770. Subtract 0.3 from this result and divide by 0.2 to obtain the value for the second component of the rating; the value obtained is (0.6770 − 0.3)/0.2 = 1.8850.

**Step 3.** Compute the ratio of the number of interceptions (6) to the number of passes attempted (356); the value obtained is 6/356 = 0.0169. Subtract this value from 0.095 and divide the result by 0.04 to obtain the value for the interceptions component of the rating; the value obtained is (0.095 − 0.0169)/0.04 = 1.9525.

**Step 4.** Compute the ratio of the number of passing yards (3029) to the number of passes attempted (356); the value obtained is 3029/356 = 8.5084. Subtract 3 from this result and divide by 4 to obtain the value for the yards component of the rating; the value obtained is (8.5084 − 3)/4 = 1.3771.

**Step 5.** Add the sum of steps 1 through 4, multiply by 100 and divide by 6. The sum of steps 1 through 4 is 1.0680 + 1.8850 + 1.9525 + 1.3771 = 6.2826. After multiplying by 100 and dividing by 6 we obtain 104.7100 or 104.7; this figure is the passing rating reported by the NFL for Steve Young.

**NFL**

The passing data reported by the NFL for the 1997 season are available on the data disk in the data set named NFL. The labels for the columns are defined as follows:

| | |
|---|---|
| Att | Number of passes attempted |
| Comp | Number of passes completed |
| Comp% | Number of passes completed divided by the number of passes attempted times 100 |
| Yds | Number of yards obtained passing |
| Yds/Att | Number of yards obtained passing divided by the number of passes attempted |
| TD | Number of touchdowns obtained passing |
| TD% | Number of touchdowns divided by the number of passes attempted times 100 |
| Long | Longest pass completed |
| Int | Number of interceptions thrown |
| Int% | Number of interceptions divided by the number of passes attempted |
| Rating | The quarterback passing rating |

## Managerial Report

1. Use methods of descriptive statistics to summarize the data. Comment on the findings.
2. Develop an estimated regression equation that can be used to predict Int% given the value of Comp%. Discuss your findings.
3. Develop an estimated regression equation that can be used to predict Rating. Discuss your findings and comment on how your estimated regression equation relates to the previous discussion of computing passing ratings.
4. If the NFL hired you to compute the passing ratings for next year, what approach would you use? Explain.

## Case Problem 3   PREDICTING STUDENT PROFICIENCY TEST SCORES

In order to predict how a school district would have scored when accounting for poverty and other income measures, *The Cincinnati Enquirer* gathered data from the Ohio Department of Education's Education Management Services and the Ohio Department of Taxation (*The Cincinnati Enquirer,* November 30, 1997). First, the newspaper obtained passage-rate data on the math, reading, science, writing, and citizenship proficiency exams given to fourth-, sixth-, ninth-, and 12th-graders in early 1996. By combining these data, they computed an overall percentage of students that passed the tests for each district.

The percentage of a school district's students on Aid for Dependent Children (ADC), the percentage who qualify for free or reduced-price lunches, and the district's median family income were also recorded. A portion of the data collected for the 608 school districts follows. The complete data set is available on the data disk in the data set named Enquirer.

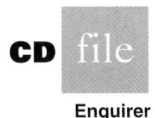

**Enquirer**

| Rank | School District | County | % Passed | % on ADC | % Free Lunch | Median Income ($) |
|------|----------------|--------|----------|----------|--------------|-------------------|
| 1 | Ottawa Hills Local | Lucas | 93.85 | 0.11 | 0.00 | 48231 |
| 2 | Wyoming City | Hamilton | 93.08 | 2.95 | 4.59 | 42672 |
| 3 | Oakwood City | Montgomery | 92.92 | 0.20 | 0.38 | 42403 |
| 4 | Madeira City | Hamilton | 92.37 | 1.50 | 4.83 | 32889 |
| 5 | Indian Hill Ex Vill | Hamilton | 91.77 | 1.23 | 2.70 | 44135 |
| 6 | Solon City | Cuyahoga | 90.77 | 0.68 | 2.24 | 34993 |
| 7 | Chagrin Falls Ex Vill | Cuyahoga | 89.89 | 0.47 | 0.44 | 38921 |
| 8 | Mariemont City | Hamilton | 89.80 | 3.00 | 2.97 | 31823 |
| 9 | Upper Arlington City | Franklin | 89.77 | 0.24 | 0.92 | 38358 |
| 10 | Granville Ex Vill | Licking | 89.22 | 1.14 | 0.00 | 36235 |

The data have been ranked based on the values in the column labeled % Passed; these data are the overall percentage of students passing the tests. Data in the column labeled % on ADC are the percentage of each school district's students on ADC, and the data in the column labeled % Free Lunch are the percentage of students who qualify for free or reduced-price lunches. The column labeled Median Income shows each district's median family income. Also shown for each school district is the county in which the school district is located. Note that in some cases the value in the % Free Lunch column is 0, indicating that the district did not participate in the free lunch program.

## Managerial Report

Use the methods presented in this and previous chapters to analyze this data set. Present a summary of your analysis, including key statistical results, conclusions, and recommendations, in a managerial report. Include any technical material you feel is appropriate in an appendix.

## Case Problem 4   ALUMNI GIVING

Alumni donations are an important source of revenue for colleges and universities. If administrators could determine the factors that increase the percentage of alumni who make a donation, they might be able to implement policies that increase revenues. Research shows that students who are more satisfied with their contact with teachers are more likely to graduate. As a result, one might suspect that smaller class sizes and lower student-faculty ratios might lead to a higher percentage of satisfied alumni, which in turn might lead to increases in the percentage of alumni who make a donation. Table 15.8 shows data for 48 national universities (*America's Best Colleges,* Year 2000 Edition). The column labeled Graduation Rate is the percentage of students who initially enrolled at the university and graduated. The column labeled % of Classes Under 20 shows the percentage of classes

**TABLE 15.8**   DATA FOR 48 NATIONAL UNIVERSITIES

**Alumni**

| School | State | Graduation Rate | % of Classes Under 20 | Student-Faculty Ratio | Alumni Giving Rate |
|--------|-------|-----------------|-----------------------|-----------------------|--------------------|
| Boston College | MA | 85 | 39 | 13 | 25 |
| Brandeis University | MA | 79 | 68 | 8 | 33 |
| Brown University | RI | 93 | 60 | 8 | 40 |
| California Institute of Technology | CA | 85 | 65 | 3 | 46 |
| Carnegie Mellon University | PA | 75 | 67 | 10 | 28 |
| Case Western Reserve Univ. | OH | 72 | 52 | 8 | 31 |
| College of William and Mary | VA | 89 | 45 | 12 | 27 |
| Columbia University | NY | 90 | 69 | 7 | 31 |
| Cornell University | NY | 91 | 72 | 13 | 35 |
| Dartmouth College | NH | 94 | 61 | 10 | 53 |
| Duke University | NC | 92 | 68 | 8 | 45 |
| Emory University | GA | 84 | 65 | 7 | 37 |
| Georgetown University | PA | 91 | 54 | 10 | 29 |
| Harvard University | MA | 97 | 73 | 8 | 46 |
| Johns Hopkins University | MD | 89 | 64 | 9 | 27 |
| Lehigh University | PA | 81 | 55 | 11 | 40 |
| Massachusetts Inst. of Technology | MA | 92 | 65 | 6 | 44 |
| New York University | NY | 72 | 63 | 13 | 13 |
| Northwestern University | IL | 90 | 66 | 8 | 30 |
| Pennsylvania State Univ. | PA | 80 | 32 | 19 | 21 |
| Princeton University | NJ | 95 | 68 | 5 | 67 |
| Rice University | TX | 92 | 62 | 8 | 40 |
| Stanford University | CA | 92 | 69 | 7 | 34 |
| Tufts University | MA | 87 | 67 | 9 | 29 |
| Tulane University | LA | 72 | 56 | 12 | 17 |
| U. of California–Berkeley | CA | 83 | 58 | 17 | 18 |
| U. of California–Davis | CA | 74 | 32 | 19 | 7 |
| U. of California–Irvine | CA | 74 | 42 | 20 | 9 |
| U. of California–Los Angeles | CA | 78 | 41 | 18 | 13 |
| U. of California–San Diego | CA | 80 | 48 | 19 | 8 |
| U. of California–Santa Barbara | CA | 70 | 45 | 20 | 12 |
| U. of Chicago | IL | 84 | 65 | 4 | 36 |
| U. of Florida | FL | 67 | 31 | 23 | 19 |
| U. of Illinois–Urbana Champaign | IL | 77 | 29 | 15 | 23 |
| U. of Michigan–Ann Arbor | MI | 83 | 51 | 15 | 13 |
| U. of North Carolina–Chapel Hill | NC | 82 | 40 | 16 | 26 |
| U. of Notre Dame | IN | 94 | 53 | 13 | 49 |
| U. of Pennsylvania | PA | 90 | 65 | 7 | 41 |
| U. of Rochester | NY | 76 | 63 | 10 | 23 |
| U. of Southern California | CA | 70 | 53 | 13 | 22 |
| U. of Texas–Austin | TX | 66 | 39 | 21 | 13 |
| U. of Virginia | VA | 92 | 44 | 13 | 28 |
| U. of Washington | WA | 70 | 37 | 12 | 12 |
| U. of Wisconsin–Madison | WI | 73 | 37 | 13 | 13 |
| Vanderbilt University | TN | 82 | 68 | 9 | 31 |
| Wake Forest University | NC | 82 | 59 | 11 | 38 |
| Washington University–St. Louis | MO | 86 | 73 | 7 | 33 |
| Yale University | CT | 94 | 77 | 7 | 50 |

offered with fewer than 20 students. The column labeled Student-Faculty Ratio is the number of students enrolled divided by the total number of faculty. Finally, the column labeled Alumni Giving Rate is the percentage of alumni who made a donation to the university.

## Managerial Report

1. Use methods of descriptive statistics to summarize the data.
2. Develop an estimated regression equation that can be used to predict the alumni giving rate given the number of students who graduate. Discuss your findings.
3. Develop an estimated regression equation that could be used to predict the alumni giving rate using the data provided.
4. What conclusion and/or recommendations can you derive from your analysis?

# Chapter 16

# REGRESSION ANALYSIS: MODEL BUILDING

**CONTENTS**

STATISTICS IN PRACTICE: MONSANTO COMPANY

## STATISTICS IN PRACTICE

### MONSANTO COMPANY*
*St. Louis, Missouri*

Monsanto Company traces its roots to one entrepreneur's investment of $500 and a dusty warehouse on the Mississippi riverfront, where in 1901 John F. Queeney began manufacturing saccharin. Today, Monsanto is one of the nation's largest chemical companies, producing more than a thousand products ranging from industrial chemicals to synthetic playing surfaces used in modern sports stadiums. Monsanto is a worldwide corporation with manufacturing facilities, laboratories, technical centers, and marketing operations in 65 countries.

Monsanto's Nutrition Chemical Division manufactures and markets a methionine supplement used in poultry, swine, and cattle feed products. Because poultry growers work with high volumes and low profit margins, cost-effective poultry feed products with the best possible nutrition value are needed. Optimal feed composition will result in rapid growth and high final body weight for a given level of feed intake. The chemical industry has worked closely with poultry growers to optimize poultry feed products. Ultimately, success depends on keeping the cost of poultry low in comparison with the cost of beef and other meat products.

Monsanto used regression analysis to model the relationship between body weight $y$ and the amount of methionine $x$ added to the poultry feed. Initially, the following simple linear estimated regression equation was developed.

$$\hat{y} = .21 + .42x$$

This estimated regression equation proved statistically significant; however, the analysis of the residuals indicated that a curvilinear relationship would be

Monsanto researchers used regression analysis to develop an optimal feed composition for poultry growers. Photo © PhotoDisc, Inc.

a better model of the relationship between body weight and methionine.

Further research conducted by Monsanto showed that although small amounts of methionine tended to increase body weight, at some point body weight leveled off and additional amounts of the methionine were of little or no benefit. In fact, when the amount of methionine increased beyond nutritional requirements, body weight tended to decline. The following estimated multiple regression equation was used to model the curvilinear relationship between body weight and methionine.

$$\hat{y} = -1.89 + 1.32x - .506x^2$$

Use of the regression results enabled Monsanto to determine the optimal level of methionine to be used in poultry feed products.

In this chapter we will extend the discussion of regression analysis by showing how curvilinear models such as the one used by Monsanto can be developed. In addition, we will describe a variety of tools that help determine which independent variables lead to the best estimated regression equation.

---

*The authors are indebted to James R. Ryland and Robert M. Schisla, Senior Research Specialists, Monsanto Nutrition Chemical Division, for providing this Statistics in Practice.

Model building is the process of developing an estimated regression equation that describes the relationship between a dependent variable and one or more independent variables. The major issues in model building are finding the proper functional form of the relationship and selecting the independent variables to be included in the model. In Section 16.1 we establish the framework for model building by introducing the concept of a general linear model. Section 16.2, which provides the foundation for the more sophisticated computer-based procedures, introduces a general approach for determining when to add or delete independent variables. In Section 16.3 we consider a larger regression problem involving eight independent variables and 25 observations. In Section 16.4 we discuss the use of variable selection procedures, including stepwise regression, the forward selection procedure, the backward elimination procedure, and best-subsets regression. We also show how to implement the backward elimination procedure using Excel. In Section 16.5 we show how the Durbin-Watson test can be used to detect serial or autocorrelation, and in Section 16.6 we show how regression analysis can be used for analysis of variance and experimental design problems.

## 16.1    GENERAL LINEAR MODEL

Suppose we have collected data for one dependent variable $y$ and $k$ independent variables $x_1, x_2, \ldots, x_k$. Our objective is to use these data to develop an estimated regression equation that provides the best relationship between the dependent and independent variables. As a general framework for developing more complex relationships among the independent variables, we introduce the concept of a **general linear model** involving $p$ independent variables.

If you can write a regression model in the form of equation (16.1), the standard multiple regression procedures described in Chapter 15 are applicable.

**General Linear Model**

$$y = \beta_0 + \beta_1 z_1 + \beta_2 z_2 + \cdots + \beta_p z_p + \epsilon \qquad \textbf{(16.1)}$$

In equation (16.1), each of the independent variables $z_j$ (where $j = 1, 2, \ldots, p$) is a function of $x_1, x_2, \ldots, x_k$ (the variables for which data have been collected). In some cases, each $z_j$ may be a function of only one $x$ variable. The simplest case is when we have collected data for just one variable $x_1$ and want to estimate $y$ by using a straight-line relationship. In this case $z_1 = x_1$, and equation (16.1) becomes

$$y = \beta_0 + \beta_1 x_1 + \epsilon \qquad \textbf{(16.2)}$$

Note that equation (16.2) is the simple linear regression model introduced in Chapter 14 with the exception that the independent variable is labeled $x_1$ instead of $x$. In the statistical modeling literature, this model is called a *simple first-order model with one predictor variable*.

### Modeling Curvilinear Relationships

More complex types of relationships can be modeled with equation (16.1). To illustrate, let us consider the problem facing Reynolds, Inc., a manufacturer of industrial scales and laboratory equipment. Managers at Reynolds want to investigate the relationship between length of employment of their salespeople and the number of electronic laboratory scales sold. Table 16.1 gives the number of months each salesperson has been employed by the firm and the number of scales sold by 15 randomly selected salespeople for the most recent sales period. Figure 16.1 is the scatter diagram for these data. The scatter diagram indicates a possible curvilinear relationship between the length of time employed and the number of units sold. Before considering how to develop a curvilinear relationship for Reynolds, let us consider the Excel output in Figure 16.2 corresponding to a simple first-order model; the estimated regression equation is

**Reynolds**

$$\text{Sales} = 111.2279 + 2.3768 \text{ Months}$$

**TABLE 16.1**

DATA FOR THE
REYNOLDS
EXAMPLE

| Months Employed | Scales Sold |
|---|---|
| 41 | 275 |
| 106 | 296 |
| 76 | 317 |
| 104 | 376 |
| 22 | 162 |
| 12 | 150 |
| 85 | 367 |
| 111 | 308 |
| 40 | 189 |
| 51 | 235 |
| 9 | 83 |
| 12 | 112 |
| 6 | 67 |
| 56 | 325 |
| 19 | 189 |

where

Sales = number of electronic laboratory scales sold

Months = the number of months the salesperson has been employed

A standardized residual plot against $\hat{y}$ (predicted Sales) is also displayed. Although the computer output shows that a linear relationship explains a high percentage of the variability in sales (R Square = .7812), the standardized residual plot suggests that a curvilinear relationship is present.

To account for the curvilinear relationship, we set $z_1 = x_1$ and $z_2 = x_1^2$ in equation (16.1) to obtain the model

$$y = \beta_0 + \beta_1 x_1 + \beta_2 x_1^2 + \epsilon \qquad (16.3)$$

This model is called a *second-order model with one predictor variable*. To develop an estimated regression equation corresponding to this second-order model, Excel's Regression Tool needs the original data in Table 16.1, as well as that data corresponding to adding a second independent variable that is the square of the number of months the employee has been with the firm. In Figure 16.3 we show the Excel output corresponding to the second-order model (the months squared data are in column B); the estimated regression equation is

Sales = 45.3476 + 6.3448 Months − .0345 MonthsSq

where

MonthsSq = the square of the number of months the
salesperson has been employed

The corresponding standardized residual plot is also shown. It shows that the previous curvilinear pattern has been removed. At the .05 level of significance, the computer output

**FIGURE 16.1**    SCATTER DIAGRAM FOR THE REYNOLDS EXAMPLE

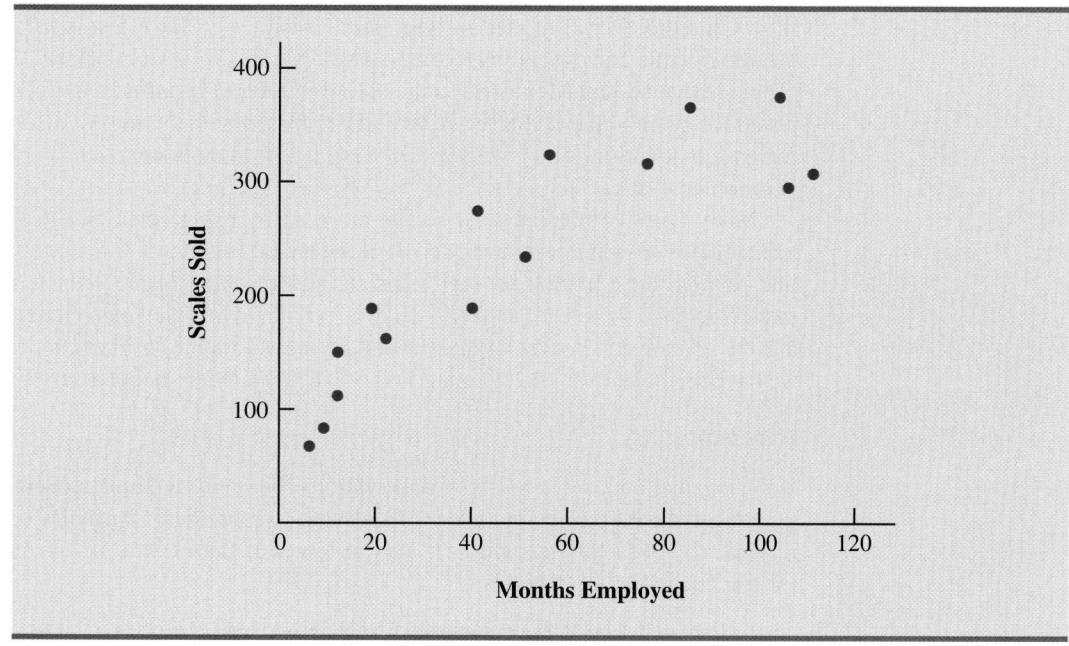

**FIGURE 16.2    EXCEL OUTPUT FOR THE REYNOLDS EXAMPLE: FIRST-ORDER MODEL**

| | A | B | C | D | E | F | G | H | I | J |
|---|---|---|---|---|---|---|---|---|---|---|
| 1 | **Months** | **Sales** | | | | | | | | |
| 2 | 41 | 275 | | | | | | | | |
| 3 | 106 | 296 | | | | | | | | |
| 4 | 76 | 317 | | | | | | | | |
| 5 | 104 | 376 | | | | | | | | |
| 6 | 22 | 162 | | | | | | | | |
| 7 | 12 | 150 | | | | | | | | |
| 8 | 85 | 367 | | | | | | | | |
| 9 | 111 | 308 | | | | | | | | |
| 10 | 40 | 189 | | | | | | | | |
| 11 | 51 | 235 | | | | | | | | |
| 12 | 9 | 83 | | | | | | | | |
| 13 | 12 | 112 | | | | | | | | |
| 14 | 6 | 67 | | | | | | | | |
| 15 | 56 | 325 | | | | | | | | |
| 16 | 19 | 189 | | | | | | | | |
| 17 | | | | | | | | | | |
| 18 | SUMMARY OUTPUT | | | | | | | | | |
| 19 | | | | | | | | | | |
| 20 | *Regression Statistics* | | | | | | | | | |
| 21 | Multiple R | 0.8838 | | | | | | | | |
| 22 | R Square | 0.7812 | | | | | | | | |
| 23 | Adjusted R Square | 0.7643 | | | | | | | | |
| 24 | Standard Error | 49.5158 | | | | | | | | |
| 25 | Observations | 15 | | | | | | | | |
| 26 | | | | | | | | | | |
| 27 | ANOVA | | | | | | | | | |
| 28 | | *df* | *SS* | *MS* | *F* | *Significance F* | | | | |
| 29 | Regression | 1 | 113783.3447 | 113783.3447 | 46.4078 | 1.24E-05 | | | | |
| 30 | Residual | 13 | 31873.5886 | 2451.8145 | | | | | | |
| 31 | Total | 14 | 145656.9333 | | | | | | | |
| 32 | | | | | | | | | | |
| 33 | | *Coefficients* | *Standard Error* | *t Stat* | *P-value* | *Lower 95%* | *Upper 95%* | *Lower 99.0%* | *Upper 99.0%* | |
| 34 | Intercept | 111.2279 | 21.6280 | 5.1428 | 0.0002 | 64.5035 | 157.9524 | 46.0783 | 176.3776 | |
| 35 | Months | 2.3768 | 0.3489 | 6.8123 | 0.0000 | 1.6230 | 3.1305 | 1.3258 | 3.4277 | |
| 36 | | | | | | | | | | |

The chart embedded in the spreadsheet shows a plot with "Standard Residuals" on the vertical axis (ranging from -2.0 to 2.0) and "Predicted Sales" on the horizontal axis (ranging from 50 to 400), with plotted residual points.

shows that the overall model is significant (*p*-value for the *F* test is 8.75E-07); note also that the *p*-value corresponding to the *t*-stat for MonthsSq is less than .05, and hence we can conclude that adding MonthsSq to the model involving Months is significant. With an Adjusted R Square value of .8859, we should be pleased with the fit provided by this estimated regression equation. Thus, we see how easy it is to handle curvilinear relationships in regression analysis.

Many types of relationships can be modeled by using equation (16.1). The regression techniques with which we have been working are definitely not limited to linear, or straight-line, relationships. In multiple regression analysis the word *linear* in the term "general linear model" refers only to the fact that $\beta_0, \beta_1, \ldots, \beta_p$ all have exponents of one; it does not imply that the relationship between $y$ and the underlying $x_i$ variables is linear. Indeed, in this section we have seen one example of equation (16.1) being used to model a curvilinear relationship.

## Interaction

If the original data set consists of observations for $y$ and two independent variables $x_1$ and $x_2$, we can develop a second-order model with two predictor variables by setting $z_1 = x_1$, $z_2 = x_2$, $z_3 = x_1^2$, $z_4 = x_2^2$, and $z_5 = x_1 x_2$ in terms of the general linear model of equation (16.1). The model obtained is

$$y = \beta_0 + \beta_1 x_1 + \beta_2 x_2 + \beta_3 x_1^2 + \beta_4 x_2^2 + \beta_5 x_1 x_2 + \epsilon \qquad (16.4)$$

**FIGURE 16.3    EXCEL OUTPUT FOR THE REYNOLDS EXAMPLE: SECOND-ORDER MODEL**

| | A | B | C | D | E | F | G | H | I | J |
|---|---|---|---|---|---|---|---|---|---|---|
| 1 | **Months** | **Months Sq** | **Sales** | | | | | | | |
| 2 | 41 | 1681 | 275 | | | | | | | |
| 3 | 106 | 11236 | 296 | | | | | | | |
| 4 | 76 | 5776 | 317 | | | | | | | |
| 5 | 104 | 10816 | 376 | | | | | | | |
| 6 | 22 | 484 | 162 | | | | | | | |
| 7 | 12 | 144 | 150 | | | | | | | |
| 8 | 85 | 7225 | 367 | | | | | | | |
| 9 | 111 | 12321 | 308 | | | | | | | |
| 10 | 40 | 1600 | 189 | | | | | | | |
| 11 | 51 | 2601 | 235 | | | | | | | |
| 12 | 9 | 81 | 83 | | | | | | | |
| 13 | 12 | 144 | 112 | | | | | | | |
| 14 | 6 | 36 | 67 | | | | | | | |
| 15 | 56 | 3136 | 325 | | | | | | | |
| 16 | 19 | 361 | 189 | | | | | | | |
| 17 | | | | | | | | | | |
| 18 | SUMMARY OUTPUT | | | | | | | | | |
| 19 | | | | | | | | | | |
| 20 | *Regression Statistics* | | | | | | | | | |
| 21 | Multiple R | 0.9498 | | | | | | | | |
| 22 | R Square | 0.9022 | | | | | | | | |
| 23 | Adjusted R Square | 0.8859 | | | | | | | | |
| 24 | Standard Error | 34.4528 | | | | | | | | |
| 25 | Observations | 15 | | | | | | | | |
| 26 | | | | | | | | | | |
| 27 | ANOVA | | | | | | | | | |
| 28 | | *df* | *SS* | *MS* | *F* | *Significance F* | | | | |
| 29 | Regression | 2 | 131413.0156 | 65706.5078 | 55.3554 | 8.75E-07 | | | | |
| 30 | Residual | 12 | 14243.9177 | 1186.9931 | | | | | | |
| 31 | Total | 14 | 145656.9333 | | | | | | | |
| 32 | | | | | | | | | | |
| 33 | | *Coefficients* | *Standard Error* | *t Stat* | *P-value* | *Lower 95%* | *Upper 95%* | *Lower 99.0%* | *Upper 99.0%* | |
| 34 | Intercept | 45.3476 | 22.7747 | 1.9911 | 0.0697 | -4.2741 | 94.9693 | -24.2185 | 114.9136 | |
| 35 | Months | 6.3448 | 1.0579 | 5.9978 | 6.24E-05 | 4.0399 | 8.6497 | 3.1136 | 9.5761 | |
| 36 | MonthsSq | -0.0345 | 0.0089 | -3.8539 | 0.0023 | -0.0540 | -0.0150 | -0.0618 | -0.0072 | |
| 37 | | | | | | | | | | |

In this second-order model, the variable $z_5 = x_1 x_2$ is added to account for the potential effects of the two variables acting together. This type of effect is called **interaction.**

To provide an illustration of interaction and what it means, let us review the regression study conducted by Tyler Personal Care for one of its new shampoo products. Two factors believed to have the most influence on sales are unit selling price and advertising expenditure. To investigate the effects of these two variables on sales, prices of $2.00, $2.50, and $3.00 were paired with advertising expenditures of $50,000 and $100,000 in 24 test markets. The unit sales that were observed (in 1000s) are reported in Table 16.2.

Table 16.3 is a summary of these data. Note that the mean sales corresponding to a price of $2.00 and an advertising expenditure of $50,000 is 461,000, and the mean sales corresponding to a price of $2.00 and an advertising expenditure of $100,000 is 808,000. Hence, with price held constant at $2.00, the difference in mean sales between advertising expenditures of $50,000 and $100,000 is $808,000 - 461,000 = 347,000$ units. When the price of the product is $2.50, the difference in mean sales is $646,000 - 364,000 = 282,000$ units. Finally, when the price is $3.00, the difference in mean sales is $375,000 - 332,000 = 43,000$ units. Clearly, the difference in mean sales between advertising expenditures of $50,000 and $100,000 depends on the price of the product. In other words, at higher selling prices, the effect of increased advertising expenditure

**TABLE 16.2**   DATA FOR THE TYLER PERSONAL CARE EXAMPLE

| Price | Advertising Expenditure ($1000s) | Sales (1000s) | Price | Advertising Expenditure ($1000s) | Sales (1000s) |
|---|---|---|---|---|---|
| $2.00 | 50 | 478 | $2.00 | 100 | 810 |
| $2.50 | 50 | 373 | $2.50 | 100 | 653 |
| $3.00 | 50 | 335 | $3.00 | 100 | 345 |
| $2.00 | 50 | 473 | $2.00 | 100 | 832 |
| $2.50 | 50 | 358 | $2.50 | 100 | 641 |
| $3.00 | 50 | 329 | $3.00 | 100 | 372 |
| $2.00 | 50 | 456 | $2.00 | 100 | 800 |
| $2.50 | 50 | 360 | $2.50 | 100 | 620 |
| $3.00 | 50 | 322 | $3.00 | 100 | 390 |
| $2.00 | 50 | 437 | $2.00 | 100 | 790 |
| $2.50 | 50 | 365 | $2.50 | 100 | 670 |
| $3.00 | 50 | 342 | $3.00 | 100 | 393 |

**CD file**

Tyler

diminishes. These observations provide evidence of interaction between the price and advertising expenditure variables.

To provide another perspective of interaction, Figure 16.4 shows a graph of the mean sales for the six price-advertising expenditure combinations. This graph also shows that the effect of advertising expenditure on mean sales depends on the price of the product; we again see the effect of interaction. When interaction between two variables is present, we cannot study the effect of one variable on the response $y$ independently of the other variable. In other words, meaningful conclusions can be developed only if we consider the joint effect that both variables have on the response.

To account for the effect of interaction, we will use the following regression model.

$$y = \beta_0 + \beta_1 x_1 + \beta_2 x_2 + \beta_3 x_1 x_2 + \epsilon \qquad (16.5)$$

where

$$y = \text{unit sales (1000s)}$$
$$x_1 = \text{price (\$)}$$
$$x_2 = \text{advertising expenditure (\$1000s)}$$

**TABLE 16.3**   MEAN SALES (1000s) FOR THE TYLER PERSONAL CARE EXAMPLE

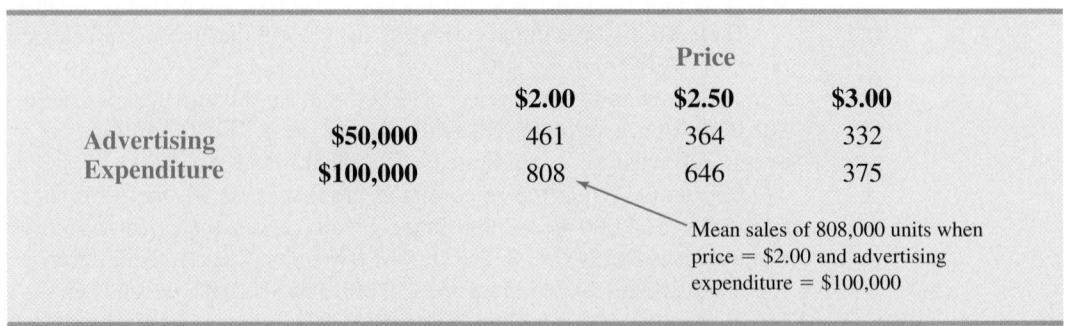

| | | Price | | |
|---|---|---|---|---|
| | | **$2.00** | **$2.50** | **$3.00** |
| Advertising | **$50,000** | 461 | 364 | 332 |
| Expenditure | **$100,000** | 808 | 646 | 375 |

Mean sales of 808,000 units when price = $2.00 and advertising expenditure = $100,000

**FIGURE 16.4**    MEAN SALES AS A FUNCTION OF SELLING AND
ADVERTISING EXPENDITURE

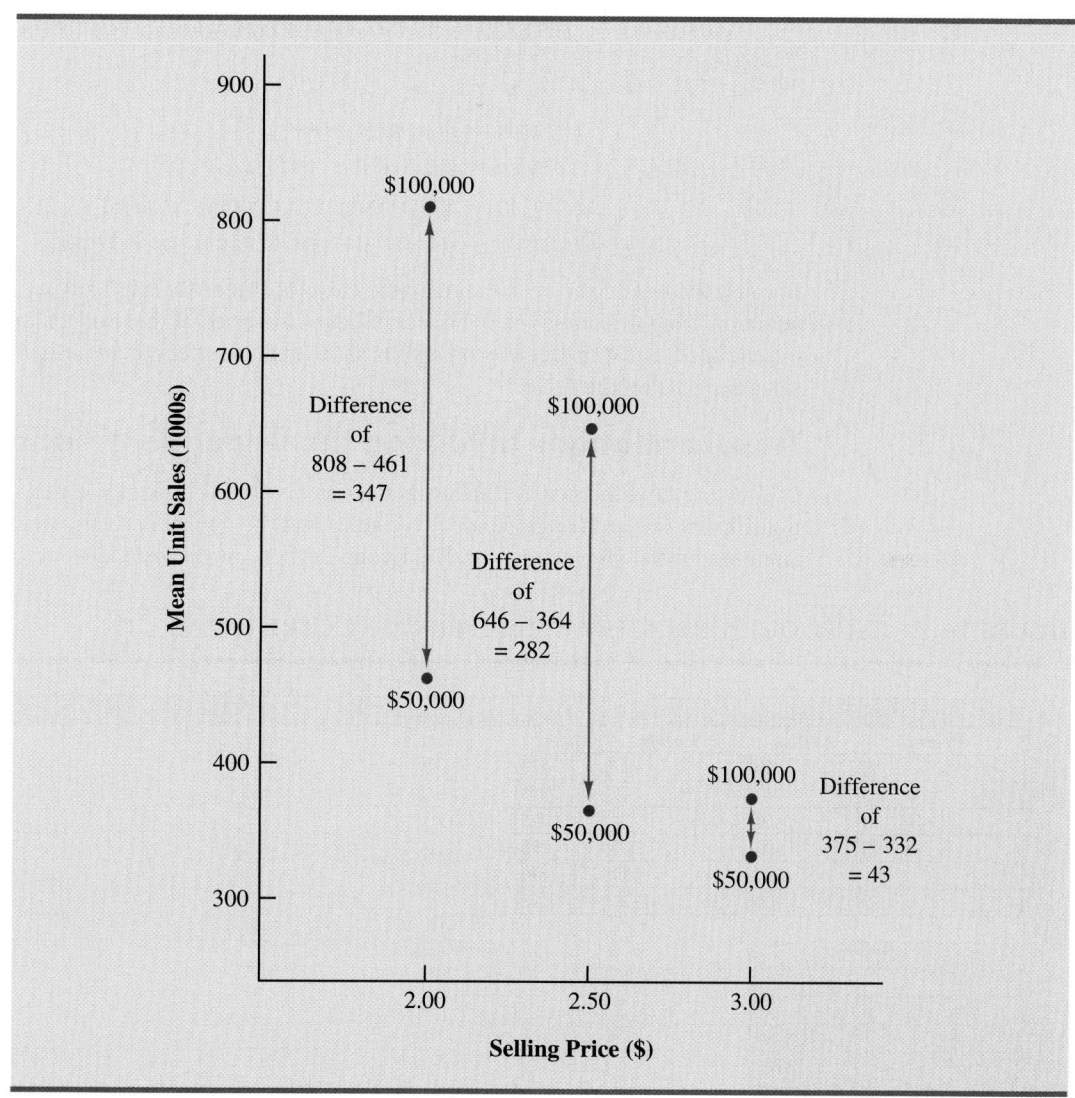

Note that equation (16.5) reflects Tyler's belief that the number of units sold depends linearly on selling price and advertising expenditure (accounted for by the $\beta_1 x_1$ and $\beta_2 x_2$ terms), and that there is interaction between the two variables (accounted for by the $\beta_3 x_1 x_2$ term).

To develop an estimated regression equation, a general linear model involving three independent variables ($z_1$, $z_2$, and $z_3$) was used.

$$y = \beta_0 + \beta_1 z_1 + \beta_2 z_2 + \beta_3 z_3 + \epsilon \qquad \text{(16.6)}$$

where

$$z_1 = x_1$$
$$z_2 = x_2$$
$$z_3 = x_1 x_2$$

Figure 16.5 is the Excel output corresponding to the interaction model for the Tyler Personal Care example. The resulting estimated regression equation is

$$\text{Sales} = -275.8333 + 175\,\text{Price} + 19.68\,\text{AdvExp} - 6.08\,\text{PriceAdv}$$

where

$$
\begin{aligned}
\text{Sales} &= \text{unit sales (1000s)} \\
\text{Price} &= \text{price of the product (\$)} \\
\text{AdvExp} &= \text{advertising expenditure (\$1000s)} \\
\text{PriceAdv} &= \text{interaction term (Price times AdvExp)}
\end{aligned}
$$

Because the $p$-value corresponding to the $t$ test for PriceAdv is 0.0000, we conclude that interaction is significant given the linear effect of the price of the product and the advertising expenditure. Thus, the regression results show that the effect of advertising expenditure on sales depends on the price.

## Transformations Involving the Dependent Variable

In showing how the general linear model can be used to model a variety of possible relationships between the independent variables and the dependent variable, we have focused attention on transformations involving one or more of the independent variables. Often it

**FIGURE 16.5**  EXCEL OUTPUT FOR THE TYLER PERSONAL CARE EXAMPLE

| | A | B | C | D | E | F | G | H | I | J |
|---|---|---|---|---|---|---|---|---|---|---|
| 1 | **Price** | **AdvExp** | **PriceAdv** | **Sales** | | | | | | |
| 2 | 2 | 50 | 100 | 478 | | | | | | |
| 3 | 2.5 | 50 | 125 | 373 | | | | | | |
| 4 | 3 | 50 | 150 | 335 | | | | | | |
| 23 | 2 | 100 | 200 | 790 | | | | | | |
| 24 | 2.5 | 100 | 250 | 670 | | | | | | |
| 25 | 3 | 100 | 300 | 393 | | | | | | |
| 26 | | | | | | | | | | |
| 27 | SUMMARY OUTPUT | | | | | | | | | |
| 28 | | | | | | | | | | |
| 29 | *Regression Statistics* | | | | | | | | | |
| 30 | Multiple R | 0.9890 | | | | | | | | |
| 31 | R Square | 0.9781 | | | | | | | | |
| 32 | Adjusted R Square | 0.9748 | | | | | | | | |
| 33 | Standard Error | 28.1739 | | | | | | | | |
| 34 | Observations | 24 | | | | | | | | |
| 35 | | | | | | | | | | |
| 36 | ANOVA | | | | | | | | | |
| 37 | | *df* | *SS* | *MS* | *F* | *Significance F* | | | | |
| 38 | Regression | 3 | 709316 | 236438.7 | 297.8692 | 9.26E-17 | | | | |
| 39 | Residual | 20 | 15875.3333 | 793.7667 | | | | | | |
| 40 | Total | 23 | 725191.3333 | | | | | | | |
| 41 | | | | | | | | | | |
| 42 | | *Coefficients* | *Standard Error* | *t Stat* | *P-value* | *Lower 95%* | *Upper 95%* | *Lower 99.0%* | *Upper 99.0%* | |
| 43 | Intercept | -275.8333 | 112.8421 | -2.4444 | 0.0239 | -511.2177 | -40.4489 | -596.9070 | 45.2404 | |
| 44 | Price | 175 | 44.5468 | 3.9285 | 0.0008 | 82.0771 | 267.9229 | 48.2494 | 301.7506 | |
| 45 | AdvExp | 19.68 | 1.4274 | 13.7878 | 1.13E-11 | 16.7026 | 22.6574 | 15.6187 | 23.7413 | |
| 46 | PriceAdv | -6.08 | 0.5635 | -10.7901 | 8.68E-10 | -7.2554 | -4.9046 | -7.6833 | -4.4767 | |
| 47 | | | | | | | | | | |

Note: Rows 5–22 are hidden.

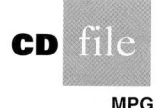

MPG

**TABLE 16.4**

WEIGHT AND
MILES-PER-
GALLON
RATING FOR
12 AUTOMOBILES

| Weight | Miles per Gallon |
|--------|------------------|
| 2289 | 28.7 |
| 2113 | 29.2 |
| 2180 | 34.2 |
| 2448 | 27.9 |
| 2026 | 33.3 |
| 2702 | 26.4 |
| 2657 | 23.9 |
| 2106 | 30.5 |
| 3226 | 18.1 |
| 3213 | 19.5 |
| 3607 | 14.3 |
| 2888 | 20.9 |

is worthwhile to consider transformations involving the dependent variable *y*. As an illustration of when we might want to transform the dependent variable, consider the data in Table 16.4, the weight and miles-per-gallon rating for 12 automobiles. The scatter diagram in Figure 16.6 shows a negative linear relationship between these two variables. Therefore, we use a simple first-order model to relate the two variables. The Excel output is in Figure 16.7; the resulting estimated regression equation is

$$\text{MPG} = 56.0957 - 0.0116 \text{ Weight}$$

where

$$\text{MPG} = \text{miles-per-gallon rating}$$
$$\text{Weight} = \text{weight of the car in pounds}$$

The model is significant (Significance *F* or *p*-value for the *F* test is 0.000) and the fit is very good (R Square = .9354).

A standardized residual plot is also displayed. The pattern we observe does not look like the horizontal band we should expect to find if the assumptions about the error term are valid. Instead, the variability in the residuals appears to increase as the value of $\hat{y}$ (weight) increases. In other words, we have the wedge-shaped pattern referred to in Chapter 14 as being indicative of a nonconstant variance. We are not justified in reaching any conclusions about the statistical significance of the resulting estimated regression equation when the underlying assumptions for the tests of significance do not appear to be satisfied.

Often the problem of nonconstant variance can be corrected by transforming the dependent variable to a different scale. For instance, if we work with the logarithm of the dependent variable instead of the original dependent variable, the effect will be to compress the values of the dependent variable and thus diminish the effects of nonconstant variance. Most statistical packages provide the ability to apply logarithmic transformations using either the base 10 (common logarithm) or the base *e* = 2.71828 . . . (natural logarithm).

**FIGURE 16.6**  SCATTER DIAGRAM FOR THE MILES-PER-GALLON PROBLEM

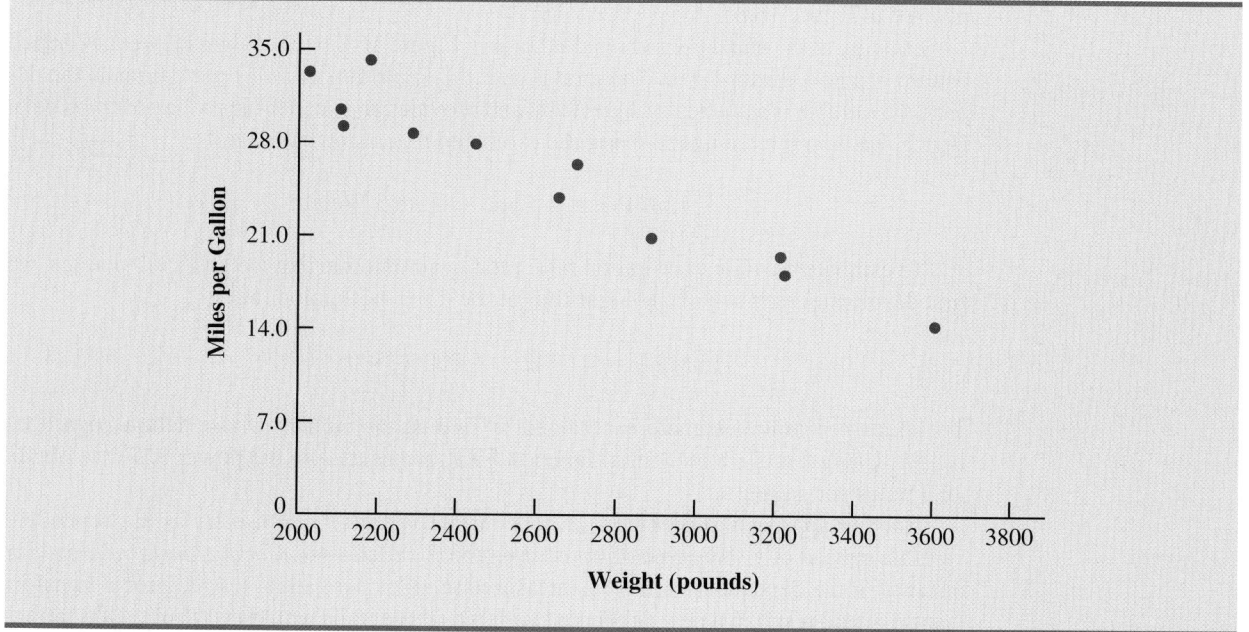

**FIGURE 16.7** EXCEL OUTPUT FOR THE MILES-PER-GALLON PROBLEM

| | A | B | C | D | E | F | G | H | I | J |
|---|---|---|---|---|---|---|---|---|---|---|
| 1 | **Weight** | **MPG** | | | | | | | | |
| 2 | 2289 | 28.7 | | | | | | | | |
| 3 | 2113 | 29.2 | | | | | | | | |
| 4 | 2180 | 34.2 | | | | | | | | |
| 11 | 3213 | 19.5 | | | | | | | | |
| 12 | 3607 | 14.3 | | | | | | | | |
| 13 | 2888 | 20.9 | | | | | | | | |
| 14 | | | | | | | | | | |
| 15 | SUMMARY OUTPUT | | | | | | | | | |
| 16 | | | | | | | | | | |
| 17 | *Regression Statistics* | | | | | | | | | |
| 18 | Multiple R | 0.9672 | | | | | | | | |
| 19 | R Square | 0.9354 | | | | | | | | |
| 20 | Adjusted R Square | 0.9289 | | | | | | | | |
| 21 | Standard Error | 1.6705 | | | | | | | | |
| 22 | Observations | 12 | | | | | | | | |
| 23 | | | | | | | | | | |
| 24 | ANOVA | | | | | | | | | |
| 25 | | *df* | *SS* | *MS* | *F* | *Significance F* | | | | |
| 26 | Regression | 1 | 403.9759 | 403.9759 | 144.7601 | 2.85E-07 | | | | |
| 27 | Residual | 10 | 27.9066 | 2.7907 | | | | | | |
| 28 | Total | 11 | 431.8825 | | | | | | | |
| 29 | | | | | | | | | | |
| 30 | | *Coefficients* | *Standard Error* | *t Stat* | *P-value* | *Lower 95%* | *Upper 95%* | *Lower 99.0%* | *Upper 99.0%* | |
| 31 | Intercept | 56.0957 | 2.5821 | 21.7245 | 9.55E-10 | 50.3423 | 61.8490 | 47.9122 | 64.2791 | |
| 32 | Weight | -0.0116 | 0.0010 | -12.0316 | 2.85E-07 | -0.0138 | -0.0095 | -0.0147 | -0.0086 | |
| 33 | | | | | | | | | | |

Note: Rows 5–10 are hidden.

We applied a natural logarithmic transformation to the miles-per-gallon data (see note on cell C2 in Figure 16.8) and developed the estimated regression equation relating weight to the natural logarithm of miles-per-gallon. The regression results obtained by using the natural logarithm of miles-per-gallon as the dependent variable, labeled LnMPG in the output, are in Figure 16.8.

Looking at the standardized residual plot in Figure 16.8, we see that the wedge-shaped pattern has now disappeared. The model with the logarithm of miles per gallon as the dependent variable is statistically significant and provides an excellent fit to the observed data. Hence, we would recommend using the estimated regression equation

$$LnMPG = 4.5242 - 0.0005 \text{ Weight}$$

To estimate the miles-per-gallon rating for an automobile that weighs 2500 pounds, we first develop an estimate of the logarithm of the miles-per-gallon rating.

$$LnMPG = 4.5242 - 0.0005(2500) = 3.27$$

The miles-per-gallon estimate is obtained by finding the number whose natural logarithm is 3.27. Using Excel's exponential function EXP, or raising $e$ to the power 3.27, we obtain 26.3 miles per gallon.

Another approach to problems of nonconstant variance is to use $1/y$ as the dependent variable instead of $y$. This type of transformation is called a *reciprocal transformation*. For instance, if the dependent variable is measured in miles per gallon, the reciprocal transformation would result in a new dependent variable whose units would be 1/(miles per gallon)

**FIGURE 16.8**    EXCEL OUTPUT FOR THE MILES-PER-GALLON: LOGARITHMIC TRANSFORMATION

Note: Rows 5–10 are hidden.

or gallons per mile. In general, there is no way to determine whether a logarithmic transformation or a reciprocal transformation will perform best without actually trying each of them.

## Nonlinear Models That Are Intrinsically Linear

Models in which the parameters $(\beta_0, \beta_1, \dots, \beta_p)$ have exponents other than one are called nonlinear models. However, for the case of the exponential model, we can perform a transformation of variables that will enable us to perform regression analysis with equation (16.1), the general linear model. The exponential model involves the following regression equation.

$$E(y) = \beta_0 \beta_1^x \qquad (16.7)$$

This model is appropriate when the dependent variable $y$ increases or decreases by a constant percentage, instead of by a fixed amount, as $x$ increases.

As an example, suppose sales for a product $y$ are related to advertising expenditure $x$ (in \$1000s) according to the following regression equation.

$$E(y) = 500(1.2)^x$$

Thus, for $x = 1$, $E(y) = 500(1.2)^1 = 600$; for $x = 2$, $E(y) = 500(1.2)^2 = 720$; and for $x = 3$, $E(y) = 500(1.2)^3 = 864$. Note that $E(y)$ is not increasing by a constant amount in this case, but by a constant percentage; the percentage increase is 20%.

We can transform this nonlinear model to a linear model by taking the logarithm of both sides of equation (16.7).

$$\log E(y) = \log \beta_0 + x \log \beta_1 \qquad (16.8)$$

Now if we let $y' = \log E(y)$ $\beta_0' = \log \beta_0$, and $\beta_1' = \log \beta_1$, we can rewrite equation (16.8) as

$$y' = \beta_0' + \beta_1' x$$

The formulas for simple linear regression can now be used to develop estimates of $\beta_0'$ and $\beta_1'$. Denoting the estimates as $b_0'$ and $b_1'$ leads to the following estimated regression equation.

$$\hat{y}' = b_0' + b_1' x \qquad (16.9)$$

To obtain predictions of the original dependent variable $y$ given a value of $x$, we would first substitute the value of $x$ into equation (16.9) and compute $\hat{y}'$. The antilog of $\hat{y}'$ would be the prediction of $y$, or the expected value of $y$.

Many nonlinear models cannot be transformed into an equivalent linear model. However, such models have had limited use in business and economic applications. Furthermore, the mathematical background needed for study of such models is beyond the scope of this text.

## EXERCISES

## Methods

1. Consider the following data for two variables, $x$ and $y$.

| $x$ | 22 | 24 | 26 | 30 | 35 | 40 |
|-----|----|----|----|----|----|----|
| $y$ | 12 | 21 | 33 | 35 | 40 | 36 |

   a. Develop an estimated regression equation for the data of the form $\hat{y} = b_0 + b_1 x$.
   b. Using the results from part (a), test for a significant relationship between $x$ and $y$; use $\alpha = .05$.
   c. Develop a scatter diagram for the data. Does the scatter diagram suggest an estimated regression equation of the form $\hat{y} = b_0 + b_1 x + b_2 x^2$? Explain.
   d. Develop an estimated regression equation for the data of the form $\hat{y} = b_0 + b_1 x + b_2 x^2$.
   e. Refer to part (d). Is the relationship between $x$, $x^2$, and $y$ significant? Use $\alpha = .05$.
   f. Predict the value of $y$ when $x = 25$.

2. Consider the following data for two variables, $x$ and $y$.

| $x$ | 9 | 32 | 18 | 15 | 26 |
|-----|---|----|----|----|----|
| $y$ | 10 | 20 | 21 | 16 | 22 |

   a. Develop an estimated regression equation for the data of the form $\hat{y} = b_0 + b_1 x$. Comment on the adequacy of this equation for predicting $y$.
   b. Develop an estimated regression equation for the data of the form $\hat{y} = b_0 + b_1 x + b_2 x^2$. Comment on the adequacy of this equation for predicting $y$.
   c. Predict the value of $y$ when $x = 20$.

3.  Consider the following data for two variables, $x$ and $y$.

| $x$ | 2 | 3 | 4 | 5 | 7 | 7 | 7 | 8 | 9 |
|-----|---|---|---|---|---|---|---|---|----|
| $y$ | 4 | 5 | 4 | 6 | 4 | 6 | 9 | 5 | 11 |

a.  Does there appear to be a linear relationship between $x$ and $y$? Explain.
b.  Develop the estimated regression equation relating $x$ and $y$.
c.  Plot the standardized residuals versus $\hat{y}$ for the estimated regression equation developed in part (b). Do the model assumptions appear to be satisfied? Explain.
d.  Perform a logarithmic transformation on the dependent variable $y$. Develop an estimated regression equation using the transformed dependent variable. Do the model assumptions appear to be satisfied by using the transformed dependent variable? Does a reciprocal transformation work better in this case? Explain.

## Applications

4.  A highway department is studying the relationship between traffic flow and speed. The following model has been hypothesized.

$$y = \beta_0 + \beta_1 x + \epsilon$$

where

$$y = \text{traffic flow in vehicles per hour}$$
$$x = \text{vehicle speed in miles per hour}$$

The following data were collected during rush hour for six highways leading out of the city.

| Traffic Flow ($y$) | Vehicle Speed ($x$) |
|:---:|:---:|
| 1256 | 35 |
| 1329 | 40 |
| 1226 | 30 |
| 1335 | 45 |
| 1349 | 50 |
| 1124 | 25 |

a.  Develop an estimated regression equation for the data.
b.  Using $\alpha = .01$, test for a significant relationship.

5.  In working further with the problem of Exercise 4, statisticians suggested the use of the following curvilinear estimated regression equation.

$$\hat{y} = b_0 + b_1 x + b_2 x^2$$

a.  Use the data of Exercise 4 to compute the coefficients of this estimated regression equation.
b.  Using $\alpha = .01$, test for a significant relationship.
c.  Estimate the traffic flow in vehicles per hour at a speed of 38 miles per hour.

**6.** A study of emergency service facilities investigated the relationship between the number of facilities and the average distance traveled to provide the emergency service (*Management Science*, July 1988). The following table gives the data collected.

| Number of Facilities | Average Distance (miles) |
|---|---|
| 9 | 1.66 |
| 11 | 1.12 |
| 16 | .83 |
| 21 | .62 |
| 27 | .51 |
| 30 | .47 |

**a.** Develop a scatter diagram for these data, treating average distance traveled as the dependent variable.
**b.** Does a simple linear model appear to be appropriate? Explain.
**c.** Develop an estimated regression equation for the data that you believe will best explain the relationship between these two variables.

**7.** The following data show the media expenditures ($ millions) and shipments in bbls. (millions) for 10 major brands of beer (*Superbrands '98,* October 20, 1997).

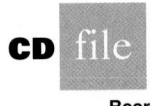

**Beer**

| Brand | Media Expenditures | Shipments |
|---|---|---|
| Budweiser | $120.0 | 36.3 |
| Bud Light | 68.7 | 20.7 |
| Miller Lite | 100.1 | 15.9 |
| Coors Light | 76.6 | 13.2 |
| Busch | 8.7 | 8.1 |
| Natural Light | 0.1 | 7.1 |
| Miller Genuine Draft | 21.5 | 5.6 |
| Miller High Life | 1.4 | 4.4 |
| Busch Light | 5.3 | 4.3 |
| Milwaukee's Best | 1.7 | 4.3 |

**a.** Develop a scatter diagram for these data with media expenditures as the independent variable.
**b.** Does a simple linear regression model appear to be appropriate?
**c.** Develop an estimated regression equation for the data that you believe will best explain the relationship between these two variables.

**8.** In Europe the number of Internet users varies widely from country to country. In 1999, 44.3% of all Swedes used the Internet, while in France the audience was less than 10%. The disparities are expected to persist even though the usage is expected to grow dramatically over the next several years. The following table shows the number of Internet users in 1999 and the projected number of users in 2005 for European countries.

**Internet**

| Country | 1999 Internet Users (%) | 2005 Projected Users (%) |
|---|---|---|
| Austria | 12.6 | 53.4 |
| Belgium | 24.2 | 60.2 |
| Denmark | 40.4 | 71.2 |
| Finland | 40.9 | 71.4 |
| France | 9.7 | 53.1 |
| Germany | 15.0 | 59.6 |

| Country | 1999 Internet Users (%) | 2005 Projected Users (%) |
|---|---|---|
| Greece | 3.4 | 15.8 |
| Ireland | 12.1 | 46.7 |
| Italy | 8.4 | 34.4 |
| Netherlands | 18.6 | 61.4 |
| Norway | 38.0 | 71.7 |
| Portugal | 4.63 | 36.6 |
| Spain | 7.4 | 39.9 |
| Sweden | 44.3 | 71.9 |
| Switzerland | 28.1 | 66.7 |
| United Kingdom | 23.6 | 66.8 |

a. Develop a scatter diagram of the data using the 1999 Internet user percentage as the independent variable. Does a simple linear regression model appear to be appropriate? Discuss.

b. Develop an estimated multiple regression equation with $x$ = the number of 1999 Internet users and $x^2$ as the two independent variables.

c. Consider the nonlinear relationship shown by equation (16.7). Use logarithms to develop an estimated regression equation for this model.

d. Do you prefer the estimated regression equation developed in part (b) or part (c)? Explain.

9. In a study to test the effect of headwinds and tailwinds on a typical golf ball distance, Titleist found that at a certain point tailwinds buy little extra distance; with headwinds, the deficit continues to increase at greater wind speeds (*Golf Magazine,* March 1997). Suppose that in a follow-up study the following data were obtained for Tour-level swing speeds with a driver. For these data wind speed is measured in miles per hour; negative values denote a headwind and positive values denote a tailwind. Distance is the number of yards of carry and roll.

**WindGolf**

| Wind Speed | Distance | Wind Speed | Distance |
|---|---|---|---|
| −30 | 202 | 0 | 269 |
| −30 | 211 | 10 | 273 |
| −30 | 206 | 10 | 286 |
| −20 | 221 | 10 | 287 |
| −20 | 239 | 20 | 283 |
| −20 | 234 | 20 | 292 |
| −10 | 240 | 20 | 298 |
| −10 | 245 | 30 | 292 |
| −10 | 260 | 30 | 301 |
| 0 | 260 | 30 | 299 |
| 0 | 278 | | |

a. Develop an estimated regression equation that shows how the number of yards of carry and roll is related to the wind speed.

b. Estimate the number of yards of carry and roll for a 15-mph headwind.

c. Estimate the number of yards of carry and roll for a 25-mph tailwind.

d. Do your results confirm the findings reported in *Golf Magazine?* Explain.

## 16.2  DETERMINING WHEN TO ADD OR DELETE VARIABLES

In this section we will show how an $F$ test can be used to determine whether it is advantageous to add one or more independent variables to a multiple regression model. This test is based on a determination of the amount of reduction in the error sum of squares resulting from adding one or more independent variables to the model. We will first illustrate how the test can be used in the context of the Butler Trucking problem.

In Chapter 15, the Butler Trucking problem was introduced to illustrate the use of multiple regression analysis. Recall that the managers wanted to develop an estimated regression equation to predict total daily travel time for trucks using two independent variables: miles traveled and number of deliveries. With miles traveled $x_1$ as the only independent variable, the least squares procedure provided the following estimated regression equation.

$$\hat{y} = 1.2739 + .0678x_1$$

In Chapter 15 we showed that the error sum of squares for this model was SSE = 8.0287. When $x_2$, the number of deliveries, was added as a second independent variable, we obtained the following estimated regression equation.

$$\hat{y} = -.8687 + .0611x_1 + .9234x_2$$

The error sum of squares for this model was SSE = 2.2994. Clearly, adding $x_2$ resulted in a reduction of SSE. The question we want to answer is: Does adding the variable $x_2$ lead to a *significant* reduction in SSE?

We use the notation $SSE(x_1)$ to denote the error sum of squares when $x_1$ is the only independent variable in the model, $SSE(x_1, x_2)$ to denote the error sum of squares when $x_1$ and $x_2$ are both in the model, and so on. Hence, the reduction in SSE resulting from adding $x_2$ to the model involving just $x_1$ is

$$SSE(x_1) - SSE(x_1, x_2) = 8.0287 - 2.2994 = 5.7293$$

An $F$ test is conducted to determine whether this reduction is significant.

The numerator of the $F$ statistic is the reduction in SSE divided by the number of independent variables added to the original model. Here only one variable, $x_2$, has been added; thus, the numerator of the $F$ statistic is

$$\frac{SSE(x_1) - SSE(x_1, x_2)}{1} = 5.7293$$

The result is a measure of the reduction in SSE per independent variable added to the model. The denominator of the $F$ statistic is the mean square error for the model that includes all of the independent variables. For Butler Trucking this corresponds to the model containing both $x_1$ and $x_2$; thus, $p = 2$ and

$$MSE = \frac{SSE(x_1, x_2)}{n - p - 1} = \frac{2.2994}{7} = .3285$$

The following $F$ statistic provides the basis for testing whether the addition of $x_2$ is statistically significant.

$$F = \frac{\dfrac{SSE(x_1) - SSE(x_1, x_2)}{1}}{\dfrac{SSE(x_1, x_2)}{n - p - 1}} \tag{16.10}$$

The numerator degrees of freedom for this $F$ test is equal to the number of variables added to the model, and the denominator degrees of freedom is equal to $n - p - 1$.

For the Butler Trucking problem, we obtain

$$F = \frac{\dfrac{5.7293}{1}}{\dfrac{2.2994}{7}} = \frac{5.7293}{.3285} = 17.44$$

Refer to Table 4 of Appendix B. We find that for a level of significance of $\alpha = .05$, $F_{.05} = 5.59$. Because $F = 17.44 > F_{.05} = 5.59$, we can reject the null hypothesis that $x_2$ is not statistically significant; in other words, adding $x_2$ to the model involving only $x_1$ results in a significant reduction in the error sum of squares.

When we want to test for the significance of adding only one independent variable to a model, the result found using the $F$ test just described could also be obtained by using the $t$ test for the significance of an individual parameter (described in Section 15.5). Indeed, the $F$ statistic we just computed is the square of the $t$ statistic used to test the significance of an individual parameter.

Because the $t$ test is equivalent to the $F$ test when only one independent variable is being added to the model, we can now further clarify the proper use of the $t$ test for testing the significance of an individual parameter. If the $t$ test shows that only one parameter is not significant, the corresponding variable can be dropped from the model. However, if the $t$ test shows that two or more parameters are not significant, no more than one independent variable can ever be dropped from a model on the basis of a $t$ test; if one variable is dropped, a second variable that was not significant initially might become significant.

We now turn to a consideration of whether the addition of more than one independent variable—as a set—results in a significant reduction in the error sum of squares.

## General Case

Consider the following multiple regression model involving $q$ independent variables, where $q < p$.

$$y = \beta_0 + \beta_1 x_1 + \beta_2 x_2 + \cdots + \beta_q x_q + \epsilon \tag{16.11}$$

If we add variables $x_{q+1}, x_{q+2}, \ldots, x_p$ to this model, we obtain a model involving $p$ independent variables.

$$y = \beta_0 + \beta_1 x_1 + \beta_2 x_2 + \cdots + \beta_q x_q \\ + \beta_{q+1} x_{q+1} + \beta_{q+2} x_{q+2} + \cdots + \beta_p x_p + \epsilon \tag{16.12}$$

To test whether the addition of $x_{q+1}, x_{q+2}, \ldots, x_p$ is statistically significant, the null and alternative hypotheses can be stated as follows.

$$H_0\colon \beta_{q+1} = \beta_{q+2} = \cdots = \beta_p = 0$$
$$H_a\colon \text{One or more of the parameters is not equal to zero}$$

The following $F$ statistic provides the basis for testing whether the additional independent variables are statistically significant.

$$F = \frac{\dfrac{\text{SSE}(x_1, x_2, \ldots, x_q) - \text{SSE}(x_1, x_2, \ldots, x_q, x_{q+1}, \ldots, x_p)}{p - q}}{\dfrac{\text{SSE}(x_1, x_2, \ldots, x_q, x_{q+1}, \ldots, x_p)}{n - p - 1}} \tag{16.13}$$

This computed $F$ value is then compared with $F_\alpha$, the table value with $p - q$ numerator degrees of freedom and $n - p - 1$ denominator degrees of freedom. If $F > F_\alpha$, we reject $H_0$ and conclude that the set of additional independent variables is statistically significant. Note that for the special case where $q = 1$ and $p = 2$, equation (16.13) reduces to equation (16.10).

Many students find equation (16.13) somewhat complex. To provide a simpler description of this $F$ ratio, we can refer to the model with the smaller number of independent variables as the reduced model and the model with the larger number of independent variables as the full model. If we let SSE(reduced) denote the error sum of squares for the reduced model and SSE(full) denote the error sum of squares for the full model, we can write the numerator of equation (16.13) as

$$\frac{\text{SSE(reduced)} - \text{SSE(full)}}{\text{number of extra terms}} \qquad \textbf{(16.14)}$$

Note that "number of extra terms" denotes the difference between the number of independent variables in the full model and the number of independent variables in the reduced model. The denominator of equation (16.13) is the error sum of squares for the full model divided by the corresponding degrees of freedom; in other words, the denominator is the mean square error for the full model. Denoting the mean square error for the full model as MSE(full) enables us to write the $F$ statistic as

$$F = \frac{\dfrac{\text{SSE(reduced)} - \text{SSE(full)}}{\text{number of extra terms}}}{\text{MSE(full)}} \qquad \textbf{(16.15)}$$

To illustrate the use of this $F$ statistic, suppose we have a regression problem involving 30 observations. One model with the independent variables $x_1$, $x_2$, and $x_3$ has an error sum of squares of 150 and a second model with the independent variables $x_1$, $x_2$, $x_3$, $x_4$, and $x_5$ has an error sum of squares of 100. Did the addition of the two independent variables $x_4$ and $x_5$ result in a significant reduction in the error sum of squares?

First, note that the degrees of freedom for SST is $30 - 1 = 29$ and that the degrees of freedom for the regression sum of squares for the full model is five (the number of independent variables in the full model). Thus, the degrees of freedom for the error sum of squares for the full model is $29 - 5 = 24$, and hence MSE(full) $= 100/24 = 4.17$. Therefore the $F$ statistic is

$$F = \frac{\dfrac{150 - 100}{2}}{4.17} = 6.00$$

This computed $F$ value is compared with the table $F$ value with two numerator and 24 denominator degrees of freedom. At the .05 level of significance, Table 4 of Appendix B shows $F_{.05} = 3.40$. Because $F = 6.00$ is greater than 3.40, we conclude that the addition of variables $x_4$ and $x_5$ is statistically significant.

## Use of *p*-Values

The *p*-value criterion can also be used to determine whether it is advantageous to add one or more independent variables to a multiple regression model. In the preceding example, we showed how to perform an $F$ test to determine whether the addition of two independent variables, $x_4$ and $x_5$, to a model with three independent variables, $x_1$, $x_2$, and $x_3$, was statistically significant. For this example, the computed $F$ statistic was 6.00 and we concluded (by comparing $F = 6.00$ to the critical value $F_{.05} = 3.40$) that the addition of variables $x_4$ and $x_5$ was significant. The $p$-value associated with $F = 6.00$ (two numerator and 24 denominator degrees of freedom) is .0077. With a $p$-value $= .0077 < \alpha = .05$, we would also conclude that the addition of the two independent variables is statistically significant. It is difficult to determine the $p$-value directly from tables of the $F$ distribution, but Excel makes computing the $p$-value easy. For instance simply enter =FDIST(6,2,24) in any cell of a worksheet to get the $p$-value for our example.

## NOTES AND COMMENTS

Computation of the $F$ statistic can also be based on the difference in the regression sums of squares. To show this form of the $F$ statistic, we first note that

$$\text{SSE(reduced)} = \text{SST} - \text{SSR(reduced)}$$
$$\text{SSE(full)} = \text{SST} - \text{SSR(full)}$$

Hence

$$\text{SSE(reduced)} - \text{SSE(full)} = [\text{SST} - \text{SSR(reduced)}] - [\text{SST} - \text{SSR(full)}]$$
$$= \text{SSR (full)} - \text{SSR(reduced)}$$

Thus,

$$F = \dfrac{\dfrac{\text{SSR(full)} - \text{SSR(reduced)}}{\text{number of extra terms}}}{\text{MSE(full)}}$$

## EXERCISES

## Methods

**10.** In a regression analysis involving 27 observations, the following estimated regression equation was developed.

$$\hat{y} = 25.2 + 5.5x_1$$

For this estimated regression equation SST $= 1550$ and SSE $= 520$.
**a.** At $\alpha = .05$, test whether $x_1$ is significant.

Suppose that variables $x_2$ and $x_3$ are added to the model and the following regression equation is obtained.

$$\hat{y} = 16.3 + 2.3x_1 + 12.1x_2 - 5.8x_3$$

For this estimated regression equation SST $= 1550$ and SSE $= 100$.
**b.** Use an $F$ test and a .05 level of significance to determine whether $x_2$ and $x_3$ together contribute significantly to the model.

**11.** In a regression analysis involving 30 observations, the following estimated regression equation was obtained.

$$\hat{y} = 17.6 + 3.8x_1 - 2.3x_2 + 7.6x_3 + 2.7x_4$$

For this estimated regression equation SST = 1805 and SSR = 1760.

**a.** At $\alpha = .05$, test the significance of the relationship among the variables.

Suppose variables $x_1$ and $x_4$ are dropped from the model and the following estimated regression equation is obtained.

$$\hat{y} = 11.1 - 3.6x_2 + 8.1x_3$$

For this model SST = 1805 and SSR = 1705.

**b.** Compute SSE($x_1, x_2, x_3, x_4$).
**c.** Compute SSE($x_2, x_3$).
**d.** Use an $F$ test and a .05 level of significance to determine whether $x_1$ and $x_4$ contribute significantly to the model.

## Applications

**12.** The following table gives some of the data available for 14 teams in the National Football League after 15 games.

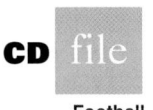

Football

| Team | Won–Lost | Total Points | Rushing Yards | Passing Yards | Interceptions Made by Team | Interceptions Made by Opponent |
|------|----------|--------------|---------------|---------------|----------------------------|--------------------------------|
| Atlanta | 5–10 | 305 | 1907 | 2473 | 19 | 23 |
| Chicago | 12–3 | 187 | 2134 | 2718 | 14 | 24 |
| Dallas | 3–12 | 358 | 1858 | 3386 | 24 | 10 |
| Detroit | 4–11 | 292 | 1184 | 1971 | 15 | 12 |
| Green Bay | 3–12 | 298 | 1274 | 3046 | 22 | 20 |
| St. Louis Rams | 9–6 | 277 | 1882 | 3604 | 17 | 22 |
| Minnesota | 10–5 | 206 | 1744 | 3633 | 16 | 35 |
| New Orleans | 9–6 | 274 | 1843 | 2963 | 15 | 17 |
| N.Y. Giants | 10–5 | 277 | 1492 | 3096 | 14 | 15 |
| Philadelphia | 9–6 | 312 | 1812 | 3247 | 17 | 29 |
| Phoenix | 7–8 | 372 | 1909 | 3633 | 19 | 14 |
| San Francisco | 10–5 | 256 | 2453 | 3131 | 14 | 21 |
| Tampa Bay | 4–11 | 340 | 1650 | 3169 | 33 | 18 |
| Washington | 7–8 | 367 | 1377 | 3930 | 24 | 14 |

**a.** Develop an estimated regression equation that can be used to predict the total points scored given the number of interceptions made by the team.

**b.** Develop an estimated regression equation that can be used to predict the total points scored given the number of interceptions made by the team, the number of rushing yards, and the number of interceptions made by the opponents.

**c.** At a .05 level of significance, test to see whether the addition of the number of rushing yards and the number of interceptions made by the opponents contributes significantly to the estimated regression equation developed in part (a). Explain.

**13.** Refer to Exercise 12.

**a.** Develop an estimated regression equation that relates the total points scored to the number of passing yards, the number of interceptions made by the team, and the number of interceptions made by the opponents.

**b.** Develop an estimated regression equation using the independent variables in part (a) and the number of rushing yards.

**c.** At a .05 level of significance, did the number of rushing yards contribute significantly to the estimated regression equation developed in part (a)? Explain.

**14.** A 10-year study conducted by the American Heart Association provided data on how age, blood pressure, and smoking relate to the risk of strokes. Data from a portion of this study follow. Risk is interpreted as the probability (times 100) that a person will have a stroke over the next 10-year period. For the smoker variable, 1 indicates a smoker and 0 indicates a nonsmoker.

**Stroke**

| Risk | Age | Blood Pressure | Smoker |
|------|-----|----------------|--------|
| 12 | 57 | 152 | 0 |
| 24 | 67 | 163 | 0 |
| 13 | 58 | 155 | 0 |
| 56 | 86 | 177 | 1 |
| 28 | 59 | 196 | 0 |
| 51 | 76 | 189 | 1 |
| 18 | 56 | 155 | 1 |
| 31 | 78 | 120 | 0 |
| 37 | 80 | 135 | 1 |
| 15 | 78 | 98 | 0 |
| 22 | 71 | 152 | 0 |
| 36 | 70 | 173 | 1 |
| 15 | 67 | 135 | 1 |
| 48 | 77 | 209 | 1 |
| 15 | 60 | 199 | 0 |
| 36 | 82 | 119 | 1 |
| 8 | 66 | 166 | 0 |
| 34 | 80 | 125 | 1 |
| 3 | 62 | 117 | 0 |
| 37 | 59 | 207 | 1 |

    **a.** Develop an estimated regression equation that can be used to predict the risk of stroke given the age and blood-pressure level.

    **b.** Consider adding two independent variables to the model developed in part (a), one for the interaction between age and blood-pressure level and the other for whether the person is a smoker. Develop an estimated regression equation using these four independent variables.

    **c.** At a .05 level of significance, test to see whether the addition of the interaction term and the smoker variable contribute significantly to the estimated regression equation developed in part (a).

**15.** The National Football League rates prospects position by position on a scale that ranges from 5 to 9. The ratings are interpreted as follows: 8–9 should start the first year; 7.0–7.9 should start; 6.0–6.9 will make the team as backup; and 5.0–5.9 can make the club and contribute. The following table shows the position, weight, speed (for 40 yards), and ratings for 40 NFL prospects (*USA Today,* April 14, 2000).

**NFL**

| Observation | Name | Position | Weight | Speed | Rating |
|-------------|------|----------|--------|-------|--------|
| 1 | Peter Warrick | Wide receiver | 194 | 4.53 | 9.0 |
| 2 | Plaxico Burress | Wide receiver | 231 | 4.52 | 8.8 |
| 3 | Sylvester Morris | Wide receiver | 216 | 4.59 | 8.3 |
| 4 | Travis Taylor | Wide receiver | 199 | 4.36 | 8.1 |
| 5 | Laveranues Coles | Wide receiver | 192 | 4.29 | 8.0 |
| 6 | Dez White | Wide receiver | 218 | 4.49 | 7.9 |
| 7 | Jerry Porter | Wide receiver | 221 | 4.55 | 7.4 |
| 8 | Ron Dugans | Wide receiver | 206 | 4.47 | 7.1 |
| 9 | Todd Pinkston | Wide receiver | 169 | 4.37 | 7.0 |
| 10 | Dennis Northcutt | Wide receiver | 175 | 4.43 | 7.0 |

(*continued*)

| Observation | Name | Position | Weight | Speed | Rating |
|---|---|---|---|---|---|
| 11 | Anthony Lucas | Wide receiver | 194 | 4.51 | 6.9 |
| 12 | Darrell Jackson | Wide receiver | 197 | 4.56 | 6.6 |
| 13 | Danny Farmer | Wide receiver | 217 | 4.60 | 6.5 |
| 14 | Sherrod Gideon | Wide receiver | 173 | 4.57 | 6.4 |
| 15 | Trevor Gaylor | Wide receiver | 199 | 4.57 | 6.2 |
| 16 | Cosey Coleman | Guard | 322 | 5.38 | 7.4 |
| 17 | Travis Claridge | Guard | 303 | 5.18 | 7.0 |
| 18 | Kaulana Noa | Guard | 317 | 5.34 | 6.8 |
| 19 | Leander Jordan | Guard | 330 | 5.46 | 6.7 |
| 20 | Chad Clifton | Guard | 334 | 5.18 | 6.3 |
| 21 | Manula Savea | Guard | 308 | 5.32 | 6.1 |
| 22 | Ryan Johanningmei | Guard | 310 | 5.28 | 6.0 |
| 23 | Mark Tauscher | Guard | 318 | 5.37 | 6.0 |
| 24 | Blaine Saipaia | Guard | 321 | 5.25 | 6.0 |
| 25 | Richard Mercier | Guard | 295 | 5.34 | 5.8 |
| 26 | Damion McIntosh | Guard | 328 | 5.31 | 5.3 |
| 27 | Jeno James | Guard | 320 | 5.64 | 5.0 |
| 28 | Al Jackson | Guard | 304 | 5.20 | 5.0 |
| 29 | Chris Samuels | Offensive tackle | 325 | 4.95 | 8.5 |
| 30 | Stockar McDougle | Offensive tackle | 361 | 5.50 | 8.0 |
| 31 | Chris McIngosh | Offensive tackle | 315 | 5.39 | 7.8 |
| 32 | Adrian Klemm | Offensive tackle | 307 | 4.98 | 7.6 |
| 33 | Todd Wade | Offensive tackle | 326 | 5.20 | 7.3 |
| 34 | Marvel Smith | Offensive tackle | 320 | 5.36 | 7.1 |
| 35 | Michael Thompson | Offensive tackle | 287 | 5.05 | 6.8 |
| 36 | Bobby Williams | Offensive tackle | 332 | 5.26 | 6.8 |
| 37 | Darnell Alford | Offensive tackle | 334 | 5.55 | 6.4 |
| 38 | Terrance Beadles | Offensive tackle | 312 | 5.15 | 6.3 |
| 39 | Tutan Reyes | Offensive tackle | 299 | 5.35 | 6.1 |
| 40 | Greg Robinson-Ran | Offensive tackle | 333 | 5.59 | 6.0 |

a. Develop dummy variables that will account for the player's position.
b. Develop an estimated regression equation to show how rating is related to position, weight, and speed.
c. At the .05 level of significance, test whether the estimated regression equation developed in part (b) represents a significant relationship between the independent variables and the dependent variable.
d. Is position a significant factor in the player's rating? Use $\alpha = .05$. Explain.

## 16.3 ANALYSIS OF A LARGER PROBLEM

In introducing multiple regression analysis, we used the Butler Trucking example extensively. The small size of this problem was an advantage in exploring introductory concepts, but would make it difficult to illustrate some of the variable selection issues involved in model building. To provide an illustration of the variable selection procedures discussed in the next section, we introduce a data set consisting of 25 observations on eight independent variables. Permission to use these data was provided by Dr. David W. Cravens of the Department of Marketing at Texas Christian University. Consequently, we refer to the data set as the Cravens data.*

The Cravens data are for a company that sells products in several sales territories, each of which is assigned to a single sales representative. A regression analysis was conducted

*For details see David W. Cravens, Robert B. Woodruff, and Joe C. Stamper, "An Analytical Approach for Evaluating Sales Territory Performance," *Journal of Marketing*, 36 (January 1972): 31–37. Copyright © 1972 American Marketing Association.

**TABLE 16.5**   THE CRAVENS DATA

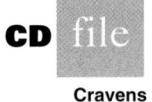

Cravens

| Sales | Time | Poten | AdvExp | Share | Change | Accounts | Work | Rating |
|---|---|---|---|---|---|---|---|---|
| 3,669.88 | 43.10 | 74,065.1 | 4,582.9 | 2.51 | 0.34 | 74.86 | 15.05 | 4.9 |
| 3,473.95 | 108.13 | 58,117.3 | 5,539.8 | 5.51 | 0.15 | 107.32 | 19.97 | 5.1 |
| 2,295.10 | 13.82 | 21,118.5 | 2,950.4 | 10.91 | −0.72 | 96.75 | 17.34 | 2.9 |
| 4,675.56 | 186.18 | 68,521.3 | 2,243.1 | 8.27 | 0.17 | 195.12 | 13.40 | 3.4 |
| 6,125.96 | 161.79 | 57,805.1 | 7,747.1 | 9.15 | 0.50 | 180.44 | 17.64 | 4.6 |
| 2,134.94 | 8.94 | 37,806.9 | 402.4 | 5.51 | 0.15 | 104.88 | 16.22 | 4.5 |
| 5,031.66 | 365.04 | 50,935.3 | 3,140.6 | 8.54 | 0.55 | 256.10 | 18.80 | 4.6 |
| 3,367.45 | 220.32 | 35,602.1 | 2,086.2 | 7.07 | −0.49 | 126.83 | 19.86 | 2.3 |
| 6,519.45 | 127.64 | 46,176.8 | 8,846.2 | 12.54 | 1.24 | 203.25 | 17.42 | 4.9 |
| 4,876.37 | 105.69 | 42,053.2 | 5,673.1 | 8.85 | 0.31 | 119.51 | 21.41 | 2.8 |
| 2,468.27 | 57.72 | 36,829.7 | 2,761.8 | 5.38 | 0.37 | 116.26 | 16.32 | 3.1 |
| 2,533.31 | 23.58 | 33,612.7 | 1,991.8 | 5.43 | −0.65 | 142.28 | 14.51 | 4.2 |
| 2,408.11 | 13.82 | 21,412.8 | 1,971.5 | 8.48 | 0.64 | 89.43 | 19.35 | 4.3 |
| 2,337.38 | 13.82 | 20,416.9 | 1,737.4 | 7.80 | 1.01 | 84.55 | 20.02 | 4.2 |
| 4,586.95 | 86.99 | 36,272.0 | 10,694.2 | 10.34 | 0.11 | 119.51 | 15.26 | 5.5 |
| 2,729.24 | 165.85 | 23,093.3 | 8,618.6 | 5.15 | 0.04 | 80.49 | 15.87 | 3.6 |
| 3,289.40 | 116.26 | 26,878.6 | 7,747.9 | 6.64 | 0.68 | 136.58 | 7.81 | 3.4 |
| 2,800.78 | 42.28 | 39,572.0 | 4,565.8 | 5.45 | 0.66 | 78.86 | 16.00 | 4.2 |
| 3,264.20 | 52.84 | 51,866.1 | 6,022.7 | 6.31 | −0.10 | 136.58 | 17.44 | 3.6 |
| 3,453.62 | 165.04 | 58,749.8 | 3,721.1 | 6.35 | −0.03 | 138.21 | 17.98 | 3.1 |
| 1,741.45 | 10.57 | 23,990.8 | 861.0 | 7.37 | −1.63 | 75.61 | 20.99 | 1.6 |
| 2,035.75 | 13.82 | 25,694.9 | 3,571.5 | 8.39 | −0.43 | 102.44 | 21.66 | 3.4 |
| 1,578.00 | 8.13 | 23,736.3 | 2,845.5 | 5.15 | 0.04 | 76.42 | 21.46 | 2.7 |
| 4,167.44 | 58.44 | 34,314.3 | 5,060.1 | 12.88 | 0.22 | 136.58 | 24.78 | 2.8 |
| 2,799.97 | 21.14 | 22,809.5 | 3,552.0 | 9.14 | −0.74 | 88.62 | 24.96 | 3.9 |

to determine whether a variety of predictor (independent) variables could explain sales in each territory. A random sample of 25 sales territories resulted in the data in Table 16.5; the variable definitions are given in Table 16.6.

As a preliminary step, let us consider the sample correlation coefficients between each pair of variables. Figure 16.9 is the correlation matrix obtained by using Excel's Correlation

**TABLE 16.6**   EXCEL VARIABLE DEFINITIONS FOR THE CRAVENS DATA

| Variable | Definition |
|---|---|
| Sales | Total sales credited to the sales representative |
| Time | Length of time employed in months |
| Poten | Market potential; total industry sales in units for the sales territory* |
| AdvExp | Advertising expenditure in the sales territory |
| Share | Market share; weighted average for the past 4 years |
| Change | Change in the market share over the previous 4 years |
| Accounts | Number of accounts assigned to the sales representative* |
| Work | Workload; a weighted index based on annual purchases and concentrations of accounts |
| Rating | Sales representative overall rating on eight performance dimensions; an aggregate rating on a 1–7 scale |

*These data were coded to preserve confidentiality.

**FIGURE 16.9** SAMPLE CORRELATION COEFFICIENTS FOR THE CRAVENS DATA

| | Sales | Time | Poten | AdvExp | Share | Change | Accounts | Work |
|---|---|---|---|---|---|---|---|---|
| Time | 0.623 | | | | | | | |
| Poten | 0.598 | 0.454 | | | | | | |
| AdvExp | 0.596 | 0.249 | 0.174 | | | | | |
| Share | 0.484 | 0.106 | -0.211 | 0.264 | | | | |
| Change | 0.489 | 0.251 | 0.268 | 0.377 | 0.085 | | | |
| Accounts | 0.754 | 0.758 | 0.479 | 0.200 | 0.403 | 0.327 | | |
| Work | -0.117 | -0.179 | -0.259 | -0.272 | 0.349 | -0.288 | -0.199 | |
| Rating | 0.402 | 0.101 | 0.359 | 0.411 | -0.024 | 0.549 | 0.229 | -0.277 |

tool. Note that the sample correlation coefficient between Sales and Time is .623, between Sales and Poten is .598, and so on.

Looking at the sample correlation coefficients between the independent variables, we see that the correlation between Time and Accounts is .758; hence, if Accounts were used as an independent variable, Time would not add much more explanatory power to the model. Recall the rule-of-thumb test from the discussion of multicollinearity in Section 15.5: multicollinearity can cause problems if the absolute value of the sample correlation coefficient exceeds .7 for any two of the independent variables. If possible, then, we should avoid including both Time and Accounts in the same regression model. The sample correlation coefficient of .549 between Change and Rating is also high and may warrant further consideration.

Looking at the sample correlation coefficients between Sales and each of the independent variables can give us a quick indication of which independent variables are, by themselves, good predictors. We see that the single best predictor of Sales is Accounts, because it has the highest sample correlation coefficient (.754). Recall that for the case of one independent variable, the square of the sample correlation coefficient is the coefficient of determination. Thus, Accounts can explain $(.754)^2(100)$, or 56.85%, of the variability in Sales. The next most important independent variables are Time, Poten, and AdvExp, each with a sample correlation coefficient of approximately .6.

Although the potential for multicollinearity problems is present, let us consider developing an estimated regression equation using all eight independent variables. Excel's Regression tool provided the results in Figure 16.10. The eight-variable multiple regression model has an adjusted coefficient of determination of .8831. Note, however, that the *P-value* column (the p-values for the t tests of individual parameters) shows that only Poten, AdvExp, and Share are significant at the $\alpha = .05$ level, given the effect of all the other variables. Hence, we might be inclined to investigate the results that would be obtained if we used just those three variables. Figure 16.11 shows the Excel results obtained for the estimated regression equation with those three variables. We see that the estimated regression equation has an adjusted coefficient of determination of .8274, which, although not quite as good as that for the eight-independent-variable estimated regression equation, is high.

How can we find an estimated regression equation that will do the best job given the data available? One approach is to compute all possible regressions. That is, we could develop eight one-variable estimated regression equations (each of which corresponds to one of the independent variables), 28 two-variable estimated regression equations (the number of combinations of eight variables taken two at a time), and so on. In all, for the Cravens data, 255 different estimated regression equations involving one or more independent variables would have to be fitted to the data.

**FIGURE 16.10**    EXCEL OUTPUT USING ALL EIGHT INDEPENDENT VARIABLES

| | A | B | C | D | E | F | G | H | I | J |
|---|---|---|---|---|---|---|---|---|---|---|
| 1 | SUMMARY OUTPUT | | | | | | | | | |
| 2 | | | | | | | | | | |
| 3 | *Regression Statistics* | | | | | | | | | |
| 4 | Multiple R | 0.9602 | | | | | | | | |
| 5 | R Square | 0.9220 | | | | | | | | |
| 6 | Adjusted R Square | 0.8831 | | | | | | | | |
| 7 | Standard Error | 449.0154 | | | | | | | | |
| 8 | Observations | 25 | | | | | | | | |
| 9 | | | | | | | | | | |
| 10 | ANOVA | | | | | | | | | |
| 11 | | *df* | *SS* | *MS* | *F* | *Significance F* | | | | |
| 12 | Regression | 8 | 38153712.1137 | 4769214 | 23.65508 | 1.81494E-07 | | | | |
| 13 | Residual | 16 | 3225836.8131 | 201614.8 | | | | | | |
| 14 | Total | 24 | 41379548.9269 | | | | | | | |
| 15 | | | | | | | | | | |
| 16 | | *Coefficients* | *Standard Error* | *t Stat* | *P-value* | *Lower 95%* | *Upper 95%* | *Lower 99.0%* | *Upper 99.0%* | |
| 17 | Intercept | -1507.8358 | 778.6084 | -1.9366 | 0.0707 | -3158.4115 | 142.7400 | -3781.9856 | 766.3141 | |
| 18 | Time | 2.0101 | 1.9305 | 1.0412 | 0.3132 | -2.0824 | 6.1026 | -3.6285 | 7.6488 | |
| 19 | Poten | 0.0372 | 0.0082 | 4.5361 | 0.0003 | 0.0198 | 0.0546 | 0.0132 | 0.0612 | |
| 20 | AdvExp | 0.1510 | 0.0471 | 3.2051 | 0.0055 | 0.0511 | 0.2508 | 0.0134 | 0.2886 | |
| 21 | Share | 199.0402 | 67.0291 | 2.9695 | 0.0090 | 56.9448 | 341.1356 | 3.2623 | 394.8181 | |
| 22 | Change | 290.8666 | 186.7769 | 1.5573 | 0.1390 | -105.0826 | 686.8158 | -254.6690 | 836.4022 | |
| 23 | Accounts | 5.5497 | 4.7754 | 1.1621 | 0.2622 | -4.5737 | 15.6732 | -8.3983 | 19.4978 | |
| 24 | Work | 19.7939 | 33.6752 | 0.5878 | 0.5649 | -51.5943 | 91.1821 | -78.5641 | 118.1519 | |
| 25 | Rating | 8.1890 | 128.4985 | 0.0637 | 0.9500 | -264.2155 | 280.5936 | -367.1277 | 383.5058 | |
| 26 | | | | | | | | | | |

**FIGURE 16.11**    EXCEL OUTPUT USING THREE INDEPENDENT VARIABLES: Poten, AdvExp, and Share

| | A | B | C | D | E | F | G | H | I | J |
|---|---|---|---|---|---|---|---|---|---|---|
| 1 | SUMMARY OUTPUT | | | | | | | | | |
| 2 | | | | | | | | | | |
| 3 | *Regression Statistics* | | | | | | | | | |
| 4 | Multiple R | 0.9214 | | | | | | | | |
| 5 | R Square | 0.8490 | | | | | | | | |
| 6 | Adjusted R Square | 0.8274 | | | | | | | | |
| 7 | Standard Error | 545.5151 | | | | | | | | |
| 8 | Observations | 25 | | | | | | | | |
| 9 | | | | | | | | | | |
| 10 | ANOVA | | | | | | | | | |
| 11 | | *df* | *SS* | *MS* | *F* | *Significance F* | | | | |
| 12 | Regression | 3 | 35130228.2856 | 11710076.0952 | 39.3501 | 8.43E-09 | | | | |
| 13 | Residual | 21 | 6249320.6413 | 297586.6972 | | | | | | |
| 14 | Total | 24 | 41379548.9269 | | | | | | | |
| 15 | | | | | | | | | | |
| 16 | | *Coefficients* | *Standard Error* | *t Stat* | *P-value* | *Lower 95%* | *Upper 95%* | *Lower 99.0%* | *Upper 99.0%* | |
| 17 | Intercept | -1603.5821 | 505.5509 | -3.1719 | 0.0046 | -2654.9330 | -552.2313 | -3034.9819 | -172.1824 | |
| 18 | Poten | 0.0543 | 0.0075 | 7.2632 | 3.74E-07 | 0.0387 | 0.0698 | 0.0331 | 0.0754 | |
| 19 | AdvExp | 0.1675 | 0.0443 | 3.7829 | 0.0011 | 0.0754 | 0.2596 | 0.0421 | 0.2928 | |
| 20 | Share | 282.7469 | 48.7556 | 5.7993 | 9.33E-06 | 181.3541 | 384.1398 | 144.7020 | 420.7919 | |
| 21 | | | | | | | | | | |

With the excellent computer packages available today, it is possible to compute all possible regressions. But doing so involves a great amount of computation and requires the model builder to review a large volume of computer output, much of which is associated with obviously poor models. Statisticians prefer a more systematic approach to selecting the subset of independent variables that provide the best estimated regression equation. In the next section, we introduce some of the more popular approaches.

## 16.4 VARIABLE SELECTION PROCEDURES

In this section we discuss four variable selection procedures: stepwise regression, forward selection, backward elimination, and best-subsets regression. Given a data set with several possible independent variables, these procedures provide a systematic approach to selecting a subset of the independent variables that provide the best model. The first three procedures are iterative; at each step of the procedure a single independent variable is added or deleted and the new model is evaluated. The process continues until a stopping criterion indicates that the procedure cannot find a better model. The best-subsets procedure is not a one-variable-at-a-time procedure; it evaluates regression models involving different subsets of the independent variables.

*Variable selection procedures are particularly useful in the early stages of building a model, but they cannot substitute for experience and judgment on the part of the analyst.*

In the stepwise regression, forward selection, and backward elimination procedures, the criterion for selecting an independent variable to add or delete from the model at each step is based on the $F$ statistic introduced in Section 16.2. Suppose, for instance, that we are considering adding $x_2$ to a model involving $x_1$ or deleting $x_2$ from a model involving $x_1$ and $x_2$. To test whether the addition or deletion of $x_2$ is statistically significant, the null and alternative hypotheses can be stated as follows:

$$H_0: \beta_2 = 0$$
$$H_a: \beta_2 \neq 0$$

In equation (16.10) in Section 16.2 we showed that

$$F = \frac{\dfrac{\text{SSE}(x_1) - \text{SSE}(x_1, x_2)}{1}}{\dfrac{\text{SSE}(x_1, x_2)}{n - p - 1}}$$

can be used as a criterion for determining whether the presence of $x_2$ in the model causes a significant reduction in the error sum of squares. The $p$-value corresponding to this $F$ statistic is the criterion used to determine whether an independent variable should be added or deleted from the regression model. The usual rejection rule applies: Reject $H_0$ if $p$-value $< \alpha$.

### Stepwise Regression

The stepwise regression procedure begins each step by determining whether any of the variables already in the model should be removed. It does so by first computing an $F$ statistic (as shown previously) and corresponding $p$-value for each independent variable in the model. The level of significance $\alpha$ for determining whether an independent variable should be removed from the model is referred to as *Alpha to remove*. If the $p$-value for any independent variable is greater than *Alpha to remove,* the independent variable with the largest $p$-value is removed from the model and the stepwise regression procedure begins a new step.

If no independent variable can be removed from the model, the procedure attempts to enter another independent variable into the model. It does so by first computing an $F$ statistic and corresponding *p*-value for each independent variable that is not in the model. The level of significance $\alpha$ for determining whether an independent variable should be entered into the model is referred to as *Alpha to enter.* The independent variable with the smallest *p*-value is entered into the model provided its *p*-value is less than *Alpha to enter.* The procedure continues in this manner until no independent variables can be deleted from or added to the model.

## Forward Selection

The forward selection procedure starts with no independent variables. It adds variables one at a time using the same procedure as stepwise regression for determining whether an independent variable should be entered into the model. However, the forward selection procedure does not permit a variable to be removed from the model once it has been entered. The procedure stops if the *p*-value for each of the independent variables not in the model is greater than *Alpha to enter.*

## Backward Elimination

The backward elimination procedure begins with a model that includes all the independent variables. It then deletes one independent variable at a time using the same procedure as stepwise regression. However, the backward elimination procedure does not permit an independent variable to be reentered once it has been removed. The procedure stops when none of the independent variables in the model have a *p*-value greater than *Alpha to remove.*

## Using Excel to Perform the Backward Elimination Procedure

Excel does not have built-in capabilities for performing the stepwise regression, forward selection, or backward elimination procedures. However, Excel's Regression tool can be used to perform the backward elimination procedure by running a series of regression problems starting with a model that involves all of the independent variables. We will illustrate the procedure using the Cravens data and a value of .05 for *Alpha to remove.*

Figure 16.10 (shown earlier) shows the Excel output for the Cravens problem using all eight independent variables. At step 1 of the backward elimination procedure, we first check to see whether the *p*-value for any independent variable is greater than *Alpha to remove* = .05. The Cravens data contain five independent variables with a *p*-value greater than .05: Time (.3132), Change (.1390), Accounts (.2622), Work (.5649), and Rating (.9500). Because Rating has the largest *p*-value, we will remove Rating from the current model and develop a new estimated regression equation involving the remaining seven independent variables; Figure 16.12 shows the Excel output for the new estimated regression equation.

Figure 16.12 shows that four of the seven independent variables have a *p*-value greater than .05: Time (.2867), Change (.0896), Accounts (.2340), Work (.5501). Because Work has the largest *p*-value greater than .05, it is selected as the next independent variable to be removed from the model. Thus, we must now develop a new estimated regression equation corresponding to six independent variables: Time, Poten, AdvExp, Share, Change, and Accounts. Instead of showing the complete regression output for this and subsequent steps of the procedure, we will summarize the key results in Table 16.7.

The column labeled All Variables in Table 16.7 shows the *p*-values for each of the eight independent variables at the start of the backward elimination procedure. Recall that we used these *p*-values to determine that Rating should be the first independent variable to remove from the model. The results after deleting Rating and developing a new estimated regression equation are shown in the column labeled Step 1. The label Deleted indicates that Rating was selected as the next independent variable to be removed from the model. Note

**FIGURE 16.12**    EXCEL OUTPUT FOR THE CRAVENS DATA AFTER DELETING RATING

| | A | B | C | D | E | F | G | H | I | J |
|---|---|---|---|---|---|---|---|---|---|---|
| 1 | SUMMARY OUTPUT | | | | | | | | | |
| 2 | | | | | | | | | | |
| 3 | *Regression Statistics* | | | | | | | | | |
| 4 | Multiple R | 0.9602 | | | | | | | | |
| 5 | R Square | 0.9220 | | | | | | | | |
| 6 | Adjusted R Square | 0.8899 | | | | | | | | |
| 7 | Standard Error | 435.6642 | | | | | | | | |
| 8 | Observations | 25 | | | | | | | | |
| 9 | | | | | | | | | | |
| 10 | ANOVA | | | | | | | | | |
| 11 | | *df* | *SS* | *MS* | *F* | *Significance F* | | | | |
| 12 | Regression | 7 | 38152893.2871 | 5450413.3267 | 28.7161 | 3.21E-08 | | | | |
| 13 | Residual | 17 | 3226655.6397 | 189803.2729 | | | | | | |
| 14 | Total | 24 | 41379548.9269 | | | | | | | |
| 15 | | | | | | | | | | |
| 16 | | *Coefficients* | *Standard Error* | *t Stat* | *P-value* | *Lower 95%* | *Upper 95%* | *Lower 99.0%* | *Upper 99.0%* | |
| 17 | Intercept | -1485.9001 | 677.6281 | -2.1928 | 0.0425 | -2915.5726 | -56.2277 | -3449.8239 | 478.0236 | |
| 18 | Time | 1.9751 | 1.7957 | 1.0999 | 0.2867 | -1.8134 | 5.7637 | -3.2292 | 7.1794 | |
| 19 | Poten | 0.0373 | 0.0079 | 4.7499 | 0.0002 | 0.0207 | 0.0539 | 0.0145 | 0.0600 | |
| 20 | AdvExp | 0.1520 | 0.0432 | 3.5139 | 0.0027 | 0.0607 | 0.2432 | 0.0266 | 0.2773 | |
| 21 | Share | 198.3252 | 64.1187 | 3.0931 | 0.0066 | 63.0464 | 333.6040 | 12.4944 | 384.1561 | |
| 22 | Change | 295.8774 | 164.3831 | 1.7999 | 0.0896 | -50.9411 | 642.6959 | -180.5430 | 772.2978 | |
| 23 | Accounts | 5.6089 | 4.5449 | 1.2341 | 0.2340 | -3.9800 | 15.1979 | -7.5633 | 18.7812 | |
| 24 | Work | 19.8989 | 32.6347 | 0.6097 | 0.5501 | -48.9544 | 88.7522 | -74.6841 | 114.4819 | |
| 25 | | | | | | | | | | |

also that the *p*-values shown in the Step 1 column correspond to the estimated regression equation obtained after deleting Rating; in other words, they are the *p*-values shown in the regression output in Figure 16.12. Similarly, the column labeled Step 2 in Table 16.7 shows that at step 2 Work was selected as the next independent variable to be removed. The *p*-values in the Step 2 column correspond to a new estimated regression equation involving only six independent variables Time, Poten, AdvExp, Share, Change, and Accounts. Note that the independent variable with the largest *p*-value is now Accounts (*p*-value = .2882); thus, in step 3 Accounts is removed from the model and a new estimated regression equation is developed. In step 4, because Change is the only independent variable remaining with a

**TABLE 16.7**    SUMMARY OF THE BACKWARD ELIMINATION PROCEDURE FOR THE CRAVENS DATA

| | All Variables P-value | Step 1 P-value | Step 2 P-value | Step 3 P-value | Step 4 P-value |
|---|---|---|---|---|---|
| **Intercept** | 0.0707 | 0.0425 | 0.01255 | 0.0125 | 0.0074 |
| **Time** | 0.3132 | 0.2867 | 0.1982 | 0.1982 | 0.0070 |
| **Poten** | 0.0003 | 0.0002 | 7.94E-05 | 7.94E-05 | 4.65E-06 |
| **AdvExp** | 0.0055 | 0.0027 | 0.0018 | 0.0018 | 0.0007 |
| **Share** | 0.0090 | 0.0066 | 0.0004 | 0.0004 | 5.2E-06 |
| **Change** | 0.1390 | 0.0896 | 0.0927 | 0.0927 | **Deleted** |
| **Accounts** | 0.2622 | 0.2340 | 0.2882 | **Deleted** | |
| **Work** | 0.5649 | 0.5501 | **Deleted** | | |
| **Rating** | 0.9500 | **Deleted** | | | |

*p*-value greater than .05, it is removed from model. Because no independent variables remain with a *p*-value greater than Alpha-to-remove = .05, the procedure now stops.

Figure 16.13 shows the Excel output corresponding to the four independent variables selected in the final step of the backward elimination procedure: Time, Poten, AdvExp, and Share. The estimated regression equation obtained using the backward elimination procedure is

$$\hat{y} = -1312.3817 + 3.8166\text{Time} + .0444\text{Poten} + .1525\text{AdvExp} + 259.4843\text{Share}$$

With an Adjusted R Square of .8752 we see that the estimated regression equation provides a good fit.

Forward selection and backward elimination are the two extremes of model building; the forward selection procedure starts with no independent variables in the model and adds independent variables one at a time, whereas the backward elimination procedure starts with all independent variables in the model and deletes variables one at a time. The two procedures may lead to the same estimated regression equation. But it is possible for them to lead to two different estimated regression equations. Which estimated regression equation to use remains a topic for discussion. Ultimately, the analyst's judgment must be applied. The best-subsets model building procedure we discuss next provides additional model-building information to be considered before a final decision is made.

*Forward selection and backward elimination are different approaches that may lead to different models.*

## Best-Subsets Regression

Stepwise regression, forward selection, and backward elimination are approaches to choosing the regression model by adding or deleting independent variables one at a time. Hence, they offer no guarantee that the best model for a given number of variables will be found. These one-variable-at-a-time procedures are properly viewed as heuristics for selecting a good regression model.

**FIGURE 16.13**    EXCEL RESULTS AFTER STEP 4 OF THE BACKWARD ELIMINATION PROCEDURE

|  | A | B | C | D | E | F | G | H | I | J |
|---|---|---|---|---|---|---|---|---|---|---|
| 1 | SUMMARY OUTPUT | | | | | | | | | |
| 2 | | | | | | | | | | |
| 3 | *Regression Statistics* | | | | | | | | | |
| 4 | Multiple R | 0.9466 | | | | | | | | |
| 5 | R Square | 0.8960 | | | | | | | | |
| 6 | Adjusted R Square | 0.8752 | | | | | | | | |
| 7 | Standard Error | 463.9334 | | | | | | | | |
| 8 | Observations | 25 | | | | | | | | |
| 9 | | | | | | | | | | |
| 10 | ANOVA | | | | | | | | | |
| 11 | | *df* | *SS* | *MS* | *F* | *Significance F* | | | | |
| 12 | Regression | 4 | 37074865.43 | 9268716 | 43.0634 | 1.47843E-09 | | | | |
| 13 | Residual | 20 | 4304683.495 | 215234.2 | | | | | | |
| 14 | Total | 24 | 41379548.93 | | | | | | | |
| 15 | | | | | | | | | | |
| 16 | | *Coefficients* | *Standard Error* | *t Stat* | *P-value* | *Lower 95%* | *Upper 95%* | *Lower 99.0%* | *Upper 99.0%* | |
| 17 | Intercept | -1312.3817 | 440.7254 | -2.9778 | 0.0074 | -2.23E+03 | -393.0449 | -2566.3936 | -58.3697 | |
| 18 | Time | 3.8166 | 1.2697 | 3.0058 | 0.0070 | 1.1680 | 6.4652 | 0.2038 | 7.4294 | |
| 19 | Poten | 0.0444 | 0.0072 | 6.2027 | 4.65E-06 | 0.0295 | 0.0593 | 0.0240 | 0.0648 | |
| 20 | AdvExp | 0.1525 | 0.0380 | 4.0144 | 0.0007 | 0.0732 | 0.2317 | 0.0444 | 0.2605 | |
| 21 | Share | 259.4843 | 42.1803 | 6.1518 | 5.20E-06 | 171.4978 | 347.4708 | 139.4673 | 379.5014 | |
| 22 | | | | | | | | | | |

Some statistical software packages have a procedure called best-subsets regression that enables the user to find, given a specified number of independent variables, the best regression equation. Typical output from such packages will enable the user to identify the two best one-variable estimated regression equations, the two best two-variable regression equations, the two best three-variable regression equations, and so on. The criterion used in determining which estimated regression equations are best for any number of predictors is usually the value of the coefficient of determination.

---

**NOTES AND COMMENTS**

1. Functions of the independent variables can be used to create new independent variables for use with any of the procedures in this section. For instance, if we wanted $x_1 x_2$ in the model to account for interaction, we would use the data for $x_1$ and $x_2$ to create the data for $z = x_1 x_2$.

2. None of the procedures that add or delete variables one at a time can be guaranteed to identify the best regression model. But they are excellent approaches to finding good models—especially when little multicollinearity is present.

---

**EXERCISES**

## Applications

16. Two experts provided subjective lists of school districts that they think are among the best in the country. For each school district, the following data were obtained: average class size, instructional spending per student, average teacher salary, combined SAT score, percentage of students taking the SAT, and percentage of graduates attending a 4-year college.

| City | Average Class Size | Average Instructional Spending per Student ($) | Average Teacher Salary ($) | Combined SAT Score/ % Taking Test | Attend 4-Year College (%) |
|---|---|---|---|---|---|
| Blue Springs, MO | 25 | 3,060 | 29,359 | 1083/(8) | 74 |
| Garden City, NY | 18 | 9,700 | 51,000 | 997/(99) | 77 |
| Indianapolis, IN | 30 | 3,222 | 30,482 | 716/(42) | 40 |
| Newport Beach, CA (Newport–Mesa) | 26 | 4,028 | 37,043 | 977/(46) | 51 |
| Novi, MI | 20 | 3,067 | 39,797 | 980/(15) | 53 |
| Piedmont, CA (Piedmont City) | 28 | 4,208 | 37,274 | 1,042/(91) | 75 |
| Pittsburgh, PA (Fox Chapel area) | 21 | 4,884 | 37,156 | 983/(80) | 66 |
| Scarsdale, NY (Edgemont) | 20 | 9,853 | 31,555 | 1,110/(98) | 87 |
| Wayne, PA (Radnor Township) | 22 | 5,022 | 40,406 | 1,040/(95) | 85 |
| Weston, MA | 21 | 4,680 | 39,800 | 1,031/(99) | 89 |
| Farmingdale, NY | 22 | 6,729 | 45,846 | 947/(75) | 81 |
| Mamaroneck, NY | 20 | 10,405 | 49,625 | 1,000/(90) | 69 |
| Mayfield, OH | 24 | 5,881 | 36,228 | 1,003/(25) | 48 |
| Morristown, NJ | 22 | 6,300 | 37,000 | 972/(80) | 64 |
| New Rochelle, NY | 23 | 8,875 | 41,650 | 1,039/(80) | 55 |
| Newtown Square, PA (Marple–Newtown) | 17 | 5,313 | 38,000 | 963/(75) | 79 |
| Omaha, NB (Westside) | 23 | 4,815 | 32,500 | 1,059/(31) | 81 |
| Shaker Heights, OH | 23 | 4,370 | 38,639 | 940/(56) | 82 |

Let the dependent variable be the percentage of graduates attending a 4-year college.
a. Develop the best one-variable estimated regression equation.
b. Develop an estimated regression equation using all five independent variables.
c. Use the backward elimination procedure to develop the best estimated regression equation.

17. Refer to the data in Exercise 12. Let the dependent variable be the number of wins.
a. Develop the best one-variable estimated regression equation.
b. Develop an estimated regression equation using all of the independent variables.
c. Use the backward elimination procedure to develop the best estimated regression equation.

18. The Ladies Professional Golfers Association (LPGA) maintains statistics on performance and earnings for members of the LPGA Tour. Year-end LPGA Tour statistics for 1997 follow (*Golfweek*, December 6, 1997). Scoring Avg. is the average score per 18 holes of golf; Driving Distance is the average number of yards per drive; Fairways is the percentage of drives landing in the fairway; Greens is the percentage of times a player was able to hit the green in regulation; Putts is the average number of putts per round; Sand Saves is the percentage of times a player was able to get "up and down" from a greenside sand bunker. A green is considered hit in regulation if any part of the ball is touching the putting surface and the number of strokes taken to hit the green is not more than the value of par minus two.

**CD file**

**LPGATour**

| Player | Scoring Avg. | Driving Distance | Fairways | Greens | Putts | Sand Saves |
|---|---|---|---|---|---|---|
| Annika Sorenstam | 70.04 | 249.00 | 75.4 | 73.2 | 29.67 | 47.3 |
| Karrie Webb | 70.00 | 254.60 | 72.1 | 75.1 | 30.20 | 38.0 |
| Kelly Robbins | 70.35 | 256.00 | 69.3 | 78.6 | 29.96 | 44.9 |
| Chris Johnson | 70.84 | 249.40 | 66.9 | 70.4 | 30.17 | 39.6 |
| Tammie Green | 71.24 | 239.40 | 70.4 | 68.6 | 29.64 | 47.2 |
| Juli Inkster | 70.64 | 251.60 | 69.0 | 69.8 | 29.35 | 46.0 |
| Liselotte Neumann | 71.28 | 243.50 | 66.6 | 65.9 | 29.36 | 48.4 |
| Laura Davies | 70.86 | 258.40 | 56.4 | 68.8 | 29.90 | 40.0 |
| Nancy Lopez | 70.70 | 245.50 | 73.4 | 73.0 | 30.23 | 43.1 |
| Betsy King | 71.52 | 245.70 | 65.9 | 66.9 | 29.63 | 37.6 |
| Lorie Kane | 71.47 | 243.30 | 74.9 | 69.4 | 30.22 | 47.8 |
| Michelle McGann | 71.52 | 256.20 | 57.8 | 69.6 | 30.05 | 51.0 |
| Donna Andrews | 71.01 | 230.60 | 79.1 | 71.7 | 29.94 | 42.3 |
| Colleen Walker | 72.31 | 230.00 | 73.6 | 63.3 | 29.58 | 40.9 |
| Rosie Jones | 71.77 | 227.20 | 77.0 | 66.0 | 29.86 | 41.0 |
| Lisa Hackney | 71.34 | 246.00 | 69.8 | 65.1 | 29.91 | 36.4 |
| Jane Geddes | 71.34 | 261.20 | 64.5 | 70.0 | 30.15 | 44.2 |
| Alison Nicholas | 72.31 | 241.70 | 71.8 | 66.4 | 30.43 | 39.4 |
| Pat Hurst | 72.14 | 251.50 | 62.4 | 69.1 | 30.58 | 29.9 |
| Cindy Figg-Currier | 71.90 | 237.20 | 70.1 | 68.0 | 30.40 | 39.3 |

a. If the average score per 18 holes of golf is the dependent variable, what is the best one-variable estimated regression equation? What does the estimated regression equation suggest for players on the LPGA Tour?
b. Use the methods in this section to develop the best estimated multiple regression equation for estimating a player's average score.
c. Does the estimated regression equation developed in part (b) appear reasonable in terms of interpretation?
d. Michele Redman has the following data: Driving Distance 231.6 yards, Fairways 75.7%, Greens 65.2%, Putts 30.69, and Sand Saves 50.5%. Estimate the average score for this professional golfer.

**19.** A sample of 16 companies taken from the *Stock Investor Pro* database was used to obtain the following data on the price/earnings (P/E) ratio, the gross profit margin, and the sales growth for each company (*Stock Investor Pro,* American Association of Individual Investors, August 21, 1997). The data in the Industry column are codes used to define the industry for each company: 1 = energy-international oil; 2 = health-drugs; and 3 = other.

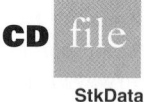

**StkData**

| Firm | P/E Ratio | Gross Profit Margin (%) | Sales Growth (%) | Industry |
|---|---|---|---|---|
| Abbott Laboratories | 22.3 | 23.7 | 10.0 | 2 |
| American Home Products | 22.6 | 21.1 | 5.3 | 2 |
| Amoco | 16.7 | 11.0 | 16.5 | 1 |
| Bristol Meyers Squibb Co. | 25.9 | 26.6 | 9.4 | 2 |
| Chevron | 18.3 | 11.6 | 18.4 | 1 |
| Exxon | 18.7 | 9.8 | 8.3 | 1 |
| General Electric Company | 13.1 | 13.4 | 13.1 | 3 |
| Hewlett-Packard | 23.3 | 9.7 | 21.9 | 3 |
| IBM | 17.3 | 11.5 | 5.6 | 3 |
| Merck & Co. Inc. | 26.2 | 25.6 | 18.9 | 2 |
| Mobil | 18.7 | 8.2 | 8.1 | 1 |
| Pfizer | 34.6 | 25.1 | 12.8 | 2 |
| Pharmacia & Upjohn, Inc. | 22.3 | 15.0 | 2.7 | 2 |
| Procter & Gamble Co. | 5.4 | 14.9 | 5.4 | 3 |
| Texaco | 12.3 | 7.3 | 23.7 | 1 |
| Travelers Group Inc. | 28.7 | 17.8 | 28.7 | 3 |

Develop an estimated regression equation that can be used to predict price/earnings ratio. Briefly discuss the process you used to develop a recommended estimated regression equation for these data.

**20.** Refer to Exercise 14. Using age, blood pressure, whether a person is a smoker, and any interaction involving those variables, develop an estimated regression equation that can be used to predict risk. Briefly describe the process you used to develop an estimated regression equation for these data.

## 16.5    RESIDUAL ANALYSIS

In Chapters 14 and 15 we showed how residual plots can be used to detect violations of assumptions about the regression model. We looked for violations of assumptions about the error term $\epsilon$ and the assumed functional form of the model. Some of the actions that can be taken when such violations are detected have been discussed in this chapter. When a different functional form is needed, curvilinear and interaction terms can be included through the use of the general linear model. When several independent variables are considered, the variable selection procedures of the preceding section may be appropriate.

We also discussed how residual analysis can be used to identify observations that can be classified as outliers or as being influential in determining the estimated regression equation. Some steps that should be taken when such observations are found were noted. In many regression studies involving data collected over time, a special type of correlation among the error terms can cause problems; it is called **serial correlation** or **autocorrelation.** In this section we show how the **Durbin-Watson test** can be used to detect significant autocorrelation.

## Autocorrelation and the Durbin-Watson Test

Often, the data used for regression studies in business and economics are collected over time. It is not uncommon for the value of $y$ at time $t$, denoted by $y_t$, to be related to the value of $y$ at previous time periods. In such cases, we say autocorrelation (also called serial correlation) is present in the data. If the value of $y$ in time period $t$ is related to its value in time period $t - 1$, first-order autocorrelation is present. If the value of $y$ in time period $t$ is related to the value of $y$ in time period $t - 2$, second-order autocorrelation is present, and so on.

When autocorrelation is present, one of the assumptions of the regression model is violated: the error terms are not independent. In the case of first-order autocorrelation, the error at time $t$, denoted $\epsilon_t$, will be related to the error at time period $t - 1$, denoted $\epsilon_{t-1}$. Two cases of first-order autocorrelation are illustrated in Figure 16.14. Panel A is the case of positive autocorrelation; panel B is the case of negative autocorrelation. With positive autocorrelation we expect a positive residual in one period to be followed by a positive residual in the next period, a negative residual in one period to be followed by a negative residual in the next period, and so on. With negative autocorrelation, we expect a positive residual in one period to be followed by a negative residual in the next period, then a positive residual, and so on.

When autocorrelation is present, serious errors can be made in performing tests of statistical significance based upon the assumed regression model. It is therefore important to be able to detect autocorrelation and take corrective action. We will show how the Durbin-Watson statistic can be used to detect first-order autocorrelation.

Suppose the values of $\epsilon$ are not independent but are related in the following manner:

$$\epsilon_t = \rho\epsilon_{t-1} + z_t \tag{16.16}$$

where $\rho$ is a parameter with an absolute value less than one and $z_t$ is a normally and independently distributed random variable with a mean of zero and a variance of $\sigma^2$. From equation (16.16) we see that if $\rho = 0$, the error terms are not related, and each has a mean of zero and a variance of $\sigma^2$. In this case, there is no autocorrelation and the regression

**FIGURE 16.14**    RESIDUAL PLOTS FOR TWO DATA SETS WITH FIRST-ORDER
AUTOCORRELATION

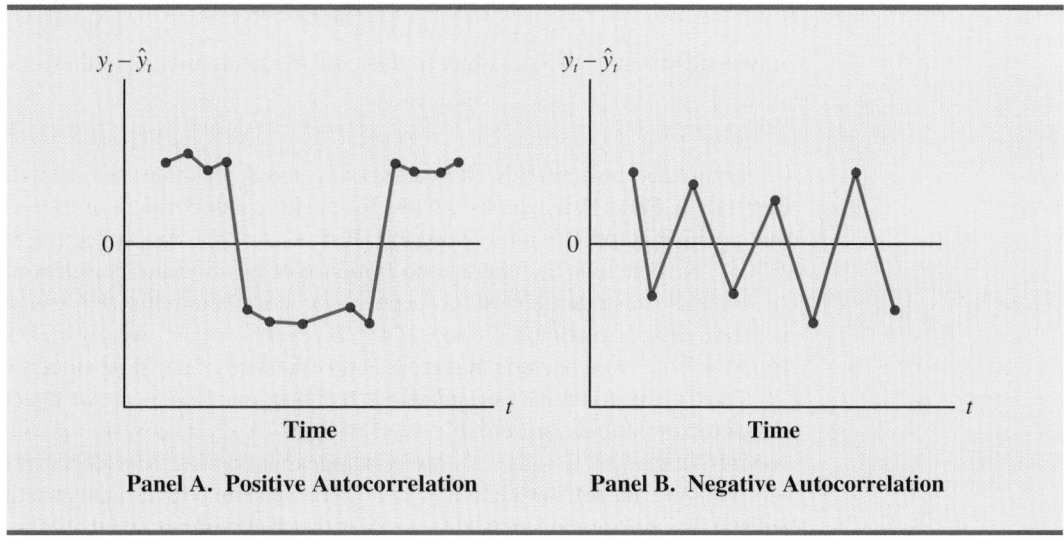

Panel A.  Positive Autocorrelation          Panel B.  Negative Autocorrelation

assumptions are satisfied. If $\rho > 0$, we have positive autocorrelation; if $\rho < 0$, we have negative autocorrelation. In either of these cases, the regression assumptions about the error term are violated.

The Durbin-Watson test for autocorrelation uses the residuals to determine whether $\rho = 0$. To simplify the notation for the Durbin-Watson statistic, we denote the $i$th residual by $e_i = y_i - \hat{y}_i$. The Durbin-Watson test statistic is computed as follows.

**Durbin-Watson Test Statistic**

$$d = \frac{\sum\limits_{t=2}^{n}(e_t - e_{t-1})^2}{\sum\limits_{t=1}^{n}e_t^2} \tag{16.17}$$

If successive values of the residuals are close together (positive autocorrelation), the value of the Durbin-Watson test statistic will be small. If successive values of the residuals are far apart (negative autocorrelation), the value of the Durbin-Watson statistic will be large.

The Durbin-Watson test statistic ranges in value from zero to four, with a value of two indicating no autocorrelation is present. Durbin and Watson have developed tables that can be used to determine when their test statistic indicates the presence of autocorrelation. Table 16.8 shows lower and upper bounds ($d_L$ and $d_U$) for hypothesis tests using $\alpha = .05$, $\alpha = .025$, and $\alpha = .01$; $n$ denotes the number of observations. The null hypothesis to be tested is always that there is no autocorrelation.

$$H_0: \rho = 0$$

The alternative hypothesis to test for positive autocorrelation is

$$H_a: \rho > 0$$

The alternative hypothesis to test for negative autocorrelation is

$$H_a: \rho < 0$$

A two-sided test is also possible. In this case the alternative hypothesis is

$$H_a: \rho \neq 0$$

Figure 16.15 shows how the values of $d_L$ and $d_U$ in Table 16.8 are used to test for autocorrelation. Panel A illustrates the test for positive autocorrelation. If $d < d_L$, we conclude that positive autocorrelation is present. If $d_L \leq d \leq d_U$, we say the test is inconclusive. If $d > d_U$, we conclude that there is no evidence of positive autocorrelation.

Panel B illustrates the test for negative autocorrelation. If $d > 4 - d_L$, we conclude that negative autocorrelation is present. If $4 - d_U \leq d \leq 4 - d_L$, we say the test is inconclusive. If $d < 4 - d_U$, we conclude that there is no evidence of negative autocorrelation.

Panel C illustrates the two-sided test. If $d < d_L$ or $d > 4 - d_L$, we reject $H_0$ and conclude that autocorrelation is present. If $d_L \leq d \leq d_U$ or $4 - d_U \leq d \leq 4 - d_L$, we say the test is inconclusive. If $d_U < d < 4 - d_U$, we conclude that there is no evidence of autocorrelation.

If significant autocorrelation is identified, we should investigate whether we have omitted one or more key independent variables that have time-ordered effects on the dependent variable. If no such variables can be identified, including an independent variable that measures the time of the observation (for instance, the value of this variable could be one for the

**TABLE 16.8**    CRITICAL VALUES FOR THE DURBIN-WATSON TEST FOR AUTOCORRELATION

NOTE: Entries in the table are the critical values for a one-tailed Durbin-Watson test for autocorrelation. For a two-tailed test, the level of significance is doubled.

**Significance Points of $d_L$ and $d_U$: $\alpha = .05$**

**Number of Independent Variables**

| | 1 | | 2 | | 3 | | 4 | | 5 | |
|---|---|---|---|---|---|---|---|---|---|---|
| $n$ | $d_L$ | $d_U$ | $d_L$ | $d_U$ | $d_L$ | $d_U$ | $d_L$ | $d_U$ | $d_L$ | $d_U$ |
| 15 | 1.08 | 1.36 | 0.95 | 1.54 | 0.82 | 1.75 | 0.69 | 1.97 | 0.56 | 2.21 |
| 16 | 1.10 | 1.37 | 0.98 | 1.54 | 0.86 | 1.73 | 0.74 | 1.93 | 0.62 | 2.15 |
| 17 | 1.13 | 1.38 | 1.02 | 1.54 | 0.90 | 1.71 | 0.78 | 1.90 | 0.67 | 2.10 |
| 18 | 1.16 | 1.39 | 1.05 | 1.53 | 0.93 | 1.69 | 0.82 | 1.87 | 0.71 | 2.06 |
| 19 | 1.18 | 1.40 | 1.08 | 1.53 | 0.97 | 1.68 | 0.86 | 1.85 | 0.75 | 2.02 |
| 20 | 1.20 | 1.41 | 1.10 | 1.54 | 1.00 | 1.68 | 0.90 | 1.83 | 0.79 | 1.99 |
| 21 | 1.22 | 1.42 | 1.13 | 1.54 | 1.03 | 1.67 | 0.93 | 1.81 | 0.83 | 1.96 |
| 22 | 1.24 | 1.43 | 1.15 | 1.54 | 1.05 | 1.66 | 0.96 | 1.80 | 0.86 | 1.94 |
| 23 | 1.26 | 1.44 | 1.17 | 1.54 | 1.08 | 1.66 | 0.99 | 1.79 | 0.90 | 1.92 |
| 24 | 1.27 | 1.45 | 1.19 | 1.55 | 1.10 | 1.66 | 1.01 | 1.78 | 0.93 | 1.90 |
| 25 | 1.29 | 1.45 | 1.21 | 1.55 | 1.12 | 1.66 | 1.04 | 1.77 | 0.95 | 1.89 |
| 26 | 1.30 | 1.46 | 1.22 | 1.55 | 1.14 | 1.65 | 1.06 | 1.76 | 0.98 | 1.88 |
| 27 | 1.32 | 1.47 | 1.24 | 1.56 | 1.16 | 1.65 | 1.08 | 1.76 | 1.01 | 1.86 |
| 28 | 1.33 | 1.48 | 1.26 | 1.56 | 1.18 | 1.65 | 1.10 | 1.75 | 1.03 | 1.85 |
| 29 | 1.34 | 1.48 | 1.27 | 1.56 | 1.20 | 1.65 | 1.12 | 1.74 | 1.05 | 1.84 |
| 30 | 1.35 | 1.49 | 1.28 | 1.57 | 1.21 | 1.65 | 1.14 | 1.74 | 1.07 | 1.83 |
| 31 | 1.36 | 1.50 | 1.30 | 1.57 | 1.23 | 1.65 | 1.16 | 1.74 | 1.09 | 1.83 |
| 32 | 1.37 | 1.50 | 1.31 | 1.57 | 1.24 | 1.65 | 1.18 | 1.73 | 1.11 | 1.82 |
| 33 | 1.38 | 1.51 | 1.32 | 1.58 | 1.26 | 1.65 | 1.19 | 1.73 | 1.13 | 1.81 |
| 34 | 1.39 | 1.51 | 1.33 | 1.58 | 1.27 | 1.65 | 1.21 | 1.73 | 1.15 | 1.81 |
| 35 | 1.40 | 1.52 | 1.34 | 1.58 | 1.28 | 1.65 | 1.22 | 1.73 | 1.16 | 1.80 |
| 36 | 1.41 | 1.52 | 1.35 | 1.59 | 1.29 | 1.65 | 1.24 | 1.73 | 1.18 | 1.80 |
| 37 | 1.42 | 1.53 | 1.36 | 1.59 | 1.31 | 1.66 | 1.25 | 1.72 | 1.19 | 1.80 |
| 38 | 1.43 | 1.54 | 1.37 | 1.59 | 1.32 | 1.66 | 1.26 | 1.72 | 1.21 | 1.79 |
| 39 | 1.43 | 1.54 | 1.38 | 1.60 | 1.33 | 1.66 | 1.27 | 1.72 | 1.22 | 1.79 |
| 40 | 1.44 | 1.54 | 1.39 | 1.60 | 1.34 | 1.66 | 1.29 | 1.72 | 1.23 | 1.79 |
| 45 | 1.48 | 1.57 | 1.43 | 1.62 | 1.38 | 1.67 | 1.34 | 1.72 | 1.29 | 1.78 |
| 50 | 1.50 | 1.59 | 1.46 | 1.63 | 1.42 | 1.67 | 1.38 | 1.72 | 1.34 | 1.77 |
| 55 | 1.53 | 1.60 | 1.49 | 1.64 | 1.45 | 1.68 | 1.41 | 1.72 | 1.38 | 1.77 |
| 60 | 1.55 | 1.62 | 1.51 | 1.65 | 1.48 | 1.69 | 1.44 | 1.73 | 1.41 | 1.77 |
| 65 | 1.57 | 1.63 | 1.54 | 1.66 | 1.50 | 1.70 | 1.47 | 1.73 | 1.44 | 1.77 |
| 70 | 1.58 | 1.64 | 1.55 | 1.67 | 1.52 | 1.70 | 1.49 | 1.74 | 1.46 | 1.77 |
| 75 | 1.60 | 1.65 | 1.57 | 1.68 | 1.54 | 1.71 | 1.51 | 1.74 | 1.49 | 1.77 |
| 80 | 1.61 | 1.66 | 1.59 | 1.69 | 1.56 | 1.72 | 1.53 | 1.74 | 1.51 | 1.77 |
| 85 | 1.62 | 1.67 | 1.60 | 1.70 | 1.57 | 1.72 | 1.55 | 1.75 | 1.52 | 1.77 |
| 90 | 1.63 | 1.68 | 1.61 | 1.70 | 1.59 | 1.73 | 1.57 | 1.75 | 1.54 | 1.78 |
| 95 | 1.64 | 1.69 | 1.62 | 1.71 | 1.60 | 1.73 | 1.58 | 1.75 | 1.56 | 1.78 |
| 100 | 1.65 | 1.69 | 1.63 | 1.72 | 1.61 | 1.74 | 1.59 | 1.76 | 1.57 | 1.78 |

(*continued*)

**TABLE 16.8**    *(continued)*

**Significance Points of $d_L$ and $d_U$: $\alpha = .025$**

**Number of Independent Variables**

| | 1 | | 2 | | 3 | | 4 | | 5 | |
|---|---|---|---|---|---|---|---|---|---|---|
| $n$ | $d_L$ | $d_U$ | $d_L$ | $d_U$ | $d_L$ | $d_U$ | $d_L$ | $d_U$ | $d_L$ | $d_U$ |
| 15 | 0.95 | 1.23 | 0.83 | 1.40 | 0.71 | 1.61 | 0.59 | 1.84 | 0.48 | 2.09 |
| 16 | 0.98 | 1.24 | 0.86 | 1.40 | 0.75 | 1.59 | 0.64 | 1.80 | 0.53 | 2.03 |
| 17 | 1.01 | 1.25 | 0.90 | 1.40 | 0.79 | 1.58 | 0.68 | 1.77 | 0.57 | 1.98 |
| 18 | 1.03 | 1.26 | 0.93 | 1.40 | 0.82 | 1.56 | 0.72 | 1.74 | 0.62 | 1.93 |
| 19 | 1.06 | 1.28 | 0.96 | 1.41 | 0.86 | 1.55 | 0.76 | 1.72 | 0.66 | 1.90 |
| 20 | 1.08 | 1.28 | 0.99 | 1.41 | 0.89 | 1.55 | 0.79 | 1.70 | 0.70 | 1.87 |
| 21 | 1.10 | 1.30 | 1.01 | 1.41 | 0.92 | 1.54 | 0.83 | 1.69 | 0.73 | 1.84 |
| 22 | 1.12 | 1.31 | 1.04 | 1.42 | 0.95 | 1.54 | 0.86 | 1.68 | 0.77 | 1.82 |
| 23 | 1.14 | 1.32 | 1.06 | 1.42 | 0.97 | 1.54 | 0.89 | 1.67 | 0.80 | 1.80 |
| 24 | 1.16 | 1.33 | 1.08 | 1.43 | 1.00 | 1.54 | 0.91 | 1.66 | 0.83 | 1.79 |
| 25 | 1.18 | 1.34 | 1.10 | 1.43 | 1.02 | 1.54 | 0.94 | 1.65 | 0.86 | 1.77 |
| 26 | 1.19 | 1.35 | 1.12 | 1.44 | 1.04 | 1.54 | 0.96 | 1.65 | 0.88 | 1.76 |
| 27 | 1.21 | 1.36 | 1.13 | 1.44 | 1.06 | 1.54 | 0.99 | 1.64 | 0.91 | 1.75 |
| 28 | 1.22 | 1.37 | 1.15 | 1.45 | 1.08 | 1.54 | 1.01 | 1.64 | 0.93 | 1.74 |
| 29 | 1.24 | 1.38 | 1.17 | 1.45 | 1.10 | 1.54 | 1.03 | 1.63 | 0.96 | 1.73 |
| 30 | 1.25 | 1.38 | 1.18 | 1.46 | 1.12 | 1.54 | 1.05 | 1.63 | 0.98 | 1.73 |
| 31 | 1.26 | 1.39 | 1.20 | 1.47 | 1.13 | 1.55 | 1.07 | 1.63 | 1.00 | 1.72 |
| 32 | 1.27 | 1.40 | 1.21 | 1.47 | 1.15 | 1.55 | 1.08 | 1.63 | 1.02 | 1.71 |
| 33 | 1.28 | 1.41 | 1.22 | 1.48 | 1.16 | 1.55 | 1.10 | 1.63 | 1.04 | 1.71 |
| 34 | 1.29 | 1.41 | 1.24 | 1.48 | 1.17 | 1.55 | 1.12 | 1.63 | 1.06 | 1.70 |
| 35 | 1.30 | 1.42 | 1.25 | 1.48 | 1.19 | 1.55 | 1.13 | 1.63 | 1.07 | 1.70 |
| 36 | 1.31 | 1.43 | 1.26 | 1.49 | 1.20 | 1.56 | 1.15 | 1.63 | 1.09 | 1.70 |
| 37 | 1.32 | 1.43 | 1.27 | 1.49 | 1.21 | 1.56 | 1.16 | 1.62 | 1.10 | 1.70 |
| 38 | 1.33 | 1.44 | 1.28 | 1.50 | 1.23 | 1.56 | 1.17 | 1.62 | 1.12 | 1.70 |
| 39 | 1.34 | 1.44 | 1.29 | 1.50 | 1.24 | 1.56 | 1.19 | 1.63 | 1.13 | 1.69 |
| 40 | 1.35 | 1.45 | 1.30 | 1.51 | 1.25 | 1.57 | 1.20 | 1.63 | 1.15 | 1.69 |
| 45 | 1.39 | 1.48 | 1.34 | 1.53 | 1.30 | 1.58 | 1.25 | 1.63 | 1.21 | 1.69 |
| 50 | 1.42 | 1.50 | 1.38 | 1.54 | 1.34 | 1.59 | 1.30 | 1.64 | 1.26 | 1.69 |
| 55 | 1.45 | 1.52 | 1.41 | 1.56 | 1.37 | 1.60 | 1.33 | 1.64 | 1.30 | 1.69 |
| 60 | 1.47 | 1.54 | 1.44 | 1.57 | 1.40 | 1.61 | 1.37 | 1.65 | 1.33 | 1.69 |
| 65 | 1.49 | 1.55 | 1.46 | 1.59 | 1.43 | 1.62 | 1.40 | 1.66 | 1.36 | 1.69 |
| 70 | 1.51 | 1.57 | 1.48 | 1.60 | 1.45 | 1.63 | 1.42 | 1.66 | 1.39 | 1.70 |
| 75 | 1.53 | 1.58 | 1.50 | 1.61 | 1.47 | 1.64 | 1.45 | 1.67 | 1.42 | 1.70 |
| 80 | 1.54 | 1.59 | 1.52 | 1.62 | 1.49 | 1.65 | 1.47 | 1.67 | 1.44 | 1.70 |
| 85 | 1.56 | 1.60 | 1.53 | 1.63 | 1.51 | 1.65 | 1.49 | 1.68 | 1.46 | 1.71 |
| 90 | 1.57 | 1.61 | 1.55 | 1.64 | 1.53 | 1.66 | 1.50 | 1.69 | 1.48 | 1.71 |
| 95 | 1.58 | 1.62 | 1.56 | 1.65 | 1.54 | 1.67 | 1.52 | 1.69 | 1.50 | 1.71 |
| 100 | 1.59 | 1.63 | 1.57 | 1.65 | 1.55 | 1.67 | 1.53 | 1.70 | 1.51 | 1.72 |

*(continued)*

**TABLE 16.8**    (*continued*)

### Significance Points of $d_L$ and $d_U$: $\alpha = .01$
### Number of Independent Variables

| | 1 | | 2 | | 3 | | 4 | | 5 | |
|---|---|---|---|---|---|---|---|---|---|---|
| $n$ | $d_L$ | $d_U$ | $d_L$ | $d_U$ | $d_L$ | $d_U$ | $d_L$ | $d_U$ | $d_L$ | $d_U$ |
| 15 | 0.81 | 1.07 | 0.70 | 1.25 | 0.59 | 1.46 | 0.49 | 1.70 | 0.39 | 1.96 |
| 16 | 0.84 | 1.09 | 0.74 | 1.25 | 0.63 | 1.44 | 0.53 | 1.66 | 0.44 | 1.90 |
| 17 | 0.87 | 1.10 | 0.77 | 1.25 | 0.67 | 1.43 | 0.57 | 1.63 | 0.48 | 1.85 |
| 18 | 0.90 | 1.12 | 0.80 | 1.26 | 0.71 | 1.42 | 0.61 | 1.60 | 0.52 | 1.80 |
| 19 | 0.93 | 1.13 | 0.83 | 1.26 | 0.74 | 1.41 | 0.65 | 1.58 | 0.56 | 1.77 |
| 20 | 0.95 | 1.15 | 0.86 | 1.27 | 0.77 | 1.41 | 0.68 | 1.57 | 0.60 | 1.74 |
| 21 | 0.97 | 1.16 | 0.89 | 1.27 | 0.80 | 1.41 | 0.72 | 1.55 | 0.63 | 1.71 |
| 22 | 1.00 | 1.17 | 0.91 | 1.28 | 0.83 | 1.40 | 0.75 | 1.54 | 0.66 | 1.69 |
| 23 | 1.02 | 1.19 | 0.94 | 1.29 | 0.86 | 1.40 | 0.77 | 1.53 | 0.70 | 1.67 |
| 24 | 1.04 | 1.20 | 0.96 | 1.30 | 0.88 | 1.41 | 0.80 | 1.53 | 0.72 | 1.66 |
| 25 | 1.05 | 1.21 | 0.98 | 1.30 | 0.90 | 1.41 | 0.83 | 1.52 | 0.75 | 1.65 |
| 26 | 1.07 | 1.22 | 1.00 | 1.31 | 0.93 | 1.41 | 0.85 | 1.52 | 0.78 | 1.64 |
| 27 | 1.09 | 1.23 | 1.02 | 1.32 | 0.95 | 1.41 | 0.88 | 1.51 | 0.81 | 1.63 |
| 28 | 1.10 | 1.24 | 1.04 | 1.32 | 0.97 | 1.41 | 0.90 | 1.51 | 0.83 | 1.62 |
| 29 | 1.12 | 1.25 | 1.05 | 1.33 | 0.99 | 1.42 | 0.92 | 1.51 | 0.85 | 1.61 |
| 30 | 1.13 | 1.26 | 1.07 | 1.34 | 1.01 | 1.42 | 0.94 | 1.51 | 0.88 | 1.61 |
| 31 | 1.15 | 1.27 | 1.08 | 1.34 | 1.02 | 1.42 | 0.96 | 1.51 | 0.90 | 1.60 |
| 32 | 1.16 | 1.28 | 1.10 | 1.35 | 1.04 | 1.43 | 0.98 | 1.51 | 0.92 | 1.60 |
| 33 | 1.17 | 1.29 | 1.11 | 1.36 | 1.05 | 1.43 | 1.00 | 1.51 | 0.94 | 1.59 |
| 34 | 1.18 | 1.30 | 1.13 | 1.36 | 1.07 | 1.43 | 1.01 | 1.51 | 0.95 | 1.59 |
| 35 | 1.19 | 1.31 | 1.14 | 1.37 | 1.08 | 1.44 | 1.03 | 1.51 | 0.97 | 1.59 |
| 36 | 1.21 | 1.32 | 1.15 | 1.38 | 1.10 | 1.44 | 1.04 | 1.51 | 0.99 | 1.59 |
| 37 | 1.22 | 1.32 | 1.16 | 1.38 | 1.11 | 1.45 | 1.06 | 1.51 | 1.00 | 1.59 |
| 38 | 1.23 | 1.33 | 1.18 | 1.39 | 1.12 | 1.45 | 1.07 | 1.52 | 1.02 | 1.58 |
| 39 | 1.24 | 1.34 | 1.19 | 1.39 | 1.14 | 1.45 | 1.09 | 1.52 | 1.03 | 1.58 |
| 40 | 1.25 | 1.34 | 1.20 | 1.40 | 1.15 | 1.46 | 1.10 | 1.52 | 1.05 | 1.58 |
| 45 | 1.29 | 1.38 | 1.24 | 1.42 | 1.20 | 1.48 | 1.16 | 1.53 | 1.11 | 1.58 |
| 50 | 1.32 | 1.40 | 1.28 | 1.45 | 1.24 | 1.49 | 1.20 | 1.54 | 1.16 | 1.59 |
| 55 | 1.36 | 1.43 | 1.32 | 1.47 | 1.28 | 1.51 | 1.25 | 1.55 | 1.21 | 1.59 |
| 60 | 1.38 | 1.45 | 1.35 | 1.48 | 1.32 | 1.52 | 1.28 | 1.56 | 1.25 | 1.60 |
| 65 | 1.41 | 1.47 | 1.38 | 1.50 | 1.35 | 1.53 | 1.31 | 1.57 | 1.28 | 1.61 |
| 70 | 1.43 | 1.49 | 1.40 | 1.52 | 1.37 | 1.55 | 1.34 | 1.58 | 1.31 | 1.61 |
| 75 | 1.45 | 1.50 | 1.42 | 1.53 | 1.39 | 1.56 | 1.37 | 1.59 | 1.34 | 1.62 |
| 80 | 1.47 | 1.52 | 1.44 | 1.54 | 1.42 | 1.57 | 1.39 | 1.60 | 1.36 | 1.62 |
| 85 | 1.48 | 1.53 | 1.46 | 1.55 | 1.43 | 1.58 | 1.41 | 1.60 | 1.39 | 1.63 |
| 90 | 1.50 | 1.54 | 1.47 | 1.56 | 1.45 | 1.59 | 1.43 | 1.61 | 1.41 | 1.64 |
| 95 | 1.51 | 1.55 | 1.49 | 1.57 | 1.47 | 1.60 | 1.45 | 1.62 | 1.42 | 1.64 |
| 100 | 1.52 | 1.56 | 1.50 | 1.58 | 1.48 | 1.60 | 1.46 | 1.63 | 1.44 | 1.65 |

Source: J. Durbin and G. S. Watson, "Testing for Serial Correlation in Least Squares Regression II," *Biometrika,* 38 (1951), 159–178.

**FIGURE 16.15**    HYPOTHESIS TEST FOR AUTOCORRELATION USING
THE DURBIN-WATSON TEST

**Panel A.  Test for Positive Autocorrelation**

| Positive auto-correlation | Inconclusive | No evidence of positive autocorrelation |

$0$    $d_L$    $d_U$    $2$

**Panel B.  Test for Negative Autocorrelation**

| No evidence of negative autocorrelation | Inconclusive | Negative auto-correlation |

$d_L$    $d_U$    $2$    $4-d_U$    $4-d_L$    $4$

**Panel C.  Two-Sided Test for Autocorrelation**

| Positive auto-correlation | Inconclusive | No evidence of autocorrelation | Inconclusive | Negative auto-correlation |

$0$    $d_L$    $d_U$    $2$    $4-d_U$    $4-d_L$    $4$

first observation, two for the second observation, and so on) will sometimes eliminate or re-duce the autocorrelation. When these attempts to reduce or remove autocorrelation do not work, transformations on the dependent or independent variables can prove helpful; a dis-cussion of such transformations can be found in more advanced texts on regression analysis.

Note that the Durbin-Watson tables list the smallest sample size as 15. The reason is that the test is generally inconclusive for smaller sample sizes; in fact, many statisticians believe the sample size should be at least 50 for the test to produce worthwhile results.

## EXERCISES

## Applications

**21.**  Consider the data set in Exercise 19.
 **a.**  Develop the estimated regression equation that can be used to predict the price/earn-ings ratio given the profit margin.
 **b.**  At the .05 level of significance, test for any positive autocorrelation in the data.

**22.** Refer to the Cravens data set in Table 16.5. In Section 16.3 we showed that the estimated regression equation involving Poten, AdvExp, and Share had an adjusted coefficient of determination of .8274. Use the .05 level of significance and apply the Durbin-Watson test to determine whether positive autocorrelation is present.

## 16.6    MULTIPLE REGRESSION APPROACH TO ANALYSIS OF VARIANCE AND EXPERIMENTAL DESIGN

In Section 15.7 we discussed the use of dummy variables in multiple regression analysis. In this section we show how the use of dummy variables in a multiple regression equation can provide another approach to solving analysis of variance and experimental design problems. We will demonstrate the multiple regression approach to analysis of variance by applying it to the National Computer Products, Inc. (NCP) problem introduced in Chapter 13.

Recall that NCP manufactures printers and fax machines at plants in Atlanta, Dallas, and Seattle. To measure how much the employees know about total quality management, a random sample of six employees was selected from each plant and given a quality-awareness exam. The examination scores for these 18 employees are listed in Table 16.9. Managers want to use the exam scores of the 18 employees to determine whether the mean examination scores are the same at each plant.

We begin the regression approach to this problem by defining two dummy variables that will be used to indicate the plant from which each sample observation was selected. Because the NCP problem has three plants or populations, we need two dummy variables. In general, if the factor being investigated involves $k$ distinct levels or populations, we need to define $k - 1$ dummy variables. For the NCP problem we define $D$ and $S$ as shown in Table 16.10.

We can use the dummy variables $D$ and $S$ to relate the score on the quality awareness examination to the plant at which the employee works.

**TABLE 16.10**

NCP PROBLEM WITH DUMMY VARIABLES

| $D$ | $S$ | |
|---|---|---|
| 0 | 0 | Observation is associated with the Atlanta plant |
| 1 | 0 | Observation is associated with the Dallas plant |
| 0 | 1 | Observation is associated with the Seattle plant |

$$E(\text{Score}) = \text{Expected value of the score on the quality awareness examination}$$
$$= \beta_0 + \beta_1 D + \beta_2 S$$

Thus, if we are interested in the expected value of the examination score for an employee who works at the Atlanta plant, our procedure for assigning numerical values to the dummy variables $D$ and $S$ would result in setting $D = S = 0$. The multiple regression equation then reduces to

$$E(\text{Score}) = \beta_0 + \beta_1(0) + \beta_2(0) = \beta_0$$

**TABLE 16.9**    EXAMINATION SCORES FOR 18 EMPLOYEES

| Plant 1<br>Atlanta | Plant 2<br>Dallas | Plant 3<br>Seattle |
|---|---|---|
| 85 | 71 | 59 |
| 75 | 75 | 64 |
| 82 | 73 | 62 |
| 76 | 74 | 69 |
| 71 | 69 | 75 |
| 85 | 82 | 67 |

We can interpret $\beta_0$ as the expected value of the examination score for employees who work at the Atlanta plant.

Next let us consider the forms of the multiple regression equation for each of the other plants. For the Dallas plant, $D = 1$ and $S = 0$, and

$$E(\text{Score}) = \beta_0 + \beta_1(1) + \beta_2(0) = \beta_0 + \beta_1$$

For the Seattle plant, $D = 0$ and $S = 1$, and

$$E(\text{Score}) = \beta_0 + \beta_1(0) + \beta_2(1) = \beta_0 + \beta_2$$

We see that $\beta_0 + \beta_1$ represents the expected value of the examination score for employees at the Dallas plant, and $\beta_0 + \beta_2$ represents the expected value of the examination score for employees at the Seattle plant.

We now want to estimate the coefficients $\beta_0$, $\beta_1$, and $\beta_2$ and hence develop an estimate of the expected value of the examination score for each plant. The sample data consisting of 18 observations of $D$, $S$, and Score were entered into Excel. The actual input data and the output from Excel's Regression tool are in Table 16.11 and Figure 16.16, respectively.

In Figure 16.16, we see that the estimates of $\beta_0$, $\beta_1$, and $\beta_2$ are $b_0 = 79$, $b_1 = -5$, and $b_2 = -13$. Thus, the best estimate of the expected value of the examination score for each plant is as follows.

| Plant | Estimate of $E$(Score) |
|---|---|
| Atlanta | $b_0 = 79$ |
| Dallas | $b_0 + b_1 = 79 - 5 = 74$ |
| Seattle | $b_0 + b_2 = 79 - 13 = 66$ |

**TABLE 16.11** REGRESSION INPUT DATA FOR THE NCP PROBLEM

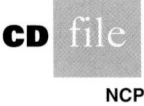

**CD** file

**NCP**

| Observation | D | S | Score |
|---|---|---|---|
| 1 | 0 | 0 | 85 |
| 2 | 0 | 0 | 75 |
| 3 | 0 | 0 | 82 |
| 4 | 0 | 0 | 76 |
| 5 | 0 | 0 | 71 |
| 6 | 0 | 0 | 85 |
| 7 | 1 | 0 | 71 |
| 8 | 1 | 0 | 75 |
| 9 | 1 | 0 | 73 |
| 10 | 1 | 0 | 74 |
| 11 | 1 | 0 | 69 |
| 12 | 1 | 0 | 82 |
| 13 | 0 | 1 | 59 |
| 14 | 0 | 1 | 64 |
| 15 | 0 | 1 | 62 |
| 16 | 0 | 1 | 69 |
| 17 | 0 | 1 | 75 |
| 18 | 0 | 1 | 67 |

**FIGURE 16.16**    EXCEL REGRESSION TOOL OUTPUT FOR THE NCP PROBLEM

| | A | B | C | D | E | F | G | H | I | J |
|---|---|---|---|---|---|---|---|---|---|---|
| 1 | Observation | D | S | Score | | | | | | |
| 2 | 1 | 0 | 0 | 85 | | | | | | |
| 3 | 2 | 0 | 0 | 75 | | | | | | |
| 4 | 3 | 0 | 0 | 82 | | | | | | |
| 12 | 11 | 1 | 0 | 69 | | | | | | |
| 13 | 12 | 1 | 0 | 82 | | | | | | |
| 14 | 13 | 0 | 1 | 59 | | | | | | |
| 15 | 14 | 0 | 1 | 64 | | | | | | |
| 16 | 15 | 0 | 1 | 62 | | | | | | |
| 17 | 16 | 0 | 1 | 69 | | | | | | |
| 18 | 17 | 0 | 1 | 75 | | | | | | |
| 19 | 18 | 0 | 1 | 67 | | | | | | |
| 20 | | | | | | | | | | |
| 21 | SUMMARY OUTPUT | | | | | | | | | |
| 22 | | | | | | | | | | |
| 23 | *Regression Statistics* | | | | | | | | | |
| 24 | Multiple R | 0.7385 | | | | | | | | |
| 25 | R Square | 0.5455 | | | | | | | | |
| 26 | Adjusted R Square | 0.4848 | | | | | | | | |
| 27 | Standard Error | 5.3541 | | | | | | | | |
| 28 | Observations | 18 | | | | | | | | |
| 29 | | | | | | | | | | |
| 30 | ANOVA | | | | | | | | | |
| 31 | | *df* | *SS* | *MS* | *F* | *Significance F* | | | | |
| 32 | Regression | 2 | 516 | 258 | 9 | 0.0027 | | | | |
| 33 | Residual | 15 | 430 | 28.66667 | | | | | | |
| 34 | Total | 17 | 946 | | | | | | | |
| 35 | | | | | | | | | | |
| 36 | | *Coefficients* | *Standard Error* | *t Stat* | *P-value* | *Lower 95%* | *Upper 95%* | *Lower 99.0%* | *Upper 99.0%* | |
| 37 | Intercept | 79 | 2.1858 | 36.14216 | 5.27E-16 | 74.3410 | 83.6590 | 72.5590 | 85.4410 | |
| 38 | D | -5 | 3.0912 | -1.61749 | 0.126603 | -11.5888 | 1.5888 | -14.1089 | 4.1089 | |
| 39 | S | -13 | 3.0912 | -4.20548 | 0.0008 | -19.5888 | -6.4112 | -22.1089 | -3.8911 | |
| 40 | | | | | | | | | | |

Note: Rows 5–11 are hidden.

Note that the best estimate of the expected value of the examination score for each plant obtained from the regression analysis is the same as the sample mean found previously by applying the ANOVA procedure. That is, 79 for Atlanta, 74 for Dallas, and 66 for Seattle.

Now let us see how we can use the output from the multiple regression package to perform the ANOVA test on the difference in the means for the three plants. First, we observe that if there is no difference in the means,

$$E(\text{Score}) \text{ for the Dallas plant } - E(\text{Score}) \text{ for the Atlanta plant } = 0$$
$$E(\text{Score}) \text{ for the Seattle plant } - E(\text{Score}) \text{ for the Atlanta plant } = 0$$

Because $\beta_0$ equals $E(\text{Score})$ for the Atlanta plant and $\beta_0 + \beta_1$ equals $E(\text{Score})$ for the Dallas plant, the first difference is equal to $(\beta_0 + \beta_1) - \beta_0 = \beta_1$. Moreover, because $\beta_0 + \beta_2$ equals $E(\text{Score})$ for the Seattle plant, the second difference is equal to $(\beta_0 + \beta_2) - \beta_0 = \beta_2$. We would conclude that there is no difference in the three means if $\beta_1 = 0$ and $\beta_2 = 0$. Hence, the null hypothesis for a test for difference of means can be stated as

$$H_0: \beta_1 = \beta_2 = 0$$

Figure 16.16 shows that the *p*-value associated with the *F* test for overall significance is .0027. Thus, at a .05 level of significance the *p*-value = .0027 < $\alpha$ = .05. Hence, we can reject $H_0$ and conclude that the means for the three plants are different.

## EXERCISES

### Methods

**23.** Consider a completely randomized design involving four treatments: A, B, C, and D. Write a multiple regression equation that can be used to analyze these data. Define all variables.

**24.** Write a multiple regression equation that can be used to analyze the data for a randomized block design involving three treatments and two blocks. Define all variables.

**25.** Write a multiple regression equation that can be used to analyze the data for a two-factorial design with two levels for factor A and three levels for factor B. Define all variables.

### Applications

**26.** The Jacobs Chemical Company wants to estimate the mean time (minutes) required to mix a batch of material on machines produced by three different manufacturers. To limit the cost of testing, four batches of material were mixed on machines produced by each of the three manufacturers. The times needed to mix the material follow.

| Manufacturer 1 | Manufacturer 2 | Manufacturer 3 |
|:---:|:---:|:---:|
| 20 | 28 | 20 |
| 26 | 26 | 19 |
| 24 | 31 | 23 |
| 22 | 27 | 22 |

    **a.** Write a multiple regression equation that can be used to analyze the data.
    **b.** What are the best estimates of the coefficients in your regression equation?
    **c.** In terms of the regression equation coefficients, what hypotheses must we test to see whether the mean time to mix a batch of material is the same for all three manufacturers?
    **d.** Using $\alpha$ = .05, what conclusion should be drawn?

**27.** Four different paints are advertised as having the same drying time. To check the manufacturers' claims, five samples were tested for each of the paints. The time in minutes until the paint was dry enough for a second coat to be applied was recorded for each sample. The data obtained follow.

| Paint 1 | Paint 2 | Paint 3 | Paint 4 |
|:---:|:---:|:---:|:---:|
| 128 | 144 | 133 | 150 |
| 137 | 133 | 143 | 142 |
| 135 | 142 | 137 | 135 |
| 124 | 146 | 136 | 140 |
| 141 | 130 | 131 | 153 |

    **a.** Using $\alpha$ = .05, test for any significant differences in mean drying time among the paints.
    **b.** What is your estimate of mean drying time for paint 2? How is it obtained from the computer output?

28. An automobile dealer conducted a test to determine if the time needed to complete a minor engine tune-up depends on whether a computerized engine analyzer or an electronic analyzer is used. Because tune-up time varies among compact, intermediate, and full-sized cars, the three types of cars were used as blocks in the experiment. The data (time in minutes) obtained follow.

|  |  | Car | | |
|  |  | Compact | Intermediate | Full-Sized |
|---|---|---|---|---|
| Analyzer | **Computerized** | 50 | 55 | 63 |
|  | **Electronic** | 42 | 44 | 46 |

Using $\alpha = .05$, test for any significant differences.

29. A mail-order catalog firm designed a factorial experiment to test the effect of the size of a magazine advertisement and the advertisement design on the number of catalog requests received (1000s). Three advertising designs and two sizes of advertisements were considered. The following data were obtained. Test for any significant effects due to type of design, size of advertisement, or interaction. Use $\alpha = .05$.

|  |  | Size of Advertisement | |
|  |  | Small | Large |
|---|---|---|---|
|  | **A** | 8 | 12 |
|  |  | 12 | 8 |
| Design | **B** | 22 | 26 |
|  |  | 14 | 30 |
|  | **C** | 10 | 18 |
|  |  | 18 | 14 |

## SUMMARY

In this chapter we discussed several concepts used by model builders in identifying the best estimated regression equation. First, we introduced the concept of a general linear model to show how the methods discussed in Chapters 14 and 15 could be extended to handle curvilinear relationships and interaction effects. Then we discussed how transformations involving the dependent variable could be used to account for problems such as nonconstant variance in the error term.

In many applications of regression analysis, a large number of independent variables are considered. We presented a general approach based on an $F$ statistic for adding or deleting variables from a regression model. We then introduced a larger problem involving 25 observations and eight independent variables. We saw that one issue encountered in solving larger problems is finding the best subset of the independent variables. To help in that task, we discussed several variable selection procedures: stepwise regression, forward selection, backward elimination, and best-subsets regression.

In Section 16.5, we extended the applications of residual analysis to show the Durbin-Watson test for autocorrelation. The chapter concluded with a discussion of how multiple regression models could be developed to provide another approach for solving analysis of variance and experimental design problems.

## GLOSSARY

**General linear model**   A model of the form $y = \beta_0 + \beta_1 z_1 + \beta_2 z_2 + \cdots + \beta_p z_p + \epsilon$, where each of the independent variables $z_j, j = 1, 2, \ldots, p$, is a function of $x_1, x_2, \ldots, x_k$, the variables for which data have been collected.

**Interaction**   The effect of two independent variables acting together.

**Variable selection procedures**   Methods for selecting a subset of the independent variables for a regression model.

**Autocorrelation**   Correlation in the errors that arises when the error terms at successive points in time are related.

**Serial correlation**   Same as autocorrelation.

**Durbin-Watson test**   A test to determine whether first-order autocorrelation is present.

## KEY FORMULAS

**General Linear Model**

$$y = \beta_0 + \beta_1 z_1 + \beta_2 z_2 + \cdots + \beta_p z_p + \epsilon \tag{16.1}$$

**General $F$ Test for Adding or Deleting $p - q$ Variables**

$$F = \frac{\dfrac{\text{SSE}(x_1, x_2, \ldots, x_q) - \text{SSE}(x_1, x_2, \ldots, x_q, x_{q+1}, \ldots, x_p)}{p - q}}{\dfrac{\text{SSE}(x_1, x_2, \ldots, x_q, x_{q+1}, \ldots, x_p)}{n - p - 1}} \tag{16.13}$$

**First-Order Autocorrelation**

$$\epsilon_t = \rho \epsilon_{t-1} + z_t \tag{16.16}$$

**Durbin-Watson Test Statistic**

$$d = \frac{\sum_{t=2}^{n}(e_t - e_{t-1})^2}{\sum_{t=1}^{n} e_t^2} \tag{16.17}$$

## SUPPLEMENTARY EXERCISES

**30.** Many international funds offer more reasonable equity valuations than those found in the United States. Because international markets often move in directions different from the U.S. market, investments in foreign markets can also reduce an investor's overall risk. The following table shows the 1-year performance through December 10, 1999, fund type (load or no-load), expense ration (%), and safety rating (0 = riskiest, 10 = safest) for 20 international funds (*Mutual Funds,* February 2000).

| Fund | Fund Type | Expense Ratio (%) | Safety Rating | Performance (%) |
|------|-----------|-------------------|---------------|-----------------|
| ABN AMRO Int'l Equity "Com" | No-load | 1.38 | 6.9 | 36 |
| Accessor Int'l Equity "Adv" | No-load | 1.59 | 7.1 | 42 |
| Artisan International | No-load | 1.45 | 6.8 | 72 |
| Columbia Int'l Stock | No-load | 1.56 | 7.1 | 54 |
| Concert Inv. "A" Int'l Equity | Load | 2.16 | 6.3 | 116 |
| Diversified Invstr Int'l Eqty | No-load | 1.40 | 7.3 | 54 |
| Driehaus Int'l Growth | No-load | 1.88 | 6.5 | 92 |
| Founders Passport | No-load | 1.52 | 7.0 | 86 |
| Guardian Baillie Fifford Int'l "A" | Load | 1.62 | 7.1 | 37 |
| Jamestown Int'l Equity | No-load | 1.56 | 7.1 | 35 |
| Julius Baer Int'l Equity | No-load | 1.79 | 6.9 | 71 |
| Aetna "I" Int'l | No-load | 1.35 | 7.3 | 46 |
| Pilgrim Int'l Value "A" | Load | 1.80 | 7.1 | 42 |
| Fidelity Diversified Int'l | No-load | 1.48 | 7.5 | 42 |
| Putnam "A" Int'l Growth | Load | 1.59 | 6.9 | 55 |
| Sit Int'l Growth | No-load | 1.50 | 6.9 | 49 |
| Touchstone Int'l Equity "A" | Load | 1.60 | 7.5 | 35 |
| United Int'l Growth "A" | Load | 1.28 | 7.1 | 47 |
| Vontobel Int'l Equity | No-load | 1.50 | 7.0 | 43 |
| Waddell & Reed Int'l Growth "B" | Load | 2.46 | 7.0 | 75 |

**MutFunds**

**a.** Use the methods in this chapter to develop an estimated regression equation that can be used to estimate the performance of a fund on the basis of the data provided.

**b.** Did the estimated regression equation developed in part (a) provide a good fit? Explain.

**c.** Acorn International is a no-load fund that has an annual expense ratio of 1.12% and a safety rating of 7.6. Use the estimated regression equation developed in part (a) to estimate the 1-year performance for Acorn International.

**31.** A study investigated the relationship between audit delay (Delay), the length of time from a company's fiscal year-end to the date of the auditor's report, and variables that describe the client and the auditor. Some of the independent variables that were included in this study follow.

Industry  A dummy variable coded 1 if the firm was an industrial company or 0 if the firm was a bank, savings and loan, or insurance company.

Public  A dummy variable coded 1 if the company was traded on an organized exchange or over the counter; otherwise coded 0.

Quality  A measure of overall quality of internal controls, as judged by the auditor, on a five-point scale ranging from "virtually none" (1) to "excellent" (5).

Finished  A measure ranging from 1 to 4, as judged by the auditor, where 1 indicates "all work performed subsequent to year-end" and 4 indicates "most work performed prior to year-end."

Suppose that a sample of 40 companies provided the following data.

| Delay | Industry | Public | Quality | Finished |
|-------|----------|--------|---------|----------|
| 62 | 0 | 0 | 3 | 1 |
| 45 | 0 | 1 | 3 | 3 |
| 54 | 0 | 0 | 2 | 2 |
| 71 | 0 | 1 | 1 | 2 |
| 91 | 0 | 0 | 1 | 1 |
| 62 | 0 | 0 | 4 | 4 |
| 61 | 0 | 0 | 3 | 2 |
| 69 | 0 | 1 | 5 | 2 |

**Audit**

(*continued*)

| Delay | Industry | Public | Quality | Finished |
|-------|----------|--------|---------|----------|
| 80 | 0 | 0 | 1 | 1 |
| 52 | 0 | 0 | 5 | 3 |
| 47 | 0 | 0 | 3 | 2 |
| 65 | 0 | 1 | 2 | 3 |
| 60 | 0 | 0 | 1 | 3 |
| 81 | 1 | 0 | 1 | 2 |
| 73 | 1 | 0 | 2 | 2 |
| 89 | 1 | 0 | 2 | 1 |
| 71 | 1 | 0 | 5 | 4 |
| 76 | 1 | 0 | 2 | 2 |
| 68 | 1 | 0 | 1 | 2 |
| 68 | 1 | 0 | 5 | 2 |
| 86 | 1 | 0 | 2 | 2 |
| 76 | 1 | 1 | 3 | 1 |
| 67 | 1 | 0 | 2 | 3 |
| 57 | 1 | 0 | 4 | 2 |
| 55 | 1 | 1 | 3 | 2 |
| 54 | 1 | 0 | 5 | 2 |
| 69 | 1 | 0 | 3 | 3 |
| 82 | 1 | 0 | 5 | 1 |
| 94 | 1 | 0 | 1 | 1 |
| 74 | 1 | 1 | 5 | 2 |
| 75 | 1 | 1 | 4 | 3 |
| 69 | 1 | 0 | 2 | 2 |
| 71 | 1 | 0 | 4 | 4 |
| 79 | 1 | 0 | 5 | 2 |
| 80 | 1 | 0 | 1 | 4 |
| 91 | 1 | 0 | 4 | 1 |
| 92 | 1 | 0 | 1 | 4 |
| 46 | 1 | 1 | 4 | 3 |
| 72 | 1 | 0 | 5 | 2 |
| 85 | 1 | 0 | 5 | 1 |

    **a.** Develop the estimated regression equation using all of the independent variables.

    **b.** Did the estimated regression equation developed in part (a) provide a good fit? Explain.

    **c.** Develop a scatter diagram showing Delay as a function of Finished. What does this scatter diagram indicate about the relationship between Delay and Finished?

    **d.** On the basis of your observations about the relationship between Delay and Finished, develop an alternative estimated regression equation to the one developed in part (a) to explain as much of the variability in Delay as possible.

**32.** Refer to the data in Exercise 31. Consider a model in which only Industry is used to predict Delay. At a .01 level of significance, test for any positive autocorrelation in the data.

**33.** Refer to the data in Exercise 31.

    **a.** Develop an estimated regression equation that can be used to predict Delay by using Industry and Quality.

    **b.** At the .05 level of significance, test for any positive autocorrelation in the data.

**34.** A study was conducted to investigate browsing activity by shoppers. Shoppers were classified as nonbrowsers, light browsers, and heavy browsers. For each shopper in the study, a measure was obtained to determine how comfortable the shopper was in the store.

Higher scores indicated greater comfort. Assume that the following data are from this study. Use a .05 level of significance to test for differences in comfort levels among the three types of browsers.

**Browsing**

| Nonbrowser | Light Browser | Heavy Browser |
|---|---|---|
| 4 | 5 | 5 |
| 5 | 6 | 7 |
| 6 | 5 | 5 |
| 3 | 4 | 7 |
| 3 | 7 | 4 |
| 4 | 4 | 6 |
| 5 | 6 | 5 |
| 4 | 5 | 7 |

35. The following data show the percentage changes in the Dow Jones Industrial Average (DJIA) in each of the 4 years of eight presidential terms (*1998 Stock Trader's Almanac*). Use regression analysis to determine what effect party and year of term in office have on the change in the Dow Jones Industrial Average.

**Election**

| President | Party | Year Elected | Year of Term | Year's Change in DJIA |
|---|---|---|---|---|
| Johnson | Democrat | 1964 | First | 10.9 |
| Johnson | Democrat | | Second | −18.9 |
| Johnson | Democrat | | Third | 15.2 |
| Johnson | Democrat | | Fourth | 4.3 |
| Nixon | Republican | 1968 | First | −15.2 |
| Nixon | Republican | | Second | 4.8 |
| Nixon | Republican | | Third | 6.1 |
| Nixon | Republican | | Fourth | 14.6 |
| Nixon | Republican | 1972 | First | −16.6 |
| Nixon | Republican | | Second | −27.6 |
| Nixon* | Republican | | Third | 38.3 |
| Nixon* | Republican | | Fourth | 17.9 |
| Carter | Democrat | 1976 | First | −17.3 |
| Carter | Democrat | | Second | −3.1 |
| Carter | Democrat | | Third | 4.2 |
| Carter | Democrat | | Fourth | 14.9 |
| Reagan | Republican | 1980 | First | −9.2 |
| Reagan | Republican | | Second | 19.6 |
| Reagan | Republican | | Third | 20.3 |
| Reagan | Republican | | Fourth | −3.7 |
| Reagan | Republican | 1984 | First | −27.7 |
| Reagan | Republican | | Second | 22.6 |
| Reagan | Republican | | Third | 2.3 |
| Reagan | Republican | | Fourth | 11.8 |
| Bush | Republican | 1988 | First | 27.0 |
| Bush | Republican | | Second | −4.3 |
| Bush | Republican | | Third | 20.3 |
| Bush | Republican | | Fourth | 4.2 |
| Clinton | Democrat | 1992 | First | 13.7 |
| Clinton | Democrat | | Second | 2.1 |
| Clinton | Democrat | | Third | 33.5 |
| Clinton | Democrat | | Fourth | 26.0 |

*Because President Nixon resigned from office in August 1974, Gerald Ford became president and completed the remainder of Nixon's term in office.

## Case Problem 1  UNEMPLOYMENT STUDY

A study provided data on variables that may be related to the number of weeks a manufacturing worker has been jobless. The dependent variable in the study (Weeks) was defined as the number of weeks a worker has been jobless due to a layoff. The following independent variables were used in the study.

| | |
|---|---|
| Age | The age of the worker |
| Educ | The number of years of education |
| Married | A dummy variable: 1 if married, 0 otherwise |
| Head | A dummy variable: 1 if the head of household, 0 otherwise |
| Tenure | The number of years on the old job |
| Manager | A dummy variable: 1 if management occupation, 0 otherwise |
| Sales | A dummy variable: 1 if sales occupation, 0 otherwise |

Assume the following data were collected for 50 displaced workers. These data are available on the data disk in the data set named Layoffs.

## Managerial Report

Use the methods presented in this and previous chapters to analyze this data set. Present a summary of your analysis, including key statistical results, conclusions, and recommendations, in a managerial report. Include any appropriate technical material (computer output, residual plots, etc.) in an appendix.

Layoffs

| Weeks | Age | Educ | Married | Head | Tenure | Manager | Sales |
|---|---|---|---|---|---|---|---|
| 37 | 30 | 14 | 1 | 1 | 1 | 0 | 0 |
| 62 | 27 | 14 | 1 | 0 | 6 | 0 | 0 |
| 49 | 32 | 10 | 0 | 1 | 11 | 0 | 0 |
| 73 | 44 | 11 | 1 | 0 | 2 | 0 | 0 |
| 8 | 21 | 14 | 1 | 1 | 2 | 0 | 0 |
| 15 | 26 | 13 | 1 | 0 | 7 | 1 | 0 |
| 52 | 26 | 15 | 1 | 0 | 6 | 0 | 0 |
| 72 | 33 | 13 | 0 | 1 | 6 | 0 | 0 |
| 11 | 27 | 12 | 1 | 1 | 8 | 0 | 0 |
| 13 | 33 | 12 | 0 | 1 | 2 | 0 | 0 |
| 39 | 20 | 11 | 1 | 0 | 1 | 0 | 0 |
| 59 | 35 | 7 | 1 | 1 | 6 | 0 | 0 |
| 39 | 36 | 17 | 0 | 1 | 9 | 1 | 0 |
| 44 | 26 | 12 | 1 | 1 | 8 | 0 | 0 |
| 56 | 36 | 15 | 0 | 1 | 8 | 0 | 0 |
| 31 | 38 | 16 | 1 | 1 | 11 | 0 | 1 |
| 62 | 34 | 13 | 0 | 1 | 13 | 0 | 0 |
| 25 | 27 | 19 | 1 | 0 | 8 | 0 | 0 |
| 72 | 44 | 13 | 1 | 0 | 22 | 0 | 0 |
| 65 | 45 | 15 | 1 | 1 | 6 | 0 | 0 |
| 44 | 28 | 17 | 0 | 1 | 3 | 0 | 1 |
| 49 | 25 | 10 | 1 | 1 | 1 | 0 | 0 |
| 80 | 31 | 15 | 1 | 0 | 12 | 0 | 0 |
| 7 | 23 | 15 | 1 | 0 | 2 | 0 | 0 |
| 14 | 24 | 13 | 1 | 1 | 7 | 0 | 0 |

| Weeks | Age | Educ | Married | Head | Tenure | Manager | Sales |
|-------|-----|------|---------|------|--------|---------|-------|
| 94 | 62 | 13 | 0 | 1 | 8 | 0 | 0 |
| 48 | 31 | 16 | 1 | 0 | 11 | 0 | 0 |
| 82 | 48 | 18 | 0 | 1 | 30 | 0 | 0 |
| 50 | 35 | 18 | 1 | 1 | 5 | 0 | 0 |
| 37 | 33 | 14 | 0 | 1 | 6 | 0 | 1 |
| 62 | 46 | 15 | 0 | 1 | 6 | 0 | 0 |
| 37 | 35 | 8 | 0 | 1 | 6 | 0 | 0 |
| 40 | 32 | 9 | 1 | 1 | 13 | 0 | 0 |
| 16 | 40 | 17 | 1 | 0 | 8 | 1 | 0 |
| 34 | 23 | 12 | 1 | 1 | 1 | 0 | 0 |
| 4 | 36 | 16 | 0 | 1 | 8 | 0 | 1 |
| 55 | 33 | 12 | 1 | 0 | 10 | 0 | 1 |
| 39 | 32 | 16 | 0 | 1 | 11 | 0 | 0 |
| 80 | 62 | 15 | 1 | 0 | 16 | 0 | 1 |
| 19 | 29 | 14 | 1 | 1 | 12 | 0 | 0 |
| 98 | 45 | 12 | 1 | 0 | 17 | 0 | 0 |
| 30 | 38 | 15 | 0 | 1 | 6 | 0 | 1 |
| 22 | 40 | 8 | 1 | 1 | 16 | 0 | 1 |
| 57 | 42 | 13 | 1 | 0 | 2 | 1 | 0 |
| 64 | 45 | 16 | 1 | 1 | 22 | 0 | 0 |
| 22 | 39 | 11 | 1 | 1 | 4 | 0 | 0 |
| 27 | 27 | 15 | 1 | 0 | 10 | 0 | 1 |
| 20 | 42 | 14 | 1 | 1 | 6 | 1 | 0 |
| 30 | 31 | 10 | 1 | 1 | 8 | 0 | 0 |
| 23 | 33 | 13 | 1 | 1 | 8 | 0 | 0 |

## Case Problem 2    ANALYSIS OF PGA TOUR STATISTICS

The Professional Golfers Association (PGA) maintains statistics on performance and earnings for members of the PGA Tour. Year-end performance statistics for 1997 appear on the data disk in the data set named PGA Tour (*Golfweek,* November 15, 1997). Each row of the data set corresponds to a PGA Tour player, and the data have been ranked according to total 1997 earnings in sponsored PGA Tour events. Descriptions for data, which appear on the disk, follow. In these descriptions a round refers to 18 holes of golf. PGA Tour events usually consist of four rounds of golf played over 4 days. Scores obtained for rounds played on Thursday and Friday of a Tour event are used to limit the size of the field for the final two rounds played on Saturday and Sunday. Players who achieve a low enough total score on Thursday and Friday to enable them to play on Saturday and Sunday are said to have made the cut.

**CD** file

**PGATour**

| | |
|---|---|
| Earnings | Total earnings in PGA Tour events |
| Events | Number of PGA Tour events entered |
| Rds. | Number of rounds completed |
| Cuts Made | Number of events in which the player makes the cut |
| Rds. in 60s | Number of rounds with a score in the 60s |
| Rds. Under Par | Number of rounds with a score less than par |
| Birdies | Average number of birdies per round |
| Scoring Avg. | Average score for all events |

| Driving Distance | Average number of yards per drive (The length of a drive is measured to the point the drive comes to rest, regardless of whether it is in the fairway. Driving distance is measured on two holes per round.) |
|---|---|
| Fairways | Average number of times a player is able to hit the fairway with his tee shot in a round |
| Greens | Average number of times a player is able to hit the green in regulation (A green is considered hit in regulation if any part of the ball is touching the putting surface and the difference between the value of par for the hole and the number of strokes taken to hit the green is at least 2.) |
| Putts | Average number of putts taken on greens hit in regulation |
| Sand Saves | Percent of time a player is able to get "up and down" once in a greenside sand bunker (Getting up and down means that the number of strokes taken to hit the ball out of the sand and into the hole is at most two.) |

## Managerial Report

Suppose that you have been hired by the commissioner of the PGA Tour to analyze the data for a presentation to be made at the annual PGA Tour dinner. The commissioner has asked whether it would be possible to use these data to determine which performance measures, such as Cuts Made, Driving Distance, Fairways, and so on, have the most effect on a player's score and amount of money earned. Use the methods presented in this and previous chapters to analyze the data. Prepare a report for the PGA Tour commissioner that summarizes your analysis, including key statistical results, conclusions, and recommendations. Include any appropriate technical material in an appendix.

## Case Problem 3    PREDICTING GRADUATION RATES FOR COLLEGES AND UNIVERSITIES

The percentage of students who enroll at a college or university and actually graduate is an important statistic for university administrators. Some of the factors related to the graduation rate include the percentage of classes with fewer than 20 students, the percentage of classes with more than 50 students, the student-faculty ratio, the percentage of students who apply to the university and are admitted, the percentage of freshmen in the top 10% of their high school class, and the academic reputation of the university. To study the effect of these factors on the graduation rate, data for 48 national universities were collected (*America's Best Colleges,* Year 2000 Edition). These data are available on the data disk in the data set named GradRate. The labels for the columns shown are defined as follows

**CD** file

**GradRate**

| State | The state in which the university is located |
|---|---|
| Region | The region of the country in which the university is located (North, South, Midwest, West) |
| Graduation Rate | The percentage of students who enroll at the university and graduate |
| % of Classes Under 20 | The percentage of classes with fewer than 20 students |
| % of Classes of 50 or More | The percentage of classes with more than 50 students |
| Student-Faculty Ratio | The ratio of the number of students enrolled divided by the total number of faculty |

| Acceptance Rate | The percentage of students who apply and are accepted |
| 1st-Year Students in Top 10% of HS Class | The percentage of students admitted who were in the top 10% of their high school class |
| Academic Reputation Score | A measure of the school's reputation determined by surveying administrators at other universities: measured on a scale from 1 (marginal) to 5 (distinguished) |

## Managerial Report

Use the methods presented in this and previous chapters to analyze this data set. Present a summary of your analysis, including key statistical results, conclusions, and recommendations, in a managerial report. Include any appropriate technical material (computer output, residual plots, etc.) in an appendix.

# NONPARAMETRIC METHODS

**CONTENTS**

## WEST SHELL REALTORS*
*Cincinnati, Ohio*

West Shell Realtors was founded in 1958 with one office and a sales staff of three people. In 1964, the company began a long-term expansion program, with new offices added almost yearly. Over the years, West Shell grew to become one of the largest realtors in Greater Cincinnati, with offices in southwest Ohio, southeast Indiana, and northern Kentucky.

Statistical analysis helps real estate firms such as West Shell monitor sales performance. Monthly reports are generated for each of West Shell's offices as well as for the total company. Statistical summaries of total sales dollars, number of units sold, and median selling price per unit are essential in keeping both office managers and the company's top managers informed of progress and trouble spots in the organization.

In addition to monthly summaries of ongoing operations, the company uses statistical considerations to guide corporate plans and strategies. West Shell has implemented a strategy of planned expansion, and with each new sales office, the company must address the question of office location. Selling prices of homes, turnover rates, and forecast sales volumes are the types of data used in evaluating and comparing alternative locations.

In one instance, West Shell identified two suburbs, Clifton and Roselawn, as prime candidates for a new office. A variety of factors were considered in comparing the two areas, including selling prices of

West Shell uses statistical analysis of home sales to remain competitive. Photo © CORBIS.

homes. West Shell employed nonparametric statistical methods with small samples to help identify any differences in sales patterns for the two areas.

Samples of 25 sales in the Clifton area and 18 sales in the Roselawn area were taken, and the Mann-Whitney-Wilcoxon rank-sum test was chosen as an appropriate statistical test of the difference in the pattern of selling prices. At the .05 level of significance, the Mann-Whitney-Wilcoxon test did not allow rejection of the null hypothesis that the two populations of selling prices were identical. Thus, West Shell was able to focus on criteria other than selling prices of homes in the site selection process.

In this chapter we will show how nonparametric statistical tests such as the Mann-Whitney-Wilcoxon test are applied. We will also discuss the proper interpretation of such tests.

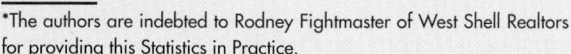

*The authors are indebted to Rodney Fightmaster of West Shell Realtors for providing this Statistics in Practice.

The statistical methods presented thus far in the text are generally known as *parametric methods.* In this chapter we introduce several **nonparametric methods.** Such methods are often applicable in situations where parametric methods are not. Nonparametric methods typically require less restrictive assumptions about the level of data measurement and fewer assumptions about the form of the probability distributions for the populations being sampled.

One consideration in determining whether a parametric or a nonparametric method is appropriate is the scale of measurement used to generate the data. As noted in Chapter 1, all data are generated by one of four scales of measurement: nominal, ordinal, interval, and ratio. Hence, all statistical analyses are conducted using either nominal, ordinal, interval, or ratio data.

Let us review and provide examples of the four scales of measurement.

1. *Nominal scale.* The scale of measurement is nominal if the data are labels or names used to define an attribute of an element. Nominal data may be numeric or nonnumeric.

   **Examples.** The exchange where a stock is listed (NYSE, NASDAQ, or AMEX) is nonnumeric nominal data. An individual's social security number is numeric nominal data.

2. *Ordinal scale.* The scale of measurement is ordinal if the data have the properties of nominal data and the order/rank of the data is meaningful. Ordinal data may be numeric or nonnumeric.

   **Examples.** The measures small, medium, and large for the size of an item are nonnumeric ordinal data. The class ranks of individuals measured as 1, 2, 3, . . . are numeric ordinal data.

3. *Interval scale.* The scale of measurement is interval if the data have the properties of ordinal data and the interval between observations is expressed in terms of a fixed unit of measure. Interval data must be numeric.

   **Example.** Measures of temperature are interval data. Suppose it is 80 degrees in one location and 40 degrees in another. We can rank the locations with respect to warmth; the first location is warmer than the second. The fixed unit of measure, a degree, enables us to say how much warmer it is at the first location: 40 degrees.

4. *Ratio scale.* The scale of measurement is ratio if the data have the properties of interval data and the ratio of measures is meaningful. Ratio data must be numeric.

   **Examples.** Measures of distance, height, weight, and time are ratio data. Note that temperature measures are not ratio data because there is no inherently defined zero point. For instance, the freezing point of water is 32 degrees on a Fahrenheit scale and zero degrees on a Celsius scale. Ratios are not meaningful with temperature data. For instance, it makes no sense to say that 80 degrees is twice as warm as 40 degrees.

*In Chapter 1 we pointed out that nominal and ordinal scales provide qualitative data. Interval and ratio scales provide quantitative data.*

Most of the statistical methods referred to as parametric require the use of interval- or ratio-scaled data. With interval or ratio data, arithmetic operations are meaningful, and means, variances, standard deviations, and so on can be computed, interpreted, and used in the analysis. With nominal or ordinal data, it is inappropriate to compute means, variances, and standard deviations; hence, parametric methods normally cannot be used. Nonparametric methods are often the only way to analyze nominal or ordinal data and draw statistical conclusions.

*If the scale of measurement is nominal or ordinal, computations of means, variances, and standard deviations are not meaningful. Thus, with these kinds of data, many of the statistical procedures discussed previously cannot be employed.*

Another consideration in determining whether a parametric method or a nonparametric method should be employed is the assumption about the population from which the data were obtained. For example, a parametric procedure for testing a hypothesis about the difference between the means of two populations was presented in Chapter 10. In the small-sample case, the $t$ distribution can be used for this test if we are willing to assume that the populations are normally distributed with equal variances. If this assumption about the populations is not appropriate, the parametric method based on the use of the $t$ distribution should not be used even if the data are interval or ratio scaled. However, nonparametric methods, which require no assumptions about the population probability distributions, are available for testing for differences between two populations. Because no probability distribution assumptions are required, nonparametric methods are often called **distribution-free methods.**

*The statistical procedures based on small samples and the $t$ distribution as discussed in Chapters 8, 9, and 10 are based on the assumption that the data are from a normal population. If this assumption is not appropriate, nonparametric methods may be applicable.*

In general, for a statistical method to be classified as nonparametric, it must satisfy at least one of the following conditions.*

---

*See W. J. Conover, *Practical Nonparametric Statistics,* 3rd ed., John Wiley & Sons, 1998.

1. The method can be used with nominal data.
2. The method can be used with ordinal data.
3. The method can be used with interval or ratio data when no assumption can be made about the population probability distribution.

If the level of data measurement is interval or ratio and if the necessary probability distribution assumptions for the population are appropriate, parametric methods provide more powerful or more discerning statistical procedures. In many cases where a nonparametric method as well as a parametric method can be applied, the nonparametric method is almost as good or almost as powerful as the parametric method. In cases where the data are nominal or ordinal or in cases where the assumptions required by parametric methods are inappropriate, only nonparametric methods are available. Because of the less restrictive data measurement requirements and the fewer assumptions needed about the population distribution, nonparametric methods are regarded as more generally applicable than parametric methods. The sign test, the Wilcoxon signed-rank test, the Mann-Whitney-Wilcoxon test, the Kruskal-Wallis test, and Spearman rank correlation are the nonparametric methods presented in this chapter.

## 17.1  SIGN TEST

A common market research application of the **sign test** involves using a sample of $n$ potential customers to identify a preference for one of two brands of a product such as coffee, soft drinks, or detergents. The $n$ expressions of preference are nominal data because the consumer simply names, or labels, a preference. Given these data, our objective is to determine whether a difference in preference exists between the two brands being compared. As we will see, the sign test is a nonparametric statistical procedure for answering this question.

### Small-Sample Case

The small-sample case for the sign test should be used whenever $n \leq 20$. Let us illustrate the use of the sign test for the small-sample case by considering a study conducted for Sun Coast Farms; Sun Coast produces an orange juice product marketed under the name Citrus Valley. A competitor of Sun Coast Farms has begun producing a new orange juice product known as Tropical Orange. In a study of consumer preferences for the two brands, 12 individuals were given unmarked samples of each product. The brand each individual tasted first was selected randomly. After tasting the two products, the individuals were asked to state a preference for one of the two samples. The purpose of the study is to determine whether consumers prefer one product over the other. Letting $p$ indicate the proportion of the population of consumers favoring Citrus Valley, we want to test the following hypotheses.

$$H_0: p = .50$$
$$H_a: p \neq .50$$

If $H_0$ cannot be rejected, we will have no evidence indicating a difference in preference for the two brands of orange juice. However, if $H_0$ can be rejected, we can conclude that the consumer preferences are different for the two brands. In that case, the brand selected by the greater number of consumers can be considered the most preferred brand.

In the following discussion we will show how the small-sample version of the sign test can be used to test these hypotheses and draw a conclusion about consumer preferences. To record the preference data for the 12 individuals participating in the study, we use a plus sign if the individual expresses a preference for Citrus Valley and a minus sign if the individual expresses a preference for Tropical Orange. Because the data are recorded in terms of plus or minus signs, this nonparametric test is called the sign test.

**TABLE 17.1**

BINOMIAL
PROBABILITIES
WITH $n = 12, p = .50$

| Number of Plus Signs | Probability |
|---|---|
| 0 | .0002 |
| 1 | .0029 |
| 2 | .0161 |
| 3 | .0537 |
| 4 | .1208 |
| 5 | .1934 |
| 6 | .2256 |
| 7 | .1934 |
| 8 | .1208 |
| 9 | .0537 |
| 10 | .0161 |
| 11 | .0029 |
| 12 | .0002 |

Under the assumption that $H_0$ is true ($p = .50$), the number of plus signs follows a binomial probability distribution with $p = .50$. With a sample size of $n = 12$, Excel's BINOMDIST function (see Chapter 5) was used to compute the probabilities for the binomial probability distribution with $p = .50$ as displayed in Table 17.1. Figure 17.1 is a graphical representation of this binomial probability distribution. It shows the probability of the number of plus signs under the assumption that $H_0$ is true and is therefore the appropriate sampling distribution for the hypothesis test.

We use the binomial sampling distribution to determine a rule for rejecting $H_0$; our approach is similar to the method we used to develop rejection rules for hypothesis testing in Chapter 9. For example, using $\alpha = .05$, we would place a rejection region or area of approximately .025 in each tail of the sampling distribution in Figure 17.1. Starting at the lower end of the distribution, we see that the probability of obtaining zero, one, or two plus signs is $.0002 + .0029 + .0161 = .0192$. Note that we stop at 2 plus signs because adding the probability of three plus signs would make the area in the lower tail equal to $.0192 + .0537 = .0729$, which substantially exceeds the desired area of .025. At the upper end of the sampling distribution, we find the same probability of .0192 corresponding to 10, 11, or 12 plus signs. Thus, the closest we can come to $\alpha = .05$ without exceeding it is $.0192 + .0192 = .0384$. We therefore adopt the following rejection rule.

A shaded rejection region cannot be shown in Figure 17.1 because the sampling distribution is not continuous. The rejection region is defined by the red colored spikes at 0, 1, 2, 10, 11, and 12.

Reject $H_0$ if the number of plus signs is less than 3 or greater than 9

The preference data obtained for the Sun Coast Farms sign test are reported in Table 17.2. Because only two plus signs are observed, the null hypothesis is rejected. The study provides evidence that consumer preference differs for the two brands of orange juice. We would advise Sun Coast Farms that consumers indicate a preference for the competitor's Tropical Orange brand.

**FIGURE 17.1**    BINOMIAL SAMPLING DISTRIBUTION FOR THE NUMBER OF PLUS SIGNS WHEN $n = 12$ AND $p = .50$

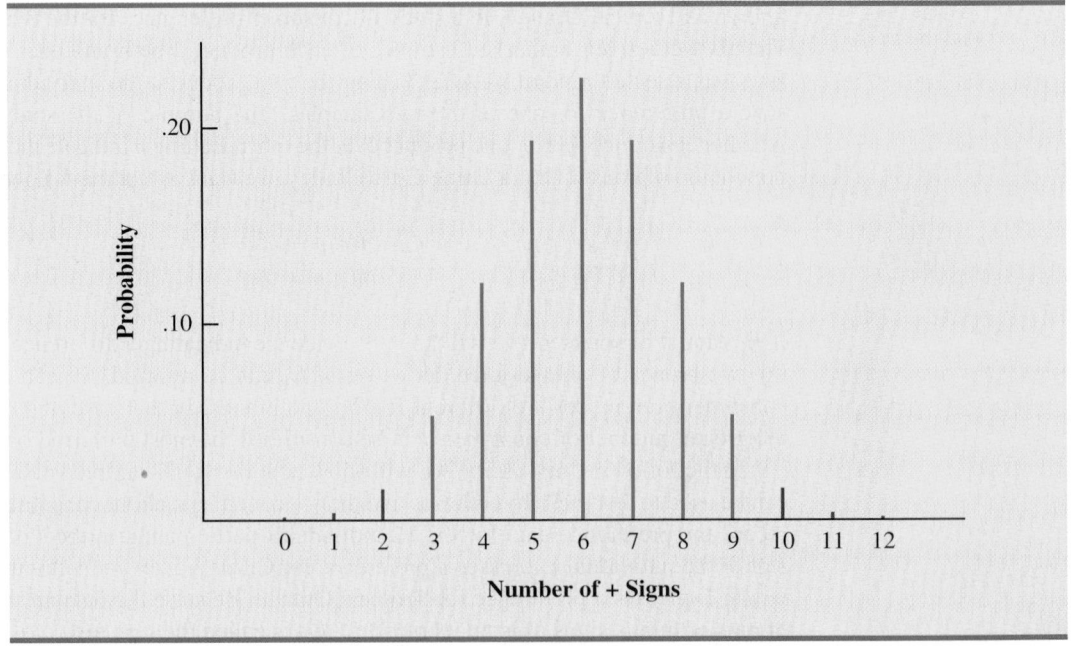

**TABLE 17.2**    PREFERENCE DATA FOR THE SUN COAST FARMS SIGN TEST

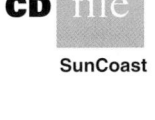

**SunCoast**

| Individual | Brand Preference | Recorded Data |
|:---:|:---:|:---:|
| 1 | Tropical Orange | − |
| 2 | Tropical Orange | − |
| 3 | Citrus Valley | + |
| 4 | Tropical Orange | − |
| 5 | Tropical Orange | − |
| 6 | Tropical Orange | − |
| 7 | Tropical Orange | − |
| 8 | Tropical Orange | − |
| 9 | Citrus Valley | + |
| 10 | Tropical Orange | − |
| 11 | Tropical Orange | − |
| 12 | Tropical Orange | − |

The approach of rejecting $H_0$ if the $p$-value $< \alpha$ can also be used for nonparametric tests. With two plus signs, the $p$-value for the Sun Coast Farms two-tailed test is $2(.0161 + .0029 + .0002) = .0384$. With the $p$-value $= .0384 < \alpha = .05$, we would reject $H_0$. For a one-tailed test, the $p$-value would be found by summing probabilities in only one tail of the sampling distribution.

In the Sun Coast Farms example, all 12 individuals in the study were able to state a preference. In many situations, one or more individuals in the sample are not able to state a definite preference. In such cases, the individual's response of no preference can be dropped and the analysis conducted with a smaller sample size.

## Using Excel

Excel's BINOMDIST function can be used to conduct a sign test. Here we show how to develop an Excel worksheet for the Sun Coast Farms sign test. Refer to Figure 17.2 as we describe the tasks involved. The formula worksheet is in the background; the value worksheet is in the foreground. Note that when using Excel, it is not necessary to record the brand preference data using + and − signs. Instead we can work directly with the actual brand preferences: Citrus Valley and Tropical Orange.

**Enter Data:**    The brand preference data are entered in column A.

**Enter Functions and Formulas:**    The descriptive statistics needed are computed in cells D3:D5. The COUNTA function is used in cell D3 to count the number of persons in the sample. Citrus Valley is entered in cell D4 to identify the response of interest (the one considered a +) and the COUNTIF function is used in cell D5 to count the number of persons stating a preference for the response of interest. All that remains is to compute the $p$-value.

The $p$-value (Lower Tail) is computed in cell D7. Recall that the form of Excel's BINOMDIST function is BINOMDIST($x, n, p$, cumulative) where $x$ is the number of successes in a sample of size $n$ with a probability of success given by $p$. We enter TRUE for cumulative if a cumulative probability (lower-tail area) is desired and FALSE for cumulative if an individual probability is desired. So we entered the formula =BINOMDIST (D5,D3,0.5,TRUE) into cell D7 to compute the cumulative probability of the number of successes shown in cell D5. The value worksheet shows a cumulative probability of 0.0193. For a discrete probability distribution, the $p$-value (Upper Tail) is not just 1 minus the $p$-value (Lower Tail). For instance, in the Sun Coast Farms case, the $p$-value (Upper Tail) is the probability of two or more successes in 12 trials. But we must compute it as 1 minus

**FIGURE 17.2**   EXCEL WORKSHEET FOR SUN COAST FARMS SIGN TEST

| | A | B | C | D | E |
|---|---|---|---|---|---|
| 1 | Brand Preference | | Sign Test Using Binomial Distribution | | |
| 2 | Tropical Orange | | | | |
| 3 | Tropical Orange | | Sample Size | =COUNTA(A2:A13) | |
| 4 | Citrus Valley | | Response of Interest | Citrus Valley | |
| 5 | Tropical Orange | | Count of Response | =COUNTIF(A2:A13,D4) | |
| 6 | Tropical Orange | | | | |
| 7 | Tropical Orange | | p-value (Lower tail) | =BINOMDIST(D5,D3,0.5,TRUE) | |
| 8 | Tropical Orange | | p-value (Upper tail) | =1-BINOMDIST(D5-1,D3,0.5,TRUE) | |
| 9 | Tropical Orange | | p-value (Two tail) | =2*MIN(D7,D8) | |
| 10 | Citrus Valley | | | | |
| 11 | Tropical Orange | | | | |
| 12 | Tropical Orange | | | | |
| 13 | Tropical Orange | | | | |
| 14 | | | | | |

| | A | B | C | D | E | F |
|---|---|---|---|---|---|---|
| 1 | Brand Preference | | Sign Test Using Binomial Distribution | | | |
| 2 | Tropical Orange | | | | | |
| 3 | Tropical Orange | | Sample Size | 12 | | |
| 4 | Citrus Valley | | Response of Interest | Citrus Valley | | |
| 5 | Tropical Orange | | Count of Response | 2 | | |
| 6 | Tropical Orange | | | | | |
| 7 | Tropical Orange | | p-value (Lower tail) | 0.0193 | | |
| 8 | Tropical Orange | | p-value (Upper tail) | 0.9968 | | |
| 9 | Tropical Orange | | p-value (Two tail) | 0.0386 | | |
| 10 | Citrus Valley | | | | | |
| 11 | Tropical Orange | | | | | |
| 12 | Tropical Orange | | | | | |
| 13 | Tropical Orange | | | | | |
| 14 | | | | | | |

the probability of 1 or fewer successes. Therefore, to compute $p$-value (Upper Tail) we enter the formula $=$ 1-BINOMDIST (D5-1,D3,0.5,TRUE) into cell D8. The value worksheet shows a $p$-value(Upper Tail) of 0.9968. The $p$-value (Two Tail) is computed in the usual way (see cell D9) as twice the minimum of the two one-tailed $p$-values. The value worksheet shows a $p$-value(Two Tail) value of 0.0386. Because $p$-value(Two Tail) $= .0386 < \alpha = .05$, we reject $H_0$ and conclude that consumer preference differs for the two brands of orange juice. Note that the $p$-value computed using Excel (.0386) differs slightly from the $p$-value we computed by hand (.0384); this difference is due simply to the fact that the binomial probabilities shown in Table 17.1 were rounded to four decimal places.

This worksheet can be used as a template for a different problem by entering the new data in column A, modifying the ranges in cells D3 and D5 to fit the new data, and typing the appropriate response in cell D4. The hypothesis test can then be conducted by choosing the appropriate $p$-value in cells D7:D9. To use this worksheet for exercises in which only the sample size and number of plus signs are given, one can ignore the data in column A, type in the sample size in cell D3, and type in the number of plus signs in cell D5. The appropriate $p$-values will then appear in cells D7:D9. We illustrate this use of the template later in the section.

## Large-Sample Case

Statisticians often recommend using a normal approximation to the sampling distribution for the number of plus signs in the large-sample case. This approach is reasonable when cumulative binomial probabilities are not readily available for computing $p$-values, or when one needs to solve a problem by hand. The normal approximation provides good results for sample sizes greater than 20. We show how such a large-sample test can be conducted here. However, whenever possible, we recommend using the worksheet in Figure 17.2, even in the large-sample case.

The large-sample sign test is equivalent to the test of a population proportion with $p = .5$ as presented in Chapter 9.

Using the null hypothesis $H_0: p = .50$ and a sample size of $n > 20$, the sampling distribution for the number of plus signs can be approximated by a normal probability distribution.

---

### Normal Approximation of the Sampling Distribution of the Number of Plus Signs for a Sign Test

$$\text{Mean: } \mu = .50n \qquad \textbf{(17.1)}$$

$$\text{Standard Deviation: } \sigma = \sqrt{.25n} \qquad \textbf{(17.2)}$$

Distribution form: approximately normal provided $n > 20$.

---

Let us consider an application of the sign test to political polling. A poll taken during a recent presidential election campaign asked 200 registered voters to rate the Democratic and Republican candidates in terms of best overall foreign policy. Results of the poll showed 72 rated the Democratic candidate higher, 103 rated the Republican candidate higher, and 25 indicated no difference between the candidates. Does the poll indicate a significant difference between the two candidates in terms of public opinion about their foreign policies?

Ties are handled by dropping the items from the analysis.

Using the sign test, we see that $n = 200 - 25 = 175$ individuals were able to indicate the candidate they believed had the best overall foreign policy. Using equations (17.1) and (17.2), we find that the sampling distribution of the number of plus signs has the following properties.

$$\mu = .50n = .50(175) = 87.5$$

$$\sigma = \sqrt{.25n} = \sqrt{.25(175)} = 6.6$$

In addition, with $n = 175$ we can assume that the sampling distribution is approximately normal. This distribution is shown in Figure 17.3. Because the distribution is approximately normal, we can use the table of areas for the standard normal probability distribution to develop the rejection rule for the test. With $\alpha = .05$, the rejection rule for this two-tailed test can be written as follows.

$$\text{Reject } H_0 \text{ if } z < -1.96 \text{ or if } z > +1.96$$

Using the number of times the Democratic candidate received the higher foreign policy rating as the number of plus signs ($x = 72$), we have the following value of the test statistic.

$$z = \frac{x - \mu}{\sigma} = \frac{72 - 87.5}{6.6} = -2.35$$

If the analysis had used the number of times the Republican candidate was rated higher, $z = 2.35$ would have led us to the same conclusion.

Because $z = -2.35$ is less than $-1.96$, the hypothesis of no difference in foreign policy for the two candidates should be rejected at the .05 level of significance. With $z = -2.35$, the cumulative normal distribution tables can be used to show that the $p$-value is $2(1.0000 - .9906) = .0188$. This study indicates that the Republican candidate is perceived to have the higher-rated foreign policy.

**FIGURE 17.3** NORMAL SAMPLING DISTRIBUTION OF THE NUMBER OF PLUS SIGNS IN THE POLITICAL POLLING EXAMPLE

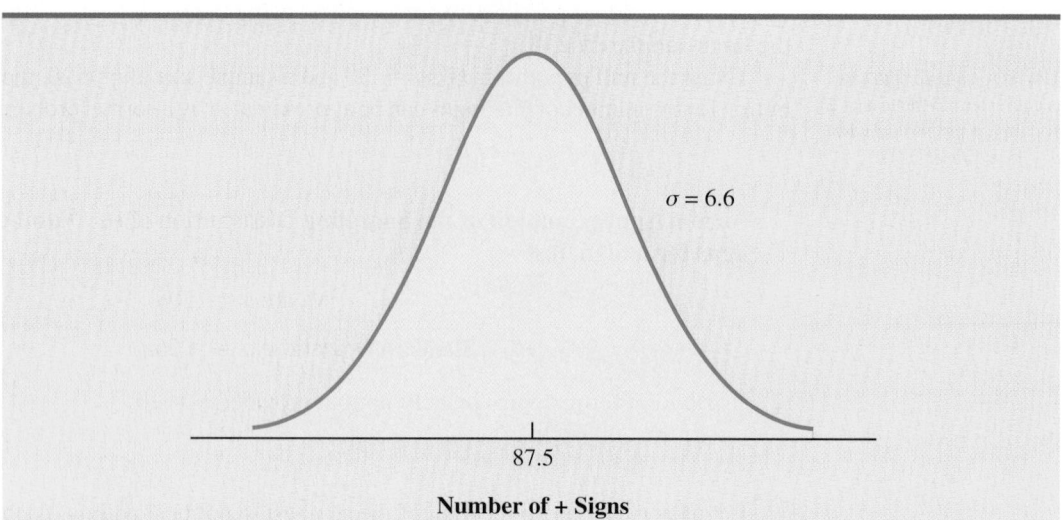

## Using Excel

Let us use the worksheet in Figure 17.2 as a template and modify it to conduct the hypothesis test involving the political candidates. The sample size is 175 and 72 people rated the Democratic candidate higher. Therefore, we enter 175 into cell D3 and 72 into cell D5 of the worksheet in Figure 17.2. The result obtained is shown in Figure 17.4. Note that $p$-value (Two Tail) = 0.0231, leads us to reject $H_0$ with $\alpha = .05$. This $p$-value is actually slightly larger than the one found using the normal approximation. In general, we recommend using the binomial probabilities whenever possible, even in the large-sample case. However, the difference caused by using the normal approximation is not that great, and both approaches lead to rejection of the null hypothesis and the conclusion of no difference in the foreign policy rating of the two candidates.

A final note about using the worksheet in Figure 17.2 as a template is in order. Although the Sun Coast Farms data is still in column A, it is not used in the computation of the $p$-values. Only the sample size in cell D3 and the number of pluses in cell D5 are used, and these are the values we just typed in for the current hypothesis test. If desired, the data in column A and the label in cell D4 can be deleted in order to clean up the worksheet when it is used to solve exercises in which the sample data are not provided.

## Hypothesis Test About a Median

In Chapter 9 we described how hypothesis tests can be used to make an inference about a population mean. We now show how the sign test can be used to conduct hypothesis tests about a population median. Recall that the median splits a population in such a way that 50% of the values are at the median or above and 50% are at the median or below. We can apply the sign test by using a plus sign whenever the data in the sample are above the hypothesized value of the median and a minus sign whenever the data in the sample are below the hypothesized value of the median. Any data exactly equal to the hypothesized value of the median should be discarded. The computations for the sign test are done in exactly the same way as before.

**FIGURE 17.4**    EXCEL WORKSHEET FOR SIGN TEST INVOLVING POLITICAL CANDIDATES

| | A | B | C | D | E | F |
|---|---|---|---|---|---|---|
| 1 | Brand Preference | | | Sign Test Using Binomial Distribution | | |
| 2 | Tropical Orange | | | | | |
| 3 | Tropical Orange | | Sample Size | 175 | | |
| 4 | Citrus Valley | | Response of Interest | Citrus Valley | | |
| 5 | Tropical Orange | | Count of Response | 72 | | |
| 6 | Tropical Orange | | | | | |
| 7 | Tropical Orange | | *p*-value (Lower tail) | =BINOMDIST(D5,D3,0.5,TRUE) | | |
| 8 | Tropical Orange | | *p*-value (Upper tail) | =1-BINOMDIST(D5-1,D3,0.5,TRUE) | | |
| 9 | Tropical Orange | | *p*-value (Two tail) | =2*MIN(D7,D8) | | |
| 10 | Citrus Valley | | | | | |
| 11 | Tropical Orange | | | | | |
| 12 | Tropical Orange | | | | | |
| 13 | Tropical Orange | | | | | |
| 14 | | | | | | |

| | A | B | C | D | E | F |
|---|---|---|---|---|---|---|
| 1 | Brand Preference | | Sign Test Using Binomial Distribution | | | |
| 2 | Tropical Orange | | | | | |
| 3 | Tropical Orange | | Sample Size | 175 | | |
| 4 | Citrus Valley | | Response of Interest | Citrus Valley | | |
| 5 | Tropical Orange | | Count of Response | 72 | | |
| 6 | Tropical Orange | | | | | |
| 7 | Tropical Orange | | *p*-value (Lower tail) | 0.0115 | | |
| 8 | Tropical Orange | | *p*-value (Upper tail) | 0.9923 | | |
| 9 | Tropical Orange | | *p*-value (Two tail) | 0.0231 | | |
| 10 | Citrus Valley | | | | | |
| 11 | Tropical Orange | | | | | |
| 12 | Tropical Orange | | | | | |
| 13 | Tropical Orange | | | | | |
| 14 | | | | | | |

For example, the following hypothesis test is being conducted about the median price of new homes in St. Louis, Missouri.

$$H_0: \text{Median} = \$130{,}000$$
$$H_a: \text{Median} \neq \$130{,}000$$

In a sample of 62 new homes, 34 have prices above \$130,000, 26 have prices below \$130,000, and two have prices of exactly \$130,000. Let us see how we can use the Excel worksheet previously developed to conduct a hypothesis test for this problem.

## Using Excel

Let us use the worksheet in Figure 17.2 as a template and modify it to conduct the hypothesis test involving the median selling price of new homes in St. Louis. The sample size is 60 and 34 of the selling prices were above \$130,000. Therefore, we enter 60 into cell D3 and 34 into cell D5 of the worksheet in Figure 17.2. The result obtained is shown in Figure 17.5. Note that *p*-value (Two Tail) = 0.3663. For any reasonable level of significance, the *p*-value would not be less than $\alpha$ and hence we would not reject $H_0$. Thus, we would not challenge the claim that the median selling price is \$130,000. Note again that the worksheet we used here is just a modification of the worksheet in Figure 17.2. Although the Sun Coast Farms data still appear in column A, the formulas in cells D3 and D5 have been replaced by the values that we typed in for the sample size and number of plus signs. Thus, if desired, the data in column A and the label in cell D4 can be deleted in order to clean up the worksheet when it is used to solve exercises in which the sample data are not provided.

**FIGURE 17.5**   EXCEL WORKSHEET FOR SIGN TEST INVOLVING MEDIAN SELLING PRICE OF HOMES

| | A | B | C | D | E | F |
|---|---|---|---|---|---|---|
| 1 | Brand Preference | | Sign Test Using Binomial Distribution | | | |
| 2 | Tropical Orange | | | | | |
| 3 | Tropical Orange | | Sample Size | 60 | | |
| 4 | Citrus Valley | | Response of Interest | Citrus Valley | | |
| 5 | Tropical Orange | | Count of Response | 34 | | |
| 6 | Tropical Orange | | | | | |
| 7 | Tropical Orange | | *p*-value (Lower tail) | =BINOMDIST(D5,D3,0.5,TRUE) | | |
| 8 | Tropical Orange | | *p*-value (Upper tail) | =1-BINOMDIST(D5-1,D3,0.5,TRUE) | | |
| 9 | Tropical Orange | | *p*-value (Two tail) | =2*MIN(D7,D8) | | |
| 10 | Citrus Valley | | | | | |
| 11 | Tropical Orange | | | | | |
| 12 | Tropical Orange | | | | | |
| 13 | Tropical Orange | | | | | |
| 14 | | | | | | |

| | A | B | C | D | E | F |
|---|---|---|---|---|---|---|
| 1 | Brand Preference | | Sign Test Using Binomial Distribution | | | |
| 2 | Tropical Orange | | | | | |
| 3 | Tropical Orange | | Sample Size | 60 | | |
| 4 | Citrus Valley | | Response of Interest | Citrus Valley | | |
| 5 | Tropical Orange | | Count of Response | 34 | | |
| 6 | Tropical Orange | | | | | |
| 7 | Tropical Orange | | *p*-value (Lower tail) | 0.8775 | | |
| 8 | Tropical Orange | | *p*-value (Upper tail) | 0.1831 | | |
| 9 | Tropical Orange | | *p*-value (Two tail) | 0.3663 | | |
| 10 | Citrus Valley | | | | | |
| 11 | Tropical Orange | | | | | |
| 12 | Tropical Orange | | | | | |
| 13 | Tropical Orange | | | | | |
| 14 | | | | | | |

## NOTES AND COMMENTS

1. The number of plus signs has been used in the calculations to determine whether to reject the null hypothesis that $p = .5$. One could just as easily use the number of minus signs; the test result would be the same.

2. Just as in the small-sample case, the sampling distribution of the number of plus signs in the large-sample case follows a binomial probability distribution with $p = .5$. So, even in the large-sample case, one can use the binomial probability distribution to conduct the hypothesis test. The normal approximation of the binomial distribution is generally considered valid whenever $np$ and $n(1 - p) \geq 5$. With $p = .5$, as it is with the sign test, this sample size requirement is satisfied with $n \geq 10$. Here, however,

we have suggested using the small-sample test and the binomial distribution unless $n > 20$ because binomial probabilities are easy to compute for $n \leq 20$. Indeed, with Excel available, there is no point in using an approximation; the exact distribution can be used easily.

3. For the sign test, the sampling distribution of the number of plus signs follows the binomial distribution with $p = .5$ and the hypotheses tested are $H_0$: $p = .5$ versus $H_a$: $p \neq .5$. The same methodology (e.g., using the binomial sampling distribution to compute $p$-values) can be used for hypothesis tests involving other values of $p$. This extension of the sign test provides a small-sample capability for hypothesis tests involving proportions (see Section 9.6).

## EXERCISES

## Methods

1.  The following table lists the preferences indicated by 10 individuals in taste tests involving two brands of a product.

| Individual | Brand A versus Brand B | Individual | Brand A versus Brand B |
|------------|------------------------|------------|------------------------|
| 1 | + | 6 | + |
| 2 | + | 7 | − |
| 3 | + | 8 | + |
| 4 | − | 9 | − |
| 5 | + | 10 | + |

With $\alpha = .05$, test for a significant difference in the preferences for the two brands. A plus sign indicates a preference for brand A over brand B.

2.  The following hypothesis test is to be conducted.

$$H_0: \text{Median} \leq 150$$
$$H_a: \text{Median} > 150$$

A sample of size 30 yields 22 cases in which a value greater than 150 is obtained, three cases in which a value of exactly 150 is obtained, and five cases in which a value less than 150 is obtained. Use $\alpha = .01$ and conduct the hypothesis test.

## Applications

3.  Are stock splits beneficial to stockholders? SNL Securities studied stock splits in the banking industry over an 18-month period and found that stock splits tended to increase the value of an individual's stock holding. Assume that in a sample of 20 recent stock splits, 14 led to an increase in value, four led to a decrease in value, and two resulted in no change. Suppose a sign test is to be used to determine whether stock splits continue to be beneficial for holders of bank stocks.
    a.   What are the null and alternative hypotheses?
    b.   With $\alpha = .05$, what is the rejection rule?
    c.   What is your conclusion?

4.  A poll asked 1253 adults a series of questions about the state of the economy and their children's future. One question was, "Do you expect your children to have a better life than you have had, a worse life, or a life about as good as yours?" The responses were 34% better, 29% worse, 33% about the same, and 4% not sure. Use the sign test and a .05 level of significance to determine whether more adults feel their children will have a better future than feel their children will have a worse future. What is your conclusion?

5.  *1996–1997 Neilsen Media Research* identified *ER* and *Seinfeld* as the top-rated network television shows. Assume that in a local television preference poll, 410 individuals were asked to indicate their favorite network television show: 185 selected *ER,* 165 selected *Seinfeld,* and 60 selected another television show. Use a .05 level of significance to test the hypothesis that *ER* and *Seinfeld* have the same level of preference. What is your conclusion?

6.  In 1996, competition in the consumer PC market was led by Packard Bell and Compaq (*USA Today,* July 21, 1997). A sample of 500 purchases showed 202 Packard Bell computers, 158 Compaq computers, and 140 other computers including IBM, Apple, and NEC. Use a .05 level of significance to test the hypothesis that Packard Bell and Compaq have the same share of the consumer PC market. What is your conclusion?

7. The median annual income of subscribers to *Barron's* magazine is $131,000 (www. barrons.mag.com, July 28, 2000). Assume a sample of 300 subscribers to *The Wall Street Journal* found 165 subscribers with an income over $131,000 and 135 subscribers with an income under $131,000. Can you conclude that there is any difference between the median incomes of the two subscriber groups? What is the *p*-value? Using $\alpha = .05$, what is your conclusion?

8. In a sample of 150 college basketball games, the home team won 98 games. Test to see whether the data support the claim of a home-team advantage in college basketball. Use a .05 level of significance. What is your conclusion?

9. The median number of part-time employees at fast-food restaurants in a particular city was known to be 15 last year. City officials think the use of part-time employees may be increasing. A sample of nine fast-food restaurants showed that more than 15 part-time employees worked at seven of the restaurants, one restaurant had exactly 15 part-time employees, and one had fewer than 15 part-time employees. Using $\alpha = .05$ determine whether the median number of part-time employees has increased.

10. According to a national survey, the median annual income adults say would make their dreams come true is $152,000. Suppose that of a sample of 225 individuals in Ohio, 122 individuals report that the amount of income needed to make their dreams come true is less than $152,000, and 103 report that the amount needed is more than $152,000. Test the null hypothesis that the median amount of annual income needed to make dreams come true in Ohio is $152,000. Use $\alpha = .05$. What is your conclusion?

11. The U.S. Bureau of Labor Statistics reported the 1996 median weekly earnings for women in administrative and managerial positions to be $585. A sample of administrative and managerial working women in the Chicago area provided the following data. Use the sample data to test $H_0$: median $\leq 585$, $H_a$: median $> 585$ for the population of administrative and managerial working women in Chicago. Use a .05 level of significance. What is your conclusion?

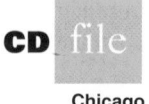

**Chicago**

| | | | | |
|---|---|---|---|---|
| 622 | 516 | 631 | 498 | 715 |
| 571 | 494 | 525 | 664 | 721 |
| 657 | 692 | 551 | 580 | 649 |
| 706 | 597 | 518 | 725 | 635 |
| 548 | 604 | 671 | 607 | 487 |
| 583 | 702 | 622 | 714 | 693 |
| 600 | 721 | 662 | 633 | 681 |
| 624 | 551 | 632 | 544 | 485 |
| 655 | 721 | 669 | 677 | 609 |
| 656 | 562 | 721 | 489 | 582 |

## 17.2 WILCOXON SIGNED-RANK TEST

The **Wilcoxon signed-rank test** is the nonparametric alternative to the parametric matched-sample test presented in Chapter 10. In the matched-sample situation, each experimental unit generates two paired or matched observations, one from population 1 and one from population 2. The differences between the values of the matched observations provide insight about the differences between the two populations.

The methodology of the parametric matched-sample analysis (the *t* test on paired differences) requires interval data and the assumption that the population of differences between the pairs of observations is *normally distributed*. With this assumption, the *t* distribution can be used to test the null hypothesis of no difference between population means. If the assumption of normally distributed differences is not appropriate, the nonparametric Wilcoxon signed-rank test can be used. We illustrate this nonparametric test by comparing the effectiveness of two production methods.

A manufacturing firm is attempting to determine whether two production methods differ in task completion time. A sample of 11 workers was selected, and each worker completed a production task using each of the production methods. The production method that each worker used first was selected randomly. Thus, each worker in the sample provided a pair of observations, as shown in Table 17.3. A positive difference in task completion times indicates that method 1 required more time, and a negative difference in times indicates that method 2 required more time. Do the data indicate that the methods are significantly different in terms of task completion times?

In effect, we have two populations of task completion times, one population associated with each method. The following hypotheses will be tested.

$$H_0: \text{The populations are identical}$$
$$H_a: \text{The populations are not identical}$$

If $H_0$ cannot be rejected, we will not have evidence to conclude that the task completion times differ for the two methods. However, if $H_0$ can be rejected, we will conclude that the two methods differ in task completion time.

The first step of the Wilcoxon signed-rank test requires a ranking of the *absolute value* of the differences between the two methods. We discard any differences of zero and then rank the remaining absolute differences from lowest to highest. Tied differences are assigned the average ranking of their positions in the combined data set. The ranking of the absolute values of differences is shown in the fourth column of Table 17.4. Note that the difference of zero for worker 8 is discarded from the rankings; then the smallest absolute difference of .1 is assigned the rank of 1. This ranking of absolute differences continues with the largest absolute difference of .9 assigned the rank of 10. The tied absolute differences for workers 3 and 5 are assigned the average rank of 3.5 and the tied absolute differences for workers 4 and 10 are assigned the average rank of 5.5.

Once the ranks of the absolute differences have been determined, the ranks are given the sign of the original difference in the data. For example, the .1 difference for worker 7, which was assigned the rank of 1, is given the value of $+1$ because the observed difference between the two methods was positive. The .2 difference, which was assigned the rank of 2, is given the value of $-2$ because the observed difference between the two methods was negative for worker 2. The complete list of signed ranks, as well as their sum, is shown in the last column of Table 17.4.

Let us return to the original hypothesis of identical population task completion times for the two methods. If the populations representing task completion times for each of the two

**TABLE 17.3**    PRODUCTION TASK COMPLETION TIMES (MINUTES)

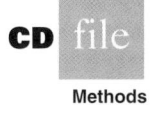

**Methods**

| | Method | | |
|---|---|---|---|
| Worker | 1 | 2 | Difference |
| 1 | 10.2 | 9.5 | .7 |
| 2 | 9.6 | 9.8 | −.2 |
| 3 | 9.2 | 8.8 | .4 |
| 4 | 10.6 | 10.1 | .5 |
| 5 | 9.9 | 10.3 | −.4 |
| 6 | 10.2 | 9.3 | .9 |
| 7 | 10.6 | 10.5 | .1 |
| 8 | 10.0 | 10.0 | .0 |
| 9 | 11.2 | 10.6 | .6 |
| 10 | 10.7 | 10.2 | .5 |
| 11 | 10.6 | 9.8 | .8 |

**TABLE 17.4**    RANKING OF ABSOLUTE DIFFERENCES FOR THE PRODUCTION TASK
COMPLETION TIME EXAMPLE

| Worker | Difference | Absolute Value of Difference | Rank | Signed Rank |
|--------|-----------|------------------------------|------|-------------|
| 1 | .7 | .7 | 8 | + 8 |
| 2 | −.2 | .2 | 2 | − 2 |
| 3 | .4 | .4 | 3.5 | + 3.5 |
| 4 | .5 | .5 | 5.5 | + 5.5 |
| 5 | −.4 | .4 | 3.5 | − 3.5 |
| 6 | .9 | .9 | 10 | +10 |
| 7 | .1 | .1 | 1 | + 1 |
| 8 | .0 | .0 | — | — |
| 9 | .6 | .6 | 7 | + 7 |
| 10 | .5 | .5 | 5.5 | + 5.5 |
| 11 | .8 | .8 | 9 | + 9 |
|    |    |    | Sum of Signed Ranks | +44.0 |

methods are identical, we would expect the positive ranks and the negative ranks to cancel each other, so that the sum of the signed rank values would be approximately zero. Thus, the test for significance under the Wilcoxon signed-rank test involves determining whether the computed sum of signed ranks (+44 in our example) is significantly different from zero.

Let $T$ denote the sum of the signed-rank values in a Wilcoxon signed-rank test. It can be shown that if the two populations are identical and the number of matched pairs of data is 10 or more, the sampling distribution of $T$ can be approximated by a normal probability distribution as follows.

**Sampling Distribution of $T$ for Identical Populations**

$$\text{Mean: } \mu_T = 0 \tag{17.3}$$

$$\text{Standard deviation: } \sigma_T = \sqrt{\frac{n(n + 1)(2n + 1)}{6}} \tag{17.4}$$

Distribution form: approximately normal provided $n \geq 10$.

For the production task completion time example, we have $n = 10$ after discarding the observation with a difference of zero (worker 8). Thus, using equation (17.4), we have

$$\sigma_T = \sqrt{\frac{10(11)(21)}{6}} = 19.62$$

Figure 17.6 is the sampling distribution of $T$ under the assumption of identical populations. The value of the test statistic $z$ is:

$$z = \frac{T - \mu_T}{\sigma_T} = \frac{44 - 0}{19.62} = 2.24$$

Testing the null hypothesis of identical populations using a level of significance of $\alpha = .05$, we reject $H_0$ if $z < -1.96$ or if $z > 1.96$. With the value of $z = 2.24$, we reject $H_0$ and conclude that the two populations are not identical and that the methods differ in task completion time. Using $z = 2.24$, the $p$-value is $2(1.0000 - .9875) = .025$. The fact that method 2 had the shorter completion times for eight of the 11 workers leads us to conclude that differences between the two populations indicate method 2 to be the better production method.

**FIGURE 17.6**  SAMPLING DISTRIBUTION OF THE WILCOXON *T* FOR THE PRODUCTION TASK COMPLETION TIME EXAMPLE

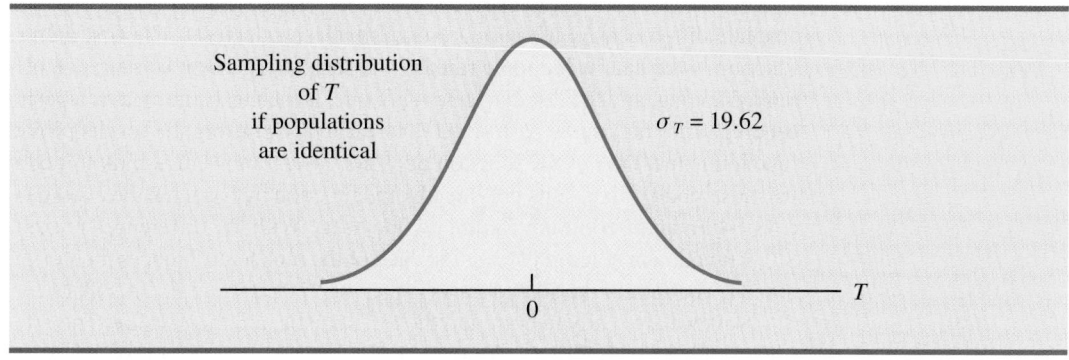

Sampling distribution
of *T*
if populations
are identical

$\sigma_T = 19.62$

*T*

0

## Using Excel

Excel does not provide any tools specifically designed for the Wilcoxon signed-rank test, but a worksheet can be developed to assist in computing the signed ranks. We now describe the development of such a worksheet. Refer to Figure 17.7 as we describe the tasks involved. The formula worksheet is in the background; the value worksheet is in the foreground.

**Enter Data:**   The data are entered in column B and C. Note that the data for worker 8 (the case of no difference) has been deleted.

**FIGURE 17.7**  EXCEL WORKSHEET FOR SIGNED-RANK TEST OF DIFFERENCES IN PRODUCTION METHODS

| | A | B | C | D | E | F | G | H |
|---|---|---|---|---|---|---|---|---|
| 1 | Worker | Method 1 | Method 2 | Difference | Absolute Value | Rank | Signed Rank | |
| 2 | 1 | 10.2 | 9.5 | =B2-C2 | =ABS(D2) | =RANK(E2,$E$2:$E$11,1) | =SIGN(D2)*F2 | |
| 3 | 2 | 9.6 | 9.8 | =B3-C3 | =ABS(D3) | =RANK(E3,$E$2:$E$11,1) | =SIGN(D3)*F3 | |
| 4 | 3 | 9.2 | 8.8 | =B4-C4 | =ABS(D4) | 3.5 | =SIGN(D4)*F4 | |
| 5 | 4 | 10.6 | 10.1 | =B5-C5 | =ABS(D5) | 5.5 | =SIGN(D5)*F5 | |
| 6 | 5 | 9.9 | 10.3 | =B6-C6 | =ABS(D6) | 3.5 | =SIGN(D6)*F6 | |
| 7 | 6 | 10.2 | 9.3 | =B7-C7 | =ABS(D7) | =RANK(E7,$E$2:$E$11,1) | =SIGN(D7)*F7 | |
| 8 | 7 | 10.6 | 10.5 | =B8-C8 | =ABS(D8) | =RANK(E8,$E$2:$E$11,1) | =SIGN(D8)*F8 | |
| 9 | 9 | 11.2 | 10.6 | =B9-C9 | =ABS(D9) | =RANK(E9,$E$2:$E$11,1) | =SIGN(D9)*F9 | |
| 10 | 10 | 10.7 | 10.2 | =B10-C10 | =ABS(D10) | 5.5 | =SIGN(D10)*F10 | |
| 11 | 11 | 10.6 | 9.8 | =B11-C11 | =ABS(D11) | =RANK(E11,$E$2:$E$11,1) | =SIGN(D11)*F11 | |
| 12 | | | | | | | =SUM(G2:G11) | |
| 13 | | | | | | | | |
| 14 | Effective Sample Size | =COUNT(A2:A11) | | | | *p*-value (Lower Tail) | =NORMSDIST(C16) | |
| 15 | Standard Deviation | =SQRT(C14*(C14+1)*(2*C14+1)/6) | | | | *p*-value (Upper Tail) | =1-NORMSDIST(C16) | |
| 16 | Test Statistic | =G12/C15 | | | | *p*-value (Two Tail) | =2*MIN(G14,G15) | |
| 17 | | | | | | | | |

| | A | B | C | D | E | F | G |
|---|---|---|---|---|---|---|---|
| 1 | Worker | Method 1 | Method 2 | Difference | Absolute Value | Rank | Signed Rank |
| 2 | 1 | 10.2 | 9.5 | 0.7 | 0.7 | 8 | 8 |
| 3 | 2 | 9.6 | 9.8 | -0.2 | 0.2 | 2 | -2 |
| 4 | 3 | 9.2 | 8.8 | 0.4 | 0.4 | 3.5 | 3.5 |
| 5 | 4 | 10.6 | 10.1 | 0.5 | 0.5 | 5.5 | 5.5 |
| 6 | 5 | 9.9 | 10.3 | -0.4 | 0.4 | 3.5 | -3.5 |
| 7 | 6 | 10.2 | 9.3 | 0.9 | 0.9 | 10 | 10 |
| 8 | 7 | 10.6 | 10.5 | 0.1 | 0.1 | 1 | 1 |
| 9 | 9 | 11.2 | 10.6 | 0.6 | 0.6 | 7 | 7 |
| 10 | 10 | 10.7 | 10.2 | 0.5 | 0.5 | 5.5 | 5.5 |
| 11 | 11 | 10.6 | 9.8 | 0.8 | 0.8 | 9 | 9 |
| 12 | | | | | | | 44 |
| 13 | | | | | | | |
| 14 | Effective Sample Size | 10 | | | | *p*-value (Lower Tail) | 0.9875 |
| 15 | Standard Deviation | 19.62 | | | | *p*-value (Upper Tail) | 0.0125 |
| 16 | Test Statistic | 2.24 | | | | *p*-value (Two Tail) | 0.0249 |
| 17 | | | | | | | |

**Enter Functions and Formulas:** The formulas in cells D2:D11 compute the differences in task completion times, and Excel's ABS function is used in cells E2:E11 to compute the absolute value of the differences. Excel's RANK function has been used in column F to rank the absolute differences in ascending order (smallest to largest). The first argument of the RANK function is the data value to be ranked, the second argument is the range of values for it to be ranked among, and the third argument is a one. If the third argument is a positive number, an ascending order ranking is performed. Our difficulty in using the results provided by the RANK function is that the RANK function does not assign an average rank to tied values. Therefore, we must modify the results provided by the function by typing in the average values for ties (see cells F4:F6 and F10 in the formula worksheet). With the differences ranked, we used Excel's SIGN function in column G to assign each of the ranked differences their original sign from column D. The sum of the signed ranks is then computed using Excel's SUM function in cell G12.

Now we are ready to compute the test statistic and the $p$-value. The effective sample size (the sample size after discarding any differences of zero) is computed using Excel's COUNT function in cell C14. The standard deviation is computed in cell C15 using equation (17.4) and Excel's SQRT function. The test statistic is computed in cell C16 as the sum of the signed ranks divided by the standard deviation. With this test statistic, $p$-value (Lower Tail) and $p$-value (Upper Tail) are computed using the NORMSDIST function in cells G14 and G15, respectively. Then, $p$-value (Two Tail) is computed in cell G16 as twice the minimum of the two one-tailed $p$-values. Because the production methods example is a two-tailed test, we use $p$-value (Two Tail) = .0249 to conduct the hypothesis test. Because $.0249 < \alpha = .05$, we reject the null hypothesis of no difference between the two production methods.

## EXERCISES

### Applications

**12.** Two fuel additives are being tested to determine their effect on miles per gallon for passenger cars. Test results for 12 cars follow; each car was tested with both fuel additives. Use $\alpha = .05$ and the Wilcoxon signed-rank test to see whether there is a significant difference in the additives.

MPG

| | Additive | | | Additive | |
|-----|-------|-------|-----|-------|-------|
| Car | 1 | 2 | Car | 1 | 2 |
| 1 | 20.12 | 18.05 | 7 | 16.16 | 17.20 |
| 2 | 23.56 | 21.77 | 8 | 18.55 | 14.98 |
| 3 | 22.03 | 22.57 | 9 | 21.87 | 20.03 |
| 4 | 19.15 | 17.06 | 10 | 24.23 | 21.15 |
| 5 | 21.23 | 21.22 | 11 | 23.21 | 22.78 |
| 6 | 24.77 | 23.80 | 12 | 25.02 | 23.70 |

**13.** A sample of 10 men was used in a study to test the effects of a relaxant on the time required to fall asleep for male adults. Data for 10 subjects showing the number of minutes required to fall asleep with and without the relaxant follow. Use a .05 level of significance to determine whether the relaxant reduces the time required to fall asleep. What is your conclusion?

Relaxant

| Subject | Without Relaxant | With Relaxant | Subject | Without Relaxant | With Relaxant |
|---------|------------------|---------------|---------|------------------|---------------|
| 1 | 15 | 10 | 6 | 7 | 5 |
| 2 | 12 | 10 | 7 | 8 | 10 |
| 3 | 22 | 12 | 8 | 10 | 7 |
| 4 | 8 | 11 | 9 | 14 | 11 |
| 5 | 10 | 9 | 10 | 9 | 6 |

**14.** Rental car gasoline prices per gallon were sampled at 10 major airports. Data for Avis and Budget car rental companies follow (*USA Today,* April 4, 2000)

| Airport | Avis | Budget |
|---------|------|--------|
| Boston Logan | 1.58 | 1.39 |
| Chicago O'Hare | 1.60 | 1.55 |
| Chicago Midway | 1.53 | 1.55 |
| Denver | 1.55 | 1.51 |
| Fort Lauderdale | 1.57 | 1.58 |
| Los Angeles | 1.80 | 1.74 |
| Miami | 1.62 | 1.60 |
| New York (JFK) | 1.69 | 1.60 |
| Orange County, CA | 1.75 | 1.59 |
| Washington (Dulles) | 1.55 | 1.54 |

CarRental

Use $\alpha = .05$ to test the hypothesis that there is no difference between the two populations. What is your conclusion?

**15.** A test was conducted of two overnight mail delivery services. Two samples of identical deliveries were set up so that both delivery services were notified of the need for a delivery at the same time. The hours required to make each delivery follow. Do the data shown suggest a difference in the delivery times for the two services? Use a .05 level of significance for the test.

| | Service | |
|---|---|---|
| **Delivery** | **1** | **2** |
| 1 | 24.5 | 28.0 |
| 2 | 26.0 | 25.5 |
| 3 | 28.0 | 32.0 |
| 4 | 21.0 | 20.0 |
| 5 | 18.0 | 19.5 |
| 6 | 36.0 | 28.0 |
| 7 | 25.0 | 29.0 |
| 8 | 21.0 | 22.0 |
| 9 | 24.0 | 23.5 |
| 10 | 26.0 | 29.5 |
| 11 | 31.0 | 30.0 |

Delivery

**16.** The 1997 price/earnings ratios for a sample of 12 stocks are shown in the following list (*Barron's,* December 8, 1997). Assume that a financial analyst has provided the estimated price/earnings ratio for 1998. Using a .05 level of significance, what is your conclusion about the differences between the price/earnings ratios for 1997 and 1998?

| Stock | 1997 P/E Ratio | 1998 P/E Ratio (Est.) |
|-------|----------------|------------------------|
| Coca-Cola | 40 | 32 |
| Du Pont | 24 | 22 |
| Eastman Kodak | 21 | 23 |
| General Electric | 30 | 23 |
| General Mills | 25 | 19 |
| IBM | 19 | 19 |
| McDonald's | 20 | 17 |
| Merck | 29 | 19 |
| Motorola | 35 | 20 |
| Philip Morris | 17 | 18 |
| Walt Disney | 33 | 27 |
| Xerox | 20 | 16 |

PERatio

**17.** Ten test-market cities were selected as part of a market research study designed to evaluate the effectiveness of a particular advertising campaign. The sales dollars for each city were recorded for the week prior to the promotional program. Then the campaign was conducted for two weeks and new sales data were collected for the week immediately after the campaign. The two sets of sales data (in $ thousands) follow.

| City | Precampaign Sales | Postcampaign Sales |
|------|:-----------------:|:------------------:|
| Kansas City | 130 | 160 |
| Dayton | 100 | 105 |
| Cincinnati | 120 | 140 |
| Columbus | 95 | 90 |
| Cleveland | 140 | 130 |
| Indianapolis | 80 | 82 |
| Louisville | 65 | 55 |
| St. Louis | 90 | 105 |
| Pittsburgh | 140 | 152 |
| Peoria | 125 | 140 |

**CD** file

**Advertising**

Use $\alpha = .05$. What conclusion do you draw about the value of the advertising program?

## 17.3 MANN-WHITNEY-WILCOXON TEST

In this section we present another nonparametric method that can be used to determine whether a difference exists between two populations. This test, unlike the signed-rank test, is not based on a matched sample. Two independent samples, one from each population, are used. The test is sometimes called the *Mann-Whitney test* and sometimes the *Wilcoxon rank-sum test.* Because the Mann-Whitney and Wilcoxon versions of this test are equivalent, we refer to the test as the **Mann-Whitney-Wilcoxon (MWW) test.**

Recall that in Chapter 10 we conducted a parametric test for the difference between the means of two populations. The following hypotheses were tested:

$$H_0: \mu_1 - \mu_2 = 0$$
$$H_a: \mu_1 - \mu_2 \neq 0$$

In the small-sample case, the hypothesis test required interval or ratio data and the assumption that both populations were normally distributed. Under these conditions, the $t$ distribution was used to test for the difference between the means of the two populations.

The nonparametric MWW test does not require interval or ratio data or the assumption that both populations are normally distributed. The only requirement of the MWW test is that the measurement scale for the data is at least ordinal. Then, instead of testing for the difference between the means of the two populations, the MWW test determines whether the two populations are identical. The hypotheses for the MWW test are as follow.

*The MWW test can be used without making the assumption that both populations are normally distributed.*

$H_0$: The two populations are identical
$H_a$: The two populations are not identical

We demonstrate how the MWW test can be applied by first showing an application for the small-sample case.

**TABLE 17.5**  HIGH SCHOOL CLASS STANDING DATA

| Garfield Students | | Mulberry Students | |
|---|---|---|---|
| **Student** | **Class Standing** | **Student** | **Class Standing** |
| Fields | 8 | Hart | 70 |
| Clark | 52 | Phipps | 202 |
| Jones | 112 | Kirkwood | 144 |
| Tibbs | 21 | Abbott | 175 |
| | | Guest | 146 |

## Small-Sample Case

The small-sample case for the MWW test should be used whenever the sample sizes for both populations are less than or equal to 10. We illustrate the use of the MWW test for the small-sample case by considering the academic potential of students attending Johnston High School. The majority of students attending Johnston High School previously attended either Garfield Junior High School or Mulberry Junior High School. The question raised by school administrators was whether the population of students who had attended Garfield was identical to the population of students who had attended Mulberry in terms of academic potential. The following hypotheses were considered.

$H_0$: The two populations are identical in terms of academic potential

$H_a$: The two populations are not identical in terms of academic potential

Using high school records, Johnston High School administrators selected a random sample of four high school students who had attended Garfield Junior High and another random sample of five students who had attended Mulberry Junior High. The current high school class standing was recorded for each of the nine students used in the study. The ordinal class standings for the nine students are listed in Table 17.5.

The first step in the MWW procedure is to rank the *combined* data from the two samples from low to high. The lowest value (class standing 8) receives a rank of 1 and the highest value (class standing 202) receives a rank of 9. The ranking of the nine students is given in Table 17.6.

The next step is to sum the ranks for each sample separately. This calculation is shown in Table 17.7. The MWW procedure can use the sum of the ranks for either sample. In the following discussion, we use the sum of the ranks for the sample of four students from Garfield. We denote this sum by the symbol $T$. Thus, for our example, $T = 11$.

**TABLE 17.6**  RANKING OF HIGH SCHOOL STUDENTS

| Student | Class Standing | Combined Sample Rank | Student | Class Standing | Combined Sample Rank |
|---|---|---|---|---|---|
| Fields | 8 | 1 | Kirkwood | 144 | 6 |
| Tibbs | 21 | 2 | Guest | 146 | 7 |
| Clark | 52 | 3 | Abbott | 175 | 8 |
| Hart | 70 | 4 | Phipps | 202 | 9 |
| Jones | 112 | 5 | | | |

**TABLE 17.7** RANK SUMS FOR HIGH SCHOOL STUDENTS FROM EACH JUNIOR HIGH SCHOOL

| | Garfield Students | | | Mulberry Students | |
|---|---|---|---|---|---|
| **Student** | **Class Standing** | **Sample Rank** | **Student** | **Class Standing** | **Sample Rank** |
| Fields | 8 | 1 | Hart | 70 | 4 |
| Clark | 52 | 3 | Phipps | 202 | 9 |
| Jones | 112 | 5 | Kirkwood | 144 | 6 |
| Tibbs | 21 | 2 | Abbott | 175 | 8 |
| | | | Guest | 146 | 7 |
| Sum of Ranks | | 11 | | | 34 |

Let us consider the properties of the sum of the ranks for the Garfield sample. With four students in the sample, Garfield could have the top four students in the study. If this were the case, $T = 1 + 2 + 3 + 4 = 10$ would be the smallest value possible for the rank sum $T$. Conversely, Garfield could have the bottom four students, in which case $T = 6 + 7 + 8 + 9 = 30$ would be the largest value possible for $T$. Hence, $T$ for the Garfield sample must take a value between 10 and 30.

Note that values of $T$ near 10 imply that Garfield has the significantly better, or higher ranking, students, whereas values of $T$ near 30 imply that Garfield has the significantly weaker, or lower ranking, students. Thus, if the two populations of students were identical in terms of academic potential, we would expect the value of $T$ to be near the average of the two values, or $(10 + 30)/2 = 20$.

Critical values of the MWW $T$ statistic are provided in Table 17.8 for cases in which both sample sizes are less than or equal to 10. In that table, $n_1$ refers to the sample size corresponding to the sample whose rank sum is being used in the test. The value of $T_L$ is read directly from the table and the value of $T_U$ is computed from (17.5).

$$T_U = n_1(n_1 + n_2 + 1) - T_L \qquad \textbf{(17.5)}$$

Neither the value of $T_L$ nor the value of $T_U$ is in the rejection region. The null hypothesis of identical populations should be rejected only if $T$ is strictly less than $T_L$ or strictly greater than $T_U$.

For example, using Table 17.8 with a .05 level of significance, we see that the lower-tail critical value for the MWW statistic with $n_1 = 4$ (Garfield) and $n_2 = 5$ (Mulberry) is $T_L = 12$. The upper-tail critical value for the MWW statistic computed by using equation (17.5) is

$$T_U = 4(4 + 5 + 1) - 12 = 28$$

Thus, the MWW decision rule indicates that the null hypothesis of identical populations can be rejected if the sum of the ranks for the first sample (Garfield) is less than 12 or greater than 28. The rejection rule can be written as

$$\text{Reject } H_0 \text{ if } T < 12 \text{ or if } T > 28$$

Referring to Table 17.7, we see that $T = 11$. Hence, the null hypothesis $H_0$ is rejected, and we can conclude that the population of students at Garfield differs from the population of students at Mulberry in terms of academic potential. The higher class ranking obtained

**TABLE 17.8**    $T_L$ VALUES FOR THE MANN-WHITNEY-WILCOXON TEST

Reject the hypothesis of identical populations if the sum of the ranks for the $n_1$ items is *less* than the value $T_L$ shown in the following table or if the sum of the ranks for the $n_1$ items is *greater* than the value $T_U$ where

$$T_U = n_1(n_1 + n_2 + 1) - T_L$$

| $\alpha = .05$ | | $n_2$ | | | | | | | | |
|---|---|---|---|---|---|---|---|---|---|---|
| | | 2 | 3 | 4 | 5 | 6 | 7 | 8 | 9 | 10 |
| $n_1$ | 2 | 3 | 3 | 3 | 3 | 3 | 3 | 4 | 4 | 4 |
| | 3 | 6 | 6 | 6 | 7 | 8 | 8 | 9 | 9 | 10 |
| | 4 | 10 | 10 | 11 | 12 | 13 | 14 | 15 | 15 | 16 |
| | 5 | 15 | 16 | 17 | 18 | 19 | 21 | 22 | 23 | 24 |
| | 6 | 21 | 23 | 24 | 25 | 27 | 28 | 30 | 32 | 33 |
| | 7 | 28 | 30 | 32 | 34 | 35 | 37 | 39 | 41 | 43 |
| | 8 | 37 | 39 | 41 | 43 | 45 | 47 | 50 | 52 | 54 |
| | 9 | 46 | 48 | 50 | 53 | 56 | 58 | 61 | 63 | 66 |
| | 10 | 56 | 59 | 61 | 64 | 67 | 70 | 73 | 76 | 79 |

| $\alpha = .10$ | | $n_2$ | | | | | | | | |
|---|---|---|---|---|---|---|---|---|---|---|
| | | 2 | 3 | 4 | 5 | 6 | 7 | 8 | 9 | 10 |
| $n_1$ | 2 | 3 | 3 | 3 | 4 | 4 | 4 | 5 | 5 | 5 |
| | 3 | 6 | 7 | 7 | 8 | 9 | 9 | 10 | 11 | 11 |
| | 4 | 10 | 11 | 12 | 13 | 14 | 15 | 16 | 17 | 18 |
| | 5 | 16 | 17 | 18 | 20 | 21 | 22 | 24 | 25 | 27 |
| | 6 | 22 | 24 | 25 | 27 | 29 | 30 | 32 | 34 | 36 |
| | 7 | 29 | 31 | 33 | 35 | 37 | 40 | 42 | 44 | 46 |
| | 8 | 38 | 40 | 42 | 45 | 47 | 50 | 52 | 55 | 57 |
| | 9 | 47 | 50 | 52 | 55 | 58 | 61 | 64 | 67 | 70 |
| | 10 | 57 | 60 | 63 | 67 | 70 | 73 | 76 | 80 | 83 |

If we had conducted the test with the rank sum of the Mulberry students, we would have had $n_1 = 5$, $n_2 = 4$, $T_L = 17$, $T_U = 33$, and $T = 34$. With $T > T_U$, we would have reached the same conclusion to reject $H_0$.

by the sample of Garfield students suggests that Garfield students are better prepared for high school than the Mulberry students.

## Large-Sample Case

When both sample sizes are greater than or equal to 10, a normal approximation of the distribution of $T$ can be used to conduct the analysis for the MWW test. We illustrate the large-sample case by considering a situation at Third National Bank.

Third National Bank has two branch offices. Data collected from two independent simple random samples, one from each branch, are given in Table 17.9. Do the data indicate whether the populations of checking account balances at the two branch banks are identical?

The first step in the MWW test is to rank the *combined* data from the lowest to the highest values. Using the combined set of 22 observations in Table 17.9, we find the lowest data

**TABLE 17.9**     ACCOUNT BALANCES FOR TWO BRANCHES OF THIRD NATIONAL BANK

| Branch 1 | | Branch 2 | |
|---|---|---|---|
| **Account** | **Balance ($)** | **Account** | **Balance ($)** |
| 1 | 1095 | 1 | 885 |
| 2 | 955 | 2 | 850 |
| 3 | 1200 | 3 | 915 |
| 4 | 1195 | 4 | 950 |
| 5 | 925 | 5 | 800 |
| 6 | 950 | 6 | 750 |
| 7 | 805 | 7 | 865 |
| 8 | 945 | 8 | 1000 |
| 9 | 875 | 9 | 1050 |
| 10 | 1055 | 10 | 935 |
| 11 | 1025 | | |
| 12 | 975 | | |

value of $750 (sixth item of sample 2) and assign to it a rank of 1. Continuing the ranking gives us the following list.

| **Balance ($)** | **Item** | **Assigned Rank** |
|---|---|---|
| 750 | 6th of sample 2 | 1 |
| 800 | 5th of sample 2 | 2 |
| 805 | 7th of sample 1 | 3 |
| 850 | 2nd of sample 2 | 4 |
| . | . | . |
| . | . | . |
| . | . | . |
| 1195 | 4th of sample 1 | 21 |
| 1200 | 3rd of sample 1 | 22 |

In ranking the combined data, we may find that two or more data values are the same. In that case, the tied values are given the *average* ranking of their positions in the combined data set. For example, the balance of $945 (eighth item of sample 1) will be assigned the rank of 11. However, the next two values in the data set are tied with values of $950 (see the sixth item of sample 1 and the fourth item of sample 2). Because these two values will be considered for assigned ranks of 12 and 13, they are both assigned the rank of 12.5. At the next highest data value of $955, we continue the ranking process by assigning $955 the rank of 14. Table 17.10 is the entire data set with the assigned rank of each observation.

The next step in the MWW test is to sum the ranks for each sample. The sums are given in Table 17.10. The test procedure can be based on the sum of the ranks for either sample. We use the sum of the ranks for the sample from branch 1. Thus, for this example, $T = 169.5$.

Given that the sample sizes are $n_1 = 12$ and $n_2 = 10$, we can use the normal approximation to the sampling distribution of the rank sum $T$. The properties of the appropriate sampling distribution are as follows:

### Sampling Distribution of $T$ for Identical Populations

$$\text{Mean: } \mu_T = \tfrac{1}{2} n_1(n_1 + n_2 + 1) \tag{17.6}$$

$$\text{Standard Deviation: } \sigma_T = \sqrt{\tfrac{1}{12} n_1 n_2(n_1 + n_2 + 1)} \tag{17.7}$$

Distribution form: approximately normal provided $n_1 \geq 10$ and $n_2 \geq 10$.

**TABLE 17.10**  COMBINED RANKING OF THE DATA IN THE TWO SAMPLES
FROM THIRD NATIONAL BANK

| | Branch 1 | | | Branch 2 | |
|---|---|---|---|---|---|
| **Account** | **Balance ($)** | **Rank** | **Account** | **Balance ($)** | **Rank** |
| 1 | 1095 | 20 | 1 | 885 | 7 |
| 2 | 955 | 14 | 2 | 850 | 4 |
| 3 | 1200 | 22 | 3 | 915 | 8 |
| 4 | 1195 | 21 | 4 | 950 | 12.5 |
| 5 | 925 | 9 | 5 | 800 | 2 |
| 6 | 950 | 12.5 | 6 | 750 | 1 |
| 7 | 805 | 3 | 7 | 865 | 5 |
| 8 | 945 | 11 | 8 | 1000 | 16 |
| 9 | 875 | 6 | 9 | 1050 | 18 |
| 10 | 1055 | 19 | 10 | 935 | 10 |
| 11 | 1025 | 17 | | Sum of Ranks | 83.5 |
| 12 | 975 | 15 | | | |
| | Sum of Ranks | 169.5 | | | |

For branch 1, we have

$$\mu_T = \tfrac{1}{2} \, 12(12 + 10 + 1) = 138$$

$$\sigma_T = \sqrt{\tfrac{1}{12} \, 12(10)(12 + 10 + 1)} = 15.17$$

Figure 17.8 is the sampling distribution of $T$. Following the usual hypothesis testing procedure, we compute the test statistic $z$ to determine whether the observed value of $T$ appears

**FIGURE 17.8**  SAMPLING DISTRIBUTION OF $T$ FOR THE THIRD NATIONAL
BANK EXAMPLE

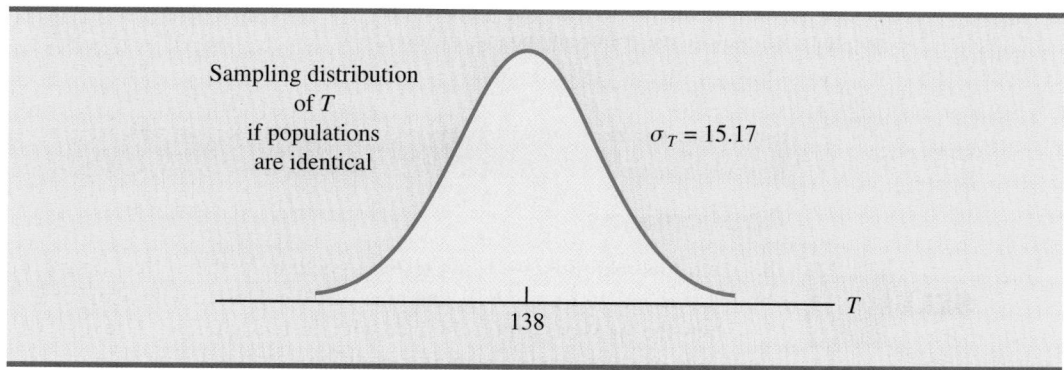

Sampling distribution
of $T$
if populations
are identical

$\sigma_T = 15.17$

$T$

138

to be from the sampling distribution of Figure 17.8. If $T$ does not appear to be from that distribution, we will reject the null hypothesis and conclude that the populations are not identical. Computing the test statistic, we have

$$z = \frac{T - \mu_T}{\sigma_T} = \frac{169.5 - 138}{15.17} = 2.08$$

If we had used the rank sum for branch 2, we would have had $n_1 = 10$, $n_2 = 12$, $\mu_T = 115$, and $T = 83.5$. With $z = -2.08$ we would again reject $H_0$.

At a .05 level of significance, we know that, to reject $H_0$, $z$ must be less than $-1.96$ or greater than $+1.96$. With $z = 2.08$, and the $p$-value $= 2(1.0000 - .9812) = .0376 < \alpha = .05$, we reject $H_0$. Thus, we conclude that the two populations are not identical. That is, the populations of account balances at the two branches are not the same.

In summary, the Mann-Whitney-Wilcoxon rank-sum test consists of the following steps to determine whether two independent random samples are selected from identical populations.

1. Rank the combined sample observations from lowest to highest, with tied values being assigned the average of the tied rankings.
2. Compute $T$, the sum of the ranks for the first sample.
3. Make the test for significant differences between the two populations by using the observed value of $T$. In the large-sample case, compute the value of the standardized test statistic $z$. Compare it to the critical value or use the corresponding $p$-value as the basis for deciding whether to reject $H_0$. In the small-sample case, use Table 17.8 to find the critical values for the test.

## Using Excel

Excel does not have any special tools for the Mann-Whitney-Wilcoxon test. However, an Excel worksheet can be used to advantage in ranking the data, summing the ranks, computing the test statistic, and computing the $p$-value in the large-sample case. The usage is similar to the use of Excel in the previous section except for assigning signs to the ranks so we will not develop a separate worksheet here.

### NOTES AND COMMENTS

The nonparametric test discussed in this section is used to determine whether two populations are identical. Parametric statistical tests, such as the $t$ test described in Chapter 10, test the equality of two population means. When we reject the hypothesis that the means are equal, we conclude that the populations differ in their means. When we reject the hypothesis that the populations are identical by using the MWW test, we cannot state how they differ. The populations could have different means, different variances, and/or different forms. Nonetheless, if we believe that the populations are the same in every aspect but the means, a rejection of $H_0$ by the nonparametric method implies that the means differ. The major advantages of the MWW test over the parametric $t$ test are that it does not require any assumptions about the form of the probability distribution from which the measurements come and it can be used with ordinal data.

### EXERCISES

## Applications

18. Two fuel additives are being tested to determine their effect on gas mileage. Seven cars were tested with additive 1 and nine cars were tested with additive 2. The following data show the miles per gallon obtained with the two additives. Use $\alpha = .05$ and the MWW test to see whether there is a significant difference in gasoline mileage for the two additives.

| Additive 1 | Additive 2 |
|:----------:|:----------:|
| 17.3 | 18.7 |
| 18.4 | 17.8 |
| 19.1 | 21.3 |
| 16.7 | 21.0 |
| 18.2 | 22.1 |
| 18.6 | 18.7 |
| 17.5 | 19.8 |
|  | 20.7 |
|  | 20.2 |

**19.** Samples of starting annual salaries for individuals entering the public accounting and financial planning professions follow (*Fortune,* June 26, 1995). Annual salaries are shown in thousands of dollars.

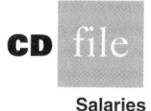

Salaries

| Public Accountant | Financial Planner | Public Accountant | Financial Planner |
|:----------:|:----------:|:----------:|:----------:|
| 25.2 | 24.0 | 30.0 | 28.6 |
| 33.8 | 24.2 | 25.9 | 24.7 |
| 31.3 | 28.1 | 34.5 | 28.9 |
| 33.2 | 30.9 | 31.7 | 26.8 |
| 29.2 | 26.9 | 26.9 | 23.9 |

**a.** Using a .05 level of significance, test the hypothesis that there is no difference between the starting annual salaries of public accountants and financial planners. What is your conclusion?

**b.** What are the sample mean annual salaries for the two professions?

**20.** The gap between the earnings of men and women with equal education is narrowing but has not closed (*USA Today,* September 15, 2000). Sample data (in $thousands) for seven men and seven women with a bachelor's degree are as follow.

| *Men* | 30.6 | 75.5 | 45.2 | 62.2 | 38.2 | 49.9 | 55.3 |
|:-----:|:----:|:----:|:----:|:----:|:----:|:----:|:----:|
| *Women* | 44.5 | 35.4 | 27.9 | 40.5 | 25.8 | 47.5 | 24.8 |

**a.** What is the median salary for men? For women?

**b.** Using $\alpha = .05$, conduct the hypothesis test for identical populations. What is your conclusion?

**21.** Mileage performance tests were conducted for two models of automobiles. Twelve automobiles of each model were selected randomly and a miles-per-gallon rating for each model was developed on the basis of 1000 miles of highway driving. The data follow.

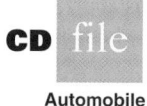

Automobile

| Model 1 | | Model 2 | |
|:--------:|:----------------:|:--------:|:----------------:|
| Automobile | Miles per Gallon | Automobile | Miles per Gallon |
| 1 | 20.6 | 1 | 21.3 |
| 2 | 19.9 | 2 | 17.6 |
| 3 | 18.6 | 3 | 17.4 |
| 4 | 18.9 | 4 | 18.5 |
| 5 | 18.8 | 5 | 19.7 |
| 6 | 20.2 | 6 | 21.1 |
| 7 | 21.0 | 7 | 17.3 |
| 8 | 20.5 | 8 | 18.8 |
| 9 | 19.8 | 9 | 17.8 |
| 10 | 19.8 | 10 | 16.9 |
| 11 | 19.2 | 11 | 18.0 |
| 12 | 20.5 | 12 | 20.1 |

Use $\alpha = .10$ and test for a significant difference in the populations of miles-per-gallon ratings for the two models.

**TABLE 17.11** P/E RATIOS FOR JAPANESE AND U.S. COMPANIES

| Japan | | United States | |
|---|---|---|---|
| **Company** | **P/E Ratio** | **Company** | **P/E Ratio** |
| Sumitomo Corp. | 153 | Gannet | 19 |
| Kinden | 21 | Motorola | 24 |
| Heiwa | 18 | Schlumberger | 24 |
| NCR Japan | 125 | Oracle Systems | 43 |
| Suzuki Motor | 31 | Gap | 22 |
| Fuji Bank | 213 | Winn-Dixie | 14 |
| Sumitomo Chemical | 64 | Ingersoll-Rand | 21 |
| Seibu Railway | 666 | American Electric Power | 14 |
| Shiseido | 33 | Hercules | 21 |
| Toho Gas | 68 | Times Mirror | 38 |
| | | WellPoint Health | 15 |
| | | Northern States Power | 14 |

22. *Business Week* annually publishes statistics on the world's 1000 largest companies. A company's price/earnings (P/E) ratio is the company's current stock price divided by the latest 12 months' earnings per share. Listed in Table 17.11 are the P/E ratios for a sample of 10 Japanese and 12 U.S. companies (*Business Week,* July 11, 1994). Is the difference in P/E ratios between the two countries significant? Use the MWW test and $\alpha = .02$ to support your conclusion.

23. Police records show the following numbers of daily crime reports for a sample of days during the winter months and a sample of days during the summer months. Using a .05 level of significance, determine whether there is a significant difference between the winter and summer months in terms of the number of crime reports.

| Winter | Summer |
|---|---|
| 18 | 28 |
| 20 | 18 |
| 15 | 24 |
| 16 | 32 |
| 21 | 18 |
| 20 | 29 |
| 12 | 23 |
| 16 | 38 |
| 19 | 28 |
| 20 | 18 |

24. A certain brand of microwave oven was priced at 10 stores in Dallas and 13 stores in San Antonio. The data follow. Use a .05 level of significance and test whether prices for the microwave oven are the same in the two cities.

| Dallas | San Antonio |
|---|---|
| 445 | 460 |
| 489 | 451 |
| 405 | 435 |
| 485 | 479 |
| 439 | 475 |
| 449 | 445 |
| 436 | 429 |
| 420 | 434 |

| Dallas | San Antonio |
|--------|-------------|
| 430 | 410 |
| 405 | 422 |
|  | 425 |
|  | 459 |
|  | 430 |

25. The National Association of Home Builders provided data on the cost of the most popular home remodeling projects (*USA Today,* June 17, 1997). Use the Mann-Whitney-Wilcoxon test to see whether it can be concluded that the cost of kitchen remodeling differs from the cost of master bedroom remodeling. Use a .05 level of significance.

| Kitchen($) | Master Bedroom($) |
|------------|-------------------|
| 25,200 | 18,000 |
| 17,400 | 22,900 |
| 22,800 | 26,400 |
| 21,900 | 24,800 |
| 19,700 | 26,900 |
| 23,000 | 17,800 |
| 19,700 | 24,600 |
| 16,900 | 21,000 |
| 21,800 |  |
| 23,600 |  |

## 17.4   KRUSKAL-WALLIS TEST

Kruskal-Wallis is an alternative to the use of ANOVA in Chapter 13, for a hypothesis test on the equality of the means of $k$ populations.

The MWW test in Section 17.3 can be used to test whether two populations are identical. It has been extended to the case of three or more populations by Kruskal and Wallis. The hypotheses for the **Kruskal-Wallis test** with $k \geq 3$ populations can be written as follows.

$$H_0: \text{All populations are identical}$$
$$H_a: \text{Not all populations are identical}$$

The Kruskal-Wallis test is based on the analysis of independent random samples from each of the $k$ populations.

In Chapter 13 we showed that analysis of variance (ANOVA) can be used to test for the equality of means among three or more populations. The ANOVA procedure requires interval or ratio data and the assumption that the $k$ populations are normally distributed.

The nonparametric Kruskal-Wallis test can be used with ordinal data as well as with interval or ratio data. In addition, the Kruskal-Wallis test does not require the assumption of normally distributed populations. Hence, whenever the data from $k \geq 3$ populations are ordinal, or whenever the assumption of normally distributed populations is questionable, the Kruskal-Wallis test provides an alternate statistical procedure for testing whether the populations are identical. We demonstrate the Kruskal-Wallis test by using it in an employee selection application.

Williams Manufacturing Company hires employees for its management staff from three local colleges. Recently, the company's personnel department has been collecting and reviewing annual performance ratings in an attempt to determine whether there are differences in performance among the managers hired from these colleges. Performance rating data are available from independent samples of seven employees from college A, six employees from college B, and seven employees from college C. These data are summarized in Table 17.12; the overall performance rating of each manager is given on a 0–100 scale, with 100 being the highest possible performance rating.

**TABLE 17.12**

PERFORMANCE EVALUATION RATINGS FOR 20 WILLIAMS EMPLOYEES

| College A | College B | College C |
|-----------|-----------|-----------|
| 25 | 60 | 50 |
| 70 | 20 | 70 |
| 60 | 30 | 60 |
| 85 | 15 | 80 |
| 95 | 40 | 90 |
| 90 | 35 | 70 |
| 80 |  | 75 |

Suppose we want to test whether the three populations are identical in terms of performance at a .05 level of significance. The Kruskal-Wallis test statistic, which is based on the sum of ranks for each of the samples, can be computed as follows.

**Kruskal-Wallis Test Statistic**

$$W = \left[ \frac{12}{n_T(n_T + 1)} \sum_{i=1}^{k} \frac{R_i^2}{n_i} \right] - 3(n_T + 1) \qquad (17.8)$$

where

$$k = \text{the number of populations}$$
$$n_i = \text{the number of items in sample } i$$
$$n_T = \Sigma n_i = \text{total number of items in all samples}$$
$$R_i = \text{sum of the ranks for sample } i$$

Kruskal and Wallis were able to show that, under the null hypothesis in which the populations are identical, the sampling distribution of $W$ can be approximated by a chi-square distribution with $k - 1$ degrees of freedom. This approximation is generally acceptable if each of the sample sizes is greater than or equal to five. Because larger values of $W$ cast doubt on the null hypothesis, the rejection region is in the upper tail.

The Kruskal-Wallis test uses only the ordinal rank of the data.

To compute the $W$ statistic for our example, we must first rank all 20 data items. The lowest data value of 15 from the college B sample receives a rank of 1, whereas the highest data value of 95 from the college A sample receives a rank of 20. The data values, their associated ranks, and the sum of the ranks for the three samples are given in Table 17.13. Note that we assign the average rank to tied items;* for example, the data values of 60, 70, 80, and 90 had ties.

The sample sizes are

$$n_1 = 7 \qquad n_2 = 6 \qquad n_3 = 7$$

and

$$n_T = \Sigma n_i = 7 + 6 + 7 = 20$$

**TABLE 17.13** COMBINED RANKINGS FOR THE 20 WILLIAMS EMPLOYEES

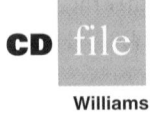

| College A | Rank | College B | Rank | College C | Rank |
|---|---|---|---|---|---|
| 25 | 3 | 60 | 9 | 50 | 7 |
| 70 | 12 | 20 | 2 | 70 | 12 |
| 60 | 9 | 30 | 4 | 60 | 9 |
| 85 | 17 | 15 | 1 | 80 | 15.5 |
| 95 | 20 | 40 | 6 | 90 | 18.5 |
| 90 | 18.5 | 35 | 5 | 70 | 12 |
| 80 | 15.5 | | | 75 | 14 |
| Sum of Ranks | 95 | | 27 | | 88 |

*If numerous tied ranks are observed, (17.8) must be modified; the modified formula is given in *Practical Nonparametric Statistics* by W. J. Conover.

We compute the $W$ statistic by using equation (17.8).

$$W = \frac{12}{20(21)}\left[\frac{(95)^2}{7} + \frac{(27)^2}{6} + \frac{(88)^2}{7}\right] - 3(20 + 1) = 8.92$$

The chi-square distribution table (Table 3 of Appendix B) shows that with $k - 1 = 2$ degrees of freedom and $\alpha = .05$ in the upper tail of the distribution, the critical chi-square value is $\chi^2 = 5.99147$. Because the test statistic $W = 8.92$ is greater than $5.99147$, we reject the null hypothesis that the three populations are identical. As a result, we conclude that manager performance differs significantly depending on the college attended. Furthermore, because the performance ratings are lowest for college B, it would be reasonable for the company to either cut back recruiting from college B or at least evaluate its graduates more thoroughly.

## Using Excel

Excel does not have a special tool for the Kruskal-Wallis test. However, an Excel worksheet can be used to simplify ranking the data and summing the ranks, as well as computing the test statistic and corresponding $p$-value. Excel's CHIDIST function is used to compute the $p$-value. We show the development of a worksheet for the Williams Company problem. Refer to Figure 17.9 as we describe the tasks involved. The formula worksheet is in the background; the value worksheet is in the foreground.

**FIGURE 17.9**    EXCEL WORKSHEET FOR THE KRUSKAL-WALLIS TEST ON THE WILLIAMS COMPANY PROBLEM

| | A | B | C | D | E |
|---|---|---|---|---|---|
| 1 | College | Performance Rating | Rank | | |
| 2 | A | 25 | =RANK(B2,$B$2:$B$21,1) | | |
| 3 | A | 70 | 12 | | |
| 4 | A | 60 | 9 | | |
| 5 | A | 85 | =RANK(B5,$B$2:$B$21,1) | | |
| 6 | A | 95 | =RANK(B6,$B$2:$B$21,1) | | |
| 7 | A | 90 | 18.5 | $n_1$ | =COUNT(B2:B8) |
| 8 | A | 80 | 15.5 | Sum A | =SUM(C2:C8) |
| 9 | B | 60 | 9 | | |
| 10 | B | 20 | =RANK(B10,$B$2:$B$21,1) | | |
| 11 | B | 30 | =RANK(B11,$B$2:$B$21,1) | | |
| 12 | B | 15 | =RANK(B12,$B$2:$B$21,1) | | |
| 13 | B | 40 | =RANK(B13,$B$2:$B$21,1) | $n_2$ | =COUNT(B9:B14) |
| 14 | B | 35 | =RANK(B14,$B$2:$B$21,1) | Sum B | =SUM(C9:C14) |
| 15 | C | 50 | =RANK(B15,$B$2:$B$21,1) | | |
| 16 | C | 70 | 12 | | |
| 17 | C | 60 | 9 | | |
| 18 | C | 80 | 15.5 | | |
| 19 | C | 90 | 18.5 | | |
| 20 | C | 70 | 12 | $n_3$ | =COUNT(B15:B21) |
| 21 | C | 75 | =RANK(B21,$B$2:$B$21,1) | Sum C | =SUM(C15:C21) |
| 22 | | | | $n_T$ | =COUNT(B2:B21) |
| 23 | Test Statistic | | =(12/(E22*(E22+1)))*(E8^2/E7+E14^2/E13+E21^2/E20)-3*(E22+1) | | |
| 24 | Degrees of Freedom | | 2 | | |
| 25 | | | | | |
| 26 | $p$-value (Lower Tail) | | =1-CHIDIST(C23,C24) | | |
| 27 | $p$-value (Upper Tail) | | =CHIDIST(C23,C24) | | |
| 28 | $p$-value (Two Tail) | | =2*MIN(C26:C27) | | |
| 29 | | | | | |

| | A | B | C | D | E | F |
|---|---|---|---|---|---|---|
| 1 | College | Performance Rating | Rank | | | |
| 2 | A | 25 | 3 | | | |
| 3 | A | 70 | 12 | | | |
| 4 | A | 60 | 9 | | | |
| 5 | A | 85 | 17 | | | |
| 6 | A | 95 | 20 | | | |
| 7 | A | 90 | 18.5 | $n_1$ | 7 | |
| 8 | A | 80 | 15.5 | Sum A | 95 | |
| 9 | B | 60 | 9 | | | |
| 10 | B | 20 | 2 | | | |
| 11 | B | 30 | 4 | | | |
| 12 | B | 15 | 1 | | | |
| 13 | B | 40 | 6 | $n_2$ | 6 | |
| 14 | B | 35 | 5 | Sum B | 27 | |
| 15 | C | 50 | 7 | | | |
| 16 | C | 70 | 12 | | | |
| 17 | C | 60 | 9 | | | |
| 18 | C | 80 | 15.5 | | | |
| 19 | C | 90 | 18.5 | | | |
| 20 | C | 70 | 12 | $n_3$ | 7 | |
| 21 | C | 75 | 14 | Sum C | 88 | |
| 22 | | | | $n_T$ | 20 | |
| 23 | | Test Statistic | 8.92 | | | |
| 24 | | Degrees of Freedom | 2 | | | |
| 25 | | | | | | |
| 26 | | $p$-value (Lower Tail) | 0.9884 | | | |
| 27 | | $p$-value (Upper Tail) | 0.0116 | | | |
| 28 | | $p$-value (Two Tail) | 0.0232 | | | |
| 29 | | | | | | |

**Enter Data:** The data are in columns A and B. The college attended is in column A and the performance rating is in column B. Note that rows 2 through 8 contain the sample of college A employees, rows 9 through 14 contain the sample of college B employees, and rows 15 through 21 contain the sample of college C employees.

**Enter Functions and Formulas:** We have used Excel's RANK funciton in column C to determine the rank order for the 20 employees. As in Section 17.2 we had to modify the results provided by the RANK function by typing in the average ranks for ties. In reviewing the formula worksheet, we see several places where providing the average rank for ties was necessary. Excel's COUNT function was used in cells E7, E13, and E20 to compute the sample size for each college, and the SUM function was used in cells E8, E14, and E21 to compute the sum of ranks for each college.

The test statistic is computed in cell C23 using an Excel formula to implement equation (17.8). A value of $k - 1 = 2$ has been entered into cell C24 for the degrees of freedom. Excel's CHIDIST function is then used to compute the $p$-value associated with the test statistic in cell C23. Recall that the form of the CHIDIST function is CHIDIST (test statistic, degrees of freedom), and that the value provided by the function is the area in the upper tail of the chi-square distribution. Thus, to obtain the $p$-value (Lower Tail) we enter the formula $=1$-CHIDIST(C23,C24) into cell C26. The $p$-value (Upper Tail) is obtained by entering the formula $=$CHIDIST(C23, C24) into cell C27, and the $p$-value (Two Tail) is obtained in cell C28 as two times the minimum of the two one-tailed $p$-values. Because the William Manufacturing example is an upper tail hypothesis test, we compare the $p$-value (Upper Tail) $= .0116$ to $\alpha = .05$. With $.0116 < \alpha = .05$, we reject $H_0$ and conclude that the three populations are not identical.

## NOTES AND COMMENTS

The Kruskal-Wallis procedure illustrated in the example began with the collection of interval-scaled data showing employee performance evaluation ratings. The procedure also would have worked had the data been the ordinal rankings of the 20 employees. In that case, the Kruskal-Wallis test could have been applied directly to the original data; the step of constructing the rank orderings from the performance evaluation ratings would have been omitted.

## EXERCISES

### Methods

**26.** Three products received the following performance ratings by a panel of 15 consumers.

| | Product | |
|---|---|---|
| **A** | **B** | **C** |
| 50 | 80 | 60 |
| 62 | 95 | 45 |
| 75 | 98 | 30 |
| 48 | 87 | 58 |
| 65 | 90 | 57 |

Use the Kruskal-Wallis test and $\alpha = .05$ to determine whether there is a significant difference in the performance ratings for the products.

27. Three admission test preparation programs are being evaluated. The scores obtained by a sample of 20 people who used the test preparation programs provided the following data. Use the Kruskal-Wallis test to determine whether there is a significant difference among the three test preparation programs. Use $\alpha = .01$.

**Program**

| A | B | C |
|-----|-----|-----|
| 540 | 450 | 600 |
| 400 | 540 | 630 |
| 490 | 400 | 580 |
| 530 | 410 | 490 |
| 490 | 480 | 590 |
| 610 | 370 | 620 |
|     | 550 | 570 |

# Applications

28. Forty-minute workouts involving one of the following activities three days a week will lead to a loss of weight. The following sample data show the number of calories burned during 40-minute workouts for three different activities. Do these data indicate differences in the amount of calories burned for the three activities? Use a .05 level of significance. What is your conclusion?

| Swimming | Tennis | Cycling |
|----------|--------|---------|
| 408 | 415 | 385 |
| 380 | 485 | 250 |
| 425 | 450 | 295 |
| 400 | 420 | 402 |
| 427 | 530 | 268 |

29. The miles-per-gallon data obtained from tests on three different automobiles are reported as follows. Use the Kruskal-Wallis test with $\alpha = .05$ to determine whether there is a significant difference in the gasoline mileage for the three automobiles.

**Automobile**

| A | B | C |
|----|----|----|
| 19 | 19 | 24 |
| 21 | 20 | 26 |
| 20 | 22 | 23 |
| 19 | 21 | 25 |
| 21 | 23 | 27 |

30. A large corporation has been sending many of its first-level managers to an off-site supervisory skills course. Four different management development centers offer this course, and the corporation wants to determine whether they differ in the quality of training provided. A sample of 20 employees who have attended these programs has been chosen and the employees ranked in terms of supervisory skills. The results follow.

| Course | Supervisory Skills Rank | | | | |
|--------|----|----|----|----|----|
| 1 | 3  | 14 | 10 | 12 | 13 |
| 2 | 2  | 7  | 1  | 5  | 11 |
| 3 | 19 | 16 | 9  | 18 | 17 |
| 4 | 20 | 4  | 15 | 6  | 8  |

Note that the top-ranked supervisor attended course 2 and the lowest-ranked supervisor attended course 4. Use $\alpha = .05$ and test to see whether there is a significant difference in the training provided by the four programs.

**31.** The better-selling candies are high in calories. Assume that the following data show the calorie content from samples of M&Ms, Kit Kat, and Milky Way II. Test for significant differences in the calorie content of these three candies. At a .05 level of significance, what is your conclusion?

| M&Ms | Kit Kat | Milky Way II |
|---|---|---|
| 230 | 225 | 200 |
| 210 | 205 | 208 |
| 240 | 245 | 202 |
| 250 | 235 | 190 |
| 230 | 220 | 180 |

## 17.5 RANK CORRELATION

The Spearman rank-correlation coefficient is equal to the Pearson correlation coefficient (see Chapter 3) applied to ordinal or rank data.

The correlation coefficient is a measure of the linear association between two variables for which interval or ratio data are available. In this section, we consider measures of association between two variables when only ordinal data are available. The **Spearman rank-correlation coefficient** $r_s$ has been developed for this purpose.

**Spearman Rank-Correlation Coefficient**

$$r_s = 1 - \frac{6\Sigma d_i^2}{n(n^2 - 1)} \tag{17.9}$$

where

$n$ = the number of elements or individuals being ranked
$x_i$ = the rank of element $i$ with respect to one variable
$y_i$ = the rank of element $i$ with respect to a second variable
$d_i = x_i - y_i$

Let us illustrate the use of the Spearman rank-correlation coefficient with an example. A company wants to determine whether individuals who were expected at the time of employment to be better salespersons actually turn out to have better sales records. To investigate this question, the vice president in charge of personnel carefully reviewed the original job interview summaries, academic records, and letters of recommendation for 10 current members of the firm's salesforce. After the review, the vice president ranked the 10 individuals in terms of their potential for success, basing the assessment solely on the information available at the time of employment. Then a list was obtained of the number of units sold by each salesperson over the first two years. On the basis of actual sales performance, a second ranking of the 10 salespersons was carried out. Table 17.14 gives the relevant data and the two rankings. The statistical question is whether there is agreement between the ranking of potential at the time of employment and the ranking based on the actual sales performance over the first two years.

Let us compute the Spearman rank-correlation coefficient for the data in Table 17.14. The computations are summarized in Table 17.15. We see that the rank-correlation coefficient is a positive .73. The Spearman rank-correlation coefficient ranges from $-1.0$ to $+1.0$ and its interpretation is similar to that of the sample correlation coefficient in that positive values near 1.0 indicate a strong association between the rankings; as one rank increases,

**TABLE 17.14**    SALES POTENTIAL AND ACTUAL TWO-YEAR SALES DATA
FOR 10 SALESPEOPLE

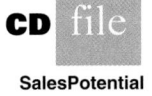

**CD** file

**SalesPotential**

| Salesperson | Ranking of Potential | Two-Year Sales (units) | Ranking According to Two-Year Sales |
|---|---|---|---|
| A | 2 | 400 | 1 |
| B | 4 | 360 | 3 |
| C | 7 | 300 | 5 |
| D | 1 | 295 | 6 |
| E | 6 | 280 | 7 |
| F | 3 | 350 | 4 |
| G | 10 | 200 | 10 |
| H | 9 | 260 | 8 |
| I | 8 | 220 | 9 |
| J | 5 | 385 | 2 |

the other rank increases. Rank correlations near $-1.0$ indicate a strong negative association between the rankings; as one rank increases, the other rank decreases. The value $r_s = .73$ indicates a positive correlation between potential and actual performance. Individuals ranked high on potential tend to rank high on performance.

## Test for Significant Rank Correlation

At this point, we have seen how sample results can be used to compute the sample rank-correlation coefficient. As with many other statistical procedures, we may want to use the sample results to make an inference about the population rank correlation $\rho_s$. To make an inference about the population rank correlation, we must test the following hypotheses.

$$H_0: \rho_s = 0$$
$$H_a: \rho_s \neq 0$$

**TABLE 17.15**    COMPUTATION OF THE SPEARMAN RANK-CORRELATION
COEFFICIENT FOR SALES POTENTIAL AND SALES PERFORMANCE

| Salesperson | $x_i$ = Ranking of Potential | $y_i$ = Ranking of Sales Performance | $d_i = x_i - y_i$ | $d_i^2$ |
|---|---|---|---|---|
| A | 2 | 1 | 1 | 1 |
| B | 4 | 3 | 1 | 1 |
| C | 7 | 5 | 2 | 4 |
| D | 1 | 6 | -5 | 25 |
| E | 6 | 7 | -1 | 1 |
| F | 3 | 4 | -1 | 1 |
| G | 10 | 10 | 0 | 0 |
| H | 9 | 8 | 1 | 1 |
| I | 8 | 9 | -1 | 1 |
| J | 5 | 2 | 3 | 9 |
| | | | | $\Sigma d_i^2 = 44$ |

$$r_s = 1 - \frac{6\Sigma d_i^2}{n(n^2 - 1)} = 1 - \frac{6(44)}{10(100 - 1)} = .73$$

Under the null hypothesis of no rank correlation ($\rho_s = 0$), the rankings are independent, and the sampling distribution of $r_s$ is as follows.

**Sampling Distribution of $r_s$**

$$\text{Mean: } \mu_{r_s} = 0 \tag{17.10}$$

$$\text{Standard Deviation: } \sigma_{r_s} = \sqrt{\frac{1}{n-1}} \tag{17.11}$$

Distribution form: approximately normal provided $n \geq 10$.

The sample rank-correlation coefficient for sales potential and sales performance is $r_s = .73$. With this value, we can test for a significant rank correlation. From equation (17.10) we have $\mu_{r_s} = 0$ and from equation (17.11) we have $\sigma_{r_s} = \sqrt{1/(10-1)} = .33$. Using the test statistic, we have

$$z = \frac{r_s - \mu_{r_s}}{\sigma_{r_s}} = \frac{.73 - 0}{.33} = 2.21$$

At a .05 level of significance, we see that the null hypothesis of no correlation will be rejected if $z < -1.96$ or if $z > 1.96$. Because $z = 2.21$ and the $p$-value $= 2(1.0000 - .9864) = .0272 < \alpha = .05$, we reject the hypothesis of no rank correlation. Thus, we can conclude that there is a significant rank correlation between sales potential and sales performance.

## Using Excel

In Chapter 3, we showed how to use Excel's CORREL function for computing the Pearson product moment correlation coefficient. The Spearman correlation coefficient is the same as the Pearson correlation coefficient applied to the ranked data. We develop a worksheet for making the necessary calculations. Refer to Figure 17.10 as we describe the

**FIGURE 17.10**   EXCEL WORKSHEET FOR COMPUTING THE SPEARMAN CORRELATION COEFFICIENT

| | A | B | C | D | E |
|---|---|---|---|---|---|
| 1 | Salesperson | Ranking of Potential | Two-Year Sales (units) | Sales Ranking | |
| 2 | A | 2 | 400 | =RANK(C2,$C$2:$C$11) | |
| 3 | B | 4 | 360 | =RANK(C3,$C$2:$C$11) | |
| 4 | C | 7 | 300 | =RANK(C4,$C$2:$C$11) | |
| 5 | D | 1 | 295 | =RANK(C5,$C$2:$C$11) | |
| 6 | E | 6 | 280 | =RANK(C6,$C$2:$C$11) | |
| 7 | F | 3 | 350 | =RANK(C7,$C$2:$C$11) | |
| 8 | G | 10 | 200 | =RANK(C8,$C$2:$C$11) | |
| 9 | H | 9 | 260 | =RANK(C9,$C$2:$C$11) | |
| 10 | I | 8 | 220 | =RANK(C10,$C$2:$C$11) | |
| 11 | J | 5 | 385 | =RANK(C11,$C$2:$C$11) | |
| 12 | | | | | |
| 13 | | Correlation | =CORREL($B$2:$B$11,$D$2:$D$11) | | |
| 14 | | | | | |

| | A | B | C | D | E |
|---|---|---|---|---|---|
| 1 | Salesperson | Ranking of Potential | Two-Year Sales (units) | Sales Ranking | |
| 2 | A | 2 | 400 | 1 | |
| 3 | B | 4 | 360 | 3 | |
| 4 | C | 7 | 300 | 5 | |
| 5 | D | 1 | 295 | 6 | |
| 6 | E | 6 | 280 | 7 | |
| 7 | F | 3 | 350 | 4 | |
| 8 | G | 10 | 200 | 10 | |
| 9 | H | 9 | 260 | 8 | |
| 10 | I | 8 | 220 | 9 | |
| 11 | J | 5 | 385 | 2 | |
| 12 | | | | | |
| 13 | | Spearman Correlation | | 0.73 | |
| 14 | | | | | |

tasks involved. The formula worksheet is in the background; the value worksheet is in the foreground.

**Enter Data:**   The data for the salespersons are entered in cells B2:C11. The data in column B are the ranks of the potential of the salespersons, and the data in columns B are sales over the first two years.

**Enter Functions and Formulas:**   We have used Excel's Rank function in column D to rank the salespersons with respect to sales over the first two years. We now want to apply Excel's CORREL function to compute the correlation between the ranks in columns B and D. Excel's CORREL function is used in cell C13 to make this calculation. In the value worksheet we see that the result is .73 and that the Pearson correlation coefficient applied to the ranked data does indeed provide the same value as the Spearman rank correlation coefficient.

## EXERCISES

## Methods

**32.**   Consider the following set of rankings for a sample of 10 elements.

| Element | $x_i$ | $y_i$ |
|---------|-------|-------|
| 1 | 10 | 8 |
| 2 | 6 | 4 |
| 3 | 7 | 10 |
| 4 | 3 | 2 |
| 5 | 4 | 5 |
| 6 | 2 | 7 |
| 7 | 8 | 6 |
| 8 | 5 | 3 |
| 9 | 1 | 1 |
| 10 | 9 | 9 |

  **a.**   Compute the Spearman rank-correlation coefficient for the data.
  **b.**   Test for significant rank correlation using $\alpha = .05$. What is your conclusion?

**33.**   Consider the following two sets of rankings for six items.

| | Case One | | | | Case Two | |
|---|---|---|---|---|---|---|
| Item | First Ranking | Second Ranking | | Item | First Ranking | Second Ranking |
| A | 1 | 1 | | A | 1 | 6 |
| B | 2 | 2 | | B | 2 | 5 |
| C | 3 | 3 | | C | 3 | 4 |
| D | 4 | 4 | | D | 4 | 3 |
| E | 5 | 5 | | E | 5 | 2 |
| F | 6 | 6 | | F | 6 | 1 |

Note that in the first case the rankings are identical, whereas in the second case the rankings are exactly opposite. What value should you expect for the Spearman rank-correlation coefficient for each of these cases? Explain. Calculate the rank-correlation coefficient for each case.

## Applications

**34.** For a sample of 11 states, the following table gives the ranks for pupil-teacher ratio (1 = lowest, 11 = highest) and expenditure per pupil (1 = highest, 11 = lowest).

| | Rank | | | | Rank | |
|---|---|---|---|---|---|---|
| **State** | **Pupil-Teacher Ratio** | **Expenditure per Pupil** | **State** | | **Pupil-Teacher Ratio** | **Expenditure per Pupil** |
| Arizona | 10 | 9 | Massachusetts | | 1 | 1 |
| Colorado | 8 | 5 | Nebraska | | 2 | 7 |
| Florida | 6 | 4 | North Dakota | | 7 | 8 |
| Idaho | 11 | 2 | South Dakota | | 5 | 10 |
| Iowa | 4 | 6 | Washington | | 9 | 3 |
| Louisiana | 3 | 11 | | | | |

At the $\alpha = .05$ level, does there appear to be a relationship between pupil-teacher ratio and expenditure per pupil?

**35.** A national study by Harris Interactive, Inc., evaluated the top Internet companies and their reputations (*The Wall Street Journal,* November 18, 1999). The following two lists show how 10 Internet companies ranked in terms of reputation and percentage of respondents who said they would purchase the company's stock. A positive rank correlation is anticipated because it seems reasonable to expect that a company with a higher reputation would be a more desirable purchase.

| Company | Reputation | Probable Purchase |
|---|---|---|
| Microsoft | 1 | 3 |
| Intel | 2 | 4 |
| Dell | 3 | 1 |
| Lucent | 4 | 2 |
| Texas Instruments | 5 | 9 |
| Cisco Systems | 6 | 5 |
| Hewlett-Packard | 7 | 10 |
| IBM | 8 | 6 |
| Motorola | 9 | 7 |
| Yahoo | 10 | 8 |

**a.** Compute the rank correlation between reputation and probable purchase.
**b.** Test for a significant positive rank correlation. What is the *p*-value?
**c.** Using $\alpha = .05$, what is your conclusion?

**36.** The 1996 rankings of a sample of professional golfers in both driving distance and putting follows (*Golf Digest,* January 1997). What is the rank correlation between driving distance and putting? Use a .10 level of significance.

| Professional Golfer | Driving Distance | Putting |
|---|---|---|
| Fred Couples | 1 | 5 |
| David Duval | 5 | 6 |
| Ernie Els | 4 | 10 |
| Nick Faldo | 9 | 2 |
| Tom Lehman | 6 | 7 |
| Justin Leonard | 10 | 3 |
| Davis Love III | 2 | 8 |
| Phil Mickelson | 3 | 9 |
| Greg Norman | 7 | 4 |
| Mark O'Meara | 8 | 1 |

**37.** A student organization surveyed both recent graduates and current students to obtain information on the quality of teaching at a particular university. An analysis of the responses provided the following rankings. Do the rankings given by the current students agree with the rankings given by the recent graduates? Use $\alpha = .10$ and test for a significant rank correlation.

| | Ranking by | |
| --- | --- | --- |
| **Professor** | **Current Students** | **Recent Graduates** |
| 1 | 4 | 6 |
| 2 | 6 | 8 |
| 3 | 8 | 5 |
| 4 | 3 | 1 |
| 5 | 1 | 2 |
| 6 | 2 | 3 |
| 7 | 5 | 7 |
| 8 | 10 | 9 |
| 9 | 7 | 4 |
| 10 | 9 | 10 |

## SUMMARY

In this chapter we have presented several statistical procedures that are classified as nonparametric methods. The parametric methods of the preceding chapters generally require interval or ratio data and often are based on assumptions about the population (for example, the assumption that the probability distribution is normal). Because nonparametric methods can be applied to nominal and ordinal data as well as interval and ratio data and do not require population distribution assumptions, they expand the class of problems that can be subjected to statistical analysis.

The sign test is a nonparametric procedure for identifying differences between two populations when the only data available are nominal data. In the small-sample case, the binominal probability distribution can be used to determine the critical values for the sign test; in the large-sample case, a normal approximation can be used. The Wilcoxon signed-rank test is a procedure for analyzing matched-sample data whenever interval- or ratio-scaled data are available for each matched pair. No assumptions are made about the population distribution. The Wilcoxon procedure tests the hypothesis that the two populations being considered are identical.

The Mann-Whitney-Wilcoxon test is a nonparametric method for testing for a difference between two populations based on two independent random samples. Tables were presented for the small-sample case, and a normal approximation was provided for the large-sample case. The Kruskal-Wallis test extends the Mann-Whitney-Wilcoxon test to the case of three or more populations. The Kruskal-Wallis test is the nonparametric analog of the parametric ANOVA test for differences among population means.

In the last section of this chapter we introduced the Spearman rank-correlation coefficient as a measure of association for two ordinal or rank-ordered sets of items. We have developed Excel worksheets for implementing most of these procedures.

## GLOSSARY

**Nonparametric methods**   Statistical methods that require few, if any, assumptions about the population probability distributions and the level of measurement.

**Distribution-free methods**   Another name for nonparametric statistical methods that indicates the lack of assumptions about the population probability distribution.

**Sign test**   A nonparametric statistical test for identifying differences between two populations based on the analysis of nominal data.

**Wilcoxon signed-rank test**   A nonparametric statistical test for identifying differences between two populations based on the analysis of two matched or paired samples.

**Mann-Whitney-Wilcoxon (MWW) test**   A nonparametric statistical test for identifying differences between two populations based on the analysis of two independent samples.

**Kruskal-Wallis test**   A nonparametric test for identifying differences among three or more populations.

**Spearman rank-correlation coefficient**   A correlation measure based on rank-ordered data for two variables.

## KEY FORMULAS

**Sign Test (Large-Sample Case)**

$$\text{Mean: } \mu = .50n \tag{17.1}$$

$$\text{Standard Deviation: } \sigma = \sqrt{.25n} \tag{17.2}$$

**Wilcoxon Signed-Rank Test**

$$\text{Mean: } \mu_T = 0 \tag{17.3}$$

$$\text{Standard Deviation: } \sigma_T = \sqrt{\frac{n(n+1)(2n+1)}{6}} \tag{17.4}$$

**Mann-Whitney-Wilcoxon Test (Large-Sample)**

$$\text{Mean: } \mu_T = \tfrac{1}{2}\, n_1(n_1 + n_2 + 1) \tag{17.6}$$

$$\text{Standard Deviation: } \sigma_T = \sqrt{\tfrac{1}{12}\, n_1 n_2 (n_1 + n_2 + 1)} \tag{17.7}$$

**Kruskal-Wallis Test Statistic**

$$W = \left[ \frac{12}{n_T(n_T + 1)} \sum_{i=1}^{k} \frac{R_i^2}{n_i} \right] - 3(n_T + 1) \tag{17.8}$$

**Spearman Rank-Correlation Coefficient**

$$r_s = 1 - \frac{6\Sigma d_i^2}{n(n^2 - 1)} \tag{17.9}$$

## SUPPLEMENTARY EXERCISES

**38.** The American Opinion Survey (*The Wall Street Journal,* March 4, 1997) asked the following question: Do you favor or oppose providing tax-funded vouchers or tax deductions to parents who send their children to private schools? Of the 2010 individuals surveyed, 905 favored the support, 1045 opposed the support, and 60 offered no opinion. Do the data indicate a significant difference in the preferences for the support for parents who send their children to private schools? Use a .05 level of significance.

**39.** The national median sales price of existing one-family homes is $118,000 (*The Wall Street Journal Almanac,* 1998). Assume that the following data were obtained for sales of existing one-family homes in Houston and Boston.

|  | Greater than $118,000 | Equal to $118,000 | Less than $118,000 |
|---|---|---|---|
| Houston | 11 | 2 | 32 |
| Boston | 27 | 1 | 13 |

    **a.** Is the median resale price in Houston lower than the national median of $118,000? Use a statistical test with $\alpha = .05$ to support your conclusion.

    **b.** Is the median resale price in Boston higher than the national median of $118,000? Use a statistical test with $\alpha = .05$ to support your conclusion.

**40.** Twelve consumers were asked to estimate the retail selling price of two models of refrigerators. Their estimates of selling price are shown in the following table. Use these data and test at the .05 level of significance to determine whether there is a difference between the two models in terms of consumers' perceptions of selling price.

**Refrigerator**

| Consumer | Model 1($) | Model 2($) | Consumer | Model 1($) | Model 2($) |
|---|---|---|---|---|---|
| 1 | 650 | 900 | 7 | 700 | 890 |
| 2 | 760 | 720 | 8 | 690 | 920 |
| 3 | 740 | 690 | 9 | 900 | 1000 |
| 4 | 700 | 850 | 10 | 500 | 690 |
| 5 | 590 | 920 | 11 | 610 | 700 |
| 6 | 620 | 800 | 12 | 720 | 700 |

**41.** A study was designed to evaluate the weight-gain potential of a new poultry feed. A sample of 12 chickens was used in a 6-week study. The weight of each chicken was recorded before and after the 6-week test period. The differences between the before and after weights of the 12 chickens are 1.5, 1.2, −.2, .0, .5, .7, .8, 1.0, .0, .6, .2, −.01. A negative value indicates a weight loss during the test period, whereas .0 indicates no weight change over the period. Use a .05 level of significance to determine whether the new feed appears to provide a weight gain for the chickens.

**42.** The following data are product weights for items produced on two production lines. Test for a difference between the product weights for the two lines. Use $\alpha = .10$.

| Production Line 1 | Production Line 2 |
|---|---|
| 13.6 | 13.7 |
| 13.8 | 14.1 |
| 14.0 | 14.2 |
| 13.9 | 14.0 |
| 13.4 | 14.6 |
| 13.2 | 13.5 |
| 13.3 | 14.4 |
| 13.6 | 14.8 |
| 12.9 | 14.5 |
| 14.4 | 14.3 |
|  | 15.0 |
|  | 14.9 |

**43.** A client wants to determine whether there is a significant difference in the time required to complete a program evaluation with the three different methods that are in common use. The times (in hours) required for each of 18 evaluators to conduct a program evaluation follow.

| Method 1 | Method 2 | Method 3 |
|:---:|:---:|:---:|
| 68 | 62 | 58 |
| 74 | 73 | 67 |
| 65 | 75 | 69 |
| 76 | 68 | 57 |
| 77 | 72 | 59 |
| 72 | 70 | 62 |

Use $\alpha = .05$ and test to see whether there is a significant difference in the time required by the three methods.

**44.** A sample of 20 engineers who have been with a company for three years has been rank-ordered with respect to managerial potential. Some of the engineers have attended the company's management development course, others have attended an off-site management development program at a local university, and the remainder have not attended any program. Use the following rankings and $\alpha = .025$ to test for a significant difference in the managerial potential of the three groups.

| Company Program | Off-Site Program | No Program |
|:---:|:---:|:---:|
| 12 | 7 | 16 |
| 20 | 1 | 9 |
| 17 | 4 | 10 |
| 19 | 2 | 15 |
| 6 | 3 | 11 |
| 18 | 8 | 13 |
| 14 | 5 | |

**45.** Course evaluation ratings for four instructors follow. Use $\alpha = .05$ and the Kruskal-Wallis procedure to test for a significant difference in teaching abilities.

| Instructor | Course Evaluation Rating | | | | | | | | |
|:---|:---:|:---:|:---:|:---:|:---:|:---:|:---:|:---:|:---:|
| Black | 88 | 80 | 79 | 68 | 96 | 69 | | | |
| Jennings | 87 | 78 | 82 | 85 | 99 | 99 | 85 | 94 | |
| Swanson | 88 | 76 | 68 | 82 | 85 | 82 | 84 | 83 | 81 |
| Wilson | 80 | 85 | 56 | 71 | 89 | 87 | | | |

**46.** A sample of 15 students received the following rankings on midterm and final examinations in a statistics course.

| Rank | | Rank | | Rank | |
|:---:|:---:|:---:|:---:|:---:|:---:|
| **Midterm** | **Final** | **Midterm** | **Final** | **Midterm** | **Final** |
| 1 | 4 | 6 | 2 | 11 | 14 |
| 2 | 7 | 7 | 5 | 12 | 15 |
| 3 | 1 | 8 | 12 | 13 | 11 |
| 4 | 3 | 9 | 6 | 14 | 10 |
| 5 | 8 | 10 | 9 | 15 | 13 |

Compute the Spearman rank-correlation coefficient for the data and test for a significant correlation with $\alpha = .10$.

# SAMPLE SURVEY

Chapter 18

**CONTENTS**

## STATISTICS IN PRACTICE

### CINERGY*
*Cincinnati, Ohio*

Cinergy, formerly Cincinnati Gas & Electric Company (CG&E), is a public utility that provides gas and electric power to customers in the Greater Cincinnati area. To improve service to its customers, Cinergy continually strives to stay up-to-date with its customers' needs. Cinergy undertook a sample survey, the Building Characteristics Survey, to learn about the energy requirements of commercial buildings in its service area.

A variety of information concerning commercial buildings was sought, such as the floor space, number of employees, energy end-use, age of the building, type of building materials, and energy conservation measures. During preparations for the survey, Cinergy analysts determined that approximately 27,000 commercial buildings were in operation in the Cinergy service area. Based on available funds and the precision desired in the results, they recommended that a sample of 616 commercial buildings be surveyed.

The sample design chosen was stratified simple random sampling. Total electrical usage over the past year for each commercial building in the service area was available from company records, and because many of the building characteristics of interest (size, number of employees, etc.) were related to usage, it was the criterion used to divide the population of buildings into six strata.

The first stratum contained the commercial buildings for the 100 largest energy users; each building in this stratum was included in the sample. Although these buildings constituted only .2% of the population, they accounted for 14.4% of the total electrical

Statistical surveys enable Cinergy Company to determine the energy needs of its customers. © PhotoDisc, Inc.

usage. For the other strata, the number of buildings sampled was determined on the basis of obtaining the greatest precision possible per unit cost.

A questionnaire was carefully developed and pretested before the actual survey was conducted. Data were collected through personal interviews. Completed surveys totaled 526 out of the sample of 616 commercial buildings. This response rate of 85.4% was considered to be excellent. Currently, Cinergy is using the survey results to improve the forecasts of energy demand and to improve service to its commercial customers.

In this chapter you will learn about the issues that statisticians consider in the design and execution of a sample survey such as the one conducted by Cinergy. Sample surveys are often used to develop profiles of a company's customers; they are also used by the government and other agencies to learn about various segments of the population.

---

*The authors are indebted to Jim Riddle of Cinergy for providing this Statistics in Practice.

## 18.1   TERMINOLOGY USED IN SAMPLE SURVEYS

In Chapter 1 we gave the following definitions of an element, a population, and a sample.

- An **element** is the entity on which data are collected.
- A **population** is the collection of all the elements of interest.
- A **sample** is a subset of the population.

To illustrate these concepts, consider the following situation. Dunning Microsystems, Inc. (DMI), a manufacturer of personal computers and peripherals, would like to collect data about the characteristics of individuals who have purchased a DMI personal computer. To obtain such data, a sample survey of DMI personal computer owners could be conducted. The *elements* in this sample survey would be individuals who have purchased a DMI personal computer. The *population* would be the collection of all people who have purchased a DMI personal computer, and the *sample* would be the subset of DMI personal computer owners who are surveyed.

In sample surveys it is necessary to distinguish between the target population and the sampled population. The **target population** is the population we want to make inferences about, while the **sampled population** is the population from which the sample is actually selected. It is important to understand that these two populations are not always the same. In the DMI example, the target population consists of all people who have purchased a DMI personal computer. The sampled population, however, might be all owners who have sent warranty registration cards back to DMI. Not every person who buys a DMI personal computer sends in the warranty card, so the sampled population would differ from the target population.

Conclusions drawn from a sample survey apply only to the sampled population. Whether these conclusions can be extended to the target population depends on the judgment of the analyst. The key issue is whether the correspondence between the sampled population and the target population on the elements of interest is close enough to allow this extension.

*If inferences from a sample are to be valid, the sampled population must be representative of the target population.*

Before sampling, the population must be divided into **sampling units.** In some cases, the sampling units are simply the elements. In other cases, the sampling units are groups of the elements. For example, suppose we want to survey certified professional engineers who are involved in the design of heating and air conditioning systems for commercial buildings. If a list of all professional engineers involved in such work were available, the sampling units would be the professional engineers we want to survey. If such a list is not available, we must find an alternative approach. A business telephone directory might provide a list of all engineering firms involved in the design of heating and air conditioning systems. Given this list, we could select a sample of the engineering firms to survey; then, for each firm surveyed, we might interview all the professional engineers. In this case, the engineering firms would be the sampling units and the engineers interviewed would be the elements.

A list of the sampling units for a particular study is called a **frame.** In the sample survey of professional engineers, the frame is defined as all engineering firms listed in the business telephone directory; the frame is not a list of all professional engineers because no such list is available. The choice of a particular frame and hence the definition of the sampling units is often determined by the availability and reliability of a list. In practice, the development of the frame can be one of the most difficult and important steps in conducting a sample survey.

## 18.2    TYPES OF SURVEYS AND SAMPLING METHODS

The three most common types of surveys are mail surveys, telephone surveys, and personal interview surveys; each of these types involves the design and administration of a questionnaire. Other types of surveys used to collect data do not involve questionnaires. For example, accounting firms are often hired to sample a company's inventory of goods to estimate the value of inventory on the company's balance sheet. In such surveys, someone simply counts the items and records the results.

In surveys that use questionnaires, the design of the questionnaire is critical. The designer must resist the temptation to include questions that *might* be of interest, because every question adds to the length of the questionnaire. Long questionnaires lead not only to

Survey costs are lower for mail and telephone surveys. But with well-trained interviewers, higher response rates and longer questionnaires are possible with personal interviews. Given the amount of data collected on each element, personal interviews were the only way to collect the data for the Cinergy study in the Statistics in Practice feature in this chapter.

respondent fatigue, but also to interviewer fatigue, especially in mail and telephone surveys. However, if personal interviews are to be used, a longer and more complex questionnaire is feasible. A large body of knowledge exists concerning the phrasing, sequencing, and grouping of questions for a questionnaire. These issues are discussed in more comprehensive books on survey sampling; several sources for this type of information are listed in the bibliography.

Sample surveys can also be classified in terms of the sampling method used. With **probabilistic sampling,** the probability of obtaining each possible sample can be computed; with a **nonprobabilistic sampling,** this probability is unknown. Nonprobabilistic sampling methods should not be used if the researcher wants to make statements about the precision of the estimates. In contrast, probabilistic sampling methods can be used to develop confidence intervals that provide bounds on the sampling error. In the following sections, four of the most popular probabilistic sampling methods are discussed: simple random sampling, stratified simple random sampling, cluster sampling, and systematic sampling.

Although statisticians prefer to use a probabilistic sampling method, nonprobabilistic sampling methods often are necessary. The advantages of nonprobabilistic sampling methods are their low expense and ease of implementation. The disadvantage is that statistically valid statements cannot be made about the precision of the estimates. Two of the more common nonprobabilistic methods are convenience sampling and judgment sampling.

With **convenience sampling,** the units included in the sample are chosen because of accessibility. For example, a professor conducting a research study at a university may ask student volunteers to participate in the study simply because they are in the professor's class; in this case, the sample of students is referred to as a convenience sample. In some situations, convenience sampling is the only practical approach. For example, to sample a shipment of oranges, an inspector might select oranges haphazardly from several crates since labeling each orange in the entire shipment to create a frame and employing a probabilistic sampling method would be impractical. Wildlife captures and volunteer panels for consumer research are other examples of convenience samples.

Although convenience sampling is a relatively easy approach to sample selection and data gathering, it is impossible to evaluate the "goodness" of the sample statistics obtained in terms of their ability to estimate the population parameters of interest. A convenience sample may provide good results or it may not; no statistically justified procedures exist for making statistical inferences from the sample results. Nevertheless, at times some researchers apply a statistical method designed for a probability sample to the data gathered from a convenience sample. In doing so, the researcher may argue that the convenience sample can be treated as though it were a random sample in the sense that it is representative of the population. However, this argument should be questioned; one should be cautious in using a convenience sample to make statistical inferences about population parameters.

In using the nonprobability sampling technique referred to as **judgment sampling,** a person knowledgeable on the subject of the study selects sampling units that he or she feels are most representative of the population. Although judgment sampling is often a relatively easy way to select samples, users of the survey results must recognize that the quality of the results is dependent on the judgment of the person selecting the sample. Consequently, caution must be exercised in using judgment samples to make statistical inferences about a population parameter. In general, no statistical statements should be made about the precision of the results from a judgment sample.

With a nonprobabilistic sampling method, if methods can be employed to ensure that a representative sample is obtained, point estimates based on the sample can be useful. However, even then the precision of the results is unknown.

Both probabilistic and nonprobabilistic sampling methods can be used to select a sample. The advantage of nonprobabilistic methods is that they are generally inexpensive and easy to use. However, if it is necessary to provide statements about the precision of the estimates, a probabilistic sampling method must be used. Almost all large sample surveys employ probabilistic sampling methods.

## 18.3 SURVEY ERRORS

Two types of errors can occur in conducting a survey. One type, **sampling error,** is defined as the magnitude of the difference between the point estimator developed from the sample and the population parameter. In other words, sampling error is the error that occurs because not every element in the population is surveyed. The second type, **nonsampling error,** refers to all other types of errors that can occur when a survey is conducted, such as measurement error, interviewer error, and processing error. Although sampling error can occur only in a sample survey, nonsampling errors can occur in both a census and a sample survey.

*A census is a survey of the entire population.*

### Nonsampling Error

One of the most common types of nonsampling error occurs whenever we incorrectly measure the characteristic of interest. Measurement error can occur in a census or a sample survey. For either type of survey, the researcher must exercise care to ensure that any measuring instruments (e.g., the questionnaire) are properly calibrated and that the people who take the measurements are properly trained. Attention to detail is the best precaution in most situations.

*Nonsampling error can be minimized by proper interviewer training, good questionnaire design, pretesting, and careful management of the process of coding and transferring the data to the computer.*

Errors due to nonresponse are a concern to both the statistician responsible for designing the survey and the manager using the results. This type of nonsampling error occurs when data cannot be obtained for some of the elements surveyed or when only partial data are obtained. The problem is most serious when a bias is created. For example, if interviews were conducted to assess women's attitudes toward working outside the home, making calls to homes only during the daytime would create an obvious bias because women who work outside the home would be excluded from the sample.

*In the 1990 U.S. Census, 25.9% of households did not respond. Census 2000 employed a sample survey of nonrespondents to estimate the characteristics of this portion of the population.*

Nonsampling errors due to lack of respondent knowledge are common in technical surveys. For example, suppose building managers were surveyed to obtain detailed information about the types of ventilation systems used in office buildings. Managers of large office buildings may be especially knowledgeable about such systems because they may attend training seminars and have support staff to help keep them current. In contrast, managers of smaller office buildings may be less knowledgeable about such systems because of the wide variety of duties they must perform. This difference in knowledge can significantly affect the survey results.

Two other types of nonsampling error are selection error and processing error. Selection errors occur when an inappropriate item is included in the survey. Suppose a sample survey was designed to develop a profile of men with beards; if some interviewers interpreted the statement "men with beards" to include men with mustaches while other interviewers did not, the resulting data would be flawed. Processing errors occur whenever data are incorrectly recorded or incorrectly transferred from recording forms, such as from questionnaires to computer files.

Although some nonsampling errors will occur in most surveys, they can be minimized by careful planning. Care should be taken to ensure that the sampled population corresponds closely to the target population, good questionnaire design principles are followed, interviewers are well trained, and so on. The final report on a survey should include some discussion of the likely impact of nonsampling errors on the results.

### Sampling Error

Recall the Dunning Microsystems (DMI) sample survey introduced in Section 18.1. Suppose DMI wants to estimate the mean age of people who have purchased a DMI personal computer. If the entire population of DMI personal computer owners could be surveyed (a census) and nonsampling errors were not present, we could determine the mean age exactly. But what if less than 100% of the population of DMI owners can be surveyed? In this case, there will most likely be a difference between the sample mean and the population mean; the absolute value of this difference is the sampling error. In practice, it is not possible to know what the sampling error will be for any one particular sample because the population mean is unknown; however, it is possible to provide probability statements about the size of the sampling error.

As stated, sampling error occurs because a sample, and not the entire population, is surveyed. Even though sampling error cannot be avoided, it can be controlled. Selecting an appropriate sampling method or design is one important way to control this type of error. In the following sections we will discuss four probabilistic sampling methods: simple random sampling, stratified simple random sampling, cluster sampling, and systematic sampling.

## 18.4 SIMPLE RANDOM SAMPLING

Recall the definition of simple random sampling from Chapter 7:

> A simple random sample of size $n$ from a finite population of size $N$ is a sample selected such that every possible sample of size $n$ has the same probability of being selected.

In Chapter 7, we showed how Excel could be used to select a simple random sample.

To conduct a sample survey using simple random sampling, we begin by developing a frame or list of all elements in the sampled population. Then a selection procedure, based on the use of random numbers, is used to ensure that each element in the sampled population has the same probability of being selected. In this section we show how estimates of a population mean, total, and proportion are made for sample surveys that use simple random sampling.

## Population Mean

In most sample surveys, the form of the probability distribution for the population is unknown. For example, in the DMI sample survey, management wants to estimate $\mu$, the mean age of people who have purchased a DMI personal computer. Most likely, DMI would not know the form of the probability distribution of age for the population of all DMI owners. Not knowing the form of the probability distribution for a population is usually not a problem because the properties of the sampling distribution of $\bar{x}$, the point estimator of $\mu$, depend primarily on the choice of the sample design.

In Chapter 7 we indicated that if a large ($n \geq 30$) simple random sample is selected, the central limit theorem enables us to conclude that the sampling distribution of $\bar{x}$ can be approximated by a normal probability distribution. In Chapter 8 we showed that for cases where the sampling distribution of $\bar{x}$ can be approximated by a normal probability distribution, an interval estimate of $\mu$ is given by

$$\bar{x} \pm z_{\alpha/2}\sigma_{\bar{x}} \tag{18.1}$$

where

$$\sigma_{\bar{x}} = \text{standard error of the mean.}$$

Recall that $1 - \alpha$ is the confidence coefficient, and $z_{\alpha/2}$ is the $z$ value providing an area of $\alpha/2$ in the upper tail of the standard normal probability distribution. For example, for a 95% confidence interval, $z_{.025} = 1.96$. Note also that the standard error of the mean, $\sigma_{\bar{x}}$, is just the standard deviation of the sampling distribution of $\bar{x}$. In general, whenever we use the term *standard error* in this chapter, we will be referring to the standard deviation of the sampling distribution for the point estimator being considered.

When a simple random sample of size $n$ is selected from a finite population of size $N$, an estimate of the standard error of the mean is

$$s_{\bar{x}} = \sqrt{\frac{N-n}{N}} \left( \frac{s}{\sqrt{n}} \right) \qquad (18.2)$$

In this case, the interval estimate of the population mean becomes

$$\bar{x} \pm z_{\alpha/2} s_{\bar{x}} \qquad (18.3)$$

Use of $z = 2$ is based on the assumption that the sampling distribution is approximately normal; approximately 95% of the data for such a distribution lie within 2 standard deviations of the mean.
In a sample survey it is common practice to use a value of $z = 2$ when developing interval estimates. Thus, when simple random sampling is used, an approximate 95% confidence interval estimate of the population mean is given by the following expression.

**Approximate 95% Confidence Interval Estimate of the Population Mean**

$$\bar{x} \pm 2 s_{\bar{x}} \qquad (18.4)$$

As an example, consider the situation of the publisher of *Great Lakes Recreation,* a regional magazine specializing in articles on boating and fishing. The magazine currently has $N = 8000$ subscribers. A simple random sample of $n = 484$ subscribers shows mean annual income to be $30,500 with a standard deviation of $7040. An unbiased estimate of the mean annual income of all subscribers is given by $\bar{x} = \$30,500$. Using the sample results and equation (18.2), we obtain the following estimate of the standard error of the mean.

$$s_{\bar{x}} = \sqrt{\frac{8000-484}{8000}} \left( \frac{7040}{\sqrt{484}} \right) = 310$$

Therefore, using equation (18.4), we find that an approximate 95% confidence interval estimate of the mean annual income for the magazine subscribers is

$$30,500 \pm 2(310) = 30,500 \pm 620$$

or $29,880 to $31,120.

The preceding procedure can be used to compute an interval estimate for other population parameters such as the population total or the population proportion. In all cases where the sampling distribution of the point estimator can be approximated by a normal probability distribution, the approximate 95% confidence interval can be written as

Point Estimator $\pm$ 2(Estimate of the Standard Error of the Point Estimator)

In sample survey terminology, the $\pm$ value is often referred to as the bound on the sampling error. It is the same as the margin of error discussed in Chapter 8.
For example, in the *Great Lakes Recreation* sample survey, an estimate of the standard error of the point estimator is $s_{\bar{x}} = \$310$, and the **bound on the sampling error** is 2($310) = $620. In general, when estimating a population mean the bound on the sampling error is $2\,s_{\bar{x}}$.

## Population Total

Consider the problem facing Northeast Electric and Gas (NEG). As part of an energy usage study, NEG needs to estimate the total square footage for the 500 public schools in its service area. We will denote the total square footage for the 500 schools as $X$; in other words,

$X$ denotes the population total. Note that if $\mu$, the mean square footage for the 500 public schools, were known, the value of $X$ could be computed by multiplying $N$ times $\mu$. However, because $\mu$ is unknown, a point estimate of $X$ is obtained by multiplying $N$ times $\bar{x}$. We will denote the point estimator of $X$ as $\hat{X}$.

**Point Estimator of a Population Total**

$$\hat{X} = N\bar{x} \tag{18.5}$$

An estimate of the standard error of this point estimator is given by

$$s_{\hat{X}} = Ns_{\bar{x}} \tag{18.6}$$

where

$$s_{\bar{x}} = \sqrt{\frac{N-n}{N}}\left(\frac{s}{\sqrt{n}}\right) \tag{18.7}$$

Note that equation (18.7) is the formula for the estimated standard error of the mean. With this standard error and equation (18.6), an approximate 95% confidence interval for the population total is given by the following expression.

When estimating a population total, the bound on the sampling error is $2s_{\hat{X}}$.

**Approximate 95% Confidence Interval Estimate of the Population Total**

$$N\bar{x} \pm 2s_{\hat{X}} \tag{18.8}$$

**NEG**

Suppose that in the NEG study a simple random sample of $n = 50$ public schools is selected from the population of $N = 500$ schools. The data for the NEG study are shown in the data set named NEG; the sample mean is $\bar{x} = 22{,}000$ square feet and the sample standard deviation is $s = 4000$ square feet. Using equation (18.5), we find that the point estimator of the population total is

$$\hat{X} = (500)(22{,}000) = 11{,}000{,}000$$

Equation (18.7) can be used to compute an estimate of the standard error of the mean.

$$s_{\bar{x}} = \sqrt{\frac{500-50}{500}}\left(\frac{4000}{\sqrt{50}}\right) = 536.66$$

Then, using equation (18.6), we can obtain an estimate of the standard error of $\hat{X}$.

$$s_{\hat{X}} = (500)(536.66) = 268{,}330$$

Therefore, using equation (18.8), we find that an approximate 95% confidence interval estimate of the total square footage for the 500 public schools in NEG's service area is

$$11{,}000{,}000 \pm 2(268{,}330) = 11{,}000{,}000 \pm 536{,}660$$

or 10,463,340 to 11,536,660 square feet.

## Population Proportion

The population proportion $p$ is the fraction of the elements in the population with some characteristic of interest. In a market research study, for example, one might be interested in the proportion of consumers preferring a certain brand of product. The sample proportion $\bar{p}$ is an unbiased point estimator of the population proportion. An estimate of the standard error of the proportion is given by

$$s_{\bar{p}} = \sqrt{\left(\frac{N - n}{N}\right)\left(\frac{\bar{p}(1 - \bar{p})}{n - 1}\right)} \qquad (18.9)$$

An approximate 95% confidence interval estimate of the population proportion is given by the following expression.

When estimating a population proportion, the bound on the sampling error is $2s_{\bar{p}}$.

**Approximate 95% Confidence Interval Estimate of the Population Proportion**

$$\bar{p} \pm 2s_{\bar{p}} \qquad (18.10)$$

As an illustration, suppose that in the Northeast Electric and Gas sampling problem, NEG would also like to estimate the proportion of the 500 public schools in its service area that use natural gas as fuel for heating. If 35 of the 50 sampled schools indicate the use of natural gas, the point estimate of the proportion of the 500 schools in the population that use natural gas is $\bar{p} = 35/50 = .70$. Using equation (18.9), we can compute an estimate of the standard error of the proportion.

$$s_{\bar{p}} = \sqrt{\left(\frac{500 - 50}{500}\right)\left(\frac{.7(1 - .7)}{50 - 1}\right)} = .0621$$

Therefore, using equation (18.10), we find that an approximate 95% confidence interval for the population proportion is

$$.7 \pm 2(.0621) = .7 \pm .1242$$

or .5758 to .8242.

As this example has shown, the width of the confidence interval can be rather large when one is estimating a population proportion. In general, large sample sizes are needed to obtain precise estimates of population proportions. A report of a sample survey of 529 mutual fund investors conducted by Louis Harris & Associates stated, "Results should be accurate to within 4.3 percentage points" (*Business Week*, August 15, 1994). This implies an approximate 95% confidence interval with a width of .086. For large populations, samples of $n = 1200$ or more are often used.

## Using Excel for Simple Random Sampling

We assume the Excel procedure described in Chapter 7 has been used to select the sample.

To show how Excel can be used to summarize the results for sample surveys that use simple random sampling, we will construct an approximate 95% confidence interval of the population mean, population total, and population proportion for the NEG study. We begin with the population total case. Refer to Figure 18.1 as we describe the tasks involved. The formula worksheet is in the background; the value worksheet is in the foreground.

**Enter Data:**  Column A identifies the school in the sample, and column B shows the number of square feet in the school.

**FIGURE 18.1    EXCEL WORKSHEET FOR THE NEG STUDY: POPULATION TOTAL**

| | A | B | C | D | E |
|---|---|---|---|---|---|
| 1 | School | Square Feet | | Interval Estimate of a Population Total | |
| 2 | 1 | 22500 | | | |
| 3 | 2 | 20335 | | Population Size | 500 |
| 4 | 3 | 26181 | | Sample Size | =COUNT(B2:B51) |
| 5 | 4 | 15998 | | Mean | =AVERAGE(B2:B51) |
| 6 | 5 | 29064 | | Standard Deviation | =STDEV(B2:B51) |
| 7 | 6 | 29278 | | | |
| 8 | 7 | 26494 | | Standard Error of Mean | =(SQRT((E3-E4)/E3))*(E6/SQRT(E4)) |
| 9 | 8 | 20293 | | Standard Error of Total | =E3*E8 |
| 10 | 9 | 19999 | | Bound on Sampling Error | =2*E9 |
| 11 | 10 | 18275 | | | |
| 12 | 11 | 21187 | | Point Estimate | =E3*E5 |
| 13 | 12 | 20772 | | Lower Limit | =E12-E10 |
| 14 | 13 | 28321 | | Upper Limit | =E12+E10 |
| 15 | 14 | 20863 | | | |
| 50 | 49 | 19627 | | | |
| 51 | 50 | 24544 | | | |
| 52 | | | | | |

Note: Rows 16–49 are hidden.

| | A | B | C | D | E |
|---|---|---|---|---|---|
| 1 | School | Square Feet | | Interval Estimate of a Population Total | |
| 2 | 1 | 22500 | | | |
| 3 | 2 | 20335 | | Population Size | 500 |
| 4 | 3 | 26181 | | Sample Size | 50 |
| 5 | 4 | 15998 | | Mean | 22000 |
| 6 | 5 | 29064 | | Standard Deviation | 4000.0103 |
| 7 | 6 | 29278 | | | |
| 8 | 7 | 26494 | | Standard Error of Mean | 536.6577 |
| 9 | 8 | 20293 | | Standard Error of Total | 268328.8497 |
| 10 | 9 | 19999 | | Bound on Sampling Error | 536657.6994 |
| 11 | 10 | 18275 | | | |
| 12 | 11 | 21187 | | Point Estimate | 11000000 |
| 13 | 12 | 20772 | | Lower Limit | 10463342.3006 |
| 14 | 13 | 28321 | | Upper Limit | 11536657.6994 |
| 15 | 14 | 20863 | | | |
| 50 | 49 | 19627 | | | |
| 51 | 50 | 24544 | | | |
| 52 | | | | | |

**Enter Functions and Formulas:**    The descriptive statistics needed are provided in cells E3:E6. Excel's COUNT, AVERAGE, and STDEV functions are used to compute the sample size, sample mean, and sample standard deviation, respectively.

Cells E8:E10 are used to compute the standard error of the mean, standard error of the total, and the bound on the sampling error. The standard error of the mean was computed using equation (18.2) by entering the formula =(SQRT((E3-E4)/E3))*(E6/SQRT(E4)) into cell E8. The standard error of the total was computed using equation (18.6) by entering the formula =E3*E8 into cell E9, and the bound on the sampling error was computed in cell E10 by entering the formula =2*E9. The value worksheet shows that the standard error of the mean is 536.6577, the standard error of the total is 268328.8497, and the bound on the sampling error is 536657.6994.

Cells E12:E14 provide the point estimate and the lower and upper limits for the confidence interval. Because the point estimate of the population total is just the population size times the sample mean, we entered the formula =E3*E5 into cell E12. To compute the lower limit of the 95% confidence interval, the formula =E12-E10 was entered into cell E13; to compute the upper limit, the formula =E12+E10 was entered into cell E14. The value worksheet shows that the point estimate of the population total is 11,000,000 and that the 95% approximate interval is 10,463,342 to 11,536,658. The differences in the Excel values and the hand calculations we computed previously are due simply to the fact that in doing the hand calculations we rounded the intermediate calculations to simplify the presentation.

It is easy to compute an approximate 95% confidence interval for the population mean in the NEG study by modifying the worksheet developed to compute the approximate 95% confidence interval of the population total. For this case, the point estimate shown in cell E12 is just the sample mean in cell E5; thus, we would enter the formula =E5 into cell E12. The bound on the sampling error would be 2 times the standard error of the mean in cell E8; thus, we would enter the formula =2*E8 into cell E10. The resulting lower and upper limits in cells E13:E14 would be the upper and lower limits of the approximate 95% confidence interval of the population mean.

To show how Excel can be used to compute an approximate 95% confidence interval of the population proportion, we will compute an approximate 95% confidence interval of the proportion of schools in the NEG study that use natural gas as fuel for heating. Refer to Figure 18.2 as we describe the tasks involved. The formula worksheet is in the background; the value worksheet is in the foreground.

**Enter Data:**    Column A identifies the school, and column B indicates whether the school uses natural gas as fuel for heating.

**Enter Functions and Formulas:**    The descriptive statistics needed are provided in cells E3:E7. The population size and response of interest are typed into cells E3 and E5. Excel's COUNTA and COUNTIF functions are used to compute the sample size and the number of schools in the sample that use natural gas. The value worksheet shows that 35 schools use natural gas and that the sample proportion is .7.

Cells E9:E10 are used to compute the standard error of the proportion and the bound on the sampling error. The standard error of the proportion was computed using equation (18.9) by entering the formula =SQRT(((E3-E4)/E3)*(E7*(1-E7))/E4-1)) into cell E9. The bound on the sampling error was computed in cell E10 by entering the formula =2*E9. The value worksheet shows that the value of the standard error of the proportion is .0621 and that the bound on the sampling error is .1242.

**FIGURE 18.2**    EXCEL WORKSHEET FOR THE NEG STUDY: POPULATION PROPORTION

Note: Rows 16–49 are hidden.

Cells E12:E14 provide the point estimate and the lower and upper limits for the confidence interval. Because the point estimate of the population proportion is just the sample proportion, we entered the formula =E7 into cell E12. To compute the lower limit of the 95% confidence interval, the formula =E12-E10 was entered into cell E13; to compute the upper limit, the formula =E12+E10 was entered into cell E14. The value worksheet shows that the point estimate of the population proportion is .7 and that the 95% approximate interval is .5758 to .8242.

## Determining the Sample Size

An important consideration in sample design is the choice of sample size. The best choice usually involves a trade-off between cost and precision. Larger samples provide greater precision (tighter bounds on the sampling error), but are more costly. Often the budget for a study will dictate how large the sample can be. In other cases, the size of the sample must be large enough to provide a specified level of precision.

A common approach to choosing the sample size is to first specify the precision desired and then determine the smallest sample size providing that precision. In this context, the term *precision* refers to the size of the approximate confidence interval; smaller confidence intervals provide more precision. Because the size of the approximate confidence interval depends on the bound $B$ on the sampling error, choosing a level of precision amounts to choosing a value for $B$. Let us see how this approach works in choosing the sample size necessary to estimate the population mean.

Equation (18.2) showed that the estimate of the standard error of the mean is

$$s_{\bar{x}} = \sqrt{\frac{N-n}{N}}\left(\frac{s}{\sqrt{n}}\right)$$

Recall that the bound on the sampling error is "2 times the estimate of the standard error of the point estimator." Thus,

$$B = 2\sqrt{\frac{N-n}{N}}\left(\frac{s}{\sqrt{n}}\right) \tag{18.11}$$

Solving equation (18.11) for $n$ will provide a bound on the sampling error equal to $B$. Doing so yields

$$n = \frac{Ns^2}{N\left(\dfrac{B^2}{4}\right) + s^2} \tag{18.12}$$

Once a desired level of precision has been selected (by choosing a value for $B$), equation (18.12) can be used to find the value of $n$ that will provide the desired level of precision. Using equation (18.12) to choose $n$ for a practical study presents problems, however. In addition to specifying the desired bound on the sampling error $B$, one must know the sample variance $s^2$. But, $s^2$ will not be known until the sample is actually taken.

Cochran* suggests several ways to develop an estimate of $s^2$ in practice. Three of them are stated as the following:

1. Take the sample in two stages. Use the value of $s^2$ found in stage 1 in equation (18.12); the resulting value of $n$ is what the size of the total sample must be. Then, select the number of additional units needed at stage 2 to provide the total sample size determined in stage 1.
2. Use the results of a pilot survey or pretest to estimate $s^2$.
3. Use information from a previous sample.

---

*William G. Cochran, *Sampling Techniques*, 3rd ed., Wiley, 1977.

Let us now consider an example involving the estimate of the population mean for starting salaries of graduates of a particular university. Suppose $N = 5000$ graduates, and we want to develop an approximate 95% confidence interval with a width of at most $1000. To provide such a confidence interval, $B = 500$. Before using equation (18.12) to determine the sample size, we need an estimate of $s^2$. Suppose a study of starting salaries conducted last year found that $s = \$3000$. We can use the data from this previous sample to estimate $s^2$. Using $B = 500$, $s = 3000$, and $N = 5000$, we can now use equation (18.12) to determine the sample size.

$$n = \frac{5000(3000)^2}{5000\left(\dfrac{(500)^2}{4}\right) + (3000)^2}$$

$$= 139.97$$

Rounding up, we see that a sample size of 140 will provide an approximate 95% confidence interval of width $1000. Keep in mind, however, that this calculation is based on the initial estimate of $s = \$3000$. If $s$ turns out to be larger in this year's sample survey, the resulting approximate confidence interval will have a width greater than $1000. Consequently, if cost considerations permit, the survey designer might choose a sample size of, say, 150 to provide added assurance that the final approximate 95% confidence interval will have a width less than $1000.

The formula for determining the sample size necessary for estimating a population total with a bound $B$ on the sampling error is as follows.

$$n = \frac{Ns^2}{\left(\dfrac{B^2}{4N}\right) + s^2} \tag{18.13}$$

In the previous example, we wanted to estimate the mean starting salary with a bound on the sampling error of $B = 500$. Suppose we are also interested in estimating the total salary of all 5000 graduates with a bound of $2 million. We can use equation (18.13) with $B = 2,000,000$ to find the sample size needed to provide such a bound on the population total.

$$n = \frac{5000(3000)^2}{\dfrac{(2,000,000)^2}{4(5000)} + (3000)^2}$$

$$= 215.31$$

Rounding up, we see that a sample size of 216 is necessary to provide an approximate 95% confidence interval with a bound of $2 million. We note here that if the same survey is expected to provide a bound of $500 on the population mean and a bound of $2 million on the population total, a sample size of at least 216 must be used. This size will provide a tighter bound than necessary on the population mean, while providing the minimum desired precision for the population total.

To choose the sample size for estimating a population proportion, we use a formula similar to the one for the population mean. We simply substitute $\bar{p}(1 - \bar{p})$ for $s^2$ in equation (18.12) to obtain

$$n = \frac{N\bar{p}(1 - \bar{p})}{N\left(\dfrac{B^2}{4}\right) + \bar{p}(1 - \bar{p})} \tag{18.14}$$

To use equation (18.14), we must specify the desired bound $B$ and provide an estimate of $\bar{p}$. If a good estimate of $\bar{p}$ is not available, we can use $\bar{p} = .5$; it will ensure that the resulting approximate confidence interval will have a bound on the sampling error at least as small as desired.

## EXERCISES

### Methods

1. Simple random sampling has been used to obtain a sample of $n = 50$ elements from a population of $N = 800$. The sample mean was $\bar{x} = 215$, and the sample standard deviation was found to be $s = 20$.
   a. Estimate the population mean.
   b. Estimate the standard error of the mean.
   c. Develop an approximate 95% confidence interval for the population mean.

2. Simple random sampling has been used to obtain a sample of $n = 80$ elements from a population of $N = 400$. The sample mean was $\bar{x} = 75$, and the sample standard deviation was found to be $s = 8$.
   a. Estimate the population total.
   b. Estimate the standard error of the population total.
   c. Develop an approximate 95% confidence interval for the population total.

3. Simple random sampling has been used to obtain a sample of $n = 100$ elements from a population of $N = 1000$. The sample proportion was $\bar{p} = .30$.
   a. Estimate the population proportion.
   b. Estimate the standard error of the proportion.
   c. Develop an approximate 95% confidence interval for the population proportion.

4. A sample is to be taken to develop an approximate 95% confidence interval estimate of the population mean. The population consists of 450 elements, and a pilot study has resulted in $s = 70$. How large must the sample be if we want to develop an approximate 95% confidence interval with a width of 30?

### Applications

5. In 1996, the Small Business Administration (SBA) granted 771 government-guaranteed loans to small businesses in North Carolina. (*The Wall Street Journal Almanac*, 1998). Suppose a sample of 50 small businesses that received an SBA loan showed an average loan of $149,670 with a standard deviation of $73,420 and that 18 of the businesses in the sample were manufacturing companies.
   a. Develop an approximate 95% confidence interval for the population mean value of a loan.
   b. Develop an approximate 95% confidence interval for the total value of all 771 SBA loans in North Carolina.
   c. In the sample, 18 of the 50 businesses were involved in manufacturing. Develop an approximate 95% confidence interval for the proportion of loans involving manufacturing companies.

6. A county in California had 724 corporate tax returns filed. The mean annual income reported was $161,220 with a standard deviation of $31,300. How large a sample will be necessary next year to develop an approximate 95% confidence interval for mean annual corporate earnings? The precision required is an interval width of no more than $5000.

## 18.5 STRATIFIED SIMPLE RANDOM SAMPLING

In **stratified simple random sampling,** the population is first divided into $H$ groups, called strata. Then for stratum $h$ a simple random sample of size $n_h$ is selected. The data from the $H$ simple random samples are combined to develop an estimate of a population parameter such as the population mean, total, or proportion.

If the variability within each stratum is smaller than the variability across the strata, a stratified simple random sample can lead to greater precision (narrower interval estimates of the population parameters). The basis for forming the various strata depends on the judgment of the designer of the sample. Depending on the application, a population might be stratified by department, location, age, product type, industry type, sales levels, and so on.

As an example, suppose the College of Business at Lakeside College wants to conduct a survey of this year's graduating class to learn about their starting salaries. The five majors in the college are accounting, finance, information systems, marketing, and operations management. Of the $N = 1500$ students who graduated this year, there were $N_1 = 500$ accounting majors, $N_2 = 350$ finance majors, $N_3 = 200$ information systems majors, $N_4 = 300$ marketing majors, and $N_5 = 150$ operations management majors. Analysis of previous salary data suggests more variability in starting salaries across majors than within each major. As a result, a stratified simple random sample of $n = 180$ students was selected; 45 of the 180 students majored in accounting ($n_1 = 45$), 40 majored in finance ($n_2 = 40$), 30 majored in information systems ($n_3 = 30$), 35 majored in marketing ($n_4 = 35$), and 30 majored in operations management ($n_5 = 30$).

## Population Mean

In stratified sampling an unbiased estimate of the population mean is obtained by computing a weighted average of the sample means for each stratum. The weights used are the fraction of the population in each stratum. The resulting point estimator, denoted $\bar{x}_{st}$, is defined as follows.

**Point Estimator of the Population Mean**

$$\bar{x}_{st} = \sum_{h=1}^{H}\left(\frac{N_h}{N}\right)\bar{x}_h \qquad (18.15)$$

$H$ = number of strata
$\bar{x}_h$ = sample mean for stratum $h$
$N_h$ = number of elements in the population in stratum $h$
$N$ = total number of elements in the population; $N = N_1 + N_2 + \cdots + N_H$

For stratified simple random sampling, the formula for computing an estimate of the standard error of the mean is a function of $s_h$, the sample standard deviation for stratum $h$. The resulting point estimator, denoted $s_{\bar{x}_{st}}$, is defined as follows.

$$s_{\bar{x}_{st}} = \sqrt{\frac{1}{N^2}\sum_{h=1}^{H}N_h(N_h - n_h)\frac{s_h^2}{n_h}} \qquad (18.16)$$

Using these results, we see that an approximate 95% confidence interval estimate of the population mean is given by the following expression.

**Approximate 95% Confidence Interval Estimate of the Population Mean**

$$\bar{x}_{st} \pm 2s_{\bar{x}_{st}} \qquad (18.17)$$

**Lakeland**

The survey of 180 graduates of the College of Business at Lakeland College provided the sample results shown in the data set named Lakeland; a summary of the starting salaries is shown in Table 18.1. The sample means for each major, or stratum, are $35,000 for

**TABLE 18.1**     LAKELAND COLLEGE SAMPLE SURVEY OF STARTING SALARIES OF GRADUATES

| Major ($h$) | $\bar{x}_h$ | $s_h$ | $N_h$ | $n_h$ |
|---|---|---|---|---|
| Accounting | $35,000 | 2000 | 500 | 45 |
| Finance | $33,500 | 1700 | 350 | 40 |
| Information systems | $41,500 | 2300 | 200 | 30 |
| Marketing | $32,000 | 1600 | 300 | 35 |
| Operations management | $36,000 | 2250 | 150 | 30 |

accounting, $33,500 for finance, $41,500 for information systems, $32,000 for marketing, and $36,000 for operations management. Using these results and equation (18.15), we can compute a point estimate of the population mean.

$$\bar{x}_{st} = \left(\frac{500}{1500}\right)(35,000) + \left(\frac{350}{1500}\right)(33,500) + \left(\frac{200}{1500}\right)(41,500)$$
$$+ \left(\frac{300}{1500}\right)(32,000) + \left(\frac{150}{1500}\right)(36,000) = 35,017$$

In Table 18.2 we show a portion of the calculations needed to estimate the standard error; note that

$$\sum_{h=1}^{5} N_h(N_h - n_h)\frac{s_h^2}{n_h} = 42,909,037,698$$

**TABLE 18.2**     PARTIAL CALCULATIONS FOR THE ESTIMATE OF THE STANDARD ERROR OF THE MEAN FOR THE LAKELAND COLLEGE SAMPLE SURVEY

| Major | $h$ | $N_h(N_h - n_h)\dfrac{s_h^2}{n_h}$ |
|---|---|---|
| Accounting | 1 | $500(500 - 45)\dfrac{(2000)^2}{45} = 20,222,222,222$ |
| Finance | 2 | $350(350 - 40)\dfrac{(1700)^2}{40} = 7,839,125,000$ |
| Information systems | 3 | $200(200 - 30)\dfrac{(2300)^2}{30} = 5,995,333,333$ |
| Marketing | 4 | $300(300 - 35)\dfrac{(1600)^2}{35} = 5,814,857,143$ |
| Operations management | 5 | $150(150 - 30)\dfrac{(2250)^2}{30} = \underline{3,037,500,000}$ |
| | | $42,909,037,698$ |

$$\sum_{h=1}^{5} N_h(N_h - n_h)\frac{s_h^2}{n_h}$$

Thus,

$$s_{\bar{x}_{st}} = \sqrt{\left(\frac{1}{(1500)^2}\right)(42,909,037,698)} = \sqrt{19,070.68} = 138$$

Hence, using expression (18.17), we find that an approximate 95% confidence interval estimate of the population mean is $35,017 \pm 2(138) = 35,017 \pm 276$, or $34,741 to $35,293.

## Using Excel: Population Mean

To show how Excel can be used for sample surveys that use stratified simple random sampling we will construct an approximate 95% confidence interval of the population mean for the Lakeland College sample survey. In a separate worksheet for each stratum (major), we have computed the sample mean and sample standard deviation for that stratum. Another worksheet is used to summarize the calculations needed to compute an approximate 95% confidence interval of the population mean. A copy of this summary worksheet is shown in Figure 18.3. The formula worksheet is in the background; the value worksheet is in the foreground.

**Enter Data:**    The worksheet shown in Figure 18.3 summarizes the starting salary data that appears in the worksheets for the separate strata of the Lakeland data set. Note that the standard deviations shown in cells C3:C7 were rounded to the nearest dollar.

**Enter Functions and Formulas:**    The descriptive statistics needed are provided in cells B3:E7. The strata means and standard deviations were calculated in the separate worksheets for each major and entered as constants in the summary worksheet. Cells F3:G7 represent partial calculations required to compute the point estimate of the population mean and the estimate of the standard error of the mean. To compute the weighted sample mean for the accounting majors we entered the formula $=(D3/\$D\$8)*B3$ into cell F3; we then copied

*Cells F3:F8 computed $\bar{x}_{st}$ using equation (18.15).*

**FIGURE 18.3**    EXCEL SUMMARY WORKSHEET FOR THE LAKELAND COLLEGE STRATIFIED SAMPLE: POPULATION MEAN this formula into cells F4:F7 to compute the weighted sample means for each of the other majors. The formula =SUM(F3:F7) was entered into cell F8 to compute the point estimator of the population mean. The computations in cells G3:G8 correspond to the calculations shown in Table 18.2. For instance the formula =D3*(D3-E3)*(C3^2/E3) was entered into cell G3 to compute the value of

$$N_h(N_h - n_h)\frac{s_h^2}{n_h}$$

for the accounting majors; copying this formula into cells G4:G7 provided similar values for each of the other majors. In cell G8 we entered the cell formula =SUM(G3:G7) to compute

$$\sum_{h=1}^{5} N_h(N_h - n_h)\frac{s_h^2}{n_h}$$

Note that the value worksheet shows that this partial calculation is 42,909,037,698. To compute the standard error of the mean we entered the formula =SQRT(1/D8^2*G8) into cell B10; we then computed the bound on the sampling error by entering the formula =2*B10 into cell B11. The value worksheet shows 138.0966 for the standard error of the mean and 276.1933 for the bound on the sampling error.

Cells B13:B15 provide the point estimate and the lower and upper limits for the confidence interval. Because the point estimate of the population mean was computed in cell F8, we entered the formula =F8 into cell B13. To compute the lower limit of the 95% confidence interval, the formula =B13-B11 was entered into cell B14; to compute the upper limit, the formula =B13+B11 was entered into cell B15. The value worksheet shows that the point estimate of the population mean is 35,016.67 and that the 95% approximate confidence interval is 34,740.47 to 35,292.86.

## Population Total

The point estimator of the population total ($X$) is obtained by multiplying $N$ times $\bar{x}_{st}$.

---

**Point Estimator of the Population Total**

$$\hat{X} = N\bar{x}_{st} \qquad\qquad (18.18)$$

---

An estimate of the standard error of this point estimator is

$$s_{\hat{X}} = Ns_{\bar{x}_{st}} \qquad\qquad (18.19)$$

Thus, an approximate 95% confidence interval for the population total is given by the following expression.

---

**Approximate 95% Confidence Interval Estimate of the Population Total**

$$N\bar{x}_{st} \pm 2s_{\hat{X}} \qquad\qquad (18.20)$$

---

Now suppose the College of Business at Lakeland College would also like to estimate the total earnings of the 1500 business graduates in order to estimate their impact on the economy. Using equation (18.18), we obtain an unbiased estimate of the total earnings.

$$\hat{X} = (1500)35,017 = 52,525,500$$

Using equation (18.19), we obtain an estimate of the standard error of the population total.

$$s_{\hat{X}} = 1500(138) = 207,000$$

Thus, using equation (18.20), we find that an approximate 95% confidence interval estimate of the total earnings of the 1500 graduates is $52,525,500 \pm 2(207,000) = 52,525,500 \pm 414,000$ or \$52,111,500 to \$52,939,500.

## Using Excel: Population Total

The worksheet that we used to compute an approximate 95% confidence interval of the population mean for the Lakeland College sample survey can be easily modified in order to compute an approximate 95% confidence interval estimate of the population total. Refer to the worksheet in Figure 18.3 as we describe the changes. The point estimator of the population total is just $N$, the total number of elements in the population, times the point estimate of the population mean, $\bar{x}_{st}$. Thus, we would enter the formula =D8*F8 into cell B13 to compute the point estimate of the population total. The point estimator of the standard error of the population total is $N$ times $s_{\bar{x}_{st}}$, the standard error of the mean. Thus, we would enter the formula =D8*SQRT(1/D8^2*G8) into cell B10 to compute the estimate of the standard error of the population total. The resulting upper and lower limits in cells B14:B15 will then provide the approximate 95% confidence interval of the population total.

## Population Proportion

An unbiased estimate of the population proportion, $p$, for stratified simple random sampling is a weighted average of the proportions for each stratum. The weights used are the fraction of the population in each stratum. The resulting point estimator, denoted $\bar{p}_{st}$, is defined as follows.

---

**Point Estimator of the Population Proportion**

$$\bar{p}_{st} = \sum_{h=1}^{H} \left( \frac{N_h}{N} \right) \bar{p}_h \tag{18.21}$$

where

$\quad H$ = the number of strata

$\quad \bar{p}_h$ = the sample proportion for stratum $h$

$\quad N_h$ = the number of elements in the population in stratum $h$

$\quad N$ = the total number of elements in the population: $N = N_1 + N_2 + \cdots + N_H$

---

An estimate of the standard error of $\bar{p}_{st}$ is given by

$$s_{\bar{p}_{st}} = \sqrt{\frac{1}{N^2} \sum_{h=1}^{H} N_h (N_h - n_h) \left[ \frac{\bar{p}_h (1 - \bar{p}_h)}{n_h - 1} \right]} \tag{18.22}$$

Thus, an approximate 95% confidence interval estimate of the population proportion is given by the following expression.

---

**Approximate 95% Confidence Interval Estimate of the Population Proportion**

$$\bar{p}_{st} \pm 2 s_{\bar{p}_{st}} \tag{18.23}$$

Suppose that in the Lakeland College survey, the college wants to estimate the proportion of graduates receiving a starting salary of $36,000 or more. The results of the sample survey of 180 graduates showed that 63 received starting salaries of $36,000 or more and that 16 of these 63 graduates majored in accounting, 3 majored in finance, 29 majored in information systems, 0 majored in marketing, and 15 majored in operations management.

Using equation (18.21), we can compute the point estimate of the proportion receiving starting salaries of $36,000 or more.

$$\bar{p}_{st} = \left(\frac{500}{1500}\right)\left(\frac{16}{45}\right) + \left(\frac{350}{1500}\right)\left(\frac{3}{40}\right) + \left(\frac{200}{1500}\right)\left(\frac{29}{30}\right) + \left(\frac{300}{1500}\right)\left(\frac{0}{35}\right) + \left(\frac{150}{1500}\right)\left(\frac{15}{30}\right)$$

$$= .3149$$

In Table 18.3 we show a portion of the calculations needed to estimate the standard error; note that

$$\sum_{h=1}^{5} N_h(N_h - n_h)\left[\frac{\bar{p}_h(1 - \bar{p}_h)}{n_h - 1}\right] = 1570.6913$$

Thus,

$$s_{\bar{p}_{st}} = \sqrt{\frac{1}{(1500)^2}(1570.6913)}$$

$$= .0264$$

Using expression (18.23), we find that an approximate 95% confidence interval for the proportion of graduates receiving starting salaries of $36,000 or more is $.3149 \pm 2(.0264) = .3149 \pm .0528$, or .2621 to .3677.

**TABLE 18.3** PARTIAL CALCULATIONS FOR THE ESTIMATE OF THE STANDARD ERROR OF $\bar{p}_{st}$ FOR THE LAKELAND COLLEGE SAMPLE SURVEY

| Major | $h$ | $N_h(N_h - n_h)\left[\dfrac{\bar{p}_h(1 - \bar{p}_h)}{n_h - 1}\right]$ | |
|---|---|---|---|
| Accounting | 1 | $500(500 - 45)\left[\dfrac{(16/45)(29/45)}{45 - 1}\right]$ | $= 1184.7363$ |
| Finance | 2 | $350(350 - 40)\left[\dfrac{(3/40)(37/40)}{40 - 1}\right]$ | $= 193.0048$ |
| Information systems | 3 | $200(200 - 30)\left[\dfrac{(29/30)(1/30)}{30 - 1}\right]$ | $= 37.7778$ |
| Marketing | 4 | $300(300 - 35)\left[\dfrac{(0/35)(35/35)}{35 - 1}\right]$ | $= 0.0000$ |
| Operations management | 5 | $150(150 - 30)\left[\dfrac{(15/30)(15/30)}{30 - 1}\right]$ | $= 155.1724$ |
| | | | $1570.6913$ |

$$\sum_{h=1}^{5} N_h(N_h - n_h)\left[\frac{\bar{p}_h(1 - \bar{p}_h)}{n_h - 1}\right]$$

## Using Excel: Population Proportion

The worksheet used to compute an approximate 95% confidence interval of the population mean for the Lakeland College sample survey can be modified in order to compute an approximate 95% confidence interval estimate of the proportion of graduates receiving a starting salary of $36,000 or more. First, using the original data, we must determine for each major the proportion of graduates in the sample that received a starting salary of $36,000 or more. This calculation can be easily made using Excel's COUNTIF function. For instance, the salary data for the accounting majors appear in the worksheet named Accounting in cells A2:A46. We can compute the number of accounting graduates who received a starting salary of $36,000 or more by entering the function =COUNTIF(A2:A46,">=36000") in any empty cell of the worksheet; the result is 16. Once the sample proportions for each stratum are obtained, it is a simple matter to modify the formulas shown in Figure 18.3 in order to display the partial calculations for the sample proportion and the standard error of the sample proportion based upon equations (18.21) and (18.22).

## Determining the Sample Size

With stratified simple random sampling we can think of choosing a sample size as a two-step process. First, a total sample size $n$ must be chosen. Second, we must decide how to assign the sampled units to the various strata. Alternatively, we could first decide how large a sample to take in each stratum and then sum the stratum sample sizes to obtain the total sample size. It is often of interest to develop estimates of the mean, total, and proportion for the individual strata, therefore a combination of these two approaches is often employed. An overall sample size $n$ and an allocation that will provide the necessary precision for the overall population parameter of interest are found. Then, if the sample sizes in some of the strata are not large enough to provide the precision necessary for the estimates within the strata, the sample sizes for those strata are adjusted upward as necessary. In this section we discuss some of the issues pertinent to allocating the total sample to the various strata and present a method for choosing the total sample size and making the allocation.

The allocation task is to decide what fraction of the total sample should be assigned to each stratum. This fraction determines how large the simple random sample will be in each stratum. The factors considered most important in making the allocation are:

1. The number of elements in each stratum.
2. The variance of the elements within each stratum.
3. The cost of selecting elements within each stratum.

Generally, larger samples should be assigned to the larger strata and to the strata with larger variances. Conversely, to get the most information for a given cost, smaller samples should be allocated to the strata where the cost per unit of sampling is greatest.

The individual stratum variances often differ greatly. For example, suppose that in a particular study we are interested in determining the mean number of employees per building; because variability is greater in a stratum with larger buildings than in one with smaller buildings, a proportionately larger sample should be taken in such a stratum. The cost of selection can be an important consideration when significant interviewer travel between sampled units is necessary in some of the strata but not in others; this issue frequently arises when some of the strata involve rural areas and others involve cities.

In many surveys the cost per unit of sampling is approximately the same for each stratum (e.g., mail and telephone surveys); in such cases, the cost of sampling can be ignored in making the allocation. We present here the appropriate formulas for choosing the sample size and making the allocation in such cases. More advanced texts on sampling provide formulas for the case when sampling costs vary significantly across strata. The formulas we present in this section will minimize the total sampling cost for a given level of precision. This method, known as *Neyman allocation,* allocates the total sample $n$ to the various strata as follows.

$$n_h = n\left(\frac{N_h s_h}{\sum\limits_{h=1}^{H} N_h s_h}\right) \tag{18.24}$$

Equation (18.24) shows that the number of units allocated to a stratum increases with the stratum size and standard deviation. Note that to make this allocation, we need to first determine the total sample size $n$. Given a specified level of precision $B$, we can use the following formulas to choose the total sample size when estimating the population mean and the population total.

**Sample Size When Estimating the Population Mean**

$$n = \frac{\left(\sum\limits_{h=1}^{H} N_h s_h\right)^2}{N^2\left(\dfrac{B^2}{4}\right) + \sum\limits_{h=1}^{H} N_h s_h^2} \tag{18.25}$$

**Sample Size When Estimating the Population Total**

$$n = \frac{\left(\sum\limits_{h=1}^{H} N_h s_h\right)^2}{\dfrac{B^2}{4} + \sum\limits_{h=1}^{H} N_h s_h^2} \tag{18.26}$$

As an example, suppose a Chevrolet dealer wants to survey the customers who have purchased a Corvette, Geo Prizm, or Cavalier to obtain information the dealer feels will be helpful in determining future advertising. In particular, suppose the dealer wants to estimate the mean monthly income for these customers with a bound on the sampling error of $100. The dealer's 600 Corvette, Geo Prizm, and Cavalier customers have been divided into three strata: 100 Corvette owners, 200 Geo Prizm owners, and 300 Cavalier owners. A pilot survey was used to estimate the standard deviation in each stratum; the results are $s_1 = \$1300$, $s_2 = \$900$, and $s_3 = \$500$ for the Corvette, Geo Prizm, and Cavalier owners, respectively.

The first step in choosing a sample size for this survey is to use equation (18.25) to determine the total sample size necessary to provide a bound of $B = \$100$ on the estimate of the population mean. First, we compute

$$\sum_{h=1}^{3} N_h s_h = 100(1300) + 200(900) + 300(500) = 460,000$$

Next, we compute

$$\sum_{h=1}^{3} N_h s_h^2 = 100(1300)^2 + 200(900)^2 + 300(500)^2 = 406,000,000$$

Substituting these values into equation (18.25), we can determine the total sample size needed to provide a bound on the sampling error of $B = \$100$.

$$n = \frac{(460{,}000)^2}{(600)^2 \dfrac{(100)^2}{4} + 406{,}000{,}000} = 162$$

Thus, a total sample size of 162 will provide the precision desired. To allocate the total sample to the three strata, we use equation (18.24).

$$n_1 = 162\left(\frac{100(1300)}{460{,}000}\right) = 46$$

$$n_2 = 162\left(\frac{200(900)}{460{,}000}\right) = 63$$

$$n_3 = 162\left(\frac{300(500)}{460{,}000}\right) = 53$$

We would therefore recommend sampling 46 Corvette owners, 63 Geo Prizm owners, and 53 Cavalier owners for a total sample size of 162 customers.

To determine the sample size when estimating a population proportion, we simply substitute $\sqrt{\bar{p}_h(1 - \bar{p}_h)}$ for $s_h$ in equation (18.25); the result is

$$n = \frac{\left(\displaystyle\sum_{h=1}^{H} N_h \sqrt{\bar{p}_h(1 - \bar{p}_h)}\right)^2}{N^2\left(\dfrac{B^2}{4}\right) + \displaystyle\sum_{h=1}^{H} N_h \bar{p}_h(1 - \bar{p}_h)} \qquad \textbf{(18.27)}$$

Once the total sample size for the population proportion estimate has been determined, allocation to the various strata is again made by using equation (18.24) with $\sqrt{\bar{p}_h(1 - \bar{p}_h)}$ substituted for $s_h$.

## NOTES AND COMMENTS

1. An advantage of stratified simple random sampling is that estimates of population parameters for each stratum are automatically available as a byproduct of the sampling procedure. For example, besides obtaining an estimate of the average starting salary for all graduates in the Lakeland College sampling problem, we obtained an estimate of the average starting salary for each major. Because each of the starting salary estimates was based on a simple random sample from each stratum, the procedure for developing an approximate confidence interval estimate for the population mean when a simple random sample is selected (see Equation (18.4)) can be used to compute an approximate 95% confidence interval estimate for the mean in each stratum. In a similar manner, interval estimates for the population total and the population proportion for each stratum can be developed by using (18.8) and (18.10), respectively.

2. Another type of allocation that is sometimes used with stratified simple random sampling is called *proportional allocation*. In this approach, the sample size allocated to each stratum is given by the following formula.

$$n_h = n\left(\frac{N_h}{N}\right) \qquad \textbf{(18.28)}$$

Proportional allocation is appropriate when the stratum variances are approximately equal and the cost per unit of sampling is about the same across strata. In the case where the stratum variances are equal, proportional allocation and the Neyman procedure result in the same allocation.

## EXERCISES

### Methods

**7.** A stratified simple random sample provided the following results.

| Stratum ($h$) | $\bar{x}_h$ | $s_h$ | $\bar{p}_h$ | $N_h$ | $n_h$ |
|---|---|---|---|---|---|
| 1 | 138 | 30 | .50 | 200 | 20 |
| 2 | 103 | 25 | .78 | 250 | 30 |
| 3 | 210 | 50 | .21 | 100 | 25 |

    **a.** Develop an estimate of the population mean for each stratum.
    **b.** Develop an approximate 95% confidence interval for the population mean in each stratum.
    **c.** Develop an approximate 95% confidence interval for the overall population mean.

**8.** Reconsider the sample results in Exercise 7.
    **a.** Develop an estimate of the population total for each stratum.
    **b.** Develop a point estimate of the total for all 550 elements in the population.
    **c.** Develop an approximate 95% confidence interval for the population total.

**9.** Reconsider the sample results in Exercise 7.
    **a.** Develop an approximate 95% confidence interval for the proportion in each stratum.
    **b.** Develop a point estimate of the population proportion for the 550 elements in the population.
    **c.** Estimate the standard error of the population proportion.
    **d.** Develop an approximate 95% confidence interval for the population proportion.

**10.** A population has been divided into three strata with $N_1 = 300$, $N_2 = 600$, and $N_3 = 500$. From a past survey, the following estimates for the standard deviations in the three strata are available: $s_1 = 150$, $s_2 = 75$, $s_3 = 100$.
    **a.** Suppose an estimate of the population mean with a bound on the error of estimate of $B = 20$ is required. How large must the sample be? How many elements should be allocated to each stratum?
    **b.** Suppose a bound of $B = 10$ is desired. How large must the sample be? How many elements should be allocated to each stratum?
    **c.** Suppose an estimate of the population total with a bound of $B = 15,000$ is requested. How large must the sample be? How many elements should be allocated to each stratum?

### Applications

**11.** A drug store chain has stores in four cities: 38 stores in Indianapolis, 45 in Louisville, 80 in St. Louis, and 70 in Memphis. Pharmacy sales in the four cities vary considerably because of the competition. The following sales data (in $1000s) are available from a sample survey. Each of the cities was considered a separate stratum, and a stratified simple random sample was taken.

| Indianapolis | Louisville | St. Louis | Memphis |
|---|---|---|---|
| 50.3 | 48.7 | 16.7 | 14.7 |
| 41.2 | 59.8 | 38.4 | 88.3 |
| 15.7 | 28.9 | 51.6 | 94.2 |
| 22.5 | 36.5 | 42.7 | 76.8 |
| 26.7 | 89.8 | 45.0 | 35.1 |
| 20.8 | 96.0 | 59.7 | 48.2 |
|  | 77.2 | 80.0 | 57.9 |
|  | 81.3 | 27.6 | 18.8 |
|  |  |  | 22.0 |
|  |  |  | 74.3 |

    **a.**  Estimate the mean sales for each city (stratum).

    **b.**  Develop an approximate 95% confidence interval for the mean sales in each city.

    **c.**  Estimate the proportion of stores with sales of $50,000 or more.

    **d.**  Develop an approximate 95% confidence interval for the proportion of stores with sales of $50,000 or more.

**12.**  Reconsider the sample survey results in Exercise 11.

    **a.**  Estimate the population total for St. Louis.

    **b.**  Estimate the population total for Indianapolis.

    **c.**  Develop an approximate 95% confidence interval for mean pharmacy sales for the drug store chain.

    **d.**  Develop an approximate 95% confidence interval for total pharmacy sales for the drug store chain.

**13.**  An accounting firm has a number of clients in the banking, insurance, and brokerage industries. There are $N_1 = 50$ banks, $N_2 = 38$ insurance companies, and $N_3 = 35$ brokerage firms. A marketing research firm has been hired to survey the accounting firm's clients in these three industries. The survey will ask a variety of questions about both the clients' businesses and their satisfaction with services provided by the accounting firm. Suppose an approximate 95% confidence interval is requested for the mean number of employees for the 123 clients with a bound on the error of estimation of $B = 30$.

    **a.**  Suppose a pilot study finds $s_1 = 80$, $s_2 = 150$, and $s_3 = 45$. Choose a total sample size, and explain how the sample size should be allocated to the three strata.

    **b.**  Suppose the pilot test is called into question and a decision is made to assume the stratum standard deviations are all equal to 100 in choosing the sample size. Choose a total sample size, and determine how many elements should be sampled in each stratum.

## 18.6   CLUSTER SAMPLING

**Cluster sampling** requires that the population be divided into $N$ groups of elements called clusters such that each element in the population belongs to one and only one cluster. For example, suppose we want to survey registered voters in the state of Ohio. One approach would be to develop a frame consisting of all registered voters in the state of Ohio and then select a simple random sample of voters from this frame. Alternatively, in cluster sampling, we might choose to define the frame as the list of the $N = 88$ counties in the state (see Figure 18.4). In this approach, each county or cluster would consist of a group of registered voters, and each registered voter in the state would belong to one and only one cluster.

    Suppose we select a simple random sample of $n = 12$ of the 88 counties. At this point, we could collect data for *all* registered voters in each of the 12 sampled clusters, an approach referred to as *single-stage cluster sampling,* or we could select a simple random sample of registered voters from each of the 12 sampled clusters, an approach referred to as *two-stage cluster sampling.* In either case, formulas are available for using the sample results to develop point and interval estimates of population parameters such as the population mean, total, or proportion. In this chapter, however, we consider only single-stage cluster sampling; more advanced texts on sampling present results for two-stage cluster sampling.

    In the sense that both stratified and cluster sampling divide the population into groups of elements, the two sampling procedures are similar. The reasons for choosing cluster sampling, however, differ from the reasons for choosing stratified sampling. Cluster sampling tends to provide better results when the elements within the clusters are heterogeneous (not alike). In the ideal case, each cluster would be a small-scale version of the entire population. In this case, sampling a small number of clusters would provide good information about the characteristics of the entire population.

    One of the primary applications of cluster sampling involves area sampling, where the clusters are counties, townships, city blocks, or other well-defined geographic sections of the

**FIGURE 18.4**     COUNTIES OF THE STATE OF OHIO USED AS CLUSTERS
OF REGISTERED VOTERS

population. Because data are collected from only a sample of the total geographic areas or clusters available, and the elements within the clusters are typically close to one another, significant savings in time and cost can be realized when a data collector or interviewer is sent to a sampled unit. As a result, even if a larger total sample size is required, cluster sampling may be less costly than either simple random sampling or stratified simple random sampling. In addition, cluster sampling can minimize the time and cost associated with developing the frame or list of elements to be sampled, because cluster sampling does not require that a list of every element in the population be developed. One needs only a list of the elements in the clusters sampled.

All the elements in the population do not need to be listed. With cluster sampling, one needs only a list of the elements in the clusters sampled.

To illustrate cluster sampling, let us consider a survey conducted by the CPA (certified public accountant) Society of the 12,000 practicing CPAs in a particular state. As part of the survey, the CPA Society collected information on income, gender, and factors related to the CPA's lifestyle. Because personal interviews were needed to obtain all the desired information, the CPA Society used a cluster sample to minimize the total travel and interviewing cost. The frame consisted of all CPA firms that were registered to practice accounting in the state. Suppose there are $N = 1000$ clusters, or CPA firms, registered to practice accounting in the state, and that a simple random sample of $n = 10$ CPA firms is to be selected.

In presenting the formulas for cluster sampling that are needed to develop approximate 95% confidence interval estimates of the population mean, total, and proportion, we will use the following notation.

$$N = \text{number of clusters in the population}$$
$$n = \text{number of clusters selected in the sample}$$
$$M_i = \text{number of elements in cluster } i$$
$$M = \text{number of elements in the population; } M = M_1 + M_2 + \cdots + M_N$$
$$\bar{M} = M/N = \text{average number of elements in a cluster}$$
$$x_i = \text{total of all observations in cluster } i$$
$$a_i = \text{number of observations in cluster } i \text{ with a certain characteristic}$$

For the CPA Society sample survey we have the following information.

$$N = 1000$$
$$n = 10$$
$$M = 12,000$$
$$\bar{M} = 12,000/1000 = 12$$

Table 18.4 shows the values of $M_i$ and $x_i$ for each of the sampled clusters as well as the number of female CPAs in the sampled firms ($a_i$).

## Population Mean

The point estimator of the population mean obtained from cluster sampling is given by the following formula.

**Point Estimator of the Population Mean**

$$\bar{x}_c = \frac{\sum\limits_{i=1}^{n} x_i}{\sum\limits_{i=1}^{n} M_i} \tag{18.29}$$

**TABLE 18.4**   RESULTS OF CPA SAMPLE SURVEY

| Firm ($i$) | CPAs ($M_i$) | Total Salary ($1000s) for Firm $i$ ($x_i$) | Female CPAs ($a_i$) |
|---|---|---|---|
| 1 | 8 | 384 | 2 |
| 2 | 25 | 1350 | 8 |
| 3 | 4 | 148 | 0 |
| 4 | 17 | 857 | 6 |
| 5 | 7 | 296 | 1 |
| 6 | 3 | 131 | 2 |
| 7 | 15 | 761 | 2 |
| 8 | 4 | 176 | 0 |
| 9 | 12 | 577 | 5 |
| 10 | 33 | 1880 | 9 |
| Totals | 128 | 6560 | 35 |

An estimate of the standard error of this point estimator is

$$s_{\bar{x}_c} = \sqrt{\left(\frac{N-n}{Nn\bar{M}^2}\right)\frac{\sum_{i=1}^{n}(x_i - \bar{x}_c M_i)^2}{n-1}} \tag{18.30}$$

Thus, the following expression gives an approximate 95% confidence interval estimate of the population mean.

**Approximate 95% Confidence Interval Estimate of the Population Mean**

$$\bar{x}_c \pm 2s_{\bar{x}_c} \tag{18.31}$$

Using the data in Table 18.4, we obtain an estimate of the mean salary for practicing certified public accountants.

$$\bar{x}_c = \frac{6560}{128} = 51.250$$

The salary data in Table 18.4, are in thousands of dollars, so an estimate of the mean salary for practicing certified public accountants in the state is $51,250.

In Table 18.5, we show a portion of the calculations needed to estimate the standard error; note that

$$\sum_{i=1}^{n}(x_i - \bar{x}_c M_i)^2 = 51,281.378$$

Thus,

$$s_{\bar{x}_c} = \sqrt{\left[\frac{1000 - 10}{(1000)(10)(12)^2}\right]\frac{51,281.378}{10 - 1}} = 1.979$$

**TABLE 18.5** PARTIAL CALCULATIONS FOR THE ESTIMATE OF THE STANDARD ERROR OF THE MEAN FOR THE CPA SAMPLE SURVEY WHERE $\bar{x}_c = 42.531$

| Firm ($i$) | $M_i$ | $x_i$ | $(x_i - 51.250M_i)^2$ | |
|-----------|-------|-------|-----------------------|---|
| 1 | 8 | 384 | $[384 - 51.250(8)]^2 =$ | 676.000 |
| 2 | 25 | 1350 | $[1350 - 51.250(25)]^2 =$ | 4,726.563 |
| 3 | 4 | 148 | $[148 - 51.250(4)]^2 =$ | 3,249.000 |
| 4 | 17 | 857 | $[857 - 51.250(17)]^2 =$ | 203.063 |
| 5 | 7 | 296 | $[296 - 51.250(7)]^2 =$ | 3,937.563 |
| 6 | 3 | 131 | $[131 - 51.250(3)]^2 =$ | 517.563 |
| 7 | 15 | 761 | $[761 - 51.250(15)]^2 =$ | 60.063 |
| 8 | 4 | 176 | $[176 - 51.250(4)]^2 =$ | 841.000 |
| 9 | 12 | 577 | $[577 - 51.250(12)]^2 =$ | 1,444.000 |
| 10 | 33 | 1880 | $[1880 - 51.250(33)]^2 =$ | 35,626.563 |
| Totals | 128 | 6560 | | 51,281.378 |

$$\sum_{i=1}^{n}(x_i - \bar{x}_c M_i)^2$$

Hence, the standard error is $1979. Using expression (18.31), we find that an approximate 95% confidence interval estimate for the mean annual salary is $51,250 \pm 2(1979) = 51,250 \pm 3958$ or $47,292 to $55,208.

## Population Total

The point estimator of the population total $X$ is obtained by multiplying $M$ times $\bar{x}_c$.

---

**Point Estimator of the Population Total**

$$\hat{X} = M\bar{x}_c \qquad\qquad (18.32)$$

---

An estimate of the standard error of this point estimator is

$$s_{\hat{X}} = Ms_{\bar{x}_c} \qquad\qquad (18.33)$$

Thus, an approximate 95% confidence interval estimate for the population total is given by the following expression.

---

**Approximate 95% Confidence Interval Estimate of the Population Total**

$$M\bar{x}_c \pm 2s_{\hat{X}} \qquad\qquad (18.34)$$

---

For the CPA sample survey,

$$\hat{X} = M\bar{x}_c = 12,000(51,250) = \$615,000,000$$
$$s_{\hat{X}} = Ms_{\bar{x}_c} = 12,000(1979) = \$23,748,000$$

Thus, using expression (18.34), we find that an approximate 95% confidence interval is $615,000,000 \pm 2(\$23,748,000) = \$615,000,000 \pm \$47,496,000$ or $567,504,000 to $662,496,000.

## Population Proportion

The point estimator of the population proportion obtained from cluster sampling follows.

---

**Point Estimator of the Population Proportion**

$$\bar{p}_c = \frac{\sum\limits_{i=1}^{n} a_i}{\sum\limits_{i=1}^{n} M_i} \qquad\qquad (18.35)$$

where

$a_i$ = number of elements in cluster $i$ with the characteristic of interest

---

An estimate of the standard error of this point estimator is

$$s_{\bar{p}_c} = \sqrt{\left(\frac{N-n}{Nn\bar{M}^2}\right)\frac{\sum\limits_{i=1}^{n}(a_i - \bar{p}_c M_i)^2}{n-1}} \qquad (18.36)$$

Thus, an approximate 95% confidence interval estimate for the population proportion is given by the following expression.

> ### Approximate 95% Confidence Interval Estimate of the Population Proportion
>
> $$\bar{p}_c \pm 2 s_{\bar{p}_c} \qquad (18.37)$$

For the CPA sample survey, we can use expression (18.35) and the data in Table 18.4 to develop an estimate of the number of practicing certified public accountants who are women.

$$\bar{p}_c = \frac{2 + 8 + \cdots + 9}{8 + 25 + \cdots + 33} = \frac{35}{128} = .2734$$

In Table 18.6 we show a portion of the calculations needed to estimate the standard error; note that

$$\sum_{i=1}^{n}(a_i - \bar{p}_c M_i)^2 = 15.2098$$

Thus,

$$s_{\bar{p}_c} = \sqrt{\left[\frac{1000 - 10}{(1000)(10)(12)^2}\right]\frac{15.2098}{10 - 1}} = .0341$$

**TABLE 18.6**  PARTIAL CALCULATIONS FOR THE ESTIMATE OF THE STANDARD ERROR OF $\bar{p}_c$ FOR THE CPA SAMPLE SURVEY WHERE $\bar{p}_c = .2734$

| Firm ($i$) | $M_i$ | $a_i$ | $(a_i - .2734M_i)^2$ |
|:---:|:---:|:---:|:---|
| 1 | 8 | 2 | $[2 - .2734(8)]^2 =$ .0350 |
| 2 | 25 | 8 | $[8 - .2734(25)]^2 =$ 1.3572 |
| 3 | 4 | 0 | $[0 - .2734(4)]^2 =$ 1.1960 |
| 4 | 17 | 6 | $[6 - .2734(17)]^2 =$ 1.8284 |
| 5 | 7 | 1 | $[1 - .2734(7)]^2 =$ .8350 |
| 6 | 3 | 2 | $[2 - .2734(3)]^2 =$ 1.3919 |
| 7 | 15 | 2 | $[2 - .2734(15)]^2 =$ 4.4142 |
| 8 | 4 | 0 | $[0 - .2734(4)]^2 =$ 1.1960 |
| 9 | 12 | 5 | $[5 - .2734(12)]^2 =$ 2.9556 |
| 10 | 33 | 9 | $[9 - .2734(33)]^2 =$ .0005 |
| Totals | 128 | 35 | 15.2098 |

$$\sum_{i=1}^{n}(a_i - \bar{p}_c M_i)^2$$

Hence, using expression (18.37), we find that an approximate 95% confidence interval for the proportion of practicing CPAs who are women is $.2734 \pm 2(.0341) = .2734 \pm .0682$ or .2052 to .3416.

## Using Excel for Cluster Sampling

The calculations required to develop an approximate 95% confidence interval of the population mean, population total, and population proportion for cluster sampling can be easily made in an Excel worksheet. For instance, to compute an approximate 95% confidence interval estimate of the population mean for the CPA sample survey, we simply develop a worksheet similar in appearance to Table 18.5. Using the partial output from this worksheet, cell formulas for equations (18.29) and (18.30) can be entered into the worksheet in order to compute point estimates of the population mean and standard error of the mean. The bound on the sampling error can then be computed and used to develop the lower and upper limits for the confidence interval. Although the details vary somewhat for developing interval estimates for estimating the population total and the population proportion, similar worksheets can also be developed for these two cases.

## Determining the Sample Size

Once the clusters have been formed, the primary issue in choosing a sample size is selecting the number of clusters $n$. The procedure for cluster sampling is similar to that for other methods of sampling. An acceptable level of precision is specified by choosing a value for $B$, the bound on the sampling error. Then a formula is developed for finding the value of $n$ that will provide the desired precision.

The average cluster size and the variance between clusters are key factors in deciding how many clusters to include in the sample. If the clusters are similar, the variance between them will be small, and the number of clusters sampled can be smaller. Also, if the average number of elements per cluster is larger, the number of clusters sampled can be smaller. The formulas for making an exact determination of sample size are included in more advanced texts on sampling.

## EXERCISES

### Methods

**14.** A sample of four clusters is to be taken from a population with $N = 25$ clusters and $M = 300$ elements. The values of $M_i$, $x_i$, and $a_i$ for each cluster in the sample follow.

| Cluster ($i$) | $M_i$ | $x_i$ | $a_i$ |
|:---:|:---:|:---:|:---:|
| 1 | 7 | 95 | 1 |
| 2 | 18 | 325 | 6 |
| 3 | 15 | 190 | 6 |
| 4 | 10 | 140 | 2 |
| Totals | 50 | 750 | 15 |

**a.** Develop point estimates of the population mean, total, and proportion.
**b.** Estimate the standard error for the estimates in part (a).
**c.** Develop an approximate 95% confidence interval for the population mean.
**d.** Develop an approximate 95% confidence interval for the population total.
**e.** Develop an approximate 95% confidence interval for the population proportion.

15. A sample of six clusters is to be taken from a population with $N = 30$ clusters and $M = 600$ elements. The following table shows values of $M_i$, $x_i$, and $a_i$ for each cluster in the sample.

| Cluster ($i$) | $M_i$ | $x_i$ | $a_i$ |
|---|---|---|---|
| 1 | 35 | 3,500 | 3 |
| 2 | 15 | 965 | 0 |
| 3 | 12 | 960 | 1 |
| 4 | 23 | 2,070 | 4 |
| 5 | 20 | 1,100 | 3 |
| 6 | 25 | 1,805 | 2 |
| Totals | 130 | 10,400 | 13 |

a. Develop point estimates of the population mean, total, and proportion.
b. Develop an approximate 95% confidence interval for the population mean.
c. Develop an approximate 95% confidence interval for the population total.
d. Develop an approximate 95% confidence interval for the population proportion.

## Applications

16. A public utility is conducting a survey of mechanical engineers to learn more about the factors influencing the choice of heating, ventilation, and air conditioning (HVAC) equipment for new commercial buildings. A total of 120 firms in the utility's service area are engaged in designing HVAC systems. The sampling plan is to use cluster sampling with each firm representing a cluster. For each firm in the sample, all of the mechanical engineers will be interviewed. Approximately 500 mechanical engineers are believed to be employed by the 120 firms. A sample of 10 firms was taken. Among other things, the age of each respondent was recorded as well as whether the respondent had attended the local university.

| Cluster ($i$) | $M_i$ | Total of Respondents' Ages | Number Attending Local University |
|---|---|---|---|
| 1 | 12 | 520 | 8 |
| 2 | 1 | 33 | 0 |
| 3 | 2 | 70 | 1 |
| 4 | 1 | 29 | 1 |
| 5 | 6 | 270 | 3 |
| 6 | 3 | 129 | 2 |
| 7 | 2 | 102 | 0 |
| 8 | 1 | 48 | 1 |
| 9 | 9 | 337 | 7 |
| 10 | 13 | 462 | 12 |
| Totals | 50 | 2000 | 35 |

a. Estimate the mean age of mechanical engineers engaged in this type of work.
b. Estimate the proportion of mechanical engineers in the utility's service area who attended the local university.
c. Develop an approximate 95% confidence interval for the mean age of mechanical engineers designing HVAC systems for commercial buildings.
d. Develop an approximate 95% confidence interval for the proportion of mechanical engineers in the utility's service area who attended the local university.

17. A national real estate company has just acquired a smaller firm that has 150 offices and 6000 agents in Los Angeles and other parts of Southern California. The national firm has conducted a sample survey to learn about attitudes and other characteristics of its new employees. A sample of eight offices has been taken, and all of the agents at these offices have completed the questionnaire. Results of the survey for the eight offices follow.

| Office | Agents | Average Age | College Graduates | Male Agents |
|--------|--------|-------------|-------------------|-------------|
| 1 | 17 | 37 | 3 | 4 |
| 2 | 35 | 32 | 14 | 12 |
| 3 | 26 | 36 | 8 | 7 |
| 4 | 66 | 30 | 38 | 28 |
| 5 | 43 | 41 | 18 | 12 |
| 6 | 12 | 52 | 2 | 6 |
| 7 | 48 | 35 | 20 | 17 |
| 8 | 57 | 44 | 25 | 26 |

**a.** Estimate the mean age of the agents.

**b.** Estimate the proportion of agents who are college graduates and the proportion who are male.

**c.** Develop an approximate 95% confidence interval for the mean age of the agents.

**d.** Develop an approximate 95% confidence interval for the proportion of agents who are college graduates.

**e.** Develop an approximate 95% confidence interval for the proportion of agents who are male.

## 18.7 SYSTEMATIC SAMPLING

**Systematic sampling** is often used as an alternative to simple random sampling. In some sampling situations, especially those with large populations, it can be time-consuming to select a simple random sample by first finding a random number and then counting or searching through the frame until the corresponding element is found. Systematic sampling offers an alternative to simple random sampling in such cases. For example, if a sample size of 50 from a population containing 5000 elements is desired, we might sample one element for every $5000/50 = 100$ elements in the population. A systematic sample for this case would involve randomly selecting one of the first 100 elements from the frame. The remaining sample elements are identified by starting with the first sampled element and then selecting every 100th element that follows in the frame. In effect, the sample of 50 is identified by moving systematically through the population and identifying every 100th element after the first randomly selected element. The sample of 50 will often be easier to select in this manner than it would be if simple random sampling were used. The first element selected is a random choice, allowing for the assumption that a systematic sample has the properties of a simple random sample. This assumption is usually appropriate when the frame is a random ordering of the elements in the population.

## SUMMARY

We have provided a brief introduction to the field of survey sampling in this chapter. The purpose of survey sampling is to collect data in order to make estimates of population parameters such as the population mean, total, or proportion. Survey sampling as a method of data collection can be contrasted with conducting experiments to generate data. When survey sampling is used, the design of the sampling plan is of critical importance in determining which data will be collected. When experiments are conducted (see Chapter 13), the data are generated. In such cases, experimental design issues are of critical importance in determining which data will be generated, or created.

Two types of errors can occur with sample surveys: sampling error and nonsampling error. Sampling error is the error that occurs because a sample, and not the entire population, is used to estimate a population parameter. Nonsampling error refers to all the other types of errors that can occur, such as measurement, interviewer, nonresponse, and processing error. Nonsampling errors are controlled by proper questionnaire design, thorough training of interviewers, careful verification of data, and so on. Sampling errors are minimized by a proper choice of sample design and by selecting an appropriate sample size.

We discussed four commonly used sample designs in this chapter: simple random sampling, stratified simple random sampling, cluster sampling, and systematic sampling. The objective of sample design is to get the most precise estimates for the least cost. When the population can be divided into strata so that the elements within each stratum are relatively homogeneous, stratified simple random sampling will provide more precision (smaller approximate confidence intervals) than simple random sampling. When the elements can be grouped in clusters so that all the elements in a cluster are close together geographically, cluster sampling often reduces interviewer cost; in these situations, cluster sampling will often provide the most precision per dollar. Systematic random sampling was presented as an alternative to simple random sampling.

Excel worksheets were developed to assist in summarizing the data obtained in a survey. Worksheets are especially helpful in summarizing the detailed calculations necessary to combine the results for individual strata and individual clusters in stratified and cluster sampling.

## GLOSSARY

**Element**   The entity on which data are collected.

**Population**   The collection of all elements of interest.

**Sample**   A subset of the population.

**Target population**   The population about which inferences are made.

**Sampled population**   The population from which the sample is taken.

**Sampling units**   The units selected for sampling. A sampling unit may include more than one element.

**Frame**   A list of the sampling units for a study. The sample is drawn by selecting units from the frame.

**Probabilistic sampling**   Any method of sampling for which the probability of obtaining each possible sample can be computed.

**Nonprobabilistic sampling**   Any method of sampling for which the probability of selecting a sample cannot be computed.

**Convenience sampling**   A nonprobabilistic method of sampling whereby elements are selected on the basis of convenience.

**Judgment sampling**   A nonprobabilistic method of sampling whereby element selection is based on the judgment of the person doing the study.

**Sampling error**   The error that occurs because a sample, and not the entire population, is used to estimate a population parameter.

**Nonsampling error**   All types of errors other than sampling error, such as measurement error, interviewer error, and processing error.

**Simple random sample**   A sample selected in such a manner that each sample of size $n$ has the same probability of being selected.

**Bound on the sampling error**   A number added to and subtracted from a point estimate to create an approximate 95% confidence interval. It is given by two times the standard error of the point estimator.

**Stratified simple random sampling**   A probabilistic method of selecting a sample in which the population is first divided into strata and a simple random sample is then taken from each stratum.

**Cluster sampling**   A probabilistic method of sampling in which the population is first divided into clusters and then one or more clusters are selected for sampling. In single-stage cluster sampling, every element in each selected cluster is sampled; in two-stage cluster sampling, a sample of the elements in each selected cluster is collected.

**Systematic sampling**   A method of choosing a sample by randomly selecting the first element and then selecting every $k$th element thereafter.

## KEY FORMULAS

### SIMPLE RANDOM SAMPLING

**Interval Estimate of the Population Mean**

$$\bar{x} \pm z_{\alpha/2}\sigma_{\bar{x}} \tag{18.1}$$

**Estimate of the Standard Error of the Mean**

$$s_{\bar{x}} = \sqrt{\frac{N-n}{N}}\left(\frac{s}{\sqrt{n}}\right) \tag{18.2}$$

**Interval Estimate of the Population Mean**

$$\bar{x} \pm z_{\alpha/2}s_{\bar{x}} \tag{18.3}$$

**Approximate 95% Confidence Interval Estimate of the Population Mean**

$$\bar{x} \pm 2s_{\bar{x}} \tag{18.4}$$

**Point Estimator of a Population Total**

$$\hat{X} = N\bar{x} \tag{18.5}$$

**Estimate of the Standard Error of $\hat{X}$**

$$s_{\hat{X}} = Ns_{\bar{x}} \tag{18.6}$$

**Approximate 95% Confidence Interval Estimate of the Population Total**

$$N\bar{x} \pm 2s_{\hat{X}} \tag{18.8}$$

**Estimate of the Standard Error of the Proportion**

$$s_{\bar{p}} = \sqrt{\left(\frac{N-n}{N}\right)\left(\frac{\bar{p}(1-\bar{p})}{n-1}\right)} \tag{18.9}$$

**Approximate 95% Confidence Interval Estimate of the Population Proportion**

$$\bar{p} \pm 2s_{\bar{p}} \tag{18.10}$$

**Sample Size for an Estimate of the Population Mean**

$$n = \frac{Ns^2}{N\left(\dfrac{B^2}{4}\right) + s^2} \tag{18.12}$$

**Sample Size for an Estimate of the Population Total**

$$n = \frac{Ns^2}{\left(\dfrac{B^2}{4N}\right) + s^2} \qquad \text{(18.13)}$$

**Sample Size for an Estimate of the Population Proportion**

$$n = \frac{N\bar{p}(1 - \bar{p})}{N\left(\dfrac{B^2}{4}\right) + \bar{p}(1 - \bar{p})} \qquad \text{(18.14)}$$

## STRATIFIED SIMPLE RANDOM SAMPLING

**Point Estimator of the Population Mean**

$$\bar{x}_{\text{st}} = \sum_{h=1}^{H} \left(\frac{N_h}{N}\right)\bar{x}_h \qquad \text{(18.15)}$$

**Estimate of the Standard Error of the Mean**

$$s_{\bar{x}_{\text{st}}} = \sqrt{\frac{1}{N^2}\sum_{h=1}^{H} N_h(N_h - n_h)\frac{s_h^2}{n_h}} \qquad \text{(18.16)}$$

**Approximate 95% Confidence Interval Estimate of the Population Mean**

$$\bar{x}_{\text{st}} \pm 2s_{\bar{x}_{\text{st}}} \qquad \text{(18.17)}$$

**Point Estimator of the Population Total**

$$\hat{X} = N\bar{x}_{\text{st}} \qquad \text{(18.18)}$$

**Estimate of the Standard Error of $\hat{X}$**

$$s_{\hat{X}} = Ns_{\bar{x}_{\text{st}}} \qquad \text{(18.19)}$$

**Approximate 95% Confidence Interval Estimate of the Population Total**

$$N\bar{x}_{\text{st}} \pm 2s_{\hat{X}} \qquad \text{(18.20)}$$

**Point Estimator of the Population Proportion**

$$\bar{p}_{\text{st}} = \sum_{h=1}^{H} \left(\frac{N_h}{N}\right)\bar{p}_h \qquad \text{(18.21)}$$

**Estimate of the Standard Error of $\bar{p}_{\text{st}}$**

$$s_{\bar{p}_{\text{st}}} = \sqrt{\frac{1}{N^2}\sum_{h=1}^{H} N_h(N_h - n_h)\left[\frac{\bar{p}_h(1 - \bar{p}_h)}{n_h - 1}\right]} \qquad \text{(18.22)}$$

**Approximate 95% Confidence Interval Estimate of the Population Proportion**

$$\bar{p}_{\text{st}} \pm 2s_{\bar{p}_{\text{st}}} \qquad \text{(18.23)}$$

**Allocating the Total Sample $n$ to the Strata: Neyman Allocation**

$$n_h = n\left(\frac{N_h s_h}{\displaystyle\sum_{h=1}^{H} N_h s_h}\right) \qquad \text{(18.24)}$$

**Sample Size When Estimating the Population Mean**

$$n = \frac{\left(\sum_{h=1}^{H} N_h s_h\right)^2}{N^2\left(\dfrac{B^2}{4}\right) + \sum_{h=1}^{H} N_h s_h^2} \tag{18.25}$$

**Sample Size When Estimating the Population Total**

$$n = \frac{\left(\sum_{h=1}^{H} N_h s_h\right)^2}{\dfrac{B^2}{4} + \sum_{h=1}^{H} N_h s_h^2} \tag{18.26}$$

**Sample Size for the Estimate of the Population Proportion**

$$n = \frac{\left(\sum_{h=1}^{H} N_h \sqrt{\bar{p}_h(1 - \bar{p}_h)}\right)^2}{N^2\left(\dfrac{B^2}{4}\right) + \sum_{h=1}^{H} N_h \bar{p}_h(1 - \bar{p}_h)} \tag{18.27}$$

**Proportional Allocation of Sample $n$ to the Strata**

$$n_h = n\left(\frac{N_h}{N}\right) \tag{18.28}$$

**CLUSTER SAMPLING**

**Point Estimator of the Population Mean**

$$\bar{x}_c = \frac{\sum_{i=1}^{n} x_i}{\sum_{i=1}^{n} M_i} \tag{18.29}$$

**Estimate of the Standard Error of the Mean**

$$s_{\bar{x}_c} = \sqrt{\left(\frac{N - n}{Nn\bar{M}^2}\right)\frac{\sum_{i=1}^{n}(x_i - \bar{x}_c M_i)^2}{n - 1}} \tag{18.30}$$

**Approximate 95% Confidence Interval Estimate of the Population Mean**

$$\bar{x}_c \pm 2s_{\bar{x}_c} \tag{18.31}$$

**Point Estimator of the Population Total**

$$\hat{X} = M\bar{x}_c \tag{18.32}$$

**Estimate of the Standard Error of $\hat{X}$**

$$s_{\hat{X}} = Ms_{\bar{x}_c} \tag{18.33}$$

Approximate 95% Confidence Interval Estimate of the Population Total

$$M\bar{x}_c \pm 2s_{\hat{X}} \tag{18.34}$$

Point Estimator of the Population Proportion

$$\bar{p}_c = \frac{\sum_{i=1}^{n} a_i}{\sum_{i=1}^{n} M_i} \tag{18.35}$$

Estimate of the Standard Error of $\bar{p}_c$

$$s_{\bar{p}_c} = \sqrt{\left(\frac{N-n}{Nn\bar{M}^2}\right) \frac{\sum_{i=1}^{n}(a_i - \bar{p}_c M_i)^2}{n-1}} \tag{18.36}$$

Approximate 95% Confidence Interval Estimate of the Population Proportion

$$\bar{p}_c \pm 2s_{\bar{p}_c} \tag{18.37}$$

## SUPPLEMENTARY EXERCISES

**18.** To assess consumer acceptance of a new series of ads for Miller Lite Beer, Louis Harris conducted a nationwide poll of 363 adults who had seen the Miller Lite ads (*USA Today,* November 17, 1997). The following responses are based on that survey. (Note: Because the survey sampled a small fraction of all adults, assume $(N - n)/N = 1$ in any formulas involving the standard error.)

    **a.** Nineteen percent of all respondents indicated they liked the ads a lot. Develop a 95% confidence interval for the population proportion of adults who like the ads a lot.

    **b.** Thirty-one percent of the respondents disliked the new ads. Develop a 95% confidence interval for the population proportion of adults who dislike the new ads.

    **c.** Seventeen percent of the respondents felt the ads are very effective. Develop a 95% confidence interval for the proportion of adults who think the ads are very effective.

    **d.** Louis Harris reported that the "margin of error is five percentage points." What does this statement mean and how do you think they arrived at this number?

    **e.** How might nonsampling error bias the results of such a survey?

**19.** *The Wall Street Journal* conducted a survey of subscribers to its interactive edition. One question asked the 504 respondents whether they used a laptop computer when traveling; 55% said they did. Another question asked respondents whether they used an express or package service when traveling; 31% said they did (*The Wall Street Journal Interactive Edition Subscriber Survey,* 2000).

    **a.** Develop an estimate of the standard error of the proportion for the proportion that uses a laptop computer.

    **b.** Develop an estimate of the standard error of the proportion for the proportion that uses express or package service.

    **c.** Are the estimates of the standard error the same in parts (a) and (b)? If they differ, explain why.

    **d.** Develop an approximate 95% confidence interval for the proportion that uses a laptop computer.

    **e.** Develop an approximate 95% confidence interval for the proportion that uses an express or package service.

**20.** A quality of life survey was conducted with employees of a manufacturing firm. Of the firm's 3000 employees, a sample of 300 were sent questionnaires. Two hundred usable questionnaires were obtained for a response rate of 67%.

    **a.** The mean annual salary for the sample was $\bar{x} = \$23{,}200$ with $s = \$3000$. Develop an approximate 95% confidence interval for the mean annual salary of the population.

    **b.** Using the information in part (a), develop an approximate 95% confidence interval for the total salary of all 3000 employees.

    **c.** Seventy-three percent of respondents reported that they were "generally satisfied" with their job. Develop an approximate 95% confidence interval for the population proportion.

    **d.** Comment on whether you think the results in part (c) might be biased. Would your opinion change if you knew the respondents were guaranteed anonymity?

**21.** A U.S. Senate Judiciary Committee report showed the number of homicides in each state for 1991. In Indiana, Ohio, and Kentucky, the number of homicides was, respectively, 380, 760, and 260. Suppose a stratified random sample with the following results was taken to learn more about the victims and the cause of death.

| Stratum | Sample Size | Shootings | Beatings | Urban Victims |
|---|---|---|---|---|
| Indiana | 30 | 10 | 9 | 21 |
| Ohio | 45 | 19 | 12 | 34 |
| Kentucky | 25 | 7 | 11 | 15 |

    **a.** Develop an approximate 95% confidence interval for the proportion of shooting deaths in Indiana.

    **b.** Develop an estimate for the total number of shooting deaths in Ohio.

    **c.** Develop an approximate 95% confidence interval for the proportion of shooting deaths in Ohio.

    **d.** Develop an approximate 95% confidence interval for the proportion of shooting deaths across all three states.

**22.** Refer again to the data in Exercise 21.

    **a.** Develop an estimate of the total number of deaths (in the three states) due to beatings.

    **b.** Develop an approximate 95% confidence interval for the proportion of deaths across all three states due to beatings.

    **c.** Develop an approximate 95% confidence interval for the proportion of urban victims.

    **d.** Develop an estimate of the total number of urban victims.

**23.** A stratified simple random sample is to be taken of a bank's customers to learn about a variety of attitudinal and demographic issues. The stratification is to be based on savings account balances as of June 30, 2001. A frequency distribution showing the number of accounts in each stratum, together with the standard deviation of account balances by stratum, follows.

| Stratum ($) | Accounts | Standard Deviation of Account Balances |
|---|---|---|
| 0.00–1,000.00 | 3000 | 80 |
| 1,000.01–2,000.00 | 600 | 150 |
| 2,000.01–5,000.00 | 250 | 220 |
| 5,000.01–10,000.00 | 100 | 700 |
| over 10,000.00 | 50 | 3000 |

    **a.** Assuming the cost per unit sampled is approximately equal across strata, determine the total number of persons to include in the sample. Assume we want a bound on the error of estimate of the population mean for savings account balances of $B = \$20$.

    **b.** Use the Neyman allocation procedure to determine the number of customers to be sampled for each stratum.

**24.** A public agency is interested in learning more about the persons living in nursing homes in a particular city. A total of 100 nursing homes are caring for 4800 people in the city and a cluster sample of six homes has been taken. Each person in the six homes has been interviewed. A portion of the sample results follows.

| Home | Residents | Average Age of Residents | Disabled Residents |
|------|-----------|--------------------------|--------------------|
| 1 | 14 | 61 | 12 |
| 2 | 7 | 74 | 2 |
| 3 | 96 | 78 | 30 |
| 4 | 23 | 69 | 8 |
| 5 | 71 | 73 | 10 |
| 6 | 29 | 84 | 22 |

**a.** Develop an estimate of the mean age of nursing home residents in this city.

**b.** Develop an approximate 95% confidence interval for the proportion of disabled persons in the city's nursing homes.

**c.** Estimate the total number of disabled persons residing in nursing homes in this city.

# STATISTICAL METHODS FOR QUALITY CONTROL

**Chapter 19**

**CONTENTS**

## STATISTICS IN PRACTICE

### DOW CHEMICAL*
*Freeport, Texas*

Dow Chemical, Texas Operations, began in 1940 when The Dow Chemical Company purchased 800 acres of Texas land on the Gulf Coast to build a magnesium production facility. That original site has expanded to cover more than 5000 acres and is one of the largest petrochemical complexes in the world. Among the products from Texas Operations are magnesium, styrene, plastics, adhesives, solvent, glycol, and chlorine. Some products are made solely for use in other processes, but many end up as essential ingredients in products such as pharmaceuticals, toothpastes, dog food, water hoses, ice chests, milk cartons, garbage bags, shampoos, and furniture.

Dow's Texas Operations produce more than 30% of the world's magnesium, an extremely lightweight metal used in products ranging from tennis rackets to suitcases to "mag" wheels. The Magnesium Department was the first group in Texas Operations to train its technical people and managers in the use of statistical quality control. Some of the earliest successful applications of statistical quality control were in chemical processing.

In one application involving the operation of a drier, samples of the output were taken at periodic intervals; the average value for each sample was computed and recorded on a chart called an $\bar{x}$ chart. Such a chart enabled Dow analysts to monitor trends in the output that might indicate the process was not operating correctly. In one instance, analysts began to observe values for the sample mean that were not indicative of a process operating within its design lim-

Statistical quality control has enabled Dow Chemical to improve its processing methods and output.
© PhotoDisc, Inc.

its. On further examination of the control chart and the operation itself, the analysts found that the variation could be traced to problems involving one operator. The $\bar{x}$ chart recorded after that operator was retrained showed a significant improvement in the process quality.

Dow Chemical has achieved quality improvements everywhere statistical quality control has been used. Documented savings of several hundred thousand dollars per year have been realized, and new applications are continually being discovered.

In this chapter we will show how an $\bar{x}$ chart such as the one used by Dow Chemical can be developed. Such charts are a part of statistical quality control known as statistical process control. We will also discuss methods of quality control for situations in which a decision to accept or reject a group of items is based on a sample.

*The authors are indebted to Clifford B. Wilson, Magnesium Technical Manager, The Dow Chemical Company, for providing this Statistics in Practice.

The American Society for Quality Control (ASQC) defines *quality* as "the totality of features and characteristics of a product or service that bears on its ability to satisfy given needs." In other words, quality measures how well a product or service meets customer needs. Organizations recognize that to be competitive in today's global economy, they must strive for high levels of quality. As a result, they have increased the emphasis on methods for monitoring and maintaining quality.

*Quality assurance* refers to the entire system of policies, procedures, and guidelines established by an organization to achieve and maintain quality. Quality assurance consists of two principal functions: quality engineering and quality control. The objective of *quality engineering* is to include quality in the design of products and processes and to identify potential quality problems prior to production. Quality control consists of making a series of inspections and measurements to determine whether quality standards are being met. If quality standards are not being met, corrective and/or preventive action can be taken to achieve and maintain conformance. As we will show in this chapter, statistical techniques are extremely useful in quality control.

Dr. W. Edwards Deming is credited with being the person who convinced top managers in Japan to use the methods of statistical quality control.

Traditional manufacturing approaches to quality control are being replaced by improved managerial tools and techniques. Competition with high quality Japanese products has provided the impetus for this. Ironically, it was two U.S. consultants, Dr. W. Edwards Deming and Dr. Joseph Juran, who helped educate the Japanese in quality management.

Although quality is everybody's job, Deming stressed that quality improvements must be led by managers. He developed a list of 14 points that he believed are the key responsibilities of managers. For instance, Deming stated that managers must cease dependence on mass inspection; must end the practice of awarding business solely on the basis of price; must seek continual improvement in all production processes and services; must foster a team-oriented environment; and must eliminate numerical goals, slogans, and work standards that prescribe numerical quotas. Perhaps most important, managers must create a work environment in which a commitment to quality and productivity is maintained at all times.

In 1987, the U.S. Congress enacted Public Law 107, the Malcolm Baldrige National Quality Improvement Act. The Baldrige Award is given annually to U.S. firms that excel in quality. This award, along with the perspectives of individuals such as Dr. Deming and Dr. Juran, has helped top managers recognize that improving service quality and product quality is the most critical challenge facing their companies. Winners of the Malcolm Baldrige Award include Motorola, IBM, Xerox, and FedEx. In this chapter we present two statistical methods used in quality control. The first method, *statistical process control,* uses graphical displays known as *control charts* to monitor a production process; the goal is to determine whether the process can be continued or whether it should be adjusted to achieve a desired quality level. The second method, *acceptance sampling,* is used in situations where a decision to accept or reject a group of items must be based on the quality found in a sample.

The most important use of a control chart is in improving the process.

## 19.1    STATISTICAL PROCESS CONTROL

In this section we consider quality control procedures for a production process whereby goods are manufactured continuously. On the basis of sampling and inspection of production output, a decision will be made to either continue the production process or adjust it to bring the items or goods being produced up to acceptable quality standards.

Despite high standards of quality in manufacturing and production operations, machine tools will invariably wear out, vibrations will throw machine settings out of adjustment, purchased materials will be defective, and human operators will make mistakes. Any or all of these factors can result in poor quality output. Fortunately, procedures are available for monitoring production output so that poor quality can be detected early and the production process can be adjusted or corrected.

If the variation in the quality of the production output is due to assignable causes such as tools wearing out, incorrect machine settings, poor quality raw materials, or operator error, the process should be adjusted or corrected as soon as possible. Alternatively, if the variation is due to what are called common causes—that is, randomly occurring variations in materials, temperature, humidity, and so on, which the manufacturer cannot possibly control—the process does not need to be adjusted. The main objective of statistical process control is to determine whether variations in output are due to assignable causes or common causes.

Whenever assignable causes are detected, we conclude that the process is *out of control.* In that case, corrective action will be taken to bring the process back to an acceptable level of quality. However, if the variation in the output of a production process is due only to common causes, we conclude that the process is in *statistical control,* or simply *in control;* in such cases, no changes or adjustments are necessary.

The statistical procedures for process control are based on the hypothesis testing methodology presented in Chapter 9. The null hypothesis $H_0$ is formulated in terms of the production process being in control. The alternative hypothesis $H_a$ is formulated in terms of the production process being out of control. Table 19.1 shows that correct decisions to continue an in-control process and adjust an out-of-control process are possible. However, as with other hypothesis testing procedures, both a Type I error (adjusting an in-control process) and a Type II error (allowing an out-of-control process to continue) are also possible.

*Process control procedures are closely related to hypothesis testing procedures discussed earlier in this text. Control charts provide an ongoing test of the hypothesis that the process is in control*

## Control Charts

A **control chart** provides a basis for deciding whether the variation in the output is due to common causes (in control) or assignable causes (out of control). Whenever an out-of-control situation is detected, adjustments and/or other corrective action will be taken to bring the process back into control.

*Control charts that are based on data that can be measured on a continuous scale are called variables control charts. The $\bar{x}$ chart is a variables control chart.*

Control charts can be classified by the type of data they contain. An $\bar{x}$ **chart** is used if the quality of the output is measured in terms of a variable such as length, weight, temperature, and so on. In that case, the decision to continue or to adjust the production process will be based on the mean value found in a sample of the output. To introduce some of the concepts common to all control charts, let us consider some specific features of an $\bar{x}$ chart.

Figure 19.1 shows the general structure of an $\bar{x}$ chart. The center line of the chart corresponds to the mean of the process when the process is in control. The vertical line identifies $\bar{x}$ on the scale of measurement for the variable of interest. Each time a sample is taken from the production process, a value of the sample mean $\bar{x}$ is computed and a data point showing the value of $\bar{x}$ is plotted on the control chart.

The two lines labeled UCL and LCL are important in determining whether the process is in control or out of control. The lines are called the *upper control limit* and the *lower control limit,* respectively. They are chosen so that when the process is in control, there will be a high probability that the value of $\bar{x}$ will be between the two control limits. Values outside the control limits provide strong statistical evidence that the process is out of control and corrective action should be taken.

Over time, more and more data points ($\bar{x}$ values) will be added to the control chart. The order of the data points will be from left to right as the process is sampled. In essence, every time a point is plotted on the control chart, we are carrying out a hypothesis test to determine whether the process is in control.

**TABLE 19.1**     DECISIONS AND STATES OF THE PROCESS

| | | State of Production Process | |
|---|---|---|---|
| | | $H_0$ **True**<br>**Process in Control** | $H_0$ **False**<br>**Process Out of Control** |
| **Decision** | **Continue Process** | Correct decision | Type II error<br>(allowing an out-of-control process<br>to continue) |
| | **Adjust Process** | Type I error<br>(adjusting an in-control process) | Correct decision |

**FIGURE 19.1**   $\bar{x}$ CHART STRUCTURE

In addition to the $\bar{x}$ chart, other control charts can be used to monitor the range of the measurements in the sample (**R chart**), the proportion of defective items in the sample (**p chart**), and the number of defective items in the sample (**np chart**). In each case, the control chart has an LCL, a center line, and a UCL similar to the $\bar{x}$ chart in Figure 19.1. The major difference among the charts is what the vertical axis measures; for instance, in a p chart the vertical axis denotes the proportion of defective items in the sample instead of the sample mean. In the following discussion, we will illustrate the construction and use of the $\bar{x}$ chart, R chart, p chart, and np chart.

## $\bar{x}$ Chart: Process Mean and Standard Deviation Known

To illustrate the construction of an $\bar{x}$ chart, let us consider the situation at KJW Packaging. This company operates a production line that fills cereal cartons. Suppose KJW knows that when the process is operating correctly—and hence the system is in control—the mean filling weight is $\mu = 16.05$ ounces, and the process standard deviation is $\sigma = .10$ ounces. In addition, assume the filling weights ($x$) are normally distributed. The distribution of filling weights is shown in Figure 19.2.

The sampling distribution of $\bar{x}$, as presented in Chapter 7, can be used to determine the variation that can be expected in $\bar{x}$ values for a process that is in control. Let us first briefly review the properties of the sampling distribution of $\bar{x}$. First, recall that the expected value or mean of $\bar{x}$, $E(\bar{x})$, is equal to $\mu$; in this case $\mu$ is the mean filling weight when the production line is in control. For samples of size $n$, the formula for the standard deviation of $\bar{x}$, called the *standard error of the mean*, is

$$\sigma_{\bar{x}} = \frac{\sigma}{\sqrt{n}} \qquad\qquad (19.1)$$

In addition, because the filling weights ($x$) are normally distributed, the sampling distribution of $\bar{x}$ is normal for any sample size. Thus, the sampling distribution of $\bar{x}$ is a normal probability distribution with mean $\mu$ and standard deviation $\sigma_{\bar{x}}$. This distribution is shown in Figure 19.3. Note that the sampling distribution has the same mean (16.05) as the distribution of individual filling weights.

The sampling distribution of $\bar{x}$ is used to determine what values of $\bar{x}$ are reasonable if the process is in control. The general practice in quality control is to define as reasonable any value of $\bar{x}$ that is within 3 standard deviations above or below the mean value. Recall

**FIGURE 19.2**   DISTRIBUTION OF CEREAL CARTON FILLING WEIGHTS

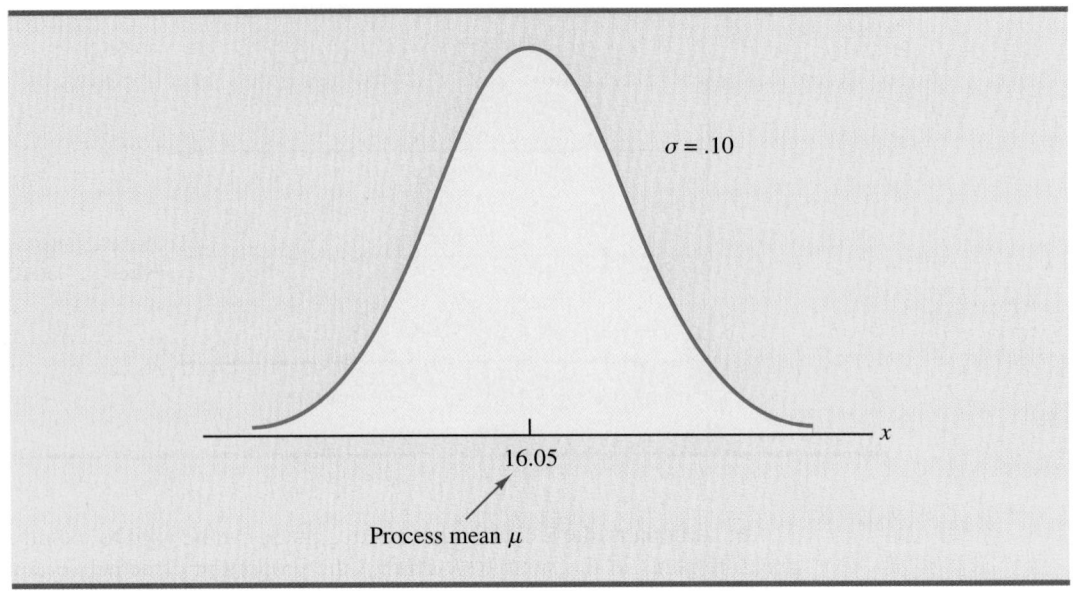

from the study of the normal probability distribution, that approximately 99.7% of the values of a normally distributed random variable are within $\pm 3$ standard deviations of its mean value. Thus, if a value of $\bar{x}$ is within the interval $\mu - 3\sigma_{\bar{x}}$ to $\mu + 3\sigma_{\bar{x}}$, we will assume that the process is in control. In summary, then, the control limits for an $\bar{x}$ chart are as follow.

**Control Limits for an $\bar{x}$ Chart: Process Mean and Standard Deviation Known**

$$\text{UCL} = \mu + 3\sigma_{\bar{x}} \qquad (19.2)$$
$$\text{LCL} = \mu - 3\sigma_{\bar{x}} \qquad (19.3)$$

**FIGURE 19.3**   SAMPLING DISTRIBUTION OF $\bar{x}$ FOR A SAMPLE OF $n$ FILLING WEIGHTS

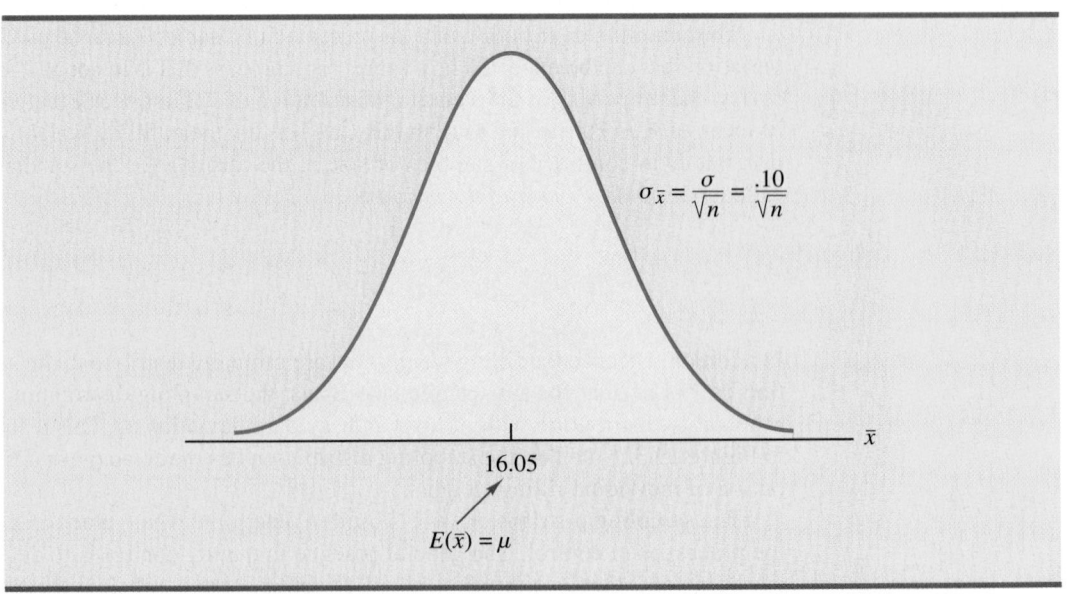

Reconsider the KJW Packaging example with the process distribution of filling weights shown in Figure 19.2 and the sampling distribution of $\bar{x}$ shown in Figure 19.3. Assume that a quality control inspector periodically samples six cartons and uses the sample mean filling weight to determine whether the process is in control or out of control. Using equation (19.1), we find that the standard error of the mean is $\sigma_{\bar{x}} = \sigma/\sqrt{n} = .10/\sqrt{6} = .04$. Thus, with the process mean at 16.05, the control limits are UCL = 16.05 + 3(.04) = 16.17 and LCL = 16.05 − 3(.04) = 15.93. Figure 19.4 is a control chart showing the results of 10 samples taken over a 10-hour period. For ease of reading, the sample numbers 1 through 10 are listed below the chart.

Note that the mean for the fifth sample in Figure 19.4 shows that the process is out of control. The fifth sample mean is below the LCL indicating that underfilling is occurring and that assignable causes of output variation are present. As a result, corrective action was taken at this point to bring the process back into control. The fact that the remaining points on the $\bar{x}$ chart are within the upper and lower control limits indicates that the corrective action was successful.

## $\bar{x}$ Chart: Process Mean and Standard Deviation Unknown

In the KJW Packaging example, we showed how an $\bar{x}$ chart can be developed when the mean and standard deviation of the process are known before sampling. In most situations, the process mean and standard deviation must be estimated by using samples that are selected from the process when it is assumed to be operating in control. For instance, KJW might select a random sample of five boxes each morning and five boxes each afternoon for 10 days of operation. For each subgroup, or sample, the mean and standard deviation of the sample are computed. The overall averages of both the sample means and the sample standard deviations can then be used to construct control charts for both the process mean and the process standard deviation.

In practice, it is more common to monitor the variability of the process by using the range instead of the standard deviation because the range is easier to compute. The range can be used to provide good estimates of the process standard deviation; thus it can be used to construct upper and lower control limits for the $\bar{x}$ chart with little computational effort. To illustrate, let us consider the problem facing Jensen Computer Supplies, Inc.

**FIGURE 19.4    $\bar{x}$ CHART FOR THE CEREAL CARTON FILLING PROCESS**

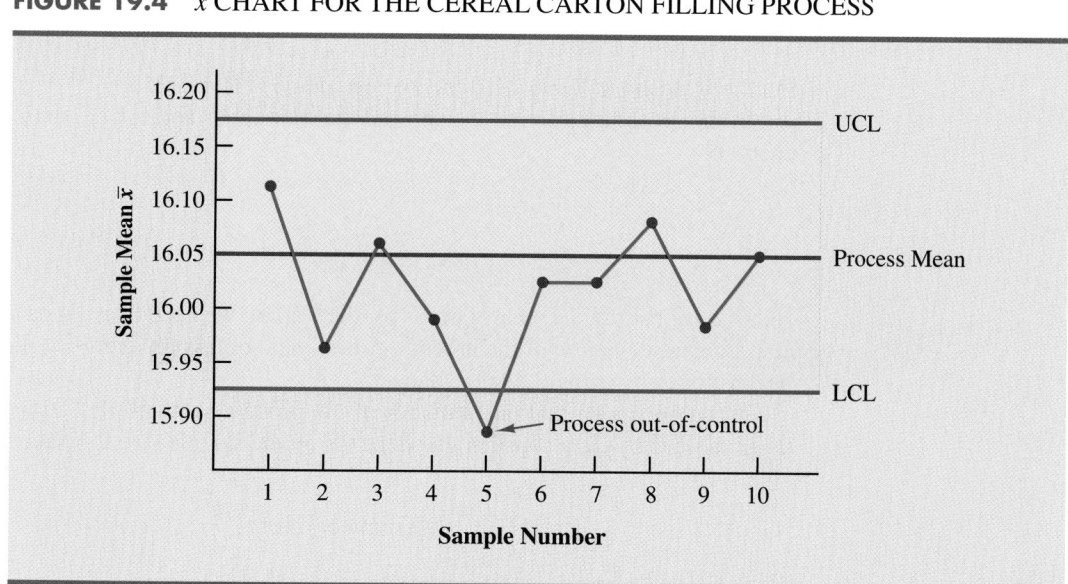

Jensen Computer Supplies (JCS) manufactures 3.5-inch-diameter computer disks. Suppose random samples of five disks are taken during the first hour of operation, during the second hour of operation, and so on, until 20 samples have been selected. Table 19.2 provides the diameter of each disk sampled as well as the mean $\bar{x}_j$ and range $R_j$ for each of the samples.

The estimate of the process mean $\mu$ for $k$ samples of size $n$ is given by the overall sample mean.

**Overall Sample Mean**

$$\bar{\bar{x}} = \frac{\bar{x}_1 + \bar{x}_2 + \cdots + \bar{x}_k}{k} \tag{19.4}$$

where

$$\bar{x}_j = \text{mean of the } j\text{th sample } j = 1, 2, \ldots, k$$
$$k = \text{number of samples}$$

For the JCS data in Table 19.2, $k = 20$ and the overall sample mean is $\bar{\bar{x}} = 3.4995$. This value will be the center line for the $\bar{x}$ chart. The range of each sample, denoted $R_j$, is simply the difference between the largest and smallest values in each sample. The average range is computed as follows.

**Average Range**

$$\bar{R} = \frac{R_1 + R_2 + \cdots + R_k}{k} \tag{19.5}$$

where

$$R_j = \text{range of the } j\text{th sample}, j = 1, 2, \ldots, k$$
$$k = \text{number of samples}$$

For the JCS data in Table 19.2, the average range is $\bar{R} = .0253$.

In the preceding section we showed that the upper and lower control limits for the $\bar{x}$ chart are

$$\mu \pm 3 \frac{\sigma}{\sqrt{n}} \tag{19.6}$$

Hence, to construct the control limits for the $\bar{x}$ chart, we need to estimate $\mu$ and $\sigma$, the mean and standard deviation of the process. An estimate of $\mu$ is given by $\bar{\bar{x}}$. An estimate of $\sigma$ can be developed by using the range data.

It can be shown that an estimator of the process standard deviation $\sigma$ is the average range divided by $d_2$, a constant that depends on the sample size $n$. That is,

$$\text{Estimator of } \sigma = \frac{\bar{R}}{d_2} \tag{19.7}$$

**TABLE 19.2**    DATA FOR JENSEN COMPUTER SUPPLIES

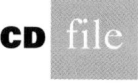

**CD** file

Jensen

| Sample Number | Observations | | | | | Sample Mean $\bar{x}_j$ | Sample Range $R_j$ |
|---|---|---|---|---|---|---|---|
| 1 | 3.5056 | 3.5086 | 3.5144 | 3.5009 | 3.5030 | 3.5065 | .0135 |
| 2 | 3.4882 | 3.5085 | 3.4884 | 3.5250 | 3.5031 | 3.5026 | .0368 |
| 3 | 3.4897 | 3.4898 | 3.4995 | 3.5130 | 3.4969 | 3.4978 | .0233 |
| 4 | 3.5153 | 3.5120 | 3.4989 | 3.4900 | 3.4837 | 3.5000 | .0316 |
| 5 | 3.5059 | 3.5113 | 3.5011 | 3.4773 | 3.4801 | 3.4951 | .0340 |
| 6 | 3.4977 | 3.4961 | 3.5050 | 3.5014 | 3.5060 | 3.5012 | .0099 |
| 7 | 3.4910 | 3.4913 | 3.4976 | 3.4831 | 3.5044 | 3.4935 | .0213 |
| 8 | 3.4991 | 3.4853 | 3.4830 | 3.5083 | 3.5094 | 3.4970 | .0264 |
| 9 | 3.5099 | 3.5162 | 3.5228 | 3.4958 | 3.5004 | 3.5090 | .0270 |
| 10 | 3.4880 | 3.5015 | 3.5094 | 3.5102 | 3.5146 | 3.5047 | .0266 |
| 11 | 3.4881 | 3.4887 | 3.5141 | 3.5175 | 3.4863 | 3.4989 | .0312 |
| 12 | 3.5043 | 3.4867 | 3.4946 | 3.5018 | 3.4784 | 3.4932 | .0259 |
| 13 | 3.5043 | 3.4769 | 3.4944 | 3.5014 | 3.4904 | 3.4935 | .0274 |
| 14 | 3.5004 | 3.5030 | 3.5082 | 3.5045 | 3.5234 | 3.5079 | .0230 |
| 15 | 3.4846 | 3.4938 | 3.5065 | 3.5089 | 3.5011 | 3.4990 | .0243 |
| 16 | 3.5145 | 3.4832 | 3.5188 | 3.4935 | 3.4989 | 3.5018 | .0356 |
| 17 | 3.5004 | 3.5042 | 3.4954 | 3.5020 | 3.4889 | 3.4982 | .0153 |
| 18 | 3.4959 | 3.4823 | 3.4964 | 3.5082 | 3.4871 | 3.4940 | .0259 |
| 19 | 3.4878 | 3.4864 | 3.4960 | 3.5070 | 3.4984 | 3.4951 | .0206 |
| 20 | 3.4969 | 3.5144 | 3.5053 | 3.4985 | 3.4885 | 3.5007 | .0259 |

The American Society for Testing and Materials Manual on Presentation of Data and Control Chart Analysis provides values for $d_2$ as shown in Table 19.3. For instance, when $n = 5$, $d_2 = 2.326$, and the estimate of $\sigma$ is the average range divided by 2.326. If we substitute $\bar{\bar{x}}$ for $\mu$ and $\bar{R}/d_2$ for $\sigma$ in equation (19.6), we can write the control limits for the $\bar{x}$ chart as

$$\bar{\bar{x}} \pm 3 \frac{\bar{R}/d_2}{\sqrt{n}} = \bar{\bar{x}} \pm \frac{3}{d_2\sqrt{n}} \bar{R} = \bar{\bar{x}} \pm A_2\bar{R} \tag{19.8}$$

Note that $A_2 = 3/(d_2\sqrt{n})$ is a constant that depends only on the sample size. Values for $A_2$ are also provided in Table 19.3. For $n = 5$, $A_2 = .577$; thus, the control limits for Jensen's $\bar{x}$ chart are

$$3.4995 \pm (.577)(.0253) = 3.4995 \pm .0146$$

Hence, UCL = 3.514 and LCL = 3.485.

Figure 19.5 shows the $\bar{x}$ chart for Jensen Computer Supplies. We used the data in Table 19.2 and Excel's Chart Wizard to construct the chart. We have added the labels for the control limits and center line. The center line is shown at the overall sample mean $\bar{\bar{x}} = 3.499$. The upper control limit (UCL) is 3.514, which is 3 "sigma limits" above $\bar{\bar{x}}$. The lower control limit (LCL) is 3.485, which is 3 "sigma limits" below $\bar{\bar{x}}$. The $\bar{x}$ chart shows the 20 sample means plotted over time. Because all 20 sample means are within the control limits, this confirms our assumption that the data were collected during a period the

**TABLE 19.3** FACTORS FOR $\bar{x}$ AND $R$ CONTROL CHARTS

| Observations in Sample, $n$ | $d_2$ | $A_2$ | $d_3$ | $D_3$ | $D_4$ |
|---|---|---|---|---|---|
| 2 | 1.128 | 1.880 | 0.853 | 0 | 3.267 |
| 3 | 1.693 | 1.023 | 0.888 | 0 | 2.574 |
| 4 | 2.059 | 0.729 | 0.880 | 0 | 2.282 |
| 5 | 2.326 | 0.577 | 0.864 | 0 | 2.114 |
| 6 | 2.534 | 0.483 | 0.848 | 0 | 2.004 |
| 7 | 2.704 | 0.419 | 0.833 | 0.076 | 1.924 |
| 8 | 2.847 | 0.373 | 0.820 | 0.136 | 1.864 |
| 9 | 2.970 | 0.337 | 0.808 | 0.184 | 1.816 |
| 10 | 3.078 | 0.308 | 0.797 | 0.223 | 1.777 |
| 11 | 3.173 | 0.285 | 0.787 | 0.256 | 1.744 |
| 12 | 3.258 | 0.266 | 0.778 | 0.283 | 1.717 |
| 13 | 3.336 | 0.249 | 0.770 | 0.307 | 1.693 |
| 14 | 3.407 | 0.235 | 0.763 | 0.328 | 1.672 |
| 15 | 3.472 | 0.223 | 0.756 | 0.347 | 1.653 |
| 16 | 3.532 | 0.212 | 0.750 | 0.363 | 1.637 |
| 17 | 3.588 | 0.203 | 0.744 | 0.378 | 1.622 |
| 18 | 3.640 | 0.194 | 0.739 | 0.391 | 1.608 |
| 19 | 3.689 | 0.187 | 0.734 | 0.403 | 1.597 |
| 20 | 3.735 | 0.180 | 0.729 | 0.415 | 1.585 |
| 21 | 3.778 | 0.173 | 0.724 | 0.425 | 1.575 |
| 22 | 3.819 | 0.167 | 0.720 | 0.434 | 1.566 |
| 23 | 3.858 | 0.162 | 0.716 | 0.443 | 1.557 |
| 24 | 3.895 | 0.157 | 0.712 | 0.451 | 1.548 |
| 25 | 3.931 | 0.153 | 0.708 | 0.459 | 1.541 |

Source: Adapted from Table 27 of ASTM STP 15D, *ASTM Manual on Presentation of Data and Control Chart Analysis.* Copyright 1976 American Society of Testing and Materials, Philadelphia, PA. Reprinted with permission.

process was in control. This chart can now be used to monitor the process mean on an ongoing basis.

## $R$ Chart

Let us now consider a range chart or $R$ **chart** that can be used to control the variability of a process. To develop the $R$ chart, we need to think of the range of a sample as a random variable with its own mean and standard deviation. The average range $\bar{R}$ provides an estimate of the mean of this random variable. Moreover, it can be shown that an estimate of the standard deviation of the range is

$$\hat{\sigma}_R = d_3 \frac{\bar{R}}{d_2} \tag{19.9}$$

where $d_2$ and $d_3$ are constants that depend on the sample size; values of $d_2$ and $d_3$ are provided in Table 19.3. Thus, the UCL for the $R$ chart is given by

$$\bar{R} + 3\hat{\sigma}_R = \bar{R} + 3d_3 \frac{\bar{R}}{d_2} = \bar{R}\left(1 + 3\frac{d_3}{d_2}\right) \tag{19.10}$$

**FIGURE 19.5**   $\bar{x}$ CHART FOR JENSEN COMPUTER SUPPLIES

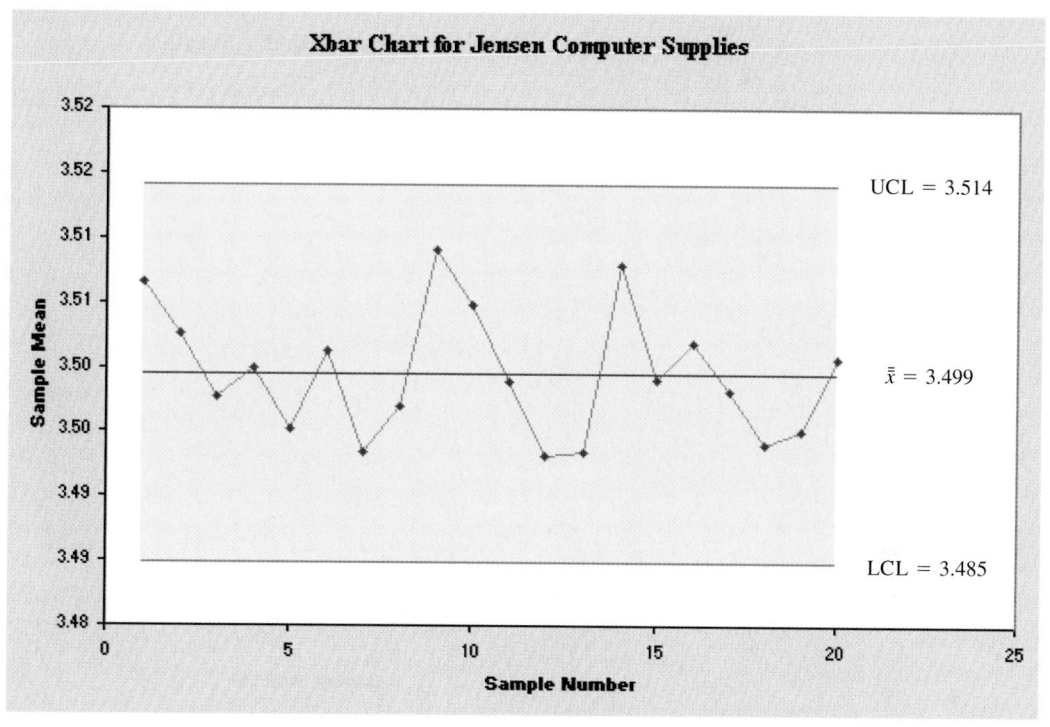

and the LCL is

$$\bar{R} - 3\hat{\sigma}_R = \bar{R} - 3d_3\frac{\bar{R}}{d_2} = \bar{R}\!\left(1 - 3\frac{d_3}{d_2}\right) \qquad \textbf{(19.11)}$$

If we let

$$D_4 = 1 + 3\frac{d_3}{d_2} \qquad \textbf{(19.12)}$$

$$D_3 = 1 - 3\frac{d_3}{d_2} \qquad \textbf{(19.13)}$$

we can write the control limits for the $R$ chart as

$$\text{UCL} = \bar{R}D_4 \qquad \textbf{(19.14)}$$
$$\text{LCL} = \bar{R}D_3 \qquad \textbf{(19.15)}$$

Values for $D_3$ and $D_4$ are also provided in Table 19.3. Note that for $n = 5$, $D_3 = 0$, and $D_4 = 2.114$. Thus, with $\bar{R} = .0253$, the control limits are

$$\text{UCL} = .0253(2.114) = .0535$$
$$\text{LCL} = .0253(0) = 0$$

Figure 19.6 shows the $R$ chart for Jensen Computer Supplies. We used the data in Table 19.2 and Excel's Chart Wizard to construct the chart. The center line is shown at the overall mean

**FIGURE 19.6**    *R* CHART FOR JENSEN COMPUTER SUPPLIES

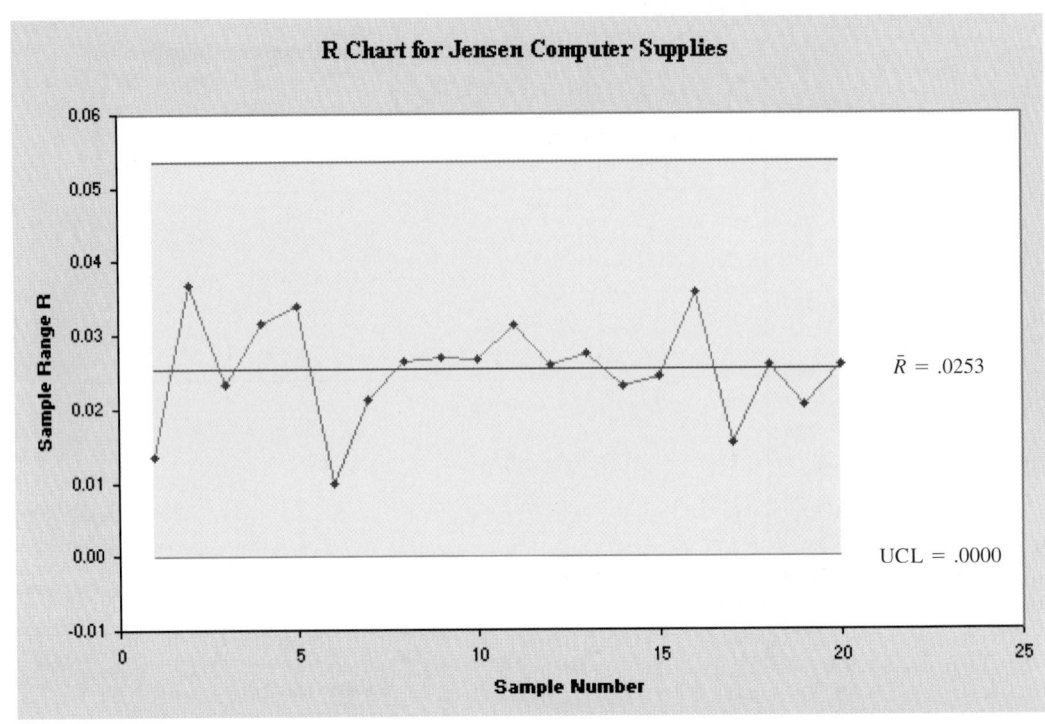

of the 20 sample ranges, $\bar{R}$ = .0253. The UCL is .0535 or 3 sigma limits above $\bar{R}$. The LCL is 0.0 or 3 sigma limits below $\bar{R}$. The *R* chart shows the 20 sample ranges plotted over time. Because all 20 sample ranges are within the control limits, we confirm that the process was in control during the sampling period.

*If the R chart indicates that the process is out of control, the $\bar{x}$ chart should not be interpreted until the R chart indicates the process variability is in control.*

## Using Excel to Construct an *R* Chart and an $\bar{x}$ Chart

The $\bar{x}$ chart in Figure 19.5 and the *R* chart in Figure 19.6 were constructed using Excel. Here we show how the data in Table 19.2 can be used to construct an *R* chart and an $\bar{x}$ chart using Excel. Figure 19.7 is an Excel worksheet containing the Jensen Computer Supplies data.

**FIGURE 19.7**    EXCEL WORKSHEET OF 20 SAMPLES OF SIZE 5 FOR JENSEN COMPUTER SUPPLIES

*Note: Rows 7–18 (samples 6–17) are hidden.*

|   | A | B | C | D | E | F | G |
|---|---|---|---|---|---|---|---|
| 1 | Sample | Observation 1 | Observation 2 | Observation 3 | Observation 4 | Observation 5 | |
| 2 | 1 | 3.5056 | 3.5086 | 3.5144 | 3.5009 | 3.5030 | |
| 3 | 2 | 3.4882 | 3.5085 | 3.4884 | 3.5250 | 3.5031 | |
| 4 | 3 | 3.4897 | 3.4898 | 3.4995 | 3.5130 | 3.4969 | |
| 5 | 4 | 3.5153 | 3.5120 | 3.4989 | 3.4900 | 3.4837 | |
| 6 | 5 | 3.5059 | 3.5113 | 3.5011 | 3.4773 | 3.4801 | |
| 19 | 18 | 3.4959 | 3.4823 | 3.4964 | 3.5082 | 3.4871 | |
| 20 | 19 | 3.4878 | 3.4864 | 3.4960 | 3.5070 | 3.4984 | |
| 21 | 20 | 3.4969 | 3.5144 | 3.5053 | 3.4985 | 3.4885 | |
| 22 | | | | | | | |

**FIGURE 19.8**    EXCEL WORKSHEET SHOWING RANGE DATA AND COMPUTATION OF LCL, MEAN, AND UCL

| | A | B | C | D | E | F |
|---|---|---|---|---|---|---|
| 1 | Sample | R | LCL | Mean | UCL | |
| 2 | 1 | =MAX(Data!B2:F2)-MIN(Data!B2:F2) | =$D$23*$B$22 | =$B$22 | =$D$24*$B$22 | |
| 3 | 2 | =MAX(Data!B3:F3)-MIN(Data!B3:F3) | =$D$23*$B$22 | =$B$22 | =$D$24*$B$22 | |
| 4 | 3 | =MAX(Data!B4:F4)-MIN(Data!B4:F4) | =$D$23*$B$22 | =$B$22 | =$D$24*$B$22 | |
| 5 | 4 | =MAX(Data!B5:F5)-MIN(Data!B5:F5) | =$D$23*$B$22 | =$B$22 | =$D$24*$B$22 | |
| 6 | 5 | =MAX(Data!B6:F6)-MIN(Data!B6:F6) | =$D$23*$B$22 | =$B$22 | =$D$24*$B$22 | |
| 19 | 18 | =MAX(Data!B19:F19)-MIN(Data!B19:F19) | =$D$23*$B$22 | =$B$22 | =$D$24*$B$22 | |
| 20 | 19 | =MAX(Data!B20:F20)-MIN(Data!B20:F20) | =$D$23*$B$22 | =$B$22 | =$D$24*$B$22 | |
| 21 | 20 | =MAX(Data!B21:F21)-MIN(Data!B21:F21) | =$D$23*$B$22 | =$B$22 | =$D$24*$B$22 | |
| 22 | Mean(Rbar) | =AVERAGE($B$2:$B$21) | | | | |
| 23 | | | | D3 | 0 | |
| 24 | | | | D4 | 2.114 | |
| 25 | | | | | | |

| | A | B | C | D | E | F |
|---|---|---|---|---|---|---|
| 1 | Sample | R | LCL | Mean | UCL | |
| 2 | 1 | 0.0135 | 0.0000 | 0.0253 | 0.0534 | |
| 3 | 2 | 0.0368 | 0.0000 | 0.0253 | 0.0534 | |
| 4 | 3 | 0.0233 | 0.0000 | 0.0253 | 0.0534 | |
| 5 | 4 | 0.0316 | 0.0000 | 0.0253 | 0.0534 | |
| 6 | 5 | 0.0340 | 0.0000 | 0.0253 | 0.0534 | |
| 19 | 18 | 0.0259 | 0.0000 | 0.0253 | 0.0534 | |
| 20 | 19 | 0.0206 | 0.0000 | 0.0253 | 0.0534 | |
| 21 | 20 | 0.0259 | 0.0000 | 0.0253 | 0.0534 | |
| 22 | Mean(Rbar) | 0.0253 | | | | |
| 23 | | | | D3 | 0.0000 | |
| 24 | | | | D4 | 2.1140 | |
| 25 | | | | | | |

Note: Rows 7–18 (samples 6–17) are hidden.

The average value for the range is needed to compute the lower and upper control limits for the $\bar{x}$ chart. So we will construct the $R$ chart first. Our approach will be to first develop a worksheet with the needed data. Then the Chart Wizard will be used to develop the $R$ chart. A similar procedure is followed to construct the $\bar{x}$ chart. Figure 19.8 contains the data developed for the $R$ chart. The formula worksheet is in the background; the value worksheet is in the foreground.

**Enter Data:**    The data for the diameter measurements for the 20 samples selected by Jensen Computer Supplies are contained in the worksheet in Figure 19.7. We will use the data in this worksheet to construct the worksheets shown in Figures 19.8 and 19.9. For future reference, the worksheet in Figure 19.7 is named Data. The only values entered directly into the worksheets in Figures 19.8 and 19.9 are the sample numbers 1–20 in column A, the heading in cells A1:E1, and cells C23 and C24.

**FIGURE 19.9**    EXCEL WORKSHEET SHOWING $\bar{x}$ DATA AND COMPUTATION OF LCL, MEAN, AND UCL

| | A | B | C | D | E | F |
|---|---|---|---|---|---|---|
| 1 | Sample | xbar | LCL | Mean | UCL | |
| 2 | 1 | =AVERAGE(Data!B2:F2) | =$B$22-$D$23*$D$24 | =$B$22 | =$B$22+$D$23*$D$24 | |
| 3 | 2 | =AVERAGE(Data!B3:F3) | =$B$22-$D$23*$D$24 | =$B$22 | =$B$22+$D$23*$D$24 | |
| 4 | 3 | =AVERAGE(Data!B4:F4) | =$B$22-$D$23*$D$24 | =$B$22 | =$B$22+$D$23*$D$24 | |
| 5 | 4 | =AVERAGE(Data!B5:F5) | =$B$22-$D$23*$D$24 | =$B$22 | =$B$22+$D$23*$D$24 | |
| 6 | 5 | =AVERAGE(Data!B6:F6) | =$B$22-$D$23*$D$24 | =$B$22 | =$B$22+$D$23*$D$24 | |
| 19 | 18 | =AVERAGE(Data!B19:F19) | =$B$22-$D$23*$D$24 | =$B$22 | =$B$22+$D$23*$D$24 | |
| 20 | 19 | =AVERAGE(Data!B20:F20) | =$B$22-$D$23*$D$24 | =$B$22 | =$B$22+$D$23*$D$24 | |
| 21 | 20 | =AVERAGE(Data!B21:F21) | =$B$22-$D$23*$D$24 | =$B$22 | =$B$22+$D$23*$D$24 | |
| 22 | Mean | =AVERAGE(B2:B21) | | | | |
| 23 | | | | A2 | 0.577 | |
| 24 | | | | Rbar | 0.025275 | |
| 25 | | | | | | |

| | A | B | C | D | E | F |
|---|---|---|---|---|---|---|
| 1 | Sample | xbar | LCL | Mean | UCL | |
| 2 | 1 | 3.5065 | 3.4849 | 3.4995 | 3.5141 | |
| 3 | 2 | 3.5026 | 3.4849 | 3.4995 | 3.5141 | |
| 4 | 3 | 3.4978 | 3.4849 | 3.4995 | 3.5141 | |
| 5 | 4 | 3.5000 | 3.4849 | 3.4995 | 3.5141 | |
| 6 | 5 | 3.4951 | 3.4849 | 3.4995 | 3.5141 | |
| 19 | 18 | 3.4940 | 3.4849 | 3.4995 | 3.5141 | |
| 20 | 19 | 3.4951 | 3.4849 | 3.4995 | 3.5141 | |
| 21 | 20 | 3.5007 | 3.4849 | 3.4995 | 3.5141 | |
| 22 | Mean | 3.4995 | | | | |
| 23 | | | | A2 | 0.577 | |
| 24 | | | | Rbar | 0.0253 | |
| 25 | | | | | | |

Note: Rows 7–18 (samples 6–17) are hidden.

**Enter Functions and Formulas:** The worksheet in Figure 19.8 contains the formulas needed to construct an $R$ chart using the Chart Wizard. Here we describe how this worksheet was constructed. Column A contains the sample numbers 1–20 as noted. Column B contains the Excel formulas needed to compute the range for each sample from the data in cells B2:F21 of the Data worksheet shown in Figure 19.7. Excel's MAX and MIN functions are used. The cell references in the formulas are to cells in the Data worksheet; note that the worksheet name followed by an exclamation point must precede a cell reference when the cells referenced are in another worksheet of the same workbook. We see, in the value worksheet, that the ranges computed are the same as in Table 19.2. The AVERAGE function has been used in cell B22 to compute the average of the ranges for the 20 samples.

In order to compute the LCL and UCL we must know $D_3$ and $D_4$. These values have been obtained from Table 19.3 and placed into cells D23 and D24, respectively. The formulas in cells C2:C21 are identical; they compute the LCL by multiplying $D_3$ (cell D23) times the average range (cell B22). The formulas in cells D2:D21 are also identical; they provide the average range. Finally, the formulas in cells E2:E21 (also identical) are used to compute the UCL by multiplying $D_4$ (cell D24) times the average range (cell B22).

**Apply Tools:** The following steps describe how to use Excel's Chart Wizard to construct the $R$ chart from the data in cells A2:E21 of Figure 19.8.

**Step 1.** Select cells A2:E21

**Step 2.** Select the **Chart Wizard** button on the standard toolbar (or select the **Insert** pull-down menu and choose the **Chart** option)

**Step 3.** When the **Chart Wizard—Step 1 of 4—Chart Type** dialog box appears:
    Choose **XY (Scatter)** in the **Chart type** list
    Choose **Scatter with data points connected by Lines** from the **Chart sub-type** display
    Select **Next>**

**Step 4.** When the **Chart Wizard—Step 2 of 4—Chart Source Data** dialog box appears:
    Select **Next>**

**Step 5.** When the **Chart Wizard—Step 3 of 4—Chart Options** dialog box appears:
    Select the **Titles** tab and then
        Type **R Chart for Jensen Computer Supplies** in the **Chart title** box
        Type **Sample Number** in the **Value (X)** axis box
        Type **Sample Range R** in the **Value (Y)** axis box
    Select the **Legend** tab and then
        Remove the check in the **Show Legend** Box
    Select the **Gridlines** tab and then
        Remove the check in the **Major gridlines** box
    Select **Next>**

**Step 6.** When the **Chart Wizard—Step 4 of 4—Chart Location** dialog box appears:
    Specify a location for the chart (we chose the **As new sheet** option)
    Select **Finish**

The resulting $R$ chart will appear in a new sheet entitled "Chart 1" in your workbook.

You will need to do some editing of your chart to make it look like Figure 19.6. To make the UCL line look like it does in Figure 19.6 follow these steps:

**Step 1.** Right click on the UCL line at one of the data points and select **Format Data Series**

**Step 2.** When the Format Data Series dialog box appears:
    In the **Line** section:
        Choose black for **Color**
        Choose the second line from the bottom for **Weight**

In the **Marker** section:
>    Choose the "long dash" for **Style**
>    Choose black for **Foreground**
>    Click **OK**

The UCL line will now appear as a solid black line. You should then follow the same steps for the average and LCL lines to make them look as they do in Figure 19.6. As a final step you will need to right click on the vertical axis to format the axis labels as shown in Figure 19.6. You will probably also want to resize the chart to satisfy your own preference. Just select the chart and move the drag handles until the chart looks the way you want it.

The procedure for constructing an $\bar{x}$ chart is similar to what we have just described so we will not provide step-by-step instructions. Figure 19.9 shows the worksheet developed to provide the data needed to construct an $\bar{x}$ chart. It is analogous to the worksheet developed for the $R$ chart in Figure 19.8. We used the Chart Wizard with this worksheet to construct the $\bar{x}$ chart shown in Figure 19.5. The steps followed are almost identical to those we just described for the $R$ chart, so we will not repeat them here.

## *p* **Chart**

Control charts that are based on data indicating the presence of a defect or the number of defects are called attributes control charts. A *p* chart is an attributes control chart.

Let us consider the case in which the output quality is measured in terms of the items being either nondefective or defective. The decision to continue or to adjust the production process will be based on $\bar{p}$, the proportion of defective items found in a sample of the output. The control chart used to monitor the proportion of defective items is called a **p chart.**

To illustrate the construction of a *p* chart, consider the use of automated mail-sorting machines in a post office. These automated machines scan the zip codes on letters and divert each letter to its proper carrier route. Even when a machine is operating properly, some letters are diverted to incorrect routes. Suppose that when a machine is operating correctly, or in a state of control, 3% of the letters are incorrectly diverted. Thus $p$, the proportion of letters incorrectly diverted when the process is in control, is .03.

The sampling distribution of $\bar{p}$, as presented in Chapter 7, can be used to determine the variation that can be expected in $\bar{p}$ values for a process that is in control. Recall that the expected value or mean of $\bar{p}$ is $p$, the proportion defective when the process is in control. With samples of size $n$, the formula for the standard deviation of $\bar{p}$, called the standard error of the proportion, is

$$\sigma_{\bar{p}} = \sqrt{\frac{p(1-p)}{n}} \tag{19.16}$$

We also learned in Chapter 7 that the sampling distribution of $\bar{p}$ can be approximated by a normal probability distribution whenever the sample size is large. With $\bar{p}$, the sample size can be considered large whenever the following two conditions are satisfied.

$$np \geq 5$$
$$n(1-p) \geq 5$$

In summary, whenever the sample size is large, the sampling distribution of $\bar{p}$ can be approximated by a normal probability distribution with mean $p$ and standard deviation $\sigma_{\bar{p}}$. This distribution is shown in Figure 19.10.

To establish control limits for a *p* chart, we follow the same procedure we used to establish control limits for an $\bar{x}$ chart. That is, the limits for the control chart are set at

**FIGURE 19.10**   SAMPLING DISTRIBUTION OF $\bar{p}$

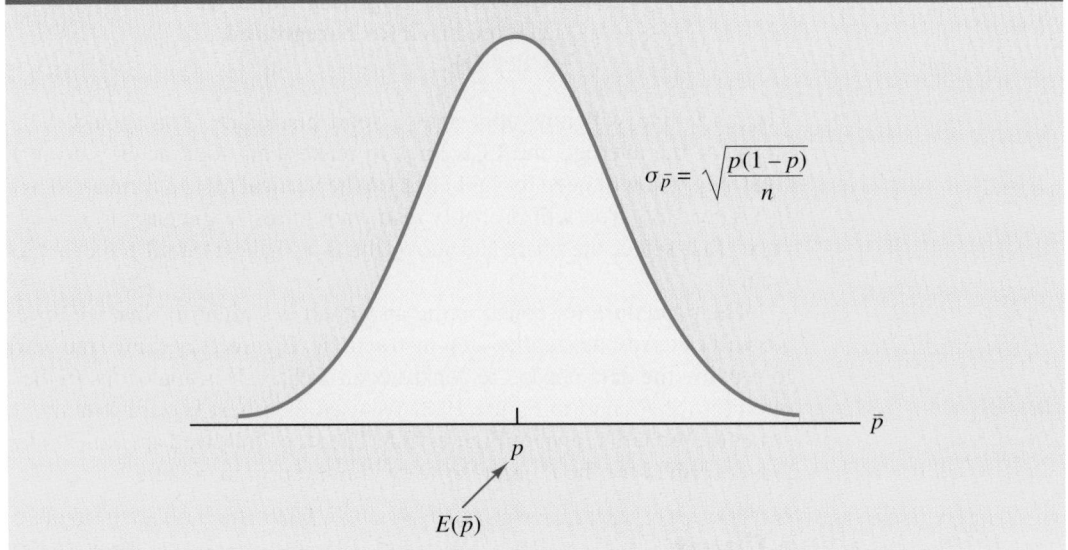

$$\sigma_{\bar{p}} = \sqrt{\frac{p(1-p)}{n}}$$

$E(\bar{p})$

3 standard errors above and below the proportion defective when the process is in control. Thus, we have the following control limits.

---

**Control Limits for a $p$ Chart**

$$\text{UCL} = p + 3\sigma_{\bar{p}}$$
$$\text{LCL} = p - 3\sigma_{\bar{p}}$$

---

With $p = .03$ and samples of size $n = 200$, equation (19.16) shows that the standard error is

$$\sigma_{\bar{p}} = \sqrt{\frac{.03(1 - .03)}{200}} = .0121$$

Hence, the control limits are UCL $= .03 + 3(.0121) = .0663$, and LCL $= .03 - 3(.0121) = -.0063$. Whenever equation (19.18) provides a negative value for LCL, LCL is reset to zero in the control chart.

Figure 19.11 is the control chart for the mail-sorting process. The points plotted show the sample proportion defective found in samples of letters taken from the process. All points are within the control limits, and the sorting process shows no evidence of being out of control. In fact, the $p$ chart indicates that the process should continue to operate.

If the proportion of defective items for a process that is in control is not known, that value is first estimated by using sample data. Suppose, for example, that $k$ different samples, each of size $n$, are selected from a process that is in control. The fraction or proportion of defective items in each sample is then determined. Treating all the data collected as one large sample, we can determine the average number of defective items for all the data; that value can then be used to provide an estimate of $p$, the proportion of defective items observed when the process is in control. Note that this estimate of $p$ also enables us to estimate the standard error of the proportion; upper and lower control limits can then be established.

**FIGURE 19.11**    $p$ CHART FOR THE PROPORTION DEFECTIVE IN A MAIL-SORTING
PROCESS

## $np$ Chart

An *$np$ chart* is a control chart developed for the number of defective items observed in a sample. In this case, $n$ is the sample size and $p$ is the probability of observing a defective item when the process is in control. Whenever the sample size is large, that is when $np \geq 5$ and $n(1 - p) \geq 5$, the distribution of the number of defective items observed in a sample size $n$ can be approximated by a normal probability distribution with mean $np$ and standard deviation $\sqrt{np(1 - p)}$. Thus, for the mail-sorting example, with $n = 200$ and $p = .03$, the number of defective items observed in a sample of 200 letters can be approximated by a normal probability distribution with a mean of $200(.03) = 6$ and a standard deviation of $\sqrt{200(.03)(.97)} = 2.4125$.

The control limits for an $np$ chart are set at 3 standard deviations above and below the expected number of defective items observed when the process is in control. Thus, we have the following control limits.

**Control Limits for an $np$ Chart**

$$\text{UCL} = np + 3\sqrt{np(1 - p)} \tag{19.19}$$

$$\text{LCL} = np - 3\sqrt{np(1 - p)} \tag{19.20}$$

For the mail-sorting process example, with $p = .03$ and $n = 200$, the control limits are UCL $= 6 + 3(2.4125) = 13.2375$, and LCL $= 6 - 3(2.4125) = -1.2375$. Because equation (19.20) provides a negative value for LCL, it is reset to zero in the control chart. Hence, if the number of letters diverted to incorrect routes is greater than 13, the process is concluded to be out of control.

The information provided by an $np$ chart is equivalent to the information provided by the $p$ chart; the only difference is that the $np$ chart is a plot of the number of defective items observed whereas the $p$ chart is a plot of the proportion of defective items observed. Thus, if we were to conclude that a particular process is out of control on the basis of a $p$ chart, the process would also be concluded to be out of control on the basis of an $np$ chart.

# Interpretation of Control Charts

Control charts are designed to identify when assignable causes of variation are present. Managers must then authorize action to eliminate the assignable cause and return the process to an in-control state.

The location and pattern of points in a control chart enable us to determine, with a small probability of error, whether a process is in statistical control. A primary indication that a process may be out of control is a data point outside the control limits, such as point 5 in Figure 19.4. Such a point is statistical evidence that the process is out of control; in such cases, corrective action should be taken as soon as possible.

In addition to points outside the control limits, certain patterns of the points within the control limits can be warning signals of quality control problems. For example, assume that all the data points are within the control limits but that a large number of points are on one side of the center line. This pattern may indicate that an equipment problem, a change in materials, or some other assignable cause of a shift in quality has occurred. Careful investigation of the production process should be undertaken to determine whether quality has changed.

Even if all points are within the upper and lower control limits, a process may not be in control. Trends in the sample data points or unusually long runs above or below the center line may also indicate out-of-control conditions.

Another pattern to watch for in control charts is a gradual shift, or trend, over time. For example, as tools wear out, the dimensions of machined parts will gradually deviate from their designed levels. Gradual changes in temperature or humidity, general equipment deterioration, dirt buildup, or operator fatigue may also result in a trend pattern in control charts. Six or seven points in a row that indicate either an increasing or decreasing trend should be cause for concern, even if the data points are all within the control limits. When such a pattern occurs, the process should be reviewed for possible changes or shifts in quality. Corrective action to bring the process back into control may be necessary.

## NOTES AND COMMENTS

1. Because the control limits for the $\bar{x}$ chart depend on the value of the average range, these limits will not have much meaning unless the process variability is in control. In practice, the $R$ chart is usually constructed before the $\bar{x}$ chart; if the $R$ chart indicates that the process variability is in control, then the $\bar{x}$ chart is constructed.

2. The $p$ and $np$ control charts can also be constructed using Excel's Chart Wizard. For instance, to develop a $p$ chart, start by organizing the data for $\bar{p}$, LCL, mean, and UCL in a worksheet similar to Figures 19.8 or 19.9. Then use the Chart Wizard in the same way we did earlier to construct an $R$ chart.

3. An $np$ chart is used to monitor a process in terms of the number of defects. The Motorola Six-Sigma Quality Level sets a goal of producing no more than 3.4 defects per million operations (*American Production and Inventory Control,* July 1991); this goal implies $p = .0000034$.

## EXERCISES

### Methods

1. A process that is in control has a mean of $\mu = 12.5$ and a standard deviation of $\sigma = .8$.
   a. Construct an $\bar{x}$ chart if samples of size 4 are to be used.
   b. Repeat part (a) for samples of size 8 and 16.
   c. What happens to the limits of the control chart as the sample size is increased? Discuss why this change is reasonable.

2. Twenty-five samples, each of size 5, were selected from a process that was in control. The sum of all the data collected was 677.5 pounds.
   a. What is an estimate of the process mean (in terms of pounds per unit) when the process is in control?
   b. Develop the control chart for this process if samples of size 5 will be used. Assume that the process standard deviation is .5 when the process is in control, and that the mean of the process is the estimate developed in part (a).

3. Twenty-five samples of 100 items each were inspected when a process was considered to be operating satisfactorily. In the 25 samples, 135 items were found to be defective.
   a. What is an estimate of the proportion defective when the process is in control?
   b. What is the standard error of the proportion if samples of size 100 will be used for statistical process control?
   c. Compute the upper and lower control limits for the control chart.

4. A process sampled 20 times with a sample of size 8 resulted in $\bar{\bar{x}} = 28.5$ and $\bar{R} = 1.6$. Compute the upper and lower control limits for the $\bar{x}$ and $R$ charts for this process.

## Applications

5. Temperature is used to measure the output of a production process. When the process is in control, the mean of the process is $\mu = 128.5$ and the standard deviation is $\sigma = .4$.
   a. Construct an $\bar{x}$ chart if samples of size 6 are to be used.
   b. Is the process in control for a sample providing the following data?

   | 128.8 | 128.2 | 129.1 | 128.7 | 128.4 | 129.2 |

   c. Is the process in control for a sample providing the following data?

   | 129.3 | 128.7 | 128.6 | 129.2 | 129.5 | 129.0 |

6. A quality control process monitors the weight per carton of laundry detergent. Control limits are set at UCL = 20.12 ounces and LCL = 19.90 ounces. Samples of size 5 are used for the sampling and inspection process. What are the process mean and process standard deviation for the manufacturing operation?

7. The Goodman Tire and Rubber Company periodically tests its tires for tread wear under simulated road conditions. To study and control the manufacturing process, 20 samples, each containing three radial tires, were chosen from different shifts over several days of operation, resulting in the following data. Assuming that these data were collected when the manufacturing process was believed to be operating in control, develop the $R$ and $\bar{x}$ charts.

**CD file**

Tires

| Sample | Tread Wear* | | |
|--------|------|------|------|
| 1 | 31 | 42 | 28 |
| 2 | 26 | 18 | 35 |
| 3 | 25 | 30 | 34 |
| 4 | 17 | 25 | 21 |
| 5 | 38 | 29 | 35 |
| 6 | 41 | 42 | 36 |
| 7 | 21 | 17 | 29 |
| 8 | 32 | 26 | 28 |
| 9 | 41 | 34 | 33 |
| 10 | 29 | 17 | 30 |
| 11 | 26 | 31 | 40 |
| 12 | 23 | 19 | 25 |
| 13 | 17 | 24 | 32 |
| 14 | 43 | 35 | 17 |
| 15 | 18 | 25 | 29 |
| 16 | 30 | 42 | 31 |
| 17 | 28 | 36 | 32 |
| 18 | 40 | 29 | 31 |
| 19 | 18 | 29 | 28 |
| 20 | 22 | 34 | 26 |

*Hundredths of an inch

8. Over several weeks of normal, or in-control, operation, 20 samples of 150 packages each of synthetic-gut tennis strings were tested for breaking strength. A total of 141 packages of the 3000 tested failed to conform to the manufacturer's specifications.
   a. What is an estimate of the process proportion defective when the system is in control?
   b. Compute the upper and lower control limits for a $p$ chart.
   c. With the results of part (b), what conclusion should be drawn about the process if tests on a new sample of 150 packages find 12 defective? Do there appear to be assignable causes in this situation?
   d. Compute the upper and lower control limits for an $np$ chart.
   e. Answer part (c) using the results of part (d).
   f. Which control chart would be preferred in this situation? Explain.

9. An automotive industry supplier produces pistons for several models of automobiles. Twenty samples, each consisting of 200 pistons, were selected when the process was known to be operating correctly. The numbers of defective pistons found in the samples follow.

| 8  | 10 | 6  | 4 | 5 | 7 | 8 | 12 | 8 | 15 |
|----|----|----|---|---|---|---|----|---|----|
| 14 | 10 | 10 | 7 | 5 | 8 | 6 | 10 | 4 | 8  |

   a. What is an estimate of the proportion defective for the piston manufacturing process when it is in control?
   b. Construct a $p$ chart for the manufacturing process, assuming each sample has 200 pistons.
   c. With the results of part (b), what conclusion should be made if a sample of 200 has 20 defective pistons?
   d. Compute the upper and lower control limits for an $np$ chart.
   e. Answer part (c) using the results of part (d).

## 19.2   ACCEPTANCE SAMPLING

In acceptance sampling, the items of interest can be incoming shipments of raw materials or purchased parts as well as finished goods from final assembly. Suppose we want to decide whether to accept or reject a group of items on the basis of specified quality characteristics. In quality control terminology, the group of items is a **lot**, and **acceptance sampling** is a statistical method that enables us to make an accept-reject decision based on the sample of items from the lot.

The general steps of acceptance sampling are shown in Figure 19.12. After a lot is received, a sample is selected for inspection. The results of the inspection are compared to specified quality characteristics. If the quality is satisfactory, the lot is accepted and sent to production or shipped to customers. If the quality is not satisfactory, the lot is rejected. Managers must then decide on the disposition of the lot. In some cases, the decision may be to keep the lot and remove the unacceptable or nonconforming items. In other cases, the lot may be returned to the supplier at the supplier's expense; the extra work and cost placed on the supplier can motivate the supplier to provide high-quality lots. Finally, if the rejected lot consists of finished goods, the goods must be scrapped or reworked to meet acceptable quality standards.

The statistical procedure of acceptance sampling is based on the hypothesis testing methodology presented in Chapter 9. The null and alternative hypotheses are stated as follows.

$$H_0: \text{Good-quality lot}$$
$$H_a: \text{Poor-quality lot}$$

Table 19.4 shows the results of the hypothesis testing procedure. Note that correct decisions correspond to accepting a good-quality lot and rejecting a poor-quality lot. However, as with

**FIGURE 19.12    ACCEPTANCE SAMPLING PROCEDURE**

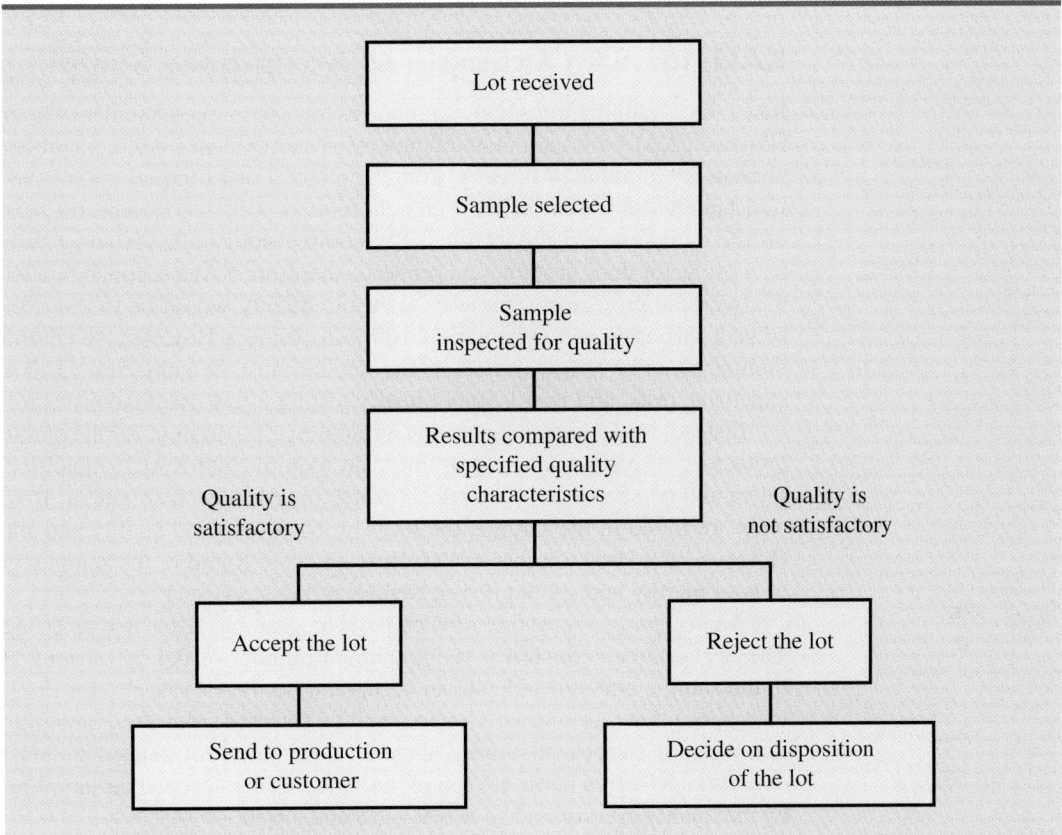

other hypothesis testing procedures, we need to be aware of the possibilities of making a Type I error (rejecting a good-quality lot) or a Type II error (accepting a poor-quality lot).

Because the probability of a Type I error creates a risk for the producer of the lot, it is known as the **producer's risk.** For example, a producer's risk of .05 indicates a 5% chance that a good-quality lot will be erroneously rejected. Because the probability of a Type II error creates a risk for the consumer of the lot, it is known as the **consumer's risk.** For example, a consumer's risk of .10 means that there is a 10% chance that a poor-quality lot will be erroneously accepted and thus used in production or shipped to the customer. Specific values for the producer's risk and the consumer's risk can be controlled by the person

**TABLE 19.4    THE OUTCOMES OF ACCEPTANCE SAMPLING**

|  |  | State of the Lot | |
|---|---|---|---|
|  |  | $H_0$ **True**<br>**Good-Quality Lot** | $H_0$ **False**<br>**Poor-Quality Lot** |
| **Decision** | **Accept the Lot** | Correct decision | Type II error<br>(accepting a poor-quality lot) |
|  | **Reject the Lot** | Type I error<br>(rejecting a good-quality lot) | Correct decision |

designing the acceptance sampling procedure. To illustrate how to assign risk values, let us consider the problem faced by KALI, Inc.

## KALI, Inc.: An Example of Acceptance Sampling

KALI, Inc., manufactures home appliances that are marketed under a variety of trade names. However, KALI does not manufacture every component used in its products. Several components are purchased directly from suppliers. For example, one of the components that KALI purchases for use in home air conditioners is an overload protector, a device that turns off the compressor if it overheats. The compressor can be seriously damaged if the overload protector does not function properly, therefore KALI is concerned about the quality of the overload protectors. One way to ensure quality would be to test every component received; this approach is known as 100% inspection. However, to determine proper functioning of an overload protector, the device must be subjected to time-consuming and expensive tests, and KALI cannot justify testing every overload protector it receives.

Instead, KALI uses an acceptance sampling plan to monitor the quality of the overload protectors. The acceptance sampling plan requires that KALI's quality control inspectors select and test a sample of overload protectors from each shipment. If very few defective units are found in the sample, the lot is probably of good quality and should be accepted. However, if a large number of defective units are found in the sample, the lot is probably of poor quality and should be rejected.

An *acceptance sampling plan* consists of a sample size $n$ and an acceptance criterion $c$. The acceptance criterion is the maximum number of defective items that can be found in the sample and still indicate an acceptable lot. For example, for the KALI problem let us suppose that a sample of 15 items will be selected from each incoming shipment or lot. Furthermore, suppose that the manager of quality control states that the lot can be accepted only if no defective items are found. In this case, the acceptance sampling plan established by the quality control manager is $n = 15$ and $c = 0$.

This acceptance sampling plan is easy for the quality control inspector to implement. The inspector simply selects a sample of 15 items, performs the tests, and reaches a conclusion based on the following decision rule.

- *Accept the lot* if zero defects are found.
- *Reject the lot* if one or more defects are found.

Before implementing this acceptance sampling plan, the quality control manager wants to evaluate the risks or errors possible under the plan. The plan will be implemented only if both the producer's risk (Type I error) and the consumer's risk (Type II error) are controlled at reasonable levels.

## Computing the Probability of Accepting a Lot

The key to analyzing both the producer's risk and the consumer's risk is a "What-if?" type of analysis. That is, we will assume that a lot has some known percentage of defective items and compute the probability of accepting the lot for a given sampling plan. By varying the assumed percentage of defective items, we can examine the effect of the sampling plan on both types of risks.

Let us begin by assuming that a large shipment of overload protectors has been received and that 5% of the overload protectors in the shipment are defective. For a shipment or lot with 5% of the items defective, what is the probability that the $n = 15$, $c = 0$ sampling plan will lead us to accept the lot? Because each overload protector tested will be either defective or nondefective and because the lot size is large, the number of defective items in a sample of 15 has a *binomial probability distribution*. The binomial probability function, which was presented in Chapter 5, follows.

**Binomial Probability Function for Acceptance Sampling**

$$f(x) = \frac{n!}{x!(n-x)!} p^x(1-p)^{(n-x)} \qquad \textbf{(19.21)}$$

where

$$n = \text{the sample size}$$
$$p = \text{the proportion of defective items in the lot}$$
$$x = \text{the number of defective items in the sample}$$
$$f(x) = \text{the probability of } x \text{ defective items in the sample}$$

For the KALI acceptance sampling plan, $n = 15$; thus, for a lot with 5% defective ($p = .05$), we have

$$f(x) = \frac{15!}{x!(15-x)!} (.05)^x(1 - .05)^{(15-x)} \qquad \textbf{(19.22)}$$

Using equation (19.22), $f(0)$ will provide the probability that zero overload protectors will be defective and the lot will be accepted. In using equation (19.22), recall that $0! = 1$. Thus, the probability computation for $f(0)$ is

$$f(0) = \frac{15!}{0!(15-0)!} (.05)^0(1 - .05)^{(15-0)}$$

$$= \frac{15!}{0!(15)!} (.05)^0(.95)^{15} = (.95)^{15} = .4633$$

We now know that the $n = 15$, $c = 0$ sampling plan has a .4633 probability of accepting a lot with 5% defective items. Hence, a corresponding probability of rejecting a lot with 5% defective items is $1 - .4633 = .5367$.

Excel's BINOMDIST function can also be used to compute these probabilities. See Chapter 5.

In Table 19.5 we show the probability that the $n = 15$, $c = 0$ sampling plan will lead to the acceptance of lots with 1%, 2%, 3%, ... defective items. The probabilities in the table were computed by using $p = .01$, $p = .02$, $p = .03$, ... in the binomial probability function (19.21).

**TABLE 19.5**    PROBABILITY OF ACCEPTING THE LOT FOR THE KALI PROBLEM WITH $n = 15$ AND $c = 0$

| Percent Defective in the Lot | Probability of Accepting the Lot |
|:---:|:---:|
| 1 | .8601 |
| 2 | .7386 |
| 3 | .6333 |
| 4 | .5421 |
| 5 | .4633 |
| 10 | .2059 |
| 15 | .0874 |
| 20 | .0352 |
| 25 | .0134 |

With the data in Table 19.5, a graph of the probability of accepting the lot versus the percent defective in the lot can be drawn as shown in Figure 19.13. This graph, or curve, is called the **operating characteristic (OC) curve** for the $n = 15$, $c = 0$ acceptance sampling plan.

Perhaps we should consider other sampling plans, ones with different sample sizes $n$ and/or different acceptance criteria $c$. First consider the case in which the sample size remains $n = 15$ but the acceptance criterion increases from $c = 0$ to $c = 1$. That is, we will now accept the lot if zero or one defective item is found in the sample. For a lot with 5% defective items ($p = .05$), the binomial probability function in equation (19.21) can be used to compute $f(0)$ and $f(1)$. Summing these two probabilities provides the probability that the $n = 15$, $c = 1$ sampling plan will accept the lot. We find that with $n = 15$ and $p = .05$, $f(0) = .4633$ and $f(1) = .3658$. Thus, we find a $.4633 + .3658 = .8291$ probability that the $n = 15$, $c = 1$ plan will lead to the acceptance of a lot with 5% defective items.

Figure 19.14 shows the operating characteristic curves for four alternative acceptance sampling plans for the KALI problem. Samples of size 15 and 20 are considered. Note that regardless of the proportion defective in the lot, the $n = 15$, $c = 1$ sampling plan provides the highest probabilities of accepting the lot. The $n = 20$, $c = 0$ sampling plan provides the lowest probabilities of accepting the lot; however, that plan also provides the highest probabilities of rejecting the lot.

## Selecting an Acceptance Sampling Plan

Now that we know how to use the binomial probability distribution to compute the probability of accepting a lot with a given proportion defective, we are ready to select the values of $n$ and $c$ that determine the desired acceptance sampling plan for the applica-

**FIGURE 19.13**    OPERATING CHARACTERISTIC CURVE FOR THE $n = 15$, $c = 0$ ACCEPTANCE SAMPLING PLAN

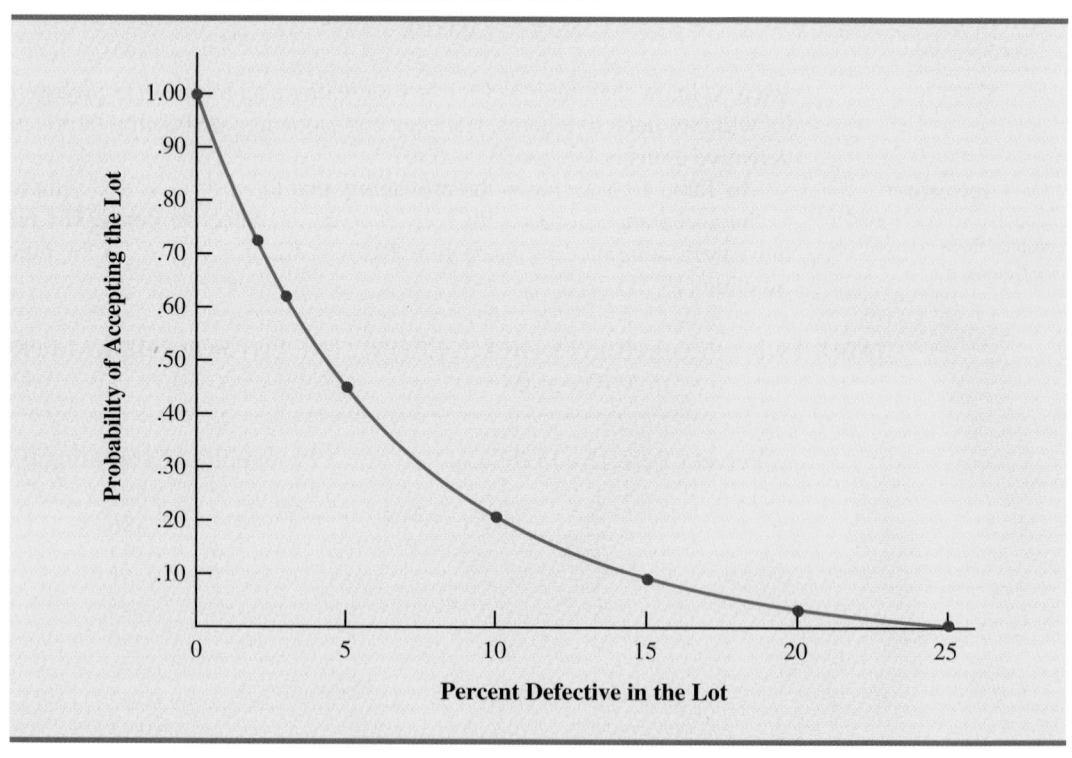

**FIGURE 19.14**    OPERATING CHARACTERISTIC CURVES FOR FOUR ACCEPTANCE
SAMPLING PLANS

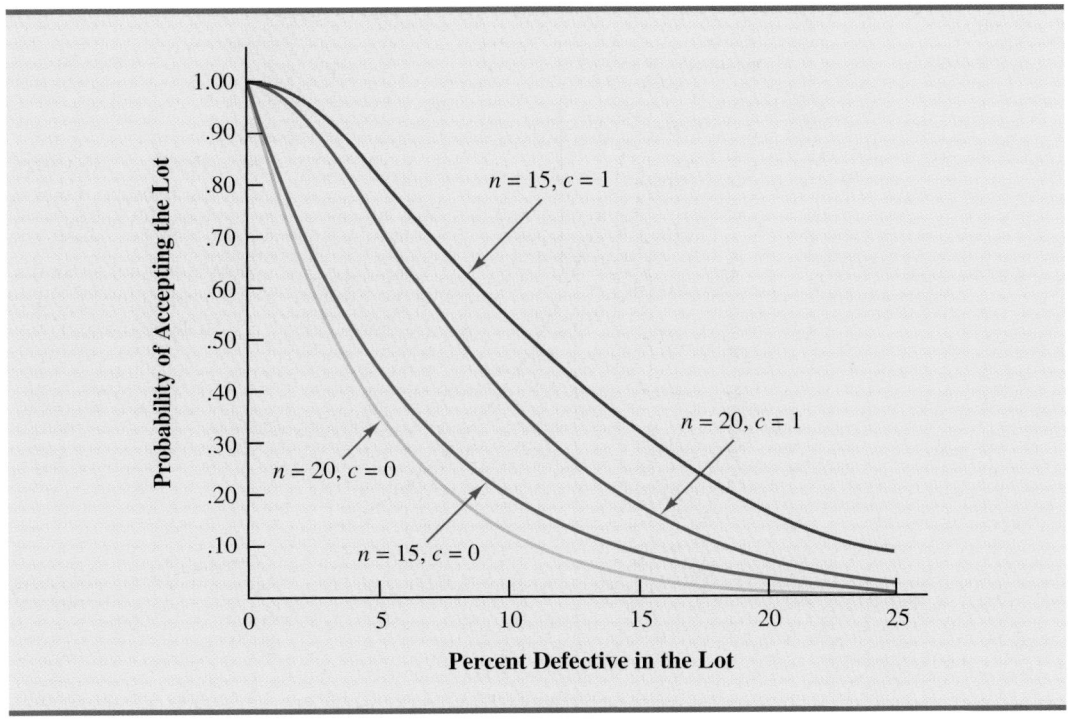

tion being studied. In formulating an acceptance plan, managers must specify two values
for the fraction defective in the lot. One value, denoted $p_0$, will be used to control for
the producer's risk, and the other value, denoted $p_1$, will be used to control for the consumer's risk.

In showing how this can be done, we will use the following notation.

$\alpha$ = the producer's risk; the probability that a lot with $p_0$ defective will be rejected

$\beta$ = the consumer's risk; the probability that a lot with $p_1$ defective will be accepted

Suppose that for the KALI problem, the managers specify that $p_0 = .03$ and $p_1 = .15$. From
the OC curve for $n = 15$, $c = 0$ in Figure 19.15, we see that $p_0 = .03$ provides a producer's
risk of approximately $1 - .63 = .37$, and $p_1 = .15$ provides a consumer's risk of approximately .09. Thus, if the managers are willing to tolerate both a .37 probability of rejecting
a lot with 3% defective items (producer's risk) and a .09 probability of accepting a lot with
15% defective items (consumer's risk), the $n = 15$, $c = 0$ acceptance sampling plan would
be acceptable.

Suppose, however, that the managers request a producer's risk of $\alpha = .10$ and a consumer's risk of $\beta = .20$. We see that now the $n = 15$, $c = 0$ sampling plan has a better-than-
desired consumer's risk but an unacceptably large producer's risk. The fact that $\alpha = .37$
indicates that 37% of the lots will be erroneously rejected when only 3% of the items in
them are defective. The producer's risk is too high, and a different acceptance sampling plan
should be considered.

Using $p_0 = .03$, $\alpha = .10$, $p_1 = .15$, and $\beta = .20$ in Figure 19.14 shows that the acceptance sampling plan with $n = 20$ and $c = 1$ comes closest to meeting both the producer's

**FIGURE 19.15**  OPERATING CHARACTERISTIC CURVE FOR $n = 15$, $c = 0$ WITH $p_0 = .03$ and $p_1 = .15$

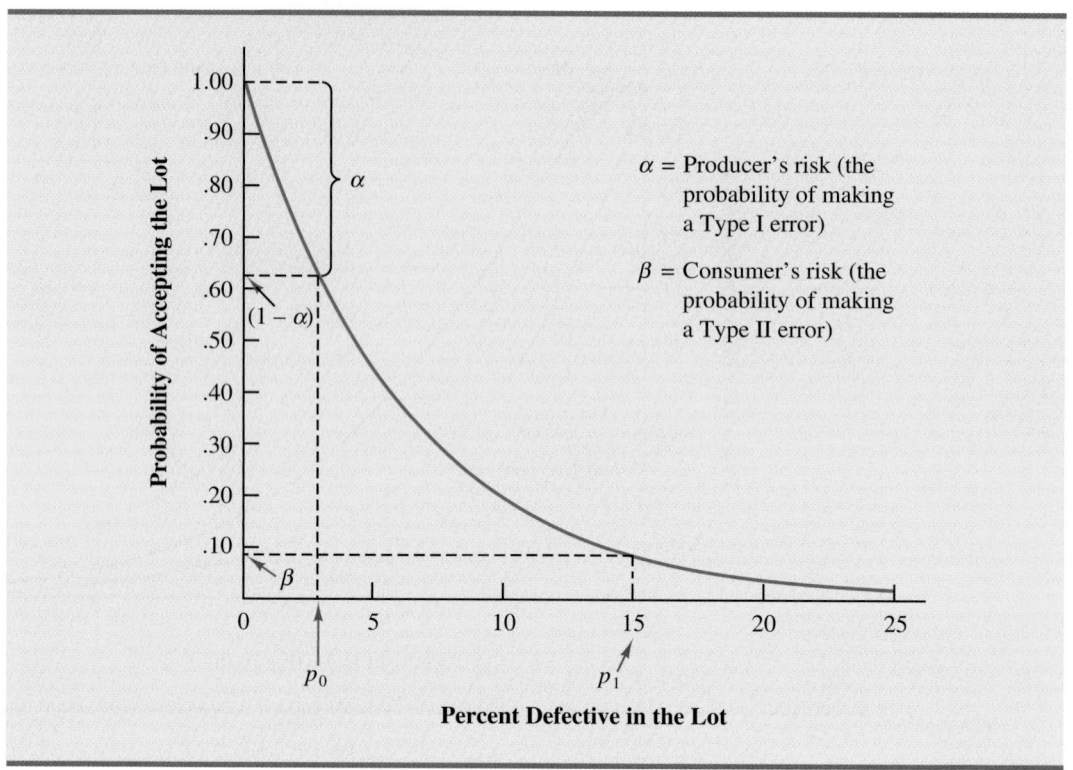

and the consumer's risk requirements. Exercise 13 at the end of this section will ask you to compute the producer's risk and the consumer's risk for the $n = 20$, $c = 1$ sampling plan.

As shown in this section, several computations and several operating characteristic curves may need to be considered to determine the sampling plan with the desired producer's and consumer's risks. Fortunately, tables of sampling plans are published. For example, the American Military Standard Table, MIL-STD-105D, provides information helpful in designing acceptance sampling plans. More advanced texts on quality control, such as those listed in the bibliography, describe the use of such tables. The advanced texts also discuss the role of sampling costs in determining the optimal sampling plan.

## Multiple Sampling Plans

The acceptance sampling procedure that we have presented for the KALI problem is a *single-sample plan*. It is called a single-sample plan because only one sample or sampling stage is used. After the number of defective components in the sample is determined, a decision must be made to accept or reject the lot. An alternative to the single-sample plan is a **multiple sampling plan**, in which two or more stages of sampling are used. At each stage a decision is made among three possibilities: stop sampling and accept the lot, stop sampling and reject the lot, or continue sampling. Although more complex, multiple sampling plans often result in a smaller total sample size than single-sample plans with the same $\alpha$ and $\beta$ probabilities.

The logic of a two-stage, or double-sample, plan is shown in Figure 19.16. Initially a sample of $n_1$ items is selected. If the number of defective components $x_1$ is less than or equal to $c_1$, accept the lot. If $x_1$ is greater than or equal to $c_2$, reject the lot. If $x_1$ is between $c_1$ and $c_2$ $(c_1 < x_1 < c_2)$, select a second sample of $n_2$ items. Determine the combined, or total number of defects from the first sample $(x_1)$ and the second sample $(x_2)$. If $x_1 + x_2 \leq c_3$, accept the lot; otherwise reject the lot. The development of the double-sample plan is more difficult because the sample sizes $n_1$ and $n_2$ and the acceptance numbers $c_1$, $c_2$, and $c_3$ must meet acceptable levels of both the producer's and consumer's risks.

**FIGURE 19.16**   A TWO-STAGE ACCEPTANCE SAMPLING PLAN

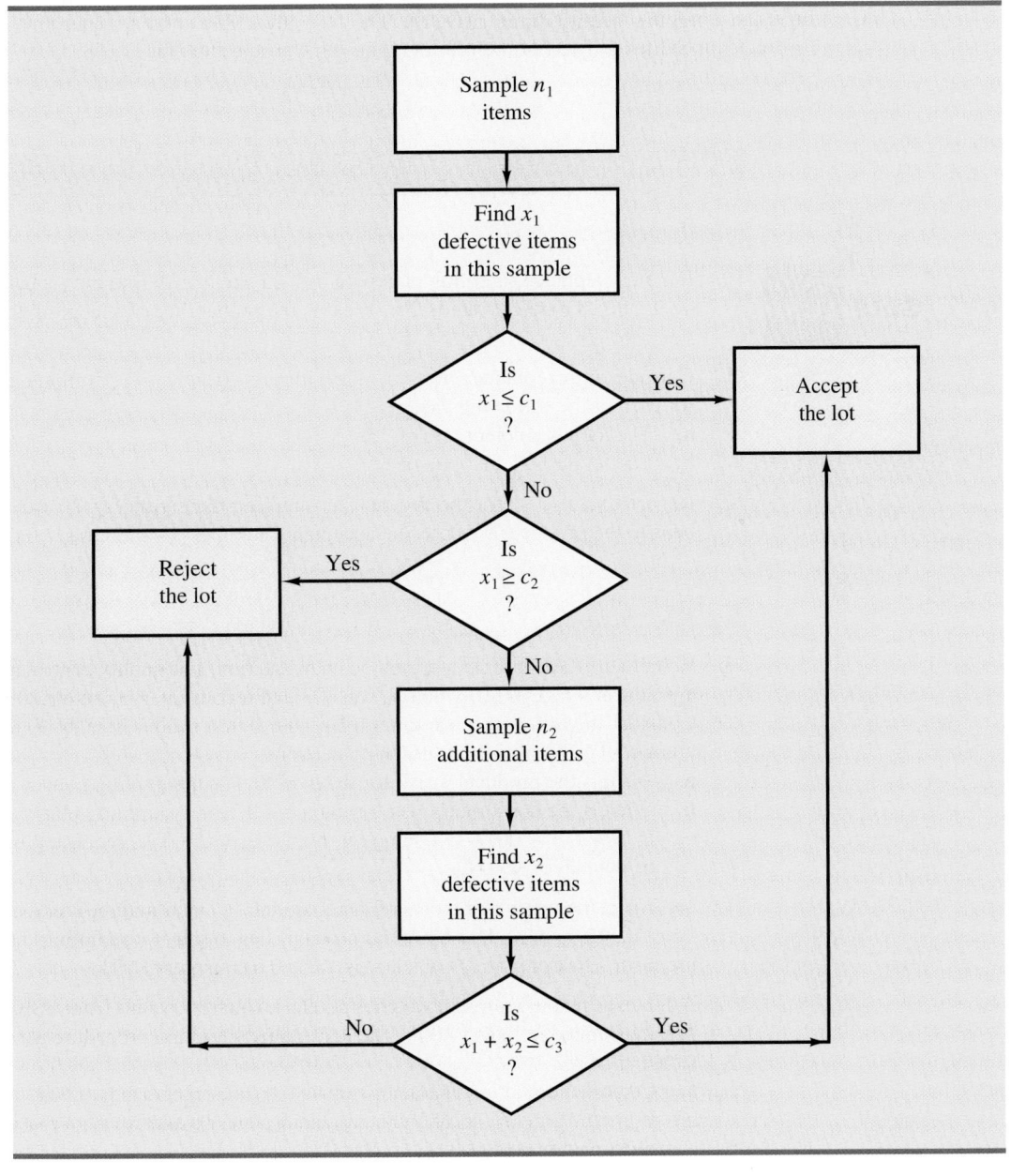

## NOTES AND COMMENTS

1. The use of the binomial probability distribution for acceptance sampling is based on the assumption of large lots. If the lot size is small, the hypergeometric probability distribution is the appropriate distribution.

2. In the MIL-ST-105D sampling tables, $p_0$ is called the acceptable quality level (AQL). In some sampling tables, $p_1$ is called the lot tolerance percent defective (LTPD) or the rejectable quality level (RQL). Many of the published sampling plans also use quality indexes such as the indifference quality level (IQL) and the average outgoing quality limit (AOQL). The more advanced texts listed in the bibliography provide a complete discussion of these other indexes.

3. In this section we provided an introduction to *attributes sampling plans.* In these plans each item sampled is classified as nondefective or defective. In *variables sampling plans,* a sample is taken and a measurement of the quality characteristic is taken. For example, for gold jewelry a measurement of quality may be the amount of gold it contains. A simple statistic such as the average amount of gold in the sample jewelry is computed and compared with an allowable value to determine whether to accept or reject the lot.

## EXERCISES

### Methods

**10.** For an acceptance sampling plan with $n = 25$ and $c = 0$, find the probability of accepting a lot when the defect rate is 2%. What is the probability of accepting the lot if the defect rate is 6%?

**11.** Consider an acceptance sampling plan with $n = 20$ and $c = 0$. Compute the producer's risk for each of the following cases.
   **a.** The lot has a defect rate of 2%.
   **b.** The lot has a defect rate of 6%.

**12.** Repeat Exercise 11 for the acceptance sampling plan with $n = 20$ and $c = 1$. What happens to the producer's risk as the acceptance number $c$ is increased? Explain.

### Applications

**13.** Refer to the KALI problem presented in this section. The quality control manager requested a producer's risk of .10 when $p_0$ was .03 and a consumer's risk of .20 when $p_1$ was .15. Consider the acceptance sampling plan based on a sample size of 20 and an acceptance number of 1. Answer the following questions.
   **a.** What is the producer's risk for the $n = 20$, $c = 1$ sampling plan?
   **b.** What is the consumer's risk for the $n = 20$, $c = 1$ sampling plan?
   **c.** Does the $n = 20$, $c = 1$ sampling plan satisfy the risks requested by the quality control manager? Discuss.

**14.** To inspect incoming shipments of raw materials, a manufacturer is considering samples of sizes 10, 15, and 20. Use binomial probabilities to select a sampling plan that provides a producer's risk of $\alpha = .03$ when $p_0$ is .05 and a consumer's risk of $\beta = .12$ when $p_1$ is .30.

**15.** A domestic manufacturer of watches purchases quartz crystals from a Swiss firm. The crystals are shipped in lots of 1000. The acceptance sampling procedure uses 20 randomly selected crystals.
   **a.** Construct operating characteristic curves for acceptance numbers of 0, 1, and 2.
   **b.** If $p_0$ is .01 and $p_1 = .08$, what are the producer's and consumer's risks for each sampling plan in part (a)?

## SUMMARY

In this chapter we discussed how statistical methods can be used to assist in the control of quality. We first presented the $\bar{x}$, $R$, $p$, and $np$ control charts as graphical aids in monitoring process quality. Control limits are established for each chart; samples are selected periodically and the data plotted on the control chart. Data outside the control limits indicate that the process is out of control and that corrective action should be taken. Patterns of data within the control limits can also indicate potential quality control problems and suggest that corrective action may be warranted.

We also considered the technique known as acceptance sampling. With this procedure, a sample is selected and inspected. The number of defective items in the sample provides the basis for accepting or rejecting the lot. The sample size and the acceptance criterion can be adjusted to control both the producer's risk (Type I error) and the consumer's risk (Type II error).

## GLOSSARY

**Quality control**   A series of inspections and measurements used to determine whether quality standards are being met.

**Assignable causes**   Variations in process outputs that are due to factors such as machine tools wearing out, incorrect machine settings, poor-quality raw materials, operator error, and so on. Corrective action should be taken when assignable causes of output variation are detected.

**Common causes**   Normal or natural variations in process outputs that are due purely to chance. No corrective action is necessary when output variations are due to common causes.

**Control chart**   A graphical tool used to help determine whether a process is in control or out of control.

**$\bar{x}$ chart**   A control chart used to monitor the mean value of a variable such as a length, weight, temperature, and so on.

**$R$ chart**   A control chart used to monitor the range of values for a variable.

**$p$ chart**   A control chart used to monitor the proportion defective generated by a process.

**$np$ chart**   A control chart used to monitor the number of defective items generated by a process.

**Lot**   A group of items such as incoming shipments of raw materials or purchased parts as well as finished goods from final assembly.

**Acceptance sampling**   A statistical procedure in which the number of defective items found in a sample is used to determine whether a lot should be accepted or rejected.

**Producer's risk**   The risk of rejecting a good-quality lot; a Type I error.

**Consumer's risk**   The risk of accepting a poor-quality lot; a Type II error.

**Acceptance criterion**   The maximum number of defective items that can be found in the sample and still allow acceptance of the lot.

**Operating characteristic curve**   A graph showing the probability of accepting the lot as a function of the percentage defective in the lot. This curve can be used to help determine whether a particular acceptance sampling plan meets both the producer's and the consumer's risk requirements.

**Multiple sampling plan** A form of acceptance sampling in which more than one sample or stage is used. On the basis of the number of defective items found in a sample, a decision will be made to accept the lot, reject the lot, or continue sampling.

## KEY FORMULAS

**Standard Error of the Mean**

$$\sigma_{\bar{x}} = \frac{\sigma}{\sqrt{n}} \tag{19.1}$$

**Control Limits for an $\bar{x}$ Chart: Process Mean and Standard Deviation Known**

$$UCL = \mu + 3\sigma_{\bar{x}} \tag{19.2}$$
$$LCL = \mu - 3\sigma_{\bar{x}} \tag{19.3}$$

**Overall Sample Mean**

$$\bar{\bar{x}} = \frac{\bar{x}_1 + \bar{x}_2 + \cdots + \bar{x}_k}{k} \tag{19.4}$$

**Average Range**

$$\bar{R} = \frac{R_1 + R_2 + \cdots + R_k}{k} \tag{19.5}$$

**Control Limits for an $\bar{x}$ Chart: Process Mean and Standard Deviation Unknown**

$$\bar{\bar{x}} \pm A_2\bar{R} \tag{19.8}$$

**Control Limits for an $R$ Chart**

$$UCL = \bar{R}D_4 \tag{19.14}$$
$$LCL = \bar{R}D_3 \tag{19.15}$$

**Standard Error of the Proportion**

$$\sigma_{\bar{p}} = \sqrt{\frac{p(1 - p)}{n}} \tag{19.16}$$

**Control Limits for a $p$ Chart**

$$UCL = p + 3\sigma_{\bar{p}} \tag{19.17}$$
$$LCL = p - 3\sigma_{\bar{p}} \tag{19.18}$$

**Control Limits for an $np$ Chart**

$$UCL = np + 3\sqrt{np(1 - p)} \tag{19.19}$$
$$LCL = np - 3\sqrt{np(1 - p)} \tag{19.20}$$

**Binomial Probability Function for Acceptance Sampling**

$$f(x) = \frac{n!}{x!(n-x)!} p^x (1-p)^{(n-x)} \qquad \textbf{(19.21)}$$

## SUPPLEMENTARY EXERCISES

16. Samples of size 5 provided the following 20 sample means for a production process that is believed to be in control.

| | | |
|---|---|---|
| 95.72 | 95.24 | 95.18 |
| 95.44 | 95.46 | 95.32 |
| 95.40 | 95.44 | 95.08 |
| 95.50 | 95.80 | 95.22 |
| 95.56 | 95.22 | 95.04 |
| 95.72 | 94.82 | 95.46 |
| 95.60 | 95.78 | |

   a. Based on these data, what is an estimate of the mean when the process is in control?

   b. Assuming that the process standard deviation is $\sigma = .50$, develop a control chart for this production process. Assume that the mean of the process is the estimate developed in part (a).

   c. Are any of the 20 sample means outside the control limits?

17. Product filling weights are normally distributed with a mean of 350 grams and a standard deviation of 15 grams.

   a. Develop the control limits for samples of size 10, 20, and 30.

   b. What happens to the control limits as the sample size is increased?

   c. What happens when a Type I error is made?

   d. What happens when a Type II error is made?

   e. What is the probability of a Type I error for samples of size 10, 20, and 30?

   f. What is the advantage of increasing the sample size for control chart purposes? What error probability is reduced as the sample size is increased?

18. Twenty-five samples of size 5 resulted in $\bar{\bar{x}} = 5.42$ and $\bar{R} = 2.0$. Compute control limits for the $\bar{x}$ and $R$ charts, and estimate the standard deviation of the process.

19. The following are quality control data for a manufacturing process at Kensport Chemical Company. The data show the temperature in degrees centigrade at five points in time during a manufacturing cycle. The company is interested in using control charts to monitor the temperature of its manufacturing process. Construct the $\bar{x}$ chart and $R$ chart. What conclusions can be made about the quality of the process?

| Sample | $\bar{x}$ | $R$ | Sample | $\bar{x}$ | $R$ |
|---|---|---|---|---|---|
| 1 | 95.72 | 1.0 | 11 | 95.80 | .6 |
| 2 | 95.24 | .9 | 12 | 95.22 | .2 |
| 3 | 95.18 | .8 | 13 | 95.56 | 1.3 |
| 4 | 95.44 | .4 | 14 | 95.22 | .5 |
| 5 | 95.46 | .5 | 15 | 95.04 | .8 |
| 6 | 95.32 | 1.1 | 16 | 95.72 | 1.1 |
| 7 | 95.40 | .9 | 17 | 94.82 | .6 |
| 8 | 95.44 | .3 | 18 | 95.46 | .5 |
| 9 | 95.08 | .2 | 19 | 95.60 | .4 |
| 10 | 95.50 | .6 | 20 | 95.74 | .6 |

**20.** The following data were collected for the Master Blend Coffee production process. The data show the filling weights based on samples of 3-pound cans of coffee. Use these data to construct the $\bar{x}$ and $R$ chart. What conclusions can be made about the quality of the production process?

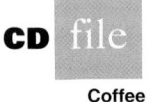

**CD** file

Coffee

|          | Observations |      |      |      |      |
| -------- | ------------ | ---- | ---- | ---- | ---- |
| Sample   | 1            | 2    | 3    | 4    | 5    |
| 1        | 3.05         | 3.08 | 3.07 | 3.11 | 3.11 |
| 2        | 3.13         | 3.07 | 3.05 | 3.10 | 3.10 |
| 3        | 3.06         | 3.04 | 3.12 | 3.11 | 3.10 |
| 4        | 3.09         | 3.08 | 3.09 | 3.09 | 3.07 |
| 5        | 3.10         | 3.06 | 3.06 | 3.07 | 3.08 |
| 6        | 3.08         | 3.10 | 3.13 | 3.03 | 3.06 |
| 7        | 3.06         | 3.06 | 3.08 | 3.10 | 3.08 |
| 8        | 3.11         | 3.08 | 3.07 | 3.07 | 3.07 |
| 9        | 3.09         | 3.09 | 3.08 | 3.07 | 3.09 |
| 10       | 3.06         | 3.11 | 3.07 | 3.09 | 3.07 |

**21.** Consider the following situations. Comment on whether the sample results might cause concern about the quality of the process.

  **a.** A $p$ chart has LCL = 0 and UCL = .068. When the process is in control, the proportion defective is .033. Plot the following seven sample results: .035, .062, .055, .049, .058, .066, and .055. Discuss.

  **b.** An $\bar{x}$ chart has LCL = 22.2 and UCL = 24.5. The mean is $\mu$ = 23.35 when the process is in control. Plot the following seven sample results: 22.4, 22.6, 22.65, 23.2, 23.4, 23.85, and 24.1. Discuss.

**22.** Managers of 1200 different retail outlets make twice-a-month restocking orders from a central warehouse. Past experience has shown that 4% of the orders have one or more errors such as wrong item shipped, wrong quantity shipped, and item requested but not shipped. Random samples of 200 orders are selected monthly and checked for accuracy.

  **a.** Construct a control chart for this situation.

  **b.** Six months of data show the following numbers of orders with one or more errors: 10, 15, 6, 13, 8, and 17. Plot the data on the control chart. What does your plot indicate about the order process?

**23.** An $n$ = 10, $c$ = 2 acceptance sampling plan is being considered; assume that $p_0$ = .05 and $p_1$ = .20.

  **a.** Compute both the producer's and the consumer's risks for this acceptance sampling plan.

  **b.** Would the producer, the consumer, or both be unhappy with the proposed sampling plan?

  **c.** What change in the sampling plan, if any, would you recommend?

**24.** An acceptance sampling plan with $n$ = 15 and $c$ = 1 has been designed with a producer's risk of .075.

  **a.** Was the value of $p_0$ .01, .02, .03, .04, or .05? What does this value mean?

  **b.** What is the consumer's risk associated with this plan if $p_1$ is .25?

**25.** A manufacturer produces lots of a canned food product. Let $p$ denote the proportion of the lots that do not meet the product quality specifications. An $n$ = 25, $c$ = 0 acceptance sampling plan will be used.

  **a.** Compute points on the operating characteristic curve when $p$ = .01, .03, .10, and .20.

  **b.** Plot the operating characteristic curve.

  **c.** What is the probability that the acceptance sampling plan will reject a lot that has .01 defective?

**26.** Sometimes an acceptance sampling plan will be based on a large sample. In this case, the normal approximation of the binomial probability distribution can be used to compute the producer's and the consumer's risks associated with the plan. The normal distribution can be used to approximate binomial probabilities using a mean of $np$ and a standard deviation of $\sqrt{np(1 - p)}$. Assume that an acceptance sampling plan is $n = 250$, $c = 10$.

   **a.** What is the producer's risk if $p_0$ is .02? A continuity correction factor should be used in this case. Thus, the probability of acceptance is based on the normal probability of the random variable being less than or equal to 10.5.

   **b.** What is the consumer's risk if $p_1$ is .08?

   **c.** What is an advantage of a large sample size for acceptance sampling? What is a disadvantage?

# APPENDIXES

## General

Bowerman, B. L., and R. T. O'Connell, *Applied Statistics: Improving Business Processes,* Irwin, 1996.

Freedman, D., R. Pisani, and R. Purves, *Statistics,* 3rd ed., W. W. Norton, 1997.

Hogg, R. V., and A. T. Craig, *Introduction to Mathematical Statistics,* 5th ed., Prentice Hall, 1994.

Hogg, R. V., and E. A. Tanis, *Probability and Statistical Inference,* 6th ed., Prentice Hall, 2001.

Miller, I., and M. Miller, *John E. Freund's Mathematical Statistics,* Prentice Hall, 1998.

Tanur, J. M., *Statistics: A Guide to the Unknown,* 4th ed., Brooks/Cole, 2002.

## Experimental Design

Cochran, W. G., and G. M. Cox, *Experimental Designs,* 2d ed., Wiley, 1992.

Hicks, C. R., and K. V. Turner, *Fundamental Concepts in the Design of Experiments,* 5th ed., Oxford University Press, 1999.

Montgomery, D. C., *Design and Analysis of Experiments,* 5th ed., Wiley, 2000.

Wu, C. F. Jeff, and M. Hamada, *Experiments: Planning, Analysis, and Parameter Optimization,* Wiley, 2000.

## Nonparametric Methods

Conover, W. J., *Practical Nonparametric Statistics,* 3rd ed., Wiley, 1998.

Gibbons, J. D., and S. Chakraborti, *Nonparametric Statistical Inference,* 3rd ed., Marcel Dekker, 1992.

Siegel, S., and N. J. Castellan, *Nonparametric Statistics for the Behavioral Sciences,* 2d ed., McGraw-Hill, 1988.

Sprent, P., *Applied Non-Parametric Statistical Methods,* CRC, 1993.

## Probability

Hogg, R. V., and E. A. Tanis, *Probability and Statistical Inference,* 6th ed., Prentice Hall, 2001.

Ross, S. M., *Introduction to Probability Models,* 7th ed., Academic Press, 2000.

Wackerly, D. D., W. Mendenhall, and R. L. Scheaffer, *Mathematical Statistics with Applications,* 6th ed., Duxbury, 2002.

## Quality Control

Deming, W. E., *Quality, Productivity, and Competitive Position,* MIT, 1982.

Evans, J. R., and W. M. Lindsay, *The Management and Control of Quality,* 4th ed., South-Western, 1998.

Gryna, F. M., and I. M. Juran, *Quality Planning and Analysis: From Product Development Through Use,* 3rd ed., McGraw-Hill, 1993.

Ishikawa, K., *Introduction to Quality Control,* Klower Academic, 1991.

Montgomery, D. C., *Introduction to Statistical Quality Control,* 3rd ed., Wiley, 1996.

## Regression Analysis

Chatterjee, S., and B. Price, *Regression Analysis by Example,* 3rd ed., Wiley, 1999.

Draper, N. R., and H. Smith, *Applied Regression Analysis,* 3rd ed., Wiley, 1998.

Graybill, F. A., and H. Iyer, *Regression Analysis: Concepts and Applications,* Duxbury Press, 1994.

Kleinbaum, D. G., L. L. Kupper, and K. E. Muller, *Applied Regression Analysis and Other Multivariate Methods,* 3rd ed., Duxbury Press, 1997.

Kutner, M. H., C. J. Nachtschiem, W. Wasserman, and J. Neter, *Applied Linear Statistical Models,* 4th ed., Irwin, 1996.

Mendenhall, M., and T. Sincich, *A Second Course in Statistics: Regression Analysis,* 5th ed., Prentice Hall, 1996.

## Sampling

Cochran, W. G., *Sampling Techniques,* 3rd ed., Wiley, 1977.

Hansen, M. H., W. N. Hurwitz, W. G. Madow, and M. N. Hanson, *Sample Survey Methods and Theory,* Wiley, 1993.

Kish, L., *Survey Sampling,* Wiley, 1995.

Levy, P. S., and S. Lemeshow, *Sampling of Populations: Methods and Applications,* 3rd ed., Wiley, 1999.

Scheaffer, R. L., W. Mendenhall, and L. Ott, *Elementary Survey Sampling,* 5th ed., Duxbury, 1996.

# Appendix B    Tables

.9907

## TABLE 1   CUMULATIVE PROBABILITIES FOR THE STANDARD NORMAL DISTRIBUTION

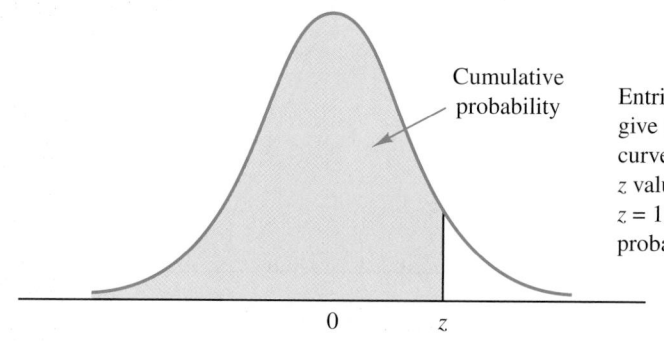

Cumulative probability

Entries in the table give the area under the curve to the left of the $z$ value. For example, for $z = 1.25$ the cumulative probability is .8944.

| $z$ | .00 | .01 | .02 | .03 | .04 | .05 | .06 | .07 | .08 | .09 |
|-----|-----|-----|-----|-----|-----|-----|-----|-----|-----|-----|
| .0 | .5000 | .5040 | .5080 | .5120 | .5160 | .5199 | .5239 | .5279 | .5319 | .5359 |
| .1 | .5398 | .5438 | .5478 | .5517 | .5557 | .5596 | .5636 | .5675 | .5714 | .5753 |
| .2 | .5793 | .5832 | .5871 | .5910 | .5948 | .5987 | .6026 | .6064 | .6103 | .6141 |
| .3 | .6179 | .6217 | .6255 | .6293 | .6331 | .6368 | .6406 | .6443 | .6480 | .6517 |
| .4 | .6554 | .6591 | .6628 | .6664 | .6700 | .6736 | .6772 | .6808 | .6844 | .6879 |
| .5 | .6915 | .6950 | .6985 | .7019 | .7054 | .7088 | .7123 | .7157 | .7190 | .7224 |
| .6 | .7257 | .7291 | .7324 | .7357 | .7389 | .7422 | .7454 | .7486 | .7517 | .7549 |
| .7 | .7580 | .7611 | .7642 | .7673 | .7704 | .7734 | .7764 | .7794 | .7823 | .7852 |
| .8 | .7881 | .7910 | .7939 | .7967 | .7995 | .8023 | .8051 | .8078 | .8106 | .8133 |
| .9 | .8159 | .8186 | .8212 | .8238 | .8264 | .8289 | .8315 | .8340 | .8365 | .8389 |
| 1.0 | .8413 | .8438 | .8461 | .8485 | .8508 | .8531 | .8554 | .8577 | .8599 | .8621 |
| 1.1 | .8643 | .8665 | .8686 | .8708 | .8729 | .8749 | .8770 | .8790 | .8810 | .8830 |
| 1.2 | .8849 | .8869 | .8888 | .8907 | .8925 | .8944 | .8962 | .8980 | .8997 | .9015 |
| 1.3 | .9032 | .9049 | .9066 | .9082 | .9099 | .9115 | .9131 | .9147 | .9162 | .9177 |
| 1.4 | .9192 | .9207 | .9222 | .9236 | .9251 | .9265 | .9279 | .9292 | .9306 | .9319 |
| 1.5 | .9332 | .9345 | .9357 | .9370 | .9382 | .9394 | .9406 | .9418 | .9429 | .9441 |
| 1.6 | .9452 | .9463 | .9474 | .9484 | .9495 | .9505 | .9515 | .9525 | .9535 | .9545 |
| 1.7 | .9554 | .9564 | .9573 | .9582 | .9591 | .9599 | .9608 | .9616 | .9625 | .9633 |
| 1.8 | .9641 | .9649 | .9656 | .9664 | .9671 | .9678 | .9686 | .9693 | .9699 | .9706 |
| 1.9 | .9713 | .9719 | .9726 | .9732 | .9738 | .9744 | .9750 | .9756 | .9761 | .9767 |
| 2.0 | .9772 | .9778 | .9783 | .9788 | .9793 | .9798 | .9803 | .9808 | .9812 | .9817 |
| 2.1 | .9821 | .9826 | .9830 | .9834 | .9838 | .9842 | .9846 | .9850 | .9854 | .9857 |
| 2.2 | .9861 | .9864 | .9868 | .9871 | .9875 | .9878 | .9881 | .9884 | .9887 | .9890 |
| 2.3 | .9893 | .9896 | .9898 | .9901 | .9904 | .9906 | .9909 | .9911 | .9913 | .9913 |
| 2.4 | .9918 | .9920 | .9922 | .9925 | .9927 | .9929 | .9931 | .9932 | .9934 | .9936 |
| 2.5 | .9938 | .9940 | .9941 | .9943 | .9945 | .9946 | .9948 | .9949 | .9951 | .9952 |
| 2.6 | .9953 | .9955 | .9956 | .9957 | .9959 | .9960 | .9961 | .9962 | .9963 | .9964 |
| 2.7 | .9965 | .9966 | .9967 | .9968 | .9969 | .9970 | .9971 | .9972 | .9973 | .9974 |
| 2.8 | .9974 | .9975 | .9976 | .9977 | .9977 | .9978 | .9979 | .9979 | .9980 | .9981 |
| 2.9 | .9981 | .9982 | .9982 | .9983 | .9984 | .9984 | .9985 | .9985 | .9986 | .9986 |
| 3.0 | .9986 | .9987 | .9987 | .9988 | .9988 | .9989 | .9989 | .9989 | .9990 | .9990 |

### TABLE 2  $t$ DISTRIBUTION

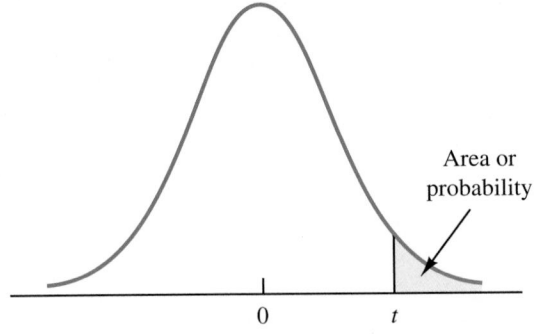

Area or probability

Entries in the table give $t$ values for an area or probability in the upper tail of the $t$ distribution. For example, with 10 degrees of freedom and a .05 area in the upper tail, $t_{.05} = 1.812$.

| Degrees of Freedom | Area in Upper Tail | | | | |
|---|---|---|---|---|---|
| | .10 | .05 | .025 | .01 | .005 |
| 1 | 3.078 | 6.314 | 12.706 | 31.821 | 63.656 |
| 2 | 1.886 | 2.920 | 4.303 | 6.965 | 9.925 |
| 3 | 1.638 | 2.353 | 3.182 | 4.541 | 5.841 |
| 4 | 1.533 | 2.132 | 2.776 | 3.747 | 4.604 |
| 5 | 1.476 | 2.015 | 2.571 | 3.365 | 4.032 |
| 6 | 1.440 | 1.943 | 2.447 | 3.143 | 3.707 |
| 7 | 1.415 | 1.895 | 2.365 | 2.998 | 3.499 |
| 8 | 1.397 | 1.860 | 2.306 | 2.896 | 3.355 |
| 9 | 1.383 | 1.833 | 2.262 | 2.821 | 3.250 |
| 10 | 1.372 | 1.812 | 2.228 | 2.764 | 3.169 |
| 11 | 1.363 | 1.796 | 2.201 | 2.718 | 3.106 |
| 12 | 1.356 | 1.782 | 2.179 | 2.681 | 3.055 |
| 13 | 1.350 | 1.771 | 2.160 | 2.650 | 3.012 |
| 14 | 1.345 | 1.761 | 2.145 | 2.624 | 2.977 |
| 15 | 1.341 | 1.753 | 2.131 | 2.602 | 2.947 |
| 16 | 1.337 | 1.746 | 2.120 | 2.583 | 2.921 |
| 17 | 1.333 | 1.740 | 2.110 | 2.567 | 2.898 |
| 18 | 1.330 | 1.734 | 2.101 | 2.552 | 2.878 |
| 19 | 1.328 | 1.729 | 2.093 | 2.539 | 2.861 |
| 20 | 1.325 | 1.725 | 2.086 | 2.528 | 2.845 |
| 21 | 1.323 | 1.721 | 2.080 | 2.518 | 2.831 |
| 22 | 1.321 | 1.717 | 2.074 | 2.508 | 2.819 |
| 23 | 1.319 | 1.714 | 2.069 | 2.500 | 2.807 |
| 24 | 1.318 | 1.711 | 2.064 | 2.492 | 2.797 |
| 25 | 1.316 | 1.708 | 2.060 | 2.485 | 2.787 |
| 26 | 1.315 | 1.706 | 2.056 | 2.479 | 2.779 |
| 27 | 1.314 | 1.703 | 2.052 | 2.473 | 2.771 |
| 28 | 1.313 | 1.701 | 2.048 | 2.467 | 2.763 |
| 29 | 1.311 | 1.699 | 2.045 | 2.462 | 2.756 |
| 30 | 1.310 | 1.697 | 2.042 | 2.457 | 2.750 |
| 40 | 1.303 | 1.684 | 2.021 | 2.423 | 2.704 |
| 60 | 1.296 | 1.671 | 2.000 | 2.390 | 2.660 |
| 120 | 1.289 | 1.658 | 1.980 | 2.358 | 2.617 |
| ∞ | 1.282 | 1.645 | 1.960 | 2.326 | 2.576 |

TABLE 3   CHI-SQUARE DISTRIBUTION

Entries in the table give $\chi_\alpha^2$ values, where $\alpha$ is the area or probability in the upper tail of the chi-square distribution. For example, with 10 degrees of freedom and a .01 area in the upper tail, $\chi_{.01}^2 = 23.2093$.

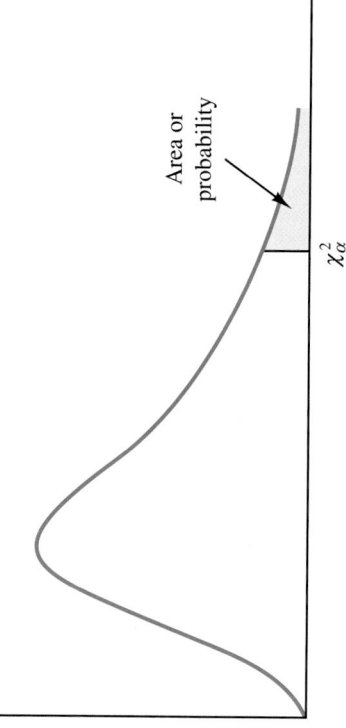

Area or probability

$\chi_\alpha^2$

| Degrees of Freedom | Area in Upper Tail | | | | | | | | | | |
|---|---|---|---|---|---|---|---|---|---|---|---|
| | .995 | .99 | .975 | .95 | .90 | .10 | .05 | .025 | .01 | .005 |
| 1 | $392.704 \times 10^{-10}$ | $157.088 \times 10^{-9}$ | $982.069 \times 10^{-9}$ | $393.214 \times 10^{-8}$ | .0157908 | 2.70554 | 3.84146 | 5.02389 | 6.63490 | 7.87944 |
| 2 | .0100251 | .0201007 | .0506356 | .102587 | .210720 | 4.60517 | 5.99147 | 7.37776 | 9.21034 | 10.5966 |
| 3 | .0717212 | .114832 | .215795 | .351846 | .584375 | 6.25139 | 7.81473 | 9.34840 | 11.3449 | 12.8381 |
| 4 | .206990 | .297110 | .484419 | .710721 | 1.063623 | 7.77944 | 9.48773 | 11.1433 | 13.2767 | 14.8602 |
| 5 | .411740 | .554300 | .831211 | 1.145476 | 1.61031 | 9.23635 | 11.0705 | 12.8325 | 15.0863 | 16.7496 |
| 6 | .675727 | .872085 | 1.237347 | 1.63539 | 2.20413 | 10.6446 | 12.5916 | 14.4494 | 16.8119 | 18.5476 |
| 7 | .989265 | 1.239043 | 1.68987 | 2.16735 | 2.83311 | 12.0170 | 14.0671 | 16.0128 | 18.4753 | 20.2777 |
| 8 | 1.344419 | 1.646482 | 2.17973 | 2.73264 | 3.48954 | 13.3616 | 15.5073 | 17.5346 | 20.0902 | 21.9550 |
| 9 | 1.734926 | 2.087912 | 2.70039 | 3.32511 | 4.16816 | 14.6837 | 16.9190 | 19.0228 | 21.6660 | 23.5893 |
| 10 | 2.15585 | 2.55821 | 3.24697 | 3.94030 | 4.86518 | 15.9871 | 18.3070 | 20.4831 | 23.2093 | 25.1882 |
| 11 | 2.60321 | 3.05347 | 3.81575 | 4.57481 | 5.57779 | 17.2750 | 19.6751 | 21.9200 | 24.7250 | 26.7569 |
| 12 | 3.07382 | 3.57056 | 4.40379 | 5.22603 | 6.30380 | 18.5494 | 21.0261 | 23.3367 | 26.2170 | 28.2995 |
| 13 | 3.56503 | 4.10691 | 5.00874 | 5.89186 | 7.04150 | 19.8119 | 22.3621 | 24.7356 | 27.6883 | 29.8194 |
| 14 | 4.07468 | 4.66043 | 5.62872 | 6.57063 | 7.78953 | 21.0642 | 23.6848 | 26.1190 | 29.1413 | 31.3193 |
| 15 | 4.60094 | 5.22935 | 6.26214 | 7.26094 | 8.54675 | 22.3072 | 24.9958 | 27.4884 | 30.5779 | 32.8013 |
| 16 | 5.14224 | 5.81221 | 6.90766 | 7.96164 | 9.31223 | 23.5418 | 26.2962 | 28.8454 | 31.9999 | 34.2672 |
| 17 | 5.69724 | 6.40776 | 7.56418 | 8.67176 | 10.0852 | 24.7690 | 27.5871 | 30.1910 | 33.4087 | 35.7185 |
| 18 | 6.26481 | 7.01491 | 8.23075 | 9.39046 | 10.8649 | 25.9894 | 28.8693 | 31.5264 | 34.8053 | 37.1564 |
| 19 | 6.84398 | 7.63273 | 8.90655 | 10.1170 | 11.6509 | 27.2036 | 30.1435 | 32.8523 | 36.1908 | 38.5822 |

**TABLE 3** CHI-SQUARE DISTRIBUTION (*Continued*)

| Degrees of Freedom | Area in Upper Tail | | | | | | | | | |
|---|---|---|---|---|---|---|---|---|---|---|
| | .995 | .99 | .975 | .95 | .90 | .10 | .05 | .025 | .01 | .005 |
| 20 | 7.43386 | 8.26040 | 9.59083 | 10.8508 | 12.4426 | 28.4120 | 31.4104 | 34.1696 | 37.5662 | 39.9968 |
| 21 | 8.03366 | 8.89720 | 10.28293 | 11.5913 | 13.2396 | 29.6151 | 32.6705 | 35.4789 | 38.9321 | 41.4010 |
| 22 | 8.64272 | 9.54249 | 10.9823 | 12.3380 | 14.0415 | 30.8133 | 33.9244 | 36.7807 | 40.2894 | 42.7958 |
| 23 | 9.26042 | 10.19567 | 11.6885 | 13.0905 | 14.8479 | 32.0069 | 35.1725 | 38.0757 | 41.6384 | 44.1813 |
| 24 | 9.88623 | 10.8564 | 12.4011 | 13.8484 | 15.6587 | 33.1963 | 36.4151 | 39.3641 | 42.9798 | 45.5585 |
| 25 | 10.5197 | 11.5240 | 13.1197 | 14.6114 | 16.4734 | 34.3816 | 37.6525 | 40.6465 | 44.3141 | 46.9278 |
| 26 | 11.1603 | 12.1981 | 13.8439 | 15.3791 | 17.2919 | 35.5631 | 38.8852 | 41.9232 | 45.6417 | 48.2899 |
| 27 | 11.8076 | 12.8786 | 14.5733 | 16.1513 | 18.1138 | 36.7412 | 40.1133 | 43.1944 | 46.9630 | 49.6449 |
| 28 | 12.4613 | 13.5648 | 15.3079 | 16.9279 | 18.9392 | 37.9159 | 41.3372 | 44.4607 | 48.2782 | 50.9933 |
| 29 | 13.1211 | 14.2565 | 16.0471 | 17.7083 | 19.7677 | 39.0875 | 42.5569 | 45.7222 | 49.5879 | 52.3356 |
| 30 | 13.7867 | 14.9535 | 16.7908 | 18.4926 | 20.5992 | 40.2560 | 43.7729 | 46.9792 | 50.8922 | 53.6720 |
| 40 | 20.7065 | 22.1643 | 24.4331 | 26.5093 | 29.0505 | 51.8050 | 55.7585 | 59.3417 | 63.6907 | 66.7659 |
| 50 | 27.9907 | 29.7067 | 32.3574 | 34.7642 | 37.6886 | 63.1671 | 67.5048 | 71.4202 | 76.1539 | 79.4900 |
| 60 | 35.5346 | 37.4848 | 40.4817 | 43.1879 | 46.4589 | 74.3970 | 79.0819 | 83.2976 | 88.3794 | 91.9517 |
| 70 | 43.2752 | 45.4418 | 48.7576 | 51.7393 | 55.3290 | 85.5271 | 90.5312 | 95.0231 | 100.425 | 104.215 |
| 80 | 51.1720 | 53.5400 | 57.1532 | 60.3915 | 64.2778 | 96.5782 | 101.879 | 106.629 | 112.329 | 116.321 |
| 90 | 59.1963 | 61.7541 | 65.6466 | 69.1260 | 73.2912 | 107.565 | 113.145 | 118.136 | 124.116 | 128.299 |
| 100 | 67.3276 | 70.0648 | 74.2219 | 77.9295 | 82.3581 | 118.498 | 124.342 | 129.561 | 135.807 | 140.169 |

This table is reprinted by permission of Oxford University Press on behalf of The Biometrika Trustees from Table 8, Percentage Points of the $\chi^2$ Distribution, by E. S. Pearson and H. O. Hartley, *Biometrika Tables for Statisticians*, Vol. I, 3rd ed., 1966.

# TABLE 4  F DISTRIBUTION

Entries in the table give $F_\alpha$ values, where $\alpha$ is the area or probability in the upper tail of the $F$ distribution. For example, with 12 numerator degress of freedom, 15 denominator degrees of freedom, and a .05 area in the upper tail, $F_{.05} = 2.48$.

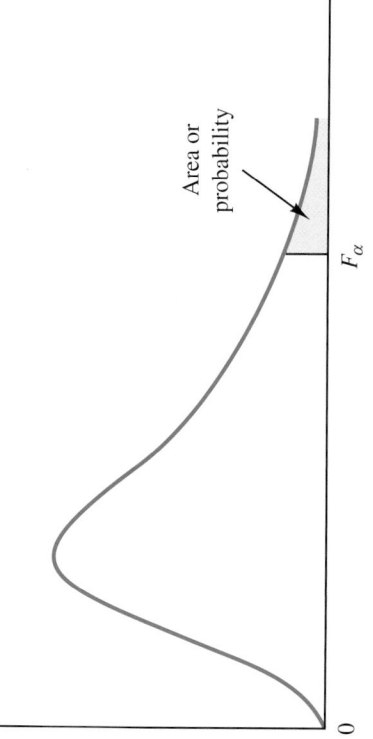

Area or probability

$F_\alpha$

**Table of $F_{.05}$ Values**

| Denominator Degrees of Freedom | Numerator Degrees of Freedom | | | | | | | | | | | | | | | | | | |
|---|---|---|---|---|---|---|---|---|---|---|---|---|---|---|---|---|---|---|---|
| | 1 | 2 | 3 | 4 | 5 | 6 | 7 | 8 | 9 | 10 | 12 | 15 | 20 | 24 | 30 | 40 | 60 | 120 | ∞ |
| 1 | 161.4 | 199.5 | 215.7 | 224.6 | 230.2 | 234.0 | 236.8 | 238.9 | 240.5 | 241.9 | 243.9 | 245.9 | 248.0 | 249.1 | 250.1 | 251.1 | 252.2 | 253.3 | 254.3 |
| 2 | 18.51 | 19.00 | 19.16 | 19.25 | 19.30 | 19.33 | 19.35 | 19.37 | 19.38 | 19.40 | 19.41 | 19.43 | 19.45 | 19.45 | 19.46 | 19.47 | 19.48 | 19.49 | 19.50 |
| 3 | 10.13 | 9.55 | 9.28 | 9.12 | 9.01 | 8.94 | 8.89 | 8.85 | 8.81 | 8.79 | 8.74 | 8.70 | 8.66 | 8.64 | 8.62 | 8.59 | 8.57 | 8.55 | 8.53 |
| 4 | 7.71 | 6.94 | 6.59 | 6.39 | 6.26 | 6.16 | 6.09 | 6.04 | 6.00 | 5.96 | 5.91 | 5.86 | 5.80 | 5.77 | 5.75 | 5.72 | 5.69 | 5.66 | 5.63 |
| 5 | 6.61 | 5.79 | 5.41 | 5.19 | 5.05 | 4.95 | 4.88 | 4.82 | 4.77 | 4.74 | 4.68 | 4.62 | 4.56 | 4.53 | 4.50 | 4.46 | 4.43 | 4.40 | 4.36 |
| 6 | 5.99 | 5.14 | 4.76 | 4.53 | 4.39 | 4.28 | 4.21 | 4.15 | 4.10 | 4.06 | 4.00 | 3.94 | 3.87 | 3.84 | 3.81 | 3.77 | 3.74 | 3.70 | 3.67 |
| 7 | 5.59 | 4.74 | 4.35 | 4.12 | 3.97 | 3.87 | 3.79 | 3.73 | 3.68 | 3.64 | 3.57 | 3.51 | 3.44 | 3.41 | 3.38 | 3.34 | 3.30 | 3.27 | 3.23 |
| 8 | 5.32 | 4.46 | 4.07 | 3.84 | 3.69 | 3.58 | 3.50 | 3.44 | 3.39 | 3.35 | 3.28 | 3.22 | 3.15 | 3.12 | 3.08 | 3.04 | 3.01 | 2.97 | 2.93 |
| 9 | 5.12 | 4.26 | 3.86 | 3.63 | 3.48 | 3.37 | 3.29 | 3.23 | 3.18 | 3.14 | 3.07 | 3.01 | 2.94 | 2.90 | 2.86 | 2.83 | 2.79 | 2.75 | 2.71 |
| 10 | 4.96 | 4.10 | 3.71 | 3.48 | 3.33 | 3.22 | 3.14 | 3.07 | 3.02 | 2.98 | 2.91 | 2.85 | 2.77 | 2.74 | 2.70 | 2.66 | 2.62 | 2.58 | 2.54 |
| 11 | 4.84 | 3.98 | 3.59 | 3.36 | 3.20 | 3.09 | 3.01 | 2.95 | 2.90 | 2.85 | 2.79 | 2.72 | 2.65 | 2.61 | 2.57 | 2.53 | 2.49 | 2.45 | 2.40 |
| 12 | 4.75 | 3.89 | 3.49 | 3.26 | 3.11 | 3.00 | 2.91 | 2.85 | 2.80 | 2.75 | 2.69 | 2.62 | 2.54 | 2.51 | 2.47 | 2.43 | 2.38 | 2.34 | 2.30 |
| 13 | 4.67 | 3.81 | 3.41 | 3.18 | 3.03 | 2.92 | 2.83 | 2.77 | 2.71 | 2.67 | 2.60 | 2.53 | 2.46 | 2.42 | 2.38 | 2.34 | 2.30 | 2.25 | 2.21 |
| 14 | 4.60 | 3.74 | 3.34 | 3.11 | 2.96 | 2.85 | 2.76 | 2.70 | 2.65 | 2.60 | 2.53 | 2.46 | 2.39 | 2.35 | 2.31 | 2.27 | 2.22 | 2.18 | 2.13 |

**TABLE 4** *F* DISTRIBUTION (*Continued*)

## Table of $F_{.05}$ Values

| Denominator Degrees of Freedom | Numerator Degrees of Freedom | | | | | | | | | | | | | | | | | | |
|---|---|---|---|---|---|---|---|---|---|---|---|---|---|---|---|---|---|---|---|
| | 1 | 2 | 3 | 4 | 5 | 6 | 7 | 8 | 9 | 10 | 12 | 15 | 20 | 24 | 30 | 40 | 60 | 120 | ∞ |
| 15 | 4.54 | 3.68 | 3.29 | 3.06 | 2.90 | 2.79 | 2.71 | 2.64 | 2.59 | 2.54 | 2.48 | 2.40 | 2.33 | 2.29 | 2.25 | 2.20 | 2.16 | 2.11 | 2.07 |
| 16 | 4.49 | 3.63 | 3.24 | 3.01 | 2.85 | 2.74 | 2.66 | 2.59 | 2.54 | 2.49 | 2.42 | 2.35 | 2.28 | 2.24 | 2.19 | 2.15 | 2.11 | 2.06 | 2.01 |
| 17 | 4.45 | 3.59 | 3.20 | 2.96 | 2.81 | 2.70 | 2.61 | 2.55 | 2.49 | 2.45 | 2.38 | 2.31 | 2.23 | 2.19 | 2.15 | 2.10 | 2.06 | 2.01 | 1.96 |
| 18 | 4.41 | 3.55 | 3.16 | 2.93 | 2.77 | 2.66 | 2.58 | 2.51 | 2.46 | 2.41 | 2.34 | 2.27 | 2.19 | 2.15 | 2.11 | 2.06 | 2.02 | 1.97 | 1.92 |
| 19 | 4.38 | 3.52 | 3.13 | 2.90 | 2.74 | 2.63 | 2.54 | 2.48 | 2.42 | 2.38 | 2.31 | 2.23 | 2.16 | 2.11 | 2.07 | 2.03 | 1.98 | 1.93 | 1.88 |
| 20 | 4.35 | 3.49 | 3.10 | 2.87 | 2.71 | 2.60 | 2.51 | 2.45 | 2.39 | 2.35 | 2.28 | 2.20 | 2.12 | 2.08 | 2.04 | 1.99 | 1.95 | 1.90 | 1.84 |
| 21 | 4.32 | 3.47 | 3.07 | 2.84 | 2.68 | 2.57 | 2.49 | 2.42 | 2.37 | 2.32 | 2.25 | 2.18 | 2.10 | 2.05 | 2.01 | 1.96 | 1.92 | 1.87 | 1.81 |
| 22 | 4.30 | 3.44 | 3.05 | 2.82 | 2.66 | 2.55 | 2.46 | 2.40 | 2.34 | 2.30 | 2.23 | 2.15 | 2.07 | 2.03 | 1.98 | 1.94 | 1.89 | 1.84 | 1.78 |
| 23 | 4.28 | 3.42 | 3.03 | 2.80 | 2.64 | 2.53 | 2.44 | 2.37 | 2.32 | 2.27 | 2.20 | 2.13 | 2.05 | 2.01 | 1.96 | 1.91 | 1.86 | 1.81 | 1.76 |
| 24 | 4.26 | 3.40 | 3.01 | 2.78 | 2.62 | 2.51 | 2.42 | 2.36 | 2.30 | 2.25 | 2.18 | 2.11 | 2.03 | 1.98 | 1.94 | 1.89 | 1.84 | 1.79 | 1.73 |
| 25 | 4.24 | 3.39 | 2.99 | 2.76 | 2.60 | 2.49 | 2.40 | 2.34 | 2.28 | 2.24 | 2.16 | 2.09 | 2.01 | 1.96 | 1.92 | 1.87 | 1.82 | 1.77 | 1.71 |
| 26 | 4.23 | 3.37 | 2.98 | 2.74 | 2.59 | 2.47 | 2.39 | 2.32 | 2.27 | 2.22 | 2.15 | 2.07 | 1.99 | 1.95 | 1.90 | 1.85 | 1.80 | 1.75 | 1.69 |
| 27 | 4.21 | 3.35 | 2.96 | 2.73 | 2.57 | 2.46 | 2.37 | 2.31 | 2.25 | 2.20 | 2.13 | 2.06 | 1.97 | 1.93 | 1.88 | 1.84 | 1.79 | 1.73 | 1.67 |
| 28 | 4.20 | 3.34 | 2.95 | 2.71 | 2.56 | 2.45 | 2.36 | 2.29 | 2.24 | 2.19 | 2.12 | 2.04 | 1.96 | 1.91 | 1.87 | 1.82 | 1.77 | 1.71 | 1.65 |
| 29 | 4.18 | 3.33 | 2.93 | 2.70 | 2.55 | 2.43 | 2.35 | 2.28 | 2.22 | 2.18 | 2.10 | 2.03 | 1.94 | 1.90 | 1.85 | 1.81 | 1.75 | 1.70 | 1.64 |
| 30 | 4.17 | 3.32 | 2.92 | 2.69 | 2.53 | 2.42 | 2.33 | 2.27 | 2.21 | 2.16 | 2.09 | 2.01 | 1.93 | 1.89 | 1.84 | 1.79 | 1.74 | 1.68 | 1.62 |
| 40 | 4.08 | 3.23 | 2.84 | 2.61 | 2.45 | 2.34 | 2.25 | 2.18 | 2.12 | 2.08 | 2.00 | 1.92 | 1.84 | 1.79 | 1.74 | 1.69 | 1.64 | 1.58 | 1.51 |
| 60 | 4.00 | 3.15 | 2.76 | 2.53 | 2.37 | 2.25 | 2.17 | 2.10 | 2.04 | 1.99 | 1.92 | 1.84 | 1.75 | 1.70 | 1.65 | 1.59 | 1.53 | 1.47 | 1.39 |
| 120 | 3.92 | 3.07 | 2.68 | 2.45 | 2.29 | 2.17 | 2.09 | 2.02 | 1.96 | 1.91 | 1.83 | 1.75 | 1.66 | 1.61 | 1.55 | 1.50 | 1.43 | 1.35 | 1.25 |
| ∞ | 3.84 | 3.00 | 2.60 | 2.37 | 2.21 | 2.10 | 2.01 | 1.94 | 1.88 | 1.83 | 1.75 | 1.67 | 1.57 | 1.52 | 1.46 | 1.39 | 1.32 | 1.22 | 1.00 |

## Table of $F_{.025}$ Values

| Denominator Degrees of Freedom | Numerator Degrees of Freedom | | | | | | | | | | | | | | | | | | |
|---|---|---|---|---|---|---|---|---|---|---|---|---|---|---|---|---|---|---|---|
| | 1 | 2 | 3 | 4 | 5 | 6 | 7 | 8 | 9 | 10 | 12 | 15 | 20 | 24 | 30 | 40 | 60 | 120 | ∞ |
| 1 | 647.80 | 799.50 | 864.20 | 899.60 | 921.80 | 937.10 | 948.20 | 956.70 | 963.30 | 968.60 | 976.70 | 984.90 | 993.10 | 997.20 | 1,001 | 1,006 | 1,010 | 1,014 | 1,018 |
| 2 | 38.51 | 39.00 | 39.17 | 39.25 | 39.30 | 39.33 | 39.36 | 39.37 | 39.39 | 39.40 | 39.41 | 39.43 | 39.45 | 39.46 | 39.46 | 39.47 | 39.48 | 39.49 | 39.50 |
| 3 | 17.44 | 16.04 | 15.44 | 15.10 | 14.88 | 14.73 | 14.62 | 14.54 | 14.47 | 14.42 | 14.34 | 14.25 | 14.17 | 14.12 | 14.08 | 14.04 | 13.99 | 13.95 | 13.90 |
| 4 | 12.22 | 10.65 | 9.98 | 9.60 | 9.36 | 9.20 | 9.07 | 8.98 | 8.90 | 8.84 | 8.75 | 8.66 | 8.56 | 8.51 | 8.46 | 8.41 | 8.36 | 8.31 | 8.26 |

TABLE 4  F DISTRIBUTION (*Continued*)

**Table of $F_{.025}$ Values**

| Denominator Degrees of Freedom | Numerator Degrees of Freedom | | | | | | | | | | | | | | | | | | |
|---|---|---|---|---|---|---|---|---|---|---|---|---|---|---|---|---|---|---|---|
| | 1 | 2 | 3 | 4 | 5 | 6 | 7 | 8 | 9 | 10 | 12 | 15 | 20 | 24 | 30 | 40 | 60 | 120 | ∞ |
| 5 | 10.01 | 8.43 | 7.76 | 7.39 | 7.15 | 6.98 | 6.85 | 6.76 | 6.68 | 6.62 | 6.52 | 6.43 | 6.33 | 6.28 | 6.23 | 6.18 | 6.12 | 6.07 | 6.02 |
| 6 | 8.81 | 7.26 | 6.60 | 6.23 | 5.99 | 5.82 | 5.70 | 5.60 | 5.52 | 5.46 | 5.37 | 5.27 | 5.17 | 5.12 | 5.07 | 5.01 | 4.96 | 4.90 | 4.85 |
| 7 | 8.07 | 6.54 | 5.89 | 5.52 | 5.29 | 5.21 | 4.99 | 4.90 | 4.82 | 4.76 | 4.67 | 4.57 | 4.47 | 4.42 | 4.36 | 4.31 | 4.25 | 4.20 | 4.14 |
| 8 | 7.57 | 6.06 | 5.42 | 5.05 | 4.82 | 4.65 | 4.53 | 4.43 | 4.36 | 4.30 | 4.20 | 4.10 | 4.00 | 3.95 | 3.89 | 3.84 | 3.78 | 3.73 | 3.67 |
| 9 | 7.21 | 5.71 | 5.08 | 4.72 | 4.48 | 4.32 | 4.20 | 4.10 | 4.03 | 3.96 | 3.87 | 3.77 | 3.67 | 3.61 | 3.56 | 3.51 | 3.45 | 3.39 | 3.33 |
| 10 | 6.94 | 5.46 | 4.83 | 4.47 | 4.24 | 4.07 | 3.95 | 3.85 | 3.78 | 3.72 | 3.62 | 3.52 | 3.42 | 3.37 | 3.31 | 3.26 | 3.20 | 3.14 | 3.08 |
| 11 | 6.72 | 5.26 | 4.63 | 4.28 | 4.04 | 3.88 | 3.76 | 3.66 | 3.59 | 3.53 | 3.43 | 3.33 | 3.23 | 3.17 | 3.12 | 3.06 | 3.00 | 2.94 | 2.88 |
| 12 | 6.55 | 5.10 | 4.47 | 4.12 | 3.89 | 3.73 | 3.61 | 3.51 | 3.44 | 3.37 | 3.28 | 3.18 | 3.07 | 3.02 | 2.96 | 2.91 | 2.85 | 2.79 | 2.72 |
| 13 | 6.41 | 4.97 | 4.35 | 4.00 | 3.77 | 3.60 | 3.48 | 3.39 | 3.31 | 3.25 | 3.15 | 3.05 | 2.95 | 2.89 | 2.84 | 2.78 | 2.72 | 2.66 | 2.60 |
| 14 | 6.30 | 4.86 | 4.24 | 3.89 | 3.66 | 3.50 | 3.38 | 3.29 | 3.21 | 3.15 | 3.05 | 2.95 | 2.84 | 2.79 | 2.73 | 2.67 | 2.61 | 2.55 | 2.49 |
| 15 | 6.20 | 4.77 | 4.15 | 3.80 | 3.58 | 3.41 | 3.29 | 3.20 | 3.12 | 3.06 | 2.96 | 2.86 | 2.76 | 2.70 | 2.64 | 2.59 | 2.52 | 2.46 | 2.40 |
| 16 | 6.12 | 4.69 | 4.08 | 3.73 | 3.50 | 3.34 | 3.22 | 3.12 | 3.05 | 2.99 | 2.89 | 2.79 | 2.68 | 2.63 | 2.57 | 2.51 | 2.45 | 2.38 | 2.32 |
| 17 | 6.04 | 4.62 | 4.01 | 3.66 | 3.44 | 3.28 | 3.16 | 3.06 | 2.98 | 2.92 | 2.82 | 2.72 | 2.62 | 2.56 | 2.50 | 2.44 | 2.38 | 2.32 | 2.25 |
| 18 | 5.98 | 4.56 | 3.95 | 3.61 | 3.38 | 3.22 | 3.10 | 3.01 | 2.93 | 2.87 | 2.77 | 2.67 | 2.56 | 2.50 | 2.44 | 2.38 | 2.32 | 2.26 | 2.19 |
| 19 | 5.92 | 4.51 | 3.90 | 3.56 | 3.33 | 3.17 | 3.05 | 2.96 | 2.88 | 2.82 | 2.72 | 2.62 | 2.51 | 2.45 | 2.39 | 2.33 | 2.27 | 2.20 | 2.13 |
| 20 | 5.87 | 4.46 | 3.86 | 3.51 | 3.29 | 3.13 | 3.01 | 2.91 | 2.84 | 2.77 | 2.68 | 2.57 | 2.46 | 2.41 | 2.35 | 2.29 | 2.22 | 2.16 | 2.09 |
| 21 | 5.83 | 4.42 | 3.82 | 3.48 | 3.25 | 3.09 | 2.97 | 2.87 | 2.80 | 2.73 | 2.64 | 2.53 | 2.42 | 2.37 | 2.31 | 2.25 | 2.18 | 2.11 | 2.04 |
| 22 | 5.79 | 4.38 | 3.78 | 3.44 | 3.22 | 3.05 | 2.93 | 2.84 | 2.76 | 2.70 | 2.60 | 2.50 | 2.39 | 2.33 | 2.27 | 2.21 | 2.14 | 2.08 | 2.00 |
| 23 | 5.75 | 4.35 | 3.75 | 3.41 | 3.18 | 3.02 | 2.90 | 2.81 | 2.73 | 2.67 | 2.57 | 2.47 | 2.36 | 2.30 | 2.24 | 2.18 | 2.11 | 2.04 | 1.97 |
| 24 | 5.72 | 4.32 | 3.72 | 3.38 | 3.15 | 2.99 | 2.87 | 2.78 | 2.70 | 2.64 | 2.54 | 2.44 | 2.33 | 2.27 | 2.21 | 2.15 | 2.08 | 2.01 | 1.94 |
| 25 | 5.69 | 4.29 | 3.69 | 3.35 | 3.13 | 2.97 | 2.85 | 2.75 | 2.68 | 2.61 | 2.51 | 2.41 | 2.30 | 2.24 | 2.18 | 2.12 | 2.05 | 1.98 | 1.91 |
| 26 | 5.66 | 4.27 | 3.67 | 3.33 | 3.10 | 2.94 | 2.82 | 2.73 | 2.65 | 2.59 | 2.49 | 2.39 | 2.28 | 2.22 | 2.16 | 2.09 | 2.03 | 1.95 | 1.88 |
| 27 | 5.63 | 4.24 | 3.65 | 3.31 | 3.08 | 2.92 | 2.80 | 2.71 | 2.63 | 2.57 | 2.47 | 2.36 | 2.25 | 2.19 | 2.13 | 2.07 | 2.00 | 1.93 | 1.85 |
| 28 | 5.61 | 4.22 | 3.63 | 3.29 | 3.06 | 2.90 | 2.78 | 2.69 | 2.61 | 2.55 | 2.45 | 2.34 | 2.23 | 2.17 | 2.11 | 2.05 | 1.98 | 1.91 | 1.83 |
| 29 | 5.59 | 4.20 | 3.61 | 3.27 | 3.04 | 2.88 | 2.76 | 2.67 | 2.59 | 2.53 | 2.43 | 2.32 | 2.21 | 2.15 | 2.09 | 2.03 | 1.96 | 1.89 | 1.81 |
| 30 | 5.57 | 4.18 | 3.59 | 3.25 | 3.03 | 2.87 | 2.75 | 2.65 | 2.57 | 2.51 | 2.41 | 2.31 | 2.20 | 2.14 | 2.07 | 2.01 | 1.94 | 1.87 | 1.79 |
| 40 | 5.42 | 4.05 | 3.46 | 3.13 | 2.90 | 2.74 | 2.62 | 2.53 | 2.45 | 2.39 | 2.29 | 2.18 | 2.07 | 2.01 | 1.94 | 1.88 | 1.80 | 1.72 | 1.64 |
| 60 | 5.29 | 3.93 | 3.34 | 3.01 | 2.79 | 2.63 | 2.51 | 2.41 | 2.33 | 2.27 | 2.17 | 2.06 | 1.94 | 1.88 | 1.82 | 1.74 | 1.67 | 1.58 | 1.48 |
| 120 | 5.15 | 3.80 | 3.23 | 2.89 | 2.67 | 2.52 | 2.39 | 2.30 | 2.22 | 2.16 | 2.05 | 1.94 | 1.82 | 1.76 | 1.69 | 1.61 | 1.53 | 1.43 | 1.31 |
| ∞ | 5.02 | 3.69 | 3.12 | 2.79 | 2.57 | 2.41 | 2.29 | 2.19 | 2.11 | 2.05 | 1.94 | 1.83 | 1.71 | 1.64 | 1.57 | 1.48 | 1.39 | 1.27 | 1.00 |

**TABLE 4**  *F* DISTRIBUTION (*Continued*)

**Table of $F_{.01}$ Values**

|  |  | | | | | | | Numerator Degrees of Freedom | | | | | | | | | | | |
|---|---|---|---|---|---|---|---|---|---|---|---|---|---|---|---|---|---|---|---|
| Denominator Degrees of Freedom | 1 | 2 | 3 | 4 | 5 | 6 | 7 | 8 | 9 | 10 | 12 | 15 | 20 | 24 | 30 | 40 | 60 | 120 | ∞ |
| 1 | 4,052 | 4,999.5 | 5,403 | 5,625 | 5,764 | 5,859 | 5,928 | 5,982 | 6,022 | 6,056 | 6,106 | 6,157 | 6,209 | 6,235 | 6,261 | 6,287 | 6,313 | 6,339 | 6,366 |
| 2 | 98.50 | 99.00 | 99.17 | 99.25 | 99.30 | 99.33 | 99.36 | 99.37 | 99.39 | 99.40 | 99.42 | 99.43 | 99.45 | 99.46 | 99.47 | 99.47 | 99.48 | 99.49 | 99.50 |
| 3 | 34.12 | 30.82 | 29.46 | 28.71 | 28.24 | 27.91 | 27.67 | 27.49 | 27.35 | 27.23 | 27.05 | 26.87 | 26.69 | 26.60 | 26.50 | 26.41 | 26.32 | 26.22 | 26.13 |
| 4 | 21.20 | 18.00 | 16.69 | 15.98 | 15.52 | 15.21 | 14.98 | 14.80 | 14.66 | 14.55 | 14.37 | 14.20 | 14.02 | 13.93 | 13.84 | 13.75 | 13.65 | 13.56 | 13.46 |
| 5 | 16.26 | 13.27 | 12.06 | 11.39 | 10.97 | 10.67 | 10.46 | 10.29 | 10.16 | 10.05 | 9.89 | 9.72 | 9.55 | 9.47 | 9.38 | 9.29 | 9.20 | 9.11 | 9.06 |
| 6 | 13.75 | 10.92 | 9.78 | 9.15 | 8.75 | 8.47 | 8.26 | 8.10 | 7.98 | 7.87 | 7.72 | 7.56 | 7.40 | 7.31 | 7.23 | 7.14 | 7.06 | 6.97 | 6.88 |
| 7 | 12.25 | 9.55 | 8.45 | 7.85 | 7.46 | 7.19 | 6.99 | 6.84 | 6.72 | 6.62 | 6.47 | 6.31 | 6.16 | 6.07 | 5.99 | 5.91 | 5.82 | 5.74 | 5.65 |
| 8 | 11.26 | 8.65 | 7.59 | 7.01 | 6.63 | 6.37 | 6.18 | 6.03 | 5.91 | 5.81 | 5.67 | 5.52 | 5.36 | 5.28 | 5.20 | 5.12 | 5.03 | 4.95 | 4.86 |
| 9 | 10.56 | 8.02 | 6.99 | 6.42 | 6.06 | 5.80 | 5.61 | 5.47 | 5.35 | 5.26 | 5.11 | 4.96 | 4.81 | 4.73 | 4.65 | 4.57 | 4.48 | 4.40 | 4.31 |
| 10 | 10.04 | 7.56 | 6.55 | 5.99 | 5.64 | 5.39 | 5.20 | 5.06 | 4.94 | 4.85 | 4.71 | 4.56 | 4.41 | 4.33 | 4.25 | 4.17 | 4.08 | 4.00 | 3.91 |
| 11 | 9.65 | 7.21 | 6.22 | 5.67 | 5.32 | 5.07 | 4.89 | 4.74 | 4.63 | 4.54 | 4.40 | 4.25 | 4.10 | 4.02 | 3.94 | 3.86 | 3.78 | 3.69 | 3.60 |
| 12 | 9.33 | 6.93 | 5.95 | 5.41 | 5.06 | 4.82 | 4.64 | 4.50 | 4.39 | 4.30 | 4.16 | 4.01 | 3.86 | 3.78 | 3.70 | 3.62 | 3.54 | 3.45 | 3.36 |
| 13 | 9.07 | 6.70 | 5.74 | 5.21 | 4.86 | 4.62 | 4.44 | 4.30 | 4.19 | 4.10 | 3.96 | 3.82 | 3.66 | 3.59 | 3.51 | 3.43 | 3.34 | 3.25 | 3.17 |
| 14 | 8.86 | 6.51 | 5.56 | 5.04 | 4.69 | 4.46 | 4.28 | 4.14 | 4.03 | 3.94 | 3.80 | 3.66 | 3.51 | 3.43 | 3.35 | 3.27 | 3.18 | 3.09 | 3.00 |
| 15 | 8.68 | 6.36 | 5.42 | 4.89 | 4.56 | 4.32 | 4.14 | 4.00 | 3.89 | 3.80 | 3.67 | 3.52 | 3.37 | 3.29 | 3.21 | 3.13 | 3.05 | 2.96 | 2.87 |
| 16 | 8.53 | 6.23 | 5.29 | 4.77 | 4.44 | 4.20 | 4.03 | 3.89 | 3.78 | 3.69 | 3.55 | 3.41 | 3.26 | 3.18 | 3.10 | 3.02 | 2.93 | 2.84 | 2.75 |
| 17 | 8.40 | 6.11 | 5.18 | 4.67 | 4.34 | 4.10 | 3.93 | 3.79 | 3.68 | 3.59 | 3.46 | 3.31 | 3.16 | 3.08 | 3.00 | 2.92 | 2.83 | 2.75 | 2.65 |
| 18 | 8.29 | 6.01 | 5.09 | 4.58 | 4.25 | 4.01 | 3.84 | 3.71 | 3.60 | 3.51 | 3.37 | 3.23 | 3.08 | 3.00 | 2.92 | 2.84 | 2.75 | 2.66 | 2.57 |
| 19 | 8.18 | 5.93 | 5.01 | 4.50 | 4.17 | 3.94 | 3.77 | 3.63 | 3.52 | 3.43 | 3.30 | 3.15 | 3.00 | 2.92 | 2.84 | 2.76 | 2.67 | 2.58 | 2.49 |
| 20 | 8.10 | 5.85 | 4.94 | 4.43 | 4.10 | 3.87 | 3.70 | 3.56 | 3.46 | 3.37 | 3.23 | 3.09 | 2.94 | 2.86 | 2.78 | 2.69 | 2.61 | 2.52 | 2.42 |
| 21 | 8.02 | 5.78 | 4.87 | 4.37 | 4.04 | 3.81 | 3.64 | 3.51 | 3.40 | 3.31 | 3.17 | 3.03 | 2.88 | 2.80 | 2.72 | 2.64 | 2.55 | 2.46 | 2.36 |
| 22 | 7.95 | 5.72 | 4.82 | 4.31 | 3.99 | 3.76 | 3.59 | 3.45 | 3.35 | 3.26 | 3.12 | 2.98 | 2.83 | 2.75 | 2.67 | 2.58 | 2.50 | 2.40 | 2.31 |
| 23 | 7.88 | 5.66 | 4.76 | 4.26 | 3.94 | 3.71 | 3.54 | 3.41 | 3.30 | 3.21 | 3.07 | 2.93 | 2.78 | 2.70 | 2.62 | 2.54 | 2.45 | 2.35 | 2.26 |
| 24 | 7.82 | 5.61 | 4.72 | 4.22 | 3.90 | 3.67 | 3.50 | 3.36 | 3.26 | 3.17 | 3.03 | 2.89 | 2.74 | 2.66 | 2.58 | 2.49 | 2.40 | 2.31 | 2.21 |
| 25 | 7.77 | 5.57 | 4.68 | 4.18 | 3.85 | 3.63 | 3.46 | 3.32 | 3.22 | 3.13 | 2.99 | 2.85 | 2.70 | 2.62 | 2.54 | 2.45 | 2.36 | 2.27 | 2.17 |
| 26 | 7.72 | 5.53 | 4.64 | 4.14 | 3.82 | 3.59 | 3.42 | 3.29 | 3.18 | 3.09 | 2.96 | 2.81 | 2.66 | 2.58 | 2.50 | 2.42 | 2.33 | 2.23 | 2.13 |
| 27 | 7.68 | 5.49 | 4.60 | 4.11 | 3.78 | 3.56 | 3.39 | 3.26 | 3.15 | 3.06 | 2.93 | 2.78 | 2.63 | 2.55 | 2.47 | 2.38 | 2.29 | 2.20 | 2.10 |
| 28 | 7.64 | 5.45 | 4.57 | 4.07 | 3.75 | 3.53 | 3.36 | 3.23 | 3.12 | 3.03 | 2.90 | 2.75 | 2.60 | 2.52 | 2.44 | 2.35 | 2.26 | 2.17 | 2.06 |
| 29 | 7.60 | 5.42 | 4.54 | 4.04 | 3.73 | 3.50 | 3.33 | 3.20 | 3.09 | 3.00 | 2.87 | 2.73 | 2.57 | 2.49 | 2.41 | 2.33 | 2.23 | 2.14 | 2.03 |

**TABLE 4**  *F* DISTRIBUTION (*Continued*)

**Table of $F_{.01}$ Values**

| Denominator Degrees of Freedom | Numerator Degrees of Freedom | | | | | | | | | | | | | | | | | | |
|---|---|---|---|---|---|---|---|---|---|---|---|---|---|---|---|---|---|---|---|
| | 1 | 2 | 3 | 4 | 5 | 6 | 7 | 8 | 9 | 10 | 12 | 15 | 20 | 24 | 30 | 40 | 60 | 120 | ∞ |
| 30 | 7.56 | 5.39 | 4.51 | 4.02 | 3.70 | 3.47 | 3.30 | 3.17 | 3.07 | 2.98 | 2.84 | 2.70 | 2.55 | 2.47 | 2.39 | 2.30 | 2.21 | 2.11 | 2.01 |
| 40 | 7.31 | 5.18 | 4.31 | 3.83 | 3.51 | 3.29 | 3.12 | 2.99 | 2.89 | 2.80 | 2.66 | 2.52 | 2.37 | 2.29 | 2.20 | 2.11 | 2.02 | 1.92 | 1.80 |
| 60 | 7.08 | 4.98 | 4.13 | 3.65 | 3.34 | 3.12 | 2.95 | 2.82 | 2.72 | 2.63 | 2.50 | 2.35 | 2.20 | 2.12 | 2.03 | 1.94 | 1.84 | 1.73 | 1.60 |
| 120 | 6.85 | 4.79 | 3.95 | 3.48 | 3.17 | 2.96 | 2.79 | 2.66 | 2.56 | 2.47 | 2.34 | 2.19 | 2.03 | 1.95 | 1.86 | 1.76 | 1.66 | 1.53 | 1.38 |
| ∞ | 6.63 | 4.61 | 3.78 | 3.32 | 3.02 | 2.80 | 2.64 | 2.51 | 2.41 | 2.32 | 2.18 | 2.04 | 1.88 | 1.79 | 1.70 | 1.59 | 1.47 | 1.32 | 1.00 |

This table is reprinted by permission of Oxford University Press on behalf of The Biometrika Trustees from Table 18, Percentage Points of the *F* Distribution, by E. S. Pearson and H. O. Hartley, *Biometrika Tables for Statisticians*, Vol. 1, 3rd ed., 1966.

# Appendix C    Summation Notation

## Summations

*Definition*

$$\sum_{i=1}^{n} x_i = x_1 + x_2 + \cdots + x_n \tag{C.1}$$

Example for $x_1 = 5$, $x_2 = 8$, $x_3 = 14$:

$$\sum_{i=1}^{3} x_i = x_1 + x_2 + x_3$$
$$= 5 + 8 + 14$$
$$= 27$$

*Result 1*

For a constant $c$:

$$\sum_{i=1}^{n} c = \underbrace{(c + c + \cdots + c)}_{n \text{ times}} = nc \tag{C.2}$$

Example for $c = 5$, $n = 10$:

$$\sum_{i=1}^{10} 5 = 10(5) = 50$$

Example for $c = \bar{x}$:

$$\sum_{i=1}^{n} \bar{x} = n\bar{x}$$

*Result 2*

$$\sum_{i=1}^{n} cx_i = cx_1 + cx_2 + \cdots + cx_n$$
$$= c(x_1 + x_2 + \cdots + x_n) = c\sum_{i=1}^{n} x_i \tag{C.3}$$

Example for $x_1 = 5$, $x_2 = 8$, $x_3 = 14$, $c = 2$:

$$\sum_{i=1}^{3} 2x_i = 2\sum_{i=1}^{3} x_i = 2(27) = 54$$

*Result 3*

$$\sum_{i=1}^{n} (ax_i + by_i) = a\sum_{i=1}^{n} x_i + b\sum_{i=1}^{n} y_i \tag{C.4}$$

Example for $x_1 = 5$, $x_2 = 8$, $x_3 = 14$, $a = 2$, $y_1 = 7$, $y_2 = 3$, $y_3 = 8$, $b = 4$:

$$\sum_{i=1}^{3}(2x_i + 4y_i) = 2\sum_{i=1}^{3}x_i + 4\sum_{i=1}^{3}y_i$$
$$= 2(27) + 4(18)$$
$$= 54 + 72$$
$$= 126$$

## Double Summations

Consider the following data involving the variable $x_{ij}$, where $i$ is the subscript denoting the row position and $j$ is the subscript denoting the column position:

|       |   | Column | | |
|-------|---|--------|--------|--------|
|       |   | **1** | **2** | **3** |
|       | **1** | $x_{11} = 10$ | $x_{12} = 8$ | $x_{13} = 6$ |
| **Row** | | | | |
|       | **2** | $x_{21} = 7$ | $x_{22} = 4$ | $x_{23} = 12$ |

*Definition*

$$\sum_{i=1}^{n}\sum_{j=1}^{m}x_{ij} = (x_{11} + x_{12} + \cdots + x_{1m}) + (x_{21} + x_{22} + \cdots + x_{2m})$$
$$+ (x_{31} + x_{32} + \cdots + x_{3m}) + \cdots + (x_{n1} + x_{n2} + \cdots + x_{nm}) \qquad \textbf{(C.5)}$$

Example:

$$\sum_{i=1}^{2}\sum_{j=1}^{3}x_{ij} = x_{11} + x_{12} + x_{13} + x_{21} + x_{22} + x_{23}$$
$$= 10 + 8 + 6 + 7 + 4 + 12$$
$$= 47$$

*Definition*

$$\sum_{i=1}^{n}x_{ij} = x_{1j} + x_{2j} + \cdots + x_{nj} \qquad \textbf{(C.6)}$$

Example:

$$\sum_{i=1}^{2}x_{i2} = x_{12} + x_{22}$$
$$= 8 + 4$$
$$= 12$$

## Shorthand Notation

Sometimes when a summation is for all values of the subscript, we use the following shorthand notations:

$$\sum_{i=1}^{n}x_i = \sum x_i \qquad \textbf{(C.7)}$$

$$\sum_{i=1}^{n}\sum_{j=1}^{m}x_{ij} = \sum\sum x_{ij} \qquad \textbf{(C.8)}$$

$$\sum_{i=1}^{n}x_{ij} = \sum_{i}x_{ij} \qquad \textbf{(C.9)}$$

## Chapter 1

**2. a.** 9
 **b.** 4
 **c.** Qualitative: country and room rate
   Quantitative: number of rooms and overall score
 **d.** Country is nominal; room rate is ordinal; number of rooms and overall score are ratio

**4. a.** 10
 **b.** *Fortune* 500 largest U.S. corporations
 **c.** $14,227.59 million
 **d.** $14,227.59 million

**6.** Questions a, c, and d are quantitative
   Questions b and e are qualitative

**8. a.** 2013
 **b.** Qualitative
 **c.** Percentages
 **d.** 563 or 564

**10. a.** Quantitative; ratio
 **b.** Qualitative; nominal
 **c.** Qualitative; ordinal
 **d.** Qualitative; nominal
 **e.** Quantitative; ratio

**12. a.** All visitors to Hawaii
 **b.** Yes
 **c.** Questions 1 and 4 provide quantitative data
   Questions 2 and 3 provide qualitative data

**14. a.** 4
 **b.** All are quantitative
 **c.** Time series

**16. a.** Product taste tests and test marketing
 **b.** Specially designed statistical studies

**18. a.** 40%
 **b.** Qualitative

**20. a.** 56% and $387,325
 **b.** 3.73
 **c.** $387,325

**22. a.** All adult viewers reached by the station
 **b.** Viewers contacted in the telephone survey
 **c.** Sample

**24. a.** Correct
 **b.** Incorrect
 **c.** Correct
 **d.** Incorrect
 **e.** Incorrect

## Chapter 2

**2. a.** .20
 **b.** 40
 **c/d.**

| Class | Frequency | Percent Frequency |
|-------|-----------|-------------------|
| A | 44 | 22 |
| B | 36 | 18 |
| C | 80 | 40 |
| D | 40 | 20 |
| Total | 200 | 100 |

**4. a.** Qualitative
 **b.**

| TV Show | Frequency | Percent Frequency |
|---------|-----------|-------------------|
| Millionaire | 24 | 48 |
| Frasier | 15 | 30 |
| Chicago Hope | 7 | 14 |
| Charmed | 4 | 8 |
| Total | 50 | 100 |

 **d.** Millionaire has the largest market share; Frasier is second

**6. a.**

| Book | Frequency | Percent Frequency |
|------|-----------|-------------------|
| *7 Habits* | 10 | 16.66 |
| *Millionaire* | 16 | 26.67 |
| *Motley* | 9 | 15.00 |
| *Dad* | 13 | 21.67 |
| *WSJ Guide* | 6 | 10.00 |
| Other | 6 | 10.00 |
| Total | 60 | 100.00 |

 **b.** First 5: *Millionaire, Dad, Motley, 7 Habits, WSJ Guide*
 **c.** 48.33%

**8. a.**

| Position | Frequency | Relative Frequency |
|----------|-----------|--------------------|
| P | 17 | .309 |
| H | 4 | .073 |
| 1 | 5 | .091 |
| 2 | 4 | .073 |
| 3 | 2 | .036 |
| S | 5 | .091 |
| L | 6 | .109 |
| C | 5 | .091 |
| R | 7 | .127 |
| Totals | 55 | 1.000 |

**b.** Pitcher
**c.** 3rd base
**d.** Right field
**e.** Infielders 16 to outfielders 18

**10. a.** Quality classifications
**b.**

| Rating | Frequency | Relative Frequency |
|--------|-----------|--------------------|
| Poor | 2 | .03 |
| Fair | 4 | .07 |
| Good | 12 | .20 |
| Very good | 24 | .40 |
| Excellent | 18 | .30 |
| Totals | 60 | 1.00 |

**12.**

| Class | Cumulative Frequency | Cumulative Relative Frequency |
|-------|----------------------|-------------------------------|
| ≤19 | 10 | .20 |
| ≤29 | 24 | .48 |
| ≤39 | 41 | .82 |
| ≤49 | 48 | .96 |
| ≤59 | 50 | 1.00 |

**14. a/b.**

| Class | Frequency | Percent Frequency |
|-------|-----------|-------------------|
| 6.0–7.9 | 4 | 20 |
| 8.0–9.9 | 2 | 10 |
| 10.0–11.9 | 8 | 40 |
| 12.0–13.9 | 3 | 15 |
| 14.0–15.9 | 3 | 15 |
| Totals | 20 | 100 |

**16. a.**

| Stock Price ($) | Frequency | Relative Frequency | Percent Frequency |
|-----------------|-----------|--------------------|-------------------|
| 10.00–19.99 | 10 | .40 | 40 |
| 20.00–29.99 | 4 | .16 | 16 |
| 30.00–39.99 | 6 | .24 | 24 |
| 40.00–49.99 | 2 | .08 | 8 |
| 50.00–59.99 | 1 | .04 | 4 |
| 60.00–69.99 | 2 | .08 | 8 |
| Total | 25 | 1.00 | 100 |

**b.**

| Earnings per Share ($) | Frequency | Relative Frequency | Percent Frequency |
|------------------------|-----------|--------------------|-------------------|
| −3.00 to −2.01 | 2 | .08 | 8 |
| −2.00 to −1.01 | 0 | .00 | 0 |
| −1.00 to −0.01 | 2 | .08 | 8 |
| 0.00 to 0.99 | 9 | .36 | 36 |
| 1.00 to 1.99 | 9 | .36 | 36 |
| 2.00 to 2.99 | 3 | .12 | 12 |
| Total | 25 | 1.00 | 100 |

**18. a.** Lowest salary: $93,000
Highest salary: $178,000
**b.**

| Salary ($1000s) | Frequency | Relative Frequency | Percent Frequency |
|-----------------|-----------|--------------------|-------------------|
| 91–105 | 4 | 0.08 | 8 |
| 106–120 | 5 | 0.10 | 10 |
| 121–135 | 11 | 0.22 | 22 |
| 136–150 | 18 | 0.36 | 36 |
| 151–165 | 9 | 0.18 | 18 |
| 166–180 | 3 | 0.06 | 6 |
| Total | 50 | 1.00 | 100 |

**c.** 20/50
**d.** 24%

**20. a.** 48.9%
**b.** 43.4%
**c.** 51.1%
**d.** 97.075 million
**e.** 46.6125 million

**22.**

```
5 | 7  8
6 | 4  5  8
7 | 0  2  2  5  5  6  8
8 | 0  2  3  5
```

**24.** Leaf Unit = 10

```
11 | 6
12 | 0  2
13 | 0  6  7
14 | 2  2  7
15 | 5
16 | 0  2  8
17 | 0  2  3
```

**26.** Leaf Unit = .1

```
0 | 4  7  8  9  9
1 | 1  2  9
2 | 0  0  1  3  5  5  6  8
3 | 4  9
4 | 8
5 |
6 |
7 | 1
```

**28. a.**
```
0 | 5  8
1 | 1  1  3  3  4  4
1 | 5  6  7  8  9  9
2 | 2  3  3  3  5  5
2 | 6  8
3 |
3 | 6  7  7  9
4 | 0
4 | 7  8
5 |
5 |
6 | 0
```

**b.**

| 2000 P/E Forecast | Frequency | Relative Frequency |
|---|---|---|
| 5–9 | 2 | 6.7 |
| 10–14 | 6 | 20.0 |
| 15–19 | 6 | 20.0 |
| 20–24 | 6 | 20.0 |
| 25–29 | 2 | 6.7 |
| 30–34 | 0 | 0.0 |
| 35–39 | 4 | 13.3 |
| 40–44 | 1 | 3.3 |
| 45–49 | 2 | 6.7 |
| 50–54 | 0 | 0.0 |
| 55–59 | 0 | 0.0 |
| 60–64 | 1 | 3.3 |
| Total | 30 | 100.0 |

**30. b.** Negative relationship

**32. a.**

| Sales/ Margins/ ROE | EPS Rating | | | | | |
|---|---|---|---|---|---|---|
| | 0– 19 | 20– 39 | 40– 59 | 60– 79 | 80– 100 | Total |
| A | | | | 1 | 8 | 9 |
| B | | 1 | 4 | 5 | 2 | 12 |
| C | 1 | | 1 | 2 | 3 | 7 |
| D | 3 | 1 | | 1 | | 5 |
| E | | 2 | 1 | | | 3 |
| Total | 4 | 4 | 6 | 9 | 13 | 36 |

**b.**

| Sales/ Margins/ ROE | EPS Rating | | | | | |
|---|---|---|---|---|---|---|
| | 0– 19 | 20– 39 | 40– 59 | 60– 79 | 80– 100 | Total |
| A | | | | 11.11 | 88.89 | 100 |
| B | | 8.33 | 33.33 | 41.67 | 16.67 | 100 |
| C | 14.29 | | 14.29 | 28.57 | 42.86 | 100 |
| D | 60.00 | 20.00 | | 20.00 | | 100 |
| E | | 66.67 | 33.33 | | | 100 |

Higher EPS ratings seem to be associated with higher ratings on Sales/Margins/ROE

**34.** No apparent relationship

**36. a.**

| Vehicle | Frequency | Percent Frequency |
|---|---|---|
| F-Series | 17 | 34 |
| Silverado | 12 | 24 |
| Taurus | 8 | 16 |
| Camry | 7 | 14 |
| Accord | 6 | 12 |
| | 50 | 100 |

**b.** Ford F-Series Pickup and Chevrolet Silverado

**38. a.**

| Movie | Frequency | Percent Frequency |
|---|---|---|
| *Blair Witch Project* | 159 | 36.0 |
| *Phantom Menace* | 89 | 20.2 |
| *Beloved* | 85 | 19.3 |
| *Primary Colors* | 57 | 12.9 |
| *Truman Show* | 51 | 11.6 |
| Total | 441 | 100.0 |

**c.** 56.2%

**40.**

| Closing Price | Freq. | Rel. Freq. | Cum. Freq. | Cum. Rel. Freq. |
|---|---|---|---|---|
| 0–9⅞ | 9 | .225 | 9 | .225 |
| 10–19⅞ | 10 | .250 | 19 | .475 |
| 20–29⅞ | 5 | .125 | 24 | .600 |
| 30–39⅞ | 11 | .275 | 35 | .875 |
| 40–49⅞ | 2 | .050 | 37 | .925 |
| 50–59⅞ | 2 | .050 | 39 | .975 |
| 60–69⅞ | 0 | .000 | 39 | .975 |
| 70–79⅞ | 1 | .025 | 40 | 1.000 |
| Totals | 40 | 1.000 | | |

**42.**

| Income ($) | Frequency | Relative Frequency |
|---|---|---|
| 18,000–21,999 | 13 | 0.255 |
| 22,000–25,999 | 20 | 0.392 |
| 26,000–29,999 | 12 | 0.235 |
| 30,000–33,999 | 4 | 0.079 |
| 34,000–37,999 | 2 | 0.039 |
| Total | 51 | 1.000 |

**44. a. High Temperature**

```
3 |
4 |
5 | 7
6 | 1 4 4 4 4 6 8
7 | 3 5 7 9
8 | 0 1 1 4 6
9 | 0 2 3
```

**b. Low Temperature**

```
3 | 9
4 | 3 6 8
5 | 0 0 0 2 4 4 5 5 7 9
6 | 1 8
7 | 2 4 5 5
8 |
9 |
```

**c.** The range of low temperatures is below the range of high temperatures

**d.** 8 cities

**e.**

| | Frequency | |
|---|---|---|
| Temperature | High Temp. | Low Temp. |
| 30–39 | 0 | 1 |
| 40–49 | 0 | 3 |
| 50–59 | 1 | 10 |
| 60–69 | 7 | 2 |
| 70–79 | 4 | 4 |
| 80–89 | 5 | 0 |
| 90–99 | 3 | 0 |
| Total | 20 | 20 |

**46. a.**

| | Satisfaction Score | | | | | | |
|---|---|---|---|---|---|---|---|
| Occupation | 30–39 | 40–49 | 50–59 | 60–69 | 70–79 | 80–89 | Total |
| Cabinetmaker | | | 2 | 4 | 3 | 1 | 10 |
| Lawyer | 1 | 5 | 2 | 1 | 1 | | 10 |
| Physical Therapist | | | 5 | 2 | 1 | 2 | 10 |
| Systems Analyst | | 2 | 1 | 4 | 3 | | 10 |
| Total | 1 | 7 | 10 | 11 | 8 | 3 | 40 |

**b.**

| | Satisfaction Score | | | | | | |
|---|---|---|---|---|---|---|---|
| Occupation | 30–39 | 40–49 | 50–59 | 60–69 | 70–79 | 80–89 | Total |
| Cabinetmaker | | | 20 | 40 | 30 | 10 | 100 |
| Lawyer | 10 | 50 | 20 | 10 | 10 | | 100 |
| Physical Therapist | | | 50 | 20 | 10 | 20 | 100 |
| Systems Analyst | | 20 | 10 | 40 | 30 | | 100 |

**c.** Cabinetmakers seem to have the highest job satisfaction scores; lawyers seem to be the lowest

**48. b.**

| Year | Freq. | Fuel | Freq. |
|---|---|---|---|
| 1973 or before | 247 | Elect. | 149 |
| 1974–79 | 54 | Nat. Gas | 317 |
| 1980–86 | 82 | Oil | 17 |
| 1987–91 | 121 | Propane | 7 |
| Total | 504 | Other | 14 |
| | | Total | 504 |

**50. a.** Crosstabulation of market value and profit

| Market Value ($1000s) | Profit ($1000s) | | | | Total |
|---|---|---|---|---|---|
| | 0– 300 | 300– 600 | 600– 900 | 900– 1200 | |
| 0–8000 | 23 | 4 | | | 27 |
| 8000–16,000 | 4 | 4 | 2 | 2 | 12 |
| 16,000–24,000 | | 2 | 1 | 1 | 4 |
| 24,000–32,000 | | | 1 | 2 | 1 | 4 |
| 32,000–40,000 | | | 2 | 1 | 3 |
| Total | 27 | 13 | 6 | 4 | 50 |

**b.** Crosstabulation of row percentages

| Market Value ($1000s) | Profit ($1000s) | | | | Total |
|---|---|---|---|---|---|
| | 0– 300 | 300– 600 | 600– 900 | 900– 1200 | |
| 0–8000 | 85.19 | 14.81 | 0.00 | 0.00 | 100 |
| 8000–16,000 | 33.33 | 33.33 | 16.67 | 16.67 | 100 |
| 16,000–24,000 | 0.00 | 50.00 | 25.00 | 25.00 | 100 |
| 24,000–32,000 | 0.00 | 25.00 | 50.00 | 25.00 | 100 |
| 32,000–40,000 | 0.00 | 66.67 | 33.33 | 0.00 | 100 |

**c.** A positive relationship is indicated between profit and market value; as profit goes up, market value goes up

**52. b.** A positive relationship is demonstrated between market value and stockholders' equity

# Chapter 3

**2.** 16, 16.5

**4.** 59.727, 57, 53

**6. a.** 92.25; 80.5; multimodal
**b.** 66.7; 68; 70
**c.** 500 @ $50
**d.** Yes

**8. a.** 38.75, 29
**b.** 38.5
**c.** 29.5, 47.5
**d.** 31

**10. a.** 48.33, 49; do not report a mode
**b.** 45, 55

**12. a.** $639
**b.** 98.8 pictures
**c.** 110.2 minutes

**14.** 16, 4

**16. a.** 22
**b.** 75.2
**c.** 8.67
**d.** 4.87

**18. a.** Mainland: 115.13; 111.56
Asia: 36.62; 36.695

**b.** Mainland: 86.24; 26.82; 23.30
Asia: 42.97; 11.40; 31.13
**c.** Greater mean and standard deviation for Mainland.

**20.** *Dawson:* range = 2, $s$ = .67
*Clark:* range = 8, $s$ = 2.58

**22. a.** 161, 92.5; 56, 19.5
**b.** 2705.3816, 52.01; 290.8526, 17.05
**c.** 56.38, 25.56
**d.** Greater for 500 @ $50

**24.** *Quarter-milers:* $s$ = .0564, Coef. of Var. = 5.8
*Milers:* $s$ = .1295, Coef. of Var. = 2.9

**26.** .20, 1.50, 0, −.50, −2.20

**28. a.** 95%
**b.** Almost all
**c.** 68%

**30. a.** 34%
**b.** 81.5%
**c.** 16%

**32. a.** −.95
**b.** 3.90
**c.** Labor cost in part (b) is an outlier

**34. a.** 100; 13.88 or approximately 14
**b.** 16%
**c.** 11.1 and 10.77; no outliers

**36.** 15, 22.5, 26, 29, 34

**38.** 5, 8, 10, 15, 18

**40. a.** 5, 9.6, 14.5, 19.2, 52.7
**b.** Limits: −4.8, 33.6
**c.** 41.6 is an outlier
52.7 is an outlier

**42. a.** 105.7933, 52.7
**b.** 15.7, 78.3
**c.** Silicon Graphics, Toys R Us
**d.** 26.73; much greater

**44. a.** 37.48, 23.67
**b.** 7.91, 51.92
**c.** Limits: −58.11, 117.94
Russia and Turkey are outliers

**46. b.** There appears to be a positive linear relationship between $x$ and $y$
**c.** $s_{xy}$ = 26.5
**d.** $r_{xy}$ = .693

**48.** −.91; negative relationship

**50. a.** .92
**b.** Strong positive linear relationship

**52. a.** 3.69
**b.** 3.175

**54. a.** 2.50
**b.** Yes

**56.** 10.74, 25.63, 5.06

**58. a.** 138.52, 129, 0
 **b.** No, much more
 **c.** 95, 169
 **d.** 467, 74
 **e.** 9271.01, 96.29
 **f.** Yes, the $467 value

**60. a.** 18.57, 16.5
 **b.** 53.49, 7.31
 **c.** Quantex
 **d.** 1.15
 **e.** $-.90$
 **f.** No

**62. a.** $\bar{x} = 83.135$ $s = 16.173$
 **b.** $50,789 to $115,481
 **c.** same range as in part (b); higher probability
 **d.** Danbury, CT is an outlier

**64. a.** 502.67; positive linear relationship
 **b.** .933; strong linear relationship

**66. b.** .9856, strong positive relationship

**68. a.** 817
 **b.** 833

**70. a.** 60.68
 **b.** $s = 5.59$

## Chapter 4

**2.** 20 ways

**4. b.** (H,H,H) (H,H,T) (H,T,H) (H,T,T)
 (T,H,H) (T,H,T) (T,T,H) (T,T,T)
 **c.** $\frac{1}{8}$

**6.** .40, .26, .34; relative frequency method

**8. a.** 4; Commission Positive—Council Approves,
 Commission Positive—Council Disapproves
 Commission Negative—Council Approves,
 Commission Negative—Council Disapproves

**10. a.** .60
 **b.** .09
 **c.** .78
 **d.** 86
 **e.** $1.53 billion

**12. a.** 1,906,884
 **b.** 1/1,906,884
 **c.** 1/80,089,128

**14. a.** $\frac{1}{4}$
 **b.** $\frac{1}{2}$
 **c.** $\frac{3}{4}$

**16. a.** 36
 **c.** $\frac{1}{6}$
 **d.** $\frac{5}{18}$
 **e.** No; $P(\text{odd}) = P(\text{even}) = \frac{1}{2}$
 **f.** Classical

**18. a.** $P(0) = .05$
 **b.** $P(4 \text{ or } 5) = .20$
 **c.** $P(0, 1, \text{ or } 2) = .55$

**20. a.** .112
 **b.** .086
 **c.** .49

**22. a.** .40, .40, .60
 **b.** .80, yes
 **c.** $A^c = (E_3, E_4, E_5)$; $C^c = (E_1, E_4)$;
  $P(A^c) = .60$; $P(C^c) = .40$
 **d.** $(E_1, E_2, E_5)$; .60
 **e.** .80

**24.** .43

**26. a.** .30, .23
 **b.** .17
 **c.** .64

**28. a.** .698
 **b.** .302

**30. a.** .67
 **b.** .80
 **c.** No

**32. a.**

|  | Single | Married | Total |
|---|---|---|---|
| Under 30 | .55 | .10 | .65 |
| 30 or Over | .20 | .15 | .35 |
| Total | .75 | .25 | 1.0 |

 **b.** Higher probability of under 30
 **c.** Higher probability of single
 **d.** .55
 **e.** .8462
 **f.** No

**34. a.** .44
 **b.** .15
 **c.** .0225
 **d.** .0025
 **e.** .136
 **f.** .106

**36. b.** .075
 **c.** .20
 **d.** .25
 **e.** .15
 **f.** .60
 **g.** .275

**38. a.** 52/1035
 **b.** .0004
 **c.** .0676

**40. a.** .10, .20, .09
 **b.** .51
 **c.** .26, .51, .23

**42. a.** .21
 **b.** Yes

**44.** .6754

**46. a.** .68
  **b.** 52
  **c.** 10

**48. a.** .61
  **b.** 18–34 and 65+
  **c.** .30

**50. a.** 76
  **b.** .24

**52. b.** .2022
  **c.** .4618
  **d.** .4005

**54. a.** .49
  **b.** .44
  **c.** .54
  **d.** No
  **e.** Yes

**56. a.** .25
  **b.** .125
  **c.** .0125
  **d.** .10
  **e.** No

**58.** 3.44%

**60. a.** .0625
  **b.** .0132
  **c.** Three

# Chapter 5

**2. a.** $x$ = time in minutes to assemble product
  **b.** Any positive value: $x > 0$
  **c.** Continuous

**4.** $x = 0, 1, 2, \ldots, 12$

**6. a.** $0, 1, 2, \ldots, 20$; discrete
  **b.** $0, 1, 2, \ldots$; discrete
  **c.** $0, 1, 2, \ldots, 50$; discrete
  **d.** $0 \le x \le 8$; continuous
  **e.** $x > 0$; continuous

**8. a.**

| $x$ | 1 | 2 | 3 | 4 |
|---|---|---|---|---|
| $f(x)$ | .15 | .25 | .40 | .20 |

  **c.** $f(x) \ge 0, \Sigma f(x) = 1$

**10. a.**

| $x$ | 1 | 2 | 3 | 4 | 5 |
|---|---|---|---|---|---|
| $f(x)$ | .05 | .09 | .03 | .42 | .41 |

  **b.**

| $x$ | 1 | 2 | 3 | 4 | 5 |
|---|---|---|---|---|---|
| $f(x)$ | .04 | .10 | .12 | .46 | .28 |

  **c.** .83
  **d.** .28
  **e.** Senior executives more satisfied

**12. a.** Yes
  **b.** .65

**14. a.** .05
  **b.** .70
  **c.** .40

**16. a.** 5.20
  **b.** 4.56, 2.14

**18. a.** $E(x) = 2.3$, same
  **b.** $Var(x) = 1.23, \sigma = 1.11$

**20. a.** 166
  **b.** $-94$; concern is to protect against the expense of a big accident

**22. a.** 445
  **b.** 1250 loss

**24. a.** Medium: 145; large: 140
  **b.** Medium: 2725; large: 12,400

**26. a.** $f(0) = .3487$
  **b.** $f(2) = .1937$
  **c.** .9298
  **d.** .6513
  **e.** 1
  **f.** $\sigma^2 = .9000, \sigma = .9487$

**28. a.** .3292
  **b.** .6422
  **c.** .0182

**30. a.** Probability of a defective part must be .03 for each trial; trials must be independent
  **c.** 2
  **d.**

| Number of defects | 0 | 1 | 2 |
|---|---|---|---|
| Probability | .9409 | .0582 | .0009 |

**32. a.** .90
  **b.** .99
  **c.** .999
  **d.** Yes

**34. a.** .0634
  **b.** .0634
  **c.** .9729

**38. a.** $f(x) = \dfrac{3^x e^{-3}}{x!}$
  **b.** .2241
  **c.** .1494
  **d.** .8008

**40. a.** .1952
  **b.** .1048
  **c.** .0183
  **d.** .0907

**42. a.** .1465
  **b.** 1
  **c.** .8647

**44. a.** $\mu = 1.25$
  **b.** .2865
  **c.** .3581
  **d.** .3554

**46. a.** 50
   **b.** .067
   **c.** .4667
   **d.** .30

**48. a.** .50
   **b.** .3333

**50. a.** .01
   **b.** .07
   **c.** .92
   **d.** .07

**52. a.** .5333
   **b.** .6667
   **c.** .7778
   **d.** $n = 7$

**54. a.** $f(x) \geq 0$ and $\Sigma f(x) = 1$
   **b.** 3.64, .6704
   **c.** Appears overvalued

**56. a.** .0364
   **b.** .4420
   **c.** 48
   **d.** 6.7882

**58. a.** .9510
   **b.** .0480
   **c.** .0490

**60. a.** 328
   **b.** 13.91
   **c.** 13.91

**62. a.** .2240
   **b.** .5767

**64. a.** .5333
   **b.** .1333
   **c.** .3333

## Chapter 6

**2. b.** .50
   **c.** .60
   **d.** 15
   **e.** 8.33

**4. b.** .50
   **c.** .30
   **d.** .40

**6. a.** .40
   **b.** .64
   **c.** .68

**10. a.** .3413
   **b.** .4332
   **c.** .4772
   **d.** .4938

**12. a.** .2967
   **b.** .4418
   **c.** .3300

   **d.** .5910
   **e.** .8849
   **f.** .2389

**14. a.** $z = 1.96$
   **b.** $z = .61$
   **c.** $z = 1.12$
   **d.** $z = .44$

**16. a.** $z = 2.33$
   **b.** $z = 1.96$
   **c.** $z = 1.645$
   **d.** $z = 1.28$

**18. a.** .2451
   **b.** .1170
   **c.** 69.48 minutes or more

**20. a.** .025
   **b.** 5.16%
   **c.** 33.72 or more

**22. a.** .4194
   **b.** $517.44 or more
   **c.** .0166

**24. a.** 902.75, 114.185
   **b.** .1841
   **c.** .1977
   **d.** 1,091 million

**26. a.** .5276
   **b.** .3935
   **c.** .4724
   **d.** .1341

**28. a.** .3935
   **b.** .2231
   **c.** .3834

**30. a.** 50 hours
   **b.** .3935
   **c.** .1353

**32. a.** $f(x) = 30e^{-30x}$
   **b.** .0821
   **c.** .7135

**34. a.** $63,000
   **b.** $43,800 or less
   **c.** 12.92%
   **d.** $87,675

**36. a.** $220.33
   **b.** .5999
   **c.** $1656.78

**38. a.** .0228
   **b.** $50

**40. a.** 38.3%
   **b.** 3.59% better, 96.41% worse
   **c.** 38.21%

**42.** $\mu = 19.23$ ounces

**44. a.** 4 hours
  **b.** $1/4\ e^{-x/4}$
  **c.** .7788
  **d.** .1353

**46. a.** 2 minutes
  **b.** .2212
  **c.** .3935
  **d.** .0821

## Chapter 7

**2.** 22, 147, 229, 289

**4. a.** Number companies: 1-AT&T, 2-IBM, . . . , 10-Pfizer
  Sample: Microsoft, Motorola, Cisco, Johnson & Johnson, AT&T
  **b.** America Online, Johnson & Johnson, General Electric, Motorola, Intel
  **c.** 252

**6.** 2782, 493, 825, 1807, 289

**8. a.** Wisconsin, Clemson, Washington, USC, Oklahoma, Colorado. 21 random numbers used
  **b.** Nebraska, Florida State, Michigan, Texas, Washington, TCU. 25 random numbers used

**10.** Finite, infinite, infinite, infinite, finite

**12. a.** .50
  **b.** .3667

**14. a.** .19
  **b.** .32
  **c.** .79

**16.** .80

**20.** 3.54, 2.50, 2.04, 1.77
  $\sigma_{\bar{x}}$ decreases as $n$ increases

**22. a.** Only for $n = 30$ and $n = 40$
  **b.** $n = 30$; normal with $E(\bar{x}) = 400$
  and $\sigma_{\bar{x}} = 9.13$
  $n = 40$; normal with $E(\bar{x}) = 400$
  and $\sigma_{\bar{x}} = 7.91$

**24. a.** Normal with $E(\bar{x}) = 51,800$ and $\sigma_{\bar{x}} = 516.40$
  **b.** $\sigma_{\bar{x}}$ decreases to 365.15
  **c.** $\sigma_{\bar{x}}$ decreases as $n$ increases

**26. a.** Normal with $E(\bar{x}) = 1.20$ and $\sigma_{\bar{x}} = .014$
  **b.** .8414
  **c.** .5224

**28. a.** .5036, .6212, .7888, .9232, .9876
  **b.** Smaller standard error

**30. a.** Normal with $E(\bar{x}) = 166,500$ and $\sigma_{\bar{x}} = 4200$
  **b.** .9826
  **c.** .7660, .4514, .1896
  **d.** Increase the sample size

**32. a.** No, 40/4000 < .05
  **b.** With: 1.2902
  Without: 1.2965
  **c.** .8764

**34. a.** .6156
  **b.** .8530

**36. a.** .6156
  **b.** .7814
  **c.** .9488
  **d.** .9942
  **e.** High probability with larger $n$

**38. a.** Normal with $E(\bar{p}) = .76$ and $\sigma_{\bar{p}} = .0214$
  **b.** .8384
  **c.** .9452

**40. a.** Normal with $E(\bar{p}) = .25$ and $\sigma_{\bar{p}} = .0306$
  **b.** .6730
  **c.** .8968

**42. a.** Normal with $E(\bar{p}) = .15$ and $\sigma_{\bar{p}} = .0505$
  **b.** .4448
  **c.** .8389

**44.** 112, 145, 73, 324, 293, 875, 318, 618

**46. a.** Normal with $E(\bar{x}) = 31.5$ and $\sigma_{\bar{x}} = 1.70$
  **b.** .4448
  **c.** .9232

**48. a.** 8.4853
  **b.** .50
  **c.** .4448
  **d.** .5934

**50. a.** 625
  **b.** .7888

**52. a.** Normal with $E(\bar{p}) = .74$ and $\sigma_{\bar{p}} = .031$
  **b.** .8030
  **c.** .4778

**54. a.** .9606
  **b.** .0495

**56. a.** 48
  **b.** Normal, $E(\bar{p}) = .26$, $\sigma_{\bar{p}} = .0625$
  **c.** .2119

## Chapter 8

**2. a.** 30.60 to 33.40
  **b.** 30.34 to 33.66
  **c.** 29.81 to 34.19

**4.** 62

**6. a.** $\bar{x} = 369$
  **b.** $s = 50$
  **c.** 362.80 to 375.20

**8. a.** 11,769 to 12,231
  **b.** 11,725 to 12,275
  **c.** 11,638 to 12,362
  **d.** Width increases to be more confident

**10.** 7.25 to 8.25

**12. a.** 3.8
  **b.** .81
  **c.** 2.99 to 4.61

**14. a.** 1.734
   **b.** $-1.321$
   **c.** 3.365
   **d.** $-1.761$ and 1.761
   **e.** $-2.048$ and 2.048

**16. a.** 15.97 to 18.53
   **b.** 15.71 to 18.79
   **c.** 15.14 to 19.36

**18. a.** 1.58
   **b.** .1474
   **c.** 1.49 to 1.67

**20. a.** 21.15 to 23.65
   **b.** 21.12 to 23.68
   **c.** Intervals are essentially the same

**22. a.** 6.86
   **b.** 6.54 to 7.18

**24. a.** 9
   **b.** 35
   **c.** 78

**26. a.** 340
   **b.** 1358
   **c.** 8487

**28. a.** 53
   **b.** 75
   **c.** 129
   **d.** Must increase $n$

**30.** 59

**32. a.** .6733 to .7267
   **b.** .6682 to .7318

**34.** 1068

**36. a.** .4393
   **b.** .3870 to .4916

**38. a.** .0430
   **b.** .2170 to .3030
   **c.** 822

**40. a.** .2505
   **b.** .0266

**42.** 601, 1068, 2401, 9604

**44. a.** 2009
   **b.** 47,991 to 52,009

**46. a.** 49.8
   **b.** 15.99
   **c.** 47.58 to 52.02

**48. a.** 13.2
   **b.** 7.8
   **c.** 7.62 to 18.78
   **d.** Wide interval; large $n$ desirable

**50.** 37

**52.** 176

**54. a.** .5420
   **b.** .0508
   **c.** .4912 to .5928

**56. a.** 1267
   **b.** 1509

**58. a.** .68
   **b.** .6391 to .7209

**60. a.** .3101
   **b.** .2898 to .3304
   **c.** 8219; No, this sample size is unnecessarily large

# Chapter 9

**2. a.** $H_0: \mu \leq 14$
      $H_a: \mu > 14$

**4. a.** $H_0: \mu \geq 220$
      $H_a: \mu < 220$

**6. a.** $H_0: \mu \leq 1$
      $H_a: \mu > 1$
   **b.** Claiming $\mu > 1$ when it is not true
   **c.** Claiming $\mu \leq 1$ when it is not true

**8. a.** $H_0: \mu \geq 220$
      $H_a: \mu < 220$
   **b.** Claiming $\mu < 220$ when it is not true
   **c.** Claiming $\mu \geq 220$ when it is not true

**10. a.** Reject $H_0$ if $z > 2.05$
   **b.** 1.36
   **c.** .0869
   **d.** Do not reject $H_0$

**12. a.** .0344; reject $H_0$
   **b.** .3264; do not reject $H_0$
   **c.** .0668; do not reject $H_0$
   **d.** Approximately 0; reject $H_0$
   **e.** 8413

**14. a.** Reject if $z > 2.33$
   **b.** 3.11
   **c.** Reject $H_0$

**16.** $z = -2.74$; reject $H_0$
   $p$-value $= .0031$

**18. a.** $H_0: \mu \leq 5.72$
      $H_a: \mu > 5.72$
   **b.** 2.12
   **c.** .0170
   **d.** Reject $H_0$

**20. a.** Reject $H_0$ if $z < -2.33$ or $z > 2.33$
   **b.** $-1.13$
   **c.** .2584
   **d.** Do not reject $H_0$

**22. a.** .0718; do not reject $H_0$
   **b.** .6528; do not reject $H_0$
   **c.** .0404; reject $H_0$
   **d.** Approximately 0; reject $H_0$
   **e.** .3174; do not reject $H_0$

**24. a.** $z = -1.06$; do not reject $H_0$
**b.** .0872

**26. a.** $z = 6.37$; reject $H_0$

**28. a.** $H_0: \mu = 1075$
$H_a: \mu \neq 1075$
**b.** $z = 1.43$
**c.** .1528
**d.** Do not reject $H_0$

**30. a.** 18
**b.** 1.41
**c.** Reject $H_0$ if $t < -2.571$ or $t > 2.571$
**d.** $-3.46$
**e.** Reject $H_0$

**32. a.** .01; reject $H_0$
**b.** .10; do not reject $H_0$
**c.** .03; reject $H_0$
**d.** .15; do not reject $H_0$
**e.** .003; reject $H_0$

**34. a.** $t = -1.90$; do not reject $H_0$
**b.** Approximately .07

**36. a.** $\mu = 4000$
$\mu \neq 4000$
**b.** Reject $H_0$ if $t < -2.160$ or if $t > 2.160$
**c.** 1.63
**d.** Do not reject $H_0$
**e.** Between .10 and .20

**38.** $t = 2.45$; reject $H_0$

**40. a.** Reject $H_0$ if $z < -1.96$ or $z > 1.96$
**b.** $-1.25$
**c.** .2112
**d.** Do not reject $H_0$

**42. a.** $H_0: p \leq .4$
$H_a: p > .4$
**b.** Reject $H_0$ if $z > 1.645$
**c.** 1.99
**d.** Reject $H_0$

**44. a.** .62
**b.** $z = 3.13$; reject $H_0$
**c.** Yes; it shows Burger King is preferred

**46. a.** .6381
**b.** 2.83
**c.** .0046
**d.** Reject $H_0$

**48. a.** $-1.20$
**b.** .1151
**c.** Do not reject $H_0$

**50. a.** .2912
**b.** Type II error
**c.** .0031

**52. a.** Concluding $\mu \leq 15$ when it is not true
**b.** .2676
**c.** .0179

**54. a.** Concluding $\mu = 28$ when it is not true
**b.** .0853, .6179, .6179, .0853
**c.** .9147

**56.** .1151, .0015
Increasing $n$ reduces $\beta$

**58.** 214

**60.** 109

**62.** 324

**64. a.** $H_0: \mu \leq 45,250$
$H_a: \mu > 45,250$
**b.** 2.71
**c.** .0034
**d.** Reject $H_0$

**66.** $z = 2.26$; $p$-value $= .0119$
Reject $H_0$

**68. a.** $z = 1.80$; do not reject $H_0$
**b.** .0718
**c.** 549 to 575

**70.** $z = -3.84$; reject $H_0$

**72. a.** Show $p < .50$
**b.** $z = -6.62$; reject $H_0$

**74. a.** .6502
**b.** $-.98$
**c.** .3270
**d.** Do not reject $H_0$

**76. a.** .352
**b.** $-2.64$
**c.** .0041
**d.** Reject $H_0$

**78. a.** .2912
**b.** .7939
**c.** Can't make Type II error

**80. a.** 45
**b.** .0192, .2358, .7291, .7291, .2358, .0192

## Chapter 10

**2. a.** 2.4
**b.** 5.27
**c.** .09 to 4.71

**4. a.** .60
**b.** .56 to .64

**6.** $-.51$ to 1.27

**8. a.** 1200
**b.** 438 to 1962
**c.** Populations normal with equal variances

**10. a.** 2.18
**b.** 4.41
**c.** .71 to 3.65

**12. a.** $z = -1.53$; do not reject $H_0$
**b.** .1260

**14. a.** $H_0: \mu_1 - \mu_2 = 0$
$H_a: \mu_1 - \mu_2 \neq 0$
  **b.** Reject if $z < -1.96$ or $z > 1.96$
  **c.** 2.18
  **d.** Reject $H_0$
  **e.** .0292

**16.** Customers at the two stores differ in terms of mean ages. $p$-value $= .0160$.

**18.** $z = 3.88$
Reject $H_0$

**20. a.** 1.08
  **b.** .2802
  **c.** Do not reject $H_0$

**22. a.** $H_0: \mu_1 - \mu_2 \leq 0$
$H_a: \mu_1 - \mu_2 > 0$
  **b.** Reject $H_0$ if $t > 1.711$
  **c.** 2.07
  **d.** Reject $H_0$
  **e.** .025

**24. a.** 3, $-1$, 3, 5, 3, 0, 1
  **b.** 2
  **c.** 2.082
  **d.** 2
  **e.** .07 to 3.93

**26.** .16 to .35

**28.** $t = 1.63$; do not reject $H_0$

**30. a.** Cannot reject the hypothesis that a \$10 price differential exists.
  **b.** 6.45 to 11.27

**32. a.** .12
  **b.** .0586 to .1814
  **c.** .0469 to .1931

**34.** .0009 to .1391

**36.** .07 to .24

**38.** $z = 3.94$; reject $H_0$

**40. a.** There is a difference between the recall rates.
  **b.** .02 to .22

**42.** $p$-value $= .0322$, reject $H_0$

**44.** System B has a lower mean checkout time.

**46.** $t = 2.29$; reject $H_0$

**48.** .029 to .171

**50. a.** There is a difference between claim rates.
  **b.** .0468 to .1332

# Chapter 11

**2. a.** 15.76 to 46.95
  **b.** 14.46 to 53.33
  **c.** 3.8 to 7.3

**4. a.** .22 to .71
  **b.** .47 to .84

**6. a.** 13.30
  **b.** 7.97 to 38.23

**8. a.** .00845
  **b.** .0919
  **c.** .0042 to .0244 for $\sigma^2$
    .0651 to .1561 for $\sigma$

**10.** $\chi^2 = 206.22$; reject $H_0$

**12. a.** .8106
  **b.** $\chi^2 = 9.49$; do not reject $H_0$

**14.** $F = 2.42$; reject $H_0$

**16.** $F = 2.63$; reject $H_0$

**18.** $F = 3.54$; do not reject $H_0$

**20.** $F = 5.29$; reject $H_0$

**22. a.** $F = 4$; reject $H_0$
  **b.** Drive carefully on wet pavement

**24.** 10.72 to 24.68

**26. a.** $\chi^2 = 27.44$; reject $H_0$
  **b.** .00012 to .00042

**28.** $\chi^2 = 31.5$; reject $H_0$

**30. a.** 15
  **b.** 6.25 to 11.13

**32.** $F = 1.39$; do not reject $H_0$

**34.** $F = 2.08$; reject $H_0$

# Chapter 12

**2.** $\chi^2 = 15.33$, $\chi^2_{.05} = 7.81$; reject $H_0$

**4.** $\chi^2 = 29.51$, $\chi^2_{.05} = 11.07$; reject $H_0$
Percentage figures have changed

**6.** $\chi^2 = 10.69$, $\chi^2_{.10} = 9.24$; reject $H_0$

**8.** $\chi^2 = 16.31$, $\chi^2_{.01} = 11.34$; reject $H_0$

**10.** $\chi^2 = 19.78$, $\chi^2_{.05} = 9.49$; reject $H_0$

**12. a.** $\chi^2 = 7.36$, $\chi^2_{.05} = 5.99$; reject $H_0$
  **b.** Domestic, 47.2%

**14.** $\chi^2 = 13.43$, $\chi^2_{.05} = 11.07$; reject $H_0$

**16. a.** $\chi^2 = 7.85$, $\chi^2_{.05} = 7.81$; reject $H_0$
  **b.** Pharmaceutical, 98.6%

**18.** $\chi^2 = 13.42$, $\chi^2_{.01} = 13.28$; reject $H_0$

**20.** $\chi^2 = 9.03$, $\chi^2_{.05} = 7.81$; reject $H_0$

**22.** $\chi^2 = 4.30$, $\chi^2_{.05} = 5.99$; do not reject $H_0$

**24.** $\chi^2 = 2.8$, $\chi^2_{.10} = 6.25$; do not reject $H_0$

**26.** $\chi^2 = 8.04$, $\chi^2_{.05} = 7.81$; reject $H_0$

**28.** $\chi^2 = 31.43$, $\chi^2_{.05} = 7.81$; reject $H_0$

**30.** $\chi^2 = 42.53$, $\chi^2_{.05} = 9.49$; reject $H_0$

**32.** $\chi^2 = 23.37$, $\chi^2_{.05} = 7.81$; reject $H_0$

**34. a.** $\chi^2 = 12.86$, $\chi^2_{.01} = 9.21$; reject $H_0$
 **b.** 66.9, 30.3, 2.9 for men
  54.0, 42.0, 4.0 for women

**36.** $\chi^2 = 6.20$, $\chi^2_{.05} = 12.59$; do not reject $H_0$

**38.** $\chi^2 = 7.78$, $\chi^2_{.05} = 7.81$; do not reject $H_0$

## Chapter 13

**2. a.** MSTR $= 268$
 **b.** MSE $= 92$
 **c.** Cannot reject $H_0$ because $F = 2.91 < F_{.05} = 4.26$
 **d.**

| Source of Variation | Sum of Squares | Degrees of Freedom | Mean Square | F |
|---|---|---|---|---|
| Treatments | 536 | 2 | 268 | 2.91 |
| Error | 828 | 9 | 92 | |
| Total | 1364 | 11 | | |

**4. b.** Reject $H_0$ because $F = 80 > F_{.05} = 2.76$

**6.** Reject $H_0$ because $F = 10.63 > F_{.05} = 4.26$

**8.** Significant difference;
 $F = 7.00 > F_{.05} = 3.68$

**10.** No significant difference;
 $p$-value $= .4034$

**12. a.** Significant; $F = 7.87 > F_{.05} = 4.26$
 **b.** 1 and 2; 2 and 3 (LSD $= 15.34$)

**14.** $-8.54$ to $-1.46$

**16. a.** Significant difference; $F = 19.86 > F_{.05} = 3.10$
 **b.** Significant difference; $2.3 > $ LSD $= 1.19$

**18.** 1 and 2: significant difference (LSD $= 3.52$)
 1 and 3: significant difference (LSD $= 3.17$)
 2 and 3: no significant difference (LSD $= 3.65$)

**20. a.**

| Source of Variation | Sum of Squares | Degrees of Freedom | Mean Square | F |
|---|---|---|---|---|
| Treatments | 1488 | 2 | 744 | 5.50 |
| Error | 2030 | 15 | 135.3 | |
| Total | 3518 | 17 | | |

 **b.** Significant difference between A and C

**22. a.** $H_0: \mu_1 = \mu_2 = \mu_3 = \mu_4 = \mu_5$
  $H_a$: Not all the population means are equal
 **b.** Reject $H_0$ because $F = 14.07 > 2.69$

**24.** Significant difference; $F = 43.99 > F_{.05} = 3.21$

**26. b.** Significant difference; $F = 9.87 > F_{.05} = 3.35$

**28.** Not significant; $F = 1.78 < F_{.05} = 3.89$

**30.** Not significant; $F = 2.54 < F_{.05} = 3.24$

**32.** Means are all different (LSD $= 2.53$)

**34.** Significant; $F = 6.60 > F_{.05} = 4.46$

**36.** Significant; $F = 12.60 > F_{.05} = 3.07$

**38.** Significant; $F = 7.12 > F_{.05} = 3.26$

**40.** Significant difference
 $F = 22.42 > F_{.05} = 2.96$

**42.** Factor A is significant because $F = 3.72 > F_{.05} = 3.01$
 Factor B is significant because $F = 4.94 > F_{.05} = 3.40$
 Interaction is significant because $F = 12.52 > F_{.05} = 2.51$

**44.** No significant effect due to the loading and unloading method, the type of ride, or interaction

**46.** Factor A is not significant
 Factor B is significant
 Interaction is significant

**48.** Significant difference;
 $p$-value $= .000 < \alpha = .05$

**50.** Significant difference

**52.** Significant difference

**54.** Significant; $F = 7.23 > F_{.05} = 4.26$

**56.** Not significant; $F = 1.48 < F_{.05} = 3.35$

**58.** Significant; $F = 5.19 > F_{.05} = 4.26$

**60.** Significant; $F = 6.99 > F_{.05} = 4.46$

**62.** Significant difference; $p$-value $= .000 < \alpha = .05$

**64.** Type of machine is significant; type of loading system and interaction are not significant

## Chapter 14

**2. b.** There appears to be a linear relationship between $x$ and $y$
 **d.** $\hat{y} = 30.33 - 1.88x$
 **e.** 19.05

**4. b.** There appears to be a linear relationship between $x$ and $y$
 **d.** $\hat{y} = -240.5 + 5.5x$
 **e.** 106 pounds

**6. c.** $\hat{y} = 6.02 - .07x$
 **e.** .42

**8. a.** $\hat{y} = 107.13 + 3.07x$
 **c.** 153.2

**10. b.** $\hat{y} = 51.82 + .145x$
 **c.** 84.4

**12. c.** $\hat{y} = 1293 + .3165x$
 **d.** 25,031

**14. b.** $\hat{y} = 49.63 + 2.455x$
 **c.** 69.3%

**16. a.** SSE $= 6.33$, SST $= 114.80$, SSR $= 108.47$
 **b.** $r^2 = .945$
 **c.** $r = -.9721$

**18. a.** SSE = 85,135.14, SST = 335,000,
SSR = 249,864.86
**b.** $r^2 = .746$
**c.** $r = +.8637$

**20. a.** $\hat{y} = -48.11 + 2.3325x$
**b.** $r^2 = .82$
**c.** \$173,500

**22. a.** $\hat{y} = -1.0183 + .1258x$
**b.** $r^2 = .3631$
**c.** $r = +.6026$

**24. a.** 2.11
**b.** 1.453
**c.** .262
**d.** Significant
$t = -7.18 < -t_{.025} = -3.182$
**e.** Significant
$F = 51.41 > F_{.05} = 10.13$

**26. a.** Significant
$t = 3.43 > t_{.025} = 2.776$
**b.** Significant
$F = 11.74 > F_{.05} = 7.71$

**28.** They are related because $F = 20.17 > F_{.05} = 4.67$

**30.** No significant relationship

**32. a.** $\hat{y} = 6.1092 + .8951x$
**b.** Significant relationship
**c.** $r^2 = .82$; a good fit

**34. a.** $\hat{y} = 80.0 + 50.0x$
**b.** 30
**c.** $F = 83.17 > F_{.05} = 4.20$; reject $H_0: \beta_1 = 0$
**d.** \$680,000

**36. a.** $\hat{y} = -42.7965 + 1.0043x$
**b.** Significant
**c.** 0.4288; not a good fit

**38. b.** There appears to be a linear relationship between the two variables
**c.** $\hat{y} = 37.0747 - 0.7792x$
**d.** Significant relationship
**e.** 0.43; not a good fit

**40. a.** 1.453
**b.** 22.53 to 26.85
**c.** 1.61
**d.** 19.57 to 29.81

**42. a.** \$3343.53 to \$3724.07
**b.** \$3086.34 to \$3981.26

**44. a.** \$11,740 to \$14,420
**b.** \$9,300 to \$16,860
**c.** Yes, \$20,400 is much larger than anticipated
**d.** Any deductions exceeding \$16,800

**46. a.** $\hat{y} = 67.0476 + 5.8167x$
**b.** $r^2 = .894$; very good fit.
**c.** 250.59 to 290.67
**d.** 215.39 to 325.87

**48. a.** $\hat{y} = 2.322 + .6366x$
**b.** Assumption that variance is the same for all values of $x$ is questionable. The variance appears to increase for larger values of $x$.

**50. b.** The assumptions concerning the error terms appear reasonable.

**52. a.** The scatter diagram indicates that $x = 135$, $y = 145$ may be an outlier.
**b.** The standard residual for $x = 135$, $y = 145$ is 2.13; thus, it is an outlier.

**54. a.** $\hat{y} = 4.0890 + .1995x$
**b.** We would treat observation 1 as an outlier

**56. a.** $\hat{y} = 707.0299 + .0048x$

**60. a.** $\hat{y} = 9.2649 + .7105x$
**b.** Significant relationship
**c.** $r^2 = .744$; good fit
**d.** \$13.53

**62. a.** Market beta = .9498
**b.** Significant relationship
**c.** $r^2 = .470$; not a good fit
**d.** Woolworth has a higher risk

**64. a.** $\hat{y} = 10.5280 + .9534x$
**b.** Significant relationship; $p$-value = .0001
**c.** \$2874 to \$4952
**d.** Yes

**66. a.** Negative linear relationship
**b.** $\hat{y} = 8.0978 - .3442x$
**c.** Significant relationship; $p$-value = .0022
**d.** $r^2 = .711$; reasonably good fit
**e.** 5.2 to 7.6 days

**68. a.** $\hat{y} = 5.8470 + .8295x$
**b.** Significant relationship; $p$-value = .000
**c.** 84.65 points
**d.** 65.35 to 103.96

# Chapter 15

**2. a.** $\hat{y} = 45.0594 + 1.9436x_1$; $\hat{y} = 132.52$
**b.** $\hat{y} = 85.2171 + 4.3215x_2$; $\hat{y} = 150.04$
**c.** $\hat{y} = -18.3683 + 2.0102x_1 + 4.7378x_2$;
$\hat{y} = 143.16$

**4. a.** \$255,000

**6. a.** Speed = 49.78 + .0151 Weight
**b.** Speed = 80.4873 - .0031 Weight + .1047 Horsepower

**8. a.** Return = 247.3579 - 32.8445 Safety +
34.5887 ExpRatio
**b.** 70.2

**10. a.** Revenue = 33.3352 + 7.9840 Cars
**b.** Increase of 1000 cars will increase revenue by \$7.984 million
**c.** Revenue = 105.9727 + 8.9427 Cars - .1914 Locations

**12. a.** .926
**b.** .905
**c.** Yes

**14. a.** .75
**b.** .68

**16. a.** No, $R^2 = .3112$
**b.** Multiple regression analysis

**18. a.** $R^2 = .9416$, $R_a^2 = .9318$
**b.** The fit is good

**20. a.** Significant; $p$-value $= .0001$
**b.** Significant; $p$-value $= .000$
**c.** Significant; $p$-value $= .0016$

**22. a.** SSE $= 4000$, $s^2 = 571.43$,
MSR $= 6000$
**b.** Significant; $F = 10.50 > F_{.05} = 4.74$

**24. a.** Reject $H_0$: $\beta_1 = \beta_2 = 0$; $p$-value $= .000$
**b.** Weight: Cannot reject $H_0$: $\beta_1 = 0$; $p$-value $= .3861$
Horsepower: Reject $H_0$: $\beta_2 = 0$; $p$-value $= .000$

**26. a.** Significant; $p$-value $= .000$
**b.** Significant; $p$-value $= .000$
**c.** Not significant; $p$-value $= .0868$

**28. a.** 132.16 to 154.16
**b.** 111.13 to 175.18

**30. a.** 101.29
**b.** 99.490 to 103.089
**c.** 94.596 to 107.984

**32. a.** $x_2 = 0$ if level 1; $x_2 = 1$ if level 2
$E(y) = \beta_0 + \beta_1 x_1 + \beta_2 x_2$
**b.** $E(y) = \beta_0 + \beta_1 x_1$
**c.** $E(y) = \beta_0 + \beta_1 x_1 + \beta_2$
**d.** $\beta_2 = E(y \mid \text{level 2}) - E(y \mid \text{level 1})$

**34. a.** $15,300
**b.** $56,100
**c.** $41,600

**36. a.** $\hat{y} = 1.8602 + 0.2914$ Months $+ 1.1024$ Type $-$
0.6091 Person
**b.** Significant; $p$-value $= .0021 < \alpha = .05$
**c.** Person is not significant

**38. a.** $\hat{y} = -91.7595 + 1.0767$ Age $+ .2518$ Pressure $+$
8.7399 Smoker
**b.** Significant; $p$-value $= .0102 < \alpha = .05$
**c.** 95% prediction interval is 21.35 to 47.18 or a probability of .2135 to .4718; quit smoking and begin some type of treatment to reduce his blood pressure

**40. a.** $\hat{y} = -53.28 + 3.11x$
**b.** $-1.27, -.15, 1.39, .49, -.45$; no

**42. b.** Unusual trend
**c.** No outliers

**44. b.** 3.19

**46. b.** Significant; $p$-value $= .000$
**c.** Both are significant

**48. b.** Significant; $F = 22.79 > F_{.05} = 5.79$
**c.** $R_a^2 = .861$; good fit
**d.** Both are significant

**50. a.** Speed $= 97.5702 + .0693$ Price $- .0008$ Weight
$+ .0590$ Horsepwr $- 2.4836$ Zero60
**b.** Significant relationship
**c.** Price and Weight are not significant
**d.** Speed $= 103.1028 + .0558$ Horsepwr
$- 3.1876$ Zero60
**e.** Unusual trend
**f.** Observation 2 is an outlier

**52. a.** Resale% $= 38.7718 + .0008$ Price
**b.** Not a good fit; R Square $= .3671$
**c.** Resale% $= 42.5539 + 9.0903$ Type 1 $+ 7.9172$ Type 2
$+ .0003$ Price
where Type 1 $= 1$ if a full-size pickup and Type 2 $= 1$ if a sport utility vehicle
**d.** Significant relationship; $p$-value corresponding to $F =$
14.7892 $= .000 < \alpha = .05$

# Chapter 16

**2. a.** $\hat{y} = 9.3152 + .4242x$; $p$-value $= .1171$ indicates that the relationship between $x$ and $y$ is not significant
**b.** $\hat{y} = -8.1014 + 2.4127x - .0480x^2$
$R_a^2 = .9324$; a good fit
**c.** 20.953

**4. a.** $\hat{y} = 943.0476 + 8.7143x$
**b.** Significant; $p$-value $= .0049 < \alpha = .01$

**6. b.** No, the relationship appears to be curvilinear
**c.** Several possible models; e.g.,
$\hat{y} = 2.90 - .185x + .00351x^2$

**8. a.** It appears that a simple linear regression model is not appropriate
**b.** 2005% $= 17.0988 + 3.1462$ 1999% $- .0445$ 1999%Sq
**c.** Log 2000% $= 1.1742 + .4489$ Log1999%
**d.** Part (b); higher percentage of variability is explained

**10. a.** Significant; $F = 49.52 > 4.24$
**b.** Significant; $F = 48.3 > 3.42$

**12. a.** $\hat{y} = 170.1724 + 6.6130$ TeamInt
**b.** $\hat{y} = 280.3430 + 5.1762$ TeamInt $- .0037$ Rushing
$- 3.9182$ OpponInt
**c.** Addition of the two independent variables is not significant

**14. a.** $\hat{y} = -110.9423 + 1.3150$ Age $+ .2964$ Pressure
**b.** $\hat{y} = -123.1650 + 1.5130$ Age $+ .4483$ Pressure
$+ 8.8656$ Smoker $- .0028$ AgePress
**c.** Significant

**16. a.** %College $= -26.6126 + .0970$ SATScore
   **b.** %College $= 33.7086 - 1.5577$ Size $- .0024$ Spending
   $- .0003$ Salary $+ .0769$ SATScore
   $+ .2852$ %TakeSAT
   **c.** %College $= -26.9312 + .0838$ SATScore
   $+ .2045$ %TakeSAT

**18. a.** Greens
   **b.** ScoreAvg $= 58.1979 - .0100$ Distance $-$
   $.1519$ Greens $+ .8686$ Putts
   **c.** Yes
   **d.** 72.64

**20.** $\hat{y} = -91.7595 + 1.0767$ Age $+ .2518$ Pressure
   $+ 8.7399$ Smoker

**22.** $d = 1.60$; test is inconclusive

**24.**

| $x_1$ | $x_2$ | Treatment |
|-------|-------|-----------|
| 0 | 0 | 1 |
| 1 | 0 | 2 |
| 0 | 1 | 3 |

$x_3 = 0$ if block 1; $x_3 = 1$ if block 2
$E(y) = \beta_0 + \beta_1 x_1 + \beta_2 x_2 + \beta_3 x_3$

**26. a.**

| $D_1$ | $D_2$ | Manufacturer |
|-------|-------|--------------|
| 0 | 0 | 1 |
| 1 | 0 | 2 |
| 0 | 1 | 3 |

$E(y) = \beta_0 + \beta_1 D_1 + \beta_2 D_2$
   **b.** $\hat{y} = 23 + 5D_1 - 2D_2$
   **c.** $H_0: \beta_1 = \beta_2 = 0$
   **d.** Mean time is not the same for each manufacturer;
   $p$-value $= .0043$

**28.** Significant difference between the two analyzers

**30. a.** Let ExS denote the interaction between expense ratio
   and safety rating
   Perform% $= 23.3240 + 222.4310$ Expense%
   $- 28.8689$ ExS
   **b.** Adjusted R Square $= .653$
   **c.** 26.7 or approximately 27%

**32. a.** Delay $= 63 + 11.0741$ Industry; no significant positive
   autocorrelation

**34.** Significant differences between comfort levels for the
   three types of browsers

## Chapter 17

**2.** $z = 3.27$; reject $H_0$
**4.** $z = 3.15$; reject $H_0$
**6.** $z = 2.32$; reject $H_0$
**8.** $z = 3.76$; reject $H_0$
**10.** $z = 1.27$; do not reject $H_0$
**12.** $z = 2.43$; reject $H_0$

**14.** $z = 2.29$; reject $H_0$
   Prices differ
**16.** $z = 2.62$; reject $H_0$
**18.** $T = 34$; reject $H_0$
**20.** $T = 36$; reject $H_0$
**22.** $z = 2.77$; reject $H_0$
   P/E ratios differ
**24.** $z = -.25$; do not reject $H_0$
**26.** $W = 10.22$; reject $H_0$
**28.** $W = 9.26$; reject $H_0$
**30.** $W = 8.03$; reject $H_0$
**32. a.** .68
   **b.** $z = 2.06$; reject $H_0$
**34.** $z = .72$; do not reject $H_0$
**36.** $r_s = -.709$; $z = -2.13$; reject $H_0$
**38.** $z = 3.17$; reject $H_0$
**40. a.** $z = -3.20$; reject $H_0$
   Houston is below national median
   **b.** $z = 2.21$; reject $H_0$
   Philadelphia is above national median
**42.** $z = -2.97$; reject $H_0$
**44.** $W = 12.61$; reject $H_0$
**46.** $r_s = .76$; $z = 2.84$; reject $H_0$

## Chapter 18

**2. a.** 30,000
   **b.** 320
   **c.** 29,360 to 30,640
**4.** 73
**6.** 337
**8. a.** stratum 1: 27,600
   stratum 2: 25,750
   stratum 3: 21,000
   **b.** 74,350
   **c.** 70,599.88 to 78,100.12
**10. a.** $n = 93, n_1 = 30, n_2 = 30, n_3 = 33$
   **b.** $n = 306, n_1 = 98, n_2 = 98$
   $n_3 = 109$
   **c.** $n = 275, n_1 = 88, n_2 = 88, n_3 = 98$
**12. a.** $3,617,000
   **b.** $1,122,265
   **c.** $41,066 to $56,499
   **d.** $9,568,261 to $13,164,197
**14. a.** 15, 4500, .30
   **b.** 1.4708, 441.24, .0484
   **c.** 12.0584 to 17.9416
   **d.** 3617.52 to 5382.48
   **e.** .2032 to .3968

**16. a.** 40
  **b.** .70
  **c.** 35.8634 to 44.1366
  **d.** .5234 to .8766

**18. a.** .1488 to .2312
  **b.** .2615 to .3585
  **c.** .1306 to .2094

**20. a.** $22,790 to $23,610
  **b.** $68,370,366 to $70,829,634
  **c.** .6692 to .7908

**22. a.** 431
  **b.** .2175 to .3983
  **c.** .6230 to .8002
  **d.** 996

**24. a.** 75.275
  **b.** .198 to .502
  **c.** 1680

# Chapter 19

**2. a.** 5.42
  **b.** UCL = 6.09, LCL = 4.75

**4.**

|  | R Chart | $\bar{x}$ Chart |
|---|---|---|
| UCL | 2.98 | 29.10 |
| LCL | .22 | 27.90 |

**6.** 20.01, .082

**8. a.** .0470
  **b.** UCL = .0989, LCL = −.0049 (use LCL = 0)
  **c.** $\bar{p}$ = .08; in control
  **d.** UCL = 14.826, LCL = −0.726 (use LCL = 0)
     Process is out of control if more than 14 defective
  **e.** In control with 12 defective
  **f.** *np* chart

**10.** $p$ = .02; $f(0)$ = .6035
    $p$ = .06; $f(0)$ = .2129

**12.** $p_0$ = .02; producer's risk = .0599
    $p_0$ = .06; producer's risk = .3396
    Producer's risk decreases as the acceptance number $c$ is increased

**14.** $n$ = 20, $c$ = 3

**16. a.** 95.4
  **b.** UCL = 96.07, LCL = 94.73
  **c.** No

**18.**

|  | R Chart | $\bar{x}$ Chart |
|---|---|---|
| UCL | 4.23 | 6.57 |
| LCL | 0 | 4.27 |

Estimate of standard deviation = .86

**20.**

|  | R Chart | $\bar{x}$ Chart |
|---|---|---|
| UCL | .1121 | 3.112 |
| LCL | 0 | 3.051 |

**22. a.** UCL = .0817, LCL = −.0017 (use LCL = 0)

**24. a.** .03
  **b.** $\beta$ = .0802

**26. a.** Producer's risk = .0064
  **b.** Consumer's risk = .0136
  **c.** *Advantage:* excellent control
     *Disadvantage:* cost

## Chapter 1

**2. a.** 9
**b.** 4
**c.** Country and room rate are qualitative variables; number of rooms and the overall score are quantitative variables
**d.** Country is nominal; room rate is ordinal; number of rooms and overall score are ratio

**3. a.** Average number of rooms = 808/9 = 89.78 or approximately 90 rooms
**b.** 2 of 9 are located in England; approximately 22%
**c.** 4 of 9 have a room rate of $$; approximately 44%

**4. a.** 10
**b.** *Fortune* 500 largest U.S. industrial corporations
**c.** Average revenue = $142,275.9/10 = $14,227.59 million
**d.** Using the sample average, statistical inference would let us estimate the average revenue for the population of 500 corporations as $14,227.59 million

**13. a.** Quantitative
**b.** Time series with 7 observations
**c.** Number of riverboat casinos
**d.** Time series shows a rapid increase; an increase would be expected in 1998, but it appears that the rate of increase is slowing

## Chapter 2

**3. a.** 360° × 58/120 = 174°
**b.** 360° × 42/120 = 126°
**c.**

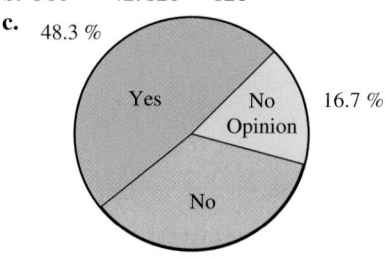

**d.**

**7.**

| Rating | Frequency | Relative Frequency |
|---|---|---|
| Outstanding | 19 | .38 |
| Very good | 13 | .26 |
| Good | 10 | .20 |
| Average | 6 | .12 |
| Poor | 2 | .04 |

Management should be pleased with these results: 64% of the ratings are very good to outstanding, and 84% of the ratings are good or better; comparing these ratings to previous results will show whether the restaurant is making improvements in its customers' ratings of food quality

**12.**

| Class | Cumulative Frequency | Cumulative Relative Frequency |
|---|---|---|
| ≤19 | 10 | .20 |
| ≤29 | 24 | .48 |
| ≤39 | 41 | .82 |
| ≤49 | 48 | .96 |
| ≤59 | 50 | 1.00 |

**15. a/b.**

| Waiting Time | Frequency | Relative Frequency |
|---|---|---|
| 0–4 | 4 | .20 |
| 5–9 | 8 | .40 |
| 10–14 | 5 | .25 |
| 15–19 | 2 | .10 |
| 20–24 | 1 | .05 |
| Totals | 20 | 1.00 |

**c/d.**

| Waiting Time | Cumulative Frequency | Cumulative Relative Frequency |
|---|---|---|
| ≤4 | 4 | .20 |
| ≤9 | 12 | .60 |
| ≤14 | 17 | .85 |
| ≤19 | 19 | .95 |
| ≤24 | 20 | 1.00 |

**e.** 12/20 = .60

**23.** Leaf unit = .1

| | |
|---|---|
| 6 | 3 |
| 7 | 5  5  7 |
| 8 | 1  3  4  8 |
| 9 | 3  6 |
| 10 | 0  4  5 |
| 11 | 3 |

**25.**

| | |
|---|---|
| 9 | 8  9 |
| 10 | 2  4  6  6 |
| 11 | 4  5  7  8  8  9 |
| 12 | 2  4  5  7 |
| 13 | 1  2 |
| 14 | 4 |
| 15 | 1 |

**29. a.**

| | | y | | |
|---|---|---|---|---|
| | | **1** | **2** | **Total** |
| | **A** | 5 | 0 | 5 |
| *x* | **B** | 11 | 2 | 13 |
| | **C** | 2 | 10 | 12 |
| | **Total** | 18 | 12 | 30 |

**b.**

| | | y | | |
|---|---|---|---|---|
| | | **1** | **2** | **Total** |
| | **A** | 100.0 | 0.0 | 100.0 |
| *x* | **B** | 84.6 | 15.4 | 100.0 |
| | **C** | 16.7 | 83.3 | 100.0 |

**c.**

| | | y | |
|---|---|---|---|
| | | **1** | **2** |
| | **A** | 27.8 | 0.0 |
| *x* | **B** | 61.1 | 16.7 |
| | **C** | 11.1 | 83.3 |
| | **Total** | 100.0 | 100.0 |

**d.** *A* values are always in $y = 1$
    *B* values are most often in $y = 1$
    *C* values are most often in $y = 2$

**30. a.**

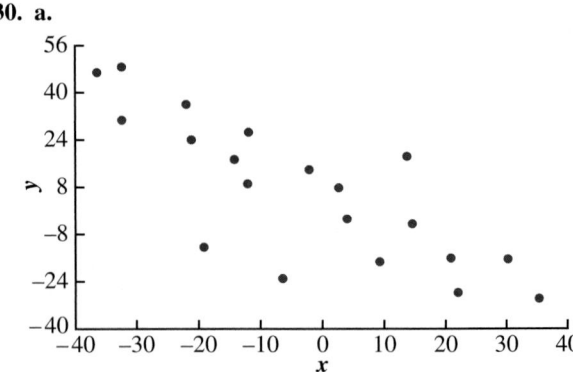

**b.** There is a negative relationship between *x* and *y*; *y* decreases as *x* increases.

## Chapter 3

**3.** Arrange data in order: 15, 20, 25, 25, 27, 28, 30, 34

$i = \dfrac{20}{100}(8) = 1.6$; round up to position 2

20th percentile = 20

$i = \dfrac{25}{100}(8) = 2$; use positions 2 and 3

25th percentile $= \dfrac{20 + 25}{2} = 22.5$

$i = \dfrac{65}{100}(8) = 5.2$; round up to position 6

65th percentile = 28

$i = \dfrac{75}{100}(8) = 6$; use positions 6 and 7

75th percentile $= \dfrac{28 + 30}{2} = 29$

**8. a.** $\bar{x} = \dfrac{\Sigma x_i}{n} = \dfrac{775}{20} = 38.75$

Mode = 29 (appears three times)

**b.** Data in order: 22, 24, 29, 29, 29, 30, 31, 31, 32, 37, 40, 41, 44, 44, 46, 49, 50, 52, 57, 58

Median (10th and 11th positions)

$\dfrac{37 + 40}{2} = 38.5$

At home workers are slightly younger

**c.** $i = \dfrac{25}{100}(20) = 5$; use positions 5 and 6

$$Q_1 = \frac{29 + 30}{2} = 29.5$$

$i = \dfrac{75}{100}(20) = 15$; use positions 15 and 16

$$Q_3 = \frac{46 + 49}{2} = 47.5$$

**d.** $i = \dfrac{32}{100}(20) = 6.4$; round up to position 7

32nd percentile = 31
At least 32% of the people are 31 or younger

**15.** Range = $34 - 15 = 19$
Arrange data in order: 15, 20, 25, 25, 27, 28, 30, 34

$i = \dfrac{25}{100}(8) = 2;\ Q_1 = \dfrac{20 + 25}{2} = 22.5$

$i = \dfrac{75}{100}(8) = 6;\ Q_3 = \dfrac{28 + 30}{2} = 29$

IQR $= Q_3 - Q_1 = 29 - 22.5 = 6.5$

$\bar{x} = \dfrac{\sum x_i}{n} = \dfrac{204}{8} = 25.5$

| $x_i$ | $(x_i - \bar{x})$ | $(x_i - \bar{x})^2$ |
|-------|-------------------|---------------------|
| 27 | 1.5 | 2.25 |
| 25 | −.5 | .25 |
| 20 | −5.5 | 30.25 |
| 15 | −10.5 | 110.25 |
| 30 | 4.5 | 20.25 |
| 34 | 8.5 | 72.25 |
| 28 | 2.5 | 6.25 |
| 25 | −.5 | .25 |
| | | 242.00 |

$$s^2 = \frac{\sum(x_i - \bar{x})^2}{n - 1} = \frac{242}{8 - 1} = 34.57$$

$$s = \sqrt{34.57} = 5.88$$

**16. a.** Range = $190 - 168 = 22$

**b.** $\bar{x} = \dfrac{\sum x_i}{n} = \dfrac{1068}{6} = 178$

$s^2 = \dfrac{\sum(x_i - \bar{x})^2}{n - 1}$

$= \dfrac{4^2 + (-10)^2 + 6^2 + 12^2 + (-8)^2 + (-4)^2}{6 - 1}$

$= \dfrac{376}{5} = 75.2$

**c.** $s = \sqrt{75.2} = 8.67$

**d.** $\dfrac{s}{\bar{x}}(100) = \dfrac{8.67}{178}(100) = 4.87$

**27.** Chebyshev's theorem: *at least* $(1 - 1/z^2)$

**a.** $z = \dfrac{40 - 30}{5} = 2;\ 1 - \dfrac{1}{(2)^2} = .75$

**b.** $z = \dfrac{45 - 30}{5} = 3;\ 1 - \dfrac{1}{(3)^2} = .89$

**c.** $z = \dfrac{38 - 30}{5} = 1.6;\ 1 - \dfrac{1}{(1.6)^2} = .61$

**d.** $z = \dfrac{42 - 30}{5} = 2.4;\ 1 - \dfrac{1}{(2.4)^2} = .83$

**e.** $z = \dfrac{48 - 30}{5} = 3.6;\ 1 - \dfrac{1}{(3.6)^2} = .92$

**38.** Arrange data in order: 5, 6, 8, 10, 10, 12, 15, 16, 18

$i = \dfrac{25}{100}(9) = 2.25$; round up to position 3

$Q_1 = 8$

Median (5th position) = 10

$i = \dfrac{75}{100}(9) = 6.75$; round up to position 7

$Q_3 = 15$

5-number summary: 5, 8, 10, 15, 18

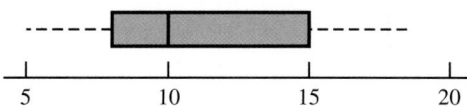

**41. a.** Arrange data in order low to high

$i = \dfrac{25}{100}(21) = 5.25$; round up to 6th position

$Q_1 = 1872$

Median (11th position) = 4019

$i = \dfrac{75}{100}(21) = 15.75$; round up to 16th position

$Q_3 = 8305$

5-number summary: 608, 1872, 4019, 8305, 14,138

**b.** IQR $= Q_3 - Q_1 = 8305 - 1872 = 6433$
Lower limit: $1872 - 1.5(6433) = -7777$
Upper limit: $8305 + 1.5(6433) = 17,955$

**c.** No; data are within limits

**d.** 41,138 would be an outlier; data value should be reviewed and corrected

**e.**

| | | | | | |
|---|---|---|---|---|---|
| 0 | 3,000 | 6,000 | 9,000 | 12,000 | 15,000 |

**45. b.** There appears to be a negative linear relationship between $x$ and $y$

**c.**

| $x_i$ | $y_i$ | $x_i - \bar{x}$ | $y_i - \bar{y}$ | $(x_i - \bar{x})(y_i - \bar{y})$ |
|---|---|---|---|---|
| 4 | 50 | −4 | 4 | −16 |
| 6 | 50 | −2 | 4 | −8 |
| 11 | 40 | 3 | −6 | −18 |
| 3 | 60 | −5 | 14 | −70 |
| 16 | 30 | 8 | −16 | −128 |
| 40 | 230 | 0 | 0 | −240 |

$\bar{x} = 8; \bar{y} = 46$

$$s_{xy} = \frac{\Sigma(x_i - \bar{x})(y_i - \bar{y})}{n - 1} = \frac{-240}{4} = -60$$

The sample covariance indicates a negative linear association between $x$ and $y$

**d.** $r_{xy} = \dfrac{s_{xy}}{s_x s_y} = \dfrac{-60}{(5.43)(11.40)} = -.969$

The sample correlation coefficient of $-.969$ is indicative of a strong negative linear relationship

**53. a.**

| $f_i$ | $M_i$ | $f_i M_i$ |
|---|---|---|
| 4 | 5 | 20 |
| 7 | 10 | 70 |
| 9 | 15 | 135 |
| 5 | 20 | 100 |
| 25 | | 325 |

$$\bar{x} = \frac{\Sigma f_i M_i}{n} = \frac{325}{25} = 13$$

**b.**

| $f_i$ | $M_i$ | $(M_i - \bar{x})$ | $(M_i - \bar{x})^2$ | $f_i(M_i - \bar{x})^2$ |
|---|---|---|---|---|
| 4 | 5 | −8 | 64 | 256 |
| 7 | 10 | −3 | 9 | 63 |
| 9 | 15 | 2 | 4 | 36 |
| 5 | 20 | 7 | 49 | 245 |
| 25 | | | | 600 |

$$s^2 = \frac{\Sigma f_i (M_i - \bar{x})^2}{n - 1} = \frac{600}{25 - 1} = 25$$

$$s = \sqrt{25} = 5$$

**54. a.**

| Grade $x_i$ | Weight $w_i$ |
|---|---|
| 4 (A) | 9 |
| 3 (B) | 15 |
| 2 (C) | 33 |
| 1 (D) | 3 |
| 0 (F) | 0 |
| | 60 credit hours |

$$\bar{x} = \frac{\Sigma w_i x_i}{\Sigma w_i} = \frac{9(4) + 15(3) + 33(2) + 3(1)}{9 + 15 + 33 + 3}$$

$$= \frac{150}{60} = 2.5$$

**b.** Yes

## Chapter 4

**2.** $\dbinom{6}{3} = \dfrac{6!}{3!3!} = \dfrac{6 \cdot 5 \cdot 4 \cdot 3 \cdot 2 \cdot 1}{(3 \cdot 2 \cdot 1)(3 \cdot 2 \cdot 1)} = 20$

| | | | |
|---|---|---|---|
| ABC | ACE | BCD | BEF |
| ABD | ACF | BCE | CDE |
| ABE | ADE | BCF | CDF |
| ABF | ADF | BDE | CEF |
| ACD | AEF | BDF | DEF |

**6.** $P(E_1) = .40, P(E_2) = .26, P(E_3) = .34$

The relative frequency method was used

**9.** $\dbinom{50}{4} = \dfrac{50!}{4!46!} = \dfrac{50 \cdot 49 \cdot 48 \cdot 47}{4 \cdot 3 \cdot 2 \cdot 1} = 230,300$

**10. a.** Use the relative frequency approach:

$P(\text{California}) = 1,434/2,374 = .60$

**b.** Number not from 4 states

$= 2,374 - 1,434 - 390 - 217 - 112$

$= 221$

$P(\text{Not from 4 States}) = 221/2,374 = .09$

**c.** $P(\text{Not in Early Stages}) = 1 - .22 = .78$

**d.** Estimate of number of Massachusetts' companies in early stage of development $= (.22)390 \approx 86$

**e.** If we assume the size of the awards did not differ by states, we can multiply the probability an award went to Colorado by the total venture funds disbursed to get an estimate

Estimate of Colorado funds $= (112/2374)(\$32.4)$

$= \$1.53$ billion

Authors' Note: The actual amount going to Colorado was $1.74 billion

**15. a.** $S = \{$ace of clubs, ace of diamonds, ace of hearts, ace of spades$\}$

**b.** $S = \{2$ of clubs, 3 of clubs, . . . , 10 of clubs, J of clubs, Q of clubs, K of clubs, A of clubs$\}$

**c.** There are 12; jack, queen, or king in each of the four suits

**d.** *For* (a): 4/52 = 1/13 = .08

*For* (b): 13/52 = 1/4 = .25

*For* (c): 12/52 = .23

**17. a.** (4, 6), (4, 7), (4, 8)
  **b.** .05 + .10 + .15 = .30
  **c.** (2, 8), (3, 8), (4, 8)
  **d.** .05 + .05 + .15 = .25
  **e.** .15

**23. a.** $P(A) = P(E_1) + P(E_4) + P(E_6)$
  $= .05 + .25 + .10 = .40$
  $P(B) = P(E_2) + P(E_4) + P(E_7)$
  $= .20 + .25 + .05 = .50$
  $P(C) = P(E_2) + P(E_3) + P(E_5) + P(E_7)$
  $= .20 + .20 + .15 + .05 = .60$
  **b.** $A \cup B = \{E_1, E_2, E_4, E_6, E_7\}$
  $P(A \cup B) = P(E_1) + P(E_2) + P(E_4) + P(E_6) + P(E_7)$
  $= .05 + .20 + .25 + .10 + .05$
  $= .65$
  **c.** $A \cap B = \{E_4\}, P(A \cap B) = P(E_4) = .25$
  **d.** Yes, they are mutually exclusive
  **e.** $B^c = \{E_1, E_3, E_5, E_6\}$
  $P(B^c) = P(E_1) + P(E_3) + P(E_5) + P(E_6)$
  $= .05 + .20 + .15 + .10$
  $= .50$

**28.** Let $B$ = rented a car for business reasons
  $P$ = rented a car for personal reasons
  **a.** $P(B \cup P) = P(B) + P(P) - P(B \cap P)$
  $= .540 + .458 - .300$
  $= .698$
  **b.** $P(\text{Neither}) = 1 - .698 = .302$

**30. a.** $P(A \mid B) = \dfrac{P(A \cap B)}{P(B)} = \dfrac{.40}{.60} = .6667$

  **b.** $P(B \mid A) = \dfrac{P(A \cap B)}{P(A)} = \dfrac{.40}{.50} = .80$

  **c.** No, because $P(A \mid B) \neq P(A)$

**33. a.**

**Reason for Applying**

| | Quality | Cost/Convenience | Other | Total |
|---|---|---|---|---|
| **Full-time** | .218 | .204 | .039 | .461 |
| **Part-time** | .208 | .307 | .024 | .539 |
| **Total** | .426 | .511 | .063 | 1.000 |

  **b.** A student is most likely to cite cost or convenience as the first reason (probability = .511); school quality is the first reason cited by the second largest number of students (probability = .426)
  **c.** $P(\text{quality} \mid \text{full-time}) = .218/.461 = .473$
  **d.** $P(\text{quality} \mid \text{part-time}) = .208/.539 = .386$
  **e.** For independence, we must have $P(A)P(B) = P(A \cap B)$; from the table
  $P(A \cap B) = .218, P(A) = .461, P(B) = .426$

$P(A)P(B) = (.461)(.426) = .196$
Because $P(A)P(B) \neq P(A \cap B)$, the events are not independent

**39. a.** Yes, because $P(A_1 \cap A_2) = 0$
  **b.** $P(A_1 \cap B) = P(A_1)P(B \mid A_1) = .40(.20) = .08$
  $P(A_2 \cap B) = P(A_2)P(B \mid A_2) = .60(.05) = .03$
  **c.** $P(B) = P(A_1 \cap B) + P(A_2 \cap B) = .08 + .03 = .11$
  **d.** $P(A_1 \mid B) = \dfrac{.08}{.11} = .7273$

  $P(A_2 \mid B) = \dfrac{.03}{.11} = .2727$

**42.** $M$ = missed payment
  $D_1$ = customer defaults
  $D_2$ = customer does not default
  $P(D_1) = .05, P(D_2) = .95, P(M \mid D_2) = .2, P(M \mid D_1) = 1$
  **a.** $P(D_1 \mid M) = \dfrac{P(D_1)P(M \mid D_1)}{P(D_1)P(M \mid D_1) + P(D_2)P(M \mid D_2)}$
  $= \dfrac{(.05)(1)}{(.05)(1) + (.95)(.2)}$
  $= \dfrac{.05}{.24} = .21$

  **b.** Yes, the probability of default is greater than .20

# Chapter 5

**1. a.** Head, Head $(H, H)$
  Head, Tail $(H, T)$
  Tail, Head $(T, H)$
  Tail, Tail $(T, T)$
  **b.** $x$ = number of heads on two coin tosses
  **c.**

| Outcome | Values of $x$ |
|---|---|
| $(H, H)$ | 2 |
| $(H, T)$ | 1 |
| $(T, H)$ | 1 |
| $(T, T)$ | 0 |

  **d.** Discrete; it may assume 3 values: 0, 1, and 2

**3.** Let: $Y$ = position is offered
  $N$ = position is not offered
  **a.** $S = \{(Y, Y, Y), (Y, Y, N), (Y, N, Y), (Y, N, N), (N, Y, Y),$
  $(N, Y, N), (N, N, Y), (N, N, N)\}$
  **b.** Let $N$ = number of offers made; $N$ is a discrete random variable
  **c.**

| Experimental Outcome | $(Y, Y, Y)$ | $(Y, Y, N)$ | $(Y, N, Y)$ | $(Y, N, N)$ | $(N, Y, Y)$ | $(N, Y, N)$ | $(N, N, Y)$ | $(N, N, N)$ |
|---|---|---|---|---|---|---|---|---|
| Value of $N$ | 3 | 2 | 2 | 1 | 2 | 1 | 1 | 0 |

**7. a.** $f(x) \geq 0$ for all values of $x$
  $\Sigma f(x) = 1$; therefore, it is a proper probability distribution
  **b.** Probability $x = 30$ is $f(30) = .25$
  **c.** Probability $x \leq 25$ is $f(20) + f(25) = .20 + .15 = .35$
  **d.** Probability $x > 30$ is $f(35) = .40$

**8. a.**

| x | f(x) |
|---|------|
| 1 | 3/20 = .15 |
| 2 | 5/20 = .25 |
| 3 | 8/20 = .40 |
| 4 | 4/20 = .20 |
| Total | 1.00 |

**b.**

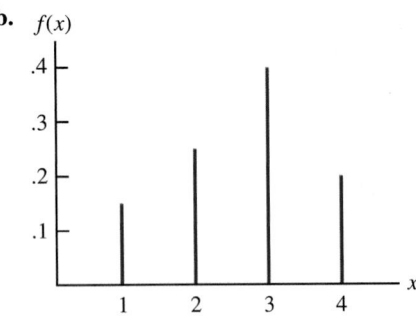

f(x)

**c.** $f(x) \geq 0$ for $x = 1, 2, 3, 4$
$\Sigma f(x) = 1$

**16. a.**

| y | f(y) | yf(y) |
|---|------|-------|
| 2 | .20 | .40 |
| 4 | .30 | 1.20 |
| 7 | .40 | 2.80 |
| 8 | .10 | .80 |
| Totals | 1.00 | 5.20 |

$$E(y) = \mu = 5.20$$

**b.**

| y | y − μ | (y − μ)² | f(y) | (y − μ)²f(y) |
|---|-------|----------|------|--------------|
| 2 | −3.20 | 10.24 | .20 | 2.048 |
| 4 | −1.20 | 1.44 | .30 | .432 |
| 7 | 1.80 | 3.24 | .40 | 1.296 |
| 8 | 2.80 | 7.84 | .10 | .784 |
| | | | Total | 4.560 |

$$\text{Var}(y) = 4.56$$
$$\sigma = \sqrt{4.56} = 2.14$$

**18. a/b.**

| x | f(x) | xf(x) | (x − μ) | (x − μ)² | (x − μ)²f(x) |
|---|------|-------|---------|----------|--------------|
| 0 | .01 | .00 | −2.3 | 5.29 | .0529 |
| 1 | .23 | .23 | −1.3 | 1.69 | .3887 |
| 2 | .41 | .82 | −0.3 | 0.09 | .0369 |
| 3 | .20 | .60 | 0.7 | 0.49 | .0980 |
| 4 | .10 | .40 | 1.7 | 2.89 | .2890 |
| 5 | .05 | .25 | 2.7 | 7.29 | .3645 |
| | E(x) = 2.30 | | | Var(x) = 1.2300 | |

$$\sigma = 1.11$$

The expected value, $E(x) = 2.3$, of the probability distribution is the same as the average reported in the *1997 Statistical Abstract of the United States*

$$\text{Var}(x) = 1.23 \text{ television sets squared}$$
$$\sigma = \sqrt{1.23} = 1.11 \text{ television sets}$$

**25. a.**

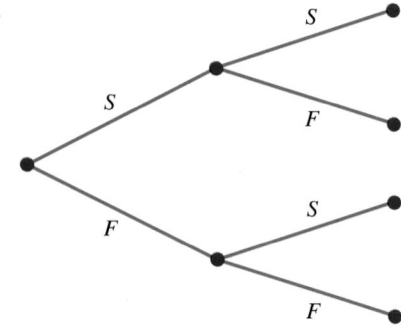

**b.** $f(1) = \binom{2}{1}(.4)^1(.6)^1 = \frac{2!}{1!1!}(.4)(.6) = .48$

**c.** $f(0) = \binom{2}{0}(.4)^0(.6)^2 = \frac{2!}{0!2!}(1)(.36) = .36$

**d.** $f(2) = \binom{2}{2}(.4)^2(.6)^0 = \frac{2!}{2!0!}(.16)(.1) = .16$

**e.** $P(x \geq 1) = f(1) + f(2) = .48 + .16 = .64$

**f.** $E(x) = np = 2(.4) = .8$
$\text{Var}(x) = np(1 - p) = 2(.4)(.6) = .48$
$\sigma = \sqrt{.48} = .6928$

**30. a.** Probability of a defective part being produced must be .03 for each trial; trials must be independent

**b.** Let $D$ = defective
$G$ = not defective

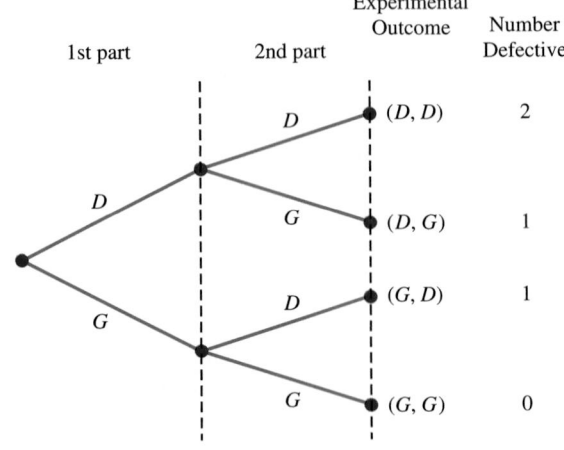

**c.** Two outcomes result in exactly one defect

**d.** $P(\text{no defects}) = (.97)(.97) = .9409$
$P(1 \text{ defect}) = 2(.03)(.97) = .0582$
$P(2 \text{ defects}) = (.03)(.03) = .0009$

**39. a.** $f(x) = \dfrac{2^x e^{-2}}{x!}$

**b.** $\mu = 6$ for 3 time periods

**c.** $f(x) = \dfrac{6^x e^{-6}}{x!}$

**d.** $f(2) = \dfrac{2^2 e^{-2}}{2!} = \dfrac{4(.1353)}{2} = .2706$

**e.** $f(6) = \dfrac{6^6 e^{-6}}{6!} = .1606$

**f.** $f(5) = \dfrac{4^5 e^{-4}}{5!} = .1563$

**40. a.**    $\mu = 48(5/60) = 4$

$f(3) = \dfrac{4^3 e^{-4}}{3!} = \dfrac{(64)(.0183)}{6} = .1952$

**b.**    $\mu = 48(15/60) = 12$

$f(10) = \dfrac{12^{10} e^{-12}}{10!} = .1048$

**c.**    $\mu = 48(5/60) = 4$; one can expect 4 callers to be
waiting after 5 minutes

$f(0) = \dfrac{4^0 e^{-4}}{0!} = .0183$; the probability none will
be waiting after 5 minutes
is .0183

**d.**    $\mu = 48(3/60) = 2.4$

$f(0) = \dfrac{2.4^0 e^{-2.4}}{0!} = .0907$; the probability of no
interruptions in 3 minutes
is .0907

**46. a.** $f(1) = \dfrac{\binom{3}{1}\binom{10-3}{4-1}}{\binom{10}{4}} = \dfrac{\left(\dfrac{3!}{1!2!}\right)\left(\dfrac{7!}{3!4!}\right)}{\dfrac{10!}{4!6!}}$

$= \dfrac{(3)(35)}{210} = .50$

**b.** $f(2) = \dfrac{\binom{3}{2}\binom{10-3}{2-2}}{\binom{10}{2}} = \dfrac{(3)(1)}{45} = .067$

**50.** $N = 60, n = 10$

**a.** $r = 20, x = 0$

$f(0) = \dfrac{\binom{20}{0}\binom{40}{10}}{\binom{60}{10}} = \dfrac{(1)\left(\dfrac{40!}{10!30!}\right)}{\dfrac{60!}{10!50!}}$

$= \left(\dfrac{40!}{10!30!}\right)\left(\dfrac{10!50!}{60!}\right)$

$= \dfrac{40 \cdot 39 \cdot 38 \cdot 37 \cdot 36 \cdot 35 \cdot 34 \cdot 33 \cdot 32 \cdot 31}{60 \cdot 59 \cdot 58 \cdot 57 \cdot 56 \cdot 55 \cdot 54 \cdot 53 \cdot 52 \cdot 51}$

$\approx .01$

**b.** $r = 20, x = 1$

$f(1) = \dfrac{\binom{20}{1}\binom{40}{9}}{\binom{60}{10}} = 20\left(\dfrac{40!}{9!31!}\right)\left(\dfrac{10!50!}{60!}\right)$

$\approx .07$

**c.** $1 - f(0) - f(1) = 1 - .08 = .92$

**d.** Same as the probability one will be from Hawaii; in
part (b) it was equal to approximately .07

## Chapter 6

**1. a.**

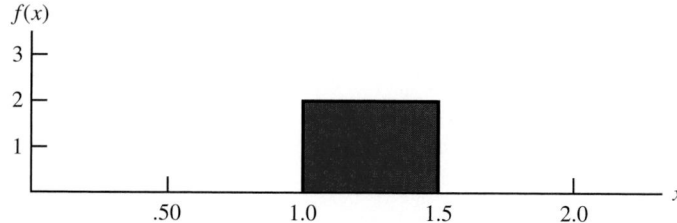

**b.** $P(x = 1.25) = 0$; the probability of any single point is
zero since the area under the curve above any single
point is zero

**c.** $P(1.0 \leq x \leq 1.25) = 2(.25) = .50$

**d.** $P(1.20 < x < 1.5) = 2(.30) = .60$

**4. a.**

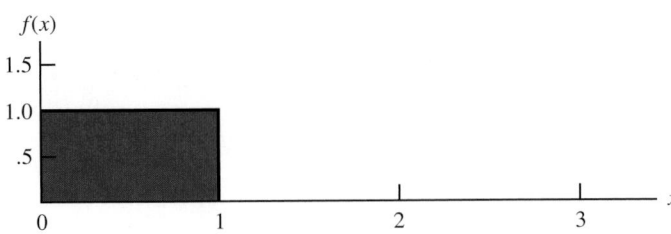

**b.** $P(.25 < x < .75) = 1(.50) = .50$
**c.** $P(x \le .30) = 1(.30) = .30$
**d.** $P(x > .60) = 1(.40) = .40$

**13. a.** $.6879 - .0239 = .6640$
**b.** $.8888 - .6985 = .1903$
**c.** $.9599 - .8508 = .1091$

**15. a.** Look in the table for an area of $1.000 - .2119 = .7881$; $z = .80$ cuts off an area of .2119 in the upper tail. Thus, for an area of .2119 in the lower tail, $z = -.80$
**b.** Look in the table for an area of .9515; $z = 1.66$
**c.** Look in the table for an area of .6026; $z = .26$
**d.** Look in the table for an area of .9948; $z = 2.56$
**e.** Look in the table for an area of .6915; because the value we are seeking is below the mean, the $z$ value must be negative; thus, $z = -.50$

**18. a.** Find $P(x \ge 60)$

At $x = 60$, $z = \dfrac{60 - 49}{16} = \dfrac{11}{16} = .69$

$P(x < 60) = .7549$
$P(x \ge 60) = 1 - P(x < 60) = 1 - .7549 = .2451$

**b.** Find $P(x \le 30)$

At $x = 30$, $z = \dfrac{30 - 49}{16} = -1.19$

$P(x \le 30) = 1.000 - .8830$
$= .1170$

**c.** Find $z$-score so that $P(z \ge z\text{-score}) = .10$
A $z$-score of 1.28 cuts off 10% in upper tail
Now, solve for corresponding value of $x$

$1.28 = \dfrac{x - 49}{16}$

$x = 49 + (16)(1.28)$
$= 69.48$

So, 10% of subscribers spend 69.48 minutes or more reading *The Wall Street Journal*

**27. a.** $P(x \le x_0) = 1 - e^{-x_0/3}$
**b.** $P(x \le 2) = 1 - e^{-2/3} = 1 - .5134 = .4866$
**c.** $P(x \ge 3) = 1 - P(x \le 3) = 1 - (1 - e^{-3/3})$
$= e^{-1} = .3679$
**d.** $P(x \le 5) = 1 - e^{-5/3} = 1 - .1889 = .8111$
**e.** $P(2 \le x \le 5) = P(x \le 5) - P(x \le 2)$
$= .8111 - .4866 = .3245$

**29. a.**

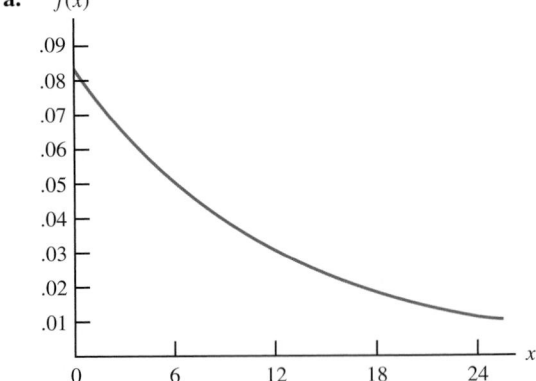

**b.** $P(x \le 12) = 1 - e^{-12/12} = 1 - .3679 = .6321$
**c.** $P(x \le 6) = 1 - e^{-6/12} = 1 - .6065 = .3935$
**d.** $P(x \ge 30) = 1 - P(x < 30)$
$= 1 - (1 - e^{-30/12})$
$= .0821$

# Chapter 7

**1. a.** AB, AC, AD, AE, BC, BD, BE, CD, CE, DE
**b.** With 10 samples, each has a $\frac{1}{10}$ probability
**c.** E and C because 8 and 0 do not apply; 5 identifies E; 7 does not apply; 5 is skipped because E is already in the sample; 3 identifies C; 2 is not needed because the sample of size 2 is complete

**3.** 459, 147, 385, 113, 340, 401, 215, 2, 33, 348

**11. a.** $\bar{x} = \dfrac{\Sigma x_i}{n} = \dfrac{54}{6} = 9$

**b.** $s = \sqrt{\dfrac{\Sigma(x_i - \bar{x})^2}{n - 1}}$

$\Sigma(x_i - \bar{x})^2 = (-4)^2 + (-1)^2 + 1^2 + (-2)^2 + 1^2 + 5^2$
$= 48$

$s = \sqrt{\dfrac{48}{6 - 1}} = 3.1$

**13. a.** $\bar{x} = \dfrac{\Sigma x_i}{n} = \dfrac{465}{5} = 93$

**b.**

| $x_i$ | $(x_i - \bar{x})$ | $(x_i - \bar{x})^2$ |
|---|---|---|
| 94 | +1 | 1 |
| 100 | +7 | 49 |
| 85 | −8 | 64 |
| 94 | +1 | 1 |
| 92 | −1 | 1 |
| Totals 465 | 0 | 116 |

$$s = \sqrt{\frac{\Sigma(x_i - \bar{x})^2}{n-1}} = \sqrt{\frac{116}{4}} = 5.39$$

**19. a.** The sampling distribution is normal with

$$E(\bar{x}) = \mu = 200$$

$$\sigma_{\bar{x}} = \frac{\sigma}{\sqrt{n}} = \frac{50}{\sqrt{100}} = 5$$

For +5, $(\bar{x} - \mu) = 5$,

$$z = \frac{\bar{x} - \mu}{\sigma_{\bar{x}}} = \frac{5}{5} = 1$$

$$P(0 \le z \le 1) = .3413$$

$$\text{Area} = .3413 \times 2 = .6826$$

**b.** For ±10, $(\bar{x} - \mu) = 10$,

$$z = \frac{\bar{x} - \mu}{\sigma_{\bar{x}}} = \frac{10}{5} = 2$$

$$P(0 \le z \le 2) = .4772$$

$$\text{Area} = .4772 \times 2 = .9544$$

**25. a.**

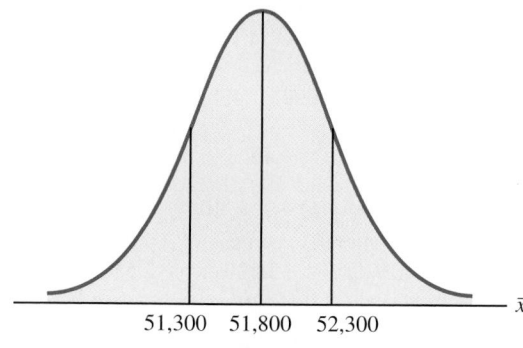

$$\sigma_{\bar{x}} = \frac{\sigma}{\sqrt{n}} = \frac{4000}{\sqrt{60}} = 516.40$$

$$z = \frac{52,300 - 51,800}{516.40} = +.97$$

$$\text{Area} = .3340 \times 2 = .6680$$

**b.** $\sigma_{\bar{x}} = \dfrac{\sigma}{\sqrt{n}} = \dfrac{4000}{\sqrt{120}} = 365.15$

$$z = \frac{52,300 - 51,800}{365.15} = +1.37$$

$$P(0 \le z \le 1.37) = .4147$$

$$\text{Area} = .4147 \times 2 = .8294$$

**34. a.** $E(\bar{p}) = .40$

$$\sigma_{\bar{p}} = \sqrt{\frac{p(1-p)}{n}} = \sqrt{\frac{(.40)(.60)}{200}} = .0346$$

$$z = \frac{\bar{p} - p}{\sigma_{\bar{p}}} = \frac{.03}{.0346} = .87$$

$$P(0 \le z \le .87) = .3078$$

$$\text{Area} = .3078 \times 2 = .6156$$

**b.** $z = \dfrac{\bar{p} - p}{\sigma_{\bar{p}}} = \dfrac{.05}{.0346} = 1.45$

$$P(0 \le z \le 1.45) = .4265$$

$$\text{Area} = .4265 \times 2 = .8530$$

**37. a.**

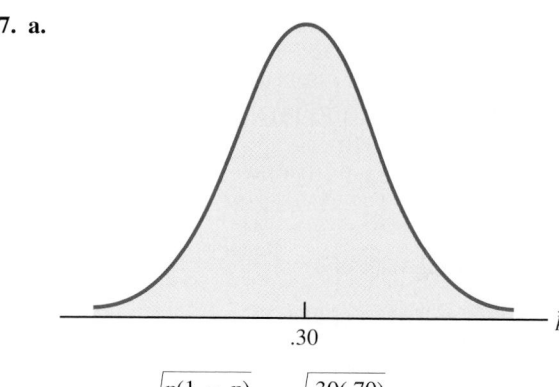

$$\sigma_{\bar{p}} = \sqrt{\frac{p(1-p)}{n}} = \sqrt{\frac{.30(.70)}{100}} = .0458$$

The normal distribution is appropriate because $np = 100(.30) = 30$ and $n(1-p) = 100(.70) = 70$ are both greater than 5

**b.** $P(.20 \le \bar{p} \le .40) = ?$

$$z = \frac{.40 - .30}{.0458} = 2.18$$

$$P(0 \le z \le 2.18) = .4854$$

$$\text{Area} = .4854 \times 2 = .9708$$

**c.** $P(.25 \le \bar{p} \le .35) = ?$

$$z = \frac{.35 - .30}{.0458} = 1.09$$

$$P(0 \le z \le 1.09) = .3621$$

$$\text{Area} = .3621 \times 2 = .7242$$

## Chapter 8

**2.** Use $\bar{x} \pm z_{\alpha/2}(\sigma/\sqrt{n})$ with the sample standard deviation $s$ used to estimate $\sigma$

**a.** $32 \pm 1.645 \, (6/\sqrt{50})$
$32 \pm 1.4$; (30.6 to 33.4)

**b.** $32 \pm 1.96(6/\sqrt{50})$
$32 \pm 1.66$; (30.34 to 33.66)

**c.** $32 \pm 2.58(6/\sqrt{50})$
$32 \pm 2.19$; (29.81 to 34.19)

**5. a.** $\sigma_{\bar{x}} = \sigma/\sqrt{n} = 5.00/\sqrt{49} = .7143$

**b.** $1.96\sigma/\sqrt{n} = 1.96 \, (5.00/\sqrt{49}) = 1.4$

**c.** $34.80 \pm 1.4$ or (33.40 to 36.20)

**15. a.** $\bar{x} = \dfrac{\Sigma x_i}{n} = \dfrac{80}{8} = 10$

**b.** $s = \sqrt{\dfrac{\Sigma(x_i - \bar{x})^2}{n-1}} = \sqrt{\dfrac{84}{8-1}} = 3.46$

**c.** With 7 degrees of freedom, $t_{.025} = 2.365$

$$\bar{x} \pm t_{.025}\dfrac{s}{\sqrt{n}}$$

$$10 \pm 2.365\dfrac{3.46}{\sqrt{8}}$$

$$10 \pm 2.90; (7.10 \text{ to } 12.90)$$

**17.** At 90%, $80 \pm t_{.05}(s/\sqrt{n})$ with degrees of freedom = 17

$t_{.05} = 1.740$

$80 \pm 1.740(10/\sqrt{18})$

$80 \pm 4.10; (75.90 \text{ to } 84.10)$

At 95%, $80 \pm t_{.025}(10/\sqrt{18})$ with degrees of freedom = 17

$t_{.025} = 2.110$

$80 \pm 2.110 (10/\sqrt{18})$

$80 \pm 4.97; (75.03 \text{ to } 84.97)$

**24. a.** Planning value of $\sigma = \dfrac{\text{Range}}{4} = \dfrac{36}{4} = 9$

**b.** $n = \dfrac{z_{.025}^2 \sigma^2}{E^2} = \dfrac{(1.96)^2(9)^2}{(3)^2} = 34.57;$ use $n = 35$

**c.** $n = \dfrac{(1.96)^2(9)^2}{(3)^2} = 77.79;$ use $n = 78$

**25. a.** Use $n = \dfrac{z_{\alpha/2}^2 \sigma^2}{E^2}$

$n = \dfrac{(1.96)^2(6.82)^2}{(1.5)^2} = 79.41;$ use $n = 80$

**b.** $n = \dfrac{(1.645)^2(6.82)^2}{(2)^2} = 31.47;$ use $n = 32$

**31. a.** $\bar{p} = \dfrac{100}{400} = .25$

**b.** $\sqrt{\dfrac{\bar{p}(1-\bar{p})}{n}} = \sqrt{\dfrac{.25(.75)}{400}} = .0217$

**c.** $\bar{p} \pm z_{.025}\sqrt{\dfrac{\bar{p}(1-\bar{p})}{n}}$

$.25 \pm 1.96(.0217)$

$.25 \pm .0424; (.2076 \text{ to } .2924)$

**35. a.** $\bar{p} = 562/814 = .6904$

**b.** $1.645\sqrt{\dfrac{.6904(1-.6904)}{814}} = .0267$

**c.** $.6904 \pm .0267; (.6637 \text{ to } .7171)$

**39. a.** $n = \dfrac{1.96^2 p(1-p)}{E^2}$

$n = \dfrac{1.96^2(.33)(.67)}{(.03)^2} = 943.75;$ use $n = 944$

**b.** $n = \dfrac{2.576^2(.33)(.67)}{(.03)^2} = 1630.19;$ use $n = 1631$

## Chapter 9

**2. a.** $H_0: \mu \le 14$
$H_a: \mu > 14$

**b.** No evidence that the new plan increases sales

**c.** The research hypothesis $\mu > 14$ is supported; the new plan increases sales

**5. a.** Rejecting $H_0: \mu \le 8.6$ when it is true

**b.** Accepting $H_0: \mu \le 8.6$ when it is false

**10. a.** $z = 2.05$
Reject $H_0$ if $z > 2.05$

**b.** $z = \dfrac{\bar{x} - \mu}{s/\sqrt{n}} = \dfrac{16.5 - 15}{7/\sqrt{40}} = 1.36$

**c.** Area for $z = 1.36 = .9131$
$p$-value $= 1 - .9131 = .0869$

**d.** Do not reject $H_0$

**13. a.** $H_0: \mu \ge 1056$
$H_a: \mu < 1056$

**b.** Reject $H_0$ if $z < -1.645$

**c.** $z = \dfrac{\bar{x} - \mu}{s/\sqrt{n}} = \dfrac{910 - 1056}{1600/\sqrt{400}} = -1.83$

**d.** Reject $H_0$; conclude $\mu < 1056$

**e.** $p$-value $= 1 - .9664 = .0336$

**20. a.** Reject $H_0$ if $z < -2.33$ or $z > 2.33$

**b.** $z = \dfrac{\bar{x} - \mu}{\sigma/\sqrt{n}} = \dfrac{14.2 - 15}{5/\sqrt{50}} = -1.13$

**c.** $p$-value $= 2(1 - .8708) = .2584$

**d.** Do not reject $H_0$

**23. a.** Reject $H_0$ if $z < -1.96$ or $z > 1.96$

**b.** $z = \dfrac{\bar{x} - \mu_0}{s/\sqrt{n}} = \dfrac{38.5 - 39.2}{4.8/\sqrt{112}} = -1.54$

**c.** Do not reject $H_0$

**d.** $p$-value $= 2(.5000 - .4382) = .1236$

**30. a.** $\bar{x} = \dfrac{\Sigma x_i}{n} = \dfrac{108}{6} = 18$

**b.** $s = \sqrt{\dfrac{\Sigma(x_i - \bar{x})}{n-1}} = \sqrt{\dfrac{10}{6-1}} = 1.414$

**c.** Reject $H_0$ if $t < -2.571$ or $t > 2.571$

**d.** $t = \dfrac{\bar{x} - \mu}{s/\sqrt{n}} = \dfrac{18 - 20}{1.41/\sqrt{6}} = -3.46$

**e.** Reject $H_0$; conclude $H_a$ is true

**33. a.** $H_0: \mu = 3.00$
$H_a: \mu \ne 3.00$

**b.** Reject $H_0$ if $t < -2.262$ or if $t > 2.262$

**c.** $\bar{x} = \Sigma x_i/n = {}^{28}\!/_{10} = 2.80$

**d.** $s = \sqrt{\dfrac{\Sigma(x_i - \bar{x})^2}{n-1}} = .70$

**e.** $t = \dfrac{\bar{x} - \mu_0}{s/\sqrt{n}} = \dfrac{2.80 - 3.00}{.70/\sqrt{10}} = -.90$

**f.** Do not reject $H_0$

**g.** $t_{.10} = 1.383;$ $p$-value greater than $2(.10) = .20$

**40. a.** Reject $H_0$ if $z < -1.96$ or $z > 1.96$

**b.** $\sigma_{\bar{p}} = \sqrt{\dfrac{.20(.80)}{400}} = .02$

$z = \dfrac{\bar{p} - p}{\sigma_{\bar{p}}} = \dfrac{.175 - .20}{.02} = -1.25$

**c.** $p\text{-value} = 2(1 - .8944) = .2112$

**d.** Do not reject $H_0$

**43.** $H_0: p \geq .64$
$H_a: p < .64$
Reject $H_0$ if $z < -1.645$
$\bar{p} = {}^{52}\!/_{100} = .52$

$z = \dfrac{.52 - .64}{\sqrt{\dfrac{.64(.36)}{100}}} = -2.5$

Reject $H_0$

**50.**

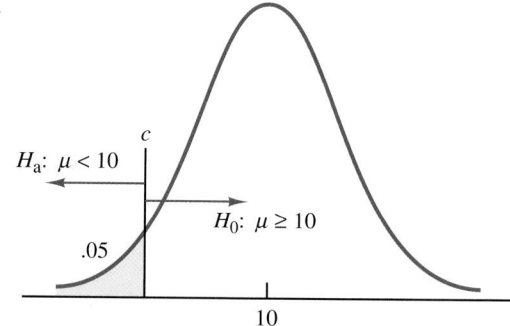

$c = 10 - 1.645(5/\sqrt{120}) = 9.25$
Reject $H_0$ if $\bar{x} < 9.25$

**a.** When $\mu = 9$,

$z = \dfrac{9.25 - 9}{5/\sqrt{120}} = .55$

$P(H_0) = (.5000 - .2088) = .2912$

**b.** Type II error

**c.** When $\mu = 8$,

$z = \dfrac{9.25 - 8}{5/\sqrt{120}} = 2.74$

$\beta = (.5000 - .4969) = .0031$

**53. a.** $H_0: \mu \geq 25$
$H_a: \mu < 25$
Reject $H_0$ if $z < -2.05$

$z = \dfrac{\bar{x} - \mu_0}{\sigma/\sqrt{n}} = \dfrac{\bar{x} - 25}{3/\sqrt{30}} = -2.05$

Solve for $\bar{x} = 23.88$
Decision Rule: Accept $H_0$ if $\bar{x} \geq 23.88$
Reject $H_0$ if $\bar{x} < 23.88$

**b.** For $\mu = 23$,

$z = \dfrac{23.88 - 23}{3/\sqrt{30}} = 1.61$

$\beta = .5000 - .4463 = .0537$

**c.** For $\mu = 24$,

$z = \dfrac{23.88 - 24}{3/\sqrt{30}} = -.22$

$\beta = .5000 - .0871 = .5871$

**d.** The Type II error cannot be made in this case; note that when $\mu = 25.5$, $H_0$ is true: the Type II error can only be made when $H_0$ is false

**58.** $n = \dfrac{(z_\alpha - z_\beta)\sigma^2}{(\mu_0 - \mu_a)^2} = \dfrac{(1.645 + 1.28)^2(5)^2}{(10 - 9)^2} = 214$

**61.** At $\mu_0 = 400$, $\alpha = .02$; $z_{.02} = 2.05$
At $\mu_a = 385$, $\beta = .10$; $z_{.10} = 1.28$
With $\sigma = 30$,

$n = \dfrac{(z_\alpha + z_\beta)^2\sigma^2}{(\mu_0 - \mu_a)^2} = \dfrac{(2.05 + 1.28)^2(30)^2}{(400 - 385)^2} = 44.4$ or 45

## Chapter 10

**1. a.** $\bar{x}_1 - \bar{x}_2 = 13.6 - 11.6 = 2$

**b.** $s_{\bar{x}_1 - \bar{x}_2} = \sqrt{\dfrac{s_1^2}{n_1} + \dfrac{s_2^2}{n_2}} = \sqrt{\dfrac{(2.2)^2}{50} + \dfrac{3^2}{35}} = .595$

$2 \pm 1.645(.595)$
$2 \pm .98$ or 1.02 to 2.98

**c.** $2 \pm 1.96(.595)$
$2 \pm 1.17$, or .83 to 3.17

**8. a.** $\bar{x}_1 - \bar{x}_2 = 45{,}700 - 44{,}500 = 1200$

**b.** Pooled variance

$s^2 = \dfrac{7(700)^2 + 11(850)^2}{18} = 632{,}083$

$s_{\bar{x}_1 - \bar{x}_2} = \sqrt{632{,}083\left(\dfrac{1}{8} + \dfrac{1}{12}\right)} = 362.88$

With 18 degrees of freedom $t_{.025} = 2.101$,
$1200 \pm 2.101(362.88)$
$1200 \pm 762$, or 438 to 1962

**c.** Populations are normally distributed with equal variances

**11. a.** $s_{\bar{x}_1 - \bar{x}_2} = \sqrt{\dfrac{s_1^2}{n_1} + \dfrac{s_2^2}{n_2}} = \sqrt{\dfrac{(5.2)^2}{40} + \dfrac{6^2}{50}} = 1.18$

$z = \dfrac{(\bar{x}_1 - \bar{x}_2) - (\mu_1 - \mu_2)}{s_{\bar{x}_1 - \bar{x}_2}}$

$= \dfrac{(25.2 - 22.8)}{1.18} = 2.03$

Reject $H_0$ if $z > 1.645$; therefore reject $H_0$; conclude $H_a$ is true and $\mu_1 > \mu_2$

**b.** $p\text{-value} = 1 - .9788 = .0212$

**16.** $H_0: \mu_1 - \mu_2 = 0$
$H_a: \mu_1 - \mu_2 \neq 0$
Reject $H_0$ if $z < -1.96$ or if $z > 1.96$

$z = \dfrac{(\bar{x}_1 - \bar{x}_2) - 0}{\sqrt{\sigma_1^2/n_1 + \sigma_2^2/n_2}} = \dfrac{40 - 35}{\sqrt{(9)^2/36 + (10)^2/49}}$

$= 2.41$

$p$-value $= 2(1 - .9920) = .0160$

Reject $H_0$; customers at the two stores differ in terms of mean ages

**23. a.** $1, 2, 0, 0, 2$

**b.** $\bar{d} = \dfrac{\Sigma d_i}{n} = \dfrac{5}{5} = 1$

**c.** $s_d = \sqrt{\dfrac{\Sigma(d_i - \bar{d})^2}{n - 1}} = \sqrt{\dfrac{4}{5 - 1}} = 1$

**d.** With 4 degrees of freedom, $t_{.05} = 2.132$; reject $H_0$ if $t > 2.132$

$$t = \frac{\bar{d} - \mu_d}{s_d/\sqrt{n}} = \frac{1 - 0}{1/\sqrt{5}} = 2.24$$

Reject $H_0$; conclude $\mu_d > 0$

**25.** $d$ = rating after $-$ rating before

$H_0$: $\mu_d \leq 0$

$H_a$: $\mu_d > 0$

With 7 degrees of freedom, reject $H_0$ if $t > 1.895$

$\bar{d} = .625$ and $s_d = 1.3025$,

$$t = \frac{\bar{d} - \mu_d}{s_d/\sqrt{n}} = \frac{.625 - 0}{1.3025/\sqrt{8}} = 1.36$$

Do not reject $H_0$; we cannot conclude that seeing the commercial improves the potential to purchase

**33. a.** $\bar{p} = \dfrac{n_1\bar{p}_1 + n_2\bar{p}_2}{n_1 + n_2} = \dfrac{200(.22) + 300(.16)}{200 + 300} = .184$

$$s_{\bar{p}_1 - \bar{p}_2} = \sqrt{(.184)(.816)\left(\frac{1}{200} + \frac{1}{300}\right)} = .0354$$

Reject $H_0$ if $z > 1.645$

$$z = \frac{(.22 - .16) - 0}{.0354} = 1.69$$

Reject $H_0$

**b.** $p$-value $= (1 - .9545) = .0455$

## Chapter 11

**2.** $s^2 = 25$

**a.** With 19 degrees of freedom, $\chi^2_{.05} = 30.1435$ and $\chi^2_{.95} = 10.1170$

$$\frac{19(25)}{30.1435} \leq \sigma^2 \leq \frac{19(25)}{10.1170}$$

$$15.76 \leq \sigma^2 \leq 46.95$$

**b.** With 19 degrees of freedom, $\chi^2_{.025} = 32.8523$ and $\chi^2_{.975} = 8.90655$

$$\frac{19(25)}{32.8523} \leq \sigma^2 \leq \frac{19(25)}{8.90655}$$

$$14.46 \leq \sigma^2 \leq 53.33$$

**c.** $3.8 \leq \sigma \leq 7.3$

**9.** $H_0$: $\sigma^2 \leq .0004$

$H_a$: $\sigma^2 > .0004$

$n = 30$

$$\chi^2_{.05} = 42.5569 \ (29 \text{ degrees of freedom})$$

$$\chi^2 = \frac{(29)(.0005)}{.0004} = 36.25$$

Do not reject $H_0$; the product specification does not appear to be violated

**15.** We recommend placing the larger sample variance in the numerator; with $\alpha = .05$, $F_{.025,20,24} = 2.33$: reject $H_0$ if $F > 2.33$

$$F = \frac{8.2}{4.0} = 2.05; \text{ do not reject } H_0$$

Or, had we used the lower tail $F$ value,

$$F_{.025,20,24} = \frac{1}{F_{.025,24,20}} = \frac{1}{2.46} = .41$$

$$F = \frac{4.0}{8.2} = .49$$

$F > .41$; do not reject $H_0$

**17. a.** Let: $\sigma_1^2$ = variance in repair costs for 4-year-old automobiles

$\sigma_2^2$ = variance in repair costs for 2-year-old automobiles

$H_0$: $\sigma_1^2 \leq \sigma_2^2$

$H_a$: $\sigma_1^2 > \sigma_2^2$

**b.** $s_1^2 = (170)^2 = 28,900$

$s_2^2 = (100)^2 = 10,000$

$$F = \frac{s_1^2}{s_2^2} = \frac{28,900}{10,000} = 2.89$$

$F_{.01,24,24} = 2.66$

Reject $H_0$; conclude that automobiles 4 years old have a larger variance in annual repair costs compared to automobiles 2 years old; this conclusion is expected due to the fact that older automobiles are more likely to have some expensive repairs that lead to greater variance in the annual repair costs

## Chapter 12

**1.** Expected frequencies: $e_1 = 200(.40) = 80$

$e_2 = 200(.40) = 80$

$e_3 = 200(.20) = 40$

Actual frequencies: $f_1 = 60, f_2 = 120, f_3 = 20$

$$\chi^2 = \frac{(60 - 80)^2}{80} + \frac{(120 - 80)^2}{80} + \frac{(20 - 40)^2}{40}$$

$$= \frac{400}{80} + \frac{1600}{80} + \frac{400}{40}$$

$$= 5 + 20 + 10 = 35$$

$\chi^2_{.01} = 9.21034$, with $k - 1 = 3 - 1 = 2$ degrees of freedom

Because $\chi^2 = 35 > 9.21034$, reject the null hypothesis; that is, the population proportions are not as stated in the null hypothesis

3. $H_0$: $p_{ABC} = .29$, $p_{CBS} = .28$, $p_{NBC} = .25$, $p_{Other} = .18$
   $H_a$: The proportions are not
   $p_{ABC} = .29$, $p_{CBS} = .28$, $p_{NBC} = .25$, $p_{Other} = .18$
   Expected frequencies: $300(.29) = 87$, $300(.28) = 84$
   $\qquad\qquad\qquad\qquad 300(.25) = 75$, $300(.18) = 54$
   $\qquad e_1 = 87$, $e_2 = 84$, $e_3 = 75$, $e_4 = 54$
   Actual frequencies: $f_1 = 95$, $f_2 = 70$, $f_3 = 89$, $f_4 = 46$
   $\chi^2_{.05} = 7.81$ (3 degrees of freedom)
   $$\chi^2 = \frac{(95 - 87)^2}{87} + \frac{(70 - 84)^2}{84} + \frac{(89 - 75)^2}{75}$$
   $$+ \frac{(46 - 54)^2}{54} = 6.87$$

Do not reject $H_0$; there is no significant change in the viewing audience proportions

9. $H_0$: The column variable is independent of the row variable

   $H_a$: The column variable is not independent of the row variable

   Expected frequencies:

|   | A | B | C |
|---|---|---|---|
| P | 28.5 | 39.9 | 45.6 |
| Q | 21.5 | 30.1 | 34.4 |

$$\chi^2 = \frac{(20 - 28.5)^2}{28.5} + \frac{(44 - 39.9)^2}{39.9} + \frac{(50 - 45.6)^2}{45.6}$$
$$+ \frac{(30 - 21.5)^2}{21.5} + \frac{(26 - 30.1)^2}{30.1} + \frac{(30 - 34.4)^2}{34.4}$$
$$= 7.86$$

$\chi^2_{.025} = 7.37776$, with $(2 - 1)(3 - 1) = 2$ degrees of freedom

Because $\chi^2 = 7.86 > 7.37776$, reject $H_0$; that is, conclude that the column variable is not independent of the row variable

11. $H_0$: Type of ticket purchased is independent of the type of flight

   $H_a$: Type of ticket purchased is not independent of the type of flight

   Expected frequencies:
   $e_{11} = 35.59 \qquad e_{12} = 15.41$
   $e_{21} = 150.73 \qquad e_{22} = 65.27$
   $e_{31} = 455.68 \qquad e_{32} = 197.32$

| Ticket | Flight | Observed Frequency ($f_i$) | Expected Frequency ($e_i$) | $(f_i - e_i)^2/e_i$ |
|---|---|---|---|---|
| First | Domestic | 29 | 35.59 | 1.22 |
| First | International | 22 | 15.41 | 2.82 |
| Business | Domestic | 95 | 150.73 | 20.61 |
| Business | International | 121 | 65.27 | 47.59 |
| Full-fare | Domestic | 518 | 455.68 | 8.52 |
| Full-fare | International | 135 | 197.32 | 19.68 |
| Totals | | 920 | | 100.43 |

$\chi^2_{.05} = 5.99$ with $(3 - 1)(2 - 1) = 2$ degrees of freedom
Because $100.43 > 5.99$ we reject $H_0$; type of ticket purchased is not independent of the type of flight

20. First estimate $\mu$ from the sample data (sample size = 120)
$$\bar{x} = \frac{0(39) + 1(30) + 2(30) + 3(18) + 4(3)}{120}$$
$$= \frac{156}{120} = 1.3$$

Therefore, we use Poisson probabilities with $\mu = 1.3$ to compute expected frequencies

| $x$ | Observed Frequency | Poisson Probability | Expected Frequency | Difference ($f_i - e_i$) |
|---|---|---|---|---|
| 0 | 39 | .2725 | 32.700 | 6.300 |
| 1 | 30 | .3543 | 42.516 | -12.516 |
| 2 | 30 | .2303 | 27.636 | 2.364 |
| 3 | 18 | .0998 | 11.976 | 6.024 |
| 4 or more | 3 | .0430 | 5.160 | -2.160 |

$$\chi^2 = \frac{(6.300)^2}{32.700} + \frac{(-12.516)^2}{42.516} + \frac{(2.364)^2}{27.636} + \frac{(6.024)^2}{11.976}$$
$$+ \frac{(-2.160)^2}{5.160} = 9.0348$$

$\chi^2_{.05} = 7.81473$ with $5 - 1 - 1 = 3$ degrees of freedom

Because $\chi^2 = 9.0348 > 7.81473$, reject $H_0$; that is, conclude that the data do not follow a Poisson probability distribution

21. With $n = 30$ we will use six classes with a probability of .1667 associated with each class
   $$\bar{x} = 22.80, \ s = 6.2665$$
   The $z$ values that create 6 intervals, each with probability .1667 are $-.98$, $-.43$, 0, .43, .98

| $z$ | Cutoff value of $x$ |
|---|---|
| $-.98$ | $22.8 - .98(6.2665) = 16.66$ |
| $-.43$ | $22.8 - .43(6.2665) = 20.11$ |
| $0$ | $22.8 + .00(6.2665) = 22.80$ |
| $.43$ | $22.8 + .43(6.2665) = 25.49$ |
| $.98$ | $22.8 + .98(6.2665) = 28.94$ |

| Interval | Observed Frequency | Expected Frequency | Difference |
|---|---|---|---|
| less than 16.66 | 3 | 5 | $-2$ |
| 16.66–20.11 | 7 | 5 | 2 |
| 20.11–22.80 | 5 | 5 | 0 |
| 22.80–25.49 | 7 | 5 | 2 |
| 25.49–28.94 | 3 | 5 | $-2$ |
| 28.94 and up | 5 | 5 | 0 |

$$\chi^2 = \frac{(-2)^2}{5} + \frac{(2)^2}{5} + \frac{(0)^2}{5} + \frac{(2)^2}{5} + \frac{(-2)^2}{5} + \frac{(0)^2}{5}$$

$$= \frac{16}{5} = 3.20$$

$\chi^2_{.025} = 9.34840$ with $6 - 2 - 1 = 3$ degrees of freedom

Because $\chi^2 = 3.20 \leq 9.34840$, do not reject $H_0$

The claim that the data come from a normal distribution cannot be rejected

## Chapter 13

**1. a.** $\bar{\bar{x}} = (30 + 45 + 36)/3 = 37$

$$\text{SSTR} = \sum_{j=1}^{k} n_j(\bar{x}_j - \bar{\bar{x}})^2$$

$$= 5(30 - 37)^2 + 5(45 - 37)^2 + 5(36 - 37)^2$$

$$= 570$$

$$\text{MSTR} = \frac{\text{SSTR}}{k - 1} = \frac{570}{2} = 285$$

**b.** $\text{SSE} = \sum_{j=1}^{k}(n_j - 1)s_j^2$

$$= 4(6) + 4(4) + 4(6.5) = 66$$

$$\text{MSE} = \frac{\text{SSE}}{n_T - k} = \frac{66}{15 - 3} = 5.5$$

**c.** $F = \frac{\text{MSTR}}{\text{MSE}} = \frac{285}{5.5} = 51.82$

$F_{.05} = 3.89$ (2 degrees of freedom numerator and 12 denominator)

Because $F = 51.82 > F_{.05} = 3.89$, we reject the null hypothesis that the means of the three populations are equal

**d.**

| Source of Variation | Sum of Squares | Degrees of Freedom | Mean Square | $F$ |
|---|---|---|---|---|
| Treatments | 570 | 2 | 285 | 51.82 |
| Error | 66 | 12 | 5.5 | |
| Total | 636 | 14 | | |

**6.**

| | Mfg 1 | Mfg 2 | Mfg 3 |
|---|---|---|---|
| Sample mean | 23 | 28 | 21 |
| Sample variance | 6.67 | 4.67 | 3.33 |

$$\bar{\bar{x}} = (23 + 28 + 21)/3 = 24$$

$$\text{SSTR} = \sum_{j=1}^{k} n_j(\bar{x}_j - \bar{\bar{x}})^2$$

$$= 4(23 - 24)^2 + 4(28 - 24)^2$$

$$+ 4(21 - 24)^2 = 104$$

$$\text{MSTR} = \frac{\text{SSTR}}{k - 1} = \frac{104}{2} = 52$$

$$\text{SSE} = \sum_{j=1}^{k}(n_j - 1)s_j^2$$

$$= 3(6.67) + 3(4.67) + 3(3.33) = 44.01$$

$$\text{MSE} = \frac{\text{SSE}}{n_T - k} = \frac{44.01}{12 - 3} = 4.89$$

$$F = \frac{\text{MSTR}}{\text{MSE}} = \frac{52}{4.89} = 10.63$$

$F_{.05} = 4.26$ (2 degrees of freedom numerator and 9 denominator)

Because $F = 10.63 > F_{.05} = 4.26$, we reject the null hypothesis that the mean time needed to mix a batch of material is the same for each manufacturer

**11. a.** $\text{LSD} = t_{\alpha/2}\sqrt{\text{MSE}\left(\frac{1}{n_i} + \frac{1}{n_j}\right)}$

$$= t_{.025}\sqrt{5.5\left(\frac{1}{5} + \frac{1}{5}\right)}$$

$$= 2.179\sqrt{2.2} = 3.23$$

$|\bar{x}_1 - \bar{x}_2| = |30 - 45| = 15 > \text{LSD}$; significant difference
$|\bar{x}_1 - \bar{x}_3| = |30 - 36| = 6 > \text{LSD}$; significant difference
$|\bar{x}_2 - \bar{x}_3| = |45 - 36| = 9 > \text{LSD}$; significant difference

**b.** $\bar{x}_1 - \bar{x}_2 \pm t_{\alpha/2}\sqrt{\text{MSE}\left(\frac{1}{n_1} + \frac{1}{n_2}\right)}$

$$(30 - 45) \pm 2.179\sqrt{5.5\left(\frac{1}{5} + \frac{1}{5}\right)}$$

$$-15 \pm 3.23 = -18.23 \text{ to } -11.77$$

**13.** $LSD = t_{\alpha/2}\sqrt{MSE\left(\dfrac{1}{n_1} + \dfrac{1}{n_3}\right)}$

$= t_{.025}\sqrt{4.89\left(\dfrac{1}{4} + \dfrac{1}{4}\right)}$

$= 2.262\sqrt{2.45} = 3.54$

Because $|\bar{x}_1 - \bar{x}_3| = |23 - 21| = 2 < 3.54$, there does not appear to be any significant difference between the means for manufacturer 1 and manufacturer 2.

**14.** $\bar{x}_1 - \bar{x}_2 \pm LSD$

$23 - 28 \pm 3.54$

$-5 \pm 3.54 = -8.54$ to $-1.46$

**19. a.** $\bar{\bar{x}} = (156 + 142 + 134)/3 = 144$

$SSTR = \displaystyle\sum_{j=1}^{k} n_j(\bar{x}_j - \bar{\bar{x}})^2$

$= 6(156 - 144)^2 + 6(142 - 144)^2 + 6(134 - 144)^2$

$= 1488$

**b.** $MSTR = \dfrac{SSTR}{k-1} = \dfrac{1488}{2} = 744$

**c.** $s_1^2 = 164.4, \quad s_2^2 = 131.2, \quad s_3^2 = 110.4$

$SSE = \displaystyle\sum_{j=1}^{k} (n_j - 1)s_j^2$

$= 5(164.4) + 5(131.2) + 5(110.4)$

$= 2030$

**d.** $MSE = \dfrac{SSE}{n_T - k} = \dfrac{2030}{18 - 3} = 135.3$

**e.** $F = \dfrac{MSTR}{MSE} = \dfrac{744}{135.3} = 5.50$

$F_{.05} = 3.68$ (2 degrees of freedom numerator and 15 denominator)

Because $F = 5.50 > F_{.05} = 3.68$, we reject the hypothesis that the means for the three treatments are equal

**34. *Treatment Means***

$\bar{x}_{.1} = 13.6, \quad \bar{x}_{.2} = 11.0, \quad \bar{x}_{.3} = 10.6$

***Block Means***

$\bar{x}_{1.} = 9, \bar{x}_{2.} = 7.67, \bar{x}_{3.} = 15.67, \bar{x}_{4.} = 18.67, \bar{x}_{5.} = 7.67$

***Overall Mean***

$\bar{\bar{x}} = 176/15 = 11.73$

*Step 1*

$SST = \displaystyle\sum_i \sum_j (x_{ij} - \bar{\bar{x}})^2$

$= (10 - 11.73)^2 + (9 - 11.73)^2 + \cdots + (8 - 11.73)^2$

$= 354.93$

*Step 2*

$SSTR = b\displaystyle\sum_j(\bar{x}_{.j} - \bar{\bar{x}})^2$

$= 5[(13.6 - 11.73)^2 + (11.0 - 11.73)^2 + (10.6 - 11.73)^2] = 26.53$

*Step 3*

$SSBL = k\displaystyle\sum_j(\bar{x}_{i.} - \bar{\bar{x}})^2$

$= 3[(9 - 11.73)^2 + (7.67 - 11.73)^2 + (15.67 - 11.73)^2 + (18.67 - 11.73)^2 + (7.67 - 11.73)^2] = 312.32$

*Step 4*

$SSE = SST - SSTR - SSBL$

$= 354.93 - 26.53 - 312.32 = 16.08$

| Source of Variation | Sum of Squares | Degrees of Freedom | Mean Square | F |
|---|---|---|---|---|
| Treatments | 26.53 | 2 | 13.27 | 6.60 |
| Blocks | 312.32 | 4 | 78.08 | |
| Error | 16.08 | 8 | 2.01 | |
| Total | 354.93 | 14 | | |

$F_{.05} = 4.46$ (2 numerator degrees of freedom and 8 denominator)

Because $F = 6.60 > F_{.05} = 4.46$, we reject the null hypothesis that the means of the three treatments are equal

**41.** See Table E13.41

*Step 1*

$SST = \displaystyle\sum_i \sum_j \sum_k (x_{ijk} - \bar{\bar{x}})^2$

$= (135 - 111)^2 + (165 - 111)^2 + \cdots + (136 - 111)^2 = 9028$

**TABLE E13.41**

| | | Factor B | | | Factor A Means |
|---|---|---|---|---|---|
| | | Level 1 | Level 2 | Level 3 | |
| Factor A | Level 1 | $\bar{x}_{11} = 150$ | $\bar{x}_{12} = 78$ | $\bar{x}_{13} = 84$ | $\bar{x}_{1.} = 104$ |
| | Level 2 | $\bar{x}_{21} = 110$ | $\bar{x}_{22} = 116$ | $\bar{x}_{23} = 128$ | $\bar{x}_{2.} = 118$ |
| | Factor B Means | $\bar{x}_{.1} = 130$ | $\bar{x}_{.2} = 97$ | $\bar{x}_{.3} = 106$ | $\bar{\bar{x}} = 111$ |

*Step 2*

$$SSA = br \sum_i (\bar{x}_{i\cdot} - \bar{\bar{x}})^2$$

$$= 3(2)[(104 - 111)^2 + (118 - 111)^2] = 588$$

*Step 3*

$$SSB = ar \sum_j (\bar{x}_{\cdot j} - \bar{\bar{x}})^2$$

$$= 2(2)[(130 - 111)^2 + (97 - 111)^2 + (106 - 111)^2]$$

$$= 2328$$

*Step 4*

$$SSAB = r \sum_i \sum_j (\bar{x}_{ij} - \bar{x}_{i\cdot} - \bar{x}_{\cdot j} + \bar{\bar{x}})^2$$

$$= 2[(150 - 104 - 130 + 111)^2$$

$$+ (78 - 104 - 97 + 111)^2 + \cdots$$

$$+ (128 - 118 - 106 + 111)^2] = 4392$$

*Step 5*

$$SSE = SST - SSA - SSB - SSAB$$

$$= 9028 - 588 - 2328 - 4392 = 1720$$

| Source of Variation | Sum of Squares | Degrees of Freedom | Mean Square | F |
|---|---|---|---|---|
| Factor A | 588 | 1 | 588 | 2.05 |
| Factor B | 2328 | 2 | 1164 | 4.06 |
| Interaction | 4392 | 2 | 2196 | 7.66 |
| Error | 1720 | 6 | 286.67 | |
| Total | 9028 | 11 | | |

$F_{.05} = 5.99$ (1 degree of freedom numerator and 6 denominator)

$F_{.05} = 5.14$ (2 degrees of freedom numerator and 6 denominator)

Because $F = 2.05 < F_{.05} = 5.99$, factor A is not significant
Because $F = 4.06 < F_{.05} = 5.14$, factor B is not significant
Because $F = 7.66 > F_{.05} = 5.14$, interaction is significant

# Chapter 14

**1. a.**

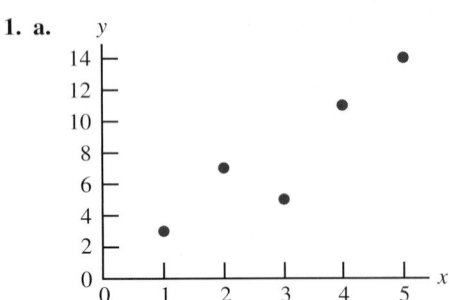

**b.** There appears to be a linear relationship between $x$ and $y$

**c.** Many different straight lines can be drawn to provide a linear approximation of the relationship between $x$ and $y$; in part (d) we will determine the equation of a straight line that "best" represents the relationship according to the least squares criterion

**d.** Summations needed to compute the slope and $y$-intercept:

$\sum x_i = 15, \quad \sum y_i = 40, \quad \sum(x_i - \bar{x})(y_i - \bar{y}) = 26,$
$\sum(x_i - \bar{x})^2 = 10$

$$b_1 = \frac{\sum(x_i - \bar{x})(y_i - \bar{y})}{\sum(x_i - \bar{x})^2} = \frac{26}{10} = 2.6$$

$$b_0 = \bar{y} - b_1\bar{x} = 8 - (2.6)(3) = 0.2$$

$$\hat{y} = 0.2 - 2.6x$$

**e.** $\hat{y} = .2 + 2.6x = .2 + 2.6(4) = 10.6$

**4. a.**

**b.** It indicates there may be a linear relationship between the variables

**c.** Many different straight lines can be drawn to provide a linear approximation of the relationship between $x$ and $y$; in part (d) we will determine the equation of a straight line that "best" represents the relationship according to the least squares criterion

**d.** Summations needed to compute the slope and $y$-intercept:

$\sum x_i = 325, \quad \sum y_i = 585, \quad \sum(x_i - \bar{x})(y_i - \bar{y}) = 110,$
$\sum(x_i - \bar{x})^2 = 20$

$$b_1 = \frac{\sum(x_i - \bar{x})(y_i - \bar{y})}{\sum(x_i - \bar{x})^2} = \frac{110}{20} = 5.5$$

$$b_0 = \bar{y} - b_1\bar{x} = 117 - (5.5)(65) = -240.5$$

$$\hat{y} = -240.5 + 5.5x$$

**e.** $\hat{y} = -240.5 + 5.5(63) = 106$

The estimate of weight is 106 pounds

**15. a.** $\hat{y}_i = .2 + 2.6x_i$ and $\bar{y} = 8$

| $x_i$ | $y_i$ | $\hat{y}_i$ | $y_i - \hat{y}_i$ | $(y_i - \hat{y}_i)^2$ | $y_i - \bar{y}$ | $(y_i - \bar{y})^2$ |
|---|---|---|---|---|---|---|
| 1 | 3 | 2.8 | .2 | .04 | −5 | 25 |
| 2 | 7 | 5.4 | 1.6 | 2.56 | −1 | 1 |
| 3 | 5 | 8.0 | −3.0 | 9.00 | −3 | 9 |
| 4 | 11 | 10.6 | .4 | .16 | 3 | 9 |
| 5 | 14 | 13.2 | .8 | .64 | 6 | 36 |
| | | | | SSE = 12.40 | | SST = 80 |

$$SSR = SST - SSE = 80 - 12.4 = 67.6$$

**b.** $r^2 = \dfrac{SSR}{SST} = \dfrac{67.6}{80} = .845$

The least squares line provided a good fit; 84.5% of the variability in $y$ has been explained by the least squares line

**c.** $r = \sqrt{.845} = +.9192$

**18. a.** The estimated regression equation and the mean for the dependent variable:

$\hat{y} = 1790.5 + 581.1x, \quad \bar{y} = 3650$

The sum of squares due to error and the total sum of squares:

$SSE = \Sigma(y_i - \hat{y}_i)^2 = 85,135.14,$
$SST = \Sigma(y_i - \bar{y})^2 = 335,000$

Thus, $SSR = SST - SSE$
$\qquad = 335,000 - 85,135.14 = 249,864.86$

**b.** $r^2 = \dfrac{SSR}{SST} = \dfrac{249,864.86}{335,000} = .746$

The least squares line accounted for 74.6% of the total sum of squares

**c.** $r = \sqrt{.746} = +.8637$

**23. a.** $s^2 = MSE = \dfrac{SSE}{n-2} = \dfrac{12.4}{3} = 4.133$

**b.** $s = \sqrt{MSE} = \sqrt{4.133} = 2.033$

**c.** $\Sigma(x_i - \bar{x})^2 = 10$

$s_{b_1} = \dfrac{s}{\sqrt{\Sigma(x_i - \bar{x})^2}} = \dfrac{2.033}{\sqrt{10}} = .643$

**d.** $t = \dfrac{b_1 - \beta_1}{s_{b_1}} = \dfrac{2.6 - 0}{.643} = 4.04$

$t_{.025} = 3.182$ (3 degrees of freedom)

Because $t = 4.04 > t_{.05} = 3.182$, we reject $H_0: \beta_1 = 0$

**e.** $MSR = \dfrac{SSR}{1} = 67.6$

$F = \dfrac{MSR}{MSE} = \dfrac{67.6}{4.133} = 16.36$

$F_{.05} = 10.13$ (1 degree of freedom numerator and 3 denominator)

Because $F = 16.36 > F_{.05} = 10.13$, we reject $H_0: \beta_1 = 0$

| Source of Variation | Sum of Squares | Degrees of Freedom | Mean Square | F |
|---|---|---|---|---|
| Regression | 67.6 | 1 | 67.6 | 16.36 |
| Error | 12.4 | 3 | 4.133 | |
| Total | 80 | 4 | | |

**26. a.** $s^2 = MSE = \dfrac{SSE}{n-2} = \dfrac{85,135.14}{4} = 21,283.79$

$s = \sqrt{MSE} = \sqrt{21,283.79} = 145.89$

$\Sigma(x_i - \bar{x})^2 = .74$

$s_{b_1} = \dfrac{s}{\sqrt{\Sigma(x_i - \bar{x})^2}} = \dfrac{145.89}{\sqrt{.74}} = 169.59$

$t = \dfrac{b_1 - \beta_1}{s_{b_1}} = \dfrac{581.08 - 0}{169.59} = 3.43$

$t_{.025} = 2.776$ (4 degrees of freedom)

Because $t = 3.43 > t_{.025} = 2.776$, we reject $H_0: \beta_1 = 0$

**b.** $MSR = \dfrac{SSR}{1} = \dfrac{249,864.86}{1} = 249,864.86$

$F = \dfrac{MSR}{MSE} = \dfrac{249,864.86}{21,283.79} = 11.74$

$F_{.05} = 7.71$ (1 degree of freedom numerator and 4 denominator)

Because $F = 11.74 > F_{.05} = 7.71$, we reject $H_0: \beta_1 = 0$

**c.**

| Source of Variation | Sum of Squares | Degrees of Freedom | Mean Square | F |
|---|---|---|---|---|
| Regression | 29,864.86 | 1 | 29,864.86 | 11.74 |
| Error | 85,135.14 | 4 | 21,283.79 | |
| Total | 335,000 | 5 | | |

**39. a.** $s = 2.033$

$\bar{x} = 3, \Sigma(x_i - \bar{x})^2 = 10$

$s_{\hat{y}_p} = s\sqrt{\dfrac{1}{n} + \dfrac{(x_p - \bar{x})^2}{\Sigma(x_i - \bar{x})^2}}$

$= 2.033\sqrt{\dfrac{1}{5} + \dfrac{(4-3)^2}{10}} = 1.11$

**b.** $\hat{y} = .2 + 2.6x = .2 + 2.6(4) = 10.6$

$\hat{y}_p \pm t_{\alpha/2}s_{\hat{y}_p}$

$10.6 \pm 3.182(1.11)$

$10.6 \pm 3.53$, or 7.07 to 14.13

**c.** $s_{ind} = s\sqrt{1 + \dfrac{1}{n} + \dfrac{(x_p - \bar{x})^2}{\Sigma(x_i - \bar{x})^2}}$

$= 2.033\sqrt{1 + \dfrac{1}{5} + \dfrac{(4-3)^2}{10}} = 2.32$

**d.** $\hat{y}_p \pm t_{\alpha/2}s_{ind}$

$10.6 \pm 3.182(2.32)$

$10.6 \pm 7.38$, or 3.22 to 17.98

**42. a.** $s = 145.89, \bar{x} = 3.2, \Sigma(x_i - \bar{x})^2 = .74$

$\hat{y} = 1790.5 + 581.1x = 1790.5 + 581.1(3)$
$\qquad = 3533.8$

$s_{\hat{y}_p} = s\sqrt{\dfrac{1}{n} + \dfrac{(x_p - \bar{x})^2}{\Sigma(x_i - \bar{x})^2}}$

$= 145.89\sqrt{\dfrac{1}{6} + \dfrac{(3-3.2)^2}{.74}} = 68.54$

$\hat{y}_p \pm t_{\alpha/2}s_{\hat{y}_p}$

$3533.8 \pm 2.776(68.54)$

$3533.8 \pm 190.27$, or \$3343.53 to \$3724.07

**b.** $\hat{y} = 1790.5 + 581.1x = 1790.5 + 581.1(3)$
$= 3533.8$

$$s_{ind} = s\sqrt{1 + \frac{1}{n} + \frac{(x_p - \bar{x})^2}{\Sigma(x_i - \bar{x})^2}}$$

$$= 145.89\sqrt{1 + \frac{1}{6} + \frac{(3 - 3.2)^2}{0.74}} = 161.19$$

$\hat{y}_p \pm t_{\alpha/2}s_{ind}$
$3533.8 \pm 2.776(161.19)$
$3533.8 \pm 447.46$, or \$3086.34 to \$3981.26

**47. a.** Using Excel's Regression tool the estimated regression equation is $\hat{y} = -7.0222 + 1.5873x$ or $\hat{y} = -7.02 + 1.59x$

**b.**

| $x_i$ | $y_i$ | $\hat{y}_i$ | $y_i - \hat{y}_i$ |
|-------|-------|-------------|-------------------|
| 6 | 6 | 2.52 | 3.48 |
| 11 | 8 | 10.47 | -2.47 |
| 15 | 12 | 16.83 | -4.83 |
| 18 | 20 | 21.60 | -1.60 |
| 20 | 30 | 24.78 | 5.22 |

**c.**

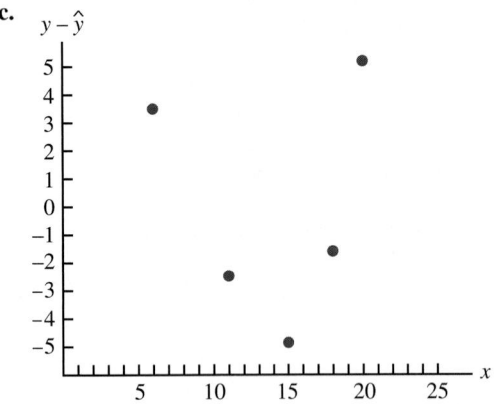

With only five observations, it is difficult to determine whether the assumptions are satisfied; however, the plot does suggest curvature in the residuals, which would indicate that the error term assumptions are not satisfied; the scatter diagram for these data also indicates that the underlying relationship between $x$ and $y$ may be curvilinear

**d.** $s^2 = 23.78$

$$h_i = \frac{1}{n} + \frac{(x_i - \bar{x})^2}{\Sigma(x_i - \bar{x})^2}$$

$$= \frac{1}{5} + \frac{(x_i - 14)^2}{126}$$

| $x_i$ | $h_i$ | $s_{y_i - \hat{y}_i}$ | $y_i - \hat{y}_i$ | Standardized Residuals |
|-------|-------|----------------------|-------------------|------------------------|
| 6 | .7079 | 2.6356 | 3.48 | 1.32 |
| 11 | .2714 | 4.1625 | -2.47 | -.59 |
| 15 | .2079 | 4.3401 | -4.83 | -1.11 |
| 18 | .3270 | 4.0005 | -1.60 | -.40 |
| 20 | .4857 | 3.4972 | 5.22 | 1.49 |

**e.** The plot of the standardized residuals against $x$ has the same shape as the original residual plot. The conclusions reached in part (c) are also appropriate here.

**49.** Using Excel's Regression tool the estimated regression equation is $\hat{y} = 29.39911 + 1.547458x$ or $\hat{y} = 29.40 + 1.55x$

**b.** Significant relationship: Significance $F$ (or $p$-value) $< \alpha = .05$

**c.**

| $x_i$ | $y_i$ | $\hat{y}_i = 29.40 + 1.55x_i$ | $y_i - \hat{y}_i$ |
|-------|-------|-------------------------------|-------------------|
| 1 | 19 | 30.95 | -11.95 |
| 2 | 32 | 32.50 | -.50 |
| 4 | 44 | 35.60 | 8.40 |
| 6 | 40 | 38.70 | 1.30 |
| 10 | 52 | 44.90 | 7.10 |
| 14 | 53 | 51.10 | 1.90 |
| 20 | 54 | 60.40 | -6.40 |

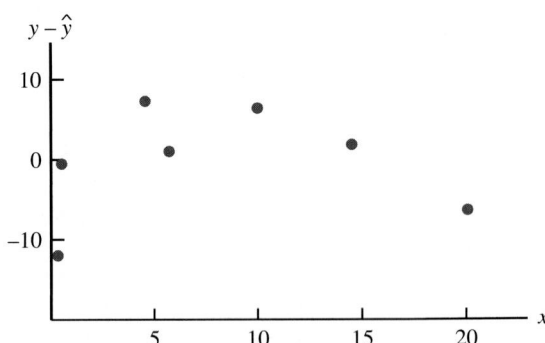

**d.** The residual plot leads us to question the assumption of a linear relationship between $x$ and $y$; even though the relationship is significant at the $\alpha = .05$ level, it would be extremely dangerous to extrapolate beyond the range of the data (e.g., $x > 20$)

**52. a.** The scatter diagram is shown:

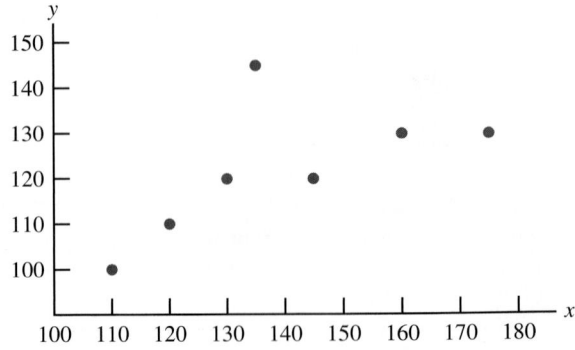

The scatter diagram indicates that the observation $x = 135$, $y = 145$ may be an outlier; the implication is that for simple linear regression outliers can be identified by looking at the scatter diagram

**b.** Using Excel, we obtained the estimated regression equation $\hat{y} = 66.1047 + .4023x$; the fitted values and standard residuals are shown:

| $\hat{y}_i$ | Standard Residuals |
|---|---|
| 120.42 | 2.13 |
| 110.36 | −.90 |
| 118.40 | .14 |
| 124.44 | −.39 |
| 136.51 | −.57 |
| 130.47 | −.04 |
| 114.38 | −.38 |

The standard residuals indicates that the observation $x = 135$, $y = 145$ is an outlier; because this observation has a standard residual of 2.13

**54. a.** The Excel output is shown in Figure E14.54a.
**b.** Excel's standard residuals are as follows:

| | | | | |
|---|---|---|---|---|
| 1.84 | 0.67 | −1.63 | −1.23 | 0.49 |
| 0.63 | −0.57 | 0.01 | −0.17 | −0.03 |

Because the standard residuals are all greater than −2 and less than 2, there does not appear to be any outliers in the data. However, the scatter diagram and the estimated regression line shown below provide visual support for the conclusion that observation 1 should be treated as an outlier.

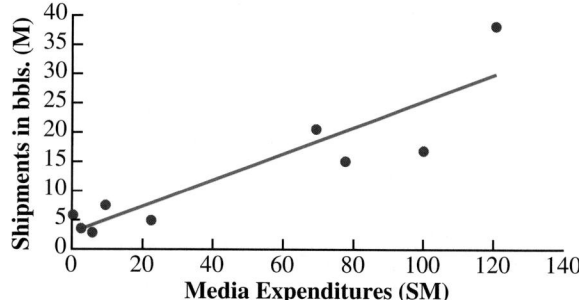

Note also the effect that observation 1 can have on the estimated regression line. For instance, if we delete observation 1 from the data, the resulting estimated regression equation is $\hat{y} = 5.1171 + .1322x$. Thus, because of the effect that this observation has on the slope and $y$-intercept, it could also be considered as an influential observation.

## Chapter 15

**2. a.** The estimated regression equation is
$$\hat{y} = 45.0594 + 1.9436x_1$$
An estimate of $y$ when $x_1 = 45$ is
$$\hat{y} = 45.0594 + 1.9436(45) = 132.52$$
**b.** The estimated regression equation is
$$\hat{y} = 85.2171 + 4.3215x_2$$
An estimate of $y$ when $x_2 = 15$ is
$$\hat{y} = 85.2171 + 4.3215(15) = 150.04$$
**c.** The estimated regression equation is
$$\hat{y} = -18.3683 + 2.0102x_1 + 4.7378x_2$$
An estimate of $y$ when $x_1 = 45$ and $x_2 = 15$ is
$$\hat{y} = -18.3683 + 2.0102(45) + 4.7378(15) = 143.16$$

**FIGURE E14.54a**

| Regression Statistics | |
|---|---|
| Multiple R | 0.8851 |
| R Square | 0.7834 |
| Adjusted R Square | 0.7563 |
| Standard Error | 5.0437 |
| Observations | 10 |

**ANOVA**

| | df | SS | MS | F | Significance F |
|---|---|---|---|---|---|
| Regression | 1 | 735.8398 | 735.8398 | 28.9261 | 0.0007 |
| Residual | 8 | 203.5092 | 25.4387 | | |
| Total | 9 | 939.349 | | | |

| | Coefficients | Standard Error | t Stat | P-value |
|---|---|---|---|---|
| Intercept | 4.0890 | 2.1684 | 1.8857 | 0.0961 |
| Media Expenditures ($M) | 0.1955 | 0.0364 | 5.3783 | 0.0007 |

**FIGURE E15.5a**

| Regression Statistics | |
|---|---|
| Multiple R | 0.8078 |
| R Square | 0.6526 |
| Adjusted R Square | 0.5946 |
| Standard Error | 1.2152 |
| Observations | 8 |

**ANOVA**

| | df | SS | MS | F | Significance F |
|---|---|---|---|---|---|
| Regression | 1 | 16.6401 | 16.6401 | 11.2688 | 0.0153 |
| Residual | 6 | 8.8599 | 1.4767 | | |
| Total | 7 | 25.5 | | | |

| | Coefficients | Standard Error | t Stat | P-value |
|---|---|---|---|---|
| Intercept | 88.6377 | 1.5824 | 56.0159 | 2.174E-09 |
| Television Advertising ($1000s) | 1.6039 | 0.4778 | 3.3569 | 0.0153 |

**5. a.** The Excel output is shown in Figure E15.5a
  **b.** The Excel output is shown in Figure E15.5b
  **c.** It is 1.6039 in part (a) and 2.2902 in part (b); in part (a) the coefficient is an estimate of the change in revenue due to a one-unit change in television advertising expenditures; in part (b) it represents an estimate of the change in revenue due to a one-unit change in television advertising expenditures when the amount of newspaper advertising is held constant

  **d.** Revenue $= 83.2301 + 2.2902(3.5) + 1.3010(1.8)$
     $= 93.59$ or $\$93,590$

**12. a.** $R^2 = \dfrac{\text{SSR}}{\text{SST}} = \dfrac{14{,}052.2}{15{,}182.9} = .926$

  **b.** $R_a^2 = 1 - (1 - R^2)\dfrac{n-1}{n-p-1}$

   $= 1 - (1 - .926)\dfrac{10-1}{10-2-1} = .905$

**FIGURE E15.5b**

| Regression Statistics | |
|---|---|
| Multiple R | 0.9587 |
| R Square | 0.9190 |
| Adjusted R Square | 0.8866 |
| Standard Error | 0.6426 |
| Observations | 8 |

**ANOVA**

| | df | SS | MS | F | Significance F |
|---|---|---|---|---|---|
| Regression | 2 | 23.4354 | 11.7177 | 28.3778 | 0.0019 |
| Residual | 5 | 2.0646 | 0.4129 | | |
| Total | 7 | 25.5 | | | |

| | Coefficients | Standard Error | t Stat | P-value |
|---|---|---|---|---|
| Intercept | 83.2301 | 1.5739 | 52.8825 | 4.57E-08 |
| Television Advertising ($1000s) | 2.2902 | 0.3041 | 7.5319 | 0.0007 |
| Newspaper Advertising ($1000s) | 1.3010 | 0.3207 | 4.0567 | 0.0098 |

**c.** Yes; after adjusting for the number of independent variables in the model, we see that 90.5% of the variability in $y$ has been accounted for

**15. a.** $R^2 = \dfrac{\text{SSR}}{\text{SST}} = \dfrac{23.435}{25.5} = .919$

$R_a^2 = 1 - (1 - R^2)\dfrac{n - 1}{n - p - 1}$

$= 1 - (1 - .919)\dfrac{8 - 1}{8 - 2 - 1} = .887$

**b.** Multiple regression analysis is preferred because both $R^2$ and $R_a^2$ show an increased percentage of the variability of $y$ explained when both independent variables are used

**19. a.** $\text{MSR} = \dfrac{\text{SSR}}{p} = \dfrac{6216.375}{2} = 3108.188$

$\text{MSE} = \dfrac{\text{SSE}}{n - p - 1} = \dfrac{507.75}{10 - 2 - 1} = 72.536$

**b.** $F = \dfrac{\text{MSR}}{\text{MSE}} = \dfrac{3108.188}{72.536} = 42.85$

$F_{.05} = 4.74$ (2 degrees of freedom numerator and 7 denominator)

Because $F = 42.85 > F_{.05} = 4.74$, the overall model is significant

**c.** $t = \dfrac{b_1}{s_{b_1}} = \dfrac{.5906}{.0813} = 7.26$

$t_{.025} = 2.365$ (7 degrees of freedom)

With $t = 7.26 > t_{.025} = 2.365$, $\beta_1$ is significant

**d.** $t = \dfrac{b_2}{s_{b_2}} = \dfrac{.4980}{.0567} = 8.78$

With $t = 8.78 > t_{.025} = 2.365$, $\beta_2$ is significant

**23. a.** $F = 28.38$

$F_{.01} = 13.27$ (2 degrees of freedom numerator and 1 denominator)

Because $F > F_{.01} = 13.27$, reject $H_0$

Alternatively, the $p$-value of .002 leads to the same conclusion

**b.** $t = 7.53$

$t_{.025} = 2.571$

Because $t > t_{.025} = 2.571$, $\beta_1$ is significant and $x_1$ should not be dropped from the model

**c.** $t = 4.06$

$t_{.025} = 2.571$

With $t > t_{.025} = 2.571$, $\beta_2$ is significant and $x_2$ should not be dropped from the model

**28. a.** Using the PredInt macro, the 95% confidence interval is 132.16 to 154.16

**b.** Using the PredInt macro, the 95% prediction interval is 111.13 to 175.18

**29. a.** See Excel output in Figure E15.5b.

$\hat{y} = 83.2301 + 2.2902(3.5) + 1.3010(1.8) = 93.588$ or $93,588

**b.** Using the PredInt macro: 92.840 to 94.335, or $92,840 to $94,335

**c.** Using the PredInt macro: 91.774 to 95.401, or $91,774 to $95,401

**32. a.** $E(y) = \beta_0 + \beta_1 x_1 + \beta_2 x_2$

where $x_2 = \begin{cases} 0 \text{ if level 1} \\ 1 \text{ if level 2} \end{cases}$

**b.** $E(y) = \beta_0 + \beta_1 x_1 + \beta_2(0) = \beta_0 + \beta_1 x_1$

**c.** $E(y) = \beta_0 + \beta_1 x_1 + \beta_2(1) = \beta_0 + \beta_1 x_1 + \beta_2$

**d.** $\beta_2 = E(y \mid \text{level 2}) - E(y \mid \text{level 1})$

$\beta_1$ is the change in $E(y)$ for a 1-unit change in $x_1$ holding $x_2$ constant

**34. a.** $15,300, because $b_3 = 15.3$

**b.** $\hat{y} = 10.1 - 4.2(2) + 6.8(8) + 15.3(0)$

$= 10.1 - 8.4 + 54.4$

$= 56.1$

Sales prediction: $56,100

**c.** $\hat{y} = 10.1 - 4.2(1) + 6.8(3) + 15.3(1)$

$= 10.1 - 4.2 + 20.4 + 15.3$

$= 41.6$

Sales prediction: $41,600

**39. a.** The Excel output is shown in Figure E15.39a

**b.**

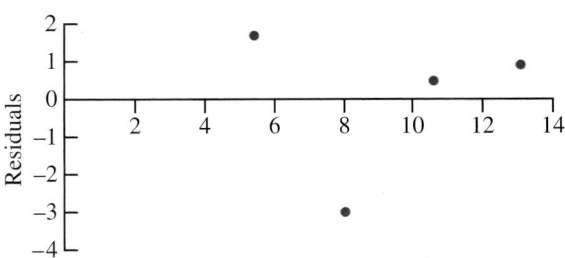

Predicted $y$

With only 5 observations it is difficult to determine if there are any violations in the assumptions. However, there is nothing unusual in the shape of the plot to question the assumptions.

**c.** The standardized residual plot is shown below:

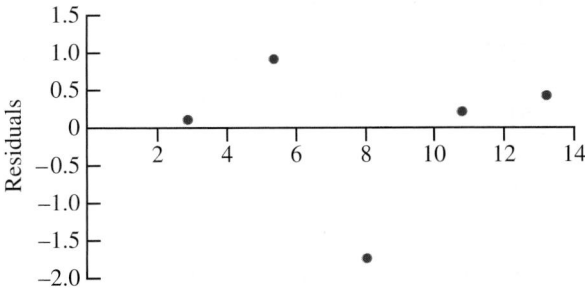

Predicted $y$

The shape of the standardized residual plot is the same as the shape of the residual plot in part (b). In addition, because none of the standard residuals is less than $-2$

**FIGURE E15.39**

| Regression Statistics | |
|---|---|
| Multiple R | 0.9192 |
| R Square | 0.845 |
| Adjusted R Square | 0.7933 |
| Standard Error | 2.0331 |
| Observations | 5 |

**ANOVA**

| | df | SS | MS | F | Significance F |
|---|---|---|---|---|---|
| Regression | 1 | 67.6 | 67.6 | 16.3548 | 0.0272 |
| Residual | 3 | 12.4 | 4.1333 | | |
| Total | 4 | 80 | | | |

| | Coefficients | Standard Error | t Stat | P-value |
|---|---|---|---|---|
| Intercept | 0.2 | 2.1323 | 0.0938 | 0.9312 |
| x | 2.6 | 0.6429 | 4.0441 | 0.0272 |

or greater than $+2$, we would conclude that there are no outliers in the data set.

**41. a.** The Excel output appears in Figure E15.5b; the estimated regression equation is $\hat{y} = 83.2301 + 2.2902x_1 + 1.3010x_2$ where $x_1$ = television advertising ($1000s) and $x_2$ = newspaper advertising ($1000s).

  **b.** Using Excel, we obtained the following values:

| $\hat{y}_i$ | Standard Residual | $\hat{y}_i$ | Standard Residual |
|---|---|---|---|
| 96.63 | $-1.16$ | 94.39 | 1.12 |
| 90.41 | $-.76$ | 94.24 | $-.44$ |
| 94.34 | 1.21 | 94.42 | $-.77$ |
| 92.21 | $-.38$ | 93.35 | 1.19 |

Predicted y

With the relatively few observations, it is difficult to determine if any of the assumptions regarding the error term have been violated. For instance, an argument could be made that there does not appear to be any pattern in the plot; alternatively an argument could be made that there is a curvilinear pattern in the plot.

**c.** The values of the standard residuals are greater than $-2$ and less than $+2$; thus, there are no outliers

## Chapter 16

**1. a.** The Excel output is shown in Figure E16.1a
  **b.** The $p$-value corresponding to $F = 6.8530$ is .0589 $> \alpha = .05$, therefore the relationship is not significant
  **c.**

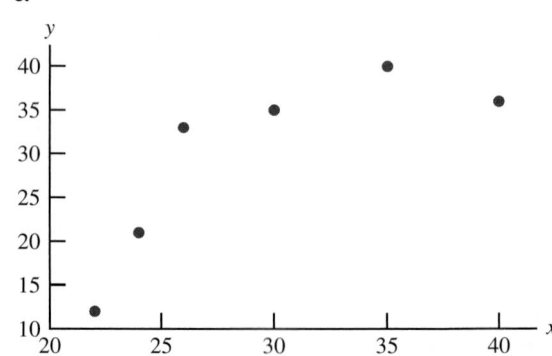

The scatter diagram suggests that a curvilinear relationship may be appropriate
  **d.** The Excel output is shown in Figure E16.1d
  **e.** The $p$-value corresponding to $F = 25.6778$ is .013 $< \alpha = .05$, therefore the relationship is significant
  **f.** $\hat{y} = -168.8848 + 12.1870(25) - .1770(25)^2 = 25.165$

**5. a.** The Excel output is shown in Figure E16.5a
  **b.** The $p$-value corresponding to $F = 73.1475$ is .0028 $< \alpha = .01$, therefore the relationship is significant; we would reject $H_0: \beta_1 = \beta_2 = 0$
  **c.** The fitted value is 1302.01 with a standard deviation of 9.93. The 95% confidence interval is 1270.41 to

**FIGURE E16.1a**

| Regression Statistics | |
|---|---|
| Multiple R | 0.7946 |
| R Square | 0.6314 |
| Adjusted R Square | 0.5393 |
| Standard Error | 7.2693 |
| Observations | 6 |

**ANOVA**

| | df | SS | MS | F | Significance F |
|---|---|---|---|---|---|
| Regression | 1 | 362.1304802 | 362.1305 | 6.8530 | 0.0589 |
| Residual | 4 | 211.3695198 | 52.8424 | | |
| Total | 5 | 573.5 | | | |

| | Coefficients | Standard Error | t Stat | P-value |
|---|---|---|---|---|
| Intercept | −6.7745 | 14.1709 | −0.4781 | 0.6576 |
| x | 1.2296 | 0.4697 | 2.6178 | 0.0589 |

1333.61; the 95% prediction interval is 1242.55 to 1361.47.

**11. a.** $SSE = 1805 - 1760 = 45$

$$F = \frac{MSR}{MSE} = \left(\frac{1760/4}{45/25}\right) = 244.44$$

$F_{.05} = 2.76$ (4 degrees of freedom numerator and 25 denominator)

Because $244.44 > 2.76$ we reject $H_0$; the relationship is significant

**b.** $SSE(x_1, x_2, x_3, x_4) = 45$

**c.** $SSE(x_2, x_3) = 1805 - 1705 = 100$

**d.** $F = \dfrac{(100 - 45)/2}{1.8} = 15.28 \qquad F_{.05} = 3.39$

With $F = 15.28 > 3.39$, $x_1$ and $x_2$ are significant

**12. a.** The Excel output is shown in Figure E16.12a

**b.** The Excel output is shown in Figure E16.12b

**c.** $F = \dfrac{[SSE(\text{reduced}) - SSE(\text{full})]/(\#\ \text{extra terms})}{MSE(\text{full})}$

$$= \frac{(23{,}157 - 14{,}317)/2}{1432} = 3.09$$

**FIGURE E16.1d**

| Regression Statistics | |
|---|---|
| Multiple R | 0.9720 |
| R Square | 0.9448 |
| Adjusted R Square | 0.9080 |
| Standard Error | 3.2482 |
| Observations | 6 |

**ANOVA**

| | df | SS | MS | F | Significance F |
|---|---|---|---|---|---|
| Regression | 2 | 541.8473 | 270.9236 | 25.6778 | 0.0130 |
| Residual | 3 | 31.6527 | 10.5509 | | |
| Total | 5 | 573.5 | | | |

| | Coefficients | Standard Error | t Stat | P-value |
|---|---|---|---|---|
| Intercept | −168.8848 | 39.7862 | −4.2448 | 0.0239 |
| x | 12.1870 | 2.6632 | 4.5760 | 0.0196 |
| xsq | −0.1770 | 0.0429 | −4.1271 | 0.0258 |

### FIGURE E16.5a

| Regression Statistics | |
|---|---|
| Multiple R | 0.9899 |
| R Square | 0.9799 |
| Adjusted R Square | 0.9665 |
| Standard Error | 15.8264 |
| Observations | 6 |

**ANOVA**

| | df | SS | MS | F | Significance F |
|---|---|---|---|---|---|
| Regression | 2 | 36643.4048 | 18321.7024 | 73.1475 | 0.0028 |
| Residual | 3 | 751.4286 | 250.4762 | | |
| Total | 5 | 37394.8333 | | | |

| | Coefficients | Standard Error | t Stat | P-value |
|---|---|---|---|---|
| Intercept | 432.5714 | 141.1763 | 3.0641 | 0.0548 |
| x | 37.4286 | 7.8074 | 4.7940 | 0.0173 |
| xsq | −0.3829 | 0.1036 | −3.6952 | 0.0344 |

$F_{.05} = 4.10$ (2 degrees of freedom numerator and 10 denominator)

With $F = 3.09 < F_{.05} = 4.10$, the addition of the two independent variables is not significant

Note: Suppose that we consider adding only the number of interceptions made by the opponents; the corresponding Excel output is shown in Figure E16.12c; in this case,

$$F = \frac{(23{,}157 - 14{,}335)/1}{1303} = 6.77$$

$F_{.05} = 4.84$ (1 degree of freedom numerator and 11 denominator)

With $F = 6.77 > F_{.05} = 4.84$, the addition of the number of interceptions made by the opponents is significant

**16. a.** The Excel output is shown in Figure E16.16a
   **b.** The Excel output is shown in Figure E16.16b
   **c.** The backward elimination procedure results in an estimated regression equation with two independent variables (see Figure 16.16c)

### FIGURE E16.12a

| Regression Statistics | |
|---|---|
| Multiple R | 0.6456 |
| R Square | 0.4167 |
| Adjusted R Square | 0.3681 |
| Standard Error | 43.9290 |
| Observations | 14 |

**ANOVA**

| | df | SS | MS | F | Significance F |
|---|---|---|---|---|---|
| Regression | 1 | 16546.1695 | 16546.1695 | 8.5742 | 0.0126 |
| Residual | 12 | 23157.0447 | 1929.7537 | | |
| Total | 13 | 39703.2143 | | | |

| | Coefficients | Standard Error | t Stat | P-value |
|---|---|---|---|---|
| Intercept | 170.1274 | 44.0201 | 3.8648 | 0.0022 |
| Team Interceptions | 6.6130 | 2.2584 | 2.9282 | 0.0126 |

**FIGURE E16.12b**

| Regression Statistics | |
|---|---|
| Multiple R | 0.7996 |
| R Square | 0.6394 |
| Adjusted R Square | 0.5312 |
| Standard Error | 37.8376 |
| Observations | 14 |

**ANOVA**

| | df | SS | MS | F | Significance F |
|---|---|---|---|---|---|
| Regression | 3 | 25386.3868 | 8462.1289 | 5.9106 | 0.0138 |
| Residual | 10 | 14316.8274 | 1431.6827 | | |
| Total | 13 | 39703.2143 | | | |

| | Coefficients | Standard Error | t Stat | P-value |
|---|---|---|---|---|
| Intercept | 280.3430 | 81.4181 | 3.4433 | 0.0063 |
| Team Interceptions | 5.1762 | 2.0735 | 2.4964 | 0.0316 |
| Rushing Yards | −0.0037 | 0.0334 | −0.1119 | 0.9131 |
| Opponent Interceptions | −3.9182 | 1.6509 | −2.3733 | 0.0391 |

**FIGURE E16.12c**

| Regression Statistics | |
|---|---|
| Multiple R | 0.7993 |
| R Square | 0.6390 |
| Adjusted R Square | 0.5733 |
| Standard Error | 36.0993 |
| Observations | 14 |

**ANOVA**

| | df | SS | MS | F | Significance F |
|---|---|---|---|---|---|
| Regression | 2 | 25368.4476 | 12684.2238 | 9.7334 | 0.0037 |
| Residual | 11 | 14334.7667 | 1303.1606 | | |
| Total | 13 | 39703.2143 | | | |

| | Coefficients | Standard Error | t Stat | P-value |
|---|---|---|---|---|
| Intercept | 273.7699 | 53.8077 | 5.0879 | 0.0004 |
| Team Interceptions | 5.2267 | 1.9308 | 2.7070 | 0.0204 |
| Opponent Interceptions | −3.9650 | 1.5239 | −2.6019 | 0.0246 |

**FIGURE E16.16a**

| Regression Statistics | |
|---|---|
| Multiple R | 0.5448 |
| R Square | 0.2968 |
| Adjusted R Square | 0.2528 |
| Standard Error | 12.8264 |
| Observations | 18 |

**ANOVA**

| | df | SS | MS | F | Significance F |
|---|---|---|---|---|---|
| Regression | 1 | 1110.8344 | 1110.8344 | 6.7521 | 0.0194 |
| Residual | 16 | 2632.2767 | 164.5173 | | |
| Total | 17 | 3743.1111 | | | |

| | Coefficients | Standard Error | t Stat | P-value |
|---|---|---|---|---|
| Intercept | −26.6126 | 37.2180 | −0.7150 | 0.4849 |
| Combined SAT Score | 0.0970 | 0.0373 | 2.5985 | 0.0194 |

**FIGURE E16.16b**

| Regression Statistics | |
|---|---|
| Multiple R | 0.7723 |
| R Square | 0.5965 |
| Adjusted R Square | 0.4283 |
| Standard Error | 11.2191 |
| Observations | 18 |

**ANOVA**

| | df | SS | MS | F | Significance F |
|---|---|---|---|---|---|
| Regression | 5 | 2232.6895 | 446.5379 | 3.5477 | 0.0336 |
| Residual | 12 | 1510.4217 | 125.8685 | | |
| Total | 17 | 3743.1111 | | | |

| | Coefficients | Standard Error | t Stat | P-value |
|---|---|---|---|---|
| Intercept | 33.7086 | 63.2773 | 0.5327 | 0.6040 |
| Average Class Size | −1.5577 | 1.0901 | −1.4289 | 0.1786 |
| Spending Per Student ($) | −0.0024 | 0.0017 | −1.4661 | 0.1683 |
| Average Teacher Salary ($) | −0.0003 | 0.0006 | −0.4045 | 0.6930 |
| Combined SAT Score | 0.0769 | 0.0374 | 2.0573 | 0.0621 |
| % Taking SAT | 0.2852 | 0.1154 | 2.4704 | 0.0295 |

**FIGURE E16.16c**

| Regression Statistics | |
|---|---|
| Multiple R | 0.6851 |
| R Square | 0.4693 |
| Adjusted R Square | 0.3986 |
| Standard Error | 11.5076 |
| Observations | 18 |

**ANOVA**

| | df | SS | MS | F | Significance F |
|---|---|---|---|---|---|
| Regression | 2 | 1756.7232 | 878.3616 | 6.6329 | 0.0086 |
| Residual | 15 | 1986.3879 | 132.4259 | | |
| Total | 17 | 3743.1111 | | | |

| | Coefficients | Standard Error | t Stat | P-value |
|---|---|---|---|---|
| Intercept | −26.9312 | 33.3916 | −0.8065 | 0.4325 |
| Combined SAT Score | 0.0838 | 0.0340 | 2.4623 | 0.0264 |
| % Taking SAT | 0.2045 | 0.0926 | 2.2085 | 0.0432 |

21. **a.** The Excel output is shown in Figure E16.21a
    **b.** The Durban-Watson statistic is $d = 1.96$; at $\alpha = .05$, $d_L = 1.10$, and $d_U = 1.37$; because $d > d_U$, there is no significant positive autocorrelation

23.

| $x_1$ | $x_2$ | $x_3$ | Treatment |
|---|---|---|---|
| 0 | 0 | 0 | A |
| 1 | 0 | 0 | B |
| 0 | 1 | 0 | C |
| 0 | 0 | 1 | D |

$$E(y) = \beta_0 + \beta_1 x_1 + \beta_2 x_2 + \beta_3 x_3$$

26. **a.**

| $D_1$ | $D_2$ | Manufacturer |
|---|---|---|
| 0 | 0 | 1 |
| 1 | 0 | 2 |
| 0 | 1 | 3 |

$$E(y) = \beta_0 + \beta_1 D_1 + \beta_2 D_2$$

**b.** See Figure E16.26b
**c.** $H_0: \beta_1 = \beta_2 = 0$
**d.** The $p$-value is $.0043 < \alpha = .05$, therefore we conclude that the mean time to mix a batch of material is not the same for each manufacturer

**FIGURE E16.21a**

| Regression Statistics | |
|---|---|
| Multiple R | 0.6246 |
| R Square | 0.3901 |
| Adjusted R Square | 0.3465 |
| Standard Error | 5.6483 |
| Observations | 16 |

**ANOVA**

| | df | SS | MS | F | Significance F |
|---|---|---|---|---|---|
| Regression | 1 | 285.6389 | 285.6389 | 8.9534 | 0.0097 |
| Residual | 14 | 446.6411 | 31.9029 | | |
| Total | 15 | 732.28 | | | |

| | Coefficients | Standard Error | t Stat | P-value |
|---|---|---|---|---|
| Intercept | 10.0518 | 3.7355 | 2.6908 | 0.0176 |
| Gross Profit Margin (%) | 0.6562 | 0.2193 | 2.9922 | 0.0097 |

**FIGURE E16.26b**

| Regression Statistics | |
|---|---|
| Multiple R | 0.8383 |
| R Square | 0.7027 |
| Adjusted R Square | 0.6366 |
| Standard Error | 2.2111 |
| Observations | 12 |

**ANOVA**

| | df | SS | MS | F | Significance F |
|---|---|---|---|---|---|
| Regression | 2 | 104 | 52 | 10.6364 | 0.0043 |
| Residual | 9 | 44 | 4.8889 | | |
| Total | 11 | 148 | | | |

| | Coefficients | Standard Error | t Stat | P-value |
|---|---|---|---|---|
| Intercept | 23 | 1.1055 | 20.8043 | 0.0000 |
| D1 | 5 | 1.5635 | 3.1980 | 0.0109 |
| D2 | −2 | 1.5635 | −1.2792 | 0.2328 |

## Chapter 17

**1.** Binomial probabilities for $n = 10$, $p = .50$

| x | Probability | x | Probability |
|---|---|---|---|
| 0 | .0010 | 6 | .2051 |
| 1 | .0098 | 7 | .1172 |
| 2 | .0439 | 8 | .0439 |
| 3 | .1172 | 9 | .0098 |
| 4 | .2051 | 10 | .0010 |
| 5 | .2461 | | |

$P(0) + P(1) = .0108$; Adding $P(2)$ exceeds .025 required in the tail; therefore, reject $H_0$ if the number of plus signs is less than 2 or greater than 8;

Number of plus signs is 7

Do not reject $H_0$; conclude that there is no indication that a difference exists

**2.** $n = 27$ cases in which a value different from 150 is obtained
Use normal approximation with $\mu = np = .5(27) = 13.5$ and $\sigma = \sqrt{.25n} = \sqrt{.25(27)} = 2.6$
Use $x = 22$ as the number of plus signs and obtain the following test statistic:

$$z = \frac{x - \mu}{\sigma} = \frac{22 - 13.5}{2.6} = 3.27$$

With $\alpha = .01$, we reject if $z > 2.33$; because $z = 3.27 > 2.33$, reject $H_0$ and conclude the median is greater than 150

**4.** We need to determine the number of "better" responses and the number of "worse" responses; the sum of the two is the sample size used for the study

$$n = .34(1253) + .29(1253) = 789.4$$

Use the large-sample test using the normal distribution; this means the value of $n(n = 789.4)$ need not be an integer. Use

$$\mu = .5n = .5(789.4) = 394.7$$
$$\sigma = \sqrt{.25n} = \sqrt{.25(789.4)} = 14.05$$

Let $p =$ proportion of adults who feel children will have a better future

$H_0: p \le .50$
$H_a: p > .50$

$$x = .34(1253) = 426.0$$
$$z = \frac{x - \mu}{\sigma} = \frac{426.0 - 394.7}{14.05} = 2.23$$

With $\alpha = .05$, we reject if $z > 1.645$; because $z = 2.23 > 1.645$, reject $H_0$ and conclude that more than half of the adults feel their children will have a better future

**12.** $H_0$: The populations are identical
$H_a$: The populations are not identical

| Additive | | | Absolute | | Signed |
|---|---|---|---|---|---|
| 1 | 2 | Difference | Value | Rank | Rank |
| 20.12 | 18.05 | 2.07 | 2.07 | 9 | +9 |
| 23.56 | 21.77 | 1.79 | 1.79 | 7 | +7 |
| 22.03 | 22.57 | −.54 | .54 | 3 | −3 |
| 19.15 | 17.06 | 2.09 | 2.09 | 10 | +10 |
| 21.23 | 21.22 | .01 | .01 | 1 | +1 |
| 24.77 | 23.80 | .97 | .97 | 4 | +4 |
| 16.16 | 17.20 | −1.04 | 1.04 | 5 | −5 |
| 18.55 | 14.98 | 3.57 | 3.57 | 12 | +12 |
| 21.87 | 20.03 | 1.84 | 1.84 | 8 | +8 |
| 24.23 | 21.15 | 3.08 | 3.08 | 11 | +11 |
| 23.21 | 22.78 | .43 | .43 | 2 | +2 |
| 25.02 | 23.70 | 1.32 | 1.32 | 6 | +6 |
| | | | | | $T = 62$ |

$\mu_T = 0$

$$\sigma_T = \sqrt{\frac{n(n + 1)(2n + 1)}{6}} = \sqrt{\frac{12(13)(25)}{6}} = 25.5$$

$$z = \frac{T - \mu_T}{\sigma_T} = \frac{62 - 0}{25.5} = 1.83$$

Two-tailed test; reject $H_0$ if $z < -1.96$ or $z > 1.96$; because $z = 2.43 > 1.96$, reject $H_0$ and conclude that there is a significant difference between the additives

**13.**

| Without Relaxant | With Relaxant | Difference | Rank of Absolute Difference | Signed Rank |
|---|---|---|---|---|
| 15 | 10 | 5 | 9 | +9 |
| 12 | 10 | 2 | 3 | +3 |
| 22 | 12 | 10 | 10 | +10 |
| 8 | 11 | -3 | 6.5 | -6.5 |
| 10 | 9 | 1 | 1 | +1 |
| 7 | 5 | 2 | 3 | +3 |
| 8 | 10 | -2 | 3 | -3 |
| 10 | 7 | 3 | 6.5 | +6.5 |
| 14 | 11 | 3 | 6.5 | +6.5 |
| 9 | 6 | 3 | 6.5 | +6.5 |
| | | | | $T = 36$ |

$\mu_T = 0$

$$\sigma_T = \sqrt{\frac{n(n + 1)(2n + 1)}{6}} = \sqrt{\frac{10(11)(21)}{6}} = 19.62$$

$$z = \frac{T - \mu_T}{\sigma_T} = \frac{36}{19.62} = 1.83$$

One-tailed test; reject $H_0$ if $z > 1.645$

Reject $H_0$; there is a significant difference in favor of the relaxant

**18.** Rank the combined samples and find rank sum for each sample; this is a small-sample test because $n_1 = 7$ and $n_2 = 9$

| Additive 1 | | Additive 2 | |
|---|---|---|---|
| **MPG** | **Rank** | **MPG** | **Rank** |
| 17.3 | 2 | 18.7 | 8.5 |
| 18.4 | 6 | 17.8 | 4 |
| 19.1 | 10 | 21.3 | 15 |
| 16.7 | 1 | 21.0 | 14 |
| 18.2 | 5 | 22.1 | 16 |
| 18.6 | 7 | 18.7 | 8.5 |
| 17.5 | 3 | 19.8 | 11 |
| | 34 | 20.7 | 13 |
| | | 20.2 | 12 |
| | | | 102 |

$T = 34$

With $\alpha = .05$, $n_1 = 7$, and $n_2 = 9$

$T_L = 41$ and $T_U = 7(7 + 9 + 1) - 41 = 78$

Because $T = 34 < 41$, reject $H_0$ and conclude that there is a significant difference in gasoline mileage

**19. a.**

| Public Accountant | Rank | Financial Planner | Rank |
|---|---|---|---|
| 25.2 | 5 | 24.0 | 2 |
| 33.8 | 19 | 24.2 | 3 |
| 31.3 | 16 | 28.1 | 10 |
| 33.2 | 18 | 30.9 | 15 |
| 29.2 | 13 | 26.9 | 8.5 |
| 30.0 | 14 | 28.6 | 11 |
| 25.9 | 6 | 24.7 | 4 |
| 34.5 | 20 | 28.9 | 12 |
| 31.7 | 17 | 26.8 | 7 |
| 26.9 | 8.5 | 23.9 | 1 |
| | 136.5 | | 73.5 |

$$\mu_T = \frac{1}{2} n_1(n_1 + n_2 + 1) = \frac{1}{2}(10)(10 + 10 + 1) = 105$$

$$\sigma_T = \sqrt{\frac{1}{12} n_1 n_2(n_1 + n_2 + 1)} = \sqrt{\frac{1}{12}(10)(10)(10 + 10 + 1)}$$

$$= 13.23$$

$T = 136.5$

Reject $H_0$ if $z < -1.645$ or if $z > 1.645$

$$z = \frac{136.5 - 105}{13.23} = 2.38$$

Reject $H_0$; salaries differ significantly for the two professions

**b.**  Public Accountant        $32,300

    Financial Planner        $26,700

**26.** Rankings:

| Product A | Product B | Product C |
|---|---|---|
| 4 | 11 | 7 |
| 8 | 14 | 2 |
| 10 | 15 | 1 |
| 3 | 12 | 6 |
| 9 | 13 | 5 |
| 34 | 65 | 21 |

$$W = \frac{12}{(15)(16)}\left[\frac{(34)^2}{5} + \frac{(65)^2}{5} + \frac{(21)^5}{5}\right] - 3(15 + 1)$$

$$= 58.22 - 48 = 10.22$$

$\chi^2_{.05} = 5.99147$ (2 degrees of freedom)

Reject $H_0$ and conclude the ratings for the products differ

**28.** Rankings:

| Swimming | Tennis | Cycling |
|---|---|---|
| 8 | 9 | 5 |
| 4 | 14 | 1 |
| 11 | 13 | 3 |
| 6 | 10 | 7 |
| 12 | 15 | 2 |
| 41 | 61 | 18 |

$$W = \frac{12}{15(15+1)}\left[\frac{41^2}{5} + \frac{61^2}{5} + \frac{18^2}{5}\right] - 3(15+1)$$
$$= 9.26$$

$\chi^2_{.05} = 5.99147$ (2 degrees of freedom)

Because $9.26 > 5.99147$, reject $H_0$ and conclude activities differ

**32. a.** $\Sigma d_i^2 = 52$

$$r_s = 1 - \frac{6\Sigma d_i^2}{n(n^2-1)} = 1 - \frac{6(52)}{10(99)} = .68$$

**b.** $\sigma_{r_s} = \sqrt{\frac{1}{n-1}} = \sqrt{\frac{1}{9}} = .33$

$$z = \frac{r_s - 0}{\sigma_{r_s}} = \frac{.68}{.33} = 2.06$$

Reject $H_0$ if $z < -1.96$ or $z > 1.96$; because $z = 2.06 > 1.96$, reject $H_0$ and conclude that significant rank correlation exists

**34.** $\Sigma d_i^2 = 250$

$$r_s = 1 - \frac{6\Sigma d_i^2}{n(n^2-1)} = 1 - \frac{6(250)}{11(120)} = -.136$$

$$\sigma_{r_s} = \sqrt{\frac{1}{n-1}} = \sqrt{\frac{1}{10}} = .32$$

$$z = \frac{r_s - 0}{\sigma_{r_s}} = \frac{-.136}{.32} = -.425$$

Reject $H_0$ if $z < -1.96$ or $z > 1.96$; because $z = -.425$, do not reject $H_0$; we cannot conclude that there is a significant relationship between the rankings

# Chapter 18

**1. a.** $\bar{x} = 215$ is an estimate of the population mean

**b.** $s_{\bar{x}} = \frac{20}{\sqrt{50}}\sqrt{\frac{800-50}{800}} = 2.7386$

**c.** $215 \pm 2(2.7386)$ or $209.5228$ to $220.4772$

**5. a.** $\bar{x} = 149{,}670$ and $s = 73{,}420$

$$s_{\bar{x}} = \sqrt{\left(\frac{771-50}{771}\right)\frac{73{,}420}{\sqrt{50}}} = 10{,}040.83$$

Approximate 95% confidence interval:
$$149{,}760 \pm 2(10{,}040.83)$$
or
$$\$129{,}588.34 \text{ to } \$169{,}751.66$$

**b.** $\hat{X} = N\bar{x} = 771(149{,}670) = 115{,}395{,}570$
$$s_{\hat{X}} = Ns_{\bar{x}} = 771(10{,}040.83) = 7{,}741{,}479.93$$

Approximate 95% confidence interval:
$$115{,}395{,}570 \pm 2(7{,}741{,}479.93)$$
or
$$\$99{,}912{,}810.14 \text{ to } \$130{,}878{,}729.86$$

**c.** $\bar{p} = {}^{18}\!/_{50} = .36$ and

$$s_{\bar{p}} = \sqrt{\left(\frac{771-50}{771}\right)\frac{(.36)(.64)}{49}} = .0663$$

Approximate 95% confidence interval:
$$.36 \pm 2(.0663)$$
or
$$.2274 \text{ to } .4926$$

This is a rather large interval; sample sizes must be rather large to obtain tight confidence intervals on a population proportion

**7. a.** Stratum 1: $\bar{x}_1 = 138$
Stratum 2: $\bar{x}_2 = 103$
Stratum 3: $\bar{x}_3 = 210$

**b.** Stratum 1

$$\bar{x}_1 = 138; s_{\bar{x}_1} = \left(\frac{30}{\sqrt{20}}\right)\sqrt{\frac{200-20}{200}} = 6.3640$$

Approximate 95% confidence interval:
$$138 \pm 2(6.3640)$$
or $125.272$ to $150.728$

Stratum 2

$$\bar{x}_2 = 103; s_{\bar{x}_2} = \left(\frac{25}{\sqrt{30}}\right)\sqrt{\frac{250-30}{250}} = 4.2817$$

Approximate 95% confidence interval:
$$103 \pm 2(4.2817)$$
or $94.4366$ to $111.5634$

Stratum 3

$$\bar{x}_3 = 210; s_{\bar{x}_3} = \left(\frac{50}{\sqrt{25}}\right)\sqrt{\frac{100-25}{100}} = 8.6603$$

Approximate 95% confidence interval:
$$210 \pm 2(8.6603)$$
or $192.6794$ to $227.3206$

**c.** $\bar{x}_{st} = \left(\frac{200}{550}\right)138 + \left(\frac{250}{550}\right)103 + \left(\frac{100}{550}\right)210$
$$= 50.1818 + 46.8182 + 38.1818 = 135.1818$$

$$s_{\bar{x}_{st}} = \sqrt{\left(\frac{1}{(550)^2}\right)\left(200(180)\frac{(30)^2}{20} + 250(220)\frac{(25)^2}{30} + 100(75)\frac{(50)^2}{25}\right)}$$
$$= \sqrt{\left(\frac{1}{(550)^2}\right)3{,}515{,}833.3} = 3.4092$$

Approximate 95% confidence interval:
$$135.1818 \pm 2(3.4092)$$
or $128.3634$ to $142.0002$

**14. a.** $\bar{x}_c = \frac{\Sigma x_i}{\Sigma M_i} = \frac{750}{50} = 15$

$$\hat{X} = M\bar{x}_c = 300(15) = 4500$$

$$\bar{p}_c = \frac{\Sigma a_i}{\Sigma M_i} = \frac{15}{50} = .30$$

**b.** $\Sigma(x_i - \bar{x}_c M_i)^2 = [95 - 15(7)]^2 + [325 - 15(18)]^2$
$$+ [190 - 15(15)]^2 + [140 - 15(10)]^2$$
$$= (-10)^2 + (55)^2 + (-35)^2 + (-10)^2$$
$$= 4450$$

$$s_{\bar{x}_c} = \sqrt{\left(\frac{25 - 4}{(25)(4)(12)^2}\right)\left(\frac{4450}{3}\right)} = 1.4708$$

$$s_{\hat{X}} = M s_{\bar{x}_c} = 300(1.4708) = 441.24$$

$$\Sigma(a_i - \bar{p}_c M_i)^2 = [1 - .3(7)]^2 + [6 - .3(18)]^2$$
$$+ [6 - .3(15)]^2 + [2 - .3(10)]^2$$
$$= (-1.1)^2 + (.6)^2 + (1.5)^2 + (-1)^2$$
$$= 4.82$$

$$s_{\bar{p}_c} = \sqrt{\left(\frac{25 - 4}{(25)(4)(12)^2}\right)\left(\frac{4.82}{3}\right)} = .0484$$

**c.**    Approximate 95% confidence interval
for population mean:
$$15 \pm 2(1.4708)$$
or 12.0584 to 17.9416

**d.**    Approximate 95% confidence interval
for population total:
$$4500 \pm 2(441.24)$$
or 3617.52 to 5382.48

**e.**    Approximate 95% confidence interval for
population proportion:
$$.30 \pm 2(.0484)$$
or .2032 to .3968

## Chapter 19

**4.** *R chart:*
$$\text{UCL} = \bar{R}D_4 = 1.6(1.864) = 2.98$$
$$\text{LCL} = \bar{R}D_3 = 1.6(.136) = .22$$
$\bar{x}$ *chart:*
$$\text{UCL} = \bar{\bar{x}} + A_2\bar{R} = 28.5 + .373(1.6) = 29.10$$
$$\text{LCL} = \bar{\bar{x}} - A_2\bar{R} = 28.5 - .373(1.6) = 27.90$$

**10.** $f(x) = \dfrac{n!}{x!(n - x)!} p^x(1 - p)^{n-x}$

When $p = .02$, the probability of accepting the lot is
$$f(0) = \frac{25!}{0!(25 - 0)!} (.02)^0(1 - .02)^{25} = .6035$$

When $p = .06$, the probability of accepting the lot is
$$f(0) = \frac{25!}{0!(25 - 0)!} (.06)^0(1 - .06)^{25} = .2129$$

# Appendix F   Excel Functions and the Function Wizard

Excel provides a wealth of functions for data management and statistical analysis. If you know what function is needed, and how to use it, you can simply enter the function into the appropriate worksheet cell. However, if you are not sure what functions are available to accomplish a task, or you are not sure how to use a particular function, Excel's Function Wizard can be helpful. The Function Wizard can be used to identify available functions and to help us use them properly.

## Functions Available and the Paste Function Dialog Box

To access the Function Wizard, select **Insert** and then choose $f_x$**Function** from the pull-down list. Alternatively, select the $f_x$ button on the standard toolbar. Using either approach will provide the paste function dialog box shown in Figure 1.

The Paste Function dialog box contains three types of information. The **Function category** box contains a list of several categories of functions that are available. Figure 1 shows that initially the **Most Recently Used** function category is highlighted. The **Function name** box contains a list of the functions that are available corresponding to the category highlighted. The Most Recently Used category is exactly what the label denotes, a list of all the functions that we have used most recently: FREQUENCY, COUNTIF, CONFIDENCE, TINV, NORMDIST, and so on. Note that we have selected the **COUNTIF** function (COUNTIF is

**FIGURE 1**   PASTE FUNCTION DIALOG BOX

highlighted in the Function name box). For the function that is highlighted, a description is displayed below the Function category and Function name boxes. We see that the COUNTIF function has two arguments, range and criteria, and that the proper syntax for the function is **COUNTIF (range,criteria).** A brief statement of what the function does is shown below the syntax. For instance, we see that the COUNTIF function "Counts the number of cells within a range that meet the given condition."

If the function highlighted is the one we want to use, we click **OK** and another dialog box will appear to guide us in setting up the function properly. Before going into the details associated with using a particular function, however, let's see what other information can be obtained through the Paste Function dialog box.

In the Function category box (see Figure 1) the function category Most Recently Used is selected. Several other function categories follow: All, Financial, Date & Time, Math & Trig, Statistical, and so on. If we want to list all of the Excel functions, we can select the All function category; a list of all the Excel functions will then appear in alphabetic order in the Function name box. Because we are primarily interested in statistical functions, let us select Statistical in the Function category box. After doing so, the Paste Function dialog box will appear as shown in Figure 2.

All of Excel's statistical functions are now shown in alphabetic order in the Function name box. For instance, we see the AVEDEV function listed first, followed by the AVERAGE function, and so on. By moving the cursor to select any of these functions we can obtain a description of that function. For instance, in Figure 2 a description of the AVEDEV function is provided. By moving the cursor down to highlight the AVERAGE function we obtain a description of it as shown in Figure 3.

By scrolling further through the list of functions in the Function name box we can obtain a brief description of what each statistical function does. This capability is especially

**FIGURE 2**    PASTE FUNCTION DIALOG BOX WITH STATISTICAL
FUNCTIONS HIGHLIGHTED

**FIGURE 3**   DESCRIPTION OF THE AVERAGE FUNCTION IN THE PASTE FUNCTION
DIALOG BOX

valuable when we want to do a particular type of statistical analysis and do not know what
Excel functions are available to help.

## Using the Function Wizard to Paste a Function into a Worksheet Cell

Once we have decided which function to use, the Function Wizard can guide us through the
process of creating the function and pasting it into a worksheet cell. Let's see how.

In Section 2.1, Excel's COUNTIF function was used to construct a frequency distribution for soft drink purchases. Figure 4 is an Excel worksheet containing the soft drink data.
From the worksheet layout, we see that the frequency of Coke Classic purchases will go
into cell D2, the frequency of Diet Coke purchases will go into cell D3, and so on. Suppose
we want to use the COUNTIF function to compute the proper frequencies for these cells and
would like some assistance from the Function Wizard. Select cell D2 and follow these steps.

Step 1. Click on $f_x$ on the standard toolbar (or select **Insert** and then choose $f_x$
**Function**)

Step 2. When the Paste Function dialog box appears:
Select **Statistical** in the Function category list box
Select **COUNTIF** in the Function name list box
Click **OK**

Step 3. When the COUNTIF function box appears (see Figure 5):
Enter $A$2:$A$51 in the **Range** box
Enter C2 in the **Criteria** box (At this point, the value of the function will appear
just below the horizontal line in the center of the dialog box. Its value is 19.)
Click **OK**

Step 4. Copy cell D2 to cells D3:D6

**FIGURE 4**    EXCEL WORKSHEET WITH SOFT DRINK DATA

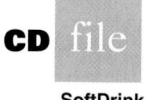

**SoftDrink**

Note: Rows 11–44 are
hidden.

|    | A | B | C | D | E |
|----|---|---|---|---|---|
| 1 | **Brand Purchased** | | **Soft Drink** | **Frequency** | |
| 2 | Coke Classic | | Coke Classic | | |
| 3 | Diet Coke | | Diet Coke | | |
| 4 | Pepsi-Cola | | Dr. Pepper | | |
| 5 | Diet Coke | | Pepsi-Cola | | |
| 6 | Coke Classic | | Sprite | | |
| 7 | Coke Classic | | | | |
| 8 | Dr. Pepper | | | | |
| 9 | Diet Coke | | | | |
| 10 | Pepsi-Cola | | | | |
| 45 | Pepsi-Cola | | | | |
| 46 | Pepsi-Cola | | | | |
| 47 | Pepsi-Cola | | | | |
| 48 | Coke Classic | | | | |
| 49 | Dr. Pepper | | | | |
| 50 | Pepsi-Cola | | | | |
| 51 | Sprite | | | | |
| 52 | | | | | |

The worksheet will now appear as in Figure 6. The formula worksheet is in the background; the value worksheet is in the foreground. We see that the Function Wizard inserted the COUNTIF function into cell D2. We then copied the contents of cell D2 into cells D3:D6. From the value worksheet we see that the proper class frequencies have been computed.

We have illustrated the use of the Function Wizard to insert the COUNTIF function. The procedure is similar for all Excel functions. The Function Wizard is especially helpful if you forget the proper name and/or syntax for a function, or when you are searching for the right function to accomplish a new task.

**FIGURE 5**    COUNTIF FUNCTION BOX

**FIGURE 6    EXCEL WORKSHEET SHOWING USE OF EXCEL'S COUNTIF FUNCTION**

Note: Rows 11–44 are hidden.

| | A | B | C | D | E |
|---|---|---|---|---|---|
| 1 | **Brand Purchased** | | **Soft Drink** | **Frequency** | |
| 2 | Coke Classic | | Coke Classic | =COUNTIF($A$2:$A$51,C2) | |
| 3 | Diet Coke | | Diet Coke | =COUNTIF($A$2:$A$51,C3) | |
| 4 | Pepsi-Cola | | Dr. Pepper | =COUNTIF($A$2:$A$51,C4) | |
| 5 | Diet Coke | | Pepsi-Cola | =COUNTIF($A$2:$A$51,C5) | |
| 6 | Coke Classic | | Sprite | =COUNTIF($A$2:$A$51,C6) | |
| 7 | Coke Classic | | | | |
| 8 | Dr. Pepper | | | | |
| 9 | Diet Coke | | | | |
| 10 | Pepsi-Cola | | | | |
| 45 | Pepsi-Cola | | | | |
| 46 | Pepsi-Cola | | | | |
| 47 | Pepsi-Cola | | | | |
| 48 | Coke Classic | | | | |
| 49 | Dr. Pepper | | | | |
| 50 | Pepsi-Cola | | | | |
| 51 | Sprite | | | | |
| 52 | | | | | |

| | A | B | C | D | E |
|---|---|---|---|---|---|
| 1 | **Brand Purchased** | | **Soft Drink** | **Frequency** | |
| 2 | Coke Classic | | Coke Classic | 19 | |
| 3 | Diet Coke | | Diet Coke | 8 | |
| 4 | Pepsi-Cola | | Dr. Pepper | 5 | |
| 5 | Diet Coke | | Pepsi-Cola | 13 | |
| 6 | Coke Classic | | Sprite | 5 | |
| 7 | Coke Classic | | | | |
| 8 | Dr. Pepper | | | | |
| 9 | Diet Coke | | | | |
| 10 | Pepsi-Cola | | | | |
| 45 | Pepsi-Cola | | | | |
| 46 | Pepsi-Cola | | | | |
| 47 | Pepsi-Cola | | | | |
| 48 | Coke Classic | | | | |
| 49 | Dr. Pepper | | | | |
| 50 | Pepsi-Cola | | | | |
| 51 | Sprite | | | | |
| 52 | | | | | |

# Index

# Modern Business Statistics with Microsoft® Excel Data Disk